The Flora of
DERBYSHIRE

ALAN WILLMOT & NICK MOYES

*"Many have aspired to write Floras
but few have completed them"*
Franklyn Perring 1974

Supported by

**Derbyshire
Wildlife Trust**

2015

Published 2015 by Pisces Publications

First published 2015.

British-Library-in-Publication Data
A catalogue record for this book is available from the British Library.

ISBN 978-1-874357-65-0

Designed and published by Pisces Publications

Visit our bookshop
www.naturebureau.co.uk/bookshop/

Pisces Publications is the imprint of NatureBureau, 36 Kingfisher Court, Hambridge Road, Newbury, Berkshire RG14 5SJ
www.naturebureau.co.uk

Printed and bound in the UK by Gomer Press Ltd

FRONT COVER PHOTOGRAPHS
Mossy Saxifrage (*Saxifraga hypnoides*) upper Cressbrook Dale (SK1775) May 2009 (Peter Smith)
Moschatel (*Adoxa moschatellina*) in spring woodland near Bretby (SK3023) April 2008 (Peter Smith)
Burnt Orchid (*Neotinea ustulata*) near Brassington (SK15) June 2006 (Peter Smith)
Jacob's-ladder (*Polemonium caeruleum*) Lathkill Dale (SK1765) July 2013 (Bill Grange)

BACK COVER PHOTOGRAPHS
Barrow Stones in the Dark Peak, September 2005 (Nick Moyes)
Cross-leaved Heath (*Erica tetralix*) Eyam Moor, July 2005 (Bill Grange)
Cresswell Crags in the Magnesian Limestone, October 2011 (DCC)
Daffodils (*Narcissus pseudonarcissus*) Cromford Canal, April 2008 (Peter Smith)
The Avenue Washlands Reserve in the Coal Measures, September 2006 (DWT)
Purple Toothwort (*Lathraea clandestina*) Hilton Gravel Pits, April 2008 (Peter Smith)
Hilton Brook in the Trent Valley, June 2007 (DWT)
Marsh-marigold (*Caltha palustris*) near Calver, April 2008 (Peter Smith)
Countryside near Coton in the Elms in the Mease Lowlands (DCC)

Contents

Figures

Tables

Foreword

Professor Clive Anthony Stace B.Sc., Ph.D., D.Sc.
Author of *New Fora of the British Isles* 3rd Edition 2010

Derbyshire is my favourite botanical county, probably because, as a southerner, the Peak District provided my first taste of more northern floras after I obtained my first job at the University of Manchester in 1962. Plants such as *Myrrhis odorata*, *Rubus chamaemorus*, *Polemonium caeruleum* and *Minuartia verna* were quite new to me then, but soon became familiar on trips from my house on the western fringe of the Park. Northern plants like these are still easily found there, and for many plants Derbyshire represents the nearest localities to south-eastern England, where so many botanists seem rooted. Derbyshire has, of course, much to offer in addition to the Peak District. For example, the flora of the eastern Magnesian Limestone, with its more southern floristic connections, provides an instructive contrast with the harder Carboniferous Limestone of the Dales. The abundance and rarity respectively of Tor-grass is illustrative.

The previous Flora (1969) was of the old school, with lists of localities and little else other than the (excellent) introductory chapters. It reflected the fashions of the time, when, for example, alien plants were considered of relatively minor interest and received scant treatment. A new, up-to-date *Flora of Derbyshire* is therefore particularly welcome. It has the now familiar large format of a modern county Flora, with informative accounts of over 1,900 species, coloured tetrad dot-maps for over 1,100 species (those with more than six localities), and a generous sprinkling of coloured photographs. Among the supporting chapters, one that I particularly like is entitled "Where to see plants in Derbyshire", which tells the reader how to discover the botanical richness of the county, reminiscent of Geoffrey Wilmore's "A tour of botanical hotspots" in *The South Yorkshire Plant Atlas* (2011). The two works, in fact, share many similarities.

There have been numerous changes to the Derbyshire flora in the almost half-century since the 1969 publication, in which, for example, *Cochlearia danica* (now a common plant of salted roadsides) was not mentioned. The new arrival of aliens such as this, and the inclusion of others previously neglected (*e.g.* no garden Golden-rods or Michaelmas Daisies in the 1969 Flora), has certainly swelled the total number of species, but even in such a well-worked county there have been important discoveries of native species. For example, a second locality for *Potentilla crantzii* was found in 1974, nearly 200 years after the first, long-extinct one, and *Sesleria caerulea* was discovered for the first time in 1989 at its southernmost British locality; both sites are in Monk's Dale National Nature Reserve. This amply illustrates the importance of continuing field-work and the pleasures that it can bring.

As usual, we are indebted not only to the two authors but also to their army of recorders for providing us with a full, accurate and fascinating account of the plants of such an important county. Thank you, and congratulations for providing what such a botanical hot-spot demands. The Flora will be valued and enjoyed by residents and visitors alike, and referred to by others not lucky enough to botanise in it.

Clive A. Stace
Middlewood Green, Suffolk

Introduction

This *Flora* is an account of the vascular plants found in Derbyshire over the last 400 years. It covers all the flowers, trees, grasses, conifers, ferns, horsetails and clubmosses ever known to have occurred in the wild here.

The main part of this book is the 1,919 accounts and around 1,100 distribution maps of the species and plant hybrids recorded here (see **Chapter 2**). Their arrangement follows the *New Flora of the British Isles* 3rd Ed. (2010) by Clive Stace, to whom we are grateful for writing the Foreword. An explanation of the accounts and maps is given at the start of that chapter.

We have tried to build on the work of past botanists and the previous three county *Floras* by summarising information on each species ever known to have grown wild in Derbyshire since records began in 1581. **Chapter 3** provides a history of botanists and botanical recording in our county.

For this book we define "Derbyshire" as being a combination of two very similar areas. Most people will be familiar with the modern geographic county of Derbyshire (including Derby City), but we also include a slightly different boundary – the Watsonian vice-county of Derbyshire (v.c.57). This is an old but unchanging definition, unaffected by the political tweaks that are made from time to time; our distribution maps show both boundaries.

Whichever boundary you prefer, visitors will surely agree that Derbyshire really is a county of contrasting geology and very varied landscapes. We have divided it into eleven different **Derbyshire Landscape Character Areas**. These are outlined in red on most distribution maps; the Areas themselves are described in detail in **Chapter 1**. Most maps show relief as a coloured background.

It has taken almost 20 years to collate the 850,000 plant records summarised in this book. This would not have been possible without the efforts of a large number of botanists and local recorders, as well as an army of volunteers at the former Derbyshire Biological Records Centre in Derby Museum. Their help is acknowledged at the end of this book. Over 575,000 individual plant records have been collected in the field since our Flora Project began in 1994. A further quarter of a million records have been included from earlier surveys, herbarium specimens and previous county *Floras*.

For the purposes of this *Flora* we regard any plant report made in Derbyshire since the start of 1987 to be a "recent record". This was the year the Botanical Society of the British Isles launched its Rare Plants Survey across the UK and began the modern period of plant recording here. We show both the earliest and the most recent known recording dates in every species account, up to and including 2013.

Inevitably there will be errors, whether in field recording, computerisation or subsequent interpretation. But over the years we have gone to considerable lengths to ensure data is accurately recorded, inputted and checked again. Any mistakes that remain are the sole responsibility of the authors. In **Chapter 8** we list all the species known to have been incorrectly attributed *in print* to our county.

Sadly, this book comes at a time when many serious losses to our county's native flora have already occurred. Many workers have shown that major habitat loss or degradation have taken place since the last *Flora* appeared in 1969, and particularly to grassland sites. The GB conservation status of every rare or threatened species is given in the systematic accounts, along with our own Derbyshire Red List assessments of local rarity or decline. These are all tabulated in **Chapter 9**, along with a list of last-minute additions resulting from publication of the first ever *Vascular Plant Red List for England*. This will undoubtedly have significant implications for many organisations involved in protecting habitats and species from further losses. A history of plant conservation in Derbyshire is given in **Chapter 4**, written by a colleague from Derbyshire Wildlife Trust.

Despite the declines in native species and their habitats, there are always novel plants for botanists and naturalists to keep a look out for. **Chapter 7** lists all new species that came to light prior to publication, but which were impossible to include in the main part of this book.

Travelling the length and breadth of the county numerous times over the years has taken us and our band of recorders into many unusual places, and sometimes revealed surprising finds. We have learnt much from one another along the way, and we hope others may find this book useful in inspiring them to identify, record, conserve and report future changes in the flora of our county. In **Chapter 5** we suggest a range of publicly accessible sites worth visiting across all parts of Derbyshire which we hope will provide a helpful introduction to discovering our county's Flora. Any new records made can be sent to the Derbyshire Wildlife Trust who will forward them to us.

Alan Willmot & Nick Moyes
Derby, September 2014

CHAPTER 1

Derbyshire – its landscapes and vegetation

Alan Willmot

Introduction

Derbyshire has a very varied geology and contains many different, but characteristic landscapes. These in their turn determine a wide mix of vegetation types. In many ways, our county is a microcosm of Great Britain, with lowland farming landscapes on the soft rocks of the Trent Valley in the south where the climate is relatively benign, to upland moorlands and blanket bog on the hard rocks of the Peak District in the north-west, where the climate can be severe. The only major British landscape elements missing are coastal ones. Derbyshire is land-locked; in fact Church Flatts Farm near Coton in the Elms in the south holds the record for being the furthest point from the sea of anywhere in Great Britain. Derbyshire lies in the East Midlands between Staffordshire to the west and Nottinghamshire to the east. This centrality of position and variety of landscape give the county a rich flora and an interesting mix of species. Many southern species reach their northern British limits here, while many northern species are at their southern extreme.

Despite being in central England and surrounded by major conurbations such as Manchester, Sheffield and Nottingham (**Figure 1.1**), Derbyshire itself has a relatively low population density compared to England as a whole. In fact it has just over

Table 1.1 Key Derbyshire statistics. This book combines both the modern geographic county and the botanical vice-county in all species maps and accounts.

"GREATER DERBYSHIRE" FACT FILE			
Area of "Greater Derbyshire" (as used in this *Flora*)	**2,725.4 km²**		
Count of Monads	**Total 2,960**;	whole 2,547;	partial 413
Count of Tetrads	**Total 771**;	whole 599;	partial 172
Count of Hectads	**Total 45**;	whole 12;	partial 33
Size of each Landscape Character Area (LCAs)			
White Peak LCA	436.1 km²		
Dark Peak LCA	606.2 km²		
South West Peak LCA	81.8 km²		
Magnesian Limestone LCA	99.2 km²		
Peak Fringe LCA	377.7 km²		
Coal Measures LCA	459.8 km²		
Claylands LCA	337.8 km²		
Trent Valley LCA	150.8 km²		
Parklands LCA	69.8 km²		
Southern Coal Measures LCA	44.0 km²		
Mease Lowlands LCA	62.1 km²		
Biodiversity features			
SAC count + area	5 sites (27,878ha)		
NNR count + area	4 sites (1,810ha)		
SSSI count + area	106 sites (31,214ha)		
LNR count + area	55 sites (742ha)		
Derbyshire LWS count + area	1,175 sites (10,035ha)		
Geographic features			
Highest Point	Kinder Scout, 636m asl		
Lowest Point	River Trent/Trent Meadows, 27m asl		
Longest River	River Derwent (106km)		
Most Northerly Point	Black Hill/Heyden Head, SE084048		
Most Southerly Point	River Mease, SK267110		
Most Easterly Point	Bismarck Plantation, SK556756		
Most Westerly Point	River Goyt/Compstall Bridge, SJ960917		
Other data			
Population of modern Derbyshire	1.024 million (at 2013)		
Area of modern Derbyshire	2,628.7 km²		
Area of Vice-county 57	2,633.4 km²		
Area difference between modern and "Greater Derbyshire"	92.0 km²		
Area difference between modern Derbyshire and Vice-county 57	4.7 km²		

Figure 1.1 Area covered by this *Flora*. Modern Derbyshire is outlined in black with vice-county in red. The Peak District National Park boundary is shown in blue, but those parts falling outside either definition of "Derbyshire" are not covered by this book.

a million inhabitants. This means that overall the landscape has a generally agricultural aspect. There are relatively few areas of woodland and some very built-up regions, with heavy industry now confined mainly to mineral and gravel extraction. However, there are still many signs of past industrial land use in the form of restored coal-mining areas and a number of old mill buildings, newly converted to offices or light industry. This rural landscape with its surrounding population, which includes around one third of the inhabitants of England within an hour's drive, means that Derbyshire is a popular tourist destination. It is estimated that almost 10 million people visit the area every year. The majority head for the **Peak District National Park** in the north of the county. The remainder visit the area to the south of the National Park, which is referred to as **Lowland Derbyshire**. This includes the **National Forest** which lies in the very southern toe of the county and which is now gradually attracting more tourists. Most holiday-makers just come to look and see, but others are attracted to the more energetic pursuits provided by the Peak District terrain. Here the southern end of the Pennines finish with a final flourish of moorlands and rocky outcrops, attracting mountain bikers, climbers and hill-walkers.

For the purposes of this book we consider both the modern geographic county of Derbyshire, and also include a slightly different boundary, known as the vice-county of Derbyshire (v.c.57). This is a definition which has not altered since the 19th century, when botanists first realised the need to have unchanging boundaries for comparison purposes, and these are still much in use today (see **Figure 1.1**). When considered together, these add an additional 92km² to the modern geographic county, which itself covers an area of 2,628km². For convenience, we tend to refer to this combined region as "Greater Derbyshire".

Natural vegetation

This mix of tourism, agriculture, mineral extraction and urbanisation means there is virtually no natural vegetation left in Derbyshire. The upland north-west corner in the Peak District is less affected by development than the lowland southern and eastern parts. The National Park still contains large areas of semi-natural vegetation in the form of moorlands where the hand of man is written less obviously on the land. In contrast, south and east Derbyshire is basically a series of artificial landscapes, a man-made palimpsest of grazing land and cereal fields, bounded by hedges or by drystone walls on the upland fringes. Before the advent of farming around 5,000 years ago, the whole of the county would have been clothed in natural vegetation. The study of plant remains preserved in peat has given us a clear picture of how this has changed. At the end of the last Ice Age the vegetation returned; at the start this would have been heathland-like tundra. Then woody plants invaded, initially forming a light woodland of **Scots Pine** (*Pinus sylvestris*) and **birch** (*Betula* spp.). Around 5500 BC, due to climatic amelioration, larger and more warmth-loving trees such as **oak** (*Quercus* spp.), **elm** (*Ulmus* spp.) and **lime** (*Tilia* spp.) moved in to replace the Pine and Birch, so producing denser forests. This forest extended far beyond the bounds of our county to cover the entire country. Indeed, it has been suggested that a Red Squirrel could theoretically have moved through this landscape from Land's End to John O'Groats without ever touching the ground.

This dense wildwood would not have been uniform in species composition, however. Where limestone underlay the soil, there would have been more Lime and Elm. Where clays and sandstones occurred, Oak would have become more dominant. In the river valleys and wetter areas these would have been replaced to a large extent by **Alder** (*Alnus glutinosa*) and **willows** (*Salix* spp.). Continuous as this forest is thought to have been, there must have been open areas within it, permitting more light-demanding species to survive. They might have been created by severe weather events, meandering rivers or by foraging animals thinning the forest canopy. These would have been deer, Boar or Aurochs, which were the forest-dwelling ancestors of domesticated cattle.

As the climate became wetter, many of the upland peats in the county began accumulating. There was little change to this dense deciduous forest until around 3000 BC when people first began to farm the region. They felled trees to provide areas for agriculture, a process which carried on gradually with occasional reversals until the fourteenth century. By that time most of Derbyshire had been cleared of trees for farming, with arable land in the lowlands and open-style grazing on moors in the uplands, much like today. Of course, clearance did not all occur at once, nor did forests disappear overnight. Some woods were no doubt clear-felled and quickly converted to arable, but most woods were probably grazed out by

stock over a period of time. In the case of medieval hunting forests, such as Duffield Frith, this period of half clearance with grazing may have continued for many hundreds of years. In some areas, such as the parklands surrounding Calke Abbey and Kedleston Hall, it is still possible to see the end of this process in the estates of veteran trees standing over open rough grazings. It is this process of clearance for agriculture, coupled with mining for rocks and minerals, and building for industry and housing that has produced the current landscapes and vegetation we see in Derbyshire today.

Derbyshire Landscape Character Areas

We have divided the county's differing landscapes into eleven separate units which we call **Derbyshire Landscape Character Areas**. They were developed specifically for this book (see **Figure 1.2**), but are basically just slightly simplified versions of the **National Character Areas** of Natural England. They appear outlined in red on the majority of distribution maps within this book.

Because two of these Landscape Character Areas are so similar (the Dark Peak and the South West Peak) we describe them together in this Chapter within the Dark Peak section. Within each Character Area attention is drawn to the more interesting types of semi-natural vegetation that are likely to interest visiting botanists.

Figure 1.2 Derbyshire Landscape Character Areas.

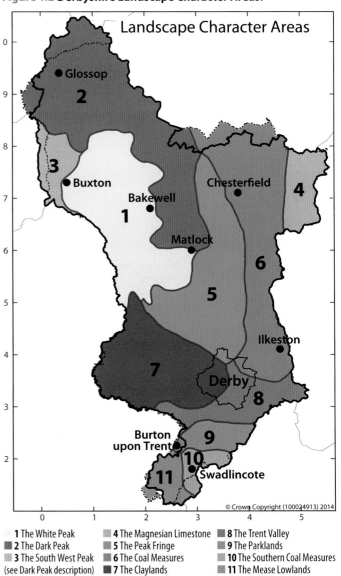

1 The White Peak **4** The Magnesian Limestone **8** The Trent Valley
2 The Dark Peak **5** The Peak Fringe **9** The Parklands
3 The South West Peak **6** The Coal Measures **10** The Southern Coal Measures
(see Dark Peak description) **7** The Claylands **11** The Mease Lowlands

© Crown Copyright (100024913) 2014

For detailed recommendations of publicly accessible sites to visit in each Landscape Character Area, refer to **Chapter 5** "Where to See Plants in Derbyshire"

Note: The descriptions of each Character Area rely heavily on the work of the Landscape Team at Derbyshire County Council, whose assistance is gratefully acknowledged. Their further subdivision and description of these Areas into smaller "Landscape Character Types" can be found on their website.

1 THE WHITE PEAK LANDSCAPE CHARACTER AREA

Landscape description and geology

The White Peak is Derbyshire's most iconic Landscape Character Area for botanists as it contains the greatest plant diversity of all those discussed here, as well as most of the prime rarities for which naturalists visit. Geographically, the White Peak forms the core of the county, extending some 35km north–south from Castleton to Ashbourne, and 25km east–west from Matlock to Buxton. It takes its name from the pale grey limestone rocks which underpin this Character Area, forming a gently rolling **Plateau**, dissected by steep-sided river valleys known locally as **Dales**. The majority of these are now dry valleys but a number contain significant watercourses, such as the River Wye in Miller's Dale. The limestone plateau rises gently from an altitude of 300m in the south to one of around 370m in the north, and exhibits many of the classic features of **karst** scenery, such as caves and sink holes. Generally referred to as **Carboniferous Limestone**, the rock is more properly known as **Dinantian Limestone**. It was deposited as calcareous sediments from the remains of innumerable sea creatures on the floor of a shallow tropical sea some 360 to 320 million years ago when the land, which is now Derbyshire, was situated just south of the equator. The seabed itself was slowly sinking, allowing great thicknesses of lime-rich sediments to build up. Occasional volcanic activity spewed molten **lava** out onto the sea bed in places, or forced it between the layers of limestone sediments as **dolerite sills**, or even ejected fine ash into the air which settled on the seabed, until life returned once again. Around the margins of this sea were muddy algal reefs, and these formed harder limestones than those originating from the sea floor deposits. Although over 1.5km deep, all these sediments were, in their turn, later buried by massive deposits of sand, grit and mud until almost 300 million years ago, when the rocks that formed from them were uplifted and folded into a huge dome, causing them to be eroded and the earlier rocks re-exposed. By coincidence, these reef limestones are at the stage of being re-exhumed today, and are now found round the edge of the limestone plateau, forming upstanding outcrops, hills and crags, as at Castleton, Matlock Bath and Dove Dale.

After their formation, the buried Carboniferous Limestone underwent a number of processes which modified it and which, much later, influenced the plants we find associated with it today. Possibly the first change was the intrusion into the limestone of magnesium-rich solutions. This caused the calcium carbonate in places to be changed into magnesium carbonate – a process known as **dolomitisation**. Such limestone erodes more readily to form isolated upstanding pinnacles of rock called **tors**. This period also saw extensive mineralisation of the limestone in the form of pipes and veins of high pressure liquids which were forced through the solid rock. On cooling, these liquids precipitated minerals such as fluorspar, calcite and barytes, as well as various lead and copper-containing ores. During a much later period of uplift the limestone was eroded by water, forming deep surface hollows in places. These were subsequently infilled with thick deposits of Tertiary age sands, gravels and clays, some 20 million years ago.

Now known as the **Brassington Formation,** they are often just referred to as **silica sand pockets**. The limestone plateau was then again uplifted, such that during the last 2 million years, the **Pleistocene** epoch, it was above sea level. In the early part of this period it was glaciated at least twice, leaving behind large patches of clay on the limestone surface, known as **glacial till**. Later on in this epoch, during the last British glaciation, the White Peak was just to the south of the main ice front. The lack of glacial ice at this time probably explains why there are virtually no limestone pavements in the county similar to those found further north on the Yorkshire limestone which was then glaciated. Though not ice-covered, our area was still subject to severe periglacial conditions of intense cold, drought and strong winds. It was under these conditions that up to half a metre of fine wind-blown material called **loess** was deposited on the surface of the plateau.

Where there are no superficial deposits, current soils are derived directly from the weathering of the limestone itself. These are well-drained inorganic soils, neutral and deep on the plateau, but shallow and calcareous on the sides of the dales. Where there are patches of glacial deposits, loess or silica sand pockets, these have all led to the formation of more acidic soils on the plateau. Finally, soils high in heavy metals such as lead have developed where mineral veins have been exposed.

The wealth and variety of rock types and minerals in the White Peak have attracted mining and quarrying from at least the Roman period when lead ore was certainly mined. This has continued, quite literally, up to the modern day when other minerals such as fluorspar and barytes found with the lead are still sought. Lead has been won from underground mines as well as from linear surface outcrops, known locally as **rakes**. All this lead-mining activity has left many areas of spoil and soil contaminated with heavy metals. Limestone quarrying over the years has produced the greatest volume of mineral extraction from this Landscape Character Area. Today the region is covered in many old abandoned and smaller quarries, plus some very large and still active modern ones, particularly near Wirksworth and Buxton. There has also been quarrying of the silica sand pockets for clay and sand to manufacture refractory bricks. The result of all this activity has been to increase the incidence of naturally occurring habitats, rather than to create new ones. The limestone quarries increased the number of rock outcrops; lead extraction increased the amount of heavy metal-polluted grassland, while only the silica

Deep Dale (Chelmorton) in the White Peak with Early-purple Orchids and Cowslips in spring (DCC)

sand mining has produced new habitats in the form of sandpits and lakes where clay has been removed.

Vegetation of the White Peak – The Dales

The White Peak is an agricultural landscape; there are some quarries and a few settlements, but basically it is an area of farmed countryside. The limestone plateau now supports highly productive "improved" grassland, used for pasture, hay and grazing. It consists of regular fields surrounded by drystone walls of grey limestone rocks, and generally holds little interest for botanists apart from along abandoned railway lines such as the High Peak and the Tissington Trails which wend their way through this botanically depauperate landscape. It is in the Dales where the floristic interest really lies. Here there are mainly open, grazed grasslands for sheep with some areas of Hazel scrub, Ash woodland, limestone outcrops and screes, plus the occasional stream with marshy areas.

The limestone grasslands – It is the grasslands of the Dales that are the jewel in the crown of Derbyshire botany. Not only are they extremely biodiverse, with up to 45 plant species per square metre, but they can be stunningly beautiful at times, too. In spring there can be carpets of gold and magenta with Cowslips (*Primula veris*) amongst drifts of Early-purple Orchid (*Orchis mascula*). Later in the year there are shows of deep-red Bloody Crane's-bill (*Geranium sanguineum*), bright yellow Common Rock-rose (*Helianthemum nummularium*) and the rich-cream of Dropwort (*Filipendula vulgaris*). Variable over the seasons, these **calcareous grasslands** also vary within the dales themselves. At one extreme, on the steepest slopes and thinnest soils on south-facing dale-sides, there are areas of open grassland dominated by short, fine-leaved grasses such as Sheep's-fescue (*Festuca ovina*) and Quaking-grass (*Briza media*). These areas tend to be richest in the more attractive species such as Common Rock-rose and Bloody Crane's-bill. At the other extreme, on the shallower hillsides, deeper soils and north-facing slopes, there are areas of taller denser grassland dominated by larger grasses such as oat-grasses (*Avenula* spp.) with wetland plants such as Meadowsweet (*Filipendula ulmaria*), Common Valerian (*Valeriana officinalis*) and Grass-of-Parnassus (*Parnassia palustris*). In between these extremes a whole range of other colourful species can occur including:

Common Bird's-foot-trefoil (*Lotus corniculatus*)
Common Milkwort (*Polygala vulgaris*)
Fairy Flax (*Linum catharticum*)
Hoary Plantain (*Plantago media*)
Jacob's-ladder (*Polemonium caeruleum*)
Limestone Bedstraw (*Galium sterneri*)
Rough Hawkbit (*Leontodon hispidus*)
Wild Thyme (*Thymus polytrichus*)

Towards the shoulders of some Dales, where slopes begin to grade out and soils become deeper, the above-mentioned calcareous grasslands can begin to be replaced by more **acid grasslands**. This may be due to rain leaching the lime from the soil or to the presence of glacial deposits or loess. Typical species here are Tormentil (*Potentilla erecta*), Heath Bedstraw (*Galium saxatile*) and even Heather (*Calluna vulgaris*), Bilberry (*Vaccinium myrtillus*) or Mat-grass (*Nardus stricta*) which can be found growing next to lime-loving species like Hoary Plantain (*Plantago media*). In a few places, where igneous intrusions force groundwater to come to the surface, flushes occur on the dalesides which may contain a suite of sedges and mosses plus occasionally the curious insect-eating Common Butterwort (*Pinguicula vulgaris*).

Limestone streams – Despite being on limestone, a number of the White Peak dales have streams in them that flow continuously, except in years of extreme drought. Others have **winterbournes,** but it is the permanent streams like the Rivers Dove and Lathkill that are scenically and floristically most attractive. Their waters are very pure and exceptionally clear. Water-starworts (*Callitriche* spp.) and water-crowfoots (*Ranunculus* spp.) float in midstream, while water-cresses (*Nasturtium* spp.) and Brooklime (*Veronica beccabunga*) line the shallow margins. On the banks there may be marshy areas with Meadowsweet (*Filipendula ulmaria*) and Hemp-agrimony (*Eupatorium cannabinum*). In places, extensive stands of the umbrella-like leaves of Butterbur (*Petasites hybridus*) shade the river margins.

Scrub occurs irregularly throughout the Dales where grazing has been less intense. These areas are not as colourful as the grasslands but can have similarly bold shows of flowers, particularly in spring. There may be clouds of Wood Anemone (*Anemone nemorosa*) or of Ramsons (*Allium ursinum*) which scent the air. The most botanically rich and interesting is that dominated by Hazel (*Corylus avellana*) and which is often referred to as **retrogressive scrub**. This is thought to have been derived from the original wildwood by the removal of trees, followed by light grazing with a later return towards woodland on the reduction of that grazing. Such areas are considered never to have been completely cleared of woody vegetation which explains their rich sylvan flora. Botanical gems of this habitat are Lily-of-the-valley (*Convallaria majalis*), Mezereon (*Daphne mezereum*) and, rarely, Dark-red Helleborine (*Epipactis atrorubens*).

Ash woodland occurs in many of the Dales on the steeper slopes, often where there is a large amount of fallen rock debris or outcrops of limestone. This is not thought to be the natural or **climatic climax** woodland of the area rather it is spontaneous re-growth of woodland after a cessation of, or reduction in, grazing. Along with the dominant Ash (*Fraxinus excelsior*) there may be a few limes (*Tilia* spp.) and oaks (*Quercus* spp.), particularly higher up the slopes where the soils are often deeper and less calcareous. These Ash woods are not as floristically rich as the Hazel Scrub but may contain Mountain Melick (*Melica nutans*), Narrow-leaved Bitter-cress (*Cardamine impatiens*) or Mountain Currant (*Ribes alpinum*). The latter typically grows as curtains tumbling down over vertical rock faces.

Rock outcrops and screes – The largest rock outcrops provide grazing-free refugia where trees can survive which have been unable to exist elsewhere because of the grazing of sheep. These include Yew (*Taxus baccata*), Rock Whitebeam (*Sorbus rupicola*) and Wild Service-tree (*S. torminalis*). These crags and smaller outcrops can shelter ferns in their crevices such as Brittle Bladder-fern (*Cystopteris fragilis*) and Green Spleenwort (*Asplenium viride*). Those ledges that dry out in summer can support small annuals such as Hutchinsia (*Hornungia petraea*) and Wall Whitlowgrass (*Draba muralis*). Screes of fallen rock fragments typically have a much more restricted flora, with Ash the commonest colonist, followed by Herb-Robert (*Geranium robertianum*) and occasionally the Limestone Fern (*Gymnocarpium robertianum*) or Red Hemp-nettle (*Galeopsis angustifolia*).

Lead mine spoil tips can occur anywhere in the White Peak where there are mineral veins – in the Dales or on the Plateau. Here the high levels of toxic lead and other heavy metals in the soil prevent the growth of most plants except for the very few which can tolerate them. Spoil tips are therefore generally very open communities with a large amount of bare soil. The two most characteristic species are Spring Sandwort (*Minuartia verna*) and Alpine Penny-cress (*Noccaea caerulescens*). These both have bright white flowers and, confusingly, both are known locally as "Leadwort". Where the concentration of lead is lower and hence there is more vegetation, other species are found including Sheep's-fescue (*Festuca ovina*), Mountain Pansy (*Viola lutea*) and Moonwort (*Botrychium lunaria*). These areas are also referred to as **metallophyte** or **calaminarian grasslands**.

Vegetation of the White Peak – The Plateau

The natural vegetation of the Plateau would have been **mixed deciduous woodland**, growing on a soil derived from various mixtures of weathered limestone, glacial clay and loess. When the trees in these woods were cleared and replaced by more shallow-rooted species, the soils became acidic with a semi-natural covering of heathland. They remained like this until the 1800s when the heathlands were ploughed up and limed to produce high quality agricultural land, now with calcareous soils. As stated above, this plateau now consists of regular pasture fields surrounded by drystone walls of grey limestone rock. Although an attractive landscape in its own way, it offers little to interest the botanist, apart from along the abandoned railway lines of the High Peak Trail and especially the Tissington Trail which provide narrow flowery ribbons snaking their way through an otherwise green desert.

The White Peak plateau at Grin Low near Buxton, June 2010 (Kieron Huston)

Limestone heath – Only tiny remnants of the originally widespread heathland now remain on a few roadsides and on the shoulders of some dales. Like most heathlands, these support only a restricted flora, dominated by Heather (*Calluna vulgaris*) and Bilberry (*Vaccinium myrtillus*) with some Western Gorse (*Ulex gallii*) and Wavy Hair-grass (*Deschampsia flexuosa*).

Silica sand pits – These constitute the only other habitat of botanical interest on the Plateau. There are around 60 known pits that have been worked to some extent and they are very variable due to the range of deposits within them. Most have patches of scrub and open disturbed areas, while many have open water or marshy areas, too. Where there are sandy deposits, these have generally been colonised by acid grassland or heath species such as Wavy Hair-grass and Heather. They are particularly known for supporting up to three species of rare fern allies, the Clubmosses: Alpine (*Diphasiastrum alpinum*), Fir (*Huperzia selago*) and Stag's-horn Clubmoss (*Lycopodium clavatum*). Unfortunately most sites are not open to the public; the only one with easy access is Green Lane Pits (SK165626).

2 THE DARK PEAK LANDSCAPE CHARACTER AREA
(Description incorporates The South West Peak Area)

Landscape description

The Dark or "High Peak" is an elevated plateau of sandstones, grits and shales to the north of the White Peak, which also extends down its flanks in the form of the **Western** and **Eastern Moors**. It constitutes the southern end of the Pennines, with the plateau forming an elevated block of land lying between Manchester to the west and Sheffield to the east. In its highest parts it is a wild open area of continuous moorland surrounded at lower altitudes by enclosed farmland and dissected by deep river valleys. The whole area is underlain by rocks of the **Namurian** or **Millstone Grit** series. These consist of a series of shales, mudstones and coarse sandstones deposited in a river delta some 330 to 320 million years ago which buried the earlier limestone sediments. All these rocks weather and erode to produce acidic nutrient-poor soils. In the case of the shales and mudstones, these are heavy wet soils, whereas the sandstones weather to produce more freely-draining sandy soils. On the highest parts of the sandstone plateau, between 530 to 630 metres altitude, the heavy rainfall and cold climate counteract this free-draining nature to produce waterlogged soils. Over the last 10,000 years this has led to the formation of **blanket peats** which lie over the landscape to a depth of up to three metres in places.

Dark Peak moorlands from Win Hill, February 2006 (Ashley Franklin)

Apart from the elevated plateau the main features of the Dark Peak are its valleys. These may be narrow and rocky with fast-flowing streams. Such valleys are locally known as **cloughs** and are generally clothed in moorland vegetation. The larger broader valleys such as the Vale of Edale and the Derwent Valley generally have enclosed farmland in their bottoms, but have rocky outcrops along their upper slopes. These outcrops are usually of coarse sandstone (often termed **gritstone**) and although only 20 metres high can extend for many kilometres. These are the famous **Edges** of the county which castellate many of the major valley sides. They often have boulder-strewn slopes below them, known as **blockfields** and may have the occasional upstanding outcrop of rock or tor above. These Edges have often been the subject of small-scale quarrying for building or grinding stones. The coarse-grained sandstones were particularly well-suited for grinding grain, hence the colloquial name of **Millstone Grit** for the rocks. Reject millstones were sometimes cast out from the quarries on to the boulder fields below the edges, or they lay in situ, abandoned and unloved following the rapid collapse of this local manufacturing industry in the early 19th century until they were adopted as the physical logo of the Peak District National Park.

Another but far less obvious feature of the landscapes of the Dark Peak is the presence of **landslides**. These occur along the sides of valleys where shales and other softer rocks underlie the gritstone edges. Shales are both impervious to water and often unable to support their own weight, so can simply collapse after periods of heavy rain, leaving large scars on the valley sides. These revegetate quickly but are visible as slumpings in many areas. The most famous place for landslides is Mam Tor, known locally as the Shivering Mountain. Here frequent landslides caused the need for continual repair and eventual closure in 1979 of the A625 road between Sheffield and Manchester. Landslides are simply an extreme expression of the weathering and subsequent erosion that affects every landscape, all the time. Another more obvious example of erosion is that of the blanket peats on the higher areas of the plateau such as Kinder Scout. There is much discussion over the exact cause of this peat erosion. Pollution, drainage, excessive burning and over-grazing have all been implicated by various authors. Whatever the actual reason, large areas of the Dark Peak plateau are currently just bare peat. In places this is being rapidly eroded by the rain down to just a bare skeleton of grey rock. Urgent action is now being taken to reverse and repair this erosion, with the blocking of gulleys and the re-planting of moorland species.

The major land use in the Dark Peak is agriculture as there are few settlements, particularly at higher altitudes, and little sign of industry apart from the abandoned quarries on the Edges. Agriculture generally takes the form of open sheep-grazing higher up on unenclosed moorland. Lower down in the more sheltered valleys, there is some limited beef cattle and dairy farming with small-scale enclosed fields surrounded by drystone gritstone walls. Most of the moors are very intensively managed for the grouse shooting industry, while some of the larger valleys have been dammed to form water storage reservoirs for the large conurbations surrounding the county. Some of these larger valleys have also been used for conifer plantations, and large blocks of dark trees have further added to the already sombre nature of the Dark Peak Landscape Character Area. Another increasingly important use of the landscape is for tourism, with hill walking and mountain biking in the valleys and on the plateau, plus rock climbing and bouldering on the Edges. Lacking the tourist comforts of toilets and cafes, the plateau gets less tourist pressure than the more lowland areas. However, there is still significant human erosion here, with the Pennine Way across Bleaklow looking like the M1 of footpaths, paved as it is now with the sandstone bases of old mill machinery, aimed at protecting the delicate peat.

Vegetation of the Dark Peak

At around 600 metres, the upper reaches of Kinder Scout and Bleaklow contain what is probably the only extensive area of virtually natural vegetation in the county. Here above the tree line, where the rainfall and low temperatures produce constantly waterlogged ground, there are large areas of **blanket bog**. Lower down where sheep grazing and moor burning for grouse prevents tree growth, there is semi-natural moorland where once there would naturally have been woodland. This moorland is generally a mixture of acid grassland, heathland and further areas of bog. A few patches of semi-natural woodland have survived in some of the high valleys. Lower down, amongst the enclosed fields of the valley bottoms, there are further extensive areas of acid grassland.

Heathland, dominated by low undershrubs such as Heather (*Calluna vulgaris*), Bilberry (*Vaccinium myrtillus*), Cowberry (*V. vitis-idaea*) and Crowberry (*Empetrum nigrum*), covers large areas of the upland moors of the Dark Peak Landscape Character Area. They are generally species-poor, but can produce beautiful landscapes moulded with the purple of the Heather in late summer. The only other abundant vascular plant here generally is Wavy Hair-grass (*Deschampsia flexuosa*). Where the ground is wetter, a range of other species can occur, including the pale-pink nodding heads of Cross-leaved Heath (*Erica tetralix*), Purple Moor-grass (*Molinia caerulea*) and Deergrass (*Trichophorum germanicum*).

Bogs – At the highest altitudes **blanket bogs** occur, covering the entire ground surface, except where eroded. Lower down, bogs are more confined to damp hollows, leaving the slightly better-drained ground to grass and heathland. These bogs are dominated by tussocks of Hare's-tail Cottongrass (*Eriophorum vaginatum*) in the drier parts, and by Common Cottongrass (*Eriophorum angustifolium*) in the wetter ones. Both can produce drifts of white fluffy seed heads that move in the wind and can look like the crests of billowing waves on a sea of green. Compared to bogs elsewhere, mosses are rare here, probably due to the high levels of industrial air pollution in these parts in the past. Where mosses do occur, the fine thread-like shoots of Cranberry (*Vaccinium oxycoccos*) are often found growing. The yellow flowers of Bog Asphodel (*Narthecium ossifragum*) will light up some of the wetter areas in summer, while the white flowers of Cloudberry (*Rubus chamaemorus*) can do the same on some of the higher drier areas. Various landscape-scale projects are currently engaged in restoring these degraded habitats.

Acid grasslands – Various types of acid grassland occur in the Derbyshire uplands. Probably the most widespread and species-rich are those dominated by a combination of two grasses: Common Bent (*Agrostis capillaris*) and Sheep's-fescue (*Festuca ovina*). A restricted range of herbaceous plants grow alongside these, the commonest being Tormentil (*Potentilla erecta*) and Heath Bedstraw (*Galium saxatile*). Rarer, but with more showy flowers, are Mountain Pansy (*Viola lutea*), Harebell (*Campanula rotundifolia*) and Bitter-vetch (*Lathyrus linifolius*). Where sheep pressure is more intense, even these few plants are grazed out and Mat-grass (*Nardus stricta*) takes over as the dominant species since sheep find its silica-rich leaves to be unpalatable.

Gritstone Edges and blockfields – Where they are not "gardened" by rock climbers, the larger outcrops can provide ledges out of reach of the ubiquitous sheep, where grazing-sensitive species such as Great Wood-rush (*Luzula sylvatica*) and Goldenrod (*Solidago virgaurea*) can survive. Crevices may provide

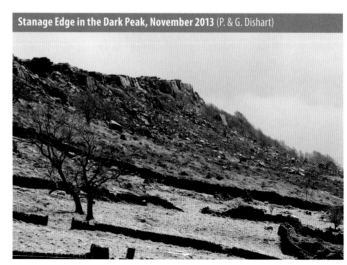

Stanage Edge in the Dark Peak, November 2013 (P. & G. Dishart)

sites for the rare and delicate Beech Fern (*Phegopteris connectilis*) and Oak Fern (*Gymnocarpium dryopteris*). A few of the deepest crevices support the extremely rare Killarney Fern (*Trichomanes speciosum*), but unfortunately it is not present as the more familiar leafy asexual stage, but only as the very diminutive algal-like sexual stage. Blockfields with their larger, deeper crevices tend to support bigger ferns such as Golden-scaled Male-fern (*Dryopteris affinis*) and Lemon-scented Fern (*Oreopteris limbosperma*).

Upland acid woodlands – These semi-natural remnants of the native woodland vegetation of the area occur in the upper parts of cloughs and on rocky hillsides where the difficult terrain has discouraged its complete clearance for agriculture. These woods are dominated by both species of oak (*Quercus petraea* and *Q. robur*) with occasional trees of Silver Birch (*Betula pendula*), Holly (*Ilex aquifolium*) and Rowan (*Sorbus aucuparia*). Where grazed by sheep, they have only a very limited and sparse understorey of heathy species including Heather, Wavy Hair-grass, Wood-sorrel (*Oxalis acetosella*) and Bilberry. Where sheep are excluded, however, they have a rich and luxuriant field layer of the same species plus others such as Wood Club-rush (*Scirpus sylvaticus*) and Upland Enchanter's-nightshade (*Circaea* × *intermedia*).

3 THE SOUTH WEST PEAK LANDSCAPE CHARACTER AREA

The small part of this National Character Area that falls within Derbyshire is so similar to the Dark Peak that all its features have been described in that section above. It lies between Buxton and Chapel-en-le-Frith, and is bounded on the west by the Goyt Valley. Although not described further here, it is shown as a distinct Derbyshire Landscape Character Area on all the distribution maps in this book.

4 THE MAGNESIAN LIMESTONE LANDSCAPE CHARACTER AREA

Landscape description
The Magnesian Limestone Landscape Character Area in Derbyshire is very different from its Carboniferous Limestone cousin further to the west. This is a mellower more-rounded landscape; the predominant colours are yellow tints rather than the harsh grey-whites of the White Peak, and its rock outcrops are less angular. This is a smaller area, too – a narrow belt of land some 20km long, north–south, and some 10km wide east–west. It occupies an elevated position 150 to 200m high in the north-eastern corner

Hardwick Estate in the Magnesian Limestone Area with the Hall in the background, October 2003 (DCC)

of Derbyshire, with the town of Bolsover at its edge, overlooking the somewhat lower Coal Measures to its west. The underlying rock is Magnesian Limestone. This was formed from sediments laid down at the bottom of a shallow, land-locked sea during the **Permian** period, some 290 to 250 million years ago. It is a relatively soft limestone that is easily weathered and eroded, resulting in a general landscape of a plateau of rounded hills. This plateau is dissected by narrow rocky gorges known locally as **Grips** which often have caves worn into their sides. The most famous are those at Creswell Crags where a rich fossil fauna and evidence of pre-historic man from 45,000 years ago has been found. Here, remains of Spotted Hyena and Mammoth have been discovered along with the earliest cave art known in Britain.

The soils derived from the breakdown of the Magnesian Limestone are light well-draining and mineral-rich, with generally a red tinge. In short, they are fertile soils which are excellent for intensive cereal cropping. This Landscape Character Area is thus predominantly one of large arable fields separated by hedges, or drystone walls in a few areas. There are also a few large areas of woodland on the plateau. The Grips are either wooded or used for grazing, since their steep sides and often waterlogged bottoms make them unsuitable for cultivation. In the past there has been some limited opencast quarrying for limestone and deep mining for the coal that lies far beneath it. Both these activities ceased some time ago, and the evidence of them has either moulded back into the landscape or been actively restored. Otherwise there is limited evidence of industry in the Area, though the situation may change in the near future as there are disputed plans for wind turbines here. The main towns are Bolsover, Clowne and Shirebrook with further urban development of this Landscape Character Area limited to a few scattered villages. Here, the older buildings, with their traditional construction materials of Magnesian Limestone and red clay pantiles, easily melt back into the landscape.

Creswell Crags in the Magnesian Limestone Area has numerous caves with some famous prehistoric cave art, May 2003 (DCC)

Vegetation of the Magnesian Limestone
There are only two types of vegetation that stand out here as being of particular interest to visiting plant-lovers. These are its woodlands and its calcareous grasslands. At best, both can only be described as semi-natural in that neither is entirely natural, nor have they been simply planted. Other habitats that exist here, albeit of generally lesser interest, include hedges and marshy areas.

Woodlands – Where not just modern plantations of Ash or conifers, the local semi-natural woodlands here can contain a rich canopy of broad-leaved trees. These include Pedunculate Oak (*Quercus robur*), the two native species of lime (*Tilia cordata* and *T. platyphyllos*) and

Ash (*Fraxinus excelsior*), plus the native conifer Yew (*Taxus baccata*). Underneath this canopy there is a variety of shrubs: Hazel (*Corylus avellana*) is usually the most abundant species with lesser amounts of Field Maple (*Acer campestre*), Spindle (*Euonymus europaeus*), Dogwood (*Cornus sanguinea*) and Wild Privet (*Ligustrum vulgare*). Beneath these are typically an even more species-rich strata of herbaceous plants which include common flowers such as Bluebell (*Hyacinthoides non-scripta*), Primrose (*Primula vulgaris*) and Dog's Mercury (*Mercurialis perennis*). There may also be rarer ones such as Columbine (*Aquilegia vulgaris*), Giant Bellflower (*Campanula latifolia*) and a particular feature of these woods, Common Gromwell (*Lithospermum officinale*), with its strange stone-like white fruits. Woodlands such as these are best seen on the sides of Grips. Here on the steepest crags the roots of trees thrust themselves into crevices, holding the rocks in place until they die and rot away, leaving the cliff face to crumble. Patches of semi-natural woodland also occur in the plateau, along the margins of plantations. In addition, trees are present along hedgerows and around stately homes such as Hardwick Hall where today's veterans were planted in "platoons" on the parkland.

Magnesian Limestone grasslands – The general grassland flora in this Landscape Character Area is basically the same as that of the more extensive Carboniferous Limestone grasslands further west, but there are some important differences. Grasslands here are generally associated with the Grips, although there are some patches on the sides of disused mineral railways and the plateau. They are dominated by a complex and variable mixture of grasses and sedges: including Sheep's-fescue (*Festuca ovina*), Sweet Vernal-grass (*Anthoxanthum odoratum*), Quaking-grass (*Briza media*), Glaucous Sedge (*Carex flacca*) and Spring-sedge (*C. caryophyllea*) amongst others. One noticeable difference is how much commoner Tor-grass (*Brachypodium rupestre*) is here, particularly where grazing is reduced. With these grasses and sedges, there is a similarly rich and varied collection of forbs. These include Cowslip (*Primula veris*), Oxeye Daisy (*Leucanthemum vulgare*), Common Rock-rose (*Helianthemum nummularium*), Hairy St John's-wort (*Hypericum hirsutum*), Fairy Flax (*Linum catharticum*) and Wild Thyme (*Thymus polytrichus*). But there are a couple of species that occur nowhere else in the county; these are Soft-leaved Sedge (*Carex montana*) and Rare Spring-sedge (*C. ericetorum*) which both occur in Markland Grips. Floristically rich as these grasslands are, there are some species missing which do occur on the Carboniferous Limestone, such as Mountain Pansy (*Viola lutea*) and Woolly Thistle (*Cirsium eriophorum*). There are other species which, although found in both areas, are markedly less frequent on the Magnesian Limestone. These include

Markland Grips in the Magnesian Limestone, June 2004 (P. & G. Dishart)

Dwarf Thistle (*Cirsium acaule*) and Smooth Lady's-mantle (*Alchemilla glabra*). Limestone heaths and heavy-metal contaminated grasslands are both absent from the Magnesian Limestone Landscape Character Area; the former probably because of the greater intensity of arable farming in this area, and the latter because no lead ore veins were ever intruded into the Magnesian Limestone.

Other habitats – Hedges are more of a feature of this Landscape Character Area than on the Carboniferous Limestone of the White Peak. They are commonly dominated by Hawthorn (*Crataegus monogyna*) and Blackthorn (*Prunus spinosa*), but can also contain a varied assortment of more calcareous-loving shrubs such as Dogwood (*Cornus sanguinea*), Spindle (*Euonymus europaeus*) and Wild Privet (*Ligustrum vulgare*). In a few places the Wild Service-tree (*Sorbus torminalis*) occurs in hedges, probably as a relic of former woodland cover. Wetlands are rare here because of the porous nature of the bedrock, but they do occur in the bottom of some grips and disused quarries. They also occur around springheads, as in Whitwell Wood where there are very rich flushes with a collection of sedges (*Carex flacca, C. hostiana* and *C. panicea*), plus Bog Pimpernel (*Anagallis tenella*) and Grass-of-Parnassus (*Parnassia palustris*).

Other lowland Derbyshire landscapes (5–11)

The term "Lowland Derbyshire" refers to those parts of the county falling outside the three Landscape Character Areas we generally regard as constituting "The Peak District" – the White Peak, Dark Peak and South West Peak. These three Character Areas, plus the Magnesian Limestone Area described above, are probably the most distinctive as far as the botanist is concerned. The remaining parts of Lowland Derbyshire contain much less semi-natural vegetation than the Peak District, and what there is differs far less from one Landscape Character Area to another. For that reason the species accounts in this book are less likely to refer to the remaining Character Areas by name, as plants found in one of them are quite likely to occur in others, too.

The remaining Character Areas below are covered by shorter descriptions of their landscapes with just a brief mention of their semi-natural vegetation. After these seven Areas are introduced individually, they are followed by general descriptions of the major habitat types present across all seven Character Areas in Lowland Derbyshire. For detailed recommendations of publicly accessible sites to visit within each Area, see **Chapter 5**, "Where to See Plants in Derbyshire".

5 THE PEAK FRINGE LANDSCAPE CHARACTER AREA

Landscape description

The Peak Fringe is very much a transitional area between the rural Peak District to the west and the industrial/urban Coal Measures to the east. It extends some 40km north–south from the outskirts of Sheffield down to Derby in the south, and some 20km from Ashbourne in the west to Ripley in the east. The land surface consists of a series of steep-sided valleys separated by ridges which are in fact the foothills of the Pennines. The general elevation is between 100 and 300m, with the highest point being at **Alport Height**, where this pocket-sized National Trust holding offers splendid views over the Area and into the White Peak landscape beyond. The underlying geology is variously Millstone Grit and Lower Coal Measures sandstones and shales, and some small but botanically very significant outliers of Carboniferous Limestone at Ashover and Crich. In places the sandstone bedrock is overlain by glacial till (boulder clay) from the earlier part of the last Ice Age. In

Crich Stand on the Carboniferous Limestone outlier in the Peak Fringe, November 2006 (Ashley Franklin)

the later part of the Ice Age this area, along with most of the county, was not ice-covered, although it was still subjected to extreme periglacial conditions.

The land-use here is mainly pastoral, but gone are the open sheep grazings of the Peak District, and in their place are small enclosed fields used for mixed stock rearing. These are mostly rough grazings and permanent pastures, with patches of scrub or trees on their steeper slopes. At higher altitudes these fields are separated by drystone walls of brown sandstone, whilst at lower altitudes they are parcelled out by hedges of hawthorn. There are also a few areas of arable farming in the shallower valleys to the south. Mining has been important in the past, with numerous small workings for limestone, gritstone, clay and even ironstone. There has also been some early small-scale industrial development in the way of textile mills which took advantage of the power available from water courses. Finally, apart from the town of Belper, there are few built-up parts as all the major local conurbations of Ashbourne, Matlock and Derby sit just outside the boundaries of this Landscape Character Area.

East Mill, Belper, on the River Derwent in the Peak Fringe, August 2012 (Ashley Franklin)

Rivers and other watercourses are important landscape elements here. The major river is the Derwent which flows north to south down the centre of the Peak Fringe in a narrow deep and well-wooded valley, now a National Heritage Corridor and a UNESCO World Heritage Site. The smaller River Ecclesbourne flows through a much wider valley to the west, while in the more upland northern parts of the Peak Fringe there are a number of smaller faster brooks. The most significant man-made waterbodies here are Carsington Reservoir and the Cromford Canal. The latter was once very rich in aquatic species, but is essentially now

derelict and dewatered for much of its length. It does, however, still retain its populations of Water Voles and Grass Snakes between Ambergate and Cromford. There are also a number of small reservoirs scattered here and there that were originally designed to power the local mills. These too have been essentially dewatered by the growth of vegetation or the collapse of dam walls through neglect.

Vegetation of the Peak Fringe

As a mainly pastoral area, the Peak Fringe is rich in grasslands but relatively few of these are "unimproved", so are of little interest to botanists. Of those that remain, some are akin to Carboniferous Limestone grasslands, others to the acid grasslands of the Millstone Grit, and some are more like the neutral grasslands of Lowland Derbyshire described below. Only small fragments of semi-natural woodland remain, except for the Derwent Valley where there are extensive areas of woodland, such as Shining Cliff Woods and Crich Chase, north of Ambergate. These are similar to upland oak woodlands, like those found in the Dark Peak. Other notable habitats are wetlands and associated water bodies in the valley bottoms, and rock outcrops in quarries. The former are described below, whilst the latter are akin to the outcrops in The White Peak and The Dark Peak Landscape Character sections described above. See the "Lowland Derbyshire Habitats" section at the end of this chapter for descriptions of the main vegetation types found here.

Millennium Meadow Local Nature Reserve at Duffield in the Peak Fringe, May 2010 (Ashley Franklin)

6 THE COAL MEASURES LANDSCAPE CHARACTER AREA

Landscape description

This Character Area constitutes a broad belt of industrialised land, 10km wide, running down the eastern side of the county for some 45km, from Dronfield in the north almost down to Derby in the south. It includes the built-up areas of Alfreton, Ripley and Ilkeston, as well as numerous coal-mining villages. The underlying rocks are Coal Measure shales, mudstones and sandstones. These were deposited in a massive swampy river delta system some 320 to 300 million years ago towards the end of the Upper Carboniferous

Ploughland with patchy hedges and isolated trees near Middle Handley in the Coal Measures, September 2002 (DCC)

period. These thick deposits have subsequently been pushed up and tilted by major earth movements, then eroded away to form a series of broadly undulating sandstone ridges sloping gently to the east, with valleys beneath them. The soft shale and mudstone deposits of the valleys produce wet, heavy clay soils which are seasonally waterlogged and generally poor for agriculture. Such land is best for growing grass, so the agriculture here is traditionally dairy farming. It is only where the belts of harder sandstone produce lighter drier soils that some arable crops are found.

The presence of coal seams within these layers led to the development of a significant mining industry in Derbyshire. Initially coal was extracted from near the surface by numerous small-scale **bell pits**, leaving a characteristically hillocky land surface, still seen in some secondary woods today. As the coal reserves near the surface were exhausted, deeper mine shafts were developed in the nineteenth century which produced large conical waste tips. **Deep mining** continued into the twentieth century, but was replaced midway through by huge **opencast mines**. These excavated large areas but, having first removed the coal, then replaced the **overburden** in an attempt to reform the previous landscapes. In fact, opencast mining was often used to remove the old pit heaps and remedy the scars on the landscapes left by the deep mines. In the process opencast working has returned the land surface to something approximating its pre-mining contours. Subsequent re-planting has been less successful in recreating pre-mining vegetation cover. Deep mining for coal required railways to remove the product and, as mines closed, so did the railways. This left behind a network of disused lines, many of which are now re-used as public routeways such as the Teversal and Five Pits Trails.

Coal mining attracted other heavy industries such as iron smelting, and each required housing for the workers and their

Jacob's Sheep graze on Coal Measure grassland at the Woodside Nature Reserve, Shipley (DWT)

families. All of this, coupled with the extraction of clay for ceramics, means this Derbyshire Landscape Character Area has seen widespread industrialisation, urbanisation and pollution. Much of the heavy industry has now gone, just leaving acres of derelict buildings or land, though some have been restored or redeveloped. Much of the pollution has gone too, but the urbanisation remains. The landscape thus remains basically one of pastoral farming interspersed with dense pockets of dereliction or urbanisation.

Vegetation of The Coal Measures

With all the industrialisation and urbanisation, there is very little space left for semi-natural vegetation here. There are a few patches of semi-natural woodland on the steeper slopes and valley bottoms. There are also unimproved grasslands and wetland communities, including rush pastures in the valley bottoms. Otherwise the botanical interest of the area is mainly in its brownfield sites. These can support some interesting open communities, though are often of a rather transitory nature, being naturally replaced by scrub or artificially restored to other economic or recreational use. See the "Lowland Derbyshire Habitats" section at the end of this chapter for descriptions of the main vegetation types found here.

Coal Measures pastoral countryside at Holbrook, March 2009 (Ashley Franklin)

7 THE CLAYLANDS LANDSCAPE CHARACTER AREA

Landscape description

This south-western corner of Derbyshire is very much a rural area – a region of deep countryside and cattle-raising on very "improved" grassland. The Claylands extends some 20km from Ashbourne in the north to Sudbury in the south, and 25km east–west, from the River Dove on the Staffordshire border to Derby City in the east. The broad valley of the River Dove forms the boundary of this area all along its western and southern borders. The hinterland is a gently undulating, rolling landscape. The underlying geology is of **Mercia Mudstones** which are Triassic clays some 250 million years old, containing occasional bands of sandstone. The Mudstones were formerly known as Keuper Marls, and in places are overlain by much more recent **glacial till** or drift, and in the valleys there are surface deposits of **fluvio-glacial sands and gravels**. Mercia Mudstones generally produce wet heavy clay soils which are very suitable for growing grass and hence supporting dairy cattle. Many fields still show **ridge and furrow** patterns which is indicative of earlier arable usage and no subsequent modern ploughing. In places these ridges even show the slight reverse-S shape characteristic of ox-ploughing. In a few areas where there are gentle slopes or sandstones below the surface, there are better drained soils which allow arable cropping. As the farming is mainly dairying, the fields are hedged with bushes and occasional hedgerow trees. There is no

Cattle grazing at Mugginton Lane End in the Claylands (DCC)

industrialisation and little urbanisation here, just isolated villages. In fact it appears that, because of the number of Deserted Medieval Villages such as Hungry Bentley and Mugginton, the area was once more heavily populated than it is now. Minor elements in the landscapes are isolated woodlands and parks around country seats as at Osmaston and Kedleston.

Vegetation of The Claylands

There are no vegetation types here that specifically characterise this Landscape Area, just a varied but thinly spread tapestry of lowland habitats. There are many hedges with mature hedgerow trees and a few areas of semi-natural lowland woodland. There are very few fields left containing species-rich unimproved grassland, and these are becoming ever rarer. There are many streams with just a few areas of associated marsh and fen. There are also veteran trees in some of the parklands, particularly at Kedleston, whilst north of Brailsford there are some vestigial patches of heathy vegetation on sandstone areas. On many farms the fields are cultivated right up to the hedgerows, which in turn are so heavily over-managed that there are no reserves of young hedgerow trees. During the Flora survey it was often difficult to find even some of the commonest hedgerow flowers in certain monads within this Landscape Character Area. See the "Lowland Derbyshire Habitats" section at the end of this chapter for descriptions of the main vegetation types found here.

A pastoral landscape in the Claylands between Great Cubley and Bentley Fields (DCC)

8 THE TRENT VALLEY LANDSCAPE CHARACTER AREA

Landscape description

This is a swathe of low-lying land running from Doveridge in the west to Long Eaton in the east, along which the River Trent flows across the southern waist of the county. It also includes the lower reaches of the Rivers Dove and Derwent. It extends for up to 40km east–west but only 5km north–south. Geologically the area is underlain by Mercia Mudstones, but this is more or less covered with a range of **fluvio-glacial sands and gravels** for large parts of it. These sands and gravels were mostly deposited by rivers flowing off glaciers further north during and after the periods when extensive ice sheets covered northern Britain in the last Ice Age. These, and more recent river deposits, form terraces that flank the rivers, and some contain evidence of prehistoric man in terms of flint hand axes such as at Hilton, whilst even earlier gravel terraces at Allenton in Derby have yielded hippopotamus remains from one of the warmer inter-glacial periods. The soils that developed in the Trent Valley Area vary with the underlying geology. Where Mercia Mudstones are at the surface, there are heavy clay loam soils which are often waterlogged and prone to flooding, especially in winter. Where the Mudstones are covered by sand and gravels, the soils are lighter and better drained. To a large extent this pattern of soil types determines the agriculture of the Area, which is a mixture of pastoral and arable. On the clay soils there are typically small hedged fields of permanent grass, and a few riverside meadows for mowing on the lower-lying land by the rivers. On the higher terraces with lighter soils, there are generally larger, more regular hedged fields for mixed grazing/arable agriculture. There is archaeological evidence from the Neolithic and Iron Age that these gravel terraces with their lighter soils had always been more attractive to farmers than the heavier valley bottom land.

River Trent at Swarkestone Bridge, November 2013 (P. & G. Dishart)

Despite the tendency of the Trent Valley Area to flood in winter, it is relatively well populated, built-up and industrially developed. The two most obvious industries are the gravel extraction workings and the large coal-fired power stations. The sets of cooling towers of the latter are generally visible on the horizon wherever one goes in this Area. The sand and gravel workings are less obvious,

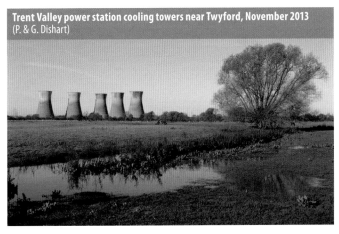

Trent Valley power station cooling towers near Twyford, November 2013 (P. & G. Dishart)

but more ubiquitous. Older examples from the earlier parts of the twentieth century have been mostly just abandoned when exhausted, although later workings now conclude with well-developed landscape restoration plans. This has left a series of flooded pits and patches of overgrown willow scrub and woodland. The former have attracted birds and other wildlife as well as offering various recreational uses, while the scrub and woodland have proved equally attractive to wildlife in a generally well-developed landscape. Not surprisingly, the built-up areas are restricted mostly to the edges of the Trent Valley and to higher ground away from winter flooding.

Vegetation of The Trent Valley

Hedges are an all-pervading feature of the landscape in this Character Area which, from the viewpoint of road users, tend to hide the extent to which the region is actually dominated by agriculture. These hedgerows often contain mature standard trees and these, coupled with lines of willows and poplars along watercourses, falsely give the impression of a well-wooded landscape in some parts. In fact ancient semi-natural woodlands are rare here, though there are some areas of developing woods in the abandoned gravel workings. Unimproved grasslands are also rare, though there are some patches of rush pastures and damp meadows by waterbodies. It is only in the matter of aquatic habitats that the area is relatively rich; both flowing and standing waterbodies are frequent. The former are represented by the major rivers of the Trent, Dove and Derwent, and by their respective tributaries which form a network across the region. There are many standing waterbodies in the flooded workings of the numerous abandoned and still-active gravel extraction pits. See the "Lowland Derbyshire Habitats" section at the end of this chapter for descriptions of the main vegetation types found here.

9 THE PARKLANDS LANDSCAPE CHARACTER AREA

Landscape description

The Parklands Landscape Character Area occupies the narrow waist of the county alongside that of the Trent Valley, and just above the final southern swelling of the county near Swadlincote. It is a small Character Area, extending barely 15km from the vicinity of Repton in the west to that of Melbourne in the east, and only 5km north–south from Repton to Swadlincote. It is a slightly elevated landscape, being raised above the surrounding areas.

Hedgerow trees give the impression of a well-wooded landscape in the Parklands between South Wood and Calke Park (DCC)

The bedrock here is relatively complex. It is mainly Mercia Mudstones of Triassic age with small outliers of the Millstone Grit series and Carboniferous Limestone which add considerable botanical interest. The land surface consists of low, gently undulating hills separated by narrow valleys. The soils are predominately productive reddish clays with some areas of better-drained sandy soils on the Millstone Grit outcrops. The slightly elevated position of the area and the gentle gradients tend to nullify any tendency of the clay soils to be too wet. The landscape is thus one of intensive, mainly arable agriculture. There are regular hedged fields with some permanent pasture, and some woodland on the steeper slopes. The area is lightly populated with very little industrial development, apart from the two large lowland reservoirs at Foremark and Staunton Harold. Much of the Parklands Landscape Character Area falls within the National Forest and this should result in significant alterations across parts of the landscape in coming years as the newly-planted woodlands mature.

As the name of this Character Area suggests, this is an historic landscape with many vestiges of its long and rich past. At Repton, which is famous both for its public school and for once being the capital of the ancient kingdom of Mercia, there is an Anglo-Saxon sepulchre built into the fabric of the church. There are parklands around the country seats of gentlemen, particularly at Calke Abbey which is now a significant National Trust property. Adjacent to Calke Park is the attractive estate village of Ticknall with its many traditional cottages. There is also the substantial Norman parish church at Melbourne next to the hall gardens and pool.

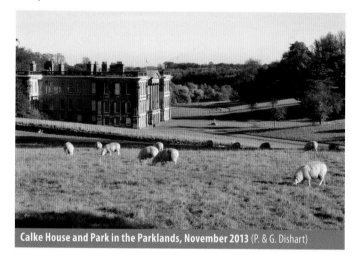

Calke House and Park in the Parklands, November 2013 (P. & G. Dishart)

Vegetation of The Parklands

As a rich agricultural area, there are few areas of semi-natural vegetation here; even the ubiquitous hedges contain relatively few trees. The major semi-natural habitat now remaining is known as **wood pasture and parkland** which, with its many mature and often veteran trees, has given this Landscape Character Area its name. The particularly large park at Calke is especially well-endowed with mature trees. There are both isolated veterans and a more modern avenue of magnificent lime trees leading from Ticknall village towards the big house. These semi-natural woodlands are increasingly being joined by modern plantations, spawned by the National Forest. At the time of writing, these mostly appear like elfin forests over grassland, but as they mature they should take on more of the appearance of natural woodlands and enrich the wildlife of the area. Elsewhere there are only very limited areas of semi-natural vegetation but these can have surprising botanical interest such as the calcareous grassland on

Veteran Oak in the Parklands at Calke, June 2006 (DWT)

the Carboniferous Limestone outlier at Ticknall, and the minute patches of heathland and wetland on the Millstone Grit at Carver's Rocks near Repton. See the "Lowland Derbyshire Habitats" section at the end of this chapter for descriptions of the main vegetation types found here.

10 THE SOUTHERN COAL MEASURES LANDSCAPE CHARACTER AREA

Landscape description

This is the smallest of Derbyshire's Landscape Character Areas. It extends barely 10km north–south and 10km east–west in an arc around the town of Swadlincote. It is sandwiched between The Parklands to the north and The Mease Lowlands to the south. It is underlain by Carboniferous age Coal Measure deposits which consist of layers of mudstones and sandstones containing bands of clays and seams of coal. All of these have contributed significantly to the development of the landscapes here. The major deposits of mudstones and sandstones originally produced a background of a gently swelling agricultural landscape of low ridges and shallow valleys, but in contrast the bands of clays and seams of coal have produced pockets of intense industrial activity. These have intruded significantly into, and generally replaced, the agricultural landscape over most of the area. The band of fireclay between Swadlincote and Moira has supported a sanitary ware pottery industry around Swadlincote with large areas of clay extraction. The coal seams were deep-mined in the past, leaving a typical

The close mix of arable farming and residential housing in the Southern Coal Measures, August 2011 (DCC)

landscape of pit heaps although these have been swept away and restored recently by a wave of opencast coal mining. In the past these extractive industries required large numbers of workers who had to be housed, and even now the area remains relatively densely populated.

Overall, this Character Area is still dominated by a mining landscape, albeit one where the original scars of mines and pits have been replaced by a restored landscape of gentle slopes and patches of young woodlands. Otherwise there is an urban landscape of redbrick houses with rural pockets. These pockets consist of a mixture of pasture and arable farming, often with a rather rundown urban fringe of horse paddocks and patchy fencing.

Vegetation of The Southern Coal Measures

With such a developed landscape of extractive industries and agriculture, there are relatively few areas of semi-natural vegetation left. There are some interesting patches for botanists, however, in the form of derelict land or **brownfield sites** such as heathy areas on the few remaining parts of pit heaps. As the area is wholly within the National Forest, there are a number of recent plantations, often on restored industrial land. Although intrinsically poor in woodland species, these should improve in interest overtime and restore some sylvan calm to a generally very disturbed area. See the "Lowland Derbyshire Habitats" section at the end of this chapter for descriptions of the main vegetation types found here.

Arable farmland appearing to be well-wooded due to hedgerow trees and copses in the Southern Coal Measures (DCC)

11 THE MEASE LOWLANDS LANDSCAPE CHARACTER AREA

Landscape description

This Area forms the southernmost extension of Derbyshire, bordered to the south and west by the valleys of the Rivers Mease and Trent, and to the north and east by the Southern Coal Measures. Again, it is a rather small lowland area though fractionally larger than the adjacent Southern Coal Measures. It extends for roughly no more than 5km in all directions from the small rural village of Coton in the Elms to the county boundary or to the Southern Coal Measures. Geologically it is underlain by Triassic Mercia Mudstones which consist of marls with interspersed bands of sandstones. These produce a gently flowing lowland landscape of low ridges and shallow valleys. These marls have eroded to produce productive reddish clay soils with more free-draining sandy soils over the sandstone bands. Despite being generally good quality farmland, the area was enclosed rather late in the 18th and 19th centuries. This produced a landscape of large

Arable fields and hedgerows at Coton in the Elms, in the Mease Lowlands (DCC)

regular fields which has been further exaggerated by hedgerow removal in the 20th century for intensive arable agriculture. Only where there are steeper slopes or heavier soils does this give way to a more mixed arable/pasture farming system. There is little urbanisation in the area; what houses there are tend to be clustered in the few scattered villages. There is also little evidence of industrialisation apart from numerous power lines on pylons that trample across the landscape. Overall the area gives the impression of a region deeply entrenched and firmly rooted in agriculture, and one only lightly touched by modern industrial Britain.

Vegetation of The Mease Lowlands

Like much of Lowland Derbyshire, this Character Area appears to be more wooded than it really is, due to trees growing in hedges and along the lines of watercourses. What little semi-natural woodland there is here is generally restricted to areas of parkland as at Catton and Grangewood Parks. This may change in the future as both this Area and that of the Southern Coal Measures are entirely within the National Forest where new woodland planting is encouraged. Apart from woodlands and hedges, semi-natural vegetation is restricted to a very few areas of unimproved grassland and watercourses. The River Mease itself is a Site of Special Scientific Interest and a Special Area of Conservation (SAC), although the designations are based on its animal life, not its plants. See the "Lowland Derbyshire habitats" section below for descriptions of the main vegetation types found here.

Isolated field trees show field enlargement near Rosliston in the Mease Lowlands (DCC)

Lowland Derbyshire habitats

Outside the three very distinctive and different landscapes of the White Peak, the Dark Peak (including the South West Peak) and the Magnesian Limestone Character Areas, there are relatively fewer areas of semi-natural habitat in the rest of Lowland Derbyshire. Despite this, there is still plenty to interest the plant-lover. This brief outline gives some idea of the range of botanical highlights present in each of the major habitat types found in Lowland Derbyshire. These are:

a) Woodlands
b) Wood pasture and parkland
c) Hedges
d) Grasslands
e) Wetlands
f) Waterbodies
g) Arable
h) Brownfield sites (Open Mosaic Habitat)

To a large extent this outline is based on the work in the *Derbyshire Local Wildlife Sites Handbook volume 2,* produced by Derbyshire Wildlife Trust in 2011. Specific recommendations for accessible sites to visit within each Landscape Character Area are given in **Chapter 5**.

a) Woodlands as described here include three main categories: ancient woodlands, secondary semi-natural woodlands and wet woodlands. **Ancient woodlands** are those known to have been present since 1600 and which are therefore presumed to be remnants of the native woods of the area. **Secondary semi-natural woodlands** are known not to have been continuously wooded since 1600. These may be either spontaneous in origin or, if plantations, have been planted with native species on or near ancient woodland sites. **Wet woodlands** occur where the water table is permanently high and the dominant species are natives. Considered separately below is **wood pasture and parkland** which, although containing trees, does appear more like open grasslands to the non-botanist.

Ancient and secondary semi-natural woods in the Peak Fringe may closely resemble the Ash woodlands of the White Peak or the upland acid woodlands of the Dark Peak in respect of tree cover. Otherwise they may contain almost any combination of the following native tree species: birch (either *Betula pendula* or *B. pubescens*), Ash (*Fraxinus excelsior*) and oak (either *Quercus petraea* or *Q. robur*). Along with these native species, there are often specimens of the non-native Sycamore (*Acer pseudoplatanus*) or Beech (*Fagus sylvatica*). There may also be rare individuals of either native lime species (*Tilia cordata* or *T. platyphyllos*) or of Holly (*Ilex aquifolium*) or Wild Cherry (*Prunus avium*) or Yew (*Taxus baccata*). The commonest shrubs under the tree cover are Hawthorn (*Crataegus monogyna*) and Hazel (*Corylus avellana*). The former is commoner in the secondary semi-natural woods and the latter in the ancient woodlands. Where woodlands are especially dry and or acidic, Holly is common as a shrub. Where soils are more nutrient-rich there may be specimens of Field Maple (*Acer campestre*) or Crab Apple (*Malus sylvestris*), and where the woods are wetter there may be plants of Guelder-rose (*Viburnum opulus*).

The **woodland floor** is generally the most species-rich layer in any wood. However, in the more acidic woodlands it may be restricted to just a jumble of Bluebells (*Hyacinthoides non-scripta*), Bracken (*Pteridium aquilinum*) and Bramble (*Rubus* spp.). On the better soils, or in the older woodlands, there may be a very varied ground flora consisting of colourful combinations of the following herbaceous species:

Wood Anemone – *Anemone nemorosa*
Pignut – *Conopodium majus*
Male-fern – *Dryopteris filix-mas*
Wood Avens – *Geum urbanum*
Dog's Mercury – *Mercurialis perennis*
Wood Millet – *Milium effusum*
Primrose – *Primula vulgaris*
Red Campion – *Silene dioica*
Common Dog-violet – *Viola riviniana*

Less variable then the drier woodlands described above, **wet woodlands** are found in the bottom of river valleys and in abandoned gravel pits. They are generally dominated by a tree layer consisting of one or more of either Alder (*Alnus glutinosa*), or Downy Birch (*Betula pubescens*) or willow (*Salix* spp.). Understorey shrubs tend to be from the same limited spectrum of species, but may also include Alder Buckthorn (*Frangula alnus*). The field layer may contain one or more of a range of species including: Bugle (*Ajuga reptans*), Lady-fern (*Athyrium filix-femina*), Marsh-marigold (*Caltha palustris*), Wood-sedge (*Carex sylvatica*) and Marsh Violet (*Viola palustris*).

b) Wood pasture and parkland consists of isolated mature trees standing amongst a grazed landscape of grassland. It may have various origins – perhaps arising from tracts of ancient hunting forest or from more modern landscape gardening. However, the interest here lies in its trees; the grazed elements of the habitat will be included under grasslands. The trees found here have generally grown in open canopy and, as such, have spreading branches and show a clear browse line where the domestic stock can nibble up to. They are also typically **veterans**, that is they have reached or passed their peak growth point, and have begun to deteriorate. They have begun to lose limbs and develop areas of rot or infection in which other organisms can grow. Ultimately they just become hollow cylinders with a few live branches, like hairs on the edge of a bald pate. Pedunculate Oaks (*Quercus robur*) are the typical parkland tree in Derbyshire, and these take 150 to 200 years or more to reach this mature state. Other veteran trees in parklands may be Beech (*Fagus sylvatica*) or Sweet Chestnut (*Castanea sativa*). Of course, veteran trees may occur elsewhere in hedges, whilst veteran Yews (*Taxus baccata*) are classically found in old churchyards.

c) Hedges are probably the most frequent and widespread of the semi-natural habitats in Lowland Derbyshire, where they form important field boundaries. It is only in the rockier parts of the Peak Fringe Landscape Character Area that hedges are commonly replaced by drystone walls. Elsewhere hedges are retained to limit the movement of stock. As in much of lowland Britain, the classic hedging plant here is Hawthorn or Quickthorn (*Crataegus monogyna*), and it was planted in its millions to create the current network of hedges we see today. Occasionally other species were planted alongside it, but generally these simply colonised the planted hedgerows over time. The commonest ones found alongside Hawthorn now are Blackthorn (*Prunus spinosa*), species of Rose (*Rosa* spp.) and of Bramble (*Rubus* spp.). Rarer shrubs, which are often thought to indicate some woodland influence or origin, are Field Maple (*Acer campestre*), Hazel (*Corylus avellana*), Holly (*Ilex aquifolium*) and Crab Apple (*Malus sylvestris*). Where soils are drier, Gorse (*Ulex europaeus*) may be found and, where soils are wetter, willows of various species or hybrid parentage (*Salix* spp.)

Lowland Derbyshire hedgerow in spring with Blackthorn blossom
(Nick Moyes)

may occur. The presence of Wild Plum (*Prunus domestica*) or Wild Privet (*Ligustrum vulgare*) in hedges usually means there is, or was, a dwelling or garden nearby.

The commonest hedgerow trees in Lowland Derbyshire are Pedunculate Oak (*Quercus robur*) and Ash (*Fraxinus excelsior*), whilst willows (*Salix* spp.) and poplars (*Populus* spp.) are frequent along hedges by watercourses. Wych Elms (*Ulmus glabra*) used to be more common before the latest outbreak of Dutch Elm disease in the 1970s, and sadly Ash may soon start to disappear following the 20012/13 arrival of Chalara fungus in Britain. Rarely, specimens of the Native Black Poplar (*Populus nigra* ssp. *betulifolia*) or the Wild Service-tree (*Sorbus torminalis*) may turn up. The over-management of many hedgerows and the indiscriminate flailing of their entire length mean that, in places, there are now no new young trees available to take the place of the current stock of mature hedgerow trees when these eventually die.

Hedges not only support shrubs and trees; woodland herbs may occur in the hedge bottom, or there may be wetland species in a ditch running alongside it. Common woodland herbs that flourish in hedgerows are Foxglove (*Digitalis purpurea*), Wood Avens (*Geum urbanum*) and Red Campion (*Silene dioica*); while typical wetland plants are Meadowsweet (*Filipendula ulmaria*), Great Willowherb (*Epilobium hirsutum*) and more rarely Common Valerian (*Valeriana officinalis*).

d) Grasslands – Species-rich unimproved grasslands are very rare in Lowland Derbyshire. Where soils are rich in calcium carbonate, grasslands may occur which are akin to those found in the

Lowland Derbyshire meadow at Shining Cliff, Whatstandwell, August 2008
(Kieron Huston)

limestone areas of the White Peak and in the Magnesian Limestone Character Areas. Where soils are dry and acidic, grasslands similar to those of the Dark Peak sometimes occur here. However, the characteristic species-rich unimproved grasslands throughout Lowland Derbyshire are described as **neutral grasslands**. They are now very rare but once were common. Agricultural improvement in the form of drainage, fertilisers and reseeding has converted the great majority of these to productive grasslands or Perennial Rye-grass (*Lolium perenne*) leys. Those that have survived support a wide range of species which produce a rich tapestry of scents and colours in early summer. Some of these grasslands are pastures used for grazing; others are meadows still mown for hay. They both support species such as:

Betony – *Betonica officinalis*
Common Knapweed – *Centaurea nigra*
Lady's Bedstraw – *Galium verum*
Meadow Vetchling – *Lathyrus pratensis*
Oxeye Daisy – *Leucanthemum vulgare*
Common Bird's-foot-trefoil – *Lotus corniculatus*
Great Burnet – *Sanguisorba officinalis*

Where the herbage is shorter as in grazed pastures, small gems may still be found like Harebell (*Campanula rotundifolia*), Dyer's Greenweed (*Genista tinctoria*) and the diminutive Adder's-tongue (*Ophioglossum vulgatum*). Where the herbage is taller as in mown meadows, more statuesque or stately plants may be found including: Wild Angelica (*Angelica sylvatica*), Saw-wort (*Serratula tinctoria*) and Pepper-saxifrage (*Silaum silaus*).

Some examples of neutral lowland grasslands occur on wetter sites. From a distance these often appear to consist only of species of rush (*Juncus* spp.), and are hence referred to as **rush pastures**. On closer inspection however they are just as species-rich and colourful as their drier cousins with plants such as:

Sneezewort – *Achillea ptarmica*
Brown Sedge – *Carex disticha*
Southern Marsh-orchid – *Dactylorhiza praetermissa*
Meadowsweet – *Filipendula ulmaria*
Jointed Rush – *Juncus articulatus*
Common Fleabane – *Pulicaria dysenterica*
Ragged-Robin – *Silene flos-cuculi*

e) Wetlands – A variety of interesting habitat types fit into this category and, in increasing order of wetness, these are: marshes, fens, reed beds and swamps. Although different from one another, they share a common range of species. **Marshes** are closest to wet grasslands but differ in that water levels are at the soil surface for at least part of the year. **Fens** are similar in terms of water levels but occur on organic soils or peats rather than the mineral soils of marshes. In both **reed beds** and **swamps** the water level is well above the soil surface throughout the year and the vegetation emerges through to stand in the air with its feet in water. Reed beds are dominated by a combination of one or more of the following large grass-like plants which are often simply referred to as "reeds". These include:

Lesser Pond-sedge – *Carex acutiformis*
Greater Pond-sedge – *Carex riparia*
Reed Sweet-grass – *Glyceria maxima*
Reed Canary-grass – *Phalaris arundinacea*
Common Reed – *Phragmites australis*
Branched Bur-reed – *Sparganium erectum*
Bulrush – *Typha latifolia*

Lacking colourful flowers, it is the size and bulk of these plants that gives them a sort of stately grandeur as they fringe the edges of water bodies or occupy the damper areas of valley bottoms. They often form transitional habitats between grasslands and open water environments. Alongside the dominant reed-like plants, there also occurs a range of less vigorous, but showier species. These tend to be more frequent and obvious in marshes and fens, but can occur in lesser amounts even in reed beds. In swamps they dominate, replacing the grass-like plants though some reeds generally co-exist with them. Some of the more attractive of these supporting players are:

Hemp-agrimony – *Eupatorium cannabinum*
Common Marsh-bedstraw – *Galium palustre*
Square-stalked St John's-wort – *Hypericum tetrapterum*
Yellow Iris – *Iris pseudacorus*
Greater Bird's-foot-trefoil – *Lotus pedunculatus*
Greater Spearwort – *Ranunculus lingua*
Marsh Woundwort – *Stachys palustris*
Common Meadow-rue – *Thalictrum flavum*

f) Waterbodies help produce some of the most beautiful and idyllic scenery in the county. Flowing waters add sparkle to views of valleys, whilst still waters can mirror stands of pondside trees. They also support attractive stands of floating and submerged vegetation. **Rivers**, **streams** and **brooks** are examples of natural **flowing waterbodies**. However, many of our larger rivers have been artificially straightened and deepened to improve the flow of water or for navigation. **Canals** and **drainage channels** are relatively rare here, but their water flow is generally so low that the flora they support is essentially the same as that found in still waterbodies.

The most iconic plants of **flowing waterbodies** are the water-crowfoots, especially species such as *Ranunculus fluitans* and *R. penicillatus*. These produce long green underwater streamer-like stems that flow with the current and have white star-like flowers protruding just above the surface. Other submerged water plants that occur are species of water-starworts (*Callitriche* spp.) and of pondweeds (*Potamogeton* spp.). Floating-leaved plants are rare in flowing waterbodies except for the quiet backwaters, while wetland species as listed above are frequent along their margins.

Water-crowfoot (*Ranunculus* sp.), Hilton Brook in Lowland Derbyshire, June 2007 (DWT)

In the case of still or **standing waterbodies**, the situation is reversed in that examples of natural ones are rare, whereas man-made ones are common. Probably the only example of a natural still waterbody habitat in Lowland Derbyshire is formed by **oxbow lakes**, such as occur near Marston on Dove. There are many types of artificial standing waterbodies, however. There are large water storage reservoirs such as at Foremark and Carsington. Redundant mill dams and ponds created to provide water for powering mills are frequent. Many mineral extraction sites have become water-filled once their mineral wealth was exhausted. One example is the borrow pits around Trentlock that were excavated to produce material for the nearby railway embankments. **Field ponds** are the commonest examples of artificial standing waterbodies, but are nevertheless rapidly disappearing from the landscape because they are no longer used to water livestock – the function for which they were created.

Standing waterbodies in lowland areas tend to be what is described as **eutrophic**, that is they contain relatively high levels of plant nutrients such as phosphorus and nitrogen. This means they support dense stands of submerged and floating aquatics, plus emergent wetland species around their margins. This in turn means they tend to rapidly fill up with decaying plant remains and soon turn into swamps or marshes. Before they do this they can support a diverse flora of submerged species which include:

Water-starworts – *Callitriche* spp.
Rigid Hornwort – *Ceratophyllum demersum*
Ivy-leaved Duckweed – *Lemna trisulca*
Water-milfoils – *Myriophyllum* spp.
Pondweeds – *Potamogeton* spp.

Rarer submerged species which can sometimes occur include Water-violet (*Hottonia palustris*) and Horned Pondweed (*Zannichellia palustris*). Typically the submerged species tend to grow in the deeper water, while those with floating leaves tend to grow in shallower water round the margins. These include:

Fat Duckweed – *Lemna gibba*
Yellow Water-lily – *Nuphar lutea*
White Water-lily – *Nymphaea alba*
Broad-leaved Pondweed – *Potamogeton natans*
Round-leaved Crowfoot – *Ranunculus omiophyllus*

Where standing waterbodies experience marked and sudden changes of water level (as can occur in storage reservoirs) a particular flora can develop on their bare exposed margins. These are known as **drawdown zone communities** and can contain Red Goosefoot (*Chenopodium rubrum*) and Redshank (*Persicaria maculosa*) along with the rarer Mudwort (*Limosella aquatica*) and Shoreweed (*Littorella uniflora*).

g) Arable – Most arable fields in Lowland Derbyshire are generally sprayed with herbicides to the extent that few other plants can survive within the crops. Amongst those that can, probably the most herbicide resistant and most frequently encountered is the diminutive yellow viola (*Viola arvensis*) or Field Pansy. Others that occur occasionally are:

Scarlet Pimpernel – *Anagallis arvensis*
Redshank – *Persicaria maculosa*
Black Nightshade – *Solanum nigrum*
Corn Spurrey – *Spergula arvensis*
Common Field-speedwell – *Veronica persica*

Common Poppies (*Papaver rhoeas*) in the corner of arable field, Dowey Lumb, July 2005 (P. & G. Dishart)

Sometimes part of a field may be missed by the turn of a tractor, resulting in a blaze of red poppies across a hillside. Very rarely small populations of the petite Dwarf Spurge (*Euphorbia exigua*) can be found in the corners of fields that have avoided the latest application of weed killer. Other plants such as Corncockle (*Agrostemma githago*) and Corn Marigold (*Glebionis segetum*) have completely gone from arable fields in Lowland Derbyshire. They only turn up now in deliberately sown wildflower seed mixes in gardens, parks and some restoration schemes.

h) Brownfield sites – Areas of demolished factories or abandoned railway sidings may not look scenically very attractive but can provide some of the happiest hunting grounds for botanists searching for something different. They can contain a rich mixture of native species, exotic plants from gardens and casuals from discarded waste. Such sites are very diverse in origin and therefore different areas will support very different species, meaning it is difficult to describe a typical flora for this type of habitat. Some may be formally termed as **Open Mosaic Habitat on Previously Developed Land** (OMH). When newly created they will support a multitude of drought-tolerant annuals such as Thyme-leaved Sandwort (*Arenaria serpyllifolia*), Common Centaury (*Centaurium erythraea*), Fairy Flax (*Linum catharticum*) or Hare's-foot Clover (*Trifolium arvense*). Common weedy herbaceous species include plants such as willowherbs (*Epilobium* spp.), Mugwort (*Artemisia vulgaris*), Creeping Bent (*Agrostis stolonifera*) and Colt's-foot (*Tussilago farfara*). But along with these will also probably be some garden plants, for example Montbretia (*Crocosmia* × *crocosmiiflora*) and Perennial Cornflower (*Centaurea montana*) and more attractive species including evening-primroses (*Oenothera* spp.) and Blue Fleabane (*Erigeron acris*). Such brownfield sites may be invaded by woody plants fairly quickly which soon shade out the more varied herbaceous ones. The typical woody species are Silver Birch (*Betula pendula*) and Sycamore (*Acer pseudoplatanus*), plus various types of shrub willow (*Salix* spp.) and Butterfly-bush (*Buddleja davidii*). It should be pointed out that such sites do not generally have public access and may contain hazards in terms of rough ground and dumped wastes. They should therefore be treated with extreme caution but, when they can be safely visited, they can be very rewarding for the botanist interested in more than just the native flora of Derbyshire.

CHAPTER 2

Species accounts and maps

Explanatory notes

The following pages provide over 1,900 species accounts of Derbyshire's vascular plants. Each plant listed in this book has an account containing up to three sections:
- All plants have a descriptive entry or **systematic account**
- Most have a **statistics box**
- Many will have a **distribution map** unless it has fewer than five plottable records.

1 SYSTEMATIC ACCOUNTS

The taxonomy and nomenclature (**order and naming**) of these species accounts follows Stace (2010), but with four exceptions:
- Hawkweeds (*Hieracium* species) follow McCosh & Rich (2011)
- Brambles (*Rubus fruticosus* agg.) follow Newton & Randall (2004)
- Dandelions (*Taraxacum* species) follow Dudman & Richards (1997)
- Aliens (not listed in Stace's *New Flora of the British Isles*) follow Clement & Foster (1994).

Each entry begins with its **scientific name** and authority, then its **common name**. The text then describes the recent ecology of the plant in Derbyshire. "Recent" refers to the **period of survey** (1987 to 2013 inclusive). The **area covered** by this Flora is actually "Greater Derbyshire", consisting of the modern **geographic county** we all know well, combined with the slightly different botanical **vice-county** of Derbyshire (v.c.57) see **Figure 2.1**. Both boundaries are shown on every map.

An account will commence with the words "Locally extinct" if the plant has not been recorded here since Clapham's 1969 Flora was published. Otherwise, each starts with its Common Name as given in Stace (2010), unless it has a very well-used Derbyshire one. Each account refers to five main aspects of a plant's current ecology in the county: its **county status**, **growth form**, **distribution**, **frequency** of occurrence and **habitats** in which it occurs. **County status** is given as either:
- Native
- Anciently established (=archaeophyte)
- Recently established (=neophyte)
- Casual or
- Planted.

For simplicity, all neophytes are described as "Established", whereas archaeophytes are described as "Anciently Established". See Glossary for further explanation.

Distributions are generally described in terms of Derbyshire **Landscape Character Areas** (explained in **Chapter 1**). If a species is on the edge of its national range, this will be noted too.

Frequency is given on the scale: *Very common; Common; Frequent; Occasional; Rare* or *Very rare*. This applies to either the whole county or selected Landscape Areas/regions: Frequency may be qualified by "locally" where appropriate. The term is not used to describe abundance. See **Glossary** for further explanation.

Habitats are described without using a particular system of classification, although terms such as woodland, grassland and marsh generally relate to those used in Phase 1 habitat surveying (JNCC 2010).

Further information is included where relevant. For hybrids, the parent names are given. For recent introductions and casuals their means of arrival and where they occur naturally is stated, if known.

Plants found in fewer than five sites are not mapped, so locality details and record dates from 1987 onwards will be stated here. These are usually given with a four-figure grid reference e.g. Allestree (SK3338). Sometimes only tetrad or hectad grid references are available. (see explanation in Glossary). A few example locations are included for many species, although particularly common ones generally have no sites listed.

2 STATISTICS BOXES

Statistics boxes are generally provided for plants that have more than a couple of recorded localities. Each contains the following fields:

Equisetum sylvaticum L.
Wood Horsetail

COUNTY STATUS: Native	
CONSERVATION STATUS: None	
FIRST YEAR: 1829 **LATEST YEAR:** 2013 **NO OF RECORDS:** 530	
RECENT SQUARES: monads 202; tetrads 146; hectads 29	
ALL SQUARES: monads 239; tetrads 169; hectads 33	

- **County status** – Native or Alien status (see Glossary)
- **Conservation status** – all national and local Conservation Statuses as a Code (see **Table 2.2**)
- **First year** – earliest known record
- **Latest year** – last year recorded, up to and including 2013
- **Number of records** – count of records (including duplicates and unconfirmed records)
- **Recent records** – count of monads, tetrads and hectads from 1987 onwards (see **Table 2.1**)
- **All records** – count of monads, tetrads and hectads, irrespective of date (see **Table 2.1**).

The number of recording squares present in Derbyshire are shown in **Table 2.1** below (see Chapter 1, Table 1.1 for additional Derbyshire data).

Table 2.1 Count of monads, tetrads and hectads falling wholly or partly in Derbyshire.

Area of "Greater Derbyshire" (modern county plus v.c.57)	2,725.4 km²		
Count of monads	**Total 2,960;**	whole 2,547;	partial 413
Count of tetrads	**Total 771;**	whole 599;	partial 172
Count of hectads	**Total 45;**	whole 12;	partial 33

Conservation Statuses are given as one or more abbreviations. These are listed in **Table 2.2**, and further explained in the **Glossary**. In 2009 the *Derbyshire Red Data List* aggregated all species of local, national and international conservation significance into one of six "DRDB Categories". **Chapter 9** tabulates the species in these categories. To show how our assessment of local plant statuses has evolved, past Derbyshire Red Data Lists have been included in these conservation status codes despite now being superseded by the 2009 assessment, shown revised in Chapter 9. A further suite of 59 additional species now have their own "England Red List" status (ERL), and these are also tabulated in that chapter. Statistics were derived from computer analysis of 850,000 plant records collated by Derbyshire Biological Records Centre at Derby Museum. Latest Year figures from 2011 onwards were added manually. Any record with an "unknown" date does not get counted in the statistics box, but will nevertheless appear on distribution maps with a pre-1987 symbol. This applies to very few species.

Table 2.2 Conservation Status abbreviations used in the species accounts in this book. See **Glossary** for further explanation and **Chapter 9** for Derbyshire Red List species.

Conservation Code	Meaning
DERBYSHIRE STATUSES	
DRDB (Cat1)	Derbyshire Red Data List 2009 (Category 1) = Internationally Rare
DRDB (Cat2)	Derbyshire Red Data List 2009 (Category 2) = Nationally Threatened
DRDB (Cat3)	Derbyshire Red Data List 2009 (Category 3) = Nationally Rare or Scarce
DRDB (Cat4)	Derbyshire Red Data List 2009 (Category 4) = Locally Rare
DRDB (Cat5a)	Derbyshire Red Data List 2009 (Category 5a) = Locally Scarce
DRDB (Cat5b)	Derbyshire Red Data List 2009 (Category 5b) = Locally Declining
DRDB (Cat6)	Derbyshire Red Data List 2009 (Category 6) = Locally Extinct
A	2002 Candidate Derbyshire RDB list (superseded – see above)
B	1996 Derbyshire RDB species (superseded – see above)
C	1997 Mid-Derbyshire Biodiversity Action Plan (superseded)
NATIONAL or INTERNATIONAL STATUSES	
Bern	Bern Convention (Appendix 1)
CitesB	Cites Annexe B
CitesD	Cites Annexe D
CR	Critically Endangered*
EN	Endangered*
ERL	England Red List
HabsRegs	Conservation of Habitats & Species Regulations 2010
NR	Nationally Rare
NS	Nationally Scarce
NT	Near Threatened*
NERC	Species of Principal Importance (=UK BAP Priority Species)
VU	Vulnerable*
WCA8	Wildlife & Countryside Act 1981 Schedule 8 (Protected Plants)
WCA9	Wildlife & Countryside Act 1981 Schedule 9(2) (Introduction banned)

= IUCN threat category applied to a plant's status across GB

3 DISTRIBUTION MAPS

Maps are provided for all species with more than five plottable records. Map symbols are normally shown to Tetrad accuracy (*i.e.* 2km × 2km grid square). Three symbols are used:

- ● **Small solid dots** = **recent records** (1987–2013)
- ○ **Larger cream circles** = **older records** (any date prior to 1987)
- ◉ **Bull's eyes** (solid dot in white circle = present across **both date classes**.

Maps are sometimes plotted with larger symbols to represent hectad records (10km by 10km squares). Hectads are only used where the majority of records were made before the Ordnance Survey National Grid system was introduced, or where critical species have few records, and their distribution is better demonstrated by coarser mapping. Very occasionally we have shown data at a 1km (monad) accuracy, e.g. *Ranunculus penicillatus* and *Cochlearia danica*, where the value of finer plotting outweighs the difficulty of seeing the presence of older records.

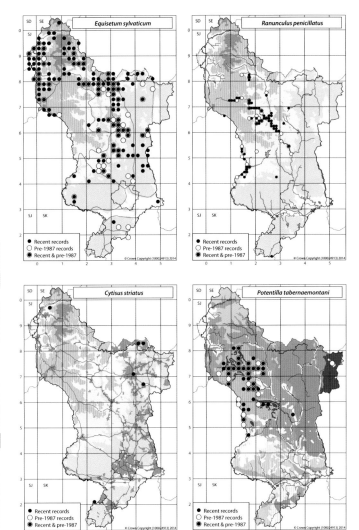

Various combinations of map backgrounds may be used. These reflect:

Relief (see **Figure 2.2** overleaf)
Landscape Character Area boundaries (see also **Figure 2.2**)
Rivers and waterbodies (see **Figure 2.3**, p.22)
Roads (see **Figure 2.4**, p.23)
Urban areas (see also **Figure 2.4**)
Geology (solid and drift) (see **Figure 2.5**, p.24).

Relief is shown on most maps in colour as follows:
- ☐ Yellow <50m above sea level
- ☐ Green 50– 150m above sea level
- ☐ Blue 150–300m above sea level
- ▨ Light purple 300–500m above sea level
- ▨ Dark purple >500m above sea level.

- **Derbyshire County boundary** is represented by a solid Black line.
- The older **Vice-county boundary** (v.c.57) is shown as a dotted Black line wherever the two diverge (see also **Figure 2.1** overleaf).
- **Grid lines** are 10km apart and represent the Ordnance Survey National Grid.
- **Derbyshire Landscape Character Areas** are shown as a solid Red Line.
- **Major rivers and waterbodies** are Blue. **Roads** are thin Red lines; **Urban areas** are Grey.

Figure 2.1 Map of "Greater Derbyshire" showing differences between modern Derbyshire boundary (black) and vice-county boundary (red). Adjacent modern counties are also shown, with corresponding vice-county numbers.

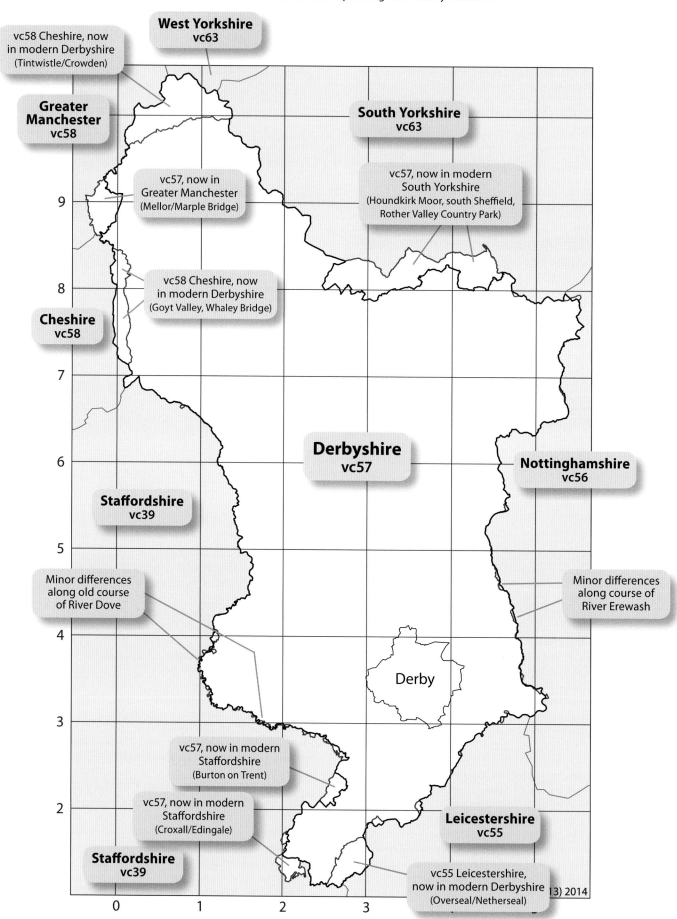

Figure 2.2 Relief map of Derbyshire showing Landscape Character Area boundaries in red (see **Chapter 1**).

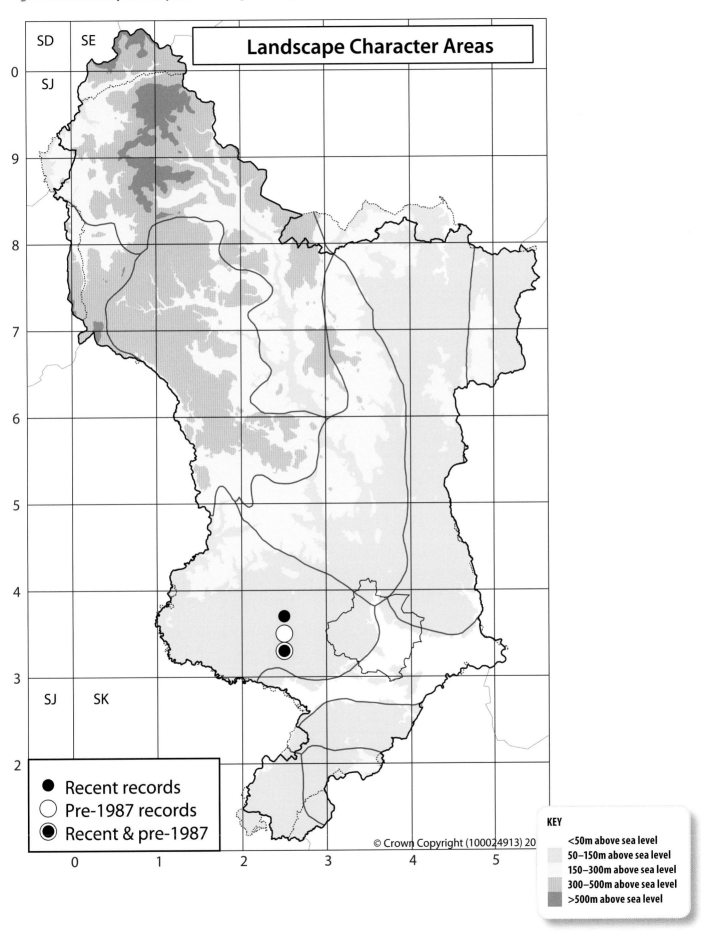

Landscape Character Areas

Recent records
Pre-1987 records
Recent & pre-1987

© Crown Copyright (100024913) 20

KEY
<50m above sea level
50–150m above sea level
150–300m above sea level
300–500m above sea level
>500m above sea level

Figure 2.3 **Relief map of Derbyshire showing main rivers, canals and large waterbodies.**

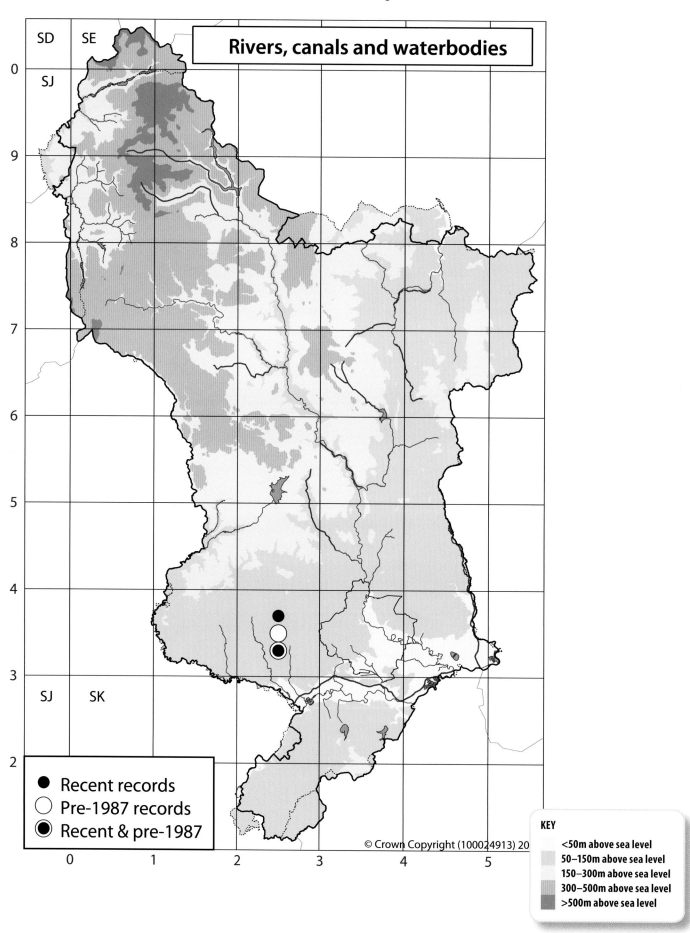

Rivers, canals and waterbodies

● Recent records
○ Pre-1987 records
◉ Recent & pre-1987

© Crown Copyright (100024913) 20

KEY

<50m above sea level
50–150m above sea level
150–300m above sea level
300–500m above sea level
>500m above sea level

Figure 2.4 Relief map of Derbyshire showing main roads (red) and urban areas (grey).

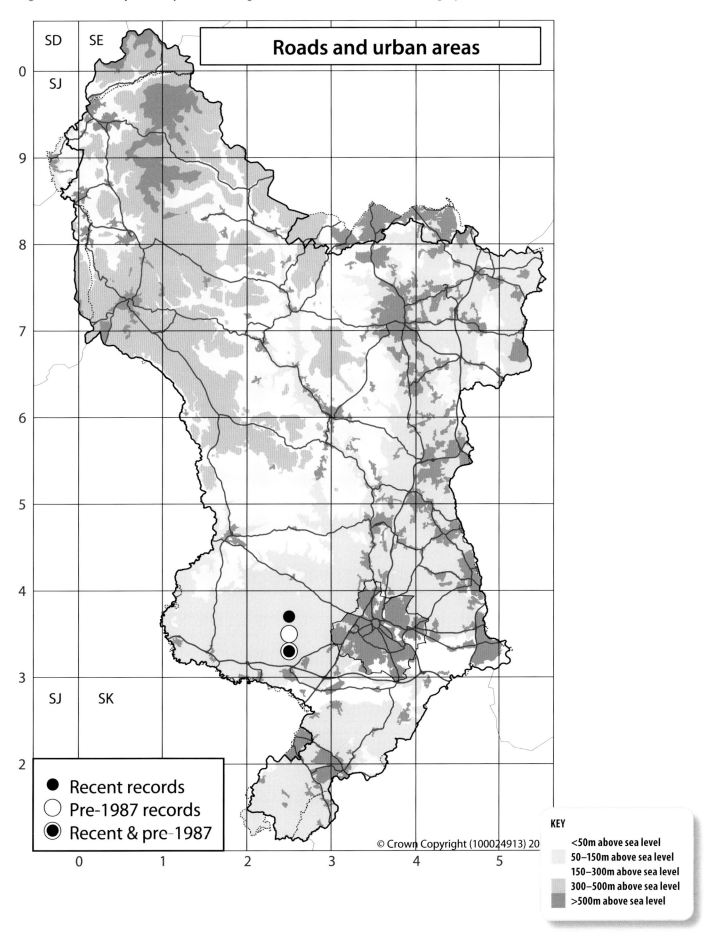

Roads and urban areas

● Recent records
○ Pre-1987 records
◉ Recent & pre-1987

© Crown Copyright (100024913) 20

KEY

<50m above sea level
50–150m above sea level
150–300m above sea level
300–500m above sea level
>500m above sea level

Figure 2.5 Map of Derbyshire showing solid and drift geology, plus waterbodies.

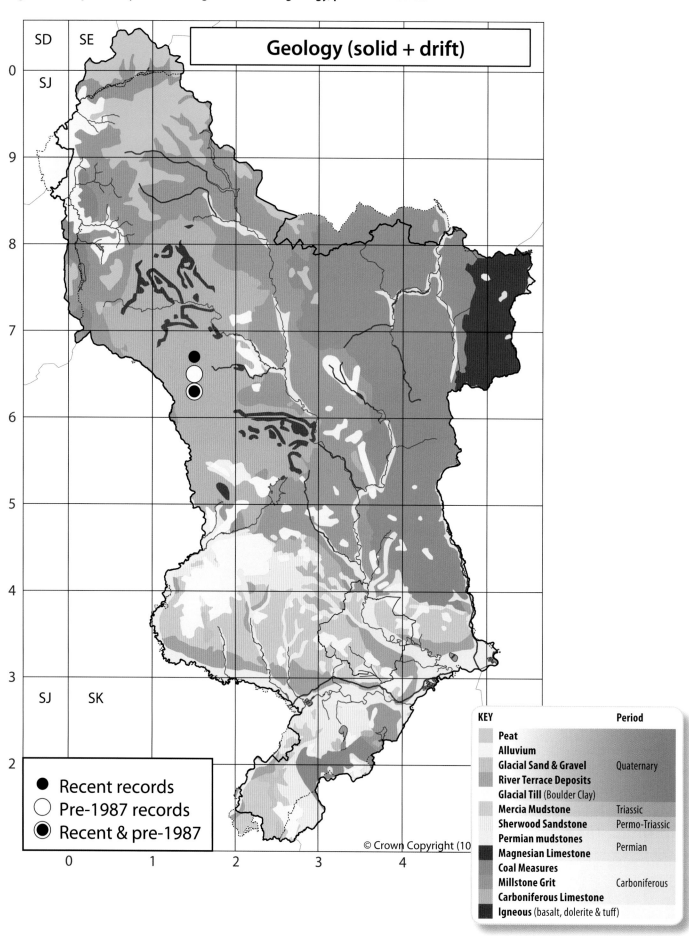

Geology (solid + drift)

● Recent records
○ Pre-1987 records
◉ Recent & pre-1987

© Crown Copyright (10

KEY	Period
Peat	
Alluvium	
Glacial Sand & Gravel	Quaternary
River Terrace Deposits	
Glacial Till (Boulder Clay)	
Mercia Mudstone	Triassic
Sherwood Sandstone	Permo-Triassic
Permian mudstones	Permian
Magnesian Limestone	
Coal Measures	
Millstone Grit	Carboniferous
Carboniferous Limestone	
Igneous (basalt, dolerite & tuff)	

LYCOPODIACEAE

Huperzia selago (L.) Bernh. ex Schrank & Mart.
Fir Clubmoss

COUNTY STATUS: Native
CONSERVATION STATUS: A, B
FIRST YEAR: 1658 LATEST YEAR: 2012 NO OF RECORDS: 85
RECENT SQUARES: monads 14; tetrads 11; hectads 7
ALL SQUARES: monads 23; tetrads 16; hectads 10

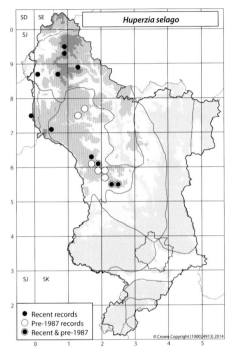

Fir Clubmoss is a very rare, native perennial found in a range of contrasting habitats. It occurs on the high moorland of the Dark Peak (Snake Pass SK0893 & Blackden Brook SK1288). In the White Peak it may be found where acid soils or substrates cover the limestone, such as the waste tips of silica sand pits (Brassington SK2354 & Friden SK1761).

These provide interesting refuges, but are unfortunately vulnerable to disturbance. Elsewhere, there are a few records from communities directly overlying the limestone (Solomon's Temple SK0571). It is a species of the upland north and west of Britain, with Derbyshire at its south-eastern limit.

Lycopodiella inundata (L.) Holub
Marsh Clubmoss

COUNTY STATUS: Native
CONSERVATION STATUS: DRDB (Cat6), EN, NS, NERC
FIRST YEAR: 1805 LATEST YEAR: 1864 NO OF RECORDS: 5
RECENT SQUARES: monads 0; tetrads 0; hectads 0
ALL SQUARES: monads 0; tetrads 0; hectads 3

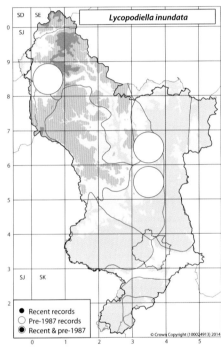

Locally extinct, Marsh Clubmoss was a very rare, native perennial that grew on the

surface of wet peat on moors and heaths. It is known only from Kinder Scout (SK08) in 1805, Chinley Hill (SK08) in 1829 and Tansley Common (SK35/36) in 1864 (Linton 1903).

Lycopodium clavatum L.
Stag's-horn Clubmoss

COUNTY STATUS: Native
CONSERVATION STATUS: DRDB (Cat5b), CitesD, B
FIRST YEAR: 1658 LATEST YEAR: 2011 NO OF RECORDS: 137
RECENT SQUARES: monads 16; tetrads 13; hectads 9
ALL SQUARES: monads 37; tetrads 29; hectads 17

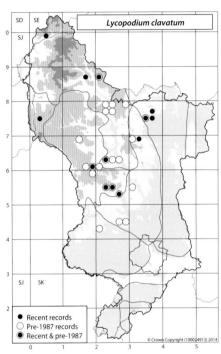

Stag's-horn Clubmoss is a very rare, native perennial of heaths and woodland rides. It occurs scattered through northern and western parts of Derbyshire. Older records (Linton 1903) also refer to the plant growing on moors where it still occasionally occurs (Ladybower SK2086). Until recently it has been particularly characteristic of heathy vegetation on silica sand pits in the White Peak (Kenslow Pits SK1861 & Bees Nest Pits SK2354). In this habitat, however, it has proved vulnerable to reworking and management changes, and has suffered a severe decline at many locations since the early 1990s.

Diphasiastrum alpinum (L.) Holub
Alpine Clubmoss

COUNTY STATUS: Native
CONSERVATION STATUS: DRDB (Cat5b), A, B
FIRST YEAR: 1729 LATEST YEAR: 2012 NO OF RECORDS: 58
RECENT SQUARES: monads 6; tetrads 4; hectads 3
ALL SQUARES: monads 11; tetrads 7; hectads 7

Alpine Clubmoss is a very rare, native perennial found in two distinct areas. It occurs on moorland in the Dark Peak

Fir Clubmoss (*Huperzia selago*), Bleaklow (SK09), August 2009 (Alan Willmot)

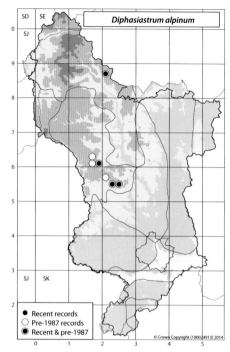

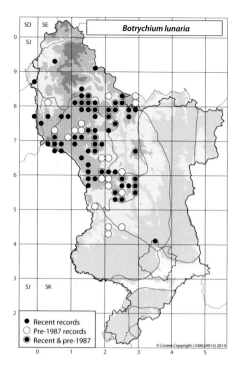

OPHIOGLOSSACEAE

Ophioglossum vulgatum L.
Adder's-tongue

COUNTY STATUS:	Native
CONSERVATION STATUS:	None

FIRST YEAR: 1792 LATEST YEAR: 2012 NO OF RECORDS: 523
RECENT SQUARES: monads 155; tetrads 128; hectads 32
ALL SQUARES: monads 225; tetrads 178; hectads 37

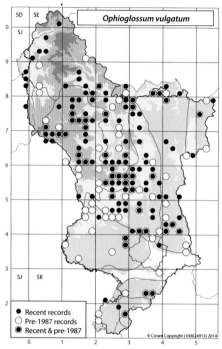

Adder's-tongue is an occasional native perennial of unimproved grasslands, open woods, heaths and marshy areas. It occurs scattered throughout the county (Miller's Dale SK1373, Woodlands Fields SK3440, Roundring Meadow SK3053, Summer Wood Field SK4079 & Mapperley Reserve SK4343). It has been lost from many grassland sites over the last thirty years due to agricultural improvement. But losses have to some extent been balanced by its ability to colonise disused gravel pits and quarries such as Ticknall Limeyards (SK3523).

Botrychium lunaria (L.) Sw.
Moonwort

COUNTY STATUS:	Native
CONSERVATION STATUS:	ERL, B

FIRST YEAR: 1789 LATEST YEAR: 2012 NO OF RECORDS: 282
RECENT SQUARES: monads 86; tetrads 66; hectads 15
ALL SQUARES: monads 112; tetrads 85; hectads 19

Moonwort is an occasional native perennial of unimproved grassland, often found in the vicinity of old lead mine workings. It is virtually confined to the White Peak, Dark Peak and South West Peak (Priestcliffe Lees SK1472, Pin Dale SK1582, Coombs Dale SK2274 & Beeley Moor SK2967). The only modern site south of the White Peak was

discovered in 2001 at Woodlands Field near Allestree (SK3440). The plant was much used by herbalists in the past which probably explains why it was impressively illustrated on a period canvas-work panel at Hardwick Hall (Mabey 1996).

EQUISETACEAE

Equisetum hyemale L.
Rough Horsetail

COUNTY STATUS:	Native
CONSERVATION STATUS:	DRDB (Cat4), A, B, C

FIRST YEAR: 1811 LATEST YEAR: 2010 NO OF RECORDS: 13
RECENT SQUARES: monads 1; tetrads 1; hectads 1
ALL SQUARES: monads 2; tetrads 2; hectads 3

Rough Horsetail (*Equisetum hyemale*), Millington Green (SK2647), June 2004 (Nick Moyes)

(Ladybower SK2187), and amongst grasses and heathers on the waste from silica sand pits in the White Peak (Kenslow Pit SK1861 & near Harborough Brickworks SK2354/SK2355). Most older records were from the former area (Derwent SK19 & Abney Moor SK17). The silica sand sites provide an important refuge for the plant, but are themselves currently vulnerable to disturbance. It is a plant of northern moorland areas, with Derbyshire on the southern limits of its British range.

SELAGINELLACEAE

Selaginella selaginoides (L.) P. Beauv.
Lesser Clubmoss

COUNTY STATUS:	Native
CONSERVATION STATUS:	DRDB (Cat6)

FIRST YEAR: 1805 LATEST YEAR: 1805 NO OF RECORDS: 1
RECENT SQUARES: monads 0; tetrads 0; hectads 0
ALL SQUARES: monads 0; tetrads 0; hectads 1

Locally extinct, Lesser Clubmoss was a native perennial of moorland and damp heaths. The only record came from Kinder Scout (SK08) in 1805.

Selaginella kraussiana (Kunze) A. Braun
Krauss's Clubmoss
Krauss's Clubmoss is a very rare, casual perennial. It is only known from two sites. It was first found on a lawn at Kedleston Hall (SK3140) by M. Bryce in 1999 and again in 2000 and 2001. A second site in the Fern Pit at Chatsworth (SK2669) was discovered in 2011. A native of central and southern Africa, it is regularly cultivated indoors and often becomes a weed of glasshouses.

Rough Horsetail is a very rare, native perennial. It is currently recorded from just one shaded streamside at Millington Green (SK2647) where it was discovered by A. Willmot in 1975 and rerecorded many times since then. There are at least two earlier records: Garneys (1881) recorded it from Repton Rocks (SK3222) and Watson (1811) from Scarcliffe Park (SK57). However, Linton (1903) either discounted or overlooked them as he later stated in his Flora it had still to be recorded in Derbyshire. It is decreasing nationally.

Equisetum fluviatile L.
Water Horsetail

COUNTY STATUS: Native	
CONSERVATION STATUS: None	
FIRST YEAR: 1789 LATEST YEAR: 2013 NO OF RECORDS: 632	
RECENT SQUARES: monads 186; tetrads 172; hectads 40	
ALL SQUARES: monads 265; tetrads 226; hectads 41	

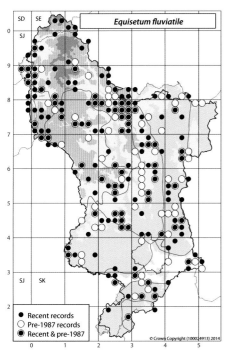

Water Horsetail is an occasional native perennial that grows throughout Derbyshire. It occurs most often at the edges of still or slowly flowing waterbodies, but is also found in marshes and fens.

Equisetum × litorale Kuehlew. ex Rupr.
Shore Horsetail

COUNTY STATUS: Native	
CONSERVATION STATUS: None	
FIRST YEAR: 1970 LATEST YEAR: 2008 NO OF RECORDS: 16	
RECENT SQUARES: monads 6; tetrads 6; hectads 6	
ALL SQUARES: monads 8; tetrads 8; hectads 8	

Shore Horsetail is a very rare, native perennial of damp open areas at the margins of ponds and streams. All recent records are from the northern half of the

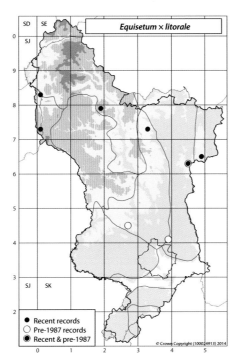

county (Abney Clough SK1979, Linacre Woods SK3272 & Row Ponds SK4563). However, older records are known from further south (Hulland Carr SK2645 & Morley Brickyards SK3841). It is the hybrid of Water (*E. fluviatile*) and Field Horsetail (*E. arvense*).

Equisetum arvense L.
Field Horsetail

COUNTY STATUS: Native	
CONSERVATION STATUS: None	
FIRST YEAR: 1829 LATEST YEAR: 2013 NO OF RECORDS: 3,397	
RECENT SQUARES: monads 1,436; tetrads 681; hectads 44	
ALL SQUARES: monads 1,540; tetrads 691; hectads 44	

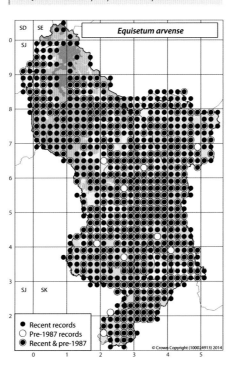

Field Horsetail is a very common, native perennial, found throughout Derbyshire apart from the highest moorland areas in the north-west. It grows on waysides, disturbed ground, waste places and cultivated land where its rhizomatous nature can make it a pervasive and troublesome weed.

Equisetum sylvaticum L.
Wood Horsetail

COUNTY STATUS: Native	
CONSERVATION STATUS: None	
FIRST YEAR: 1829 LATEST YEAR: 2013 NO OF RECORDS: 530	
RECENT SQUARES: monads 202; tetrads 146; hectads 29	
ALL SQUARES: monads 239; tetrads 169; hectads 33	

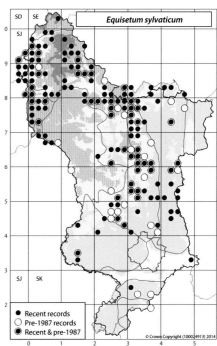

Wood Horsetail is an occasional native perennial of damp woods, stream banks and moorland flushes. It is most commonly encountered in the South West Peak, Dark Peak and Peak Fringe (Jagger's Clough SK1587, Longshaw SK2578, & Eddlestow SK3263). Elsewhere records are more widely scattered (Shirley Park SK2041 & Tibshelf SK4460), whilst other sites appear to have been lost (Bryan's Coppice, SK3619).

Equisetum palustre L.
Marsh Horsetail

COUNTY STATUS: Native	
CONSERVATION STATUS: None	
FIRST YEAR: 1811 LATEST YEAR: 2013 NO OF RECORDS: 727	
RECENT SQUARES: monads 291; tetrads 216; hectads 39	
ALL SQUARES: monads 341; tetrads 250; hectads 42	

Marsh Horsetail is an occasional native perennial of marshes, damp grasslands, fens and flushes. Recorded

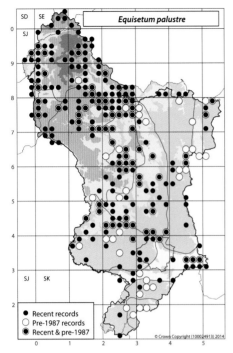

throughout the county except for parts of the Dark Peak, the White Peak and some intensively farmed lowland areas, it was once more frequent in southern Derbyshire. Most losses are probably due to drainage of agricultural land.

Equisetum telmateia Ehrh.
Great Horsetail

COUNTY STATUS:	Native
CONSERVATION STATUS:	None
FIRST YEAR: 1864	LATEST YEAR: 2013	NO OF RECORDS: 338
RECENT SQUARES:	monads 103; tetrads 79; hectads 26
ALL SQUARES:	monads 127; tetrads 95; hectads 27

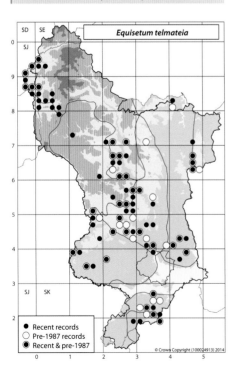

Great Horsetail is an occasional native perennial of damp shady places in woods, hedgerows, banks and waysides. This impressive plant can be found in all of the lowland Areas (Watford Lodge SK0086, Alder Carr SK2037, Birchill Bank SK2271, Carver's Rocks SK3222 & Glapwell Wood SK4766).

OSMUNDACEAE

Osmunda regalis L.
Royal Fern

COUNTY STATUS:	Native
CONSERVATION STATUS:	DRDB (Cat4)
FIRST YEAR: 1829	LATEST YEAR: 2012	NO OF RECORDS: 13
RECENT SQUARES:	monads 3; tetrads 3; hectads 2
ALL SQUARES:	monads 7; tetrads 7; hectads 7

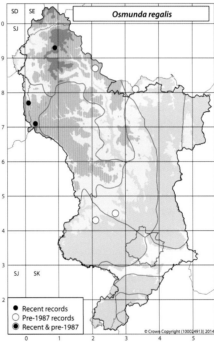

Royal Fern is a very rare, native perennial of mires and moors. There are only three recent localities, all from 2012 (Fernilee Reservoir SK0177, Featherbed Moss SK0370 & Snake Pass SK0893). Previously it had been recorded in nine sites, often in marshy woods rather than mires. Three of these were probably sites where it had been planted: Osmaston Ponds (SK24) in 1903, Brabyns Park (SJ9689) in 1984 and Beauchief Hall (SK3381) in 1970. All other records date from the late 19th century. These were Castleton (SK18) and Ladybower Inn (SK2086) in the north, Darley Dale (SK26) in the centre, and three southern sites: Breward's Carr (SK24), Shirley Wood (SK2042) and Hulland Carr (SK2645). This early loss from so many sites was no doubt due to the activity of Victorian fern collectors.

HYMENOPHYLLACEAE

Trichomanes speciosum Willd.
Killarney Fern

COUNTY STATUS:	Native
CONSERVATION STATUS:	DRDB (Cat1),HabsRegs, Bern, WCA8, NT, A, B, C
FIRST YEAR: 1990	LATEST YEAR: 2011	NO OF RECORDS: 6
RECENT SQUARES:	monads 2; tetrads 1; hectads 1
ALL SQUARES:	monads 2; tetrads 1; hectads 1

Killarney Fern is a very rare, native perennial of shaded gritstone crevices. It is known only at Froggatt Edge (SK2476 & SK2577) where it was first discovered as four small patches in 1990 (Rumsey et al. 1998) and refound in 2010 and 2011. All ferns exist as two alternating life stages: a dominant one that reproduces by spores which is what most people recognise as the fern plant, and a diminutive stage that reproduces sexually but which is rarely noticed. Killarney Fern only exists in Derbyshire as the latter sexual stage. It is assumed the other stage occurred here once, but has since been lost by environmental change, possibly climatic cooling. It grows scattered throughout the south-western, oceanic fringe of the British Isles, and is regarded as a high priority species for conservation both nationally and internationally.

SALVINIACEAE

Azolla filiculoides Lam.
Water Fern

Water Fern is an established floating waterweed of still and gently flowing waterbodies, though it can occur amongst vegetation at the edges of rivers and

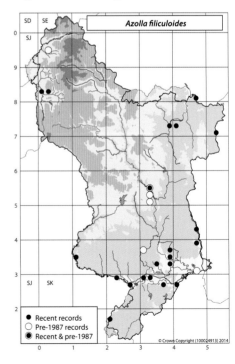

COUNTY STATUS: Established (Neophyte)
CONSERVATION STATUS: WCA9
FIRST YEAR: 1965 LATEST YEAR: 2012 NO OF RECORDS: 37
RECENT SQUARES: monads 23; tetrads 21; hectads 14
ALL SQUARES: monads 29; tetrads 26; hectads 15

canals. It is generally rare across the area, but commoner in lowland parts (Buxworth Canal Basin SK0282, Doveridge Lake SK1134 & River Derwent SK3834). It is often grown in ornamental ponds from where it escapes into more natural habitats, but its sale was banned in England in 2013. It is often said to be killed off by cold winters in the county but it survived the bad winters of the early 1980s in a shallow pool at 275 metres near Glossop. It is a native of North America.

DENNSTAEDTIACEAE

Pteridium aquilinum (L.) Kuhn
Bracken

COUNTY STATUS: Native
CONSERVATION STATUS: None
FIRST YEAR: 1829 LATEST YEAR: 2013 NO OF RECORDS: 4,435
RECENT SQUARES: monads 1,515; tetrads 601; hectads 41
ALL SQUARES: monads 1,573; tetrads 615; hectads 41

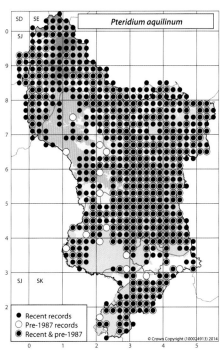

Bracken is a common native perennial found in a wide range of habitats on dry acid soils. These include woods, heaths, hedges and moors. It is widespread and dominant over large swathes of upland grazings in the Dark and South West Peak. It is much less frequent in parts of the White Peak, the southern Claylands and the Trent Valley. It is excluded from the former by shallower, more alkaline soils, and from the latter two by wetter, more

intensively farmed soils. It spread markedly through the South West and Dark Peak Areas during the 20th century. This was due to changes in farming practices and the fact that its fronds were no longer harvested for animal bedding or pottery packing (Moss 1913). It was also once collected for covering charcoal-burning hearths.

PTERIDACEAE

Cryptogramma crispa (L.) R.Br. ex Hook.
Parsley Fern

COUNTY STATUS: Native
CONSERVATION STATUS: DRDB (Cat6)
FIRST YEAR: 1805 LATEST YEAR: 1805 NO OF RECORDS: 2
RECENT SQUARES: monads 0; tetrads 0; hectads 0
ALL SQUARES: monads 0; tetrads 0; hectads 1

Locally extinct, Parsley Fern was a rare native perennial of upland rocky areas. It was known only from a single site, Chinley Hills near Chapel-en-le-Frith in 1805. By 1854 it was already regarded as extinct (Linton 1903). This site is on the south-eastern limit of its range in England.

Pteris cretica L.
Ribbon Fern

Ribbon Fern is a very rare, casual perennial of damp sheltered walls. There are only four records. There are recent ones from 2011 for Chatsworth Fern Pit (SK2669) and an old Chatsworth greenhouse wall (SK2670). There are previous ones from 1977 for Hopton Hall Gardens (SK2553) under greenhouse staging, and Markeaton Street, Derby (SK3436). The fern is commonly grown in houses as a pot plant and is a native of southern Europe.

ASPLENIACEAE

Asplenium scolopendrium L.
Hart's-tongue

COUNTY STATUS: Native
CONSERVATION STATUS: None
FIRST YEAR: 1789 LATEST YEAR: 2013 NO OF RECORDS: 1,100
RECENT SQUARES: monads 519; tetrads 337; hectads 38
ALL SQUARES: monads 550; tetrads 356; hectads 38

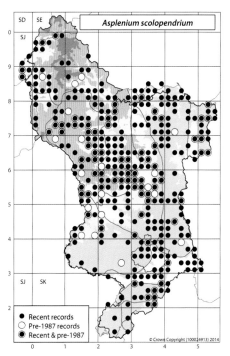

Hart's-tongue is a native evergreen perennial. It is found in a range of damp shaded habitats including woods, walls, outcrops and drains in urban areas. It occurs frequently throughout the county, especially in limestone areas or

Hart's-tongue (*Asplenium scolopendrium*), Markland Grips (SK5175), June 2009 (Peter Smith)

where limestone has been introduced for walls and paths. It is only absent from some intensively farmed lowland areas and the highest gritstone moors. It is increasing nationally (Braithwaite *et al.* 2006).

Asplenium adiantum-nigrum L.
Black Spleenwort

COUNTY STATUS: Native
CONSERVATION STATUS: None
FIRST YEAR: 1829 LATEST YEAR: 2013 NO OF RECORDS: 310
RECENT SQUARES: monads 115; tetrads 114; hectads 33
ALL SQUARES: monads 148; tetrads 130; hectads 36

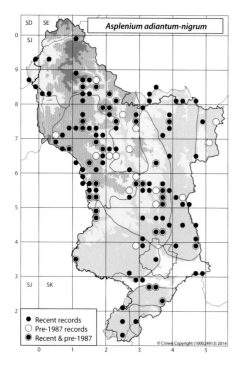

Black Spleenwort is a native evergreen perennial of rocks, walls and banks. It occurs occasionally scattered throughout the county from Blackwell Dale (SK1372) and Hathersage (SK2281) in the north, through the Tissington Trail (SK1657) and Wingfield Manor (SK3754), to Elm Farm (SK3427) in the south.

Asplenium marinum L.
Sea Spleenwort

Sea Spleenwort was an established perennial plant known only from the Derwent Hospital in Derby (SK3638). It was discovered on a gritstone wall in 1977, where it was sheltered from frost by steam from a laundry outlet. The plants disappeared with the hospital's demolition in the 1980s. It is native to British coasts and is occasionally grown in greenhouses.

Asplenium trichomanes L.
Maidenhair Spleenwort

COUNTY STATUS: Native
CONSERVATION STATUS: None
FIRST YEAR: 1789 LATEST YEAR: 2013 NO OF RECORDS: 1,038
RECENT SQUARES: monads 365; tetrads 226; hectads 34
ALL SQUARES: monads 400; tetrads 243; hectads 34

Maidenhair Spleenwort is an evergreen native perennial of shaded or moist rocks and walls. It is frequent in the White Peak but rare elsewhere. Whenever recorded to the subspecific level, ssp. *quadrivalens* D.E. Mey. is the more commonly noted form. It has been found in both gritstone and limestone areas (Crowden SK0699 v.c.58, Chee Dale SK1273 & Coombs

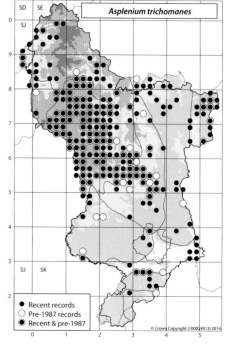

Dale SK2274). Ssp. *pachyrachis* (H. Christ) Lovis & Reichst. has only been found in the White Peak (Lathkill Dale SK1865) and is Nationally Rare.

Asplenium viride Huds.
Green Spleenwort

COUNTY STATUS: Native
CONSERVATION STATUS: DRDB (Cat5b), B
FIRST YEAR: 1789 LATEST YEAR: 2013 NO OF RECORDS: 186
RECENT SQUARES: monads 25; tetrads 16; hectads 7
ALL SQUARES: monads 33; tetrads 21; hectads 9

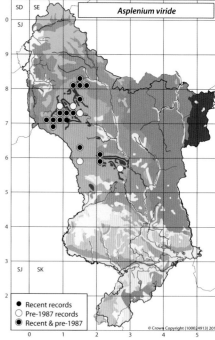

Green Spleenwort is an evergreen native perennial of damp shaded limestone outcrops. All recent records are from the

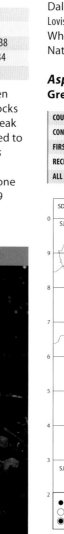

Green Spleenwort (*Asplenium viride*), a classic Derbyshire fern, 2004 (Stephen Trotter)

White Peak where it is rare and local (Woo Dale SK0972, Flag Dale SK1273, Green Dale SK1580 & Gratton Dale SK2059) but Linton (1903) gives a record from Coxbench Wood (SK34). It is a plant of upland Britain with the White Peak on the south-eastern edge of its range and its only Midlands stronghold.

Asplenium ruta-muraria L.
Wall-rue

COUNTY STATUS: Native
CONSERVATION STATUS: None
FIRST YEAR: 1724 LATEST YEAR: 2013 NO OF RECORDS: 1,135
RECENT SQUARES: monads 438; tetrads 282; hectads 37
ALL SQUARES: monads 474; tetrads 299; hectads 38

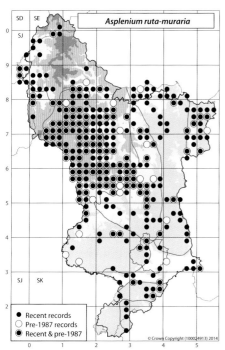

Wall-rue is an evergreen native perennial of rocks and walls in even the driest and most open localities. It is very common in the White Peak but rarer elsewhere such as at Calke Abbey (SK3622) and Derby (SK3536).

Asplenium ceterach L.
Rustyback

COUNTY STATUS: Native
CONSERVATION STATUS: B
FIRST YEAR: 1811 LATEST YEAR: 2013 NO OF RECORDS: 165
RECENT SQUARES: monads 45; tetrads 43; hectads 18
ALL SQUARES: monads 58; tetrads 56; hectads 23

Rustyback is a rare native perennial of exposed limestone rocks and mortared walls. It is occasional in the White Peak and Magnesian Limestone areas (Wolfscote Dale SK1457, Monsal Dale SK1771, Lathkill Dale SK1966, Rowthorne SK4765 & Langwith SK5270) but is rare elsewhere (Ticknall SK3422).

Rustyback (*Asplenium ceterach*), Whirlow (SK3082), July 2013 (Ken Balkow)

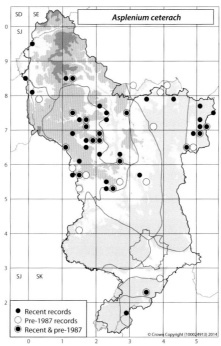

THELYPTERIDACEAE

Thelypteris palustris Schott
Marsh Fern

COUNTY STATUS: Native
CONSERVATION STATUS: DRDB (Cat3), NS, A, B
FIRST YEAR: 1991 LATEST YEAR: 2012 NO OF RECORDS: 9
RECENT SQUARES: monads 1; tetrads 1; hectads 1
ALL SQUARES: monads 1; tetrads 1; hectads 1

Marsh Fern is a very rare, native perennial of marshy areas. It has only ever been recorded from one site, Big Moor SK2674, where it was discovered in 1991 (Rotherham & Ardron 1993). Subsequently

it has been recorded there on at least seven occasions. It is a rare and decreasing plant of fens and marshes throughout Britain, north to central Scotland, and is Nationally Scarce.

Phegopteris connectilis (Michx.) Watt
Beech Fern

COUNTY STATUS: Native
CONSERVATION STATUS: B
FIRST YEAR: 1811 LATEST YEAR: 2012 NO OF RECORDS: 181
RECENT SQUARES: monads 33; tetrads 26; hectads 10
ALL SQUARES: monads 38; tetrads 30; hectads 14

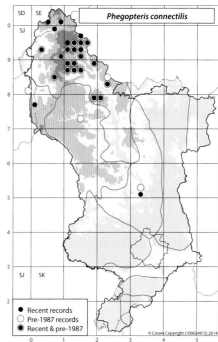

Beech Fern is a rare native perennial of damp shaded rocks in woods and along streamsides in the Dark Peak (Long Clough SK0392, Roych Clough SK0784, Jagger's Clough SK1487 & Abney Clough SK2079). The only recent records outside this Area come from the Goyt Valley (SK0176 v.c.58) and Beggarswell Wood (SK3351). There is also one older record from Priestcliffe Lees (SK1472) in the White Peak (Clapham 1969). Nationally the plant has a mainly upland distribution, with Derbyshire on the south-eastern edge of its range.

Oreopteris limbosperma (All.) Holub
Lemon-scented Fern

COUNTY STATUS: Native
CONSERVATION STATUS: None
FIRST YEAR: 1677 LATEST YEAR: 2013 NO OF RECORDS: 534
RECENT SQUARES: monads 234; tetrads 134; hectads 19
ALL SQUARES: monads 270; tetrads 157; hectads 27

Lemon-scented Fern is a locally frequent native perennial of the Dark and South West Peak where it occurs in damp areas

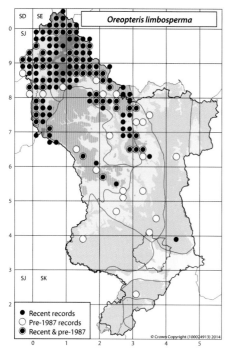

Oreopteris limbosperma

- ● Recent records
- ○ Pre-1987 records
- ◉ Recent & pre-1987

© Crown Copyright (100024913) 2014

of woods, moors and rocky banks (Whiteley Nab SK0292 & Priddock Wood SK2086). Only a small number of locations are now known outside these Areas, such as on pockets of acid soil on the Carboniferous Limestone at Parsley Hay (SK1463) and Minninglow Hill (SK2057). It has also been found at Hermit's Wood (SK4338) in the Coal Measures and at Ashover (SK3463) in the Peak Fringe. It was formerly recorded in southern and eastern areas (Cubley SK1539, Repton Shrubs SK3123, Allestree Park SK3440 & Cobnor Wood SK3575).

WOODSIACEAE

Athyrium filix-femina (L.) Roth
Lady-fern

COUNTY STATUS: Native	
CONSERVATION STATUS: None	
FIRST YEAR: 1729 **LATEST YEAR:** 2013 **NO OF RECORDS:** 1,992	
RECENT SQUARES: monads 815; tetrads 464; hectads 41	
ALL SQUARES: monads 916; tetrads 509; hectads 41	

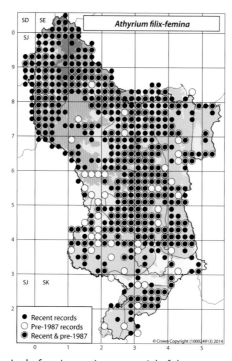

Athyrium filix-femina

- ● Recent records
- ○ Pre-1987 records
- ◉ Recent & pre-1987

© Crown Copyright (100024913) 2014

Lady-fern is a native perennial of damp shaded woods, ditches, rocky hillsides, moors and marshes, generally on acidic soils. It is common throughout the county except for the limestone Character Areas and the intensively farmed, southern parts.

Gymnocarpium dryopteris (L.) Newman
Oak Fern

COUNTY STATUS: Native	
CONSERVATION STATUS: ERL, B	
FIRST YEAR: 1805 **LATEST YEAR:** 2011 **NO OF RECORDS:** 101	
RECENT SQUARES: monads 20; tetrads 22; hectads 9	
ALL SQUARES: monads 26; tetrads 26; hectads 17	

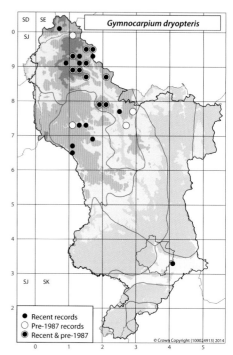

Gymnocarpium dryopteris

- ● Recent records
- ○ Pre-1987 records
- ◉ Recent & pre-1987

© Crown Copyright (100024913) 2014

Oak Fern is a rare native perennial of damp woods and shaded rocks in upland parts. It occurs in both the Dark Peak (Fair Brook SK1189, Abney Clough SK2079 & Ladybower SK2086) and the White Peak (Hurdlow SK16D & Miller's Dale SK17G) but is more frequent in the former. There is also an isolated record on a wall at Elvaston Castle (SK4033) in the south. It is a plant of upland Britain, with the Peak District on the south-eastern edge of its range.

Gymnocarpium robertianum
(Hoffm.) Newman
Limestone Fern

COUNTY STATUS: Native	
CONSERVATION STATUS: DRDB (Cat3), NS, A	
FIRST YEAR: 1790 **LATEST YEAR:** 2013 **NO OF RECORDS:** 246	
RECENT SQUARES: monads 32; tetrads 20; hectads 6	
ALL SQUARES: monads 47; tetrads 31; hectads 7	

Limestone Fern is a rare native perennial of the White Peak, particularly in the Wye Valley area. It grows in limestone screes, often with Herb-Robert, and on rock outcrops. Although the fronds produced in screes often form extensive stands, those on outcrops are generally larger and more luxuriant. Typical localities are: Deep Dale

Limestone Fern (*Gymnocarpium robertianum*), Coombs Dale (SK2274), August 2010 (Ken Balkow)

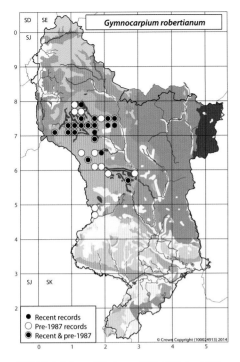

Brittle Bladder-fern (*Cystopteris fragilis*), Lathkill Dale (SK1966), May 2005 (Nick Moyes)

Hard-fern is an evergreen native perennial of woods, heaths, moors and rocky slopes on acidic substrates. It is common in the Dark and South West Peak areas (Long Clough SK0392, Alport Castles SK1491 & North Lees SK2383). It is occasional in the Peak Fringe (Peat Pits SK3252 & Dobb's Hill Plantation SK3842) but very rare elsewhere (Spring Wood SK3722).

DRYOPTERIDACEAE

Polystichum setiferum (Forssk.) T. Moore ex Woyn.
Soft Shield-fern

COUNTY STATUS: Native	
CONSERVATION STATUS: B	
FIRST YEAR: 1845 **LATEST YEAR:** 2013 **NO OF RECORDS:** 173	
RECENT SQUARES: monads 75; tetrads 64; hectads 27	
ALL SQUARES: monads 82; tetrads 69; hectads 27	

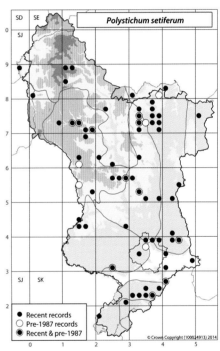

(SK0971), Priestcliffe Lees (SK1472), Lathkill Dale (SK1965) and Coombs Dale (SK2274). It is local and scattered in Britain, and Nationally Scarce.

Cystopteris fragilis (L.) Bernh.
Brittle Bladder-fern

COUNTY STATUS: Native	
CONSERVATION STATUS: None	
FIRST YEAR: 1677 **LATEST YEAR:** 2013 **NO OF RECORDS:** 680	
RECENT SQUARES: monads 237; tetrads 132; hectads 19	
ALL SQUARES: monads 252; tetrads 140; hectads 22	

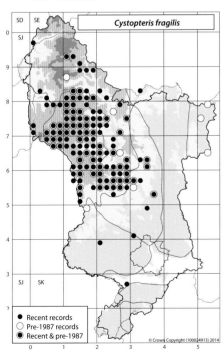

Brittle Bladder-fern is a native perennial of damp shaded limestone outcrops, mortared walls and rocky woods on

limestone. It is frequent in the White Peak but very rare elsewhere, as at Upper Derwent (SK1591), Repton (SK2927), Ramsley Moor (SK2874) and Longford Hall (SK2138) where it was found growing on a large block of imported limestone. It was previously known in the 1960s for the Magnesian Limestone (Pleasley Vale SK5265 & Whitwell Wood SK5278).

BLECHNACEAE

Blechnum spicant (L.) Roth
Hard-fern

COUNTY STATUS: Native	
CONSERVATION STATUS: None	
FIRST YEAR: 1829 **LATEST YEAR:** 2013 **NO OF RECORDS:** 965	
RECENT SQUARES: monads 421; tetrads 205; hectads 28	
ALL SQUARES: monads 441; tetrads 220; hectads 31	

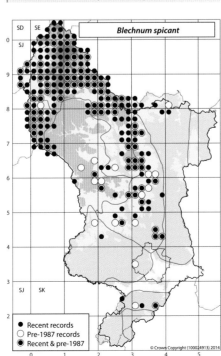

Soft Shield-fern is an occasional native perennial of deciduous woods, hedges and rock outcrops throughout the area (Chee Dale SK1273, Gulliver's Kingdom SK2957, Linacre Woods SK3272, Ticknall Limeyards SK3623 & Hermit's Wood SK4438). Clapham (1969) suggested the plant was "perhaps decreasing"; however, the number of recent records rather suggests it has been overlooked in the past. This may be because it tends to occur as solitary individuals.

Polystichum × *bicknellii* (H. Christ) Hahne
A hybrid shield-fern
This hybrid native fern has only been recorded at Lathkill Dale (SK2066) where it was found on a Bradford Botany Group meeting in 2004. It is the sterile hybrid of Soft (*P. setiferum*) and Hard

(*P. aculeatum*) Shield-fern and is probably under-recorded.

Polystichum aculeatum (L.) Roth
Hard Shield-fern

COUNTY STATUS: Native	
CONSERVATION STATUS: None	
FIRST YEAR: 1811 **LATEST YEAR:** 2013 **NO OF RECORDS:** 423	
RECENT SQUARES: monads 145; tetrads 108; hectads 27	
ALL SQUARES: monads 166; tetrads 125; hectads 29	

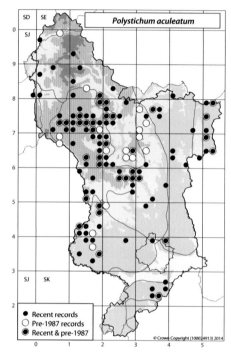

Hard Shield-fern is an evergreen native perennial of woods, hedges and shaded rock outcrops. It is occasional in the White Peak (Priestcliffe Lees SK1572 & Bruns

Wood SK2456) but rare and local elsewhere (Upper Derwent SK1193, Boylestone SK1835, Ticknall Limeyards SK3623 & Markland Grips SK5074).

Dryopteris oreades Fomin
Mountain Male-fern

COUNTY STATUS: Native	
CONSERVATION STATUS: DRDB (Cat6)	
FIRST YEAR: 1855 **LATEST YEAR:** 1855 **NO OF RECORDS:** 1	
RECENT SQUARES: monads 0; tetrads 0; hectads 0	
ALL SQUARES: monads 0; tetrads 0; hectads 0	

Locally extinct, Mountain Male-fern was a very rare, native perennial of screes in upland areas. The only reference to it is from Johnson & Sowerby (1855), stating: "in the Peak, Derbyshire". Nationally it is a plant of upland Britain which would then have been on the south-eastern limit of its range.

Dryopteris filix-mas (L.) Schott
Male-fern

COUNTY STATUS: Native	
CONSERVATION STATUS: None	
FIRST YEAR: 1789 **LATEST YEAR:** 2013 **NO OF RECORDS:** 3,543	
RECENT SQUARES: monads 1,582; tetrads 684; hectads 42	
ALL SQUARES: monads 1,636; tetrads 692; hectads 42	

Male-fern is a very common, native perennial of a wide range of damp and generally shaded habitats throughout the county on all but the most acidic substrates. It occurs in woods, hedges and scrub, as well as on banks, rocky hillsides and walls. It is generally deciduous though may remain green over winter in sheltered spots and when young (Willmot 1989).

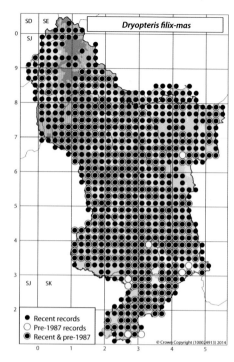

Dryopteris × *complexa* agg.
A hybrid male-fern

COUNTY STATUS: Native	
CONSERVATION STATUS: None	
FIRST YEAR: 1970 **LATEST YEAR:** 2007 **NO OF RECORDS:** 20	
RECENT SQUARES: monads 2; tetrads 2; hectads 2	
ALL SQUARES: monads 13; tetrads 13; hectads 12	

This hybrid male-fern is a very rare, native perennial of damp acid soils in woods, hedges and ditches scattered throughout the county. The only recent records are from Roman Lakes (SJ9687) plus a single plant at Haywood (SK2577). This suggests an under-recording as, when specifically looked for in the 1970s, several sites were found (Stanton Moor SK2563, Shining Cliff Wood SK3352, Breward's Carr SK3044 & Bottoms Wood SK2750). It is the hybrid of Male-fern (*D. filix-mas*) and Scaly Male-fern (*D. affinis* agg.).

Dryopteris affinis agg.
Scaly Male-fern

COUNTY STATUS: Native	
CONSERVATION STATUS: None	
FIRST YEAR: 1729 **LATEST YEAR:** 2013 **NO OF RECORDS:** 521	
RECENT SQUARES: monads 286; tetrads 212; hectads 35	
ALL SQUARES: monads 321; tetrads 239; hectads 35	

Scaly Male-fern is an occasional native perennial of deciduous woods, coniferous plantations, rocky hillsides and moorlands generally, but not exclusively, on acidic soils. It occurs throughout the county but is more common in the north-western corner, becoming rarer towards the south and east. All three British species of this aggregate have been recorded and are

Hard Shield-fern (*Polystichum aculeatum*), Via Gellia (SK2556), May 2005 (Nick Moyes)

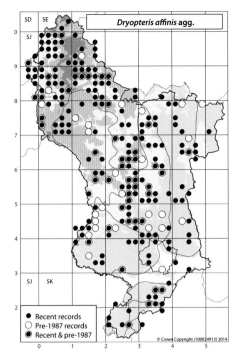

noted below, though there are very few records of each due to the problems of distinguishing one from another.

Dryopteris affinis (Lowe) Fraser-Jenk.
Golden-scaled Male-fern
Golden-scaled Male-fern is a very rare, native perennial. There are only four records, all recent, for Lane Head Road (SK0080 v.c.58), Ogden Clough (SK0198 v.c.58), Chee Tor (SK1273) and Birchen Bank (SK1098). It is probably under-recorded due to the difficulty of separating it from other members of the Scaly Male-fern aggregate.

Dryopteris cambrensis (Fraser-Jenk.) Beitel & W.R. Buck
Narrow Male-fern
Narrow Male-fern is a very rare, native perennial of the Scaly Male-fern aggregate. There are records from three sites: Tintwistle (SK0298 v.c.58) in 1999 and 2000, Heyden Bridge (SE0900 v.c.58) in 2001 and Abney Clough (SK2079) in 2011. It is probably under-recorded due to the difficulties of identification.

Dryopteris borreri (Newman) Newman ex Oberh. & Tavel
Borrer's Male-fern
Borrer's Male-fern is a rare native perennial of the Scaly Male-fern aggregate. It is recorded from eleven hectads, all recent. These are spread over the northern half of the county from Ogden Bank (SK0199 v.c.58) in the north to the Tissington Trail (SK1657) in the south. It is probably under-recorded due to the difficulty of identification.

Dryopteris submontana (Fraser-Jenk. & Jermy) Fraser-Jenk.
Rigid Buckler-fern

COUNTY STATUS: Established (Neophyte)
CONSERVATION STATUS: B
FIRST YEAR: 1970 LATEST YEAR: 2011 NO OF RECORDS: 23
RECENT SQUARES: monads 4; tetrads 4; hectads 3
ALL SQUARES: monads 5; tetrads 4; hectads 3

Rigid Buckler-fern is an established perennial of crevices in limestone rocks. It was first discovered by J. Hodgson and S. Band in 1974 at a railway cutting near Biggin (SK1657). Subsequently it has been found in three other railway cuttings on limestone outcrops: Blake Moor (SK1562), Priestcliffe Lees (SK1272) and Miller's Dale (SK1572). As all sites are man-made habitats, it is regarded as established here, but it is considered as native by some authorities (Preston *et al.* 2002). It occurs nationally in north-western England and Wales.

Dryopteris carthusiana (Vill.) H.P. Fuchs
Narrow Buckler-fern

COUNTY STATUS: Native
CONSERVATION STATUS: DRDB (Cat5b)
FIRST YEAR: 1837 LATEST YEAR: 2013 NO OF RECORDS: 275
RECENT SQUARES: monads 73; tetrads 57; hectads 22
ALL SQUARES: monads 123; tetrads 98; hectads 32

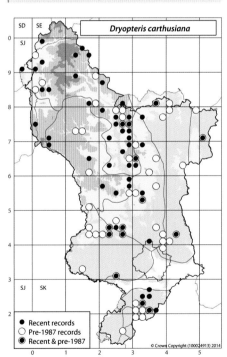

Narrow Buckler-fern is an occasional native perennial of wet woods, marshes and fens. It occurs scattered throughout Derbyshire from the lowlands to the upland moors (Bradley SK2244, Leash Fen SK2874, Shining Cliff Woods SK3352, Mapperley Reservoir SK4343 & Scarcliffe Park SK5170).

Dryopteris × deweveri (J.T. Jansen) Jansen & Wacht.
A hybrid buckler-fern
This hybrid buckler-fern is a very rare, native perennial of damp acid areas in deciduous woodlands. There are only three records all from the 1970s: Hagg Rocks (SK2957), Breward's Carr (SK3044) and High Peak Junction (SK3155). It is the hybrid of Narrow (*D. carthusiana*) and Broad Buckler-fern (*D. dilatata*) and is probably under-recorded.

Dryopteris dilatata (Hoffm.) A.Gray
Broad Buckler-fern

COUNTY STATUS: Native
CONSERVATION STATUS: None
FIRST YEAR: 1824 LATEST YEAR: 2013 NO OF RECORDS: 3,591
RECENT SQUARES: monads 1,373; tetrads 618; hectads 43
ALL SQUARES: monads 1,466; tetrads 634; hectads 43

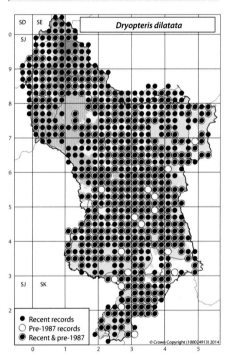

Broad Buckler-fern is a common native perennial of woods, hedges, heaths and moors generally on acidic soils. It occurs throughout the county, even in limestone areas, though here it tends to occur on tree bases and rotting logs in woods. Locally it is generally deciduous, though young plants may be evergreen (Willmot 1989).

POLYPODIACEAE

Polypodium L.
Polypodies

COUNTY STATUS: Native
CONSERVATION STATUS: None
FIRST YEAR: 1811 LATEST YEAR: 2013 NO OF RECORDS: 696
RECENT SQUARES: monads 238; tetrads 170; hectads 31
ALL SQUARES: monads 271; tetrads 192; hectads 32

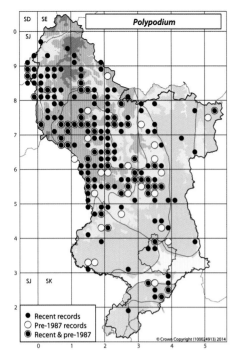

Three species of *Polypodium* are native to Britain, all of which occur here. They are very similar in appearance and in the past have been considered to form a single species. As many records only refer to this aggregate, the map and statistics here show all species combined. However, separate accounts follow for each species and their hybrids.

Polypodium vulgare L.
Polypody
Polypody is a native evergreen perennial of walls, rocks and banks, generally on acid substrates. In the west of Britain it also commonly grows on trees but rarely does so here, mostly due to a lack of moss-covered trunks in which to root. It occurs occasionally throughout northern parts of the county: Alport Valley (SK1292), Alport SK2264, Coombs Dale SK2274 and Wheatcroft SK3456. Additionally there are a few isolated records in southern Derbyshire, as at Anchor Church (SK3327). It is probably under-recorded due to confusion with other species.

Polypodium × *mantoniae* Rothm. &
U. Schneid.
A hybrid polypody
This hybrid polypody is a very rare, native perennial of limestone and gritstone, rocks and walls. There are recent records from only four sites (Coombs Dale SK2173, Chatsworth SK2670, Milltown SK3561 & Dove Valley SK1456) and four earlier ones including Monk's Dale (SK1374) and Wensley Dale (SK2660). It is probably under-recorded due to confusion with its parents: Intermediate

Polypody (*P. interjectum*) and Polypody (*P. vulgare*).

Polypodium × *font-queri* Rothm.
A hybrid polypody
This native hybrid polypody is known only from one shaded limestone crag at Hagg Rocks near Matlock (SK2956). It was discovered here in 2001 by M. Stribley, close to one of the few county sites for Southern Polypody (*P. cambricum*). Initial identification was on morphological grounds but this determination has recently been challenged by a chromosomal count.

Polypodium interjectum Shivas
Intermediate Polypody
Intermediate Polypody is an occasional native perennial of shaded rocks and walls, generally of limestone. It occurs mainly in the White Peak: Deepdale (SK1670) and Carsington Village (SK2553), and elsewhere on the Carboniferous Limestone at Butts Quarry (SK3463). There are also isolated occurrences off the Carboniferous Limestone as at Whitwell Village (SK5276) on the Magnesian Limestone, and at Allestree (SK3439) and King's Newton (SK3826). It is probably under-recorded due to confusion with its close relative, Polypody (*P. vulgare*).

Polypodium cambricum L.
Southern Polypody

COUNTY STATUS: Native	
CONSERVATION STATUS: DRDB (Cat4), B	
FIRST YEAR: 1860 **LATEST YEAR:** 2009 **NO OF RECORDS:** 14	
RECENT SQUARES: monads 2; tetrads 2; hectads 2	
ALL SQUARES: monads 2; tetrads 2; hectads 2	

Southern Polypody is a very rare, native perennial of shaded limestone outcrops. It has been known at Hagg Rocks near Matlock Bath (SK2957) since 1860. A second site was discovered in 2009 at Dove Dale's Tissington Spires (SK1452). It is a plant of western Britain, suggesting its presence in Derbyshire is as a relic of warmer climates a few thousand years ago.

PINACEAE

Abies alba Mill.
European Silver-fir
European Silver-fir is a large evergreen tree that grows as a very rare, casual in plantations and parks. It has only been recorded from two localities recently both in 1999, Ouzelden Clough (SK1590) and Lady Canning's Plantation (SK2883), and from Lathkill Dale (SK1966) in 1955. It is grown for timber and amenity,

and is native to the mountains of central Europe.

Abies procera Rehder
Noble Fir
Noble Fir is a large evergreen tree that occurs very rarely as planted specimens in woods. There are only two records: Longdendale (SK0597) in 2003 and Fairholmes (SK1789) in 1999. It is grown for timber and is a native of western North America.

Pseudotsuga menziesii (Mirb.) Franco
Douglas Fir
Douglas Fir is a large evergreen tree that occurs very rarely as planted specimens in woods and amenity plantings. There are only five records, all between 1970 and 2012: Ladybower (SK1592), Fairholmes (SK1789), Thornbridge Park (SK2070), Gladwin Wood (SK3368) and Ambergate Reservoir (SK3552). It is grown for timber and ornament, and is indigenous to western North America.

Tsuga heterophylla (Raf.) Sarg.
Western Hemlock-spruce

COUNTY STATUS: Casual	
CONSERVATION STATUS: None	
FIRST YEAR: 1974 **LATEST YEAR:** 2006 **NO OF RECORDS:** 18	
RECENT SQUARES: monads 11; tetrads 11; hectads 8	
ALL SQUARES: monads 12; tetrads 12; hectads 8	

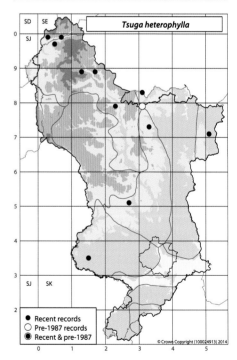

Western Hemlock-spruce is a large evergreen tree that is recorded very rarely as a casual in plantations. It occurs in the north of the county for example at Upper Derwent (SK1389), Whirlow Brook (SK38B)

and Linacre Woods (SK3272). It is grown for timber and is native to western North America.

Picea sitchensis (Bong.) Carriere
Sitka Spruce

COUNTY STATUS: Established (Neophyte)
CONSERVATION STATUS: None
FIRST YEAR: 1979 LATEST YEAR: 2010 NO OF RECORDS: 64
RECENT SQUARES: monads 40; tetrads 33; hectads 13
ALL SQUARES: monads 41; tetrads 33; hectads 13

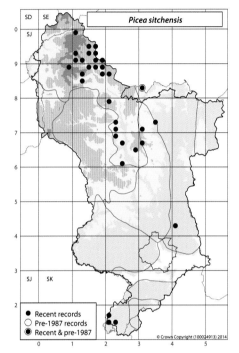

Sitka Spruce is a large evergreen tree recorded rarely as an established species in plantations and woods. It occurs mainly in the Dark Peak for example at Upper Longdendale (SK1099), Edale (SK1285), Oyster Clough (SK1291) and Clough Wood (SK2561). It is now also found in the National Forest area (Walton Wood SK2116). A native of western North America, it is grown for timber and ornament.

Picea abies (L.) H. Karst.
Norway Spruce

COUNTY STATUS: Casual
CONSERVATION STATUS: None
FIRST YEAR: 1815 LATEST YEAR: 2011 NO OF RECORDS: 95
RECENT SQUARES: monads 55; tetrads 50; hectads 25
ALL SQUARES: monads 59; tetrads 54; hectads 27

Norway Spruce is a large evergreen tree that is recorded rarely as a casual in plantations, woods and parks. It is found throughout the county from Woodlands Valley (SK1190) in the north through Wormhill (SK1273) and Scarcliffe (SK5170) to Shirley Park (SK2042) and Morley Wood (SK4041) in the south. Grown for

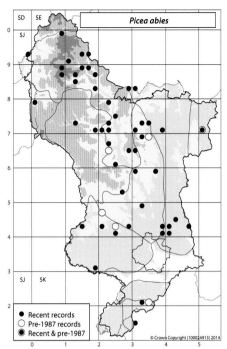

timber, amenity and Christmas trees, it is a native of mountains in eastern Europe.

Larix decidua Mill.
European Larch

COUNTY STATUS: Established (Neophyte)
CONSERVATION STATUS: None
FIRST YEAR: 1755 LATEST YEAR: 2013 NO OF RECORDS: 425
RECENT SQUARES: monads 266; tetrads 221; hectads 35
ALL SQUARES: monads 278; tetrads 228; hectads 36

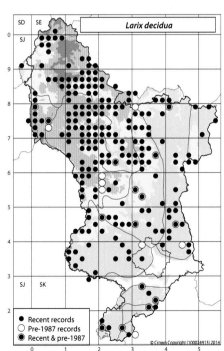

European Larch is a large tree that is occasionally established in plantations, shelter-belts, amenity plantations and parks throughout the county. It has a long history of being grown in Derbyshire for

timber and amenity since it was planted at the home of Sir Joseph Banks at Ashover in 1755 (Farey 1815). It is indigenous to the mountains of central Europe.

Larix × marschlinsii Coaz
Hybrid Larch

COUNTY STATUS: Casual
CONSERVATION STATUS: None
FIRST YEAR: 1987 LATEST YEAR: 2012 NO OF RECORDS: 51
RECENT SQUARES: monads 39; tetrads 38; hectads 19
ALL SQUARES: monads 39; tetrads 38; hectads 19

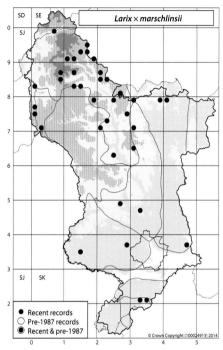

Hybrid Larch is a rare casual tree of plantations and copses. It is recorded mainly in the northern half of the county as at Ringing Roger (SK1286), Upper Derwent (SK1493) and Flash Dam (SK36C). However, there are a few records for the southern half, as at Biggin (SK24U) and Stoney Clouds (SK4737). It is much planted for timber and amenity, but is probably under-recorded for Larch. It is the hybrid of Larch (*L. decidua*) and Japanese Larch (*L. kaempferi*) that arose spontaneously in a Scottish garden in 1904.

Larix kaempferi (Lamb.) Carriere
Japanese Larch

COUNTY STATUS: Casual
CONSERVATION STATUS: None
FIRST YEAR: 1971 LATEST YEAR: 2011 NO OF RECORDS: 56
RECENT SQUARES: monads 34; tetrads 32; hectads 18
ALL SQUARES: monads 39; tetrads 34; hectads 18

Japanese Larch is a rare casual tree of plantations, copses and gardens. It occurs mainly in the north of the county as at Deep Clough (SK0497), Ditch Clough (SK1592) and Calver (SK2373). There are also a few records in the south as at Shirley Park (SK2042) and

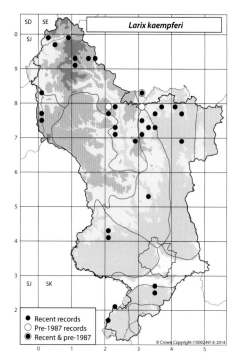

Peat Pits (SK3252). It is planted for timber and amenity, probably more often than the records here suggest. It is a native of Japan.

Pinus sylvestris L.
Scots Pine

COUNTY STATUS: Established (Neophyte)
CONSERVATION STATUS: None
FIRST YEAR: 1829 **LATEST YEAR:** 2010 **NO OF RECORDS:** 1,022
RECENT SQUARES: monads 528; tetrads 354; hectads 42
ALL SQUARES: monads 565; tetrads 376; hectads 43

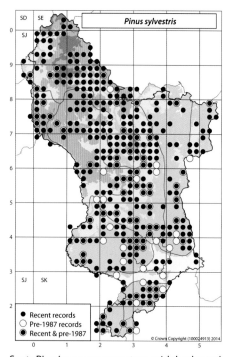

Scots Pine is an evergreen tree, widely planted for timber and amenity. It is also commonly self-sown from these specimens such that it is established in woods, copses, scrub, waste

ground and heathy areas. Including planted and self-sown trees together, it is frequent throughout the county. A large specimen at Pleasley Churchyard (SK5064) has a recently recorded girth of 2.95m. It is a native forest tree in central Scotland.

Pinus nigra J.F. Arnold
A pine species

COUNTY STATUS: Casual
CONSERVATION STATUS: None
FIRST YEAR: 1987 **LATEST YEAR:** 2013 **NO OF RECORDS:** 68
RECENT SQUARES: monads 55; tetrads 47; hectads 22
ALL SQUARES: monads 55; tetrads 47; hectads 22

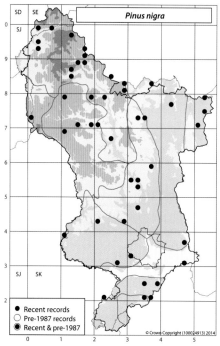

Two subspecies of this tree occur here. **Austrian Pine (ssp. nigra)** is a large evergreen tree, and a rare casual of woods, copses and amenity plantings. It occurs scattered throughout Derbyshire, from Long Clough (SK0392) and Upper Derwent (SK1789) in the north, to Abbotsholme School (SK1138) and Melbourne (SK3925) in the south. It is indigenous to central and south-eastern Europe. **Corsican Pine (ssp. laricio Maire)** is a very rare casual of plantations and amenity plantings. All nine records are recent, and occur scattered from Howden Dam (SK1692) in the north, through Creswell Crags (SK5374) to Risley Coppice (SK4436) in the south. It is a native of the central Mediterranean.

Pinus contorta Douglas ex Loudon
Lodgepole Pine

COUNTY STATUS: Casual
CONSERVATION STATUS: None
FIRST YEAR: 1988 **LATEST YEAR:** 2006 **NO OF RECORDS:** 22
RECENT SQUARES: monads 15; tetrads 14; hectads 13
ALL SQUARES: monads 15; tetrads 14; hectads 13

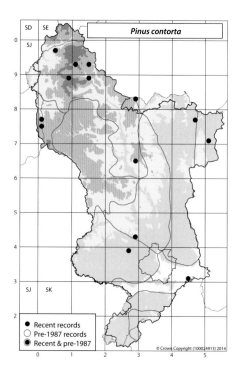

Lodgepole Pine is an evergreen tree that occurs as a very rare casual of woods and moors. It grows mostly in the north of the county where it is also a plantation tree (Hoo Moor SK0076 v.c.58, Upper Derwent SK1493 & SK1589) but there is the occasional record in the south (Kirk Langley SK2739). It is indigenous to western North America.

ARAUCARIACEAE

Araucaria araucana (Molina) K. Koch
Monkey-puzzle
Monkey-puzzle is a spiny evergreen tree found very rarely as planted specimens in parks and gardens. Our only two records are: Middle Handley Churchyard (SK4077) in 1998 and Elvaston Country Park (SK4133) in 2005. It is a native of South America.

TAXACEAE

Taxus baccata L.
Yew

COUNTY STATUS: Native
CONSERVATION STATUS: None
FIRST YEAR: 1789 **LATEST YEAR:** 2013 **NO OF RECORDS:** 1,151
RECENT SQUARES: monads 478; tetrads 328; hectads 38
ALL SQUARES: monads 510; tetrads 343; hectads 38

Yew is an occasional evergreen tree or bush that occurs as native, established and planted specimens. It is native in woods and scrub, and on cliffs in the limestone districts (Dove Dale SK1455, Ashwood Dale SK0772, Priestcliffe Lees SK1572 & Pleasley SK5164). It is planted throughout the county in woods, parks, gardens and churchyards (Sudbury Hall SK1532, Rosliston Churchyard SK2416, Melbourne Pool SK3824 & Shipley Hall

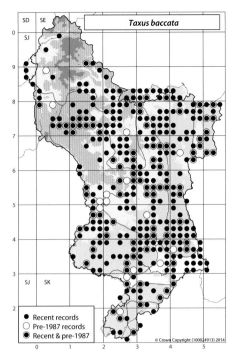

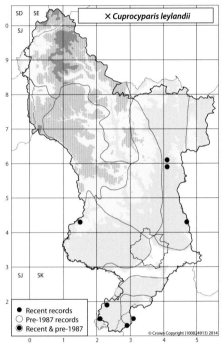

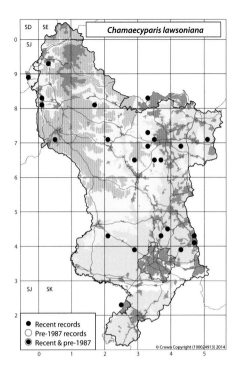

SK4344). Some churchyard trees can reach great size and age, for example Farey (1815) noted the trunk of the yew tree in Darley Churchyard as 33 feet in circumference in 1808. A recent survey measured a Yew at St Helens Church, Darley Dale (SK2662) with a girth of 8.31m at chest height. Self-sown specimens from planted trees also occur throughout Derbyshire in a wide range of habitats, including scrub, waste ground and walls. It has the local name of Vew (Grigson 1975). There are the remains of an old tree in Shining Cliff Woods called the Betty Kenny Tree (SK35). In the 18th century a charcoal burner lived near the hollow tree with his wife Betty and their children. She is reputed to have used a hollow branch as a cradle which gave rise to the rock-a-bye baby nursery rhyme (Mallett 2011).

CUPRESSACEAE

Sequoiadendron giganteum (Lindl.) Buchholz
Wellingtonia
Wellingtonia is a large evergreen tree found very rarely planted in woods, parks and large gardens. It has been recorded twelve times throughout the lowland parts of the county: the earliest record being for Limb Valley (SK3083) in 1960, and the most recent Shirley Park (SK2042) in 2003 and Scarcliffe Park (SK5171) in 2005. A large specimen at Birdsgrove Lane near Ashbourne (SK1546) was found recently with a girth of 5.69m. The tree is a native of the Sierra Nevada, California.

Cryptomeria japonica (L. f.) D. Don
Japanese Red-cedar
Japanese Red-cedar is a very rare,

established evergreen tree that occurs in plantings for timber and amenity. It is only recorded for Lady Clough (SK1092) in 2001 and Oakwood (SK3873) in 2007. It is a native of Japan and China.

× Cuprocyparis leylandii (A.B. Jacks. & Dallim.) Farjon
Leyland Cypress

COUNTY STATUS: Planted
CONSERVATION STATUS: None
FIRST YEAR: 1996 LATEST YEAR: 2008 NO OF RECORDS: 13
RECENT SQUARES: monads 5; tetrads 8; hectads 6
ALL SQUARES: monads 5; tetrads 8; hectads 6

Leyland Cypress is a very rare, evergreen tree. It is planted in copses and amenity woods, usually for shelter or screening. It grows scattered throughout the county (Snelston SK1542, Mickley SK46A & Ilkeston SK4642). It is of Welsh garden origin from the crossing of Monterey Cypress (*Cupressus macrocarpa*) with Nootka Cypress (*Xanthocyparis nootkatensis*).

Chamaecyparis lawsoniana
(A. Murray bis) Parl.
Lawson's Cypress

COUNTY STATUS: Established (Neophyte)
CONSERVATION STATUS: None
FIRST YEAR: 1987 LATEST YEAR: 2012 NO OF RECORDS: 37
RECENT SQUARES: monads 21; tetrads 24; hectads 20
ALL SQUARES: monads 21, tetrads 24, hectads 20

Lawson's Cypress is a large established evergreen tree that occurs as a rare species in forestry and amenity plantings, particularly those for shelter or screening. Records are scattered throughout the

county from Long Clough (SK0392) and Sutton Scarsdale (SK46J) in the north, to Shirley Park (SK2042) and Trent Bridge (SK2522) in the south. It is a native of western North America.

Juniperus communis L.
Common Juniper
Locally extinct, Common Juniper was a very rare, native shrub of limestone slopes in the White Peak. The only native record appears to be one made in Ashwood Dale (SK07) in 1884 (Linton 1903). However, it has been known from Grin Wood Buxton (SK0572) since at least 1969 (Clapham 1969). It was still there in 2013 and some have considered it native here too. There are a small number of other introduced records, both current (White Edge Moor SK2678) and older (Wardlow SK1774).

NYMPHAEACEAE

Nymphaea alba L.
White Water-lily

COUNTY STATUS: Native
CONSERVATION STATUS: B
FIRST YEAR: 1789 LATEST YEAR: 2013 NO OF RECORDS: 190
RECENT SQUARES: monads 67; tetrads 66; hectads 27
ALL SQUARES: monads 81; tetrads 78; hectads 27

White Water-lily is an attractive native perennial of ponds, rivers and canals, with star-like white flowers set against floating green leaves. It is occasional throughout lowland Derbyshire, but rarely occurs over 150m (North Road Ponds SK0395). Regularly planted as an ornamental, it is often impossible to

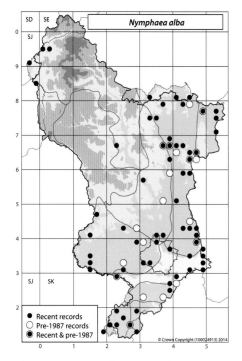

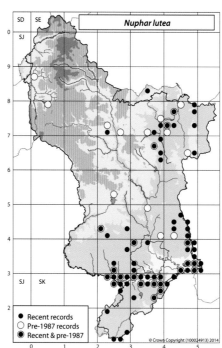

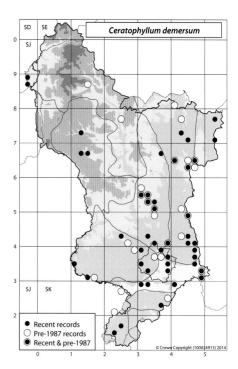

distinguish native from naturalised records, so both are mapped together here.

Nymphaea marliacea Lat.-Marl.
Garden Water-lily

Garden Water-lily is a very rare, established perennial of ponds and canals. It was discovered in the Erewash Canal (SK4835) by R. Martin in 1996. There are seven other records, found throughout the county between 2007 and 2013. Much grown in ornamental waterbodies, it appears to spread through the disposal of garden waste and deliberate introductions into more natural situations. It is of garden origin from the artificial hybridisation of White Water-lily (*N. alba*) and various exotic species.

Nuphar lutea (L.) Sm.
Yellow Water-lily

COUNTY STATUS: Native	
CONSERVATION STATUS: None	
FIRST YEAR: 1789 **LATEST YEAR:** 2013 **NO OF RECORDS:** 308	
RECENT SQUARES: monads 107; tetrads 69; hectads 16	
ALL SQUARES: monads 120; tetrads 82; hectads 22	

Yellow Water-lily is a native aquatic perennial of lakes, canals and rivers. It is occasional in lowland Derbyshire being most frequent in the south (Swarkestone Gravel Pits SK3627) and east (Erewash Canal SK44Q) of Derby. It also occurs, albeit rarely, in the more upland parts of the county (Hermitage Pond SK2271). Previously it was also recorded in the north-west (Thornsett Mill Pond SK0186). It is less often planted than other water-lilies but many records

mapped here are still probably of naturalised plants.

ARISTOLOCHIACEAE

Asarum europaeum L.
Asarabacca

Asarabacca is a very rare, established perennial of woods. There are just two old records in the south of the county: Allestree Park (SK3440) in 1963 and Derby (SK33) in 1970. It is a native of Europe.

Aristolochia clematitis L.
Birthwort

Locally extinct, Birthwort was a very rare, scrambling perennial of old gardens where it was casual. Grown as a medicinal herb, it has only been recorded at the gardens in Calke Park (SK32) towards the middle of the 19th century. It is a native of south-eastern Europe.

CERATOPHYLLACEAE

Ceratophyllum demersum L.
Rigid Hornwort

COUNTY STATUS: Native	
CONSERVATION STATUS: B	
FIRST YEAR: 1863 **LATEST YEAR:** 2012 **NO OF RECORDS:** 155	
RECENT SQUARES: monads 54; tetrads 46; hectads 17	
ALL SQUARES: monads 77; tetrads 64; hectads 23	

Rigid Hornwort is a rare submerged native perennial of ponds, streams and canals. It has been recorded recently throughout the county (Cromford Canal SK3452, Sudbury SK1531 & Wormhill SK1273) except for the Dark Peak. Its preference for nutrient-rich waters

probably means it is increasing in lowland areas (Preston *et al.* 2002). It was previously also recorded in the Dark Peak (Nether Brook SK1486).

Ceratophyllum submersum L.
Soft Hornwort

COUNTY STATUS: Native	
CONSERVATION STATUS: DRDB (Cat4), B	
FIRST YEAR: 1969 **LATEST YEAR:** 2003 **NO OF RECORDS:** 4	
RECENT SQUARES: monads 2; tetrads 2; hectads 2	
ALL SQUARES: monads 3; tetrads 3; hectads 3	

Soft Hornwort is a very rare, submerged native perennial of ponds and canals. There are only two recent records: Coton in the Elms (SK2315) and the Cromford Canal (SK2956). The two older records are both from Cromford Canal (SK3452) in 1969 and 1979.

PAPAVERACEAE

Papaver pseudoorientale (Fedde) Medw.
False-oriental Poppy

False-oriental Poppy is a very rare, casual perennial of verges and waste ground, found as a garden escape or throwout. There are only eight records scattered throughout the county between 1999 and 2013. Examples are: Glasshouse, near Hundall (SK3976), Whaley Common (SK5172), Dale Brook (SK2624), Bradwell Moor (SK1480) and Long Eaton (SK4932). It is a native of south-western Asia.

Papaver orientale L.
Oriental Poppy

Oriental Poppy is a very rare, casual perennial of verges, waste land and disturbed ground. It is often grown in gardens from where it escapes or is discarded. So far it has only been recorded at Pomeroy (SK1167), Bradwell (SK1780) and Wadshelf (SK3171), all around 1999. A native of south-western Asia, it is so similar to the False-Oriental Poppy (*P. pseudoorientale*) that it may be the same species.

Papaver atlanticum (Ball) Coss.
Atlas Poppy

Atlas Poppy is a very rare, established perennial of verges, walls and waste ground. A native of Morocco, it is often grown in gardens, from where it can escape. The only records are all from the 1970s: Tideswell (SK1574); near Chelmorton Church (SK1170); Hope Station (SK1883); and Ashbourne (SK1746). A specimen from the latter site is in Derby Museum.

Common Poppy (*Papaver rhoeas*), Melbourne (SK3924), June 2009 (Peter Smith)

Papaver somniferum L.
Opium Poppy

COUNTY STATUS: Established (Archaeophyte)
CONSERVATION STATUS: None
FIRST YEAR: 1829 LATEST YEAR: 2013 NO OF RECORDS: 416
RECENT SQUARES: monads 268; tetrads 238; hectads 37
ALL SQUARES: monads 290; tetrads 253; hectads 37

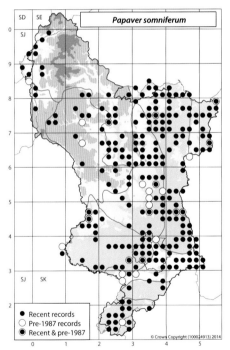

Opium Poppy is an anciently established annual of verges, waste places and disturbed ground. This native of the eastern Mediterranean is commonly grown in gardens and escapes easily. It is occasional throughout Derbyshire, but is rare in the upland north and west. Our plants are likely to be ssp. *somniferum*. White and double-flowered forms are occasionally found (Long Eaton SK4933).

Papaver rhoeas L.
Common Poppy

COUNTY STATUS: Established (Archaeophyte)
CONSERVATION STATUS: None
FIRST YEAR: 1789 LATEST YEAR: 2013 NO OF RECORDS: 832
RECENT SQUARES: monads 483; tetrads 326; hectads 37
ALL SQUARES: monads 510; tetrads 336; hectads 37

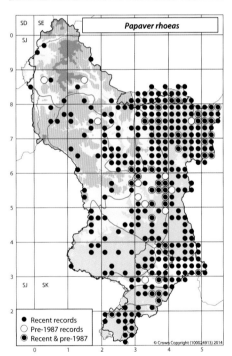

Common Poppy is an anciently established annual of arable fields, verges and newly disturbed ground. It is common in eastern Derbyshire but rarer in the west, probably because there is less arable land there. It was formerly more abundant than today, colouring many cornfields scarlet red before the intensive use of herbicides, but was probably no more widely distributed. Being such an obvious plant, it has gained

various local names. Grigson (1975) gives Earaches, Headache and Wild Maws. It is now commonly sown in wild-flower seed mixes to give an early show of colour. It also seems to appear sporadically, bringing a sudden blaze of colour to individual fields. This may be due to patchy spreading of herbicides coupled with their generally reduced application.

Papaver dubium L.
Long-headed Poppy

COUNTY STATUS: Established (Archaeophyte)
CONSERVATION STATUS: None
FIRST YEAR: 1829 LATEST YEAR: 2013 NO OF RECORDS: 350
RECENT SQUARES: monads 193; tetrads 166; hectads 33
ALL SQUARES: monads 232; tetrads 198; hectads 33

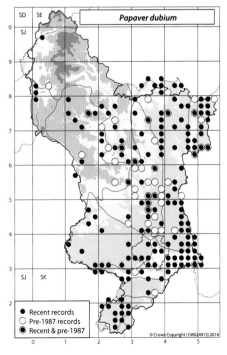

Long-headed Poppy is an anciently established annual of arable land, roadsides and waste places. Though frequent in eastern Derbyshire, it is rarer in the west where there is less arable farming, and is virtually absent from the Dark and South West Peak Character Areas.

Papaver lecoqii (Lamotte)
Yellow-juiced Poppy

COUNTY STATUS: Established (Archaeophyte)
CONSERVATION STATUS: None
FIRST YEAR: 1884 LATEST YEAR: 2011 NO OF RECORDS: 45
RECENT SQUARES: monads 12; tetrads 12; hectads 11
ALL SQUARES: monads 24; tetrads 22; hectads 18

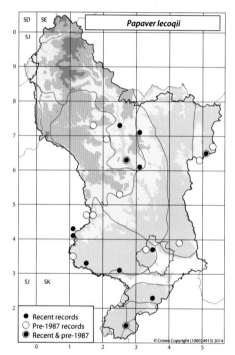

Yellow-juiced Poppy is an anciently established annual of waste places, open ground and arable fields. It occurs very rarely scattered throughout the county except for the northern parts of the Dark Peak and South West Peak Areas. Once regarded as only a subspecies of Long-headed Poppy, it is probably under-recorded.

Papaver hybridum L.
Rough Poppy

Rough Poppy is a very rare, casual annual of arable land and disturbed ground, which is native to southern and eastern England. It has only been recorded twice: Hanging Bridge (SK1545) in 1939 and Tunstead (SK1074) in 1990 where, at 320m, it holds the British altitude record (Preston *et al.* 2002).

Papaver argemone L.
Prickly Poppy

Prickly Poppy is an anciently established annual of disturbed ground and arable land on light soils, with recent records from

COUNTY STATUS: Established (Archaeophyte)
CONSERVATION STATUS: DRDB (Cat2), VU
FIRST YEAR: 1829 LATEST YEAR: 2008 NO OF RECORDS: 36
RECENT SQUARES: monads 1; tetrads 1; hectads 1
ALL SQUARES: monads 11; tetrads 10; hectads 15

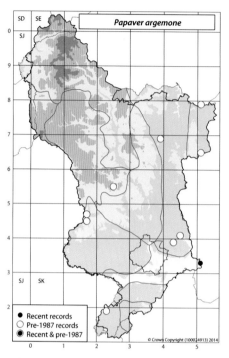

only one site, near Trent Junction (SK5032). Previous records were mainly from the south and east of the county (Ashbourne SK1746, Drakelow Reserve SK2219 & Dale Abbey SK4338). Sadly, this local decline reflects the national situation, probably due to increased herbicide use (Preston *et al.* 2002).

Meconopsis cambrica (L.) Vig.
Welsh Poppy

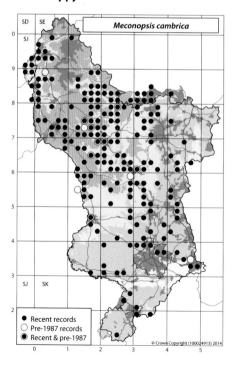

COUNTY STATUS: Established (Neophyte)
CONSERVATION STATUS: None
FIRST YEAR: 1864 LATEST YEAR: 2013 NO OF RECORDS: 383
RECENT SQUARES: monads 249; tetrads 196; hectads 36
ALL SQUARES: monads 259; tetrads 201; hectads 36

Welsh Poppy is an established perennial of cultivated and disturbed ground, waste places and verges. It occurs occasionally throughout the county, though becoming rarer in upland and intensively farmed areas. Only as a native plant of Wales and south-western England is it regarded as Nationally Scarce. However, it is much grown in gardens, from where it often escapes into the wild, so the plant's scarcity in south and east Derbyshire is surprising.

Argemone mexicana L.
Mexican Poppy

Locally extinct, Mexican Poppy was a very rare, casual annual of disturbed ground. It was found in Derby (SK3536) by D. McClintock in 1967 but there have been no further records. This fits with the national picture that has been one of decrease over recent years. It is indigenous to Central America.

Chelidonium majus L.
Greater Celandine

COUNTY STATUS: Established (Archaeophyte)
CONSERVATION STATUS: None
FIRST YEAR: 1789 LATEST YEAR: 2013 NO OF RECORDS: 423
RECENT SQUARES: monads 201; tetrads 173; hectads 33
ALL SQUARES: monads 218; tetrads 188; hectads 37

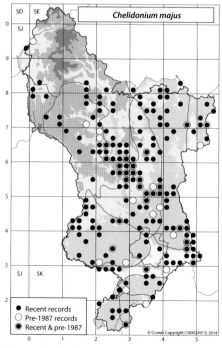

Greater Celandine is an anciently established perennial of verges, hedges and walls. It grows occasionally throughout Derbyshire, except for the northern moors of the Dark Peak. Some authorities suggest it may be native, but its close association with habitation, in our county at least, argues against this (Darley Abbey Mills SK3538, Risley Churchyard SK4635 & Chesterfield SK3871).

Eschscholzia californica Cham.
Californian Poppy

COUNTY STATUS: Casual

CONSERVATION STATUS: None

FIRST YEAR: 1985 **LATEST YEAR:** 2011 **NO OF RECORDS:** 17

RECENT SQUARES: monads 15; tetrads 15; hectads 11

ALL SQUARES: monads 16; tetrads 16; hectads 11

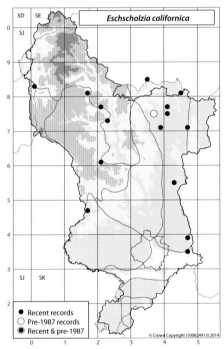

Californian Poppy is a very rare, casual annual of waste ground and roadsides. This native of south-western North America is often grown in gardens from where it can escape. Recent sites are scattered throughout Derbyshire (Ashbourne SK1746, Nether Handley Tip SK4076, Staveley SK4175, New Bolsover SK4670, Stanton North Lagoon SK4739 & Cotespark SK4254). A single pre-1987 record demonstrates how much the plant has spread locally, probably due to increased horticultural usage.

Corydalis solida (L.) Clairv.
Bird-in-a-bush

Bird-in-a-bush is a very rare, established perennial. It was first recorded in Risley (SK4635) during 1982; and recently at Repton (SK3026) in 2006 and Nutwood Reserve Derby (SK3538) in 2010. It is a native of continental Europe.

Corydalis cava (L.) Schweigg. & Koerte
Hollowroot

Hollowroot is a very rare, established perennial of woodland and a native of Europe. It was recorded in Risley (SK4635) during 1983 but there have been no further records.

Pseudofumaria lutea (L.) Borkh.
Yellow Corydalis

COUNTY STATUS: Established (Neophyte)

CONSERVATION STATUS: None

FIRST YEAR: 1796 **LATEST YEAR:** 2013 **NO OF RECORDS:** 272

RECENT SQUARES: monads 141; tetrads 128; hectads 29

ALL SQUARES: monads 163; tetrads 142; hectads 31

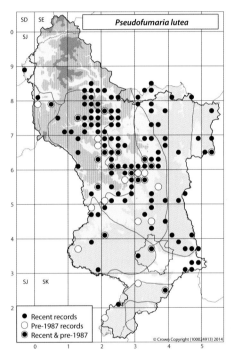

Yellow Corydalis is an established perennial of walls. It occurs occasionally throughout the county except for the Dark Peak in the north and the more intensively farmed areas in the south and east. It is commonly cultivated in gardens. It grows in most of lowland Britain, reaching its altitudinal limit of 305m at Great Hucklow in Derbyshire (Preston *et al.* 2002). It occurs naturally in the southern Alps.

Ceratocapnos claviculata (L.) Lidén
Climbing Corydalis

COUNTY STATUS: Native

CONSERVATION STATUS: None

FIRST YEAR: 1789 **LATEST YEAR:** 2011 **NO OF RECORDS:** 332

RECENT SQUARES: monads 110; tetrads 77; hectads 16

ALL SQUARES: monads 146; tetrads 100; hectads 19

Climbing Corydalis is a scrambling native annual of woods and shaded rocky places on free-draining acid soils. It is frequent in the Peak Fringe as at Holloway (SK3256). It is occasional in the southern

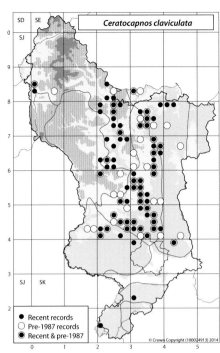

part of the Dark Peak (Furness Vale SK0083 & Baslow Edge SK2573) but only rarely grows in the rest of the county (Repton Shrubs SK3123).

Fumaria capreolata L.
White Ramping-fumitory

COUNTY STATUS: Native

CONSERVATION STATUS: DRDB (Cat4)

FIRST YEAR: 1847 **LATEST YEAR:** 2012 **NO OF RECORDS:** 8

RECENT SQUARES: monads 1; tetrads 1; hectads 1

ALL SQUARES: monads 2; tetrads 2; hectads 5

White Ramping-fumitory is a scrambling native annual of waste ground and cultivated areas. The single recent record is for Old Whittington (SK3875) in 2012. Previously it was noted for Bonsall (SK2757) in Clapham (1969); and before that for Repton (SK32), Breadsall (SK33) and Lumsdale (SK36) in Linton (1903). The earliest record was made by J. Whittaker in 1847 (Linton 1903).

Fumaria muralis Sond. ex W.D.J. Koch
Common Ramping-fumitory

COUNTY STATUS: Native

CONSERVATION STATUS: DRDB (Cat5a), A

FIRST YEAR: 1969 **LATEST YEAR:** 2010 **NO OF RECORDS:** 16

RECENT SQUARES: monads 9; tetrads 9; hectads 7

ALL SQUARES: monads 13; tetrads 13; hectads 8

Common Ramping-fumitory is a very rare, native annual of disturbed ground and old walls. It grows scattered throughout the northern (Hadfield SK0296) and western (Edlaston Hall SK1742) parts of the county with previous records covering basically the same area. When determined to subspecies level, they have

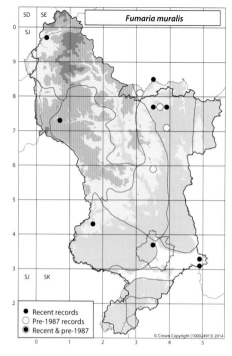

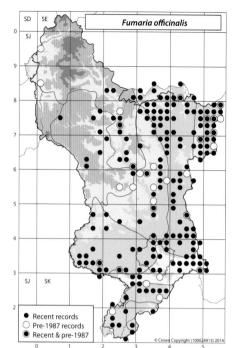

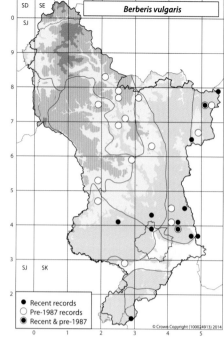

been recorded as the common ssp. *boroei* (Jord.) Pugsley.

Fumaria officinalis L.
Common Fumitory

COUNTY STATUS: Established (Archaeophyte)

CONSERVATION STATUS: None

FIRST YEAR: 1789 LATEST YEAR: 2013 NO OF RECORDS: 361

RECENT SQUARES: monads 197; tetrads 180; hectads 31

ALL SQUARES: monads 225; tetrads 197; hectads 34

Common Fumitory is a scrambling annual of cultivated ground and waste places. Anciently established, it is occasional throughout the county except for the northern moors of the Dark Peak, where it is virtually absent. Two subspecies occur here, but are rarely separated, so the statistics and map show records

for the species. **Ssp. *officinalis*** is commoner, occurring throughout its range. **Ssp. *wirtgenii*** (W.D.J. Koch) Arcang. is rarer. It is found mostly in the east, generally avoiding the heavier soils of the Trent Valley and Claylands Areas.

BERBERIDACEAE

Berberis vulgaris L.
Barberry

COUNTY STATUS: Established (Neophyte)

CONSERVATION STATUS: None

FIRST YEAR: 1789 LATEST YEAR: 2010 NO OF RECORDS: 45

RECENT SQUARES: monads 12; tetrads 12; hectads 8

ALL SQUARES: monads 29; tetrads 28; hectads 20

Barberry is a very rare, established shrub of hedges, woods and waste places. All

recent records are from the south and east of the county (Brailsford SK2440 & Markland Plantation SK5074). Previous records came from a wider area including the White and Dark Peaks (Wardlow SK1874 & Longshaw SK2578). This plant is the secondary host of the rust fungus that attacks wheat, which may explain its loss from some areas, though in others it is still being planted for ornament. It is a native of continental Europe.

Berberis thunbergii DC.
Thunberg's Barberry

Thunberg's Barberry is a recently established, spiny shrub from Japan. Our sole record was made by T. Taylor for a roadside hedge in Allestree (SK3339) in 2004.

Berberis gagnepainii C.K. Schneid.
Gagnepain's Barberry

Gagnepain's Barberry is a casual evergreen shrub from western China that is commonly planted in gardens. The only record was made by R. Burton in 2005 growing on a wayside at Monyash (SK1566).

Berberis julianae C.K. Schneid.
Chinese Barberry

Chinese Barberry is a casual evergreen shrub from central China that is frequently grown in parks and gardens. All records are by R. Martin and are from the Long Eaton area: SK4734 in 2006, SK4735 in 2007 and SK4933 in 2010. He thought they might have been bird-sown.

Berberis darwinii Hook.
Darwin's Barberry

Darwin's Barberry is a very rare, established shrub of roadsides and bushy areas where

Common Fumitory (*Fumaria officinalis*), Dronfield Woodhouse (SK3278), June 2013 (Ken Balkow)

its evergreen and spiny growth makes it an attractive and useful plant. It can occasionally spread by bird-sown seed. It is recorded for only five sites, all between 1996 and 2009: The Parks, Buxton (SK0573), Taddington By-pass (SK1471), Oakwell Brickworks (SK4641), Brailsford (SK2541) and Wingerworth (SK3568). It is indigenous to South America.

Mahonia aquifolium (Pursh) Nutt.
Oregon-grape

COUNTY STATUS: Established (Neophyte)
CONSERVATION STATUS: None
FIRST YEAR: 1953 LATEST YEAR: 2013 NO OF RECORDS: 254
RECENT SQUARES: monads 119; tetrads 108; hectads 29
ALL SQUARES: monads 141; tetrads 128; hectads 30

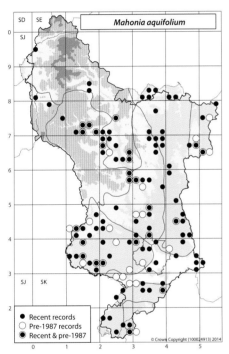

Oregon-grape is a low spiny and evergreen shrub of woods, hedges, scrub and waste places that has established itself from plantings for ornament and game cover. It occurs throughout the county except for the north-western moors. It is a native of western North America.

RANUNCULACEAE

Caltha palustris L.
Marsh-marigold

COUNTY STATUS: Native
CONSERVATION STATUS: None
FIRST YEAR: 1789 LATEST YEAR: 2013 NO OF RECORDS: 1,147
RECENT SQUARES: monads 404; tetrads 294; hectads 38
ALL SQUARES: monads 454; tetrads 325; hectads 39

Marsh-marigold is a native perennial of wet woodlands, marshes, flushes and streamsides where its bright yellow flowers herald spring. These are so striking

Globeflower (*Trollius europaeus*), Dale Road, Buxton (SK0672), June 2011 (Kieron Huston)

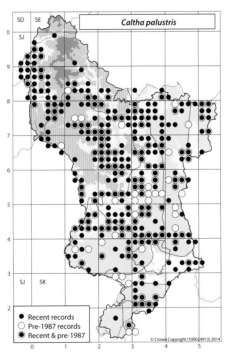

that it has acquired various local names, May Blobs being the most common, although Grigson (1975) also notes Mare-blobs and Water Blobs. It is recorded occasionally throughout the county, except for the higher parts of the White and Dark Peak Areas. Where it does grow in the Dark Peak, it has as a smaller, more prostrate form (Clapham 1969). This conspicuous plant previously grew over much the same area, though Linton (1903) noted that it was less common on limestone, as it still is. The BSBI's Local Change Survey found a national decrease due to wetland eutrophication (Braithwaite *et al.* 2006).

Trollius europaeus L.
Globeflower

COUNTY STATUS: Native
CONSERVATION STATUS: DRDB (Cat5b), B
FIRST YEAR: 1805 LATEST YEAR: 2013 NO OF RECORDS: 214
RECENT SQUARES: monads 25; tetrads 15; hectads 5
ALL SQUARES: monads 43; tetrads 26; hectads 8

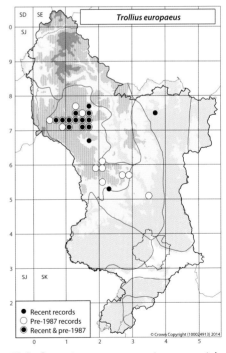

Globeflower is a very rare, native perennial of damp grasslands, scrub and open woods in the White Peak. It grows mainly in the area east of Buxton (Cunning Dale SK0773 & Miller's Dale SK1272) though there is an isolated record from further south at Brassington (SK2353). It is also recorded from Dunston Tip (SK3674) where it is no doubt a garden throwout. Previously there were more records for the southern area of the White Peak (Via Gellia SK2656) and a record from the Peak Fringe at Shiningcliff Woods (SK3451). It is a plant of the upland north and west, with Derbyshire on the south-eastern edge of its British range.

Helleborus foetidus L.
Stinking Hellebore

COUNTY STATUS: Native
CONSERVATION STATUS: DRDB (Cat3), NS, A, B, C
FIRST YEAR: 1789 LATEST YEAR: 2012 NO OF RECORDS: 115
RECENT SQUARES: monads 17; tetrads 14; hectads 8
ALL SQUARES: monads 28; tetrads 23; hectads 16

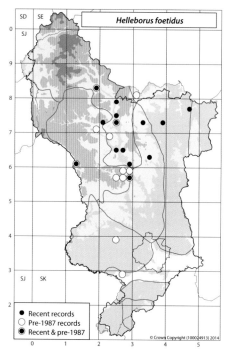

Stinking Hellebore is a rare native perennial of woods and screes in central Derbyshire. It occurs in a range of Character Areas including the White Peak (Hartington Dale SK1364), the Dark Peak (Brough SK1882) and the Peak Fringe. Although thought of in this work as a native, other authorities consider it as only doubtfully native (Clapham 1969). This is almost certainly because it is widely grown in gardens and can establish itself easily. Outside the county it is very local in southern and western Britain, and is Nationally Scarce.

Helleborus viridis L.
Green Hellebore

COUNTY STATUS: Native
CONSERVATION STATUS: DRDB (Cat5b), B
FIRST YEAR: 1789 LATEST YEAR: 2012 NO OF RECORDS: 77
RECENT SQUARES: monads 13; tetrads 12; hectads 8
ALL SQUARES: monads 26; tetrads 21; hectads 12

Green Hellebore is a rare native perennial of woodland and scrub on limestone.

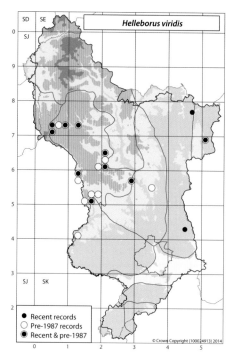

It occurs mainly in the White Peak Area (Conksbury Bridge SK2165, Cunning Dale SK0872 & Thorpe Station SK1650). However, it also occurs in the Magnesian Limestone Area (Scarcliffe Lane SK5169). Elsewhere there are only scattered records (Ilkeston Industrial Estate SK4542). These may represent relicts of previous cultivation or deliberate plantings. Previously it occurred over much the same area with a similar pattern of distribution. Nationally it has declined since 1962 probably due to woodland clearance and cessation of coppicing (Preston *et al.* 2002).

Eranthis hyemalis (L.) Salisb.
Winter Aconite

COUNTY STATUS: Established (Neophyte)
CONSERVATION STATUS: None
FIRST YEAR: 1863 LATEST YEAR: 2012 NO OF RECORDS: 17
RECENT SQUARES: monads 5; tetrads 5; hectads 5
ALL SQUARES: monads 9; tetrads 9; hectads 9

Winter Aconite is a very rare, established perennial of parks and shrubberies where it spreads after planting. Although most current records are for the central part of the county (Churchdale Hall SK2072 & Tissington SK1752), there is one record from the south (Cloud Trail SK3827). Previous records come from a similar but wider area (Whirlow Brook Park SK3083 & Lullington Hall SK2414). It is a native of southern Europe.

Nigella damascena L.
Love-in-a-mist

Love-in-a-mist is a very rare, casual annual that escapes from gardens, turning up on bare ground and rubbish tips. This native of Southern Europe was first recorded at

COUNTY STATUS: Casual
CONSERVATION STATUS: None
FIRST YEAR: 1997 LATEST YEAR: 2012 NO OF RECORDS: 13
RECENT SQUARES: monads 13; tetrads 12; hectads 9
ALL SQUARES: monads 13; tetrads 12; hectads 9

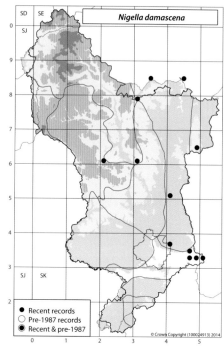

Matlock Bank (SK3060) in 1997, and now appears scattered over eastern parts, from Spondon (SK4036) in the south to Beighton (SK4484) in the north.

Aconitum napellus L.
Monk's-hood

Monk's-hood is a rare established perennial of roadsides, waste places and woods. Current records are all from northern

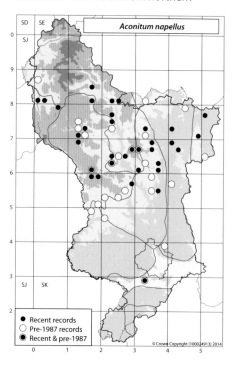

COUNTY STATUS: Established (Neophyte)
CONSERVATION STATUS: None
FIRST YEAR: 1863 LATEST YEAR: 2010 NO OF RECORDS: 93
RECENT SQUARES: monads 29; tetrads 34; hectads 17
ALL SQUARES: monads 53; tetrads 55; hectads 25

Derbyshire (Barmoor Clough SK07U & Ivy House SK1659) except for an isolated site at Twyford (SK3228). As it has been grown in gardens for a long time, it can turn up in places a long way from current habitation. Previously it occurred over much the same area with a number of these earlier records referred to ssp. *napellus*. Some records mapped here may refer to other species or hybrids as they can prove difficult to separate. It is a native of south-western Britain.

Aconitum × stoerkianum Rchb.
Hybrid Monk's-hood

COUNTY STATUS: Established (Neophyte)
CONSERVATION STATUS: None
FIRST YEAR: 1960 LATEST YEAR: 2013 NO OF RECORDS: 29
RECENT SQUARES: monads 13; tetrads 13; hectads 9
ALL SQUARES: monads 25; tetrads 25; hectads 14

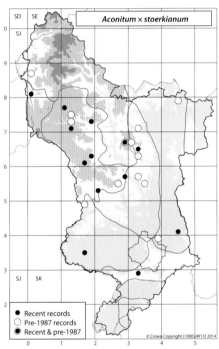

Hybrid Monk's-hood is a very rare, established perennial of damp shaded hedges and waste places. It occurs throughout the county from Hollow O'the Moor (SK1371) in the north through Bradbourne (SK2052) to Muse Lane (SK1734) in the south. It is the hybrid of Monk's-hood (*A. napellus*) and *Aconitum variegatum* L. It is either of garden origin or a natural hybrid that has been brought into cultivation.

Aconitum lycoctonum L.
Wolf's-bane

Wolf's-bane is a very rare, established

perennial and a native of central Europe. It has only been recorded from two sites: Ashwood Dale (SK0872) in 1982 and Hassop Hall (SK2272) in 1971, both in the White Peak. The local plant is ssp. *vulparia* (Rchb.) Nyman.

Consolida ajacis (L.) Schur
Larkspur

Larkspur is a very rare, casual annual of cornfields and waste ground. There are only two recent records and five older ones. The earliest, for Willington and Repton (SK32) in 1896 and 1899, relate to cornfield records (Linton 1903). Later ones refer to either garden escapes (Calver SK2374 in 1985, Froggatt SK2476 in 1984 & Holy Moor SK3267 in 1985), or to waste ground (Etwall SK2631 in 2011 & Staveley SK4375 in 2012). Larkspur grows naturally in the Mediterranean area.

Anemone nemorosa L.
Wood Anemone

COUNTY STATUS: Native
CONSERVATION STATUS: None
FIRST YEAR: 1789 LATEST YEAR: 2013 NO OF RECORDS: 1,354
RECENT SQUARES: monads 444; tetrads 301; hectads 38
ALL SQUARES: monads 494; tetrads 331; hectads 38

Wood Anemone is an occasional native perennial of woods and hedges throughout the county except for the high moors and some areas of intensive agriculture around Derby. It also grows in grassland over limestone where it is suspected of being a relic of former woodland cover (Clapham 1969). Previously it was more frequent in southern Derbyshire, this loss probably being due

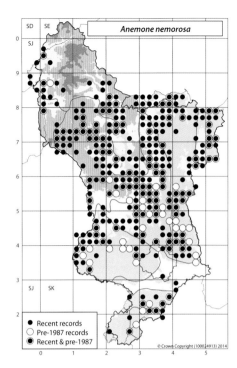

to agricultural intensification. Its white star-like flowers form an attractive sight on the floor of many woods in spring. It is not surprising that such a common showy plant has accumulated a number of local names. Mabey (1996) for example gives Moggie Nightgown that refers to the flowers smelling like mice, as moggie is a local name for a mouse.

Anemone apennina L.
Blue Anemone

Blue Anemone is a very rare, casual perennial of woods and roadsides. It has only ever been recorded in three natural-looking situations: Totley Hall Lane

Wood Anemone (*Anemone nemorosa*), Via Gellia (SK25), April 2008 (Peter Smith)

(SK3079) in 1998 and 2011, Unstone Green (SK3776) 2003 & Dore (SK3181) in 2009. It is often grown in gardens from where it escapes or is thrown out as waste. It is a native of the central Mediterranean area.

Anemone blanda Schott & Kotschy
Balkan Anemone
Balkan Anemone is an established tuberous perennial. Our sole record is from a roadside woodland near Calver (SK2474) in 1983. It is a garden throwout or escape that originates from the Balkans.

Clematis vitalba L.
Traveller's-joy

COUNTY STATUS: Native	
CONSERVATION STATUS: B	
FIRST YEAR: 1829 LATEST YEAR: 2013 NO OF RECORDS: 170	
RECENT SQUARES: monads 47; tetrads 42; hectads 18	
ALL SQUARES: monads 59; tetrads 50; hectads 22	

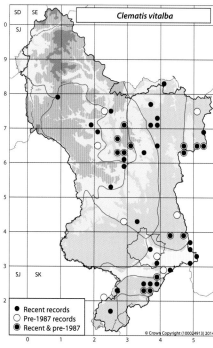

Traveller's-joy is a native woody climber of woods, hedges or scrub. This species occurs occasionally throughout Derbyshire but is absent from the Claylands and northern Dark Peak. It grows most luxuriantly on limestone such as the Carboniferous outcrops at Ticknall (SK3523) and the Magnesian Limestone at Pleasley Vale (SK5164). Here it produces thick woody climbing stems that ascend cliffs and form vast curtains over trees. Clapham (1969) only accepted the Ticknall site as native because Derbyshire is on the northern edge of its UK distribution. Other records result from garden escapes or deliberate introductions, though one such site north of Matlock holds the British altitude record at 305m (Preston *et al.* 2002).

Clematis flammula L.
Virgin's-bower
Virgin's-bower is an established woody climber of waste places. It has only ever been recorded from Rowsley (SK2664) in 1973 where seeded plants were found growing, possibly from plants at a nearby nursery. It is a native of the Mediterranean.

Ranunculus acris L.
Meadow Buttercup

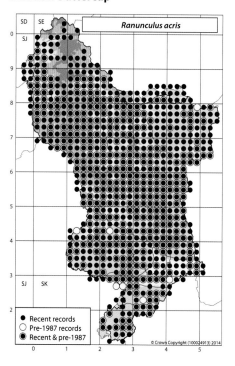

COUNTY STATUS: Native	
CONSERVATION STATUS: None	
FIRST YEAR: 1789 LATEST YEAR: 2013 NO OF RECORDS: 5,171	
RECENT SQUARES: monads 1,783; tetrads 696; hectads 43	
ALL SQUARES: monads 1,868; tetrads 703; hectads 43	

Meadow Buttercup is a very common, native perennial of unimproved grasslands and waysides. It grows throughout the county except for the highest areas of moorland in the extreme north-west. It is often so abundant that its flowers turn pastures and meadows yellow. In the past this abundant growth was often seen in a negative light, Farey (1815) lamented buttercups taking the place of valuable herbage. Nowadays it is more likely to be seen as a positive: Mabey (1996) exults in the flowers dazzling under May sunshine. Buttercup petals are often used to provide a yellow colour in well dressing pictures (Mabey 1996).

Ranunculus repens L.
Creeping Buttercup

COUNTY STATUS: Native	
CONSERVATION STATUS: None	
FIRST YEAR: 1789 LATEST YEAR: 2013 NO OF RECORDS: 7,595	
RECENT SQUARES: monads 2,342; tetrads 750; hectads 45	
ALL SQUARES: monads 2,390; tetrads 751; hectads 45	

Creeping Buttercup is a native perennial of wet grasslands, woods, marshes and waste places. Sometimes a troublesome weed of cultivated ground, it is very common throughout Derbyshire, extending even

Meadow Buttercup (*Ranunculus acris*), Rose End Meadows (SK2956), June 2008 (Peter Smith)

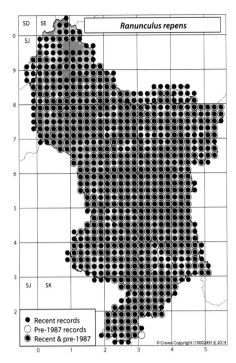

into high moorland, mostly along disturbed ground of roadsides and tracks (Fair Brook SK1089). Double-flowered plants have been found at Breaston (SK4634).

Ranunculus bulbosus L.
Bulbous Buttercup

COUNTY STATUS: Native
CONSERVATION STATUS: None
FIRST YEAR: 1789 **LATEST YEAR:** 2013 **NO OF RECORDS:** 1,477
RECENT SQUARES: monads 704; tetrads 426; hectads 37
ALL SQUARES: monads 778; tetrads 458; hectads 38

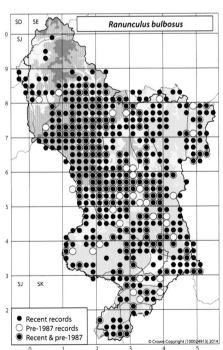

Bulbous Buttercup is a frequent native perennial of dry unimproved grasslands on all soil types except for the most acid.

Although just as widespread now as it once was, it is somewhat less abundant as it has been lost from many sites due to agricultural improvement, especially in lowland areas.

Ranunculus sardous Crantz
Hairy Buttercup

COUNTY STATUS: Native
CONSERVATION STATUS: DRDB (Cat4), A
FIRST YEAR: 1789 **LATEST YEAR:** 2004 **NO OF RECORDS:** 7
RECENT SQUARES: monads 2; tetrads 2; hectads 2
ALL SQUARES: monads 3; tetrads 3; hectads 6

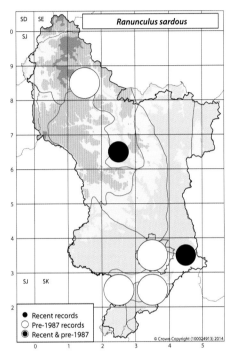

Hairy Buttercup is a very rare, native annual of disturbed ground. It has been recorded only twice recently. It was found sown at Chatsworth Garden Centre (SK26) in 1998, where it survived until 2000. It was also found on Junction 25 of the M1 (SK4735) in 2004. Previously it was recorded mostly in the south (Derby SK33 & Burton SK22), but only rarely. In 1985 there was an isolated record in the north from workings at Oxlow Rake (SK1280).

Ranunculus parviflorus L.
Small-flowered Buttercup

COUNTY STATUS: Native
CONSERVATION STATUS: DRDB (Cat6)
FIRST YEAR: 1829 **LATEST YEAR:** 1950 **NO OF RECORDS:** 10
RECENT SQUARES: monads 0; tetrads 0; hectads 0
ALL SQUARES: monads 0; tetrads 0; hectads 6

Locally extinct, Small-flowered Buttercup was a very rare, native annual of dry disturbed ground and open grasslands. It was last recorded in Linton (1903) for southern parts (Borrowash SK43, Burton SK22 & Repton SK32). There are also old records for SK44 and Buxton

SK07. It may yet return to the county as its seeds are said to be long-lived and it can reappear after disturbance (Preston *et al.* 2002).

Ranunculus arvensis L.
Corn Buttercup

COUNTY STATUS: Established (Archaeophyte)
CONSERVATION STATUS: DRDB (Cat2), CR, NERC, A, C
FIRST YEAR: 1789 **LATEST YEAR:** 1997 **NO OF RECORDS:** 52
RECENT SQUARES: monads 2; tetrads 1; hectads 1
ALL SQUARES: monads 19; tetrads 17; hectads 22

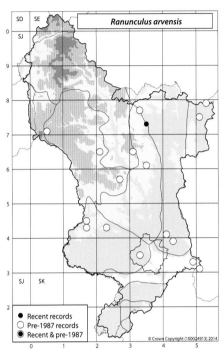

Corn Buttercup is a very rare, anciently established annual of disturbed ground. It has been recorded recently only from Cutthorpe Green (SK3472). Formerly it was not uncommon throughout the area except for the moorlands of the Dark Peak, occurring in cornfields and disturbed ground. It was recorded from near Stirrup Wood (SJ99) in the north to Askew Hill and Ticknall (SK32) in the south. This decline, which was well under way by the late 1960s, was mainly due to the improvement of weed clearance in arable fields. It has undergone a similar decline nationally and is thus a Critically Endangered UK species.

Ranunculus auricomus L.
Goldilocks Buttercup

COUNTY STATUS: Native
CONSERVATION STATUS: None
FIRST YEAR: 1829 **LATEST YEAR:** 2013 **NO OF RECORDS:** 359
RECENT SQUARES: monads 121; tetrads 92; hectads 28
ALL SQUARES: monads 140; tetrads 108; hectads 32

Goldilocks Buttercup is an occasional native perennial of woods, hedges and

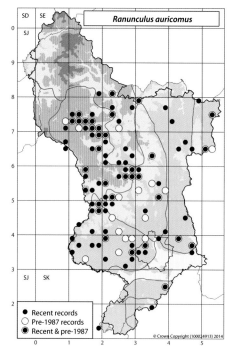

COUNTY STATUS: Native

CONSERVATION STATUS: None

FIRST YEAR: 1829 LATEST YEAR: 2013 NO OF RECORDS: 630

RECENT SQUARES: monads 283; tetrads 207; hectads 37

ALL SQUARES: monads 328; tetrads 240; hectads 39

Celery-leaved Buttercup is a native annual of the bare mud at the margins of ponds, ditches and streams. It is frequent through the Coal Measures (Netherthorpe SK4375), Claylands, Trent Valley (Hilton Gravel Pits SK2431) and other southern areas. However, it is rare over the rest of the county where it occurs for example at Hayfield (SK0587) and Over Wheal (SK1569). It previously had the same distribution but was more frequent, particularly in lowland areas, where it has been affected by the loss of field ponds.

Ranunculus lingua L.
Greater Spearwort

COUNTY STATUS: Native

CONSERVATION STATUS: B

FIRST YEAR: 1789 LATEST YEAR: 2012 NO OF RECORDS: 117

RECENT SQUARES: monads 36; tetrads 34; hectads 23

ALL SQUARES: monads 45; tetrads 44; hectads 25

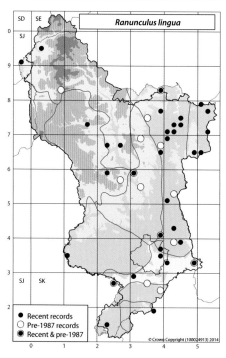

Greater Spearwort is a native creeping perennial of the sides of ponds, ditches and canals. It grows throughout the county but is rare. Examples of sites include Arkwright (SK4271) Doveridge Lake (SK1134) and North Road (SK0395). Although considered native locally, it is now so often naturalised, for example at Morley Brick Pits (SK3841) that it is impossible to determine its true natural range.

Ranunculus flammula L.
Lesser Spearwort

COUNTY STATUS: Native

CONSERVATION STATUS: ERL

FIRST YEAR: 1789 LATEST YEAR: 2013 NO OF RECORDS: 954

RECENT SQUARES: monads 391; tetrads 268; hectads 38

ALL SQUARES: monads 448; tetrads 304; hectads 40

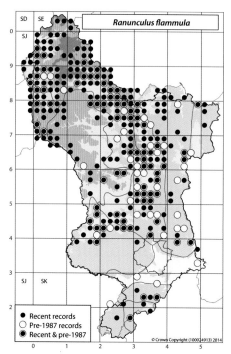

Lesser Spearwort is a native perennial of marshes, wet grasslands and flushes. It is frequent throughout the Dark Peak, South West Peak and Peak Fringe but rare elsewhere, particularly the limestone areas. Its highest record is around 600m at Seal Edge (SK1088). Past distribution was the same as now except it appears to have been more frequent in lowland areas. It is a very variable species (Clapham 1969), but all our plants seem referable to ssp. *flammula*.

Ranunculus hederaceus L.
Ivy-leaved Crowfoot

COUNTY STATUS: Native

CONSERVATION STATUS: None

FIRST YEAR: 1789 LATEST YEAR: 2013 NO OF RECORDS: 145

RECENT SQUARES: monads 55; tetrads 54; hectads 20

ALL SQUARES: monads 84; tetrads 78; hectads 31

Ivy-leaved Crowfoot is an occasional native annual or short-lived perennial, on the margins of muddy ponds and streams. It occurs mainly in the Dark Peak and Peak Fringe Areas (Ladybower SK1787, Smelting Hill Wood SK2666 & Tithe Farm Meadows SK3653). Previously it was also found in southern and eastern parts such as at Church Broughton (SK1735) and Bretby (SK3124). This loss is probably related

the margins of meadows. Records peak in early May, and are scattered across the county (Ashbourne Green SK1948, Matlock Dale SK2958 & Millers Dale Quarry SK1473). In the White Peak it is considered characteristic of ancient woodlands. It is only absent from the northern part of the Dark Peak. It formerly grew over much the same area but was more frequent in the Peak Fringe and Claylands, having apparently been lost from a number of sites.

Ranunculus sceleratus L.
Celery-leaved Buttercup

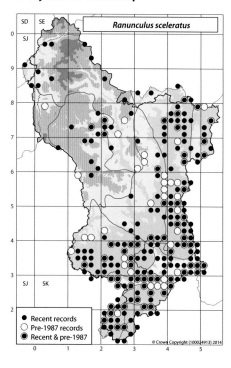

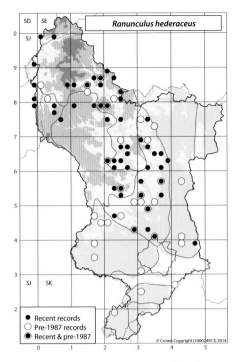

Legend:
● Recent records
○ Pre-1987 records
◉ Recent & pre-1987

© Crown Copyright (100024913) 2014

to the decrease in the number of field ponds.

Ranunculus omiophyllus Ten.
Round-leaved Crowfoot

COUNTY STATUS: Native
CONSERVATION STATUS: None
FIRST YEAR: 1879 LATEST YEAR: 2013 NO OF RECORDS: 339
RECENT SQUARES: monads 183; tetrads 124; hectads 18
ALL SQUARES: monads 203; tetrads 140; hectads 24

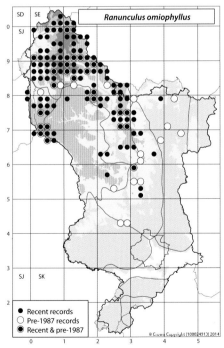

Legend:
● Recent records
○ Pre-1987 records
◉ Recent & pre-1987

© Crown Copyright (100024913) 2014

Round-leaved Crowfoot is a native annual or short-lived perennial, on the bare margins of streams, ponds and flushes in areas of nutrient poor soils. It is frequent in the South West Peak and

Dark Peak (Little Clough SK0794 & Lose Hill SK1585) but rare in the Peak Fringe and Coal Measures areas (Alderwasley SK3253 & Apperknowle SK3879). Previously it was more frequent in these latter areas, and even occurred in the Trent Valley (Newton Solney SK22 & between Calke and Melbourne SK32).

Ranunculus trichophyllus Chaix
Thread-leaved Water-crowfoot

COUNTY STATUS: Native
CONSERVATION STATUS: A
FIRST YEAR: 1886 LATEST YEAR: 2010 NO OF RECORDS: 68
RECENT SQUARES: monads 18; tetrads 17; hectads 11
ALL SQUARES: monads 40; tetrads 36; hectads 18

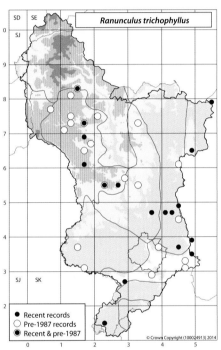

Legend:
● Recent records
○ Pre-1987 records
◉ Recent & pre-1987

© Crown Copyright (100024913) 2014

Thread-leaved Water-crowfoot is a very rare, native aquatic of still and slow-moving waterbodies in the central (Cressbrook Dale SK1772 & Cinderhill Tar Pits SK3747) and southern parts (Long Eaton SK43X) of the county. It generally grows submerged but can persist as a terrestrial plant if the waterbody dries out in summer. Previously it grew over much the same area (Cavendish Mill SK2074, Sudbury SK1631 & Swarkestone Bridge SK3628) though some sites have been lost. It is probably under-recorded as it flowers early and is thus often not critically determined.

Ranunculus × *lutzii* A. Felix
A hybrid water-crowfoot
This water-crowfoot is a very rare, native water plant, and the hybrid of Thread-leaved (*R. trichophyllus*) and Common Water-crowfoot (*R. aquatilis*).

It is only known from a listing in Stace (1975).

Ranunculus aquatilis L.
Common Water-crowfoot

COUNTY STATUS: Native
CONSERVATION STATUS: B
FIRST YEAR: 1889 LATEST YEAR: 2012 NO OF RECORDS: 138
RECENT SQUARES: monads 66; tetrads 60; hectads 26
ALL SQUARES: monads 85; tetrads 76; hectads 27

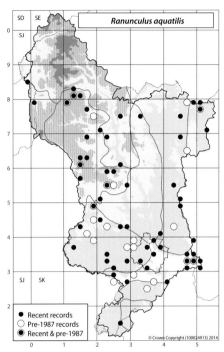

Legend:
● Recent records
○ Pre-1987 records
◉ Recent & pre-1987

© Crown Copyright (100024913) 2014

Common Water-crowfoot is an occasional native annual or short-lived perennial, of ponds and slow-flowing watercourses. It has been recorded throughout the county, for example at Forbes Hole (SK4932), Middleton Common (SK1663) and Walls Holt (SK5078), only being absent from the high moors of the north-western part of the county. Crowfoots of open water habitats are particularly difficult to separate from each other, so this species is probably under-recorded.

Ranunculus peltatus Schrank
Pond Water-crowfoot

COUNTY STATUS: Native
CONSERVATION STATUS: B
FIRST YEAR: 1881 LATEST YEAR: 2011 NO OF RECORDS: 85
RECENT SQUARES: monads 24; tetrads 31; hectads 16
ALL SQUARES: monads 47; tetrads 50; hectads 25

Pond Water-crowfoot is a rare native perennial of ponds and gently flowing watercourses. It grows throughout the county except for the Dark Peak (Highlow Farm SK16M, Repton SK3027 & Woolley Moor SK36Q). Crowfoots of open water habitats are particularly difficult to

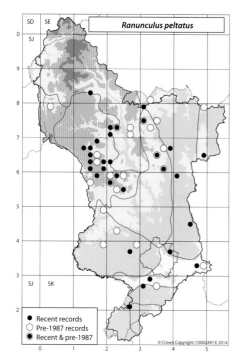

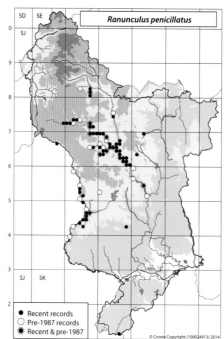

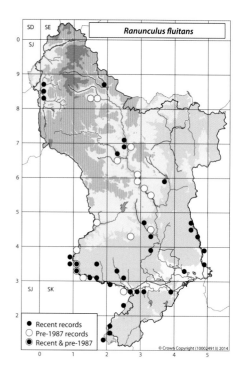

separate from each other, so it is probably under-recorded.

Ranunculus × kelchoensis S.D. Webster
Kelso Water-crowfoot

| COUNTY STATUS: Native |
| CONSERVATION STATUS: None |
| FIRST YEAR: 1888 LATEST YEAR: 1888 NO OF RECORDS: 2 |
| RECENT SQUARES: monads 0; tetrads 0; hectads 0 |
| ALL SQUARES: monads 0; tetrads 0; hectads 1 |

Locally extinct, Kelso Water-crowfoot was a very rare, native perennial of slow-flowing watercourses. It has only ever been recorded at Brailsford Brook (SK23) in 1888 (Webster 1990). The lack of subsequent records probably reflects under-recording rather than a change in its occurrence. It is the hybrid of Pond (*R. peltatus*) and River Water-crowfoot (*R. fluitans*).

Ranunculus penicillatus (Dumort.) Bab.
Stream Water-crowfoot

| COUNTY STATUS: Native |
| CONSERVATION STATUS: None |
| FIRST YEAR: 1876 LATEST YEAR: 2013 NO OF RECORDS: 165 |
| RECENT SQUARES: monads 58; tetrads 39; hectads 13 |
| ALL SQUARES: monads 77; tetrads 51; hectads 18 |

Stream Water-crowfoot is a rare native plant of fast-flowing rivers with nutrient-rich water, where it typically grows as long waving submerged streamers of green leaves and stems. It has been recorded mainly from the Rivers Dove (SK1646), Wye (SK1769) and Derwent (SK3354). Previously it was also recorded from SK24 in 1950 and the River Rother (SK47) in 1903. All local records at the

subspecies level refer to ssp. *pseudofluitans*. Crowfoots of open water habitats are particularly difficult to separate from each other, so this species is probably under-recorded.

Ranunculus × bachii Wirtg.
Wirtgen's Water-crowfoot
Wirtgen's Water-crowfoot is a very rare, native perennial that grows submerged in fast-flowing rivers. It has only ever been recorded from Alport (SK2264). The date is uncertain, but is pre-1975. It is the hybrid of River (*R. fluitans*) and Thread-leaved Water-crowfoot (*R. trichophyllus*). Due to the difficulty of determining plants in this group, it is probably under-recorded.

Ranunculus fluitans Lam.
River Water-crowfoot

| COUNTY STATUS: Native |
| CONSERVATION STATUS: C |
| FIRST YEAR: 1789 LATEST YEAR: 2012 NO OF RECORDS: 84 |
| RECENT SQUARES: monads 38; tetrads 35; hectads 16 |
| ALL SQUARES: monads 54; tetrads 49; hectads 21 |

River Water-crowfoot is a rare native of canals and rivers of moderate flow, where it grows as a submerged perennial. It occurs throughout the county where suitable habitats exist. It occurs in the Rivers Dove (SK1133), Trent (SK2826), Derwent (SK27K) and Sett (SK0086), and the Erewash Canal (SK4742). In the River Dove it still replaces Stream Water-crowfoot (R. penicillatus) downstream of Abbotsholme at SK1038 as noted by Clapham (1969). Crowfoots of open water habitats are particularly difficult to

separate from each other, so this species is probably under-recorded.

Ranunculus circinatus Sibth.
Fan-leaved Water-crowfoot

| COUNTY STATUS: Native |
| CONSERVATION STATUS: DRDB (Cat5b), A, B |
| FIRST YEAR: 1863 LATEST YEAR: 2011 NO OF RECORDS: 91 |
| RECENT SQUARES: monads 16; tetrads 15; hectads 11 |
| ALL SQUARES: monads 36; tetrads 32; hectads 19 |

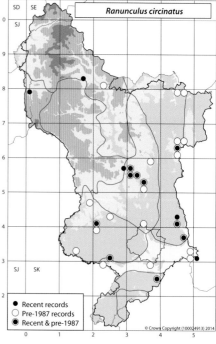

Fan-leaved Water-crowfoot is a very rare, native aquatic. It grows submerged in still and slowly moving waterbodies throughout Derbyshire. Current records are from Taxal Pond (SK0079) and Hadfield's Quarry

(SK1682) in the north, to Hilton Gravel Pits (SK2431) and Melbourne Pool (SK3924) in the south. It previously grew over a similar area of the county but was more frequent. This local decline has been matched by a national one due to habitat destruction and nutrient enrichment (Preston *et al.* 2002).

Ficaria verna Huds.
Lesser Celandine

COUNTY STATUS: Native
CONSERVATION STATUS: None
FIRST YEAR: 1789 LATEST YEAR: 2013 NO OF RECORDS: 3,166
RECENT SQUARES: monads 1,201; tetrads 604; hectads 42
ALL SQUARES: monads 1,295; tetrads 623; hectads 42

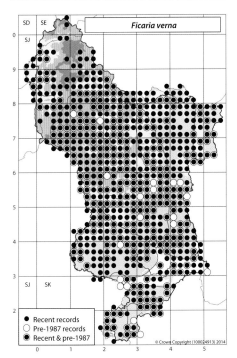

Lesser Celandine is very common and locally abundant. This perennial is native to woods, hedges and damp grasslands, only becoming rarer in the intensively-farmed south and on the northern moors. Two subspecies are present; **ssp. *verna*** and **ssp. *fertilis*** (Lawalree ex Laegaard) Stace. They occur with equal frequency and very similar distributions.

Myosurus minimus L.
Mousetail

COUNTY STATUS: Native
CONSERVATION STATUS: DRDB (Cat6), VU
FIRST YEAR: 1787 LATEST YEAR: 1903 NO OF RECORDS: 5
RECENT SQUARES: monads 0; tetrads 0; hectads 0
ALL SQUARES: monads 0; tetrads 0; hectads 4

Locally extinct, Mousetail was a very rare, native annual of arable land. It has only ever been recorded for four county sites: Drakelow (SK21), Stapenhill (SK22), Darley Dale (SK26) and near Derby (SK33) all for pre-1903. It has probably been lost locally due to general agricultural improvement.

Pheasant's Eye (*Adonis annua*), Staveley (SK4375), September 2012 (Ken Balkow)

Adonis annua L.
Pheasant's Eye

Pheasant's Eye is a very rare, casual annual of cornfields and waste ground. It was first recorded in Pilkington (1789) as "in the fields but not very common". Linton (1903) repeats this record and gives it as a garden weed in Spital (SK37). It was then recorded for Little Eaton (SK33) in 1911 and as a weed of waste ground in Staveley (SK4375) in 2012. It is a native of southern Europe.

Aquilegia vulgaris L.
Columbine

COUNTY STATUS: Native
CONSERVATION STATUS: None
FIRST YEAR: 1789 LATEST YEAR: 2013 NO OF RECORDS: 281
RECENT SQUARES: monads 110; tetrads 101; hectads 33
ALL SQUARES: monads 127; tetrads 114; hectads 33

Columbine is a rare native perennial of open woodland, scrub and damp grasslands in

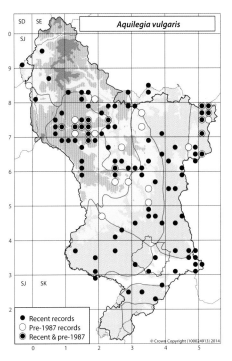

the White Peak (Priestcliffe Lees SK1472) and Magnesian Limestone Areas (Whitwell Wood SK5173). It also occurs widely scattered throughout the rest of the county where it is mostly an escape from cultivation. The flowers of the native plants are generally a rich deep blue, though colonies with white flowers are known in some dales, such as west of Hobs House, Monsal Dale (SK1771). A wine-coloured form is also known from Woo Dale (SK0972). The flowers of introduced plants are more variable in colour and often an insipid pink; some may even belong to other species.

Columbine (*Aquilegia vulgaris*) in Magnesian Limestone grassland at Markland Grips (SK5175), May 2008 (Peter Smith)

Thalictrum flavum L.
Common Meadow-rue

COUNTY STATUS:	Native
CONSERVATION STATUS:	DRDB (Cat5b), A, B
FIRST YEAR: 1789 **LATEST YEAR:** 2012 **NO OF RECORDS:** 92	
RECENT SQUARES: monads 15; tetrads 12; hectads 9	
ALL SQUARES: monads 37; tetrads 30; hectads 21	

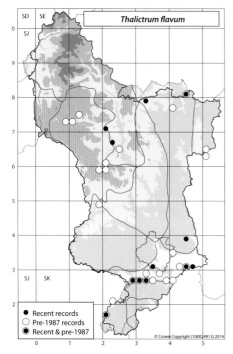

Common Meadow-rue is a very rare, native perennial of riverside grasslands and marshes. Currently it grows throughout the county (Hassop Station SK2170, Askew Hill SK3127 & Holbrook Meadows SK4680) except for the upland north-west. Previously it grew over the same area (Pikehall SK1959 & Ryelands Plantation SK2016) but was more frequent. It has also declined nationally, probably due to drainage and agricultural intensification, particularly the increased use of fertilizers. This has increased the growth of vigorous species such as Common Nettle (*Urtica dioica*) that have outcompeted it.

Thalictrum minus L.
Lesser Meadow-rue

COUNTY STATUS:	Native
CONSERVATION STATUS:	B
FIRST YEAR: 1729 **LATEST YEAR:** 2011 **NO OF RECORDS:** 171	
RECENT SQUARES: monads 25; tetrads 20; hectads 11	
ALL SQUARES: monads 42; tetrads 32; hectads 18	

Lesser Meadow-rue is a rare native perennial of cliffs, rocky outcrops and grassland in the White Peak (Miller's Dale Quarry SK1372 & Aldwark SK2357). It also occurs scattered throughout the rest of the county in grasslands and waste places as a garden escape or throwout (Breadsall

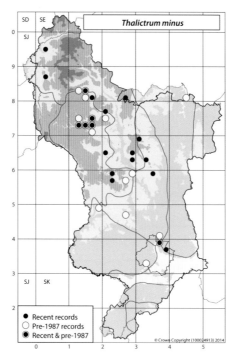

Cutting SK3739 & Glossop SK0395). Our native plants are ssp. *minus*.

PLATANACEAE

Platanus × *hispanica* Mill. ex Muenchh.
London Plane
London Plane is large casual tree of roadside verges and parkland. Probably of garden origin, it is commonly planted in urban situations due to its tolerance of air pollution. It also occurs very rarely in more natural-looking settings in southern and eastern parts where it has been recorded seven times between 1987 and 2010 (Trent Bridge SK2522, Breadsall SK3738 & the Spinkhill area SK4578). A specimen found recently at Calke Park (SK3622) has a recorded girth of 4.11m. Nationally it has a southern distribution with Derbyshire on the northern edge of its range.

BUXACEAE

Buxus sempervirens L.
Box

COUNTY STATUS:	Established (Neophyte)
CONSERVATION STATUS:	None
FIRST YEAR: 1829 **LATEST YEAR:** 2012 **NO OF RECORDS:** 33	
RECENT SQUARES: monads 18; tetrads 15; hectads 14	
ALL SQUARES: monads 22; tetrads 17; hectads 15	

Box is an established evergreen shrub or small tree of parks, hedges and woods. It is often planted for ornament and sometimes becomes naturalised. It is very rare and scattered throughout the area from Losehill Hall (SK1583) in the north, through Slinter Wood (SK2857) and

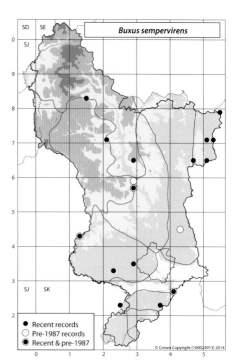

Norbury (SK1242), to Calke Park (SK3623) in the south. It is indigenous to southern England.

GUNNERACEAE

Gunnera tinctoria (Molina) Mirb.
Giant-rhubarb
Giant-rhubarb is an established perennial of marshy areas next to lakes and streams. The only record was made at Chew (SJ9992) in 1995 by E. Kearns. It is a native of western South America.

PAEONIACEAE

Paeonia officinalis L.
Garden Peony
Garden Peony is a very rare, established perennial of woods and waysides. There are only seven records scattered throughout the county between 1959 and 2012. Examples are: Barmoor Clough (SK0779), Ashford in the Water (SK1969) and Ilkeston (SK4642). It is often grown in gardens and either survives abandonment, or is thrown out when no longer required. It is a native of southern Europe.

GROSSULARIACEAE

Ribes rubrum L.
Red Currant

COUNTY STATUS:	Native
CONSERVATION STATUS:	None
FIRST YEAR: 1789 **LATEST YEAR:** 2013 **NO OF RECORDS:** 447	
RECENT SQUARES: monads 222; tetrads 205; hectads 37	
ALL SQUARES: monads 276; tetrads 247; hectads 37	

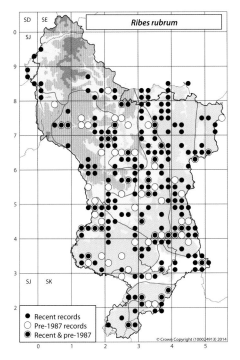

Red Currant is an occasional native shrub of woods and hedges throughout the county except for the Dark and South West Peak. It is much grown in gardens for fruit so many records are probably escapes. In fact some authorities consider all records in Britain are probably introductions (Stace 1997).

Ribes nigrum L.
Black Currant

| COUNTY STATUS: Established (Neophyte) |
| CONSERVATION STATUS: None |
| FIRST YEAR: 1854 LATEST YEAR: 2013 NO OF RECORDS: 222 |
| RECENT SQUARES: monads 105; tetrads 103; hectads 28 |
| ALL SQUARES: monads 140; tetrads 128; hectads 33 |

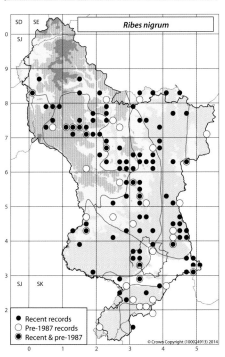

Black Currant is an established shrub of damp woods, hedges and shady stream banks. It occurs occasionally throughout Derbyshire except for the Dark Peak, the South West Peak and the Magnesian Limestone. A native of continental Europe, it is much grown in gardens for its fruit so our plants are relicts of cultivation or escapees.

Ribes sanguineum Pursh
Flowering Currant

| COUNTY STATUS: Established (Neophyte) |
| CONSERVATION STATUS: None |
| FIRST YEAR: 1969 LATEST YEAR: 2012 NO OF RECORDS: 108 |
| RECENT SQUARES: monads 68; tetrads 75; hectads 28 |
| ALL SQUARES: monads 71; tetrads 77; hectads 28 |

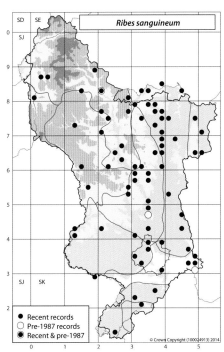

Flowering Currant is an established shrub of waste ground and abandoned cultivations. It is occasional throughout the county, but is much grown in gardens for its flowers and is sometimes self-sown. There are many more records now than in Clapham (1969). However, it is not known if this is a real increase in the wild or is due to more recording of introductions in recent times. It is a native of western North America.

Ribes odoratum H.L. Wendl.
Buffalo Currant

Buffalo Currant is a very rare, casual shrub which grows naturally in central USA. The only record was by C. Smith from a field hedge in the Loscoe/Codnor area (SK4248) in 2000. It is popular in gardens for its clove-scented yellow flowers and occurs scattered rarely through most of Great Britain.

Ribes alpinum L.
Mountain Currant

| COUNTY STATUS: Native |
| CONSERVATION STATUS: DRDB (Cat3), NS, A, B, C |
| FIRST YEAR: 1829 LATEST YEAR: 2013 NO OF RECORDS: 223 |
| RECENT SQUARES: monads 34; tetrads 29; hectads 16 |
| ALL SQUARES: monads 54; tetrads 47; hectads 17 |

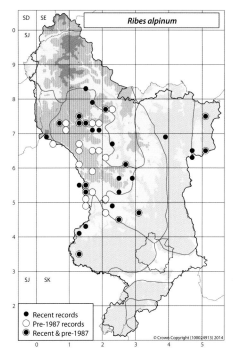

Mountain Currant is a rare native shrub of central Derbyshire. It occurs mainly in woods on limestone where it often trails over rock outcrops, forming almost vertical curtains of foliage. Localities in the White Peak include Dove Dale (SK1453) and Ashwood Dale (SK0772), and on the Magnesian Limestone, Dovedale Wood in Hardwick Park (SK4663) and Pleasley Vale (SK5164). It also occurs thinly scattered through the Coal Measures, Peak Fringe and Claylands, as at Somersal Herbert (SK1335). In these Character Areas it often occurs in hedges, so is probably a relic of cultivation. Outside the county it occurs in North Wales and northern England, though is always less frequent than in Derbyshire, and is Nationally Scarce. In 2003 Plantlife asked the public to vote between Mountain Currant and Jacob's-ladder as Derbyshire's "county plant", but the latter won.

Ribes uva-crispa L.
Gooseberry

| COUNTY STATUS: Established (Neophyte) |
| CONSERVATION STATUS: None |
| FIRST YEAR: 1789 LATEST YEAR: 2013 NO OF RECORDS: 1,194 |
| RECENT SQUARES: monads 612; tetrads 403; hectads 38 |
| ALL SQUARES: monads 664; tetrads 432; hectads 38 |

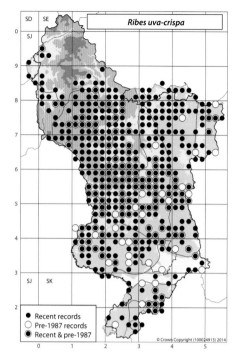

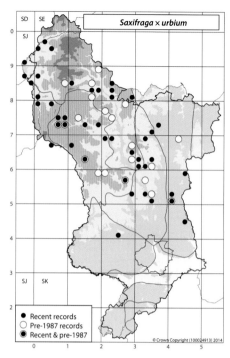

Gooseberry is an established spiny shrub of woods, hedges and shady stream banks. It occurs frequently throughout the county except for the Dark Peak. It is much grown in gardens for its fruit so many records may be escapes or throwouts. In fact some modern authorities (Stace 2010) consider all plants in the wild in Britain to be introductions.

SAXIFRAGACEAE

Astilbe × arendsii Arends
Red False-buck's-beard
Red False-buck's-beard is a very rare, established perennial, found on old railway sidings at SK0674 by J. Hawksford in 1996. Nationally it is scattered throughout the country, either as a garden throwout, escape or relic of cultivation. It is a hybrid of garden origin, but of uncertain parentage.

Rodgersia podophylla A. Gray
Rodgersia
Rodgersia is a very rare, established perennial, recorded at only one site. It was discovered as a relic of cultivation at Compstall (SJ9690) in 1993 by E. Kearns. It grows naturally in Korea and Japan.

Bergenia crassifolia (L.) Fritsch
Elephant-ears
Elephant-ears is a very rare, casual perennial of waste ground where it can occur in dense clumps due to its rhizomatous growth form. It has only been recorded three times. It was first found by J. Hodgson at Stony Ridge (SK2780) in the 1970s. Recently there have been records from Stoney Wood (SK2854) in 2012, Stanton Ironworks

(SK4739) in 2009 and a riverbank at Trent Lock (SK4831) in 2000. It is spreading in southern England due to break-up of clumps, as it cannot pollinate itself or set seed. It grows naturally in Siberia.

Saxifraga cymbalaria L.
Celandine Saxifrage
Celandine Saxifrage is a very rare, casual annual. Our only record was made at Ashbourne (SK1746) in 1983 by K.M. Hollick. It appears to be increasing in England due to escapes from gardens where it sets copious seed. It is indigenous in the eastern Mediterranean.

Saxifraga cuneifolia L.
Lesser Londonpride

COUNTY STATUS: Casual	
CONSERVATION STATUS: None	
FIRST YEAR: 1988 LATEST YEAR: 1996 NO OF RECORDS: 4	
RECENT SQUARES: monads 3; tetrads 3; hectads 3	
ALL SQUARES: monads 3; tetrads 3; hectads 3	

Lesser Londonpride is a very rare, casual perennial of walls and rocks in the White Peak. There are recent records from only three localities: Fairfield (SK0674), Parsley Hay (SK1463) and Longstone (SK1972). It is a native of southern Europe.

Saxifraga umbrosa L.
Pyrenean Saxifrage

COUNTY STATUS: Established (Neophyte)	
CONSERVATION STATUS: None	
FIRST YEAR: 1844 LATEST YEAR: 1969 NO OF RECORDS: 8	
RECENT SQUARES: monads 0; tetrads 0; hectads 0	
ALL SQUARES: monads 5; tetrads 5; hectads 6	

Locally extinct, Pyrenean Saxifrage was a very rare, established perennial of shaded rocks and walls. There are no modern records, but Clapham (1969) listed it for Sherriff Wood (SK2378) and Lodge Farm (SK1745) amongst other sites. Some of these records may be errors for Londonpride (S. × urbium), a hybrid of which this is one parent. It is a native of the Pyrenees.

Saxifraga × urbium D.A. Webb
Londonpride

COUNTY STATUS: Established (Neophyte)	
CONSERVATION STATUS: None	
FIRST YEAR: 1950 LATEST YEAR: 2013 NO OF RECORDS: 101	
RECENT SQUARES: monads 43; tetrads 45; hectads 18	
ALL SQUARES: monads 58; tetrads 60; hectads 22	

Londonpride is an established perennial of waste ground, woods and damp shaded places at the base of rock outcrops and walls. It is often associated with old railway buildings (Parsley Hay Cutting SK1463). It occurs occasionally throughout central

and northern parts, but is absent from the south. It occurs scattered through Britain, reaching its highest altitude of 335m at Parsley Hay (Preston *et al.* 2002). It is of hybrid garden origin. Pyrenean Saxifrage (*S. umbrosa*) is one of its parents and in the past has probably been recorded in error for it. The other parent is St Patrick's-cabbage (*S. spathularis*).

Saxifraga hirsuta L.
Kidney Saxifrage
Kidney Saxifrage is a very rare, established perennial of woodlands. It has only ever been recorded at Corbar Woods (SK0573). First found there in 1971 by Mrs G. Wheeldon, she then refound it at the same point some thirty years later in 2001. Nationally it is a garden escape which appears to have spread since 1962. It is a native of south-western Ireland.

Saxifraga granulata L.
Meadow Saxifrage

COUNTY STATUS: Native	
CONSERVATION STATUS: None	
FIRST YEAR: 1789 LATEST YEAR: 2013 NO OF RECORDS: 834	
RECENT SQUARES: monads 276; tetrads 155; hectads 21	
ALL SQUARES: monads 312; tetrads 182; hectads 31	

Meadow Saxifrage is a native perennial of moist unimproved grasslands. It is common in the White Peak (Via Gellia SK2556 & Peak Dale SK0976) but is rare elsewhere. It has been lost from many sites in the south of the county due to agricultural improvement (Netherseal SK2812, Mickleover SK33 & Risley Glebe SK4635). Even in its White Peak stronghold, it has been lost from 56% of its hay

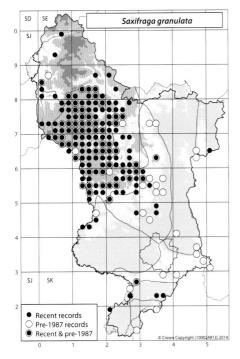

Mossy Saxifrage (*Saxifraga hypnoides*), upper Cressbrook Dale (SK1775), May 2009 (Peter Smith)

meadow sites between the mid-1980s and mid-1990s (Buckingham *et al.* 1997).

Saxifraga hypnoides L.
Mossy Saxifrage (Dovedale Moss)

COUNTY STATUS: Native
CONSERVATION STATUS: DRDB (Cat2), VU, B
FIRST YEAR: 1775 LATEST YEAR: 2013 NO OF RECORDS: 377
RECENT SQUARES: monads 84; tetrads 50; hectads 10
ALL SQUARES: monads 105; tetrads 60; hectads 11

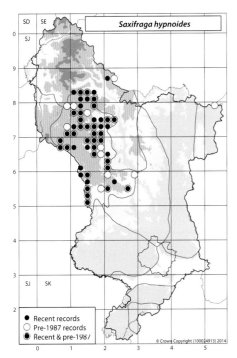

Mossy Saxifrage is an occasional native perennial of damp shaded rocks and walls in the White Peak (Deep Dale SK0971 & Lode Mill SK1455). It also occurs more rarely off the Carboniferous Limestone but

these localities are often considered garden escapes (Cutthroat Bridge SK2186). Locally it is known as **Dovedale Moss**. It is a plant of upland Britain on its eastern limit here.

Saxifraga tridactylites L.
Rue-leaved Saxifrage

COUNTY STATUS: Native
CONSERVATION STATUS: None
FIRST YEAR: 1789 LATEST YEAR: 2013 NO OF RECORDS: 570
RECENT SQUARES: monads 214; tetrads 135; hectads 22
ALL SQUARES: monads 252; tetrads 156; hectads 27

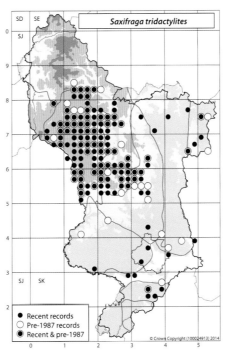

Rue-leaved Saxifrage is a native winter annual of bare shallow soil, rocks and walls throughout Derbyshire. However,

it is only common and locally abundant on limestone in the White Peak, being occasional-to-absent elsewhere (Calke Park SK3622 & Barlborough SK4777). There is little evidence of any decline locally, but nationally it is much reduced in southern and eastern England since 1950.

Chrysosplenium oppositifolium L.
Opposite-leaved Golden-saxifrage

COUNTY STATUS: Native
CONSERVATION STATUS: None
FIRST YEAR: 1789 LATEST YEAR: 2013 NO OF RECORDS: 1,622
RECENT SQUARES: monads 635; tetrads 364; hectads 39
ALL SQUARES: monads 679; tetrads 387; hectads 40

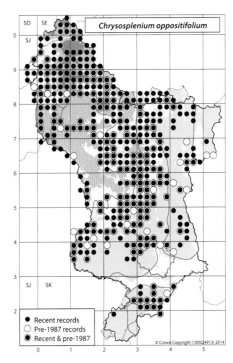

Opposite-leaved Golden-saxifrage is a native perennial of marshy areas by streams, wet areas in woods and flushes in moorland areas. It occurs frequently throughout the county but is absent from much of the White Peak and certain areas of the lowlands. Previously it grew over much the same area though has certainly been lost from several sites due to drainage.

Chrysosplenium alternifolium L.
Alternate-leaved Golden-saxifrage

COUNTY STATUS: Native	
CONSERVATION STATUS: B	
FIRST YEAR: 1789 LATEST YEAR: 2013 NO OF RECORDS: 209	
RECENT SQUARES: monads 53; tetrads 45; hectads 15	
ALL SQUARES: monads 83; tetrads 66; hectads 18	

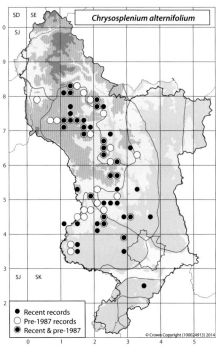

Alternate-leaved Golden-saxifrage is a native perennial of marshy areas by streams, and of wet areas in woods. In the latter habitat it often grows scattered within carpets of the commoner Opposite-leaved Golden-saxifrage (*C. oppositifolium*). It occurs occasionally throughout the White Peak, the Dark Peak, the Peak Fringe and Claylands Areas. Elsewhere it is very rare, e.g. Seven Spouts Plantation (SK3525). It was previously recorded from a slightly wider area, including the South West Peak (Ladder Hill SK0278 in 1954).

Heuchera sanguinea Engelm.
Coralbells

Coralbells is a very rare, casual perennial of waste ground. There are only two records: Wingerworth (SK3662) by D. Dupree in 1997, and New Sawley (SK4632) in 2009. It occurs as a garden throwout

scattered across south-eastern England, and is a native of southern North America.

Tolmiea menziesii (Pursh) Torr. & A. Gray
Pick-a-back-plant

COUNTY STATUS: Established (Neophyte)	
CONSERVATION STATUS: None	
FIRST YEAR: 1970 LATEST YEAR: 2011 NO OF RECORDS: 26	
RECENT SQUARES: monads 13; tetrads 10; hectads 4	
ALL SQUARES: monads 14; tetrads 11; hectads 5	

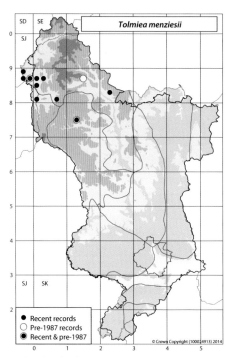

Pick-a-back-plant is a very rare, established perennial of waste ground and waysides that are damp and shaded. It occurs mainly in the Dark Peak (Bagshaw Wood SK0781 & New Mills SK0086). However, it has been recorded for the White Peak at Monks Dale (SK1374) and for the South West Peak at Horwich End (SK0080). It occurs scattered over most of Britain, although it is rarely conspicuous as the plantlets on its leaves that give it its name seldom develop in the wild. It grows naturally in western North America.

Tellima grandiflora (Pursh) Douglas ex Lindl.
Fringecups

COUNTY STATUS: Established (Neophyte)	
CONSERVATION STATUS: None	
FIRST YEAR: 1952 LATEST YEAR: 2013 NO OF RECORDS: 61	
RECENT SQUARES: monads 37; tetrads 35; hectads 18	
ALL SQUARES: monads 43; tetrads 39; hectads 20	

Fringecups is a rare established perennial of woods and damp hedges throughout the county. It is scattered over most of Britain and prefers nitrogen-rich soils (Preston *et al.* 2002). This may explain why it appears to be spreading nationally as more disposal of waste and use of fertilisers is producing

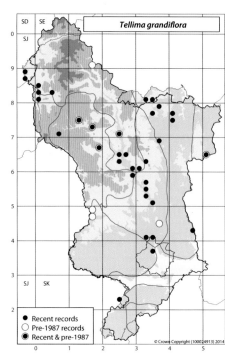

more such enriched soils. It is indigenous to western North America.

CRASSULACEAE

Crassula helmsii (Kirk) Cockayne
New Zealand Pigmyweed

COUNTY STATUS: Established (Neophyte)	
CONSERVATION STATUS: WCA9	
FIRST YEAR: 1984 LATEST YEAR: 2012 NO OF RECORDS: 68	
RECENT SQUARES: monads 41; tetrads 36; hectads 23	
ALL SQUARES: monads 42; tetrads 37; hectads 23	

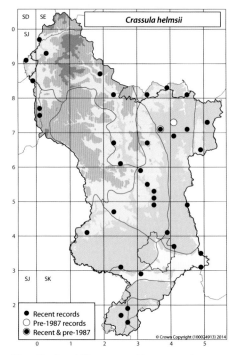

New Zealand Pigmyweed is a recently established, aquatic perennial that grows submerged or emergent in or around ponds. It was first recorded in Chesterfield (SK4072) by M. Hewitt in 1984. However, it is still rare in the county (Errwood Reservoir SK0174, Frecheville Community Pond SK3983 & Hilton Gravel Pits SK2431). Indigenous to Australia and New Zealand, it was sold at garden centres as an ornamental, but has escaped into the wild throughout Britain and is spreading quickly. Once it reaches a pond it can rapidly form pure stands over shallow water, excluding most native species. It is thus a threat to local biodiversity and its sale in England was banned in 2013.

Umbilicus rupestris (Salisb.) Dandy
Navelwort

COUNTY STATUS: Native
CONSERVATION STATUS: A, B
FIRST YEAR: 1829 **LATEST YEAR:** 2012 **NO OF RECORDS:** 55
RECENT SQUARES: monads 12; tetrads 11; hectads 11
ALL SQUARES: monads 15; tetrads 12; hectads 13

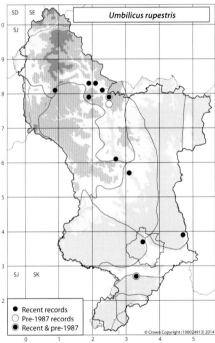

Navelwort is a very rare, native perennial of cliffs and walls. It grows scattered throughout the county, but generally avoids limestone areas. It is known from walls in the Hathersage area (SK2381), Lea Bridge (SK3156) and Darley Park (SK3537), plus the sandstone rock outcrop into which is carved the hermitage cave at Anchor Church (SK3327). It is suspected of having been planted on some walls (Thornhill SK1983) which may question its native status on walls in general. Previously it was recorded from the same area with at least one record for the Carboniferous Limestone in Dove Dale (SK15). Hodgson (2002) notes how the plant is wintergreen

here, being "dried to a crisp" by July. Nationally it is a western species with Derbyshire on the eastern edge of its range.

Sempervivum tectorum L.
House-leek

COUNTY STATUS: Established (Neophyte)
CONSERVATION STATUS: None
FIRST YEAR: 1789 **LATEST YEAR:** 2003 **NO OF RECORDS:** 18
RECENT SQUARES: monads 1; tetrads 1; hectads 1
ALL SQUARES: monads 10; tetrads 10; hectads 13

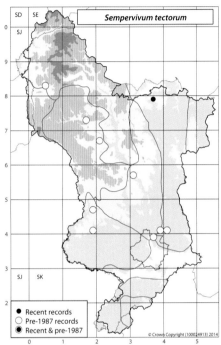

House-leek is a very rare, established plant of roofs and walls where it grows as an evergreen succulent perennial. It previously grew scattered throughout the county from New Smithy (SK0582) in the north to Morley Almshouses (SK3941) in the south. However, the only recent record is from Apperknowle (SK3278). The reason for this decrease is uncertain although it is probably real as modern recorders are more likely to record introductions than before. It is a native of central and southern Europe.

Sedum spectabile Boreau
Butterfly Stonecrop

COUNTY STATUS: Casual
CONSERVATION STATUS: None
FIRST YEAR: 1991 **LATEST YEAR:** 2009 **NO OF RECORDS:** 7
RECENT SQUARES: monads 6; tetrads 6; hectads 6
ALL SQUARES: monads 6; tetrads 6; hectads 6

Butterfly Stonecrop is a casual succulent perennial of waste ground and abandoned gardens. It is very rare, having only been recorded from a few scattered localities (Middleton Dale SK2275, Whaley Bridge

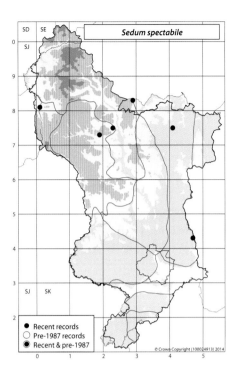

SK0181 & Cotmanhay SK4743) some of which may be errors for **Autumn Stonecrop (*S. 'Herbstfreude'*)**. It grows mostly in southern and central England, and is often a garden throwout due to its vigorous growth (Preston *et al.* 2002). It is a native of China and Japan.

Sedum telephium L.
Orpine

COUNTY STATUS: Native
CONSERVATION STATUS: None
FIRST YEAR: 1787 **LATEST YEAR:** 2013 **NO OF RECORDS:** 290
RECENT SQUARES: monads 51; tetrads 36; hectads 11
ALL SQUARES: monads 76; tetrads 53; hectads 15

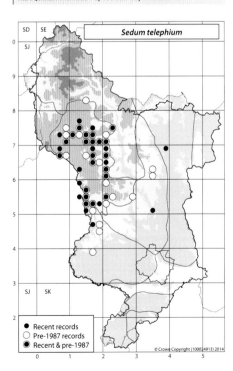

Orpine is a native succulent perennial of woods, scrub and rocky outcrops. It is occasional in the White Peak (Dove Dale SK1454 & Monsal Trail SK1971). Elsewhere it is very rare (Ambergate Station SK3451, St Augustine's SK3869 & Ashbourne SK1746). Previously it occurred over the same area but was more frequent in the Peak Fringe and Claylands. Ssp. *telephium* was recorded in SK16 during 1950. It is sometimes a garden escape, so some records mapped here may be of established plants.

Sedum anacampseros L.
Love-restoring Stonecrop

Love-restoring Stonecrop is a casual succulent perennial, indigenous to southern Europe. It has been found only once in the wild, at Ashbourne (SK1946) by K.M. Hollick in 1977. It is grown in gardens and usually reaches the wild as a throwout or garden relict.

Sedum spurium M. Bieb.
Caucasian-stonecrop

COUNTY STATUS:	Established (Neophyte)
CONSERVATION STATUS:	None
FIRST YEAR: 1960	LATEST YEAR: 2012 NO OF RECORDS: 43
RECENT SQUARES:	monads 23; tetrads 23; hectads 17
ALL SQUARES:	monads 29; tetrads 29; hectads 18

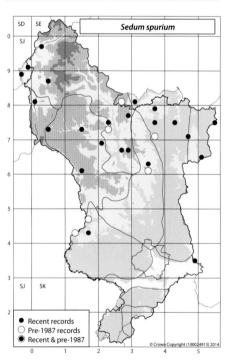

Caucasian-stonecrop is a rare established plant in northern parts of Derbyshire (Hadfield SK0296, Ashover SK3462 & Darley Moor SK1742). Here it grows as a succulent perennial on wasteland and sites of abandoned gardens. It has spread nationally in the last 50 years and appears to have increased locally too. It is a native of the Caucasus region.

Sedum rupestre L.
Reflexed Stonecrop

COUNTY STATUS:	Established (Neophyte)
CONSERVATION STATUS:	None
FIRST YEAR: 1789	LATEST YEAR: 2013 NO OF RECORDS: 291
RECENT SQUARES:	monads 169; tetrads 178; hectads 32
ALL SQUARES:	monads 177; tetrads 183; hectads 33

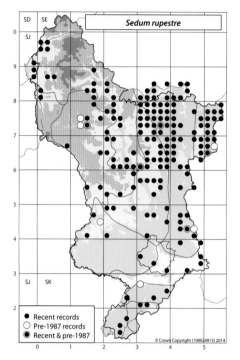

Caucasian-stonecrop (*Sedum spureum*) on a wall near Cutthorpe Hall (SK3473), July 2012 (Ken Balknow)

Reflexed Stonecrop is an occasional established succulent perennial that grows on walls and rocks throughout the county (Hayfield SK0486, Mickleover SK3035), though becoming more frequent in north-eastern parts (Clowne SK4975). Clapham (1969) comments that this European species was "rarely seen in recent years" which suggests it has increased since then.

Sedum forsterianum Sm.
Rock Stonecrop

COUNTY STATUS:	Established (Neophyte)
CONSERVATION STATUS:	None
FIRST YEAR: 1805	LATEST YEAR: 2012 NO OF RECORDS: 19
RECENT SQUARES:	monads 14; tetrads 13; hectads 8
ALL SQUARES:	monads 14; tetrads 13; hectads 10

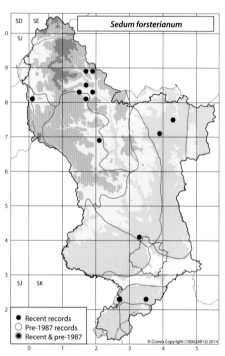

Rock Stonecrop is a very rare, established succulent perennial. It grows throughout our area on rocks and in woods (Ashes Farm SK1888 & Ticknall SK3523). It occurs as a native in Wales and the West Country.

Sedum acre L.
Biting Stonecrop

COUNTY STATUS:	Native
CONSERVATION STATUS:	None
FIRST YEAR: 1789	LATEST YEAR: 2013 NO OF RECORDS: 1,242
RECENT SQUARES:	monads 501; tetrads 341; hectads 38
ALL SQUARES:	monads 560; tetrads 364; hectads 38

Biting Stonecrop is a native succulent perennial, common in central Derbyshire but only occasional in the upland north-west and the agricultural south. Growing on rocks, walls and areas of dry open ground, in some places it can

Biting Stonecrop (*Sedum acre*), on side of Tissington Trail near Hartington (SK1461), July 2007 (Peter Smith)

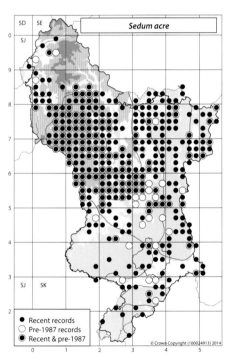

be locally abundant, especially in the White Peak.

Sedum sexangulare L.
Tasteless Stonecrop

Tasteless Stonecrop is a casual perennial succulent. It has been recorded only once in the county. It was found growing on a wall at Taxal (SK0079 v.c.58) in 1996 by G. Kay. Nationally it occurs scattered throughout Britain on walls and rocks. It is a native of Europe.

Sedum album L.
White Stonecrop

COUNTY STATUS: Established (Archaeophyte)
CONSERVATION STATUS: None
FIRST YEAR: 1829 LATEST YEAR: 2013 NO OF RECORDS: 305
RECENT SQUARES: monads 174; tetrads 172; hectads 34
ALL SQUARES: monads 186; tetrads 177; hectads 35

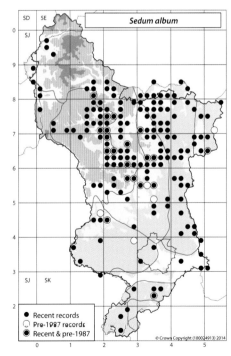

White Stonecrop is an anciently established, succulent perennial of walls, rocks and bare compacted ground. Nationally it has increased markedly

since 1962, and is now frequent in central Derbyshire, but rare in the south and virtually absent from the Dark Peak. The native range of this European plant may include some parts of the UK as well, but not Derbyshire.

Sedum anglicum Huds.
English Stonecrop

COUNTY STATUS: Native
CONSERVATION STATUS: B
FIRST YEAR: 1800 LATEST YEAR: 2013 NO OF RECORDS: 37
RECENT SQUARES: monads 21; tetrads 21; hectads 14
ALL SQUARES: monads 27; tetrads 25; hectads 14

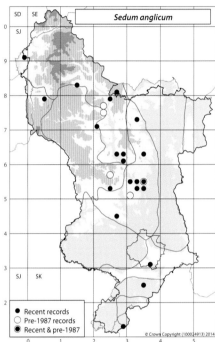

English Stonecrop is a rare native plant of rocks and bare ground throughout the area (Dirtlow Rake SK1582, Upper Hackney SK2861 & Ticknall SK3524) where it grows as a creeping succulent perennial. Previously it had a more restricted range in the county but it is uncertain if the apparent increase is real or simply due to better recording.

Sedum dasyphyllum L.
Thick-leaved Stonecrop

Thick-leaved Stonecrop is a very rare, established succulent perennial of walls. There are four recent records from the Brockwell area (SK3572, 3672 & 3772) and Hagg Wood (SK2957), plus two earlier ones (Dethick SK35 & Pinxton SK45). It is a native of mainland Europe.

Sedum hispanicum L.
Spanish Stonecrop

Spanish Stonecrop is a casual succulent perennial of bare stony ground, and a native of south-eastern Europe. Our only record is from an old aerodrome at Ashbourne (SK1946), found by K.M. Hollick in 1977.

Sedum ewersii Ledebour
A stonecrop

This stonecrop is a very rare casual of walls, found only once in the county at Fairfield (SK0674) in 1996 by A. Underhill. This is believed to be the first record in the wild in Britain.

HALORAGACEAE

Myriophyllum verticillatum L.
Whorled Water-milfoil

COUNTY STATUS: Native
CONSERVATION STATUS: DRDB (Cat2), VU, A, B, C
FIRST YEAR: 1829 LATEST YEAR: 2005 NO OF RECORDS: 20
RECENT SQUARES: monads 2; tetrads 2; hectads 2
ALL SQUARES: monads 4; tetrads 4; hectads 5

Whorled Water-milfoil is a native submerged aquatic which overwinters by means of dormant buds. The only recent records come from Forbes Hole (SK4932) and the Avenue Works (SK3967). Formerly it was recorded from a handful of localities in eastern Derbyshire, from the canal at Killamarsh (SK48) in the north, to Swarkestone (SK3628) in the south. Outside the county it is an uncommon species of base-rich waters, mostly in the east of England.

Myriophyllum aquaticum (Vell.) Verdc.
Parrot's-feather

Parrot's-feather is a very rare, established perennial, often planted in ornamental

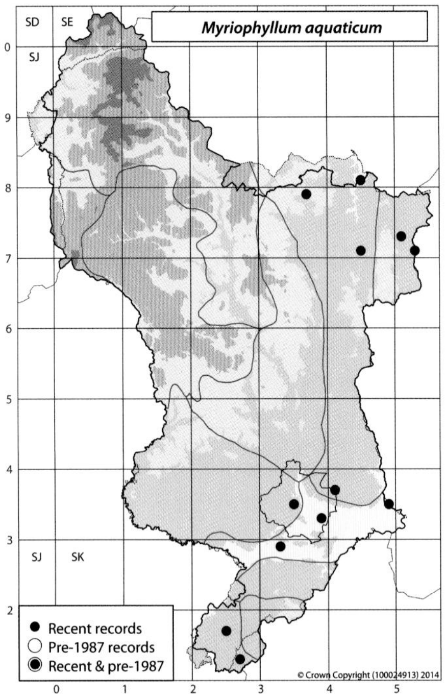
Myriophyllum aquaticum
SD
SE
SJ
SK
Recent records
Pre-1987 records
Recent & pre-1987
© Crown Copyright (100024913) 2014

COUNTY STATUS: Established (Neophyte)
CONSERVATION STATUS: WCA9
FIRST YEAR: 1997 LATEST YEAR: 2010 NO OF RECORDS: 14
RECENT SQUARES: monads 12; tetrads 12; hectads 8
ALL SQUARES: monads 12; tetrads 12; hectads 8

ponds which, if discarded, can survive in more natural situations. Its vigorous growth of velvety green leaves can smother all other plants in a pond, so it is an unwelcome invasive visitor whose sale in the UK was banned from 2013. It is increasingly recorded from southern and eastern areas (Netherseal SK2712, Twyford SK3228 & Dronfield SK3678). It is a native of central South America.

Myriophyllum spicatum L.
Spiked Water-milfoil

COUNTY STATUS: Native
CONSERVATION STATUS: None
FIRST YEAR: 1829 LATEST YEAR: 2011 NO OF RECORDS: 144
RECENT SQUARES: monads 51; tetrads 48; hectads 23
ALL SQUARES: monads 80; tetrads 72; hectads 29

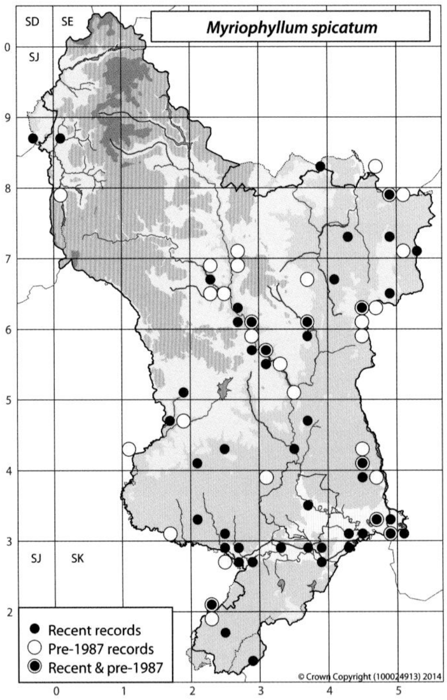
Myriophyllum spicatum
SD
SE
SJ
SK
Recent records
Pre-1987 records
Recent & pre-1987
© Crown Copyright (100024913) 2014

Spiked Water-milfoil is native perennial that grows submerged in still and slow-moving waterbodies. It occurs occasionally throughout the county except for the Dark and White Peak, where it is virtually absent, and is especially frequent in the Trent Valley.

Myriophyllum alterniflorum DC.
Alternate Water-milfoil

COUNTY STATUS: Native
CONSERVATION STATUS: DRDB (Cat5a), A, B
FIRST YEAR: 1889 LATEST YEAR: 2009 NO OF RECORDS: 18
RECENT SQUARES: monads 4; tetrads 4; hectads 4
ALL SQUARES: monads 6; tetrads 5; hectads 5

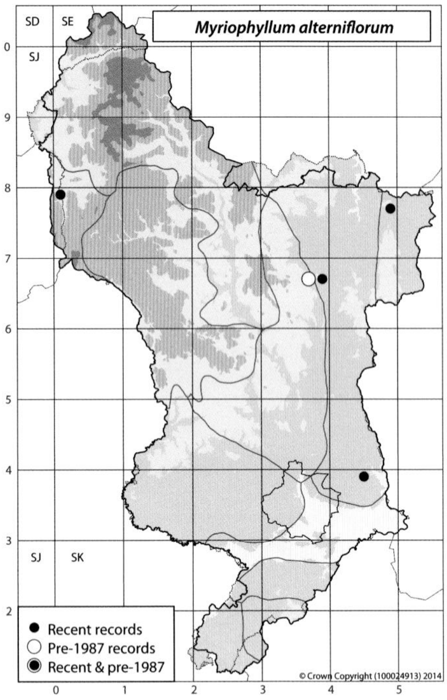
Myriophyllum alterniflorum
SD
SE
SJ
SK
Recent records
Pre-1987 records
Recent & pre-1987
© Crown Copyright (100024913) 2014

Alternate Water-milfoil is a very rare, native perennial which grows submerged in ponds and lakes, mostly in base-poor waters. It occurs scattered throughout central Derbyshire, avoiding the limestone areas. Typical localities are Taxal (SK0079 v.c.58) and Harlesthorpe Dam (SK4976). Previously it occurred in a wider range of habitats including canals, but over the same general area (e.g. canal between Renishaw and Staveley SK47).

VITACEAE

Vitis vinifera L.
Grape-vine

Grape-vine is a casual woody climber of waste ground and hedges. It is recorded from six sites between 1997 and 2012, for example: Hill Top (SK3077), Kedleston Road (SK3437), Heeley (SK3484) and Long Eaton (SK4934). It was first found at Ashbourne (SK1746) in 1975. It is either a garden escape or can grow from discarded fruit and kitchen waste, and is a native of southern and central Europe.

Parthenocissus quinquefolia (L.) Planch.
Virginia-creeper

COUNTY STATUS: Casual
CONSERVATION STATUS: WCA9
FIRST YEAR: 1971 LATEST YEAR: 2009 NO OF RECORDS: 8
RECENT SQUARES: monads 6; tetrads 6; hectads 6
ALL SQUARES: monads 8; tetrads 8; hectads 6

Virginia-creeper is a casual woody climber of waysides, woods, walls and hedges, though some authorities consider it newly established (Stace *et al.* 2003).

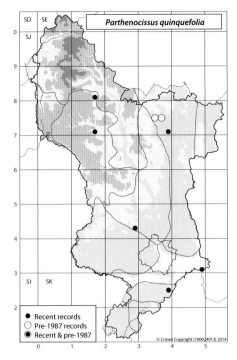

It occurs very rarely scattered through the area, as at Upperdale (SK1771), Chesterfield (SK3870), Lock Lane (SK4831) and Melbourne (SK3925). A native of North America, it is planted in gardens for autumn colour.

Parthenocissus tricuspidata (Siebold & Zucc.) Planch.
Boston-ivy
Locally extinct, Boston-ivy was a casual woody climber, known only from one record near Newbold (SK3574) in 1960. It is grown in gardens for ornament but occurs naturally in China and Japan.

FABACEAE

Robinia pseudoacacia L.
False-acacia

COUNTY STATUS:	Established (Neophyte)
CONSERVATION STATUS:	None
FIRST YEAR: 1969 LATEST YEAR: 2011 NO OF RECORDS: 41	
RECENT SQUARES: monads 24; tetrads 22; hectads 15	
ALL SQUARES: monads 29; tetrads 27; hectads 18	

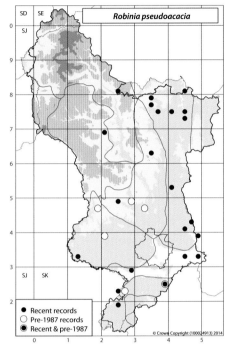

False-acacia is an established spiny tree of roadsides and plantations, originating from eastern North America. Frequently planted for ornament, it sometimes naturalises by suckers or seeds. It is occasional in eastern

and southern Derbyshire, ranging from Hathersage (SK2480) and Duckmanton (SK4472) in the north, to Doveridge (SK1333) and Melbourne Pool (SK3824) in the south.

Galega officinalis L.
Goat's-rue

COUNTY STATUS:	Established (Neophyte)
CONSERVATION STATUS:	None
FIRST YEAR: 1960 LATEST YEAR: 2012 NO OF RECORDS: 113	
RECENT SQUARES: monads 57; tetrads 46; hectads 14	
ALL SQUARES: monads 70; tetrads 55; hectads 18	

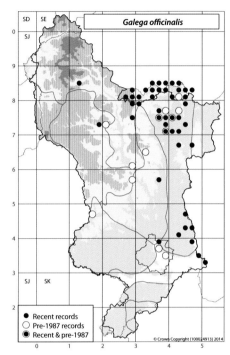

Goat's-rue is an established perennial of waysides and waste ground, grown in gardens for ornament. This native of continental Europe is occasional in the area north of Chesterfield (Chesterfield Canal SK3872 & Sheepbridge Tip SK3675), but very rare and scattered elsewhere (Shipley SK4443 & Long Eaton SK4834). Nationally it is a southern species, with Derbyshire near the northern edge of its main distribution.

Colutea arborescens L.
Bladder-senna

COUNTY STATUS:	Casual
CONSERVATION STATUS:	None
FIRST YEAR: 1941 LATEST YEAR: 2010 NO OF RECORDS: 11	
RECENT SQUARES: monads 5; tetrads 5; hectads 5	
ALL SQUARES: monads 5; tetrads 5; hectads 6	

Bladder-senna is a very rare, casual shrub of waysides and waste ground, indigenous to continental Europe and frequently grown in gardens as an ornamental. All five recent records are found in the eastern half of the county,

Goat's-rue (*Galega officinalis*), beside the A612 at Totley (SK3079), July 2002 (Ken Balkow)

from Coal Aston (SK3679) and Glapwell (SK4767) in the north, to Trent Lock (SK4831) and Long Eaton (SK5033) in the south.

Astragalus glycyphyllos L.
Wild Liquorice

COUNTY STATUS: Native

CONSERVATION STATUS: B

FIRST YEAR: 1964 LATEST YEAR: 2012 NO OF RECORDS: 43

RECENT SQUARES: monads 10; tetrads 6; hectads 2

ALL SQUARES: monads 12; tetrads 7; hectads 3

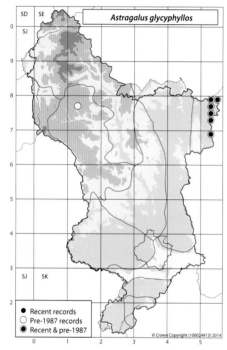

Wild Liquorice is a sprawling native perennial of wood-borders, waysides and spoil tips on the Magnesian Limestone (Creswell Colliery Tip SK5273, lay-by at Whitwell Wood SK5277 & Steetley Quarry SK5479). There is one isolated older record from Hay Dale (SK1376) in 1964.

Onobrychis viciifolia Scop.
Sainfoin

COUNTY STATUS: Established (Neophyte)

CONSERVATION STATUS: None

FIRST YEAR: 1829 LATEST YEAR: 2012 NO OF RECORDS: 20

RECENT SQUARES: monads 7; tetrads 5; hectads 3

ALL SQUARES: monads 10; tetrads 9; hectads 6

Sainfoin is a rare established perennial of waysides and waste ground on the Magnesian Limestone (Batley Lane SK4963, New Bolsover SK4670, Pleasley Vale SK4964 & the Rowthorne Trail SK4764). It has been a successful component of seed mixes on coal-tip restoration sites, such as Pleasley Colliery. It was formerly recorded in the White Peak at Matlock (SK2957) in 1976 and Taddington (SK1371) in 1970. There is also one record for Morley (SK3841) in 1969. At 335m Taddington is the highest known location in the UK (Preston *et al.* 2002). It has the local name of Ass-sweet, and is a native of southern Britain. Cultivation was attempted here in the past, but was never successful (Farey 1815).

Anthyllis vulneraria L.
Kidney Vetch

COUNTY STATUS: Native

CONSERVATION STATUS: None

FIRST YEAR: 1789 LATEST YEAR: 2013 NO OF RECORDS: 628

RECENT SQUARES: monads 171; tetrads 116; hectads 28

ALL SQUARES: monads 195; tetrads 128; hectads 31

Kidney Vetch is a frequent native perennial of grasslands in the White Peak and Magnesian Limestone, on soils that are generally calcareous and freely draining (Chee Dale SK1273, Harborough Rocks SK2455, Pleasley SK5064 & Creswell SK5274). It occurs rarely throughout the rest of the county in similar habitats (Breaston SK4634 & Langley SK4546), or on old railway land (Friar Gate Station SK3436, Long Eaton

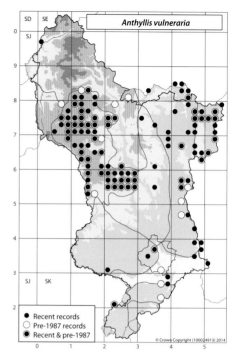

SK5033 & Stanton Ironworks SK4639). Derbyshire plants do not have the red colouring seen elsewhere. A single record of the introduced **ssp. *carpatica*** was made by W.R. Linton in 1896 from SK25 (voucher at Liverpool Museum).

Lotus tenuis Waldst. & Kit. ex Willd.
Narrow-leaved Bird's-foot-trefoil

COUNTY STATUS: Native

CONSERVATION STATUS: DRDB (Cat5a), A, B

FIRST YEAR: 1844 LATEST YEAR: 2010 NO OF RECORDS: 19

RECENT SQUARES: monads 4; tetrads 4; hectads 4

ALL SQUARES: monads 7; tetrads 8; hectads 13

Narrow-leaved Bird's-foot-trefoil is a very rare, native perennial of dry disturbed grassland. It has only been recorded recently from four localities: Congreave (SK2465), Dunston (SK3674), Lady Clough

Kidney Vetch (*Anthyllis vulneraria*), Pleasley Pit (SK5064), July 2011 (Kieron Huston)

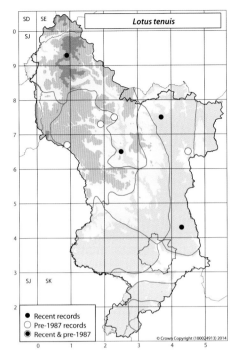

Moor (SK0992) and Mapperley Reserve (SK4343). Older records are scattered over most of the county except for the Dark Peak (Earl Sterndale SK06, Nether Langwith SK57 & Caldwell SK21).

Lotus corniculatus L.
Common Bird's-foot-trefoil

COUNTY STATUS:	Native
CONSERVATION STATUS:	None
FIRST YEAR: 1789 LATEST YEAR: 2013 NO OF RECORDS: 4,855	
RECENT SQUARES: monads 1,565; tetrads 659; hectads 42	
ALL SQUARES: monads 1,652; tetrads 671; hectads 42	

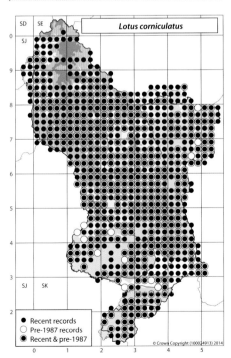

Common Bird's-foot-trefoil is a native perennial of unimproved grasslands on

all but the most acid and infertile soils. It is still very common throughout most of Derbyshire despite a recent decrease due to habitat eutrophication (Braithwaite *et al.* 2005). It is only absent from some of the northern moors and areas of intensive farming in the south. It is increasingly planted to bolster the biodiversity of restoration schemes and roadside verges, but it is often the upright alien **variety *sativus*** that is used (Anthony Hill SK0470, Diamond Hill SK0570 & Castle Gresley SK2718). It is known locally to many as Eggs-and-bacon.

Lotus pedunculatus Cav.
Greater Bird's-foot-trefoil

COUNTY STATUS:	Native
CONSERVATION STATUS:	None
FIRST YEAR: 1829 LATEST YEAR: 2013 NO OF RECORDS: 1,405	
RECENT SQUARES: monads 586; tetrads 408; hectads 41	
ALL SQUARES: monads 685; tetrads 451; hectads 41	

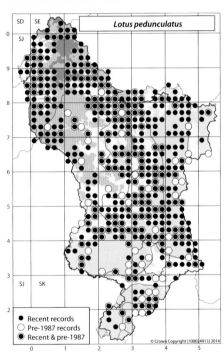

Greater Bird's-foot-trefoil is a frequent native perennial of wet grasslands, marshes and flushes throughout the county. It is recorded from Long Clough (SK0392) and the Upper Derwent Valley (SK1790) in the north to Swainspark (SK2916) and Sharp's Bottom (SK3420) in the south.

Ornithopus perpusillus L.
Bird's-foot

COUNTY STATUS:	Native
CONSERVATION STATUS:	DRDB (Cat5b), A, B
FIRST YEAR: 1789 LATEST YEAR: 2013 NO OF RECORDS: 50	
RECENT SQUARES: monads 7; tetrads 7; hectads 6	
ALL SQUARES: monads 16; tetrads 15; hectads 15	

Bird's-foot is a native winter annual of disturbed ground and field borders.

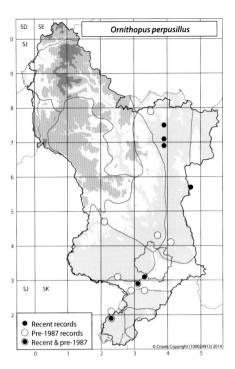

It favours gritty open soils and avoids calcareous ones. It is a lowland species occurring very rarely in the southern and eastern parts of the county (Drakelow Power Station SK2219, Stenson Bubble SK3230 & South Normanton SK4657). It formerly occurred over a slightly wider area, including Edlaston Coppy (SK14) and Longstone Edge (SK27).

Hippocrepis comosa L.
Horseshoe Vetch

Horseshoe Vetch is a very rare, native perennial of grasslands and rock outcrops on warm dry limestone slopes. All past and present records come from the White Peak

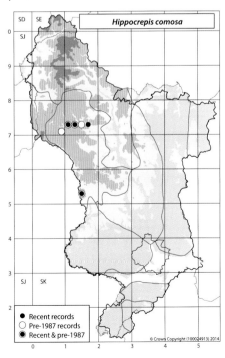

COUNTY STATUS:	Native
CONSERVATION STATUS:	DRDB (Cat5a), A, B
FIRST YEAR: 1835 LATEST YEAR: 2013 NO OF RECORDS: 58	
RECENT SQUARES:	monads 6; tetrads 4; hectads 2
ALL SQUARES:	monads 9; tetrads 6; hectads 3

(Chee Dale SK1273, SK1172, Deep Dale/ Topley Pike SK1072 & Dove Dale SK1452, SK1453). It has not been recorded for the Magnesian Limestone.

Securigera varia (L.) Lassen
Crown Vetch
Crown Vetch is an established perennial of waysides and waste ground. There are recent records from three tetrads between 1991 and 2011: Donkey Race Course (SK3672), Butterley (SK3951) and Pye Bridge (SK4353). There are previous records from Hathersage (SK2281) in 1969 and then Derby (SK3950) in 1978. A native of central and southern Europe, it probably arrived as a seed contaminant or garden escape.

Scorpiurus muricatus L.
Caterpillar-plant
Caterpillar-plant is a casual annual of disturbed ground. There are two records: imported soil at Heeley (SK3484) in 2003 and from near a bird table in Derby (SK3035) in 1976. It is indigenous to southern Europe.

Vicia cracca L.
Tufted Vetch

COUNTY STATUS:	Native
CONSERVATION STATUS:	None
FIRST YEAR: 1789 LATEST YEAR: 2013 NO OF RECORDS: 2,538	
RECENT SQUARES:	monads 1,112; tetrads 570; hectads 41
ALL SQUARES:	monads 1,197; tetrads 581; hectads 41

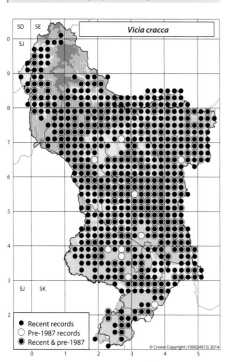

Recent records
Pre-1987 records
Recent & pre-1987
© Crown Copyright (100024913) 2014

Tufted Vetch (*Vicia cracca*), Belper Coppice (SK3547), July 2011 (Kieron Huston)

Tufted Vetch is a scrambling or climbing native perennial of meadows, marshes, waysides and wood-borders. It is common across Derbyshire, except for the northern moors and some intensively farmed areas in the south.

Vicia tenuifolia Roth
Fine-leaved Vetch
Fine-leaved Vetch is an established scrambling perennial, known only from Breadsall Cutting (SK3839). It was first discovered in 1979 and was still present in 1997, but disappeared some time after. It was introduced to England from central and southern Europe as a grain contaminant.

Vicia sylvatica L.
Wood Vetch
Wood Vetch is a very rare, native climber of woods and scrub, often on stony

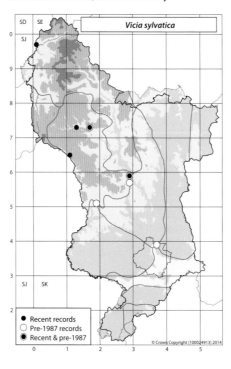

Recent records
Pre-1987 records
Recent & pre-1987
© Crown Copyright (100024913) 2014

ground. Most modern records are in the White Peak (Heights of Abraham SK2858, Cressbrook Dale SK1773 & Miller's Dale station SK1373). Other recent records are known for Unstone (SK3777) and Swallows Wood Nature Reserve (SK0097 v.c.58). It was previously recorded from these and other parts of southern Derbyshire (Coldwell Bridge SK14, Repton Shrubs SK32 & Breadsall SK3739). It has shown a similar decline nationally, possibly due to a decrease in coppicing causing plants to be shaded out (Preston *et al.* 2002).

COUNTY STATUS:	Native
CONSERVATION STATUS:	DRDB (Cat5a), A, B
FIRST YEAR: 1793 LATEST YEAR: 2011 NO OF RECORDS: 31	
RECENT SQUARES:	monads 6; tetrads 5; hectads 4
ALL SQUARES:	monads 9; tetrads 8; hectads 12

Vicia villosa Roth
Fodder Vetch
Fodder Vetch is a casual annual, introduced to England from central and southern Europe as a shoddy or grain contaminant. There are just two records: a hedge at Marple Bridge (SJ9688), found by A. Franks and J. Lowell in 1993, and a demolition site at Chesterfield (SK3870) in 2010.

Vicia hirsuta (L.) Gray
Hairy Tare

COUNTY STATUS:	Native
CONSERVATION STATUS:	None
FIRST YEAR: 1789 LATEST YEAR: 2013 NO OF RECORDS: 724	
RECENT SQUARES:	monads 393; tetrads 275; hectads 39
ALL SQUARES:	monads 434; tetrads 299; hectads 40

Hairy Tare is a scrambling native annual of wasteland, waysides and the margins of arable fields. It is frequent in southern and eastern areas (Drakelow Power Station SK2219, Kirk Hallam SK4440 & Eckington SK4279). It also occurs rarely in the White and Dark Peak Areas (Swallowhouse Mill

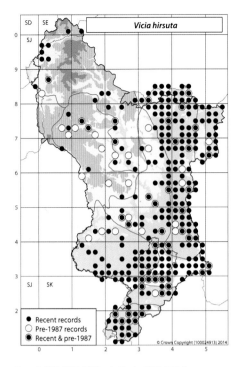

Pond SK0387, Miller's Dale SK1473 & near Dore SK2881).

Vicia tetrasperma (L.) Schreb.
Smooth Tare

COUNTY STATUS: Native
CONSERVATION STATUS: B
FIRST YEAR: 1829 LATEST YEAR: 2013 NO OF RECORDS: 159
RECENT SQUARES: monads 99; tetrads 85; hectads 28
ALL SQUARES: monads 107; tetrads 93; hectads 31

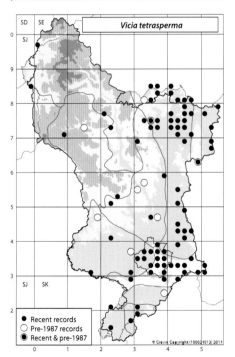

Smooth Tare is a scrambling native annual of rough ground, waysides and arable field margins, often growing alongside Hairy Tare. This beautiful but inconspicuous plant is occasional throughout the county,

though more frequent in southern and eastern parts (Mousley Bottom SJ9985, Drakelow Power Station SK2220, Barlow SK3575 & Pleasley SK4963). Derbyshire is near the northern edge of its mainly southern British distribution.

Vicia sepium L.
Bush Vetch

COUNTY STATUS: Native
CONSERVATION STATUS: None
FIRST YEAR: 1789 LATEST YEAR: 2013 NO OF RECORDS: 4,164
RECENT SQUARES: monads 1,658; tetrads 655; hectads 42
ALL SQUARES: monads 1,706; tetrads 659; hectads 42

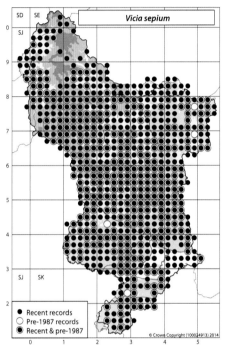

Bush Vetch is a sprawling native perennial of grasslands, waysides, hedges and wood-margins. It is common throughout the county except for the high moors and some of the more intensively farmed lowland areas.

Vicia sativa L.
Common Vetch

COUNTY STATUS: Established (Archaeophyte)
CONSERVATION STATUS: None
FIRST YEAR: 1789 LATEST YEAR: 2013 NO OF RECORDS: 1,150
RECENT SQUARES: monads 599; tetrads 388; hectads 39
ALL SQUARES: monads 651; tetrads 415; hectads 39

Three subspecies of Common Vetch occur here. **Ssp. nigra** (L.) Ehrh. is a rare casual annual of grassy habitats, and is native to coastal areas of Britain. Recent records are mainly from central parts (Gratton Grange SK2061, Hulland Ward SK2745 & Clay Cross SK36W). It was formerly known in southern Derbyshire, too. **Ssp. segetalis** (Thuill.) Gaudin is a long-established annual of rough grassy

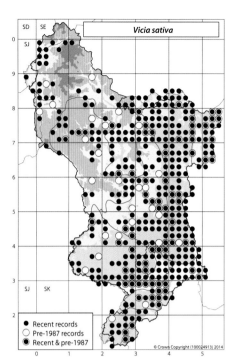

places and field borders. It is occasionally recorded in Derbyshire, but is rare in the Dark Peak. A native of continental Europe, it has sometimes been grown for fodder. **Ssp. sativa** is a rare casual annual of waysides, field borders and waste places. It occurs from Linnet Clough (SJ9788) and Standhills (SK2982) in the north to Rosliston (SK2417) and Ticknall Quarries (SK3623) in the south. It was formerly cultivated for fodder and is probably a plant of cultivated origin.

Vicia lutea L.
Yellow-vetch

Yellow-vetch is a very rare, casual annual of waste ground, first recorded by M. Smith at Fall Quarry Ashover (SK3562) in 2004, with two later records in the same area in 2005 and 2007. It is native to the coasts of southern Britain, but casual inland.

Vicia faba L.
Broad Bean

COUNTY STATUS: Casual
CONSERVATION STATUS: None
FIRST YEAR: 1992 LATEST YEAR: 2003 NO OF RECORDS: 14
RECENT SQUARES: monads 12; tetrads 12; hectads 11
ALL SQUARES: monads 12; tetrads 12; hectads 11

Broad Bean is a very rare, casual annual of waste ground, waysides and arable field margins. It is widely grown in gardens and as a fodder crop in fields, from where it spreads. It is probably of cultivated origin. In 1999 a single plant was found by N. Moyes in a flowerbed just outside Full Street Police Station in Derby (SK3536).

Lens culinaris Medik.
Lentil

Lentil is a casual climbing annual, and a native of south-western Asia. Our only record came in 2002 from the garden of G. Hirons, a lentil-eating botanist in Long Eaton (SK4734)!

Lathyrus linifolius (Reichard) Baessler
Bitter-vetch

COUNTY STATUS: Native	
CONSERVATION STATUS: ERL	
FIRST YEAR: 1811 LATEST YEAR: 2013 NO OF RECORDS: 773	
RECENT SQUARES: monads 304; tetrads 220; hectads 32	
ALL SQUARES: monads 346; tetrads 246; hectads 36	

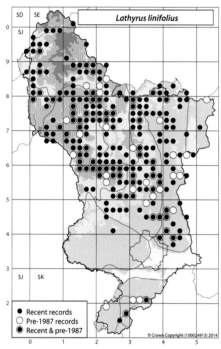

Bitter-vetch is a native perennial of unimproved grasslands, heathy grasslands and woodland margins on neutral to acid soils. It is occasional throughout the White, Dark and South West Peak Character Areas (Hayfield SK0386, Priestcliffe Lees SK1473, Gratton Dale SK2059 & Abney Clough SK2079). It is also occasional through the Peak Fringe and Coal Measures (Swainspark SK2916 & Heath Farm SK3521). It is virtually absent from the Magnesian Limestone, Claylands, Trent Valley and Mease Lowlands, probably due to the intensive agriculture in these parts.

Lathyrus pratensis L.
Meadow Vetchling

COUNTY STATUS: Native	
CONSERVATION STATUS: None	
FIRST YEAR: 1789 LATEST YEAR: 2013 NO OF RECORDS: 4,088	
RECENT SQUARES: monads 1,522; tetrads 652; hectads 42	
ALL SQUARES: monads 1,607; tetrads 661; hectads 42	

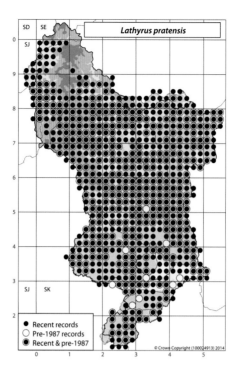

Meadow Vetchling is a very common, native climbing perennial of grasslands, waysides and waste ground. It grows throughout the county except for the high moors and some of the intensively farmed areas of southern Derbyshire.

Lathyrus tuberosus L.
Tuberous Pea

Tuberous Pea is an established climbing perennial of waste places, cultivated ground and waysides. The five recent records are from northern Derbyshire between 1998 and 2011: Dove Holes (SK0877), Brockwell Lane (SK3672), Williamthorpe Ponds (SK4366), Netherthorpe (SK4474) and Shirebrook (SK5366). Previous records have also come from the south, as at Etwall (SK2632) and Egginton (SK2631), both in the 1960s. The earliest record is from Catton (SK2013) in 1944. Indigenous to central and eastern Europe, it is grown in gardens for ornament and can be a contaminant of imported grain such as pheasant food.

Lathyrus grandiflorus Sm.
Two-flowered Everlasting-pea

COUNTY STATUS: Established (Neophyte)	
CONSERVATION STATUS: None	
FIRST YEAR: 1977 LATEST YEAR: 2012 NO OF RECORDS: 11	
RECENT SQUARES: monads 6; tetrads 6; hectads 5	
ALL SQUARES: monads 7; tetrads 7; hectads 6	

Two-flowered Everlasting-pea is an established climbing perennial of waysides, hedges and waste ground. All recent records are scattered across central Derbyshire: Rowsley Sidings

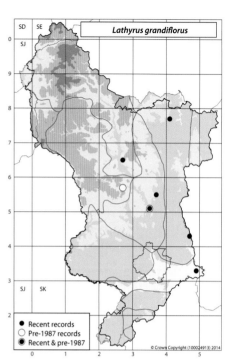

(SK2664), Malthouse Lane (SK3550), Wingfield Manor (SK3754) and Nether Handley (SK4076). It is grown in gardens for its flowers from where it can escape as a throwout, or sometimes by seed. It grows naturally in the central Mediterranean area.

Lathyrus sylvestris L.
Narrow-leaved Everlasting-pea

COUNTY STATUS: Native	
CONSERVATION STATUS: DRDB (Cat5a), B	
FIRST YEAR: 1829 LATEST YEAR: 2012 NO OF RECORDS: 18	
RECENT SQUARES: monads 4; tetrads 4; hectads 4	
ALL SQUARES: monads 9; tetrads 9; hectads 8	

Narrow-leaved Everlasting-pea is a very rare, native climbing perennial of waysides, waste ground, woods and hedges. It is also grown in gardens, so some records may refer to escapees. There are four recent sightings: Bank House Farm (SK1658) in 2000, Sawley Road (SK4632) in 2001, Highshaw (SK2187) in 2011 and Huthwaite (SK4657) in 2012. Six older sites are known. Clapham (1969) gives Weston-on-Trent (SK3927 & 4128), while Linton (1903) adds Chellaston (SK32) and the first record as Glover (1829).

Lathyrus latifolius L.
Broad-leaved Everlasting-pea

COUNTY STATUS: Established (Neophyte)	
CONSERVATION STATUS: None	
FIRST YEAR: 1970 LATEST YEAR: 2012 NO OF RECORDS: 61	
RECENT SQUARES: monads 33; tetrads 35; hectads 20	
ALL SQUARES: monads 38; tetrads 40; hectads 20	

Broad-leaved Everlasting-pea is an established scrambling perennial of waysides, waste ground and hedges. A

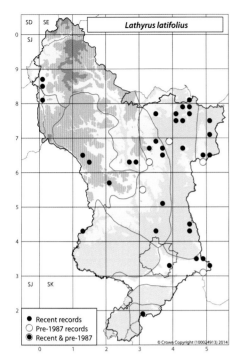

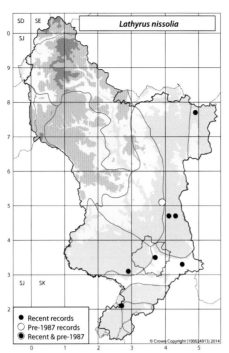

native of continental Europe, it is grown in gardens for its attractive flowers. It is rare and scattered from Watford Bridge (SK0086) and Nether Handley Tip (SK4076) in the north, through Sparklow (SK1365) to Swadlincote (SK3019) and Raynesway (SK3833) in the south. At 340m Sparklow holds the altitude record for the plant in Britain (Preston *et al.* 2002).

Lathyrus annuus L.
Fodder Pea
Locally extinct, Fodder Pea was a casual climbing annual of waysides and waste ground. It is known from just two records in Clapham's 1969 Flora: Stores Road, Derby (SK3537) and south of Little Eaton (SK3640). It is a contaminant of grain and other seed imported from the Mediterranean.

Lathyrus hirsutus L.
Hairy Vetchling
Locally extinct, Hairy Vetchling was a scrambling casual annual of waste ground and fields. It is known from just three records: Darley (SK3638) in 1969, Burton (SK22) in 1903 and South Normanton (SK45) in 1789. A native of southern Europe, it is sometimes grown in gardens and can be imported in seed.

Lathyrus nissolia L.
Grass Vetchling

COUNTY STATUS: Native	
CONSERVATION STATUS: DRDB (Cat4), A	
FIRST YEAR: 1789 **LATEST YEAR:** 2013 **NO OF RECORDS:** 22	
RECENT SQUARES: monads 7; tetrads 7; hectads 6	
ALL SQUARES: monads 7; tetrads 7; hectads 8	

Grass Vetchling is a very rare, native annual of disturbed ground and field borders. It has been recorded from seven sites recently. These include: Pride Park (SK3735) in 2012, Heanor (SK4347) in 2000 and Wilne Cross (SK4532) between 2006 and 2008, where it was found in considerable quantity. All previous records go back to the start of the 20th century and are from the same general area. Linton (1903) includes Alfreton (SK45), Darley Abbey (SK33) and gives Pilkington (1789) as the first record. Derbyshire is on the northern limit of the species as a native in England (Stace 1997).

Lathyrus aphaca L.
Yellow Vetchling
Locally extinct, Yellow Vetchling was a scrambling casual annual of cultivated and waste ground. The most recent record is from Clifton (SK1545) in 1941. Other records are from Buxton (SK0572) in 1935, Burton (SK22) in 1903 and Pinxton (SK45) in 1789. Indigenous to continental Europe, it is a contaminant of bird feed and other seeds.

Pisum sativum L.
Garden Pea

COUNTY STATUS: Casual	
CONSERVATION STATUS: None	
FIRST YEAR: 1989 **LATEST YEAR:** 2011 **NO OF RECORDS:** 7	
RECENT SQUARES: monads 6; tetrads 6; hectads 6	
ALL SQUARES: monads 6; tetrads 6; hectads 6	

Garden Pea is a casual climbing annual of field margins and waste places. Records suggest it is very rare but widely scattered across Derbyshire: Hadfield Tip (SK0296),

Fairfield (SK0674), Creswell (SK5273) and Sudbury Coppice (SK1535). However, it is probably under-recorded as few botanists deign to note this common field crop. The cultivated **Field Pea** (**var.** *arvense*) has also been found once near Fairfield (SK0674). The species is a native of southern Europe.

Ononis spinosa L.
Spiny Restharrow

COUNTY STATUS: Native	
CONSERVATION STATUS: DRDB (Cat5b), B	
FIRST YEAR: 1789 **LATEST YEAR:** 2011 **NO OF RECORDS:** 88	
RECENT SQUARES: monads 13; tetrads 11; hectads 8	
ALL SQUARES: monads 25; tetrads 22; hectads 14	

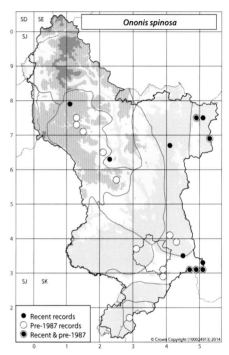

Spiny Restharrow is a very rare, native undershrub of unimproved grasslands and rough ground, particularly on heavy soils. Reports are scattered throughout Derbyshire, from Dam Dale (SK1178) and Clowne (SK4875) in the north, through Ivy Bar Brook (SK2263) and Langwith Junction (SK5268), to the flood bank of the Trent at Cranfleet Farm (SK4931) in the south. Formerly more common, and often as a disagreeable weed of pastures, it gained the local names of Hen-gorse and Fiend (Farey 1815).

Ononis × pseudohircina Schur
Hybrid Restharrow

COUNTY STATUS: Native	
CONSERVATION STATUS: None	
FIRST YEAR: 1977 **LATEST YEAR:** 2010 **NO OF RECORDS:** 6	
RECENT SQUARES: monads 4; tetrads 4; hectads 3	
ALL SQUARES: monads 4; tetrads 4; hectads 3	

Hybrid Restharrow is a very rare, native perennial. It was first discovered on the Taddington By-pass (SK1571) by J. Hodgson in 1977 (voucher in Derby Museum) and was last reported there in 1990. There have since been three more records: Wolfie Pond (SK4166), Long Eaton (SK5131) and Erewash (SK5033). Painter's 1889 Flora hints at a much earlier possible record from Baslow. The plant is the spontaneous hybrid of Common Restharrow (*O. repens*) and Spiny Restharrow (*O. spinosa*).

Ononis repens L.
Common Restharrow

COUNTY STATUS: Native	
CONSERVATION STATUS: None	
FIRST YEAR: 1650 LATEST YEAR: 2012 NO OF RECORDS: 305	
RECENT SQUARES: monads 89; tetrads 72; hectads 21	
ALL SQUARES: monads 123; tetrads 95; hectads 27	

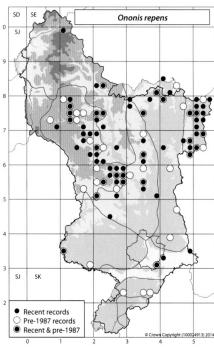

Common Restharrow is a low-growing native perennial of well-drained and unimproved grasslands. It occurs occasionally in the White Peak and Magnesian Limestone Areas, as at Dale Head (SK1276), Youlgrave (SK2164), Bonsall Leys (SK2657), Markland Grips (SK5074) and Langwith Junction (SK5268). It is rare elsewhere, but with sites ranging between Dove Bank (SK1034), Chellaston East (SK3830) and Longdendale (SK1099). Our plants are probably all ssp. *repens*.

Ononis alopecuroides L.
Salzmann's Restharrow

Locally extinct, Salzmann's Restharrow was a very rare, casual annual. The only record was made in 1968 by M. Hewitt at a roadside tip at Cross Hills, near Bolsover (SK5169), where it was probably introduced

in bird-seed (Clapham 1969). It grows naturally in the western Mediterranean.

Melilotus altissimus Thuill.
Tall Melilot

COUNTY STATUS: Established (Archaeophyte)	
CONSERVATION STATUS: None	
FIRST YEAR: 1903 LATEST YEAR: 2013 NO OF RECORDS: 229	
RECENT SQUARES: monads 111; tetrads 101; hectads 23	
ALL SQUARES: monads 146; tetrads 126; hectads 28	

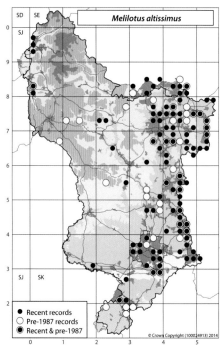

Tall Melilot is a long-established perennial of rough grassland, waysides and disturbed ground. It is occasional throughout the lowland north-western and particularly the eastern parts of Derbyshire. It ranges from Furness Vale (SK0183) and Newhall (SK2721), to Pinxton Wharf (SK4554) and Williamthorpe (SK4266). It is native to continental Europe.

Melilotus albus Medik.
White Melilot

COUNTY STATUS: Established (Neophyte)	
CONSERVATION STATUS: None	
FIRST YEAR: 1897 LATEST YEAR: 2012 NO OF RECORDS: 167	
RECENT SQUARES: monads 86; tetrads 72; hectads 22	
ALL SQUARES: monads 115; tetrads 100; hectads 25	

White Melilot is an established annual or biennial of rough ground and waste places. Recent records are occasional throughout the lowland parts of eastern Derbyshire (Long Eaton SK4933 & Steetley Quarry SK5478) with a few rare occurrences elsewhere (Manor Park SK0394 & Drakelow Power Station SK2220). Previously records were more frequent from central areas for instance Hopton Top near Brassington (SK2554). At 335m this site holds the British

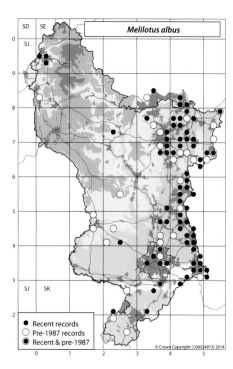

altitude record for the species (Preston *et al.* 2002). This native of southern Europe generally reaches Britain as a contaminant of wool or seed.

Melilotus officinalis (L.) Pall.
Ribbed Melilot

COUNTY STATUS: Established (Neophyte)	
CONSERVATION STATUS: None	
FIRST YEAR: 1829 LATEST YEAR: 2012 NO OF RECORDS: 279	
RECENT SQUARES: monads 138; tetrads 128; hectads 30	
ALL SQUARES: monads 162; tetrads 143; hectads 32	

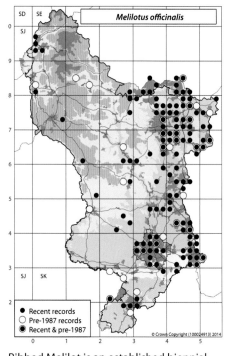

Ribbed Melilot is an established biennial of waste and rough ground. It is occasional through lowland urban areas of eastern Derbyshire (Lock Lane Ash Tip SK4831, Wyvern Centre Derby SK3735 & Williamthorpe SK4266). Elsewhere in more western and rural parts it is rare and infrequent (Simmondley SK0293 & Drakelow Power Station SK2220). It is indigenous to central and southern Europe.

Melilotus indicus (L.) All.
Small Melilot

COUNTY STATUS:	Casual
CONSERVATION STATUS:	None
FIRST YEAR: 1899	LATEST YEAR: 2009 NO OF RECORDS: 17
RECENT SQUARES:	monads 5; tetrads 5; hectads 5
ALL SQUARES:	monads 13; tetrads 13; hectads 11

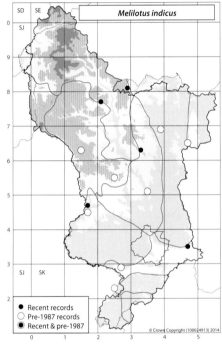

Small Melilot is a casual annual of disturbed ground. There are only five recent records from sites scattered over central Derbyshire (Kelstedge SK3262, M1 Junction 25 SK4735, Ashbourne SK1746, Dore SK2881 & Eyam Edge SK2077). Earlier records include Hopton Top (SK2554) in 1973 and Burton (SK2523) in 1969. It is generally a bird-seed or wool alien, and is native to southern Europe.

Trigonella foenum-graecum L.
Fenugreek

Locally extinct, Fenugreek was a very rare, casual annual. Our only record is from waste ground between Derby and Little Eaton (SK3639) in 1939. It is a bird-seed or spice alien from the eastern Mediterranean.

Medicago lupulina L.
Black Medick

Black Medick is a low-growing native annual of grasslands, disturbed ground, walls and limestone outcrops. It is very

COUNTY STATUS:	Native
CONSERVATION STATUS:	None
FIRST YEAR: 1829	LATEST YEAR: 2013 NO OF RECORDS: 2,267
RECENT SQUARES:	monads 1,008; tetrads 550; hectads 40
ALL SQUARES:	monads 1,079; tetrads 565; hectads 40

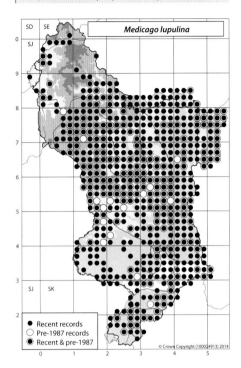

common throughout the county, except for some of the higher moors and parts of the Claylands.

Medicago sativa L.
A medick

COUNTY STATUS:	Established (Neophyte)
CONSERVATION STATUS:	None
FIRST YEAR: 1864	LATEST YEAR: 2013 NO OF RECORDS: 71
RECENT SQUARES:	monads 26; tetrads 28; hectads 10
ALL SQUARES:	monads 46; tetrads 47; hectads 20

Three subspecies have been recorded locally. **Sickle Medick** (**ssp. *falcata*** (L.) Arcang.) is a very rare, casual perennial of waste ground and tips. There are two recent records, an unlocalised one for Derby (SK33) and Hackenthorpe (SK4283). There are older records for Darley Abbey (SK3538) in 1969 and Stanton (SK4739) in 1954. The plant is indigenous to East Anglia. **Sand Lucerne** (**ssp. *varia*** (Martyn) Arcang.) is a very rare casual perennial. The only recent record is for imported soil at Middleton-by-Wirksworth (SK2755) and there is an older one for Derby (SK33) in 1950. It is sometimes grown as a fodder crop and is possibly a native in East Anglia. **Lucerne** (**ssp. *sativa***) is a rare, established perennial of field margins, waysides and waste ground. It occurs mainly in the eastern and southern lowland parts of the county as at Sawley (SK4631), Erewash Canal (SK4742), Pleasley (SK46W) and Poolsbrook (SK4473).

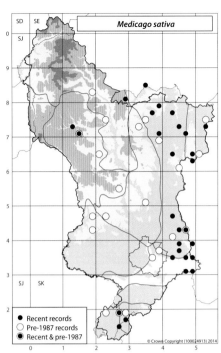

It also occurs rarely in the White Peak as at Taddington By-pass (SK1471). Older records come from the same region. It was formerly grown over a wide area as a fodder crop, so much so that its original native distribution is obscure. Map and statistics show Lucerne (ssp. *sativa*) only.

Medicago laciniata (L.) Mill.
Tattered Medick

Tattered Medick is a very rare, casual annual. The sole record was made near Dore (SK2881) in 2007 by K. Balkow. It is indigenous to North Africa.

Medicago minima (L.) Bartal.
Bur Medick

Bur Medick is a very rare, casual annual which is indigenous to eastern England. The solitary record was made near Dore (SK2881) in 2007 by K. Balkow.

Medicago polymorpha L.
Toothed Medick

Toothed Medick is a very rare, low-growing casual annual of cultivated and waste ground. There are two recent records, near Dore (SK2881) in 2007 and Britannia Mill (SK3436) in 2004. The eight older ones are all from the south. Clapham (1969) gives Snelston (SK1543), Derby Canal (SK3536) and Thrumpton (SK5131) whilst Painter (1899) gives the oldest for Mickleover (SK33). It grows naturally as a rare native on the coasts of southern England.

Medicago arabica (L.) Huds.
Spotted Medick

Spotted Medick is a very rare, casual annual of cultivated ground, waste land

COUNTY STATUS: Casual
CONSERVATION STATUS: None
FIRST YEAR: 1829 LATEST YEAR: 2010 NO OF RECORDS: 20
RECENT SQUARES: monads 8; tetrads 8; hectads 6
ALL SQUARES: monads 11; tetrads 11; hectads 11

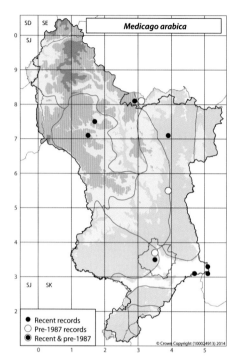

and grassy areas. It is known from several recent sites scattered throughout the county, avoiding only the extreme north and south. These include: Taddington Quarry (SK1470), Allotments in Derby (SK3434), River Trent bank (SK5031) and Old Sawley (SK4731). It is a plant of southern Britain, with Derbyshire just outside the limit of its natural range.

Trifolium ornithopodioides L.
Bird's-foot Clover
Locally extinct, Bird's-foot Clover was a low-growing casual annual. The sole county record comes from Breadsall (SK33) where it was found by H. Crewe and J. Whittaker in 1864. It is native to coastal areas in southern Britain.

Trifolium repens L.
White Clover

COUNTY STATUS: Native
CONSERVATION STATUS: None
FIRST YEAR: 1789 LATEST YEAR: 2013 NO OF RECORDS: 6,520
RECENT SQUARES: monads 2,190; tetrads 735; hectads 44
ALL SQUARES: monads 2,272; tetrads 739; hectads 44

White Clover is a creeping native perennial of grasslands and waste ground on all but the wettest and most acidic soils. It is often sown in agricultural and amenity grasslands for its ability to incorporate nitrogen into soils. It is very common throughout the county,

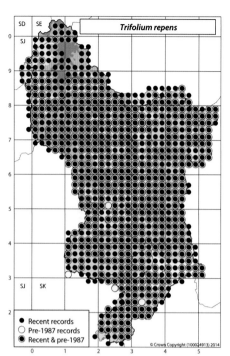

except for the high moors of the Dark Peak.

Trifolium hybridum L.
Alsike Clover

COUNTY STATUS: Established (Neophyte)
CONSERVATION STATUS: None
FIRST YEAR: 1864 LATEST YEAR: 2012 NO OF RECORDS: 368
RECENT SQUARES: monads 178; tetrads 166; hectads 35
ALL SQUARES: monads 236; tetrads 208; hectads 37

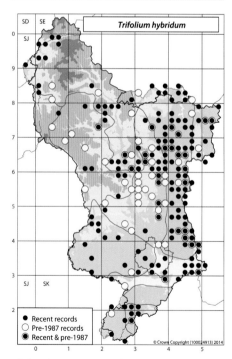

Alsike Clover is an established perennial of field borders, waysides and waste ground. It is occasional through the lowland eastern, southern and north-western parts of the county (Castle Gresley SK2817, Straw's Bridge

SK4541, Duckmanton Cutting SK4270 & Hadfield SK0296). It is rare in the upland White and Dark Peak (Friden SK1760). A native of continental Europe, it was probably introduced as a component of clover seed-mixes for forage crops or soil improvement. The local plant is ssp. *hybridum*.

Trifolium glomeratum L.
Clustered Clover
Clustered Clover is a casual annual. The sole record was made by K. Balkow near Dore (SK2881) in 2007. It is native to coasts in southern and eastern England.

Trifolium suffocatum L.
Suffocated Clover
Suffocated Clover is a casual annual. Our only record was made near Dore (SK2881) in 2007 by K. Balkow. It is native to coastal areas of southern and eastern England.

Trifolium fragiferum L.
Strawberry Clover

COUNTY STATUS: Native
CONSERVATION STATUS: DRDB (Cat4), B
FIRST YEAR: 1829 LATEST YEAR: 1979 NO OF RECORDS: 10
RECENT SQUARES: monads 0; tetrads 0; hectads 0
ALL SQUARES: monads 3; tetrads 3; hectads 6

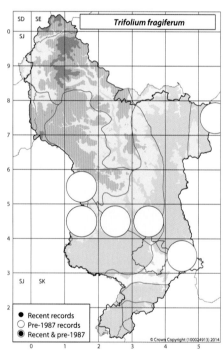

Strawberry Clover is a low-growing native perennial of damp grasslands and waysides with no modern records. The most recent are from Ashbourne Green (SK1847) in 1979 and Creswell Crags (SK5374) in 1955. It was from the former site that Keble Martin collected the specimen he drew for his 1965 "Concise British Flora in Colour" while working as curate at Ashbourne in the 1900s (Keble Martin 1968). Earlier records given in Linton's 1903 Flora are from between Fenny Bentley and Tissington (SK15); Shirley (SK24); Duffield (SK34) and Stanton-by-Dale (SK43).

Trifolium resupinatum L.
Reversed Clover
Reversed Clover is a casual annual of disturbed ground, first found by K. Balkow near Dore (SK2881) in 2007 and also at Chesterfield (SK3870) in 2009. It is indigenous to southern Europe.

Trifolium tomentosum L.
Woolly Clover
Woolly Clover is a casual annual, recorded near Dore (SK2881) in 2007 by K. Balkow. It is a native of the Mediterranean.

Trifolium aureum Pollich
Large Trefoil
Large Trefoil is a very rare, casual annual. Six out of the seven records are from waysides in the middle of last century between 1940 and 1979. Here it was probably introduced as a contaminant of seed-mixes. Examples are Spitalhill (SK1845) and Hopton Top (SK2554). At 320m the latter is the highest known British locality for this plant (Preston *et al.* 2002). There is also a Bradley Park Farm (SK24) record for 1789.

Trifolium campestre Schreb.
Hop Trefoil

COUNTY STATUS: Native
CONSERVATION STATUS: None
FIRST YEAR: 1789 LATEST YEAR: 2012 NO OF RECORDS: 459
RECENT SQUARES: monads 219; tetrads 176; hectads 32
ALL SQUARES: monads 259; tetrads 199; hectads 35

Hop Trefoil is a low-growing native annual of grass fields, arable land and waysides. Mostly found on dry soils, it is occasional

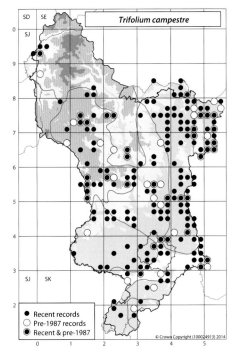

throughout Derbyshire, except for the Dark and South West Peak Areas where it is virtually absent (Gamesley SK0093, Minninglow SK2057, Willington Power Station SK3029, West Hallam SK4441 & Creswell SK5275). At 350m Minninglow is the plant's highest known site in Britain.

Trifolium dubium Sibth.
Lesser Trefoil

COUNTY STATUS: Native
CONSERVATION STATUS: None
FIRST YEAR: 1789 LATEST YEAR: 2013 NO OF RECORDS: 2,194
RECENT SQUARES: monads 1,072; tetrads 597; hectads 43
ALL SQUARES: monads 1,143; tetrads 612; hectads 43

Lesser Trefoil is a low-growing native annual of grass fields, lawns, waysides and rocky outcrops. It is common throughout

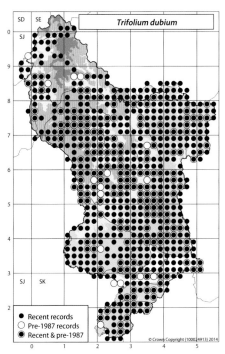

the county, except for some high moors in the Dark and South West Peak Areas.

Trifolium micranthum Viv.
Slender Trefoil

COUNTY STATUS: Native
CONSERVATION STATUS: A
FIRST YEAR: 1881 LATEST YEAR: 2012 NO OF RECORDS: 30
RECENT SQUARES: monads 8; tetrads 7; hectads 4
ALL SQUARES: monads 17; tetrads 16; hectads 14

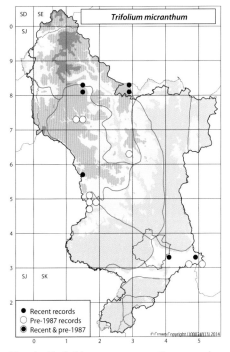

Slender Trefoil is a very rare, native annual of short open turf in pastures, lawns and waysides. It is currently thinly recorded throughout the county, from Bradwell Moor (SK1480) in the north through

Hop Trefoil (*Trifolium campestre*), Whitwell Wood (SK5277), June 2004 (Philip Precey)

Coldeaton Bridge (SK15N) to Elvaston Castle (SK4032) in the south. It previously grew over much the same area including Chee Tor (SK1273) and Hilton (SK23).

Trifolium pratense L.
Red Clover

COUNTY STATUS: Native	
CONSERVATION STATUS: None	
FIRST YEAR: 1789 **LATEST YEAR:** 2013 **NO OF RECORDS:** 5,311	
RECENT SQUARES: monads 1,911; tetrads 690; hectads 43	
ALL SQUARES: monads 1,975; tetrads 694; hectads 43	

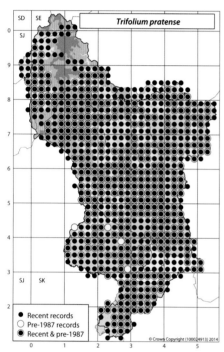

Red Clover is a very common, native perennial of grassy places, waysides and waste ground on all but the wettest and most acid soils. It is also extensively sown in agricultural and amenity grasslands, particularly to improve the nitrogen content of soils. Some botanists separate the wild type as variety *pratense* from the more robust cultivated type var. *sativum* Schreb., but none have done so in Derbyshire since Clapham's 1969 Flora.

Trifolium medium L.
Zigzag Clover

COUNTY STATUS: Native	
CONSERVATION STATUS: None	
FIRST YEAR: 1829 **LATEST YEAR:** 2013 **NO OF RECORDS:** 842	
RECENT SQUARES: monads 417; tetrads 321; hectads 38	
ALL SQUARES: monads 452; tetrads 341; hectads 38	

Zigzag Clover is a native perennial of grasslands, waysides, scrub and disturbed ground, generally on heavy soils, and is also often introduced in land reclamation schemes. It is frequent to occasional in the White Peak, Peak Fringe, Coal Measures and Magnesian Limestone Areas (Dowey

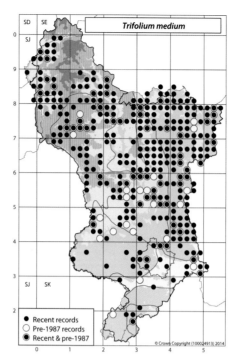

Lumb SK3780, Westhouses SK4258 & High Peak Trail SK1958). It is rare and scattered elsewhere, with examples at Melandra Castle (SK0195), Swainspark (SK2916) and Ingleby (SK3527).

Trifolium incarnatum L.
Crimson Clover

COUNTY STATUS: Casual	
CONSERVATION STATUS: None	
FIRST YEAR: 1884 **LATEST YEAR:** 2002 **NO OF RECORDS:** 13	
RECENT SQUARES: monads 3; tetrads 3; hectads 3	
ALL SQUARES: monads 7; tetrads 7; hectads 6	

Crimson Clover (ssp. *incarnatum*) is a very rare, casual annual of cultivated ground and waste places. It was once frequently planted for fodder, but is rarely grown nowadays. The only recent records are for Sheldon (SK1769), Swanwick (SK4053) and near Risley (SK4535). All others are derived from Clapham's 1969 Flora: Calver Sough (SK2374), Derby (SK33), Mackworth (SK3137), Renishaw (SK4478) and Clowne (SK4975).

Trifolium striatum L.
Knotted Clover

COUNTY STATUS: Native	
CONSERVATION STATUS: B	
FIRST YEAR: 1829 **LATEST YEAR:** 2012 **NO OF RECORDS:** 98	
RECENT SQUARES: monads 22; tetrads 18; hectads 11	
ALL SQUARES: monads 35; tetrads 28; hectads 17	

Knotted Clover is a rare native winter annual of open grassy areas on well-drained soils and rock outcrops in the White Peak (Monk's Dale SK1373, Over Haddon SK2066 & Brassington SK2354). It occurs very rarely in similar habitats elsewhere

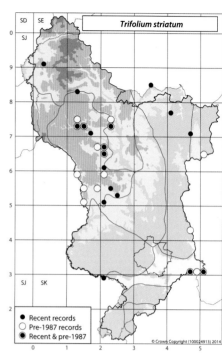

in the county (Chunal SK0390, Carr Vale SK4670 & Sawley SK4731). Derbyshire holds the altitude record for the species at 320m (Preston *et al.* 2002).

Trifolium scabrum L.
Rough Clover

Rough Clover is a casual winter annual of open grassy areas, native to coastal regions of Britain. Our only recent record is from Long Dale (SK1361), found by D. Scott in 1998. There are two earlier ones: Burton (SK22) in 1903 and Bakewell (SK26) in 1801.

Trifolium arvense L.
Hare's-foot Clover

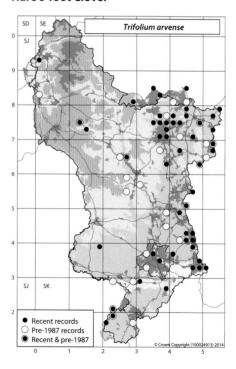

COUNTY STATUS: Native
CONSERVATION STATUS: B
FIRST YEAR: 1789 LATEST YEAR: 2012 NO OF RECORDS: 181
RECENT SQUARES: monads 62; tetrads 51; hectads 21
ALL SQUARES: monads 85; tetrads 71; hectads 26

Hare's-foot Clover is a rare native annual of open grassy areas on light sandy soils, and of well-drained disturbed ground. This neat attractive plant occurs throughout Derbyshire, from Gamesley Sidings (SK0093) and Beighton (SK4484) in the north, to Attenborough Gravel Pits (SK5133) and Drakelow (SK21J) in the south. It can be locally abundant at a site one year, then rarely seen again, as at Brook Medical Centre, Derby (SK3437) in 1996.

Trifolium subterraneum L.
Subterranean Clover

COUNTY STATUS: Native
CONSERVATION STATUS: DRDB (Cat5a), A, B
FIRST YEAR: 1866 LATEST YEAR: 2007 NO OF RECORDS: 10
RECENT SQUARES: monads 3; tetrads 3; hectads 3
ALL SQUARES: monads 4; tetrads 3; hectads 4

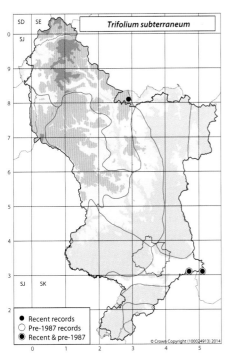

Subterranean Clover is a very rare, native annual of dry grasslands on sandy soils in the Trent Valley. The first county record came from Repton (SK32) in 1866. It has been recorded in both past and recent times as a native at just two other sites: Sawley (200 plants at SK4731 in 1990) and by the River Trent at SK5131. Recently it has been recorded as a casual near Dore (SK2881) on disturbed soil. It is a southern species, with Derbyshire localities being on the northern edge of its range (Stace, 1997).

Trifolium monanthum A.Gray
Carpet Clover
Locally extinct, Carpet Clover was a casual perennial of waste ground and is a native of western North America. The only record was made between Derby and Little Eaton (SK3639/3640) by A. Proctor in 1939, and determined by the Royal Botanic Gardens, Kew.

Trifolium nigrescens Viv.
Small White Clover
Small White Clover is a casual annual. It was discovered in 2007 at its only Derbyshire site near Dore (SK2881) by K. Balkow. It is a Mediterranean species.

Trifolium uniflorum L.
One-flowered Clover
Locally extinct, One-flowered Clover was a casual perennial of waste ground. As with *Trifolium monanthum*, the only record was made by A. Proctor in 1939, just half a mile south of Little Eaton (SK3640). It is indigenous to the eastern Mediterranean.

Lupinus arboreus Sims
Tree Lupin
Tree Lupin is a semi-evergreen casual shrub of disturbed ground. The one recent record is from Grin Low (SK0472) in 2004. There are two previous ones: Steetley Quarry (SK5478) in 1973 and Heath (SK4367) in the 1970s. This native of California is probably a garden escape here.

Lupinus × regalis Bergmans
Russell Lupin
Russell Lupin is a rare casual perennial of waste ground and waysides, such as old

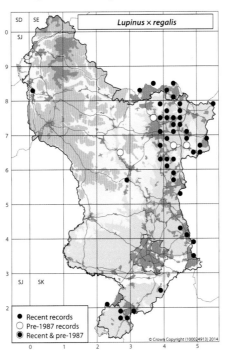

railway lines and coal tips. Records are mainly from the more urbanised southern and eastern parts (Castle Gresley SK2718, Melbourne SK3925, Shipley SK4443 & Apperknowle SK3978). This garden plant was produced by the artificial hybridisation of Tree Lupin (*L. arboreus*) with Garden Lupin (*L. polyphyllus*).

Lupinus polyphyllus Lindl.
Garden Lupin

COUNTY STATUS: Established (Neophyte)
CONSERVATION STATUS: None
FIRST YEAR: 1972 LATEST YEAR: 2010 NO OF RECORDS: 20
RECENT SQUARES: monads 12; tetrads 11; hectads 8
ALL SQUARES: monads 16; tetrads 14; hectads 10

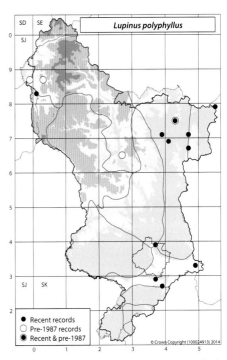

Garden Lupin is an established perennial of waste ground and waysides. It is very rare with records scattered across the county from New Mills (SK0183) and Steetley Quarry (SK5478) in the north, to King's Newton (SK3926) and Forbes Hole (SK4932) in the south. Indigenous to western North America, it was formerly grown in gardens and is probably over-recorded now for Russell Lupin (*L. × regalis*).

Lupinus nootkatensis Donn ex Sims
Nootka Lupin
Nootka Lupin is a casual perennial of disturbed ground that grows naturally in north-western North America and north-eastern Asia. It is occasionally grown

in gardens and was first recorded at Mansfield Road, Breadsall (SK3739) in 1969, and then at Carr Vale (SK4570) in 1994.

Laburnum anagyroides Medik.
Laburnum

COUNTY STATUS:	Casual
CONSERVATION STATUS:	None
FIRST YEAR: 1950 LATEST YEAR: 2013 NO OF RECORDS: 121	
RECENT SQUARES: monads 68; tetrads 81; hectads 29	
ALL SQUARES: monads 74; tetrads 87; hectads 30	

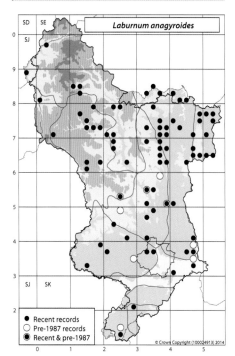

Laburnum is a small casual tree of rough ground, waysides, hedges and woodlands. It is much planted in parks and gardens, despite its poisonous seeds, which nearly killed one of the authors when he was three years old! It is found occasionally throughout Derbyshire from Hadfield (SK0296) and Bottom's Bridge (SJ9688) in the north-west, to Thulston (SK4131) and Gallows Inn (SK44Q) in the south-east. Some records may be for the similar Hybrid Laburnum (*L.* × *watereri*). Previously it was recorded only in southern Derbyshire. This distribution change may be due to more widespread planting in recent years. A specimen with a girth of 2.52m is known from a garden at Duffield Road, Derby (SK3437). It is indigenous to the mountains of central Europe.

Cytisus striatus (Hill) Rothm.
Hairy-fruited Broom

COUNTY STATUS:	Casual
CONSERVATION STATUS:	None
FIRST YEAR: 2001 LATEST YEAR: 2011 NO OF RECORDS: 8	
RECENT SQUARES: monads 7; tetrads 6; hectads 5	
ALL SQUARES: monads 7; tetrads 6; hectads 5	

Hairy-fruited Broom is a very rare, casual

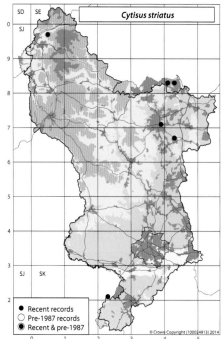

shrub of amenity plantings where it is either planted deliberately or mistakenly for Broom (*C. scoparius*). All records are recent and mostly from the northern half of the county, as on the Longdendale Trail (SK0497) and at Williamthorpe Ponds (SK4266). It shows no sign yet of spreading by seed, but this should be expected as it freely reproduces elsewhere. It is a native of the Iberian Peninsula.

Cytisus scoparius (L.) Link
Broom

COUNTY STATUS:	Native
CONSERVATION STATUS:	None
FIRST YEAR: 1789 LATEST YEAR: 2013 NO OF RECORDS: 928	
RECENT SQUARES: monads 427; tetrads 330; hectads 37	
ALL SQUARES: monads 487; tetrads 365; hectads 37	

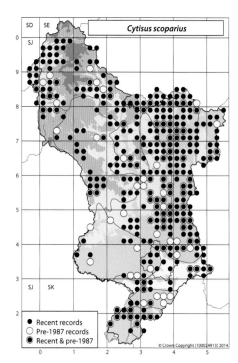

Broom is an occasional native shrub of waste ground, waysides and scrub on light non-calcareous soils. It is increasingly planted in amenity and restoration schemes for its ability to grow on and improve poor soils. It is found throughout the county, though is less frequent in the Claylands and White Peak. Our plant is ssp. *scoparius*.

Genista tinctoria L.
Dyer's Greenweed

COUNTY STATUS:	Native
CONSERVATION STATUS:	DRDB (Cat5b)
FIRST YEAR: 1789 LATEST YEAR: 2013 NO OF RECORDS: 293	
RECENT SQUARES: monads 51; tetrads 44; hectads 22	
ALL SQUARES: monads 99; tetrads 77; hectads 29	

Dyer's Greenweed is a rare native undershrub of unimproved grasslands

Dyer's Greenweed (*Genista tinctoria*), Dark Lane Rec (SK4165), June 2011 (Kieron Huston)

Gorse (*Ulex europaeus*), Rod Moor west of Dronfield Woodhouse (SK3278), April 2013 (Ken Balkow)

it is locally abundant. It was previously recorded throughout the county, except for the White Peak, as far east as Pinxton (SK45) and as far south as Willington (SK32). This marked contraction in distribution is probably due to agricultural improvement of marginal land in the lowlands.

Ulex europaeus L.
Gorse

COUNTY STATUS: Native	
CONSERVATION STATUS: None	
FIRST YEAR: 1789 LATEST YEAR: 2013 NO OF RECORDS: 2,219	
RECENT SQUARES: monads 912; tetrads 501; hectads 40	
ALL SQUARES: monads 994; tetrads 526; hectads 40	

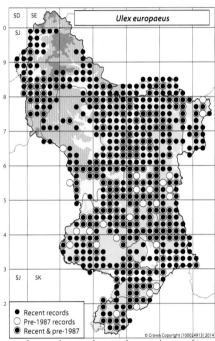

Gorse is a spiny native shrub of rough grasslands, heaths, waste ground and waysides. It is common throughout the county except for the White and Dark Peak. In the former it only grows on the deeper non-calcareous soils of the limestone plateau. In the Dark Peak it grows on the lower western and eastern moors, but avoids the higher northern moors. It frequently appears in local place names such as Gorse Covert or Gorsey Leys, and has the local name of Ling (Grigson 1975).

Ulex gallii Planch.
Western Gorse

COUNTY STATUS: Native	
CONSERVATION STATUS: C	
FIRST YEAR: 1829 LATEST YEAR: 2013 NO OF RECORDS: 509	
RECENT SQUARES: monads 231; tetrads 157; hectads 21	
ALL SQUARES: monads 280; tetrads 183; hectads 31	

Western Gorse is a spiny native shrub of moors, heaths and waysides. It is frequent throughout the South West Peak (Burbage

Genista anglica L.
Petty Whin

COUNTY STATUS: Native	
CONSERVATION STATUS: DRDB (Cat2), NT, A, B	
FIRST YEAR: 1789 LATEST YEAR: 2009 NO OF RECORDS: 59	
RECENT SQUARES: monads 7; tetrads 6; hectads 5	
ALL SQUARES: monads 17; tetrads 12; hectads 15	

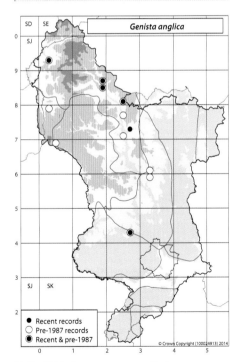

Petty Whin is a very rare, native undershrub of heathy areas and moorland. With one exception, all recently recorded sites are from the Dark Peak (Whiteley Nab SK0292 & Yorkshire Bridge SK1984). The remaining site is at Mercaston Marsh SSSI (SK2742) in the Claylands, where

on heavy soils. It occurs scattered from Long Clough (SK0392) and Parson's Wood Meadow (SK3881) in the north, through Bury Cliff (SK2161) and Grangemill (SK2457), to Breadsall (SK3638) and Dale Moor (SK4439) in the south. Our plant is ssp. *tinctoria*. It was formerly more frequent and abundant than today, and was once considered to be a serious pest of pastures, gaining unpleasant local names like Widow-wort, Widow-ways or Woodawes (Farey 1815). It was sometimes turned to the farmers' advantage when they collected and sold the plant to the dyers of Manchester (Mabey 1996).

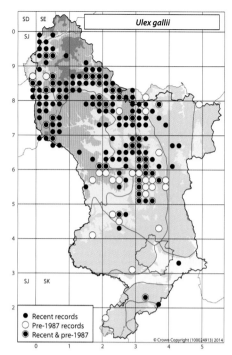

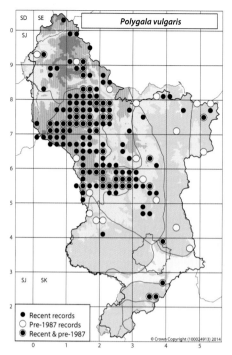

COUNTY STATUS: Native
CONSERVATION STATUS: ERL
FIRST YEAR: 1884 LATEST YEAR: 2013 NO OF RECORDS: 375
RECENT SQUARES: monads 178; tetrads 124; hectads 21
ALL SQUARES: monads 206; tetrads 147; hectads 31

South West and Dark Peak (Whiteley Nab SK0292, Berry Clough SK0272 & Hathersage Dale Bottom SK2481). Elsewhere it is rare, occurring on acid plateau soils in the White Peak (Blake Moor SK1662), in the Peak Fringe (Alport Stone SK3051), and in a few other localities. Previously it also grew in the south of the county (Overseal SK2915 & Ticknall SK3523). This local loss is in line with a national decrease in southern England since 1950 (Preston *et al.* 2002).

ROSACEAE

Physocarpus opulifolius (L.) Maxim.
Ninebark

Locally extinct, Ninebark was a very rare, casual shrub that was occasionally planted and sometimes persisted in apparently wild situations. The only record is from Lathkill Dale (SK1966) in Clapham (1969). It is a native of eastern North America.

Spiraea salicifolia L.
Bridewort

COUNTY STATUS: Established (Neophyte)
CONSERVATION STATUS: None
FIRST YEAR: 1969 LATEST YEAR: 2007 NO OF RECORDS: 17
RECENT SQUARES: monads 9; tetrads 9; hectads 6
ALL SQUARES: monads 13; tetrads 14; hectads 11

SK0372), the Dark Peak (Glossop SK0492 & Bagshaw Bridge SK1686) and the Peak Fringe (Tansley Moor SK36F & Nether Heage SK3550). Elsewhere it is very rare with just a few records, for example on the limestone plateau of the White Peak at Carsington Pasture (SK2454), and at Carver's Rocks (SK3322) in the Trent Valley. Nationally it has a western distribution with Derbyshire on the eastern edge of its main English range.

POLYGALACEAE

Polygala vulgaris L.
Common Milkwort

COUNTY STATUS: Native
CONSERVATION STATUS: None
FIRST YEAR: 1789 LATEST YEAR: 2013 NO OF RECORDS: 776
RECENT SQUARES: monads 237; tetrads 145; hectads 25
ALL SQUARES: monads 265; tetrads 164; hectads 32

Common Milkwort is a native perennial of short infertile grassland on calcareous

Common Milkwort (*Polygala vulgaris*) on Bonsall Leys (SK2657), May 2004 (Philip Precey)

or acidic soils, as well as of heathlands. It is frequent in the White Peak (Hay Dale SK17I, Meadow Place Grange SK2065 & Hopton Quarry SK2656). Elsewhere it is rare (Upper Derwent SK1490, Markland Grips SK5074 & Ticknall Quarries SK3623). There has been some loss of sites outside the White Peak since 1950 due to agricultural intensification, which mirrors a national decline over the period due to the same cause (Preston *et al.* 2002).

Polygala serpyllifolia Hose
Heath Milkwort

Heath Milkwort is a native perennial of acid grasslands and heaths. It is frequent in the

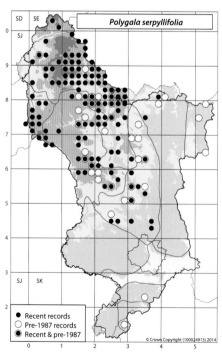

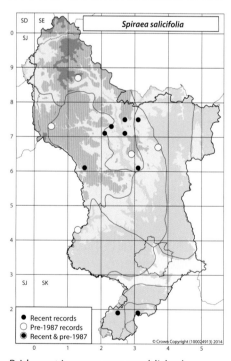

Bridewort is a very rare, established shrub of waste ground and hedges. It is

frequently planted for ornament, and occurs scattered throughout the county from Sycamore Farm (SK3074) in the north to Swadlincote in the south (SK3019).

Spiraea × pseudosalicifolia Silverside
Confused Bridewort

COUNTY STATUS: Established (Neophyte)
CONSERVATION STATUS: None
FIRST YEAR: 1994 LATEST YEAR: 2010 NO OF RECORDS: 23
RECENT SQUARES: monads 16; tetrads 15; hectads 13
ALL SQUARES: monads 16; tetrads 15; hectads 13

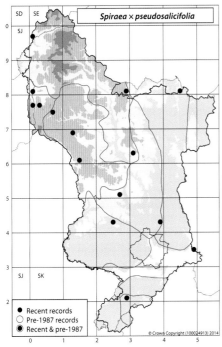

Confused Bridewort is a very rare, established shrub of waste ground, scrub and hedges. It is often planted for ornament, and occurs scattered across Derbyshire from the River Etherow (SK0196) in the north, to Newhall (SK2920) in the south. It is of garden origin from the crossing of Bridewort (*S. salicifolia*) and Steeple-bush (*S. douglasii*).

Spiraea × billardii Herincq
Billard's Bridewort

COUNTY STATUS: Casual
CONSERVATION STATUS: None
FIRST YEAR: 2000 LATEST YEAR: 2012 NO OF RECORDS: 6
RECENT SQUARES: monads 6; tetrads 6; hectads 5
ALL SQUARES: monads 6; tetrads 6; hectads 5

Billard's Bridewort is a very rare, casual shrub of hedges and waste ground. Occasionally planted for ornament, it is only known from six tetrads between 2000 and 2012 (Fairfield Common SK0674, Brailsford SK2541, Denby SK3947 & Long Eaton SK4834). It is of garden origin from the hybridisation of Pale Bridewort (*S. alba*) with Steeple-bush (*S. douglasii*).

Spiraea douglasii Hook.
Steeple-bush

COUNTY STATUS: Established (Neophyte)
CONSERVATION STATUS: None
FIRST YEAR: 1987 LATEST YEAR: 2010 NO OF RECORDS: 10
RECENT SQUARES: monads 6; tetrads 6; hectads 5
ALL SQUARES: monads 6; tetrads 6; hectads 5

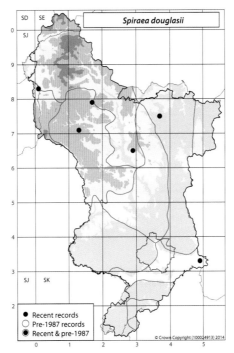

Steeple-bush is a very rare, established shrub of waste ground, tips and roadsides. It is sometimes grown in gardens and occurs scattered through the county from New Mills (SK0183) in the north, to Trent Lane (SK4932) in the south. It is a native of western North America.

Spiraea × arguta Zabel
Bridal-spray
Bridal-spray is a very rare, casual shrub of rough ground. The only record is from Ilkeston (SK4642), discovered in 2008 by C. & M. Smith.

Kerria japonica (L.) DC.
Kerria
Kerria is a very rare, established shrub of waste ground. There are only two records: an overgrown garden in the Etherow Valley (SJ9690) in the 1990s and Dronfield (SK3578) in 2012. It is indigenous to China.

Dryas octopetala L.
Mountain Avens

COUNTY STATUS: Native
CONSERVATION STATUS: DRDB (Cat6), NS, A
FIRST YEAR: 1811 LATEST YEAR: 1811 NO OF RECORDS: 1
RECENT SQUARES: monads 0; tetrads 0; hectads 0
ALL SQUARES: monads 0; tetrads 0; hectads 1

Locally extinct, Mountain Avens was a very rare, native perennial. The only record is for near Ashwood Dale (SK07) in 1811 and in the absence of other records some authors (Clapham 1969) have doubted it ever occurred here. It is a native of upland Britain and a Nationally Scarce species.

Prunus cerasifera Ehrh.
Cherry Plum

COUNTY STATUS: Casual
CONSERVATION STATUS: None
FIRST YEAR: 1969 LATEST YEAR: 2012 NO OF RECORDS: 55
RECENT SQUARES: monads 20; tetrads 30; hectads 16
ALL SQUARES: monads 30; tetrads 40; hectads 19

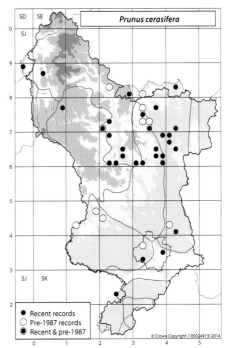

Cherry Plum is a rare casual shrub or small tree of hedges and copses. It can be a relic of cultivation or, more recently, part of amenity planting schemes. It occurs scattered through the county from the Sett Valley Trail (SK0286) and Beighton (SK4383) in the north, to Trent Bridge (SK2522) and Baldock Mill (SK4240) in the south. It is early flowering and thus often overlooked. The most commonly planted form is the purple-leaved variety *pissardii*. The species is indigenous to south-eastern Europe.

Prunus spinosa L.
Blackthorn

COUNTY STATUS: Native
CONSERVATION STATUS: None
FIRST YEAR: 1789 LATEST YEAR: 2013 NO OF RECORDS: 3,315
RECENT SQUARES: monads 1,441; tetrads 605; hectads 41
ALL SQUARES: monads 1,491; tetrads 610; hectads 41

Blackthorn is a native spiny shrub of hedges, woods, scrub and waysides. It is very common throughout the county

Blackthorn (*Prunus spinosa*), Allestree, Derby (SK3240), March 2008 (Nick Moyes)

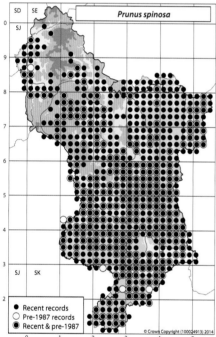

COUNTY STATUS: Established (Archaeophyte)	
CONSERVATION STATUS: None	
FIRST YEAR: 1789 **LATEST YEAR:** 2013 **NO OF RECORDS:** 674	
RECENT SQUARES: monads 394; tetrads 302; hectads 36	
ALL SQUARES: monads 449; tetrads 333; hectads 38	

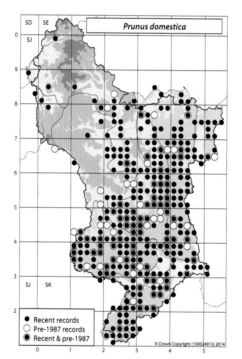

italica) was noted from Roston Common (SK1440).

Prunus avium (L.) L.
Wild Cherry

COUNTY STATUS: Native	
CONSERVATION STATUS: None	
FIRST YEAR: 1789 **LATEST YEAR:** 2013 **NO OF RECORDS:** 639	
RECENT SQUARES: monads 337; tetrads 291; hectads 38	
ALL SQUARES: monads 389; tetrads 333; hectads 39	

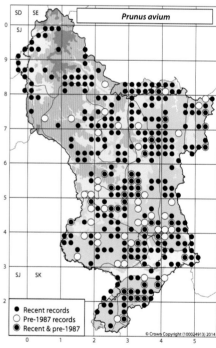

except for the higher parts of the Dark and South West Peak Areas. It suckers freely and can form dense thickets in places. A large specimen at Carsington Water (SK2550) has a recorded girth of 0.72m.

Prunus × *fruticans* Weihe
A hybrid cherry

The sole record for this native hybrid shrub is from a hedge at Kniveton (SK2249) in 1997. Probably under-recorded, it is the hybrid of Wild Plum (*P. domestica*) and Blackthorn (*P. spinosa*).

Prunus domestica L.
Wild Plum

Wild Plum is an anciently established shrub or small tree of hedges and copses near houses or gardens where it is often a relic of cultivation. It is also found on

waste ground and waysides from discarded stones. It occurs frequently throughout the lowland parts, but is rare in the White Peak and Dark Peak. The species is native to south-western Asia. Three subspecies occur here but have rarely been recorded separately. **Plum (ssp. *domestica*)** is the most commonly recorded. There are no recent records, while Clapham (1969) gives: Hulland (SK2446), Carsington (SK2452) and Repton (SK3026). **Damson (ssp. *insititia*)** has been recorded from Grange Farm (SK1640) and Stoney Clouds (SK4737). **Greengage (ssp.**

Wild Cherry is a native tree of woods and hedges found occasionally throughout the county (Millington Green SK2547, Pistern Hill SK3420 & Creswell Crags SK5374). It is planted for ornament in parks and on roadsides, for fruit in gardens, and increasingly in amenity schemes. Its natural distribution is thus very difficult to determine.

Prunus cerasus L.
Dwarf Cherry

COUNTY STATUS: Casual
CONSERVATION STATUS: None
FIRST YEAR: 1789 LATEST YEAR: 2010 NO OF RECORDS: 18
RECENT SQUARES: monads 3; tetrads 3; hectads 4
ALL SQUARES: monads 10; tetrads 10; hectads 12

Dwarf Cherry is a very rare, casual shrub or small tree of hedges and shrubberies that is occasionally grown for fruit. Recent localised records are only from Chapel-en-le-Frith (SK0579), Churchdale Hall (SK2070) and Ogston (SK3760) though there are older records from around the county. A native of south-west Asia, it is probably under-recorded due to confusion with Wild Cherry (*P. avium*).

Prunus padus L.
Bird Cherry

COUNTY STATUS: Native
CONSERVATION STATUS: None
FIRST YEAR: 1677 LATEST YEAR: 2013 NO OF RECORDS: 285
RECENT SQUARES: monads 113; tetrads 96; hectads 28
ALL SQUARES: monads 127; tetrads 109; hectads 33

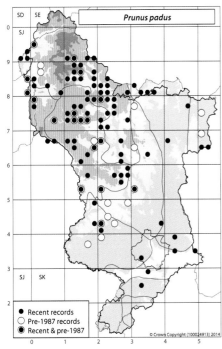

Bird Cherry is an occasional native shrub or small tree of woods, scrub and rocky places in the Dark and White Peak Areas, usually in damp and shaded situations (Dinting Wood SK0194, Miller's Dale SK1573, Bretton Clough SK2078 & the Via Gellia SK2656). It is also increasingly being used in amenity plantings (Foremark Reservoir SK3324 & Barlborough SK4776).

Prunus serotina Ehrh.
Rum Cherry
Rum Cherry is a casual shrub or small tree

that is commonly grown in gardens. The only recent record is for Pye Bridge (SK4353) in 2001 with an older record for a self-seeded garden tree at Chaddesden (SK33) in 1979. It is a native of eastern North America.

Prunus lusitanica L.
Portugal Laurel
Portugal Laurel is a casual evergreen shrub of woods and shrubberies. It is commonly planted in parks and gardens but is also frequently self-sown. Recent records are from Bottom's Bridge Wood (SJ9688), Backhill Lane (SK1955) and Miller's Green (SK2852). There is an older record from Norbury Wood (SK1242). It is indigenous to the Iberian Peninsula.

Prunus laurocerasus L.
Cherry Laurel

COUNTY STATUS: Established (Neophyte)
CONSERVATION STATUS: None
FIRST YEAR: 1975 LATEST YEAR: 2013 NO OF RECORDS: 304
RECENT SQUARES: monads 165; tetrads 153; hectads 33
ALL SQUARES: monads 168; tetrads 156; hectads 33

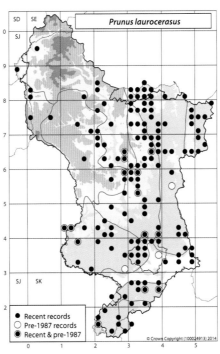

Cherry Laurel is an occasional established evergreen shrub or small tree of woods, parks and shrubberies. It is often planted, sometimes self-sown and rarely an invasive alien. It is frequent throughout the county although it generally avoids the White and Dark Peak Character Areas. It is a native of south-eastern Europe.

Chaenomeles speciosa (Sweet) Nakai
Chinese Quince
Chinese Quince is a spiny casual shrub. It is grown in gardens from where it escapes as a throwout or bird-sown seed onto verges and waste ground. There are only three records,

all between 1996 and 2005, for Rowsley Sidings (SK2663), Littleover (SK3133) and Fallgate (SK3562). It is indigenous to China.

Pyrus pyraster (L.) Burgsd.
Wild Pear
Wild Pear is an anciently established, spiny shrub or small tree of hedges and abandoned cultivations. It is often used as the stock for cultivated pears and can survive the death of the graft. The sole recent record is from Stanton Lock (SK4838) in 1999. There are six earlier records, for example Clapham (1969) gives Snelston (SK1642), and Linton (1903) Matlock (SK35) and Chesterfield (SK37). Probably under-recorded due to incomplete separation from Pear (*P. communis*), it is a native of central and southern Europe.

Pyrus communis L.
Pear

COUNTY STATUS: Established (Archaeophyte)
CONSERVATION STATUS: None
FIRST YEAR: 1789 LATEST YEAR: 2011 NO OF RECORDS: 53
RECENT SQUARES: monads 28; tetrads 34; hectads 19
ALL SQUARES: monads 30; tetrads 36; hectads 21

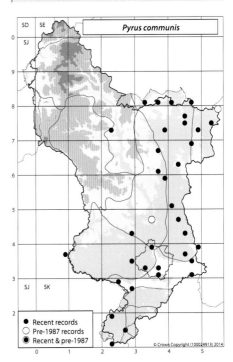

Pear is an anciently established tree of hedges and waste ground. It is often found as a relic of cultivation, but can regenerate from seeds in discarded cores. It occurs rarely throughout southern and eastern parts (Haunton SK2311, Ridgeway SK4081 & the Erewash Canal SK43Z). It is of hybrid garden origin.

Malus sylvestris (L.) Mill.
Crab Apple
Crab Apple is a spiny native shrub or small

COUNTY STATUS: Native
CONSERVATION STATUS: None
FIRST YEAR: 1789 **LATEST YEAR:** 2013 **NO OF RECORDS:** 699
RECENT SQUARES: monads 449; tetrads 323; hectads 38
ALL SQUARES: monads 458; tetrads 327; hectads 38

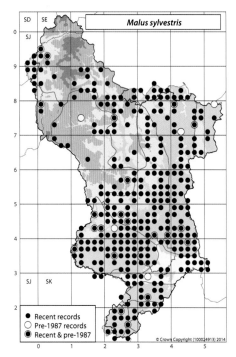

tree of hedges, scrub and woods. It is frequent throughout lowland parts of the county but rare in the White Peak and Dark Peak Areas. It is often recorded in error for Apple (*M. pumila*).

Malus pumila Mill.
Apple

Apple is an anciently established, small tree of hedges, scrub and waste ground. Even

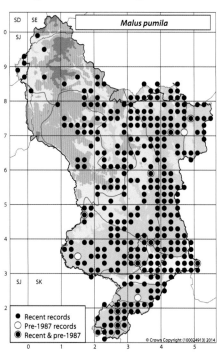

COUNTY STATUS: Established (Archaeophyte)
CONSERVATION STATUS: None
FIRST YEAR: 1963 **LATEST YEAR:** 2013 **NO OF RECORDS:** 653
RECENT SQUARES: monads 443; tetrads 330; hectads 37
ALL SQUARES: monads 449; tetrads 333; hectads 37

apparently wild-grown trees are usually relics of cultivation or the result of discarded cores. It is frequent in the lowlands, but rare in the upland Dark and White Peak Areas, other than near picnic sites.

Sorbus domestica L.
Service-tree

Locally extinct, Service-tree was a very rare, casual tree of woodlands. The sole record is from Pilkington (1789) for Crich Woods (SK35). There is also an unconfirmed record from St Chads Water (SK43) in 1996. It is a very rare native of limestone cliffs in south-western Britain and a Critically Endangered species there.

Sorbus aucuparia L.
Rowan

COUNTY STATUS: Native
CONSERVATION STATUS: None
FIRST YEAR: 1789 **LATEST YEAR:** 2013 **NO OF RECORDS:** 3,429
RECENT SQUARES: monads 1,318; tetrads 614; hectads 41
ALL SQUARES: monads 1,378; tetrads 628; hectads 41

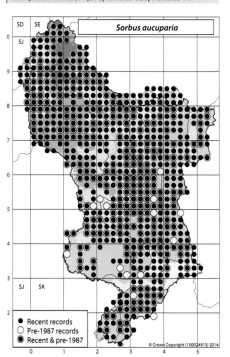

Rowan is a small native tree of woods, hedges, moors, rocky places and waste ground. It is also increasingly being planted in restoration and amenity schemes. Overall it is common throughout Derbyshire except for some areas of heavy soils in the Claylands and some calcareous soils in the White Peak. It has a long history

of use, as evidenced by its inclusion in several early accounts of the county (Farey 1815) and the number of local names in Grigson (1975) which include Quicken and Wiggen. Its berries are still used today to emphasise the outlines of well-dressing pictures. A large tree, with a girth of 4.49m was found recently at Thorny Lee, Coombs (SK0378).

Sorbus intermedia (Ehrh.) Pers.
Swedish Whitebeam

COUNTY STATUS: Established (Neophyte)
CONSERVATION STATUS: None
FIRST YEAR: 1975 **LATEST YEAR:** 2013 **NO OF RECORDS:** 122
RECENT SQUARES: monads 77; tetrads 82; hectads 31
ALL SQUARES: monads 79; tetrads 84; hectads 31

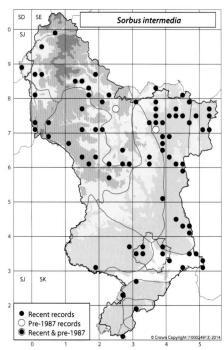

Swedish Whitebeam is an established small tree of waysides and waste ground. It is much planted in town streets, parks and amenity landscaping from where it spreads by seeds. It is occasional throughout the county from Glossop (SK0294) and Crowden (SK0799 v.c.58) in the north to Stones Bridge (SK2611) and Gresley Common (SK3018) in the south. It is a native of the Baltic region and Sweden.

Sorbus aria (L.) Crantz
Common Whitebeam

COUNTY STATUS: Native
CONSERVATION STATUS: A
FIRST YEAR: 1903 **LATEST YEAR:** 2011 **NO OF RECORDS:** 31
RECENT SQUARES: monads 5; tetrads 5; hectads 3
ALL SQUARES: monads 21; tetrads 21; hectads 18

Common Whitebeam is a very rare, native tree of woods, scrub and rocky places on

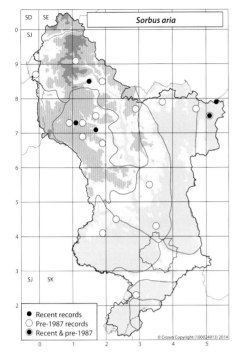

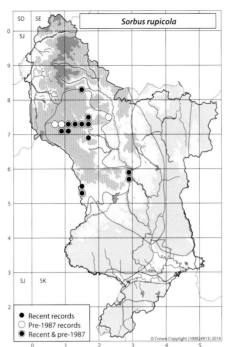

COUNTY STATUS: Native
CONSERVATION STATUS: B
FIRST YEAR: 1829 LATEST YEAR: 2010 NO OF RECORDS: 101
RECENT SQUARES: monads 19; tetrads 15; hectads 10
ALL SQUARES: monads 24; tetrads 18; hectads 13

of ancient woods and old hedges. Most records are from the north-east (Staveley SK4276, Scarcliffe Park SK5071 & Whitwell Wood SK5277) with scattered records elsewhere (Glossop SK0295 & Church Broughton SK2132). Older ones have the same distribution (Sealwood Farm SK2715 & Hagg Rocks SK2957). Nationally it is mostly a southern species with Derbyshire towards the northern limit of its main distribution. Willmot (1977) gives an account of the plant here.

Amelanchier lamarckii F.G. Schroed.
Juneberry
Juneberry is a casual shrub or small tree that sometimes escapes from ornamental plantings. The only record is from Froggatt (SK2476) in 1980. It is indigenous to North America.

Cotoneaster bacillaris Wall. ex Lindl.
Open-fruited Cotoneaster
Locally extinct, Open-fruited Cotoneaster was a very rare, casual shrub or small tree. It is grown in gardens and can escape onto roadsides and waste ground. The only record is from Alsop en le Dale (SK15) in 1925. It is a native of the Himalayas.

Cotoneaster frigidus Wall. ex Lindl.
Tree Cotoneaster
Tree Cotoneaster is an established, evergreen shrub or small tree grown as a garden ornamental. There are two recent records; Middleton Dale (SK2175) where it was considered bird-sown, and Inkersall Green (SK4172). Our one older record was also from Middleton Dale (SK2175) in 1977. It is a native of the Himalayas.

Cotoneaster × *watereri* Exell
Waterer's Cotoneaster

COUNTY STATUS: Casual
CONSERVATION STATUS: None
FIRST YEAR: 2001 LATEST YEAR: 2010 NO OF RECORDS: 5
RECENT SQUARES: monads 4; tetrads 4; hectads 4
ALL SQUARES: monads 4; tetrads 4; hectads 4

Waterer's Cotoneaster is a casual semi-evergreen shrub that is grown as a garden ornamental. It has been recorded from only four sites, all recently (Whaley Bridge SK0181 v.c.58, Chesterfield SK3871, Mickleover SK3035 & Eyam Edge SK2077). It is the artificially-produced hybrid of Tree Cotoneaster (*C. frigidus*) and Willow-leaved Cotoneaster (*C. salicifolius*).

calcareous soils. However, it has been much planted for ornament so its native distribution is uncertain. This is further obscured by the presence of Rock Whitebeam (*S. rupicola*) in similar habitats with which it has sometimes been confused. There are only five recent records: two from the White Peak (Old Dale SK1172 & Deep Dale SK1670), two from the Magnesian Limestone (Markland Grips SK5074 & Whitwell Wood SK5278) and one from the Dark Peak (Brockett Booth SK1484). Previously it was recorded rarely throughout the county both from limestone areas (Lathkill Dale SK1966, Dove Dale SK15) and elsewhere (Snake Inn SK1190 & Bretby SK2922). Nationally it is considered a native of woods and scrub on calcareous soils, with Derbyshire on the northern edge of its range (Stace 2010).

Sorbus rupicola (Syme) Hedl.
Rock Whitebeam

COUNTY STATUS: Native
CONSERVATION STATUS: DRDB (Cat3), NS, A, B
FIRST YEAR: 1864 LATEST YEAR: 2013 NO OF RECORDS: 112
RECENT SQUARES: monads 23; tetrads 13; hectads 6
ALL SQUARES: monads 28; tetrads 16; hectads 9

Rock Whitebeam is a small rare native tree of the White Peak where it grows amongst other trees and bushes on the tops and ledges of limestone cliffs. It occurs for example in Deep Dale (SK1072), Burfoot (SK1672) and the Matlock Woods (SK2959). A large tree with a girth of 2.8m was recently found at Miller's Dale (SK1673). It is scattered through upland England in

similar habitats and is a Nationally Scarce species.

Sorbus latifolia agg.
Broad-leaved Whitebeam aggregate
Broad-leaved Whitebeam aggregate is a group of small casual trees that sometimes escape from parks and ornamental plantings. There are only three records, all between 1998 and 2003: Derby (SK3830), Chesterfield (SK3872) and Chesterfield Golf Course (SK3971).

Sorbus torminalis (L.) Crantz
Wild Service-tree
Wild Service-tree is a very rare, native tree

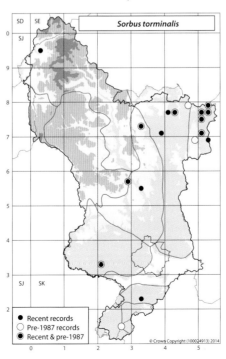

Cotoneaster salicifolius Franch.
Willow-leaved Cotoneaster

COUNTY STATUS: Casual

CONSERVATION STATUS: None

FIRST YEAR: 1999 LATEST YEAR: 2009 NO OF RECORDS: 5

RECENT SQUARES: monads 4; tetrads 4; hectads 3

ALL SQUARES: monads 4; tetrads 4; hectads 3

Willow-leaved Cotoneaster is a casual evergreen shrub. It is grown in gardens and can escape by bird-sown seed. It has only been recorded from four tetrads, all recently (Dirtlow Rake and Pin Dale SK1582, Bradwell SK1780, Longstone Edge SK2273 & West Park SK4838). It is indigenous to western China.

Cotoneaster lacteus W.W. Sm.
Late Cotoneaster
Late Cotoneaster is a casual evergreen shrub, known by a single record from the Cromford Canal (SK3156) where it was discovered by R. Martin in 2010.

Cotoneaster integrifolius (Roxb.) G. Klotz
Entire-leaved Cotoneaster

COUNTY STATUS: Established (Neophyte)

CONSERVATION STATUS: WCA9

FIRST YEAR: 1965 LATEST YEAR: 2011 NO OF RECORDS: 29

RECENT SQUARES: monads 9; tetrads 9; hectads 7

ALL SQUARES: monads 16; tetrads 16; hectads 10

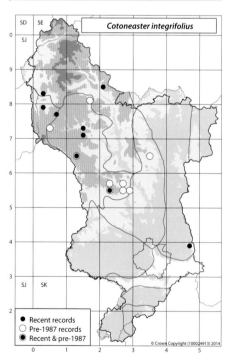

Entire-leaved Cotoneaster is an established low-growing evergreen shrub. Planted in gardens, it can persist as a relic of cultivation as at Ladybower Dam (SK2085). It can also occur as a very rare garden escape, particularly in the White Peak as at Sparklow (SK1265) and Priestcliffe Lees (SK1572). It is indigenous to western China and the Himalayas.

Cotoneaster dammeri C.K. Schneid.
Bearberry Cotoneaster
Bearberry Cotoneaster is a casual low-growing evergreen garden shrub, first found at Mapperley (SK4342) in 1998 by C. & M. Smith and subsequently at Upper Pleasley (SK4964) in 2008. It is a native of central China.

Cotoneaster simonsii Baker
Himalayan Cotoneaster

COUNTY STATUS: Established (Neophyte)

CONSERVATION STATUS: WCA9

FIRST YEAR: 1970 LATEST YEAR: 2013 NO OF RECORDS: 62

RECENT SQUARES: monads 34; tetrads 45; hectads 20

ALL SQUARES: monads 37; tetrads 48; hectads 20

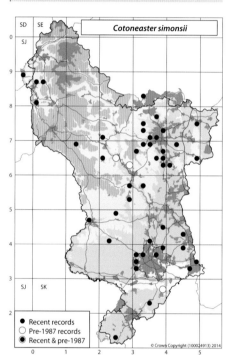

Himalayan Cotoneaster is a rare established shrub. It is popularly grown in gardens and amenity plantings. Birds readily eat the fruits, and its seeds easily spread to waste ground and waysides. It is recorded throughout the county (Hayfield SK0386, Unstone SK37T, Gorseybank SK2953, Ticknall SK3523 & Lullington SK2413). It is indigenous to the Himalayas.

Cotoneaster horizontalis Decne.
Wall Cotoneaster

COUNTY STATUS: Established (Neophyte)

CONSERVATION STATUS: WCA9

FIRST YEAR: 1968 LATEST YEAR: 2013 NO OF RECORDS: 168

RECENT SQUARES: monads 113; tetrads 111; hectads 35

ALL SQUARES: monads 115; tetrads 113; hectads 35

Wall Cotoneaster is an established low-growing shrub and a native of western China. It is much grown in gardens from where it spreads by birds or throwouts to waysides, waste ground, walls, rock outcrops and quarries. It is occasional

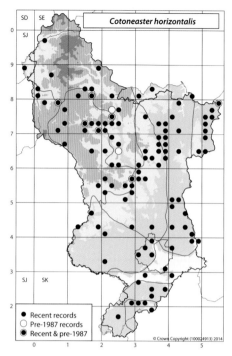

throughout the county, from Tintwistle (SK0297 v.c.58) and Ladybower Reservoir (SK1888) in the north to Rosliston (SK2416) and Smisby (SK3419) in the south.

Cotoneaster hjelmqvistii Flinck & B. Hylmoe
Hjelmqvist's Cotoneaster
Hjelmqvist's Cotoneaster is a casual low-growing shrub. The only recod was made by R. Martin at Golden Brook, Long Eaton (SK5033) in 2010.

Cotoneaster bullatus Bois
Hollyberry Cotoneaster
Hollyberry Cotoneaster is a very rare, casual shrub. It is much planted in gardens

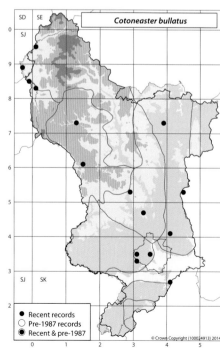

COUNTY STATUS: Casual
CONSERVATION STATUS: WCA9
FIRST YEAR: 1987 LATEST YEAR: 2012 NO OF RECORDS: 18
RECENT SQUARES: monads 15; tetrads 15; hectads 13
ALL SQUARES: monads 15; tetrads 15; hectads 13

and amenity schemes from where it escapes into woods, waysides and waste ground throughout the county. It has been recorded from Dinting Vale Wood (SK0194) in the north, through Newhaven Cottage (SK1561) and Pye Bridge (SK4453) to Weston-on-Trent (SK4027) in the south. It is indigenous to western China.

Cotoneaster rehderi Pojark.
Bullate Cotoneaster

COUNTY STATUS: Casual
CONSERVATION STATUS: None
FIRST YEAR: 1998 LATEST YEAR: 2011 NO OF RECORDS: 11
RECENT SQUARES: monads 9; tetrads 9; hectads 8
ALL SQUARES: monads 9; tetrads 9; hectads 8

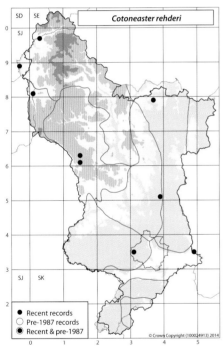

Bullate Cotoneaster is a very rare, casual shrub of waste ground and woodlands. It is often grown in gardens from where it is spread by birds. There are recent records scattered throughout Derbyshire from Hadfield (SK0296) in the north, through Hartshead Quarry (SK1460), to Mickleover (SK3035) in the south. It is a native of western China.

Cotoneaster franchetii Bois
Franchet's Cotoneaster
Franchet's Cotoneaster is a casual evergreen shrub which is indigenous to south-western China. It is grown in gardens as an ornamental from where it sometimes escapes. There are just five local records

between 1999 and 2010 (Pin Dale SK1582, Scarthin Rock SK2957, Mickleover SK3035 West Hallam SK4442 & Long Eaton SK4933).

Cotoneaster sternianus (Turrill) Boom
Stern's Cotoneaster

COUNTY STATUS: Established (Neophyte)
CONSERVATION STATUS: None
FIRST YEAR: 1995 LATEST YEAR: 2009 NO OF RECORDS: 7
RECENT SQUARES: monads 6; tetrads 6; hectads 5
ALL SQUARES: monads 6; tetrads 6; hectads 5

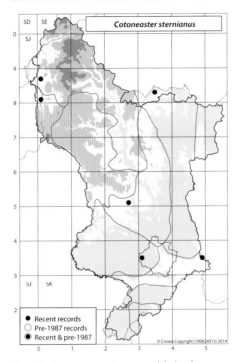

Stern's Cotoneaster is an established, evergreen shrub, popular in gardens as an ornamental from where it is bird-sown to waste ground and waysides. It occurs very rarely throughout the county from New Mills (SK0086) and Millhouses (SK3483) in the north to Mickleover (SK3035) and Erewash (SK4834) in the south. It grows naturally in south-western China.

Cotoneaster dielsianus E. Pritz. ex Diels
Diels' Cotoneaster
Diels' Cotoneaster is a casual shrub. It is often grown in gardens from where it can naturalise. It was discovered in 2005 on a disused railway siding at Long Eaton (SK4934) by R. Martin, and subsequently found at Belper (SK3447) in 2010. It is a native of China.

Pyracantha coccinea M. Roem.
Firethorn
Firethorn is an established spiny and evergreen shrub of gardens and amenity plantings. It survives as a relic of cultivation and can escape by being bird-sown or thrown out onto waysides and waste ground. It is recorded for five sites, all between 1990 and 2011: Matlock Forest

(SK2964), Mickleover (SK3035), Elm Wood (SK3632), Spital (SK3870) and Mapperley (SK4342). It is a native of southern Europe.

Pyracantha rogersiana (A.B. Jacks.) Coltm.-Rog.
Asian Firethorn
Asian Firethorn is a casual evergreen shrub. Our only record was made at Long Eaton (SK5033) in 2010 by R. Martin.

Crataegus crus-galli L.
Cockspurthorn
Cockspurthorn is an established small spiny tree. It was first recorded from a plantation at Stanton-in-the-Peak (presumed to be SK2464) by Miss M. Hewitt in 1989. It was subsequently recorded at Grassmoor (SK4167) in 2011. It occurs naturally in eastern North America.

Crataegus monogyna Jacq.
Hawthorn

COUNTY STATUS: Native
CONSERVATION STATUS: None
FIRST YEAR: 1789 LATEST YEAR: 2013 NO OF RECORDS: 8,398
RECENT SQUARES: monads 2,389; tetrads 735; hectads 44
ALL SQUARES: monads 2,425; tetrads 739; hectads 44

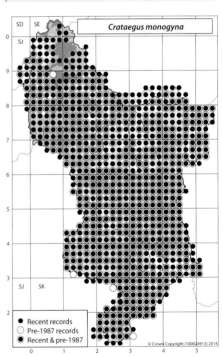

Hawthorn is a native spiny shrub or small tree of woods, scrub, open ground and waysides. The native form has been planted as the predominant species in thousands of field hedges, while pink-flowered forms are often planted for ornament. It is very common everywhere, except for a few small areas of the highest moorlands, reaching its maximum county altitude of around 400m in Upper Heyden Clough (SE0903). A large specimen with a girth of 4.8m was found recently near Barbrook Reservoir

(SK2777). It has increased in abundance in quite a few areas over the last fifty years. This causes problems for the conservation of many smaller plants and has had a detrimental impact on the scenery in a number of Dales. It has been used to veneer furniture (Farey 1815) and the fruits have the local name of Hag (Grigson 1975).

Crataegus × media Bechst.
A hybrid hawthorn

COUNTY STATUS: Native	
CONSERVATION STATUS: None	
FIRST YEAR: 1977 LATEST YEAR: 2009 NO OF RECORDS: 16	
RECENT SQUARES: monads 11; tetrads 11; hectads 8	
ALL SQUARES: monads 12; tetrads 12; hectads 9	

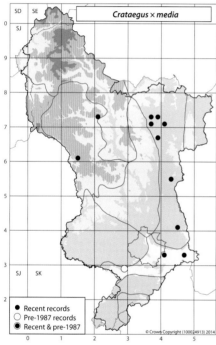

This hybrid hawthorn is a spiny native shrub or small tree of hedges and woods. It occurs very rarely scattered over central parts, from Longstone Edge (SK2173) and Brockwell (SK3771) in the north to Elvaston Castle (SK4032) and Golden Brook Storage Lagoon (SK4633) in the south. Probably under-recorded, it is the hybrid of Hawthorn (*C. monogyna*) and Midland Hawthorn (*C. laevigata*).

Crataegus laevigata (Poir.) DC.
Midland Hawthorn

COUNTY STATUS: Native	
CONSERVATION STATUS: B	
FIRST YEAR: 1903 LATEST YEAR: 2011 NO OF RECORDS: 113	
RECENT SQUARES: monads 44; tetrads 43; hectads 25	
ALL SQUARES: monads 56; tetrads 52; hectads 28	

Midland Hawthorn is a native spiny shrub or small tree of ancient woods. It is sometimes also planted in hedges, probably by mistake for Hawthorn. It

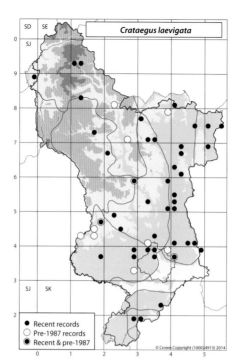

occurs rarely scattered throughout the county from Mellor (SJ9888) and Upper Derwent (SK1293) in the north, through High Tor (SK2958) to Church Gresley (SK2918) and Swadlincote (SK3018) in the south. It is a southern species with Derbyshire towards the north-western limit of its natural distribution. It is thus sometimes only regarded as native in the south of the county (Clapham 1969).

Crataegus orientalis Pall. ex M. Bieb.
Oriental Hawthorn

Oriental Hawthorn is an established, small spiny tree. It is frequently grown in gardens and parks for ornament, but is only known from wild situations in wood and scrub at Rowsley Sidings (SK2665) between 1995 and 2003. It is a native of south-eastern Europe.

Filipendula vulgaris Moench
Dropwort

COUNTY STATUS: Native	
CONSERVATION STATUS: None	
FIRST YEAR: 1829 LATEST YEAR: 2013 NO OF RECORDS: 193	
RECENT SQUARES: monads 54; tetrads 39; hectads 14	
ALL SQUARES: monads 67; tetrads 48; hectads 18	

Dropwort is an occasional native perennial of dry calcareous grasslands, mostly on steep slopes. It occurs in both the White Peak (Hay Dale SK1276 & Lathkill Dale SK1664) and the Magnesian Limestone Areas (Markland Grips SK5074). It is also grown in gardens from where it can escape to become established elsewhere in the county as at Sheepbridge (SK3674) and Langley Mill (SK4447). Previous records from the south of the county may have

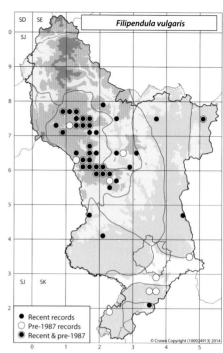

been native, for example at Knowle Hills (SK3525) and Swarkestone (SK3628).

Filipendula ulmaria (L.) Maxim.
Meadowsweet

COUNTY STATUS: Native	
CONSERVATION STATUS: None	
FIRST YEAR: 1789 LATEST YEAR: 2013 NO OF RECORDS: 3,936	
RECENT SQUARES: monads 1,268; tetrads 596; hectads 41	
ALL SQUARES: monads 1,328; tetrads 606; hectads 41	

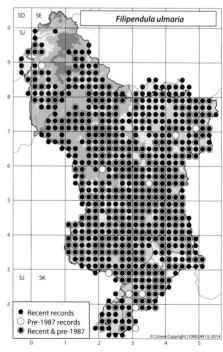

Meadowsweet is a common native perennial of damp meadows, marshes, fens, swamps and wet woodlands. It grows throughout the county except for the high moors of the Dark and South West Peak Areas.

Rubus chamaemorus L.
Cloudberry

COUNTY STATUS: Native
CONSERVATION STATUS: B
FIRST YEAR: 1700 LATEST YEAR: 2012 NO OF RECORDS: 276
RECENT SQUARES: monads 106; tetrads 45; hectads 7
ALL SQUARES: monads 114; tetrads 52; hectads 9

Cloudberry is an occasional native perennial of blanket bogs and upland moors in the

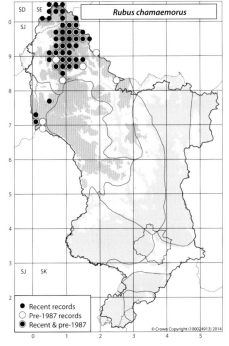

Cloudberry (*Rubus chamaemorus*), Rakes Rocks (SE0500), June 2005 (Barry Parker)

Dark and South West Peak (Crowden Moors SE0604 v.c.58, Kinder Scout SK1089 & near Cat and Fiddle SK0071). It can often be locally abundant, and even grows in areas of bare eroded peat (Clapham 1969). It is much more frequently seen in flower than fruit, probably due to sheep grazing. It was previously recorded further east in the Dark Peak than today (Ringinglow Bog SK2583 in 1970). It is a northern species on the southern limit of its English distribution here.

Rubus tricolor Focke
Chinese Bramble
Chinese Bramble is a very rare, established plant of waste ground and shrubberies. It was first recorded at Drakelow Reserve (SK2220) in 1976, where it was still present in 2008. Otherwise it is only known from five other tetrads between 1999 and 2012, all scattered over southern and eastern parts: Ashbourne Cemetery (SK1646), Woodside Reserve (SK4443), Bramley Vale (SK4666), Long Eaton (SK4934) and Clowne (SK4975). Its semi-evergreen trailing stems make it an ideal ground cover shrub in amenity plantings and restoration schemes. It is a native of China.

Rubus saxatilis L.
Stone Bramble
Stone Bramble is an occasional native perennial of rocky woods and scree

COUNTY STATUS: Native
CONSERVATION STATUS: DRDB (Cat5b)
FIRST YEAR: 1787 LATEST YEAR: 2012 NO OF RECORDS: 152
RECENT SQUARES: monads 19; tetrads 13; hectads 5
ALL SQUARES: monads 35; tetrads 20; hectads 9

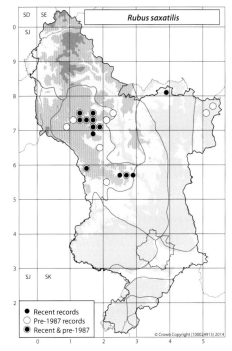

slopes in the White Peak, as at Monk's Dale (SK1374), Biggin Dale (SK1458) and Bruns Wood (SK2456). Elsewhere it is very rare with the only recent record off the Carboniferous Limestone being at Ryall's Wood (SK3980), though it was previously recorded for Markland Grips (SK5074) on the Magnesian Limestone in 1969 and near the Snake Inn (SK19) in 1903. It is generally a plant of upland Britain, on the south-eastern edge of its range here.

Rubus parviflorus Nutt.
Thimbleberry
Thimbleberry is a very rare, established shrub of waysides. The only record is from Harehill Plantation at Wingerworth (SK3567) in 1980 (specimen in Derby Museum). It is a native of western North America, grown in gardens for ornament.

Rubus idaeus L.
Raspberry

COUNTY STATUS: Native
CONSERVATION STATUS: None
FIRST YEAR: 1729 LATEST YEAR: 2013 NO OF RECORDS: 2,613
RECENT SQUARES: monads 1,048; tetrads 552; hectads 39
ALL SQUARES: monads 1,119; tetrads 569; hectads 39

Raspberry is a common native shrub of hedges, woods, waste and rough ground throughout the county, becoming rarer only on the high moors of the Dark Peak and some intensively-farmed lowland

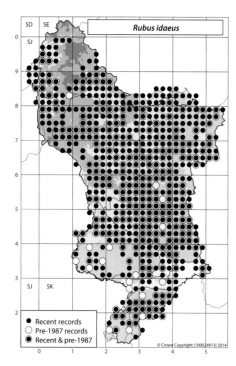

COUNTY STATUS: Native

CONSERVATION STATUS: None

FIRST YEAR: 1789 LATEST YEAR: 2013 NO OF RECORDS: 7,274

RECENT SQUARES: monads 2,207; tetrads 704; hectads 44

ALL SQUARES: monads 2,240; tetrads 705; hectads 44

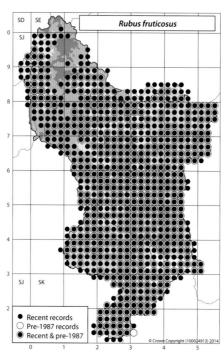

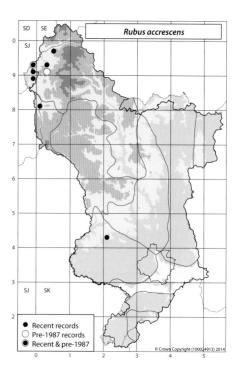

areas. It is also widely grown in gardens for fruit and many plants, particularly in the lowlands, are probably the result of escapes from cultivation.

Rubus × *pseudoidaeus* (Weihe) Lej.
A hybrid bramble

This hybrid bramble is a very rare, native shrub with just one unlocalised post-1970 record, and five others in Linton (1903) for the White Peak going back to the Via Gellia (SK25) in 1888. It is the result of the crossing of Raspberry (*R. idaeus*) with Dewberry (*R. caesius*).

Rubus cockburnianus Hemsl.
White-stemmed Bramble

White-stemmed Bramble is an established shrub of waste ground. It is often planted in gardens and restoration schemes. It is known from only three records, made between 2004 and 2012: Whaley Bridge (SK0081 v.c.58) Ringwood (SK4173) and Stanton Lagoon (SK4739). It is a native of China.

Rubus loganobaccus L.H. Bailey
Loganberry

Loganberry is a casual shrub of roadsides and waste ground. There are only two records: Pleasley Vale (SK5164) in 2006 and Brockwell Reservoir (SK3771) in 2004. It is grown in gardens where its fruits are also appreciated by birds which spread the seeds. It is of garden origin.

Rubus fruticosus agg.
Bramble aggregate

Bramble aggregate includes all subsequent *Rubus* species except the last one *Rubus caesius* (Dewberry). This aggregate is

a scrambling native perennial with biennial woody stems. It grows in a wide range of habitats including woods, scrub, waysides, moors and waste ground. It is very common throughout the county except for the high moors of the Dark Peak where it is absent. It is also widely cultivated for blackberries and so many records are probably the result of garden escapes or throwouts. The aggregate is very variable, consisting of over 300 slightly different microspecies nationally, each generally producing seed by self-fertilisation. This means each microspecies is isolated from the others. However they can occasionally cross, so increasing the problems of identifying members of the group. In fact problems of identification are so great that only a few botanists have ever studied them seriously in the county. These include a past Flora writer, W.R. Linton, and more recently R. Smith and D. Earl. This means the microspecies accounts are much less complete than for most of the other plants here, and no attempt is made to indicate frequency of occurrence.

Rubus accrescens Newton
A bramble

COUNTY STATUS: Native

CONSERVATION STATUS: None

FIRST YEAR: 1961 LATEST YEAR: 2008 NO OF RECORDS: 12

RECENT SQUARES: monads 8; tetrads 7; hectads 5

ALL SQUARES: monads 9; tetrads 8; hectads 5

This native bramble occurs in the north-western corner of the county (Stockport SJ9892, Whaley Bridge SK0081 v.c.58 & Charlestown SK0392) with an isolated record in the south (Shirley SK2042). Elsewhere in Britain it grows only in Cheshire and South Lancashire, and so is on the eastern edge of its range here (Newton & Randall 2004).

Rubus arrheniiformis W.C.R. Watson
A bramble

COUNTY STATUS: Native

CONSERVATION STATUS: DRDB (Cat6)

FIRST YEAR: 1891 LATEST YEAR: 1891 NO OF RECORDS: 1

RECENT SQUARES: monads 0; tetrads 0; hectads 0

ALL SQUARES: monads 0; tetrads 0; hectads 1

Locally extinct, this native bramble was recorded in 1891 by W.R. Linton from the Bradley and Sturston area (SK14), but there are no later records. It is a plant of southern Britain, on the northern edge of its range here (Newton & Randall 2004).

Rubus bertramii G. Braun
A bramble

This is a native bramble of damp shaded habitats on acid peaty soils. It has only been recorded for three tetrads, with recent records from Shirley Park SK2042 in 1987 and Shallcross (SK0179) in 2007, plus older ones from Hayfield (SK0388) in 1961 and 1979.

Rubus fissus Lindl.
A bramble

Locally extinct, this native bramble was last recorded in Clapham (1969) for Shirley (SK2141), where recent searches have failed to rediscover it. However, Linton (1903) recorded it as a "not uncommon" plant of "boggy places in woods and by streams". He gives several localities and a date of first recording as 1885. There is a voucher specimen in Derby Museum.

Rubus nessensis W. Hall
A bramble

This native bramble was discovered in 1979 by R. Smith at Repton Shrubs (SK3123). Its presence there was reconfirmed by him in 2005, and was found to have spread considerably. This is a distinctive species growing in a well-recorded area for brambles, so it is surprising that it had not been found earlier. A voucher specimen is in Derby Museum.

Rubus plicatus Weihe & Nees
A bramble

COUNTY STATUS: Native	
CONSERVATION STATUS: DRDB (Cat6)	
FIRST YEAR: 1889 **LATEST YEAR:** 1889 **NO OF RECORDS:** 1	
RECENT SQUARES: monads 0; tetrads 0; hectads 0	
ALL SQUARES: monads 0; tetrads 0; hectads 1	

Locally extinct, this bramble is accepted as a Derbyshire native by Newton & Randall (2004), apparently based on a specimen in Liverpool Museum collected by W.R. Linton from Bradley (SK24) in 1889. His 1903 Flora gives further records, but Clapham (1969) cast doubt on these because in Linton's day a wider concept of the species was taken.

Rubus scissus W.C.R. Watson
A bramble

This native species is one of the commoner and more widespread of the local

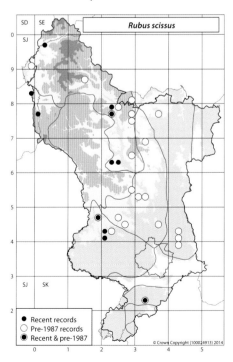

COUNTY STATUS: Native	
CONSERVATION STATUS: None	
FIRST YEAR: 1892 **LATEST YEAR:** 2008 **NO OF RECORDS:** 69	
RECENT SQUARES: monads 13; tetrads 11; hectads 8	
ALL SQUARES: monads 32; tetrads 30; hectads 19	

brambles. It occurs on woodland edges and track sides, generally in heathy areas. There are recent records from Vale House (SK0397) and Stoke Wood (SK2376) in the north, to Carver's Rocks (SK3322) in the south. Earlier records cover much the same area but appear to be more frequent. It is a plant of upland heaths that is scarce in southern Britain.

Rubus calvatus Lees ex Bloxam
A bramble

COUNTY STATUS: Native	
CONSERVATION STATUS: None	
FIRST YEAR: 1891 **LATEST YEAR:** 2008 **NO OF RECORDS:** 27	
RECENT SQUARES: monads 3; tetrads 2; hectads 1	
ALL SQUARES: monads 8; tetrads 7; hectads 9	

This native bramble has only been recorded recently from two adjacent tetrads (Shirley SK2041 & 2042). However, Clapham (1969) recorded it for three sites in the south of the county: Edlaston (SK1743), Brailsford (SK2441) and Dawson's Rocks (SK3322). Linton (1903) recorded it in the same area, and further north at Low Leighton (SK08) and Hathersage Booths (SK28). Nationally it is a plant of southern Britain (Newton & Randall 2004).

Rubus durescens W.R. Linton
A bramble

COUNTY STATUS: Native	
CONSERVATION STATUS: DRDB (Cat3), NR	
FIRST YEAR: 1890 **LATEST YEAR:** 2013 **NO OF RECORDS:** 39	
RECENT SQUARES: monads 6; tetrads 5; hectads 3	
ALL SQUARES: monads 13; tetrads 12; hectads 8	

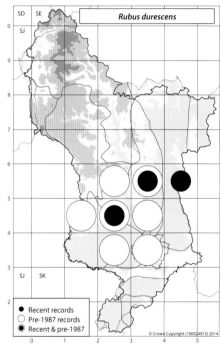

The entire global distribution of this native bramble lies within southern Derbyshire. It occurs in hedges, scrub, wood and heathy areas, and was first described and named

Rubus durescens, our endemic bramble at Alport Height (SK3051), July 2013 (Roy & Ruth Smith)

by W.R. Linton in 1892. As brambles go, it is a neat plant with deep pink flowers. He was obviously very proud of it as he illustrated it in gold on the cover of his 1903 Flora. He recorded it from between Ambergate and Wirksworth (SK25) in the north, through Bradley Wood (SK14, voucher at Derby Museum) and Duffield (SK34), to between Church Broughton and Sutton (SK23) in the south. Clapham (1969) also noted it for Bradley Wood (SK1946) and near Cross o' the Hands (SK2846). Recent records are from much the same area (Mugginton Sand Quarry SK2845, Nether Heage SK3550, Lower Hartshay SK3851 and Swanwick (SK4053, 4153). Though having no national conservation status, Cheffings & Farrell (2007) suggest populations of local endemics like these, in fewer than five hectads, should be considered threatened.

Rubus gratus Focke
A bramble

Locally extinct, the sole local record for this native bramble is by the brook in Shirley Wood (SK24) where it was noted in 1887 (Linton 1903). A voucher specimen is in Derby Museum. It is a plant of heaths and peaty soils, mainly in southern Britain (Newton & Randall 2004).

Rubus laciniatus Willd.
A bramble

| COUNTY STATUS: Established (Neophyte) |
| CONSERVATION STATUS: None |
| FIRST YEAR: 1969 LATEST YEAR: 2011 NO OF RECORDS: 11 |
| RECENT SQUARES: monads 6; tetrads 6; hectads 4 |
| ALL SQUARES: monads 8; tetrads 8; hectads 6 |

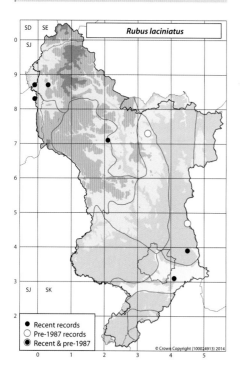

This established bramble is a plant of hedges, waysides and verges. There are recent records scattered throughout the county from New Mills (SJ9986) in the north, through the Monsal Trail at SK2170, to Thulston (SK4131) in the south. It is a cultivated plant of uncertain origin, having divided leaflets making it easily identifiable.

Rubus leptothyrsos G. Braun
A bramble

This native bramble has only been recorded three times, all in the area of Dam Farm, Ednaston (SK2342/2442) between 1961 and 1980. It is a plant of northern Britain (Newton & Randall 2004).

Rubus lindleianus Lees
A bramble

| COUNTY STATUS: Native |
| CONSERVATION STATUS: None |
| FIRST YEAR: 1884 LATEST YEAR: 2012 NO OF RECORDS: 105 |
| RECENT SQUARES: monads 38; tetrads 30; hectads 14 |
| ALL SQUARES: monads 48; tetrads 40; hectads 29 |

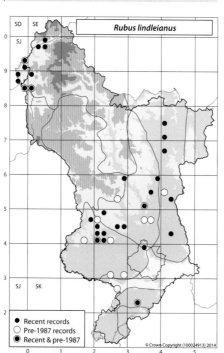

This is one of the more common native brambles. It occurs in hedges, woods, heaths, waysides and waste ground; from Hollingwood (SK4174) and the Longdendale Trail (SK0397) in the north, to Shirley Park Lane (SK2142) and Darley Tip (SK3538) in the south. It is a common and widespread plant of lowland Britain (Newton & Randall 2004).

Rubus macrophyllus Weihe & Nees
A bramble

Linton (1903) states this native bramble occurs locally in hedges, woods and bushy places, as at Alderwasley and Ambergate in 1893 (specimens in Derby Museum). He

gives an earliest date of 1852. Since then it has only been recorded at Ambergate (SK3451) in the 1980s. It is a southern species, with Derbyshire at its northern limit.

Rubus platyacanthus P.J. Muell. & Lef.
A bramble

| COUNTY STATUS: Native |
| CONSERVATION STATUS: None |
| FIRST YEAR: 1889 LATEST YEAR: 2008 NO OF RECORDS: 47 |
| RECENT SQUARES: monads 3; tetrads 3; hectads 2 |
| ALL SQUARES: monads 8; tetrads 8; hectads 17 |

This is a native bramble of hedges, scrub and open woods. It has only been recorded in recent years from Abney Clough (SK2079), Stoke Wood (SK2376) and Shirley (SK2042). However, it has been found throughout the county, from New Mills (SJ98) and Derwent Dale (SK19) in the north, to Sudbury (SK13) and Repton Rocks (SK32) in the south. All the earlier records given here are from Linton (1903).

Rubus pyramidalis Kaltenb.
A bramble

This is a rare native bramble of woods, commons and hedges. The most recent record is from near Repton Shrubs (SK3123) in 1980, though Linton (1903) recorded it from a number of other sites.

Rubus robiae (W.C.R. Watson) Newton
A bramble

There are only three recent records for this native bramble of waysides: Highfield Lane (SK2844), Shirley (SK2042) and Vale House (SK0397). Older records cover the same area: Shirley (SK24) in 1903, Spinneyford Brook (SK2445) in 1969 and Low Leighton (SK0185) in 1979. Nationally it is a plant of northern Britain (Newton & Randall 2004).

Rubus sciocharis (Sudre) W.C.R. Watson
A bramble

This native bramble has only been recorded a few times in Derbyshire. There is one 2002 record from Repton Shrubs (SK3322), and older records for the same site in 1961, plus Highoredish (SK3559) in 1980. There are specimens in Derby Museum by W.M. Rogers from Repton Rocks (SK32) in 1896.

Rubus amplificatus Lees
A bramble

| COUNTY STATUS: Native |
| CONSERVATION STATUS: None |
| FIRST YEAR: 1892 LATEST YEAR: 2000 NO OF RECORDS: 12 |
| RECENT SQUARES: monads 2; tetrads 2; hectads 1 |
| ALL SQUARES: monads 5; tetrads 6; hectads 8 |

This is a native bramble of woods and hedges. All recent records come from the north-west, for example near Thornsett (SK0087) and the New Mills area (SJ9885). It was previously recorded further afield at Baslow (SK2673) in 1969 and Hilton Gravel Pits (SK23K) in 1979. It is mainly a plant of southern Britain (Newton & Randall 2004).

Rubus cardiophyllus Lef. & P.J. Mueller.
A bramble

COUNTY STATUS: Native
CONSERVATION STATUS: None
FIRST YEAR: 1891 LATEST YEAR: 2005 NO OF RECORDS: 16
RECENT SQUARES: monads 2; tetrads 2; hectads 1
ALL SQUARES: monads 5; tetrads 5; hectads 5

This native bramble of heaths and hedges has only two recent records: Highfield Lane (SK2944) and Cross o' the Hands (SK2746). It was previously recorded from the same area plus Monsal Dale (SK17) in the north and Calke (SK32) in the south, both in 1903. Nationally it is mainly a southern species (Newton & Randall 2004).

Rubus cissburiensis W.C. Barton & Riddelsd.
A bramble

This established woodland bramble has only been recorded from two adjacent monads, in the north-west of our area: Torrs Gorge (SJ9985) in 1993 and New Mills (SK0085) in 1996 and 1997. It is a native of southern Britain (Newton & Randall 2004).

Rubus incurvatiformis Edees
A bramble

COUNTY STATUS: Native
CONSERVATION STATUS: None
FIRST YEAR: 1970 LATEST YEAR: 2008 NO OF RECORDS: 8
RECENT SQUARES: monads 4; tetrads 4; hectads 3
ALL SQUARES: monads 6; tetrads 6; hectads 4

All recent records for this native bramble are from the western half of the county: near Glossop (SK0392 & SK0492), near Hartington (SK1361) and Shirley (SK2042). It occurs mainly in north-western Britain with Derbyshire being on the south-eastern limit of its range (Newton & Randall 2004).

Rubus lindebergii P.J. Mueller
A bramble

COUNTY STATUS: Native
CONSERVATION STATUS: None
FIRST YEAR: 1888 LATEST YEAR: 2008 NO OF RECORDS: 57
RECENT SQUARES: monads 12; tetrads 10; hectads 5
ALL SQUARES: monads 17; tetrads 14; hectads 16

This bramble is a native of waysides and heaths. All recent records come from north-western Derbyshire: Stockport (SJ9892), near Highgate (SK0485) and Abney Clough (SK2079). Previously it was also found in the rest of the county: Edensor (SK26), Masson Mill (SK25), Stenson

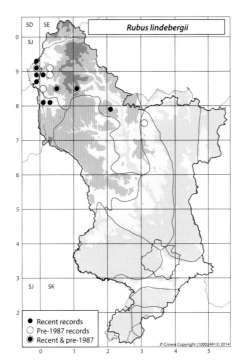

(SK33) and Repton Rocks (SK32) all for 1903. It is a plant of upland northern Britain, with Derbyshire close to the southern edge of its range (Newton & Randall 2004).

Rubus nemoralis P.J. Mueller
A bramble

COUNTY STATUS: Native
CONSERVATION STATUS: None
FIRST YEAR: 1896 LATEST YEAR: 2008 NO OF RECORDS: 78
RECENT SQUARES: monads 29; tetrads 19; hectads 6
ALL SQUARES: monads 40; tetrads 27; hectads 14

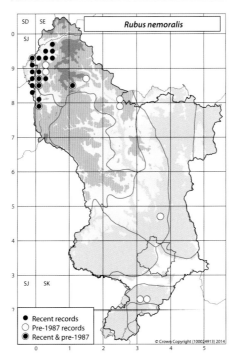

This bramble is a native of waysides and moorland. All recent records are from north-western parts, e.g. Chisworth (SJ9992), New

Mills (SK0085) and Charlesworth (SK0092). It was formerly scattered throughout the county in similar habitats and in carrs. Sites include Grindleford Station (SK27P) and Carver's Rocks (SK3322) in 1978, plus Egginton Common (SK22) and Blackwall (SK24) in 1903.

Rubus pistoris W.C. Barton & Riddelsd.
A bramble

Locally extinct, this native bramble has two old records. One is for Edlaston Hall (SK24) in 1890; the other is Charlesworth (SK09) in 1894. Both were made by W.R. Linton. A specimen collected by R. Smith at Charlesworth (SK0193) in 1980 was described as "probably this species" by A. Newton.

Rubus polyanthemus Lindeb.
A bramble

COUNTY STATUS: Native
CONSERVATION STATUS: None
FIRST YEAR: 1889 LATEST YEAR: 2012 NO OF RECORDS: 50
RECENT SQUARES: monads 19; tetrads 17; hectads 10
ALL SQUARES: monads 29; tetrads 25; hectads 20

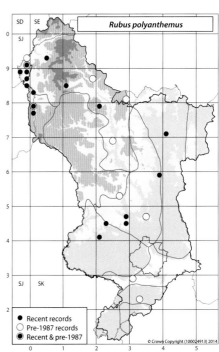

This native bramble occurs in waysides and heaths. Modern records are scattered over northern and central parts, e.g. near Glossop (SK0492), Abney Clough (SK2079), Ogston Hall (SK3859), and Hilcote (SK4457). It was formerly recorded further south, as at Dawson's Rocks (SK32) and near Culland Hall (SK23), both for 1969.

Rubus sprengelii Weihe
A bramble

This is a native plant of woods, hedges and heaths with recent records mainly from northern and central parts, as at Chinley

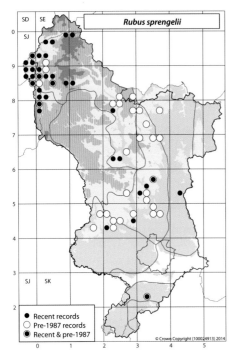

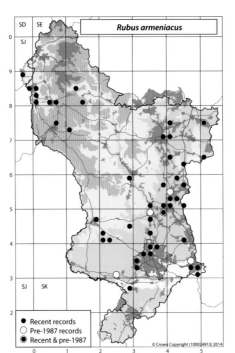

COUNTY STATUS: Native
CONSERVATION STATUS: None
FIRST YEAR: 1882 **LATEST YEAR:** 2008 **NO OF RECORDS:** 151
RECENT SQUARES: monads 57; tetrads 36; hectads 13
ALL SQUARES: monads 87; tetrads 64; hectads 26

(SK0484), Stoke Wood (SK2376), Watts Cliff Quarry (SK2262) and Common Farm Pit (SK2845). Previous records suggest a more central and southerly distribution, as at Egginton Common (SK22) and Dale (SK43) both for 1903. Nationally it is a plant of southern Britain (Newton & Randall 2004).

Rubus anglocandicans Newton
A bramble

COUNTY STATUS: Native
CONSERVATION STATUS: None
FIRST YEAR: 1895 **LATEST YEAR:** 2005 **NO OF RECORDS:** 31
RECENT SQUARES: monads 1; tetrads 1; hectads 1
ALL SQUARES: monads 2; tetrads 3; hectads 6

The only recent record for this native bramble is from Church Lane, Swarkestone (SK3728), where it has been known since 1895. All other records are from southern parts around Derby, for example: Etwall (SK23), Egginton Common (SK22), Repton (SK32) and near Trent Station (SK43), all from 1903. It is a plant of south-eastern Britain on the western edge of its range here.

Rubus armeniacus Focke
Himalayan Giant

COUNTY STATUS: Established (Neophyte)
CONSERVATION STATUS: None
FIRST YEAR: 1949 **LATEST YEAR:** 2013 **NO OF RECORDS:** 70
RECENT SQUARES: monads 55; tetrads 47; hectads 20
ALL SQUARES: monads 60; tetrads 51; hectads 23

Himalayan Giant is an established plant of waysides and waste ground, generally at lower altitudes. It is recently recorded from Stockport (SJ9689) and Markland Grips (SK5074) in the north, through Sandham Lane (SK3949), to Littleover Sewage Works (SK3133) and Willington Gravel Pit (SK2927) in the south. There were previously very few records. This apparent expansion may be either a genuine increase, or merely a reflection of a greater willingness to record introduced plants. It is an aggressive horticultural species of uncertain origins.

Rubus ulmifolius Schott
A bramble

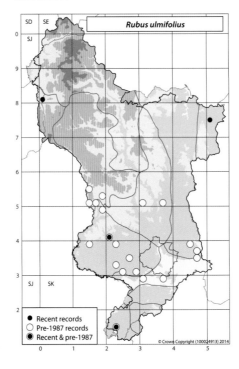

COUNTY STATUS: Native
CONSERVATION STATUS: None
FIRST YEAR: 1873 **LATEST YEAR:** 2008 **NO OF RECORDS:** 60
RECENT SQUARES: monads 3; tetrads 4; hectads 4
ALL SQUARES: monads 19; tetrads 22; hectads 23

This native bramble has only four recent records from widely separated parts of the county: Whaley Bridge (SK0181), near Hazelmere Farm (SK5174), Shirley (SK2141) and near Catton (SK21H). There are numerous older records that fill the areas between: Calton Lees (SK26) in 1903, Shottlegate (SK34) for 1903, and Swarkestone (SK32) in 1969. It is a lowland plant of southern Britain (Newton & Randall 2004), towards the northern edge of its range here.

Rubus winteri P.J. Mueller ex Focke
A bramble

COUNTY STATUS: Native
CONSERVATION STATUS: None
FIRST YEAR: 1889 **LATEST YEAR:** 2005 **NO OF RECORDS:** 12
RECENT SQUARES: monads 2; tetrads 1; hectads 1
ALL SQUARES: monads 4; tetrads 2; hectads 3

This rare native bramble was discovered on the lane at Stydd Farm by W.R. Linton in 1889. It was refound there (SK1641) in 1979 by R. Smith and at Whitwell Wood (SK5277) in 1980. It was found again at its classic Stydd Lane location in 2005. Nationally it is a plant of southern Britain (Newton & Randall 2004). Voucher specimens at Derby Museum.

Rubus bartonii Newton
A bramble

This native bramble was discovered in The Torrs (SK0085 v.c.58) in 1996 by D. Earl. It was subsequently found on the Derbyshire side of the border in New Mills (SK0085) in 1997 and 2008. Nationally it is a plant of south-western Britain and is on the north-eastern edge of its distribution here (Newton & Randall 2004). It is sometimes grown in fruit farms.

Rubus criniger (E.F. Linton) Rogers
A bramble

COUNTY STATUS: Native
CONSERVATION STATUS: None
FIRST YEAR: 1848 **LATEST YEAR:** 2008 **NO OF RECORDS:** 40
RECENT SQUARES: monads 7; tetrads 5; hectads 2
ALL SQUARES: monads 13; tetrads 11; hectads 8

There are seven recent records for this native bramble of waysides and woods including: Carver's Rocks (SK3322), Shirley (SK2042) and Yeldersley (SK2243). Previously it was recorded from much the same area but appears to have been more frequent: Bradley Wood (SK1946), Cross o'

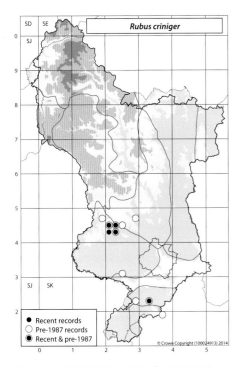

the Hands (SK2846) and Bretby (SK2923). It is a plant of southern Britain (Newton & Randall 2004).

Rubus painteri Edees
A bramble
This native bramble has only ever been recorded by D. Earl from three monads, all in the Whaley Bridge area and on one day in 2007 (SK0079, SK0179 & SK0180).

Rubus vestitus Weihe
A bramble
This is a native bramble of waysides and woods. It is one of the commoner and more widespread species, having been

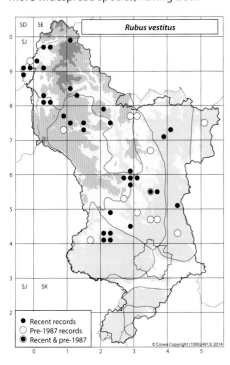

COUNTY STATUS: Native
CONSERVATION STATUS: None
FIRST YEAR: 1884 LATEST YEAR: 2013 NO OF RECORDS: 108
RECENT SQUARES: monads 43; tetrads 35; hectads 17
ALL SQUARES: monads 56; tetrads 47; hectads 32

recorded recently from the Longdendale Trail (SK0497) and Brimington Common (SK4172) in the north, to Shirley Park Lane (SK2142) and Exhibition Plantation (SK4250) in the south. It was previously recorded further south, as between Calke and Pistern Hill (SK32) and at West Hallam Station (SK43), both for 1903.

Rubus mucronulatus Boreau
A bramble
This is a native bramble of southern parts. There are recent records from only two sites: Carver's Rocks (SK3222 & 3322) in 2005 and Repton Shrubs (SK3123) in 2005. Previously it was recorded at Rosliston (SK21) in 1873 (voucher at Bolton Museum), then was not seen again until R. Smith found it in 1979 at Swains Park (SK2917). It is a plant of northern Britain on its southern limit here (Newton & Randall 2004).

Rubus wirralensis A. Newton
A bramble

COUNTY STATUS: Native
CONSERVATION STATUS: None
FIRST YEAR: 1979 LATEST YEAR: 2005 NO OF RECORDS: 14
RECENT SQUARES: monads 8; tetrads 6; hectads 3
ALL SQUARES: monads 8; tetrads 6; hectads 4

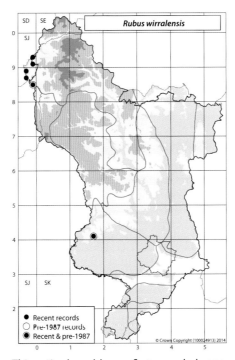

This native bramble was first recorded near Stydd Farm (SK1641) in 1979 by A. Newton. Since then it has mostly been found in the extreme north-west, as at Stockport (SJ9688),

---

New Mills (SJ9885) and Broadbottom (SJ9992 v.c.58). It is widespread in western Britain, with Derbyshire near its eastern limit (Newton & Randall 2004).

Rubus griffithianus Rogers
A bramble
This native bramble is known from just one recent site, Carver's Rocks (SK3322) in 2005. There are five earlier records, all from the same part of the county and dating from 1896 to 1969. Nationally it is a plant of central Britain, with Derbyshire on its southern limit (Newton & Randall 2004).

Rubus leightonii Lees ex Leighton
A bramble

COUNTY STATUS: Native
CONSERVATION STATUS: None
FIRST YEAR: 1896 LATEST YEAR: 1980 NO OF RECORDS: 7
RECENT SQUARES: monads 0; tetrads 0; hectads 0
ALL SQUARES: monads 1; tetrads 1; hectads 4

There are no recent records for this native bramble. Linton (1903) noted it between Willington and Findern (SK23), and at Bretby (SK32). R. Smith found it in 1980 at Hilton Gravel Pits (SK2431). It is a plant of southern Britain, close to the northern edge of its range here (Newton & Randall 2004).

Rubus newbouldii Bab.
A bramble

COUNTY STATUS: Native
CONSERVATION STATUS: None
FIRST YEAR: 1897 LATEST YEAR: 2007 NO OF RECORDS: 33
RECENT SQUARES: monads 9; tetrads 7; hectads 4
ALL SQUARES: monads 12; tetrads 9; hectads 11

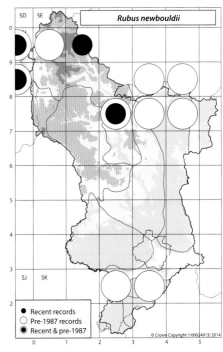

This is a native bramble of scrub, hedges and ravines. All recent records are in northern Derbyshire, from Stockport (SJ9787) and Compstall (SJ9690), to Abney Clough (SK27E) and Stoke Wood (SK2376). Linton's 1903 Flora lists it for the south of the county, as at Willington (SK22) and Repton Shrubs (SK32).

Rubus raduloides (Rogers) Sudre
A bramble

This native bramble is mainly known from specimens determined by A. Newton in Derby Museum herbarium, collected by W.R. Linton or T. Gibbs in the 1890s: Stanton Moor (SK26), Repton Shrubs (SK32), Wingerworth (SK36) and Brierley Wood (SK37). More recently it is known only from Clough Wood, Wensley (SK2461 & 2561) in 1980.

Rubus anisacanthos G. Braun
A bramble

This native bramble is known from two recent records both made in 2008, Shirley (SK2241) and Bradley Wood (SK1946). Previously it was recorded over a wider area, including Wirksworth (SK25) in 1899 and Horsley (SK34) in 1896, back until the earliest record from Brailsford (SK24) in 1888.

Rubus distractiformis Newton
A bramble

COUNTY STATUS: Native	
CONSERVATION STATUS: None	
FIRST YEAR: 1894 LATEST YEAR: 2008 NO OF RECORDS: 46	
RECENT SQUARES: monads 29; tetrads 16; hectads 5	
ALL SQUARES: monads 32; tetrads 18; hectads 5	

This native bramble has only ever been recorded from north-western Derbyshire

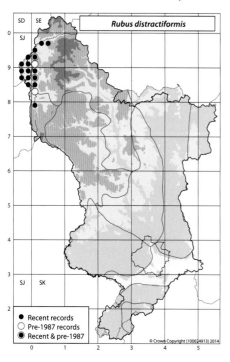

between Charlesworth (SK0992), Broadbottom (SJ9892), New Mills (SK0087) and Taxal (SK0079). Nationally it is a plant of the West Midlands on the eastern edge of its range here (Newton & Randall 2004).

Rubus drejeri G. Jensen ex Lange
A bramble

There are no recent records for this native bramble of woods, hedges and scrub. The latest is from Unthank Lane (SK3074) in 1981, with only four earlier records. These are: Wirksworth (SK25), Unstone (SK37), Brierley Wood (SK37) and "between Peacock Inn and Horsley Gate" (SK37), all from Linton (1903). Nationally it is a plant of northern Britain (Newton & Randall 2004).

Rubus infestus Weihe ex Boenn.
A bramble

COUNTY STATUS: Native	
CONSERVATION STATUS: None	
FIRST YEAR: 1889 LATEST YEAR: 2005 NO OF RECORDS: 25	
RECENT SQUARES: monads 4; tetrads 3; hectads 2	
ALL SQUARES: monads 7; tetrads 6; hectads 9	

This is a native bramble of open woods and hedges. Recent records are from three tetrads: Rowarth (SK0189) in the north, plus High Field Lane (SK2844) and Shirley (SK2141) in the south. Previously it was also recorded scattered between these sites, as at Hathersage Booths (SK28) and Ambergate (SK35), both records being for 1903. It is a northern species in Britain, towards the southern edge of its distribution here (Newton & Randall 2004).

Rubus adenanthoides Newton
A bramble

This native bramble was discovered at Vale House (SK0397) by D. Earl in 2008. There are no other records.

Rubus bloxamianus Coleman ex Purchas
A bramble

COUNTY STATUS: Native	
CONSERVATION STATUS: None	
FIRST YEAR: 1888 LATEST YEAR: 2002 NO OF RECORDS: 6	
RECENT SQUARES: monads 0; tetrads 0; hectads 0	
ALL SQUARES: monads 3; tetrads 3; hectads 4	

There are no recent localised records for this native bramble. It was previously recorded sporadically across southern Derbyshire: Willington (SK22) in 1890, Repton (SK3124) in 1961 and Horsley Carr (SK3842) in 1979. It is a plant of central England, on the northern edge of its range here (Newton & Randall 2004).

Rubus echinatoides (Rogers) Dallman
A bramble

This is a native bramble of woods and

COUNTY STATUS: Native	
CONSERVATION STATUS: None	
FIRST YEAR: 1893 LATEST YEAR: 2008 NO OF RECORDS: 60	
RECENT SQUARES: monads 10; tetrads 9; hectads 4	
ALL SQUARES: monads 26; tetrads 24; hectads 20	

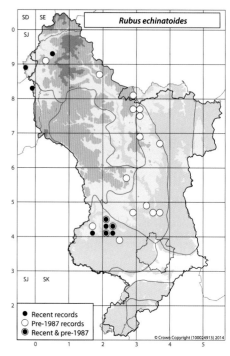

hedges. Recent records are from north-western Derbyshire (Glossop SK0492 & Kettleshulme SJ9982 v.c.58) and from the Shirley area (SK2041 & SK2142). Previously it was recorded as common throughout the county. Records extended as far south as Pistern Hill (SK32) in 1903.

Rubus echinatus Lindley
A bramble

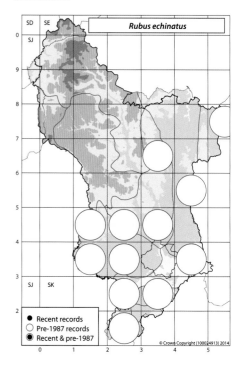

COUNTY STATUS: Native	
CONSERVATION STATUS: None	
FIRST YEAR: 1888 **LATEST YEAR:** 1980 **NO OF RECORDS:** 29	
RECENT SQUARES: monads 0; tetrads 0; hectads 0	
ALL SQUARES: monads 9; tetrads 8; hectads 12	

There are no recent records for this native bramble. It was previously recorded as an occasional plant of hedges and woods in the southern and eastern parts of the area: Swain's Park SK2917 in 1980 and Hilton Gravel Pits SK2431 in 1979. Clapham (1969) recorded it for Thurvaston (SK2438), and between Repton and Repton Shrubs (SK3024). Earlier, Linton (1903) gave records for a larger area of the south (Edlaston SK14, Linton SK21 & Risley Park SK43) plus the Magnesian Limestone at Creswell Crags (SK57). Nationally it is a plant of southern Britain towards its northern limits here (Newton & Randall 2004).

Rubus euryanthemus W.C.R. Watson
A bramble

COUNTY STATUS: Native	
CONSERVATION STATUS: None	
FIRST YEAR: 1980 **LATEST YEAR:** 1998 **NO OF RECORDS:** 2	
RECENT SQUARES: monads 1; tetrads 1; hectads 1	
ALL SQUARES: monads 2; tetrads 2; hectads 2	

This native bramble has only one recent record, Stockport (SJ9788), and an older one from Hayfield (SK0486) in 1980 (specimen in Derby Museum). It is a southern species on the northern edge of its range here (Newton & Randall 2004).

Rubus flexuosus P.J. Mueller & Lef.
A bramble

This is a native woodland species of deep shade in southern parts. It was first found at Bryan's Coppice (SK3619) in 1848, then at Carver's Rocks (SK3322) in 1888, and recorded there again almost 100 years later by R. Smith in 1978 and 1987 (specimens in Derby and Bolton Museums). It is a southern species, with Derbyshire on the northern edge of its British range (Newton & Randall 2004).

Rubus insectifolius Lef. & P.J. Mueller
A bramble

There are no recent reports for this native bramble. It was recorded for SK38 in 1980 and just listed for the county as a whole by W.R. Linton in 1899. It is a plant of south-eastern Britain (Newton & Randall 2004).

Rubus pallidus Weihe
A bramble

This is a native bramble, known from northern Derbyshire. The latest record was made at Owler Lee (SK3178) in 1980 by R. Smith. Prior to this, Linton's (1903) Flora

COUNTY STATUS: Native	
CONSERVATION STATUS: None	
FIRST YEAR: 1897 **LATEST YEAR:** 1980 **NO OF RECORDS:** 9	
RECENT SQUARES: monads 0; tetrads 0; hectads 0	
ALL SQUARES: monads 1; tetrads 1; hectads 3	

lists just a few localities: Owler Bar (SK27) in 1898, Holmesfield (SK37) in 1897 and Owler Car (SK38). Nationally it is a plant of woods and copses mainly in southern England (Newton & Randall 2004).

Rubus porphyrocaulis Newton
A bramble

COUNTY STATUS: Native	
CONSERVATION STATUS: None	
FIRST YEAR: 1970 **LATEST YEAR:** 2008 **NO OF RECORDS:** 15	
RECENT SQUARES: monads 8; tetrads 7; hectads 4	
ALL SQUARES: monads 10; tetrads 9; hectads 4	

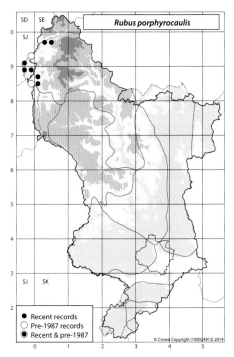

Rubus porphyrocaulis

● Recent records
○ Pre-1987 records
◉ Recent & pre-1987

© Crown Copyright (100024913) 2014

This native bramble only occurs in the extreme north-western parts of the county (Stockport SJ9791 v.c.58, New Mills SK0087 & SK0085), where records range from 1970 to 2008. Nationally it is restricted to the river valleys of the upper Mersey catchment (Newton & Randall 2004).

Rubus radula Weihe ex Boenn.
A bramble

COUNTY STATUS: Native	
CONSERVATION STATUS: None	
FIRST YEAR: 1883 **LATEST YEAR:** 1979 **NO OF RECORDS:** 12	
RECENT SQUARES: monads 0; tetrads 0; hectads 0	
ALL SQUARES: monads 1; tetrads 1; hectads 9	

This is a native bramble of hedges, woods and commons, with no modern records. It was recorded as rather rare by Linton (1903), ranging from Killamarsh (SK48) and

High Dale (SK17) in the north, to Kirk Hallam (SK44) and Denby (SK34) in the south. It was last recorded in 1979 at Hilton Gravel Pits (SK2431) by R. Smith and A. Newton.

Rubus rubristylus W.C.R. Watson
A bramble

COUNTY STATUS: Native	
CONSERVATION STATUS: DRDB (Cat 6)	
FIRST YEAR: 1894 **LATEST YEAR:** 1965 **NO OF RECORDS:** 6	
RECENT SQUARES: monads 0; tetrads 0; hectads 0	
ALL SQUARES: monads 1; tetrads 1; hectads 2	

Locally extinct, this rare native bramble of hedges and bushy places, ranged from Chisworth (SK09 in 1965 & 1894) in the north, to Repton Rocks (SK32 in 1903) in the south. Its local loss is part of a more general decline over central England (Newton & Randall 2004).

Rubus rudis Weihe
A bramble

The only recent records of this native bramble of waysides and bushy places are from Codnor Gate (SK4250) in 2000 and 2011. A nearby site at Codnor (SK4348) found by W.R. Linton in 1897 and then by R. Smith in 1979, has been lost to opencasting. Linton (1903) also recorded it on slopes west of Matlock Bath (SK25). It is mainly a plant of southern Britain (Newton & Randall 2004).

Rubus rufescens Lef. & P.J. Mueller
A bramble

This native bramble of woods and hedges has been recorded in recent times scattered over southern Derbyshire: Shirley Park Lane (SK2142), Mapperley Reserve (SK4343), and Leabrooks-Somercotes

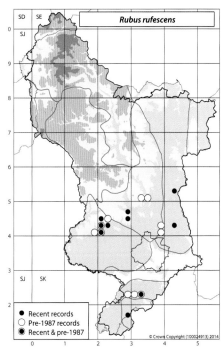

Rubus rufescens

● Recent records
○ Pre-1987 records
◉ Recent & pre-1987

© Crown Copyright (100024913) 2014

COUNTY STATUS: Native	
CONSERVATION STATUS: None	
FIRST YEAR: 1892 **LATEST YEAR:** 2012 **NO OF RECORDS:** 41	
RECENT SQUARES: monads 12; tetrads 10; hectads 5	
ALL SQUARES: monads 22; tetrads 18; hectads 12	

(SK4253). Previous records are from the same area, as well as further north as at Brierley Wood (SK37) in 1903. It is mainly a plant of southern Britain (Newton & Randall 2004).

Rubus subtercanens W.C.R. Watson
A bramble

All three records of this native bramble are from the Dore area (SK3281) where it was recorded between 1897 and 1980. Nationally it is virtually restricted to Lancashire and Cheshire (Newton & Randall 2004).

Rubus dasyphyllus (Rogers) E. Marshall
A bramble

COUNTY STATUS: Native	
CONSERVATION STATUS: None	
FIRST YEAR: 1848 **LATEST YEAR:** 2012 **NO OF RECORDS:** 247	
RECENT SQUARES: monads 151; tetrads 95; hectads 25	
ALL SQUARES: monads 176; tetrads 120; hectads 32	

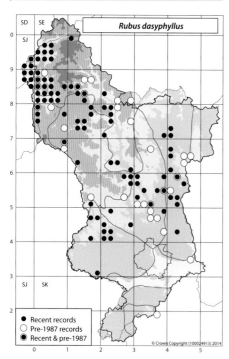

This native of woods, hedges and commons is one of the most frequent brambles in the county (Smith 1982). Recent records range from the Longdendale Trail (SK0497) and Brimington Common (SK4172) in the north, to Scropton (SK1930) and Mapperley Reserve (SK4343) in the south. It is also one of the commonest brambles nationally (Newton & Randall 2004).

Rubus hylocharis W.C.R. Watson
A bramble

This is a native bramble of woods and

COUNTY STATUS: Native	
CONSERVATION STATUS: None	
FIRST YEAR: 1892 **LATEST YEAR:** 2008 **NO OF RECORDS:** 76	
RECENT SQUARES: monads 24; tetrads 16; hectads 5	
ALL SQUARES: monads 38; tetrads 28; hectads 14	

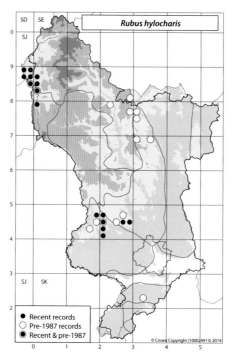

hedges. There are recent records from two distinct areas: the north-west (New Mills SJ9885 & SK0086); and the Shirley area in the south (Shirley Park SK2042). This probably reflects recording effort, as previously it was recorded more widely, from Whaley Bridge in the north (SK08) for 1903, through Dore (SK2980) and Holymoorside (SK3469) both in 1969, to Dawson's Rocks (SK3322) for 1969 in the south. It is mainly a southern species in Britain (Newton & Randall 2004).

Rubus bagnallianus Edees
A bramble

This is a native bramble with a very narrow distribution in central England (Newton & Randall 2004). There are just two localised records from the Shirley area (SK2141) in the 1970s, plus the possibility that W.R. Linton recorded it in the 1900s.

Rubus conjungens (Bab.) Rogers
A bramble

There is one recent record for this native bramble, from Woodhead (SK1199) in 2007. Previously Linton (1903) recorded it for five localities in central and southern parts of the county including: Wirksworth (SK25), Doveridge (SK13) and Bretby (SK22). It is a plant of southern Britain (Newton & Randall 2004).

Rubus eboracensis W.C.R. Watson
A bramble

COUNTY STATUS: Native	
CONSERVATION STATUS: None	
FIRST YEAR: 1906 **LATEST YEAR:** 2008 **NO OF RECORDS:** 26	
RECENT SQUARES: monads 13; tetrads 11; hectads 6	
ALL SQUARES: monads 16; tetrads 15; hectads 14	

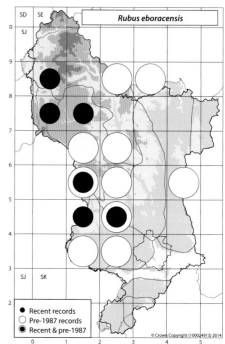

This native bramble occurs sparingly today in the western half of the county, from Fernilee (SK0180) in the north, to Shirley (SK2141) in the south. Earlier records cover much the same area but appear to be rarer, thus Clapham's (1969) comment about the species being overlooked appears to be correct. It is a plant of northern England and southern Scotland (Newton & Randall 2004).

Rubus hindii A.L. Bull
A bramble

This newly described native bramble has only ever been recorded three times in Derbyshire: twice in the Shirley area (SK2141 & SK2241) during 2008 and at Newton Station (SJ9984 v.c.58) in 1997.

Rubus intensior Edees
A bramble

COUNTY STATUS: Native	
CONSERVATION STATUS: None	
FIRST YEAR: 1891 **LATEST YEAR:** 2012 **NO OF RECORDS:** 54	
RECENT SQUARES: monads 28; tetrads 21; hectads 10	
ALL SQUARES: monads 37; tetrads 30; hectads 16	

This native bramble is recorded from north-western and central parts of the county. There are records for example from Stockport (SJ9888) and Buxton (SK0573) in the north-west, and from Common

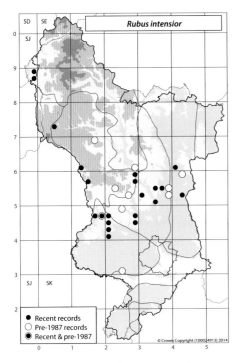

COUNTY STATUS: Native

CONSERVATION STATUS: None

FIRST YEAR: 1873 LATEST YEAR: 2008 NO OF RECORDS: 29

RECENT SQUARES: monads 8; tetrads 7; hectads 5

ALL SQUARES: monads 19; tetrads 19; hectads 15

Great Hucklow (SK1677) in the north through Pye Bridge (SK4453) to Swain's Park (SK2917) in the south.

Rubus rubriflorus Purchas
A bramble

COUNTY STATUS: Native

CONSERVATION STATUS: None

FIRST YEAR: 1887 LATEST YEAR: 2012 NO OF RECORDS: 47

RECENT SQUARES: monads 5; tetrads 6; hectads 3

ALL SQUARES: monads 12; tetrads 12; hectads 17

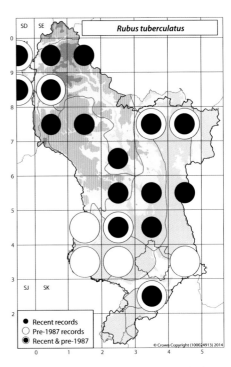

Pit Farm (SK2845) and near Pye Bridge (SK4353) in the centre. Nationally it is mainly a plant of Lancashire and Yorkshire (Newton & Randall 2004).

Rubus nemorosus Hayne & Willd.
A bramble

This native bramble was discovered at Whaley Bridge (SK0180) on a shaded bank in 2007 by D. Earl. There are no other records.

Rubus pruinosus Arrh.
A bramble

This native bramble has been recently recorded throughout the county from

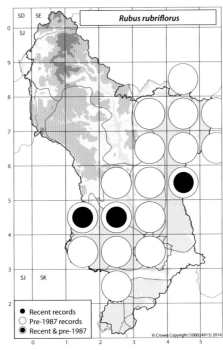

This bramble is a native plant of hedgerows. All recent records are from the Shirley area (SK14Q, SK2145 & SK2241) apart from an isolated one at Newton (SK4559). Earlier records cover a wider area from Eckington (SK48) in the north, to Egginton Common (SK22) in the south, both records from 1903. Nationally it is a plant of the north Midlands (Newton & Randall 2004).

Rubus tuberculatus Bab.
A bramble

COUNTY STATUS: Native

CONSERVATION STATUS: None

FIRST YEAR: 1896 LATEST YEAR: 2008 NO OF RECORDS: 70

RECENT SQUARES: monads 46; tetrads 37; hectads 16

ALL SQUARES: monads 50; tetrads 41; hectads 20

This native bramble occurs across Derbyshire from Woodhead (SK1099) in the north, through Leabrooks (SK4353), to Carver's Rocks (SK3322) in the south.

However, it is more frequently recorded from the Marple Bridge area (SJ9688 & SJ9890) than elsewhere.

Rubus warrenii Sudre
A bramble

COUNTY STATUS: Native

CONSERVATION STATUS: None

FIRST YEAR: 1883 LATEST YEAR: 2012 NO OF RECORDS: 218

RECENT SQUARES: monads 118; tetrads 75; hectads 22

ALL SQUARES: monads 132; tetrads 87; hectads 30

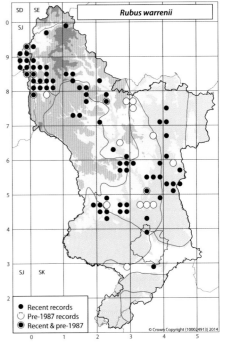

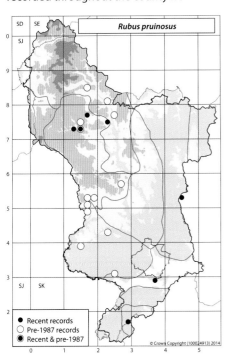

This is a native bramble of hedges and waysides throughout Derbyshire, although it becomes increasingly rare in the extreme south of the county. There are

recent reports from Charlesworth (SK0992) and near Hollingwood (SK4174) in the north, to Mugginton (SK2844) and Swarkestone (SK3728) in the south. It is a plant of northern England (Edees 1975).

Rubus caesius L.
Dewberry

COUNTY STATUS: Native	
CONSERVATION STATUS: None	
FIRST YEAR: 1789 LATEST YEAR: 2013 NO OF RECORDS: 246	
RECENT SQUARES: monads 72; tetrads 61; hectads 21	
ALL SQUARES: monads 105; tetrads 82; hectads 31	

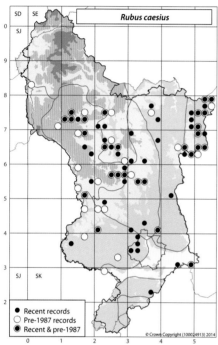

Dewberry is a native scrambling shrub of wood edges, hedges, damp woods and thickets. It is occasional in the White Peak (Upperdale SK1772 & the Via Gellia SK2756) and on the Magnesian Limestone (Scarcliffe Park SK5070). Elsewhere it is very rare (Ticknall SK3623 & Trent Lock SK4931), or virtually absent as in the Dark and South West Peak Areas.

Potentilla fruticosa L.
Shrubby Cinquefoil

Shrubby Cinquefoil is a very rare, casual shrub of waste ground and waysides. It is much grown in gardens and amenity plantings from where it escapes. There are only five records, all between 1997 and 2012: Mickleover (SK3035), Holloway (SK3256), Stretton (SK3960), Woodside (SK4443) and Hallam Fields Road (SK4739). It is a native of north-eastern England and is a species of conservation concern, but only where native.

Potentilla anserina L.
Silverweed

COUNTY STATUS: Native	
CONSERVATION STATUS: None	
FIRST YEAR: 1789 LATEST YEAR: 2013 NO OF RECORDS: 2,106	
RECENT SQUARES: monads 984; tetrads 538; hectads 40	
ALL SQUARES: monads 1,045; tetrads 556; hectads 40	

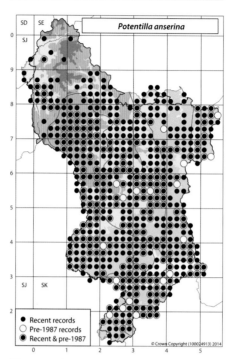

Silverweed is a creeping native perennial of waysides, waste ground and damp pastures. It is common throughout the county except for some of the high moorland areas of the north and north-west.

Potentilla argentea L.
Hoary Cinquefoil

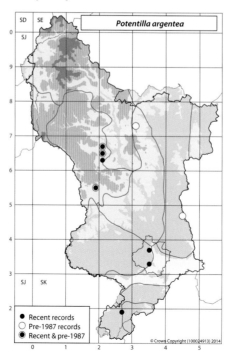

COUNTY STATUS: Native	
CONSERVATION STATUS: DRDB (Cat2), NT, A, B	
FIRST YEAR: 1710 LATEST YEAR: 2012 NO OF RECORDS: 31	
RECENT SQUARES: monads 8; tetrads 7; hectads 4	
ALL SQUARES: monads 11; tetrads 9; hectads 7	

Hoary Cinquefoil is a very rare, native perennial of dry sandy grasslands and waysides. The majority of records currently come from the White Peak (Over Haddon SK2066 and Parwich SK1854). However, there is a small group of records from the south of the county (Friar Gate Station SK3436 & Linton SK2618) which may be introductions. Previously it was more widely spread with records from Bleak House (SK3072) and Langley Mill Flash (SK4447). Nationally it has also shown a decline probably due to habitat loss (Preston et al. 2002).

Potentilla recta L.
Sulphur Cinquefoil

COUNTY STATUS: Casual	
CONSERVATION STATUS: None	
FIRST YEAR: 1969 LATEST YEAR: 2009 NO OF RECORDS: 12	
RECENT SQUARES: monads 4; tetrads 4; hectads 3	
ALL SQUARES: monads 11; tetrads 10; hectads 7	

Sulphur Cinquefoil is a very rare, casual perennial of waste ground, and a native of continental Europe. All recent records are in the Derby/Long Eaton area (Derby SK33, Shipley SK4443 & Lock Lane SK4831) but it was previously recorded more widely (Rowsley Sidings SK2665 & Lees Common SK3476). It is grown in gardens for ornament but can also be a contaminant of grass seed.

Potentilla norvegica L.
Ternate-leaved Cinquefoil

Ternate-leaved Cinquefoil is a very rare, casual perennial of waste ground and waysides, probably introduced as a contaminant of grain or bird-seed. The only records are from: Chester Green (SK3536) in 1985, Derby (SK3136) in 1969 and Trent (SK4931) in 1969. It is indigenous to northern and central Europe.

Potentilla crantzii (Crantz) Beck ex Fritsch
Alpine Cinquefoil

COUNTY STATUS: Native	
CONSERVATION STATUS: DRDB (Cat3), NS, A, B	
FIRST YEAR: 1800 LATEST YEAR: 2004 NO OF RECORDS: 16	
RECENT SQUARES: monads 3; tetrads 2; hectads 2	
ALL SQUARES: monads 3; tetrads 2; hectads 3	

Alpine Cinquefoil is a very rare, low-growing native perennial of rocky places in limestone grassland. As a native species, it has only been recorded in recent times from Monks Dale (SK1374 & 1375). Previous records are from the same site in the 1970s and Buxton (SK07) in 1800. The latter was collected by the Rev. Gisborne; a voucher specimen is in Cambridge University Herbarium. The plant was also found as a casual on Hadfield Tip (SK0196) in 1989. Elsewhere it occurs infrequently in upland Britain, and its Derbyshire locality is the most southern site in England. It is Nationally Scarce (Stewart *et al.* 1994).

Potentilla tabernaemontani Asch.
Spring Cinquefoil

COUNTY STATUS: Native
CONSERVATION STATUS: DRDB (Cat3), NS, A, B, C
FIRST YEAR: 1801 LATEST YEAR: 2013 NO OF RECORDS: 310
RECENT SQUARES: monads 58; tetrads 37; hectads 11
ALL SQUARES: monads 74; tetrads 47; hectads 12

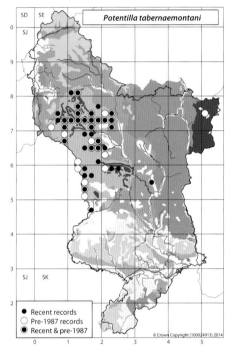

Spring Cinquefoil is an occasional native perennial of the White Peak. This attractive

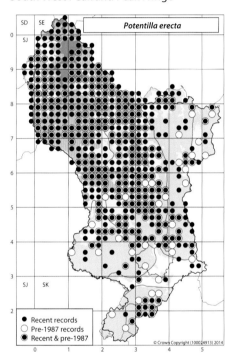

plant grows in grassland on shallow soils over limestone outcrops, mainly along the Wye valley and tributary dales (Deep Dale SK0971, Biggin Dale SK1458 & Stoney Middleton SK2275). The only other recent record comes from the limestone outlier at Crich Cliff (SK3455). It was previously recorded from Markland Grips (SK5074) in 1969 but could not be relocated in 1990. Outside Derbyshire it is very local throughout Britain and is Nationally Scarce.

Potentilla erecta (L.) Raeusch.
Tormentil

Tormentil is a low-growing native perennial of grassland, heaths and moors on well-drained acid to neutral soils. It is common throughout the White Peak, Dark Peak, South West Peak and Peak Fringe

COUNTY STATUS: Native
CONSERVATION STATUS: ERL
FIRST YEAR: 1789 LATEST YEAR: 2013 NO OF RECORDS: 3,139
RECENT SQUARES: monads 1,024; tetrads 462; hectads 40
ALL SQUARES: monads 1,106; tetrads 494; hectads 40

but is only occasional elsewhere. Both native subspecies have been recorded: ssp. *erecta* (Hope Valley SK1682, Stoney Cloud SK4737) and ssp. *strictissima* (Zimmeter) A.J. Richards (Leash Fen SK2874).

Potentilla × *suberecta* Zimmeter
A hybrid cinquefoil

COUNTY STATUS: Native
CONSERVATION STATUS: None
FIRST YEAR: 1893 LATEST YEAR: 1997 NO OF RECORDS: 9
RECENT SQUARES: monads 1; tetrads 1; hectads 1
ALL SQUARES: monads 4; tetrads 4; hectads 6

This hybrid cinquefoil is a very rare, native perennial of grasslands, heaths and rough ground. The only recent record is from Wingerworth (SK3767) in 1997, but earlier ones include: Chisworth (SK09) in 1903, Nether Heage (SK3551) in 1966 and Carver's Rocks (SK3322) in 1973. It is the hybrid of Tormentil (*P. erecta*) and Trailing Tormentil (*P. anglica*).

Potentilla anglica Laichard.
Trailing Tormentil

COUNTY STATUS: Native
CONSERVATION STATUS: None
FIRST YEAR: 1881 LATEST YEAR: 2012 NO OF RECORDS: 168
RECENT SQUARES: monads 88; tetrads 87; hectads 26
ALL SQUARES: monads 114; tetrads 108; hectads 33

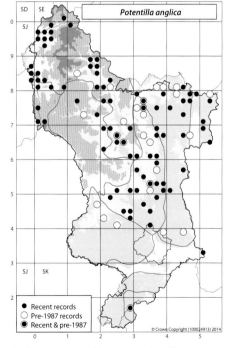

Trailing Tormentil is an occasional native perennial of wood margins, field

Spring Cinquefoil (*Potentilla tabernaemontani*), Tansley Dale (SK1774), May 2005 (Nick Moyes)

edges, waysides and waste ground. It occurs scattered throughout the county from Upper Longdendale (SK1099) and Ladybower (SK1687) in the north, to Woodlands Field (SK3440) and Swainspark (SK2916) in the south.

Potentilla × *mixta* Nolte ex Rchb.
Hybrid Cinquefoil

COUNTY STATUS: Native
CONSERVATION STATUS: None
FIRST YEAR: 1887 LATEST YEAR: 2013 NO OF RECORDS: 30
RECENT SQUARES: monads 11; tetrads 11; hectads 8
ALL SQUARES: monads 19; tetrads 19; hectads 12

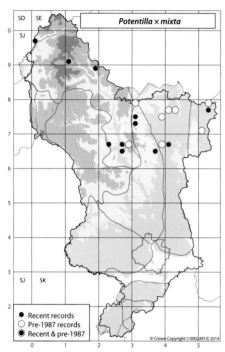

Hybrid Cinquefoil is a very rare, native perennial of waysides and waste ground. Modern records are mostly from the northern half of Derbyshire (Snake Plantation SK1091, Darley Dale SK2664, & Whitwell Wood SK5277). It was previously more common further south (Dove Dale SK15 in 1887 & Kedleston Park SK34 in 1903). This hybrid of Trailing Tormentil (*P. anglica*) and Creeping Cinquefoil (*P. reptans*) often occurs in the absence of its parents.

Potentilla reptans L.
Creeping Cinquefoil

COUNTY STATUS: Native
CONSERVATION STATUS: None
FIRST YEAR: 1789 LATEST YEAR: 2013 NO OF RECORDS: 2,530
RECENT SQUARES: monads 1,118; tetrads 560; hectads 41
ALL SQUARES: monads 1,190; tetrads 575; hectads 41

Creeping Cinquefoil is a common native perennial of waysides, waste ground, cultivated land and open grasslands. It is widespread throughout the county except

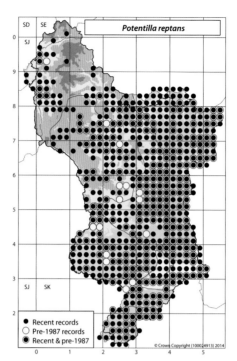

for the White Peak, where it is more local, and the Dark Peak, where it is absent from large areas.

Potentilla sterilis (L.) Garcke
Barren Strawberry

COUNTY STATUS: Native
CONSERVATION STATUS: None
FIRST YEAR: 1789 LATEST YEAR: 2013 NO OF RECORDS: 1,254
RECENT SQUARES: monads 548; tetrads 346; hectads 36
ALL SQUARES: monads 578; tetrads 357; hectads 37

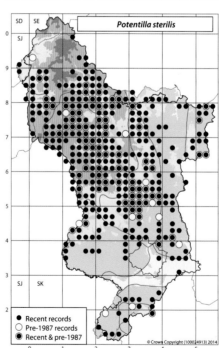

Barren Strawberry is a frequent native perennial of grasslands, light woods, walls and rock crevices on neutral to calcareous substrates. It grows throughout the county

though is more frequent in the White Peak, Peak Fringe and adjacent areas of the Dark Peak.

Comarum palustre L.
Marsh Cinquefoil

COUNTY STATUS: Native
CONSERVATION STATUS: DRDB (Cat5b), A, B
FIRST YEAR: 1763 LATEST YEAR: 2012 NO OF RECORDS: 68
RECENT SQUARES: monads 12; tetrads 10; hectads 8
ALL SQUARES: monads 24; tetrads 20; hectads 18

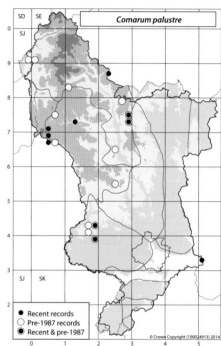

Marsh Cinquefoil is a very rare, native perennial of wet organic substrates. It grows occasionally in lowland fens but is more characteristic of moorlands. Its current distribution is in the central regions of the county (Leash Fen SK2874, Leap Edge SK0469 & Quilow Pond SK1843). It was previously scattered throughout Derbyshire, from Charlesworth Coombs (SK0191) in the north, to Gresley (SK21) in the south. It has also declined nationally due to drainage and other agricultural changes (Preston *et al.* 2002).

Fragaria vesca L.
Wild Strawberry

COUNTY STATUS: Native
CONSERVATION STATUS: ERL
FIRST YEAR: 1789 LATEST YEAR: 2013 NO OF RECORDS: 1,157
RECENT SQUARES: monads 393; tetrads 272; hectads 36
ALL SQUARES: monads 433; tetrads 293; hectads 37

Wild Strawberry is an occasional native perennial of grassland, light woods and scrub on calcareous to slightly acid soils. It is also sometimes grown in gardens from where it can escape into the wild. It is recorded throughout the county, though

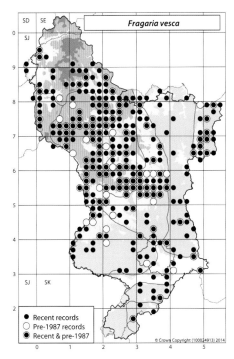

Fragaria vesca

Recent records
Pre-1987 records
Recent & pre-1987

© Crown Copyright (100024913) 2014

is commoner in the Magnesian Limestone, Peak Fringe, White Peak and adjacent parts of the Dark Peak Character Area. Sites where it has been long-recorded include Dale Head (SK1276), Bolderstone (SK1761), Bruns Wood (SK2456), Langwith Wood (SK5068) and Risley Glebe (SK4635).

Fragaria moschata (Duchesne) Weston
Hautbois Strawberry

COUNTY STATUS: Casual
CONSERVATION STATUS: None
FIRST YEAR: 1864 LATEST YEAR: 1969 NO OF RECORDS: 10
RECENT SQUARES: monads 0; tetrads 0; hectads 0
ALL SQUARES: monads 4; tetrads 4; hectads 7

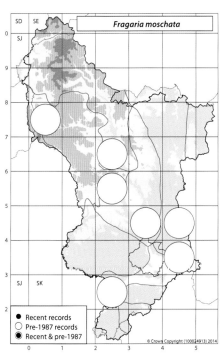

Fragaria moschata

Recent records
Pre-1987 records
Recent & pre-1987

© Crown Copyright (100024913) 2014

Locally extinct, Hautbois Strawberry was a very rare, casual perennial of roadsides and scrub. It was formerly cultivated for its fruit. There are no recent sightings but it was previously recorded across the county (Grin Plantation SK0472 in 1969, Haddon SK26 in 1903 & Egginton Station SK22 in 1903). It is a native of central Europe.

Fragaria ananassa (Duchesne) Duchesne
Garden Strawberry

COUNTY STATUS: Casual
CONSERVATION STATUS: None
FIRST YEAR: 1969 LATEST YEAR: 2013 NO OF RECORDS: 38
RECENT SQUARES: monads 20; tetrads 20; hectads 16
ALL SQUARES: monads 26; tetrads 26; hectads 19

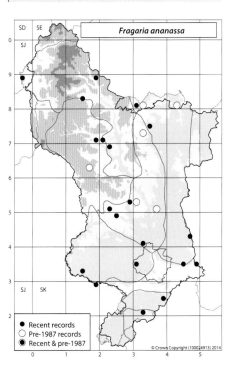

Fragaria ananassa

Recent records
Pre-1987 records
Recent & pre-1987

© Crown Copyright (100024913) 2014

Garden Strawberry is a rare casual perennial of waste places and rubbish tips. It is of garden origin and an escape or throwout found scattered throughout the area as at Ashes Farm (SK1888), Ballcross Farm (SK2269), Sudbury Hall (SK1532) and Melbourne (SK3825).

Geum rivale L.
Water Avens

COUNTY STATUS: Native
CONSERVATION STATUS: None
FIRST YEAR: 1789 LATEST YEAR: 2013 NO OF RECORDS: 690
RECENT SQUARES: monads 192; tetrads 122; hectads 24
ALL SQUARES: monads 217; tetrads 137; hectads 31

Water Avens is a frequent native perennial of marshes, damp grasslands and wet

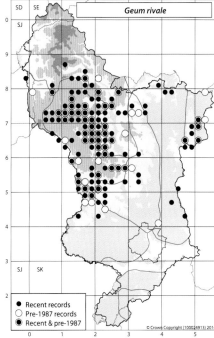

Geum rivale

Recent records
Pre-1987 records
Recent & pre-1987

© Crown Copyright (100024913) 2014

Water Avens (*Geum rivale*) in Chee Dale (SK1172), June 2008 (Peter Smith)

woodlands in the White Peak and Magnesian Limestone Character Areas (Peter Dale SK1275, Lathkill Dale SK1664, Bruns Wood SK2456 & Langwith Wood SK5068). It is also a very rare garden escape in other areas. It previously also occurred in the south, for example at Breadsall (SK33), Calke (SK32) and Repton (SK32) all for 1903. This loss is part of a general decline in central and southern England since 1950 (Preston *et al.* 2002).

Geum × intermedium Ehrh.
Hybrid Avens

COUNTY STATUS: Native	
CONSERVATION STATUS: None	
FIRST YEAR: 1793 LATEST YEAR: 2013 NO OF RECORDS: 136	
RECENT SQUARES: monads 53; tetrads 37; hectads 11	
ALL SQUARES: monads 70; tetrads 45; hectads 13	

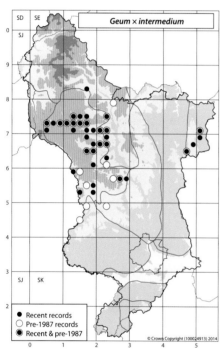

Hybrid Avens is a rare native perennial of woodlands in the White Peak and Magnesian Limestone Character Areas (Chee Dale SK1273, Lathkill Dale SK1865, Via Gellia SK2756 & Roseland Wood SK4967). It is the highly fertile hybrid of Water Avens (*G. rivale*) and Wood Avens (*G. urbanum*).

Geum urbanum L.
Wood Avens

COUNTY STATUS: Native	
CONSERVATION STATUS: None	
FIRST YEAR: 1789 LATEST YEAR: 2013 NO OF RECORDS: 3,539	
RECENT SQUARES: monads 1,371; tetrads 621; hectads 41	
ALL SQUARES: monads 1,426; tetrads 631; hectads 41	

Wood Avens is a very common, native perennial of woods, scrub and hedges on calcareous to neutral soils. It is often grown in gardens where it can occur as a

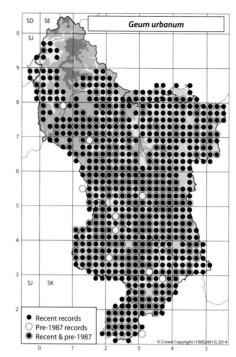

weed and escape onto roadsides or waste ground. It is recorded throughout the county except for the higher gritstone moors.

Agrimonia eupatoria L.
Agrimony

COUNTY STATUS: Native	
CONSERVATION STATUS: None	
FIRST YEAR: 1789 LATEST YEAR: 2013 NO OF RECORDS: 403	
RECENT SQUARES: monads 158; tetrads 127; hectads 29	
ALL SQUARES: monads 183; tetrads 143; hectads 31	

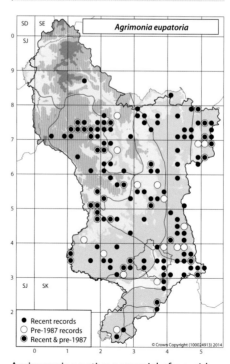

Agrimony is a native perennial of waysides, wood-margins, waste ground and other grassy places on all but the most acid

soils. It occurs occasionally throughout the county except for the Dark Peak where it is rare (Vale of Edale SK1586, Parwich SK1954, Etwall SK2733, Calke Park SK3622 & Gorse Covert SK5175).

Agrimonia procera Wallr.
Fragrant Agrimony

COUNTY STATUS: Native	
CONSERVATION STATUS: DRDB (Cat5b), A, B	
FIRST YEAR: 1881 LATEST YEAR: 2013 NO OF RECORDS: 59	
RECENT SQUARES: monads 8; tetrads 8; hectads 6	
ALL SQUARES: monads 27; tetrads 26; hectads 16	

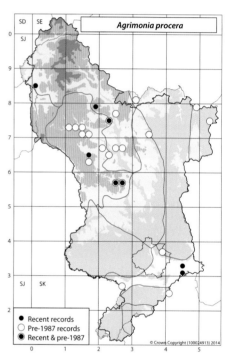

Fragrant Agrimony is a very rare, native perennial which grows in grassy areas on light soils at the edge of woods. The majority of recent records are from the White Peak (Lathkill Dale SK1765, Coombs Dale SK2274 and Ible Wood SK2656 & SK2556) with odd records elsewhere (The Torrs SK0085 and St Chads Water SK4431 & SK4432). It was formerly more frequent, particularly in the White Peak, and was also recorded for the Magnesian Limestone (Creswell Crags SK5374 in 1955).

Sanguisorba officinalis L.
Great Burnet

COUNTY STATUS: Native	
CONSERVATION STATUS: None	
FIRST YEAR: 1789 LATEST YEAR: 2013 NO OF RECORDS: 1,420	
RECENT SQUARES: monads 597; tetrads 371; hectads 38	
ALL SQUARES: monads 665; tetrads 403; hectads 39	

Great Burnet is a native perennial of damp unimproved meadows and other tall grasslands on neutral soils. It occurs frequently throughout the county except for the higher gritstone moors. Although

Great Burnet (*Sanguisorba officinalis*) at Hulland (SK2446), July 2004 (Philip Precey)

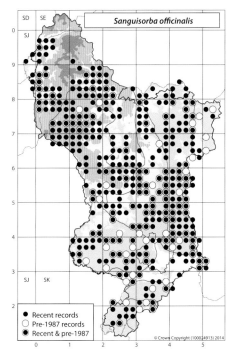

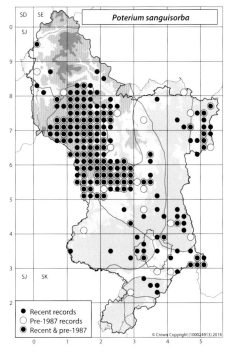

to calcareous unimproved grasslands (Sutton Church SK2334 & Lock Lane Ash Tip SK4831). It still grows on the banks of the Trent at Thrumpton Ferry (SK5031) at a site mentioned in Linton's (1903) Flora. **Fodder Burnet (ssp. *balearicum* (Bourg. ex Nyman) Stace)** is a very rare, casual perennial of grassy places. There are a dozen recent records scattered mostly over the northern half of the county (Brierley Green SK0282, Anthony Hill SK0470 & Calton Lees SK2568). It was grown for fodder and now survives as a relic of cultivation or as a contaminant of restoration schemes. It is a native of southern Europe.

Acaena novae-zelandiae Kirk
Pirri-pirri-bur
Pirri-pirri-bur is a very rare, casual perennial of open vegetation on well-drained soils. It is grown in gardens from where it sometimes escapes. The sole local record is for Holymoorside (SK3469) in 1995. It is indigenous to New Zealand and Australia.

Alchemilla alpina L.
Alpine Lady's-mantle
Alpine Lady's-mantle was discovered in Coombs Dale (SK2274) in 1971. This initially caused great interest (Band 1972b). It was short-lived however, when it was found to have been planted by a photographer to appear in a more natural setting (Band 1975). A later record from Cawdor Quarry (SK2860) in 1996, as casual, is possibly an error for a garden throwout of Silver Lady's-mantle (*A. conjuncta*). It is a native perennial of northern England and Scotland.

Alchemilla conjuncta Bab.
Silver Lady's-mantle
Silver Lady's-mantle is a very rare, casual perennial of waste ground with two recent records: Cawdor Quarry (SK2860) in 1995 and Bakewell (SK2169) in 2004. It was previously found in 1972 at a lorry park in Matlock (SK2959). It is much grown in gardens and is a native of the Alps.

Alchemilla xanthochlora Rothm.
Pale Lady's-mantle

COUNTY STATUS: Native
CONSERVATION STATUS: None
FIRST YEAR: 1903 LATEST YEAR: 2013 NO OF RECORDS: 372
RECENT SQUARES: monads 214; tetrads 151; hectads 28
ALL SQUARES: monads 236; tetrads 168; hectads 29

Pale Lady's-mantle is a frequent native perennial of grass fields and waysides in the White Peak and the adjacent parts of other Areas (Swallowhouse Mill Pond SK0387, Chee Tor SK1273 & Bruns Wood

still widespread, it has disappeared from many sites recently due to agricultural "improvement". For example, it was lost from 75% of its hay meadow sites in the Peak District between the mid-1980s and the mid-1990s (Buckingham *et al.* 1997).

Poterium sanguisorba L.
A burnet
Two subspecies are known locally. **Salad Burnet (ssp. *sanguisorba*)** is a very common, native perennial of unimproved

COUNTY STATUS: Native
CONSERVATION STATUS: None
FIRST YEAR: 1789 LATEST YEAR: 2013 NO OF RECORDS: 1,584
RECENT SQUARES: monads 381; tetrads 187; hectads 29
ALL SQUARES: monads 412; tetrads 205; hectads 33

limestone grasslands in the White Peak (Brook Bottom SK1476 & Aldwark SK2257). Although it occurs in similar habitats on the Magnesian Limestone, it is much less frequent there (Upper Langwith SK5169). It is found elsewhere, albeit rarely, in neutral

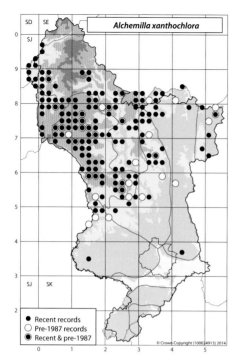

SK2556). It is very rare (Roseland Wood SK4967) or absent elsewhere. It is probably under-recorded due to the problems of separating it from other lady's-mantles.

Alchemilla filicaulis Buser.
A lady's mantle

COUNTY STATUS: Native	
CONSERVATION STATUS: None	
FIRST YEAR: 1862 **LATEST YEAR:** 2013 **NO OF RECORDS:** 486	
RECENT SQUARES: monads 188; tetrads 130; hectads 30	
ALL SQUARES: monads 233; tetrads 163; hectads 33	

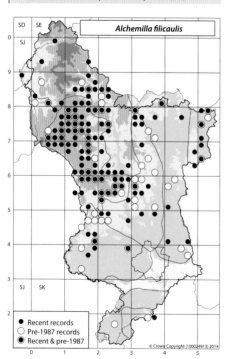

Two subspecies occur here, both of which are probably under-recorded due to the problems of distinguishing them from

other lady's-mantles. **Slender Lady's-mantle (ssp. *filicaulis*)** is a very rare, native perennial of grasslands in the White Peak. There are no recent records and only a few older ones (Taddington Dale SK1769 & Lathkill Dale SK1865, both for 1969). **Hairy Lady's-mantle (ssp. *vestita*** (Buser) M.E. Bradshaw) is an occasional native perennial of grass fields and waysides. It is most frequent in the White Peak (Wormhill SK1273 & Gratton Dale SK2059), though it does occur scattered throughout the rest of the county (Wicket Nook SK3619 & Markland Grips SK5074). It is probably the commonest lady's-mantle in the county. A record by John Ray at Poole's Hole Buxton in 1658 was most likely this plant.

Alchemilla glabra Neygenf.
Smooth Lady's-mantle

COUNTY STATUS: Native	
CONSERVATION STATUS: None	
FIRST YEAR: 1903 **LATEST YEAR:** 2013 **NO OF RECORDS:** 408	
RECENT SQUARES: monads 187; tetrads 126; hectads 21	
ALL SQUARES: monads 218; tetrads 149; hectads 23	

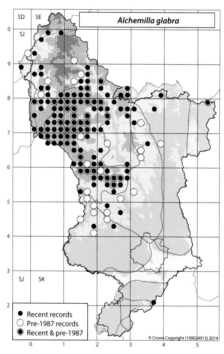

Smooth Lady's-mantle is a native perennial of grasslands and waysides. It is frequent in the White Peak (Peter Dale SK1275 & Griffe Wood Meadow SK2556) but only rare elsewhere (Birch Vale SK0286, South Wood SK3620 & Doe Lea Marsh SK3980). It is a plant of upland Britain and is almost absent from England south of our county.

Alchemilla mollis (Buser) Rothm.
Soft Lady's-mantle
Soft Lady's-mantle is an occasional established perennial of waysides, waste ground and tips throughout Derbyshire

COUNTY STATUS: Established (Neophyte)	
CONSERVATION STATUS: None	
FIRST YEAR: 1987 **LATEST YEAR:** 2013 **NO OF RECORDS:** 222	
RECENT SQUARES: monads 153; tetrads 143; hectads 35	
ALL SQUARES: monads 153; tetrads 143; hectads 35	

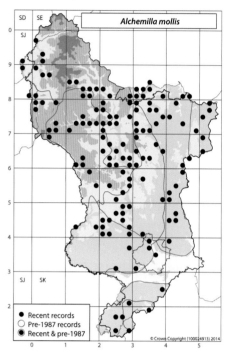

(Simmondley SK0293, Newhall SK2820 & Beauchief SK38F). It is much grown in gardens from where it escapes as seeds or is thrown out as plants. It is a native of south-eastern Europe.

Aphanes arvensis L.
Parsley-piert
Parsley-piert is a native winter annual of bare areas on light dry soils. It is locally

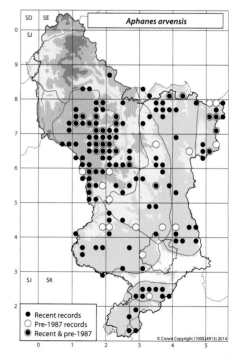

frequent near limestone outcrops in the White Peak and Magnesian Limestone (Cressbrook Dale SK1774, Kenslow Wood SK1962 & Creswell Crags SK5374). Elsewhere it is a rare weed of cultivated land, disturbed ground and sandy places, though is virtually absent from the Dark and South West Peak.

Aphanes australis Rydb.
Slender Parsley-piert

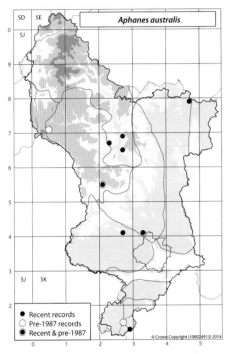

Slender Parsley-piert is a very rare, native winter annual of light dry acid soils over rocks and in arable fields. It occurs thinly scattered over central and southern Derbyshire from Park Brook (SK4679) in the north to Netherseal (SK2812) in the south. It is probably under-recorded, since not all recorders separate it from Parsley-piert.

Rosa L.
Roses

Whether native or established, all roses that grow wild in Derbyshire are spiny deciduous shrubs. They vary in growth form from weakly trailing types that climb through and over other plants, to erect self-supporting shrubs. They

are generally under-recorded as even competent botanists do not readily separate the species and their hybrids. However, individual accounts are given below for all local forms except for an undescribed one, provisionally known as **Gibb's Rose** (*Rosa gibbsii*). It often occurs in central Derbyshire and extends into Nottinghamshire. It was noted by Linton at the start of last century but he referred to it under several names. T. Gibbs of Wirksworth contributed several specimens of the plant to herbaria, and the plant is named in his honour.

Rosa multiflora Thunb.
Many-flowered Rose

Many-flowered Rose is an established climbing shrub. It was first discovered in 1980 between Curbar and Froggatt (SK2475) by M. Hewitt. There are five subsequent records including: Bakewell (SK2269) in 2013, Cotton Lane (SK3634) in 2006, Swanwick (SK4153) in 2012 and Westwood House monad (SK4361) in 2013. Used for ornamental plantings, it is a native of Eastern Asia.

Rosa arvensis Huds.
Field-rose

Field-rose is a native trailing shrub of wood margins, scrub, hedges, waysides and rough ground, often forming dense

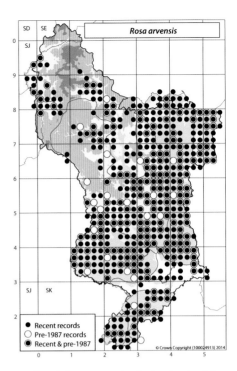

patches. It is common in the lowlands of the south and east but is only occasional in the more upland northern and western areas.

Rosa × *irregularis* Desegl. & Guillon
A hybrid rose

This hybrid rose is a very rare, native shrub with arching stems. It occurs in wood margins, hedges and scrub on the western

Field-rose (*Rosa arvensis*) in Whitwell Wood (SK5277), June 2004 (Philip Precey)

edge of the county, with recent records for Dove Dale (SK1453), Hockerley Lane (SK0081 v.c.58) and Chee Dale (SK17). It is the natural hybrid of Field-rose (*R. arvensis*) and Dog-rose (*R. canina*).

Rosa arvensis × R. caesia ssp. vosagiaca
A hybrid rose

Locally extinct, this hybrid rose is a native climbing shrub. All four records are from the Ashbourne area at end of the 19th century (Clifton SK14 in 1887 & Atlow SK24 in 1890). It is the spontaneous hybrid of Field-rose (*R. arvensis*) and Glaucous Dog-rose (*R. caesia* ssp. *vosagiaca*).

Rosa × gallicoides (Baker) Desegl.
A hybrid rose

Locally extinct, this hybrid rose is a native trailing shrub. There are two records: Stydd (SK14) and Shirley (SK24) both from 1889. It is the spontaneous hybrid of Field-rose (*R. arvensis*) and Sweet-briar (*R. rubiginosa*).

Rosa spinosissima L.
Burnet Rose

COUNTY STATUS: Native	
CONSERVATION STATUS: B	
FIRST YEAR: 1789 **LATEST YEAR:** 2012 **NO OF RECORDS:** 78	
RECENT SQUARES: monads 16; tetrads 13; hectads 7	
ALL SQUARES: monads 22; tetrads 16; hectads 10	

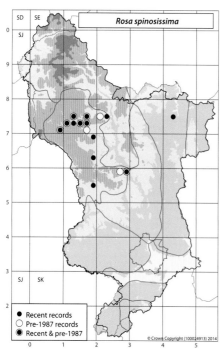

Burnet Rose is a low native shrub. It is occasional to locally frequent in the White Peak on rough grassland, in scrub and on limestone screes and outcrops (Deep Dale SK1072, High Tor Woods SK2959 & Parwich SK1854). The only recent record elsewhere is on a railway

bank at Staveley (SK4375). It is also planted from time to time in restoration schemes. Previously it was recorded more widely outside the White Peak (Chapel SK08, Rough Heanor SK33 & Dale SK43 all for 1903).

Rosa × andrzejowskii Boreau
A hybrid rose

Locally extinct, this native hybrid rose was recorded at Middleton Dale (SK27) in 1884. It is the hybrid of Burnet Rose (*R. spinosissima*) and Harsh Downy-rose (*R. tomentosa*).

Rosa × involuta Sm.
A hybrid rose

This hybrid rose is a low native shrub of rough grassland and scrub. It has only ever been recorded from the Miller's Dale/Cressbrook Dale area (SK17) in 1898 and 1972. It is the hybrid of Burnet Rose (*R. spinosissima*) and Sherard's Downy-rose (*R. sherardii*).

Rosa × sabinii Woods
A hybrid rose

This rose is an erect native shrub of rough grassland. It is the hybrid of Burnet Rose (*R. spinosissima*) and Soft Downy-rose (*R. mollis*). All records are from the White Peak (Middleton Dale SK27 in 1882, Miller's Dale SK17 in 1898 & Cressbrook Dale SK17 in 1911). It was classed as Locally extinct until 2014, when it was rediscovered by P. Anderson in Cressbrook Dale.

Rosa × biturigensis Boreau
A hybrid rose

Locally extinct, this native rose is the spontaneous hybrid of Burnet Rose (*R. spinosissima*) and Sweet-briar (*R. rubiginosa*). It has only ever been recorded at Chee Tor (SK17) in 1898.

Rosa rugosa Thunb.
Japanese Rose

COUNTY STATUS: Established (Neophyte)	
CONSERVATION STATUS: WCA9	
FIRST YEAR: 1988 **LATEST YEAR:** 2013 **NO OF RECORDS:** 63	
RECENT SQUARES: monads 37; tetrads 45; hectads 18	
ALL SQUARES: monads 37; tetrads 45; hectads 18	

Japanese Rose is a rare established shrub of waysides, rough ground and waste land. It has been recorded throughout Derbyshire, from Edale Village (SK1285) in the north, to Burton-on-Trent (SK22) in the south. It is grown in gardens for ornament or hedging, from where it escapes or is thrown-out. It is increasingly used in amenity plantings, sometimes because its spines deter trespassers. It is indigenous to Eastern Asia.

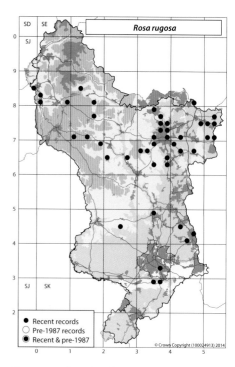

Rosa section Caninae DC.
Dog-roses

COUNTY STATUS: Native	
CONSERVATION STATUS: None	
FIRST YEAR: 1949 **LATEST YEAR:** 2013 **NO OF RECORDS:** 3,413	
RECENT SQUARES: monads 1,475; tetrads 623; hectads 41	
ALL SQUARES: monads 1,557; tetrads 634; hectads 41	

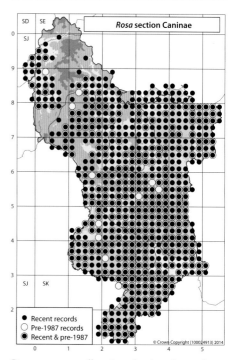

Dog-roses are all native shrubs of wood margins, hedges, rough grasslands, rock outcrops and waste places. They are very common throughout the lowland parts of the county but only frequent in the more upland Peak District. They have the local name of Briar (Grigson 1975). This section includes all subsequent roses. As a group they are well-recorded, but individual species and hybrids are not.

Rosa × andegavensis Bastard
A hybrid rose

Locally extinct, this native hybrid has only been noted once, at Dove Dale (SK15) in 1913. It is the hybrid of Dog-rose (*R. canina*) and Short-styled Field-rose (*R. stylosa*). Nationally it is a plant of southern Britain, and this report is from further north than any other native record (Preston *et al.* 2002).

Rosa canina L.
Dog-rose

COUNTY STATUS: Native	
CONSERVATION STATUS: None	
FIRST YEAR: 1789 LATEST YEAR: 2013 NO OF RECORDS: 354	
RECENT SQUARES: monads 236; tetrads 166; hectads 31	
ALL SQUARES: monads 236; tetrads 166; hectads 32	

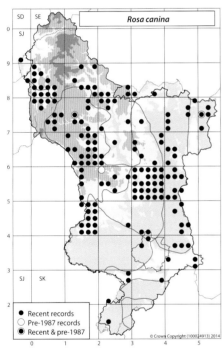

Dog-rose is a native climbing shrub of wood margins, hedges, rough grasslands, rock outcrops and waste places. It is the commonest member of the section in the area and is known from Etherow Reserve (SJ9791) and Jordanthorpe (SK38Q) in the north, to Catton (SK2215) and King's Newton (SK3826) in the south. However, recording is very patchy. Its map clearly shows certain recorders separate it from rarer members of the group whilst others do not.

Rosa × dumalis Bechst.
A hybrid rose

This native hybrid is a very rare shrub of woods, scrub, hedges, grassland and waste ground. All records are from western Derbyshire, with recent sightings mostly from the north-west (Deep Dale SK1669

COUNTY STATUS: Native	
CONSERVATION STATUS: None	
FIRST YEAR: 1840 LATEST YEAR: 2013 NO OF RECORDS: 74	
RECENT SQUARES: monads 13; tetrads 12; hectads 10	
ALL SQUARES: monads 18; tetrads 17; hectads 18	

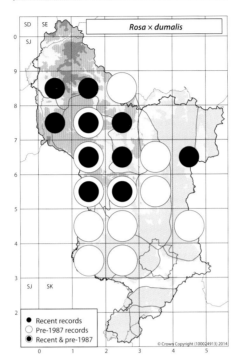

& Small Clough SK1284). Earlier records were mostly from the south-west (Thorpe SK1549 & Rough Lane SK2243 both for 1969), but this is probably an artefact of recording due to an earlier confusion with *Rosa caesia*. It is the natural hybrid of Dog-rose (*R. canina*) and *Rosa caesia*.

Rosa × dumetorum Thuill.
A hybrid rose

Locally extinct, this native hybrid shrub was recorded fourteen times, scattered over central parts between 1887 and 1918 (Longford SK23 in 1890 & Holmesfield SK37 in 1918). It is the hybrid of Dog-rose (*R. canina*) and Round-leaved Dog-rose (*R. obtusifolia*).

Rosa × scabriuscula Sm.
A hybrid rose

Locally extinct, this hybrid rose was a native climbing shrub. It was recorded twenty times, scattered over five hectads between 1884 and 1913, from Shirley (SK24) in the south to Bradwell (SK18) in the north. It is the hybrid of Dog-rose (*R. canina*) and Harsh Downy-rose (*R. tomentosa*).

Rosa × rothschildii Druce
A hybrid rose

This hybrid rose is a very rare, native shrub of coarse grassland and scrub. All recent records are from the White Peak: Peter Dale (SK1375), Monk's Dale (SK1473) and Mill Dale (SK15). It was previously known from

COUNTY STATUS: Native	
CONSERVATION STATUS: None	
FIRST YEAR: 1871 LATEST YEAR: 2002 NO OF RECORDS: 14	
RECENT SQUARES: monads 4; tetrads 3; hectads 2	
ALL SQUARES: monads 4; tetrads 3; hectads 5	

a slightly wider area including Darley Dale (SK26) in 1871 and Tansley (SK35) in 1913. It is the cross of Dog-rose (*R. canina*) and Sherard's Downy-rose (*R. sherardii*).

Rosa × molletorum Hesl.-Harr.
A hybrid rose

Locally extinct, this native hybrid rose is known only from a record in the Via Gellia (SK25) in 1913. It is the cross between Dog-rose (*R. canina*) and Soft Downy-rose (*R. mollis*). It is a plant of northern Britain, extending south only as far as Derbyshire.

Rosa × nitidula Besser
A hybrid rose

This native hybrid shrub has only been recorded here twice. It was originally discovered at Darley Dale (SK26) in 1891 and then refound near Derwent Dam (SK1789) in 2012. It is the hybrid of Dog-rose (*R. canina*) and Sweet-briar (*R. rubiginosa*).

Rosa caesia Sm.
A dog-rose

Two subspecies occur locally:

Hairy Dog-rose (ssp. *caesia*)

COUNTY STATUS: Native	
CONSERVATION STATUS: None	
FIRST YEAR: 1877 LATEST YEAR: 2010 NO OF RECORDS: 75	
RECENT SQUARES: monads 24; tetrads 19; hectads 9	
ALL SQUARES: monads 25; tetrads 20; hectads 14	

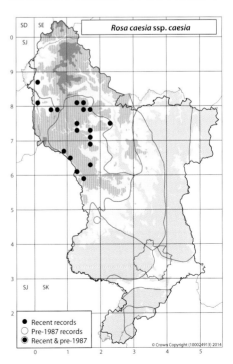

Hairy Dog-rose is a native shrub of wood margins, rough grasslands and rocky outcrops. It is recorded occasionally in the White Peak (Bradwell Moor SK1380, Deep Dale SK1669 & Biggin Dale SK1458). Elsewhere it is recorded only rarely (Sett Valley Trail SK0086, Combs Village SK0478 & Shipley Country Park SK44). Earlier records appear to avoid the White Peak, but occur around its margins (Ashbourne Green SK1847 in 1969 & Hathersage SK28 in 1892).

Glaucous Dog-rose (ssp. *vosagiaca* (N.H.F. Desp.) D.H. Kent)

COUNTY STATUS: Native
CONSERVATION STATUS: None
FIRST YEAR: 1848 LATEST YEAR: 2010 NO OF RECORDS: 125
RECENT SQUARES: monads 42; tetrads 37; hectads 11
ALL SQUARES: monads 42; tetrads 37; hectads 13

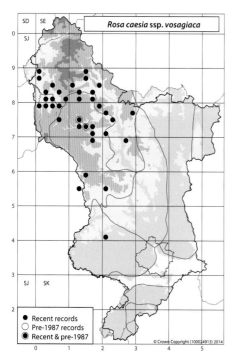

Glaucus Dog-rose is a native of scrub, rough grassland and waysides. It occurs occasionally in the upland north-western part of the county, from Rowarth (SK0189) and Rowlee Farm (SK1589) in the north, to Mill Dale (SK1354) and Shirley (SK2141) in the south.

Rosa caesia × R. obtusifolia
A hybrid rose
Locally extinct, this native hybrid rose was recorded only from Bradley (SK24) in 1889 (Graham & Primavesi 1993).

Rosa × cottetii (H. Christ) Lagger & Puget ex Cottet
A hybrid rose
This native hybrid rose has only one recent record (Monk's Dale SK1373). Previously it was scattered over central and northern parts (Bradley SK24 & Matlock Bath SK26

both for the 1880s). It is the hybrid of Glaucous Dog-rose (*R. caesia*) and Harsh Downy-rose (*R. tomentosa*).

Rosa caesia × R. sherardii
A hybrid rose
Locally extinct, this hybrid rose, a native shrub, is known only from Bradley (SK24) in 1890. It is the hybrid of Hairy Dog-rose (*R. caesia*) and Sherard's Downy-rose (*R. sherardii*).

Rosa × glaucoides Wolley-Dod
A hybrid rose
This hybrid rose is a very rare native of the White Peak. It has been recorded from five sites between 1991 and 2011: Moss Rake (SK1580), Deep Dale (SK1669), Bradwell Dale (SK1780), Coombs Dale (SK2274) and near Seymour Junction (SK4573). It is a northern plant on the southern edge of its distribution in Derbyshire, and is the hybrid of Hairy Dog-rose (*R. caesia*) and Soft Downy-rose (*R. mollis*).

Rosa caesia × R. rubiginosa
A hybrid rose
Locally extinct, this native hybrid shrub has been recorded only once, from Bradley (SK24) in 1889. It is the hybrid of Hairy Dog-rose (*R. caesia*) and Sweet-briar (*R. rubiginosa*)

Rosa obtusifolia Desv.
Round-leaved Dog-rose

COUNTY STATUS: Native
CONSERVATION STATUS: None
FIRST YEAR: 1880 LATEST YEAR: 1997 NO OF RECORDS: 19
RECENT SQUARES: monads 1; tetrads 1; hectads 1
ALL SQUARES: monads 1; tetrads 1; hectads 5

Round-leaved Dog-rose is a native shrub of hedges in the south of the county. The one recent record is from Fenny Bentley (SK1749). Previous records, which cover a wider area including Ladyhole (SK14), Brailsford (SK24), Riber (SK35) and Ockbrook (SK43), are all for the end of the 19th or early 20th century.

Rosa tomentosa Sm.
Harsh Downy-rose

COUNTY STATUS: Native
CONSERVATION STATUS: A
FIRST YEAR: 1729 LATEST YEAR: 2012 NO OF RECORDS: 28
RECENT SQUARES: monads 9; tetrads 8; hectads 6
ALL SQUARES: monads 13; tetrads 11; hectads 11

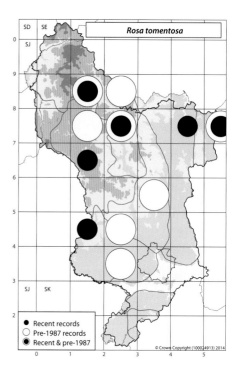

Harsh Downy-rose is a very rare, native bush of scrub, hedges and open woodlands. It is currently scattered throughout Derbyshire, from Ladybower (SK1786) and Creswell Crags (SK5374) in the north to Yeaveley (SK1840) in the south. Earlier records cover the same area (Longstone Edge SK2173 & Hollington SK23).

Rosa sherardii Davies
Sherard's Downy-rose
Sherard's Downy-rose is a rare native shrub of woods, hedges, scrub and waysides in northern Derbyshire with attractive deep rose-pink flowers. There

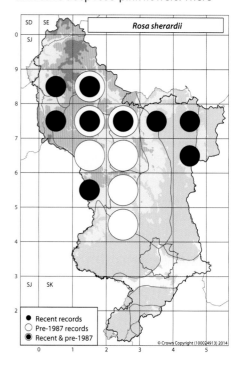

COUNTY STATUS: Native
CONSERVATION STATUS: None
FIRST YEAR: 1882 **LATEST YEAR:** 2012 **NO OF RECORDS:** 43
RECENT SQUARES: monads 15; tetrads 15; hectads 9
ALL SQUARES: monads 17; tetrads 17; hectads 13

are recent records from Rowarth (SK0189) and Bowshaw Farm (SK3479) in the north, to Biggin Dale (SK1458) and Longhedge Lane (SK4963) in the centre. It was previously recorded further south, e.g. Shirley and Bradley (SK24) in the 1880s.

Rosa mollis Sm.
Soft Downy-rose

COUNTY STATUS: Native
CONSERVATION STATUS: None
FIRST YEAR: 1789 **LATEST YEAR:** 2012 **NO OF RECORDS:** 75
RECENT SQUARES: monads 14; tetrads 12; hectads 5
ALL SQUARES: monads 31; tetrads 28; hectads 17

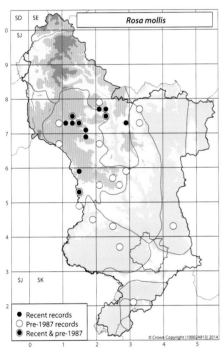

Soft Downy-rose is a rare native shrub of rough grassland and scrub in the White and Dark Peak (Priestcliffe Lees SK1473, Coombs Dale SK2274, Dove Dale SK1453 & Leash Fen SK2873). It was previously found across a wider area, generally in lowland Derbyshire (Swadlincote SK3020 in 1978 & Mapperley SK4342 in 1969). It is a plant of upland Britain, with Derbyshire on its south-eastern limit.

Rosa rubiginosa L.
Sweet-briar
Sweet-briar is a very rare, native bush of scrub. It appears to be scattered throughout the county (Drakelow SK2220, Brockwell SK3672 & Ilkeston SK4642), with

older records covering the same area, albeit more frequently (Wye Dale SK17 in 1968 & Repton SK32 in 1903). This decrease in abundance is probably due in part to the improvement of marginal land, but also to there being fewer botanists who identify critical rose species.

Rosa micrantha Borrer ex Sm.
Small-flowered Sweet-briar
Small-flowered Sweet-briar is a very rare, native shrub of scrub and hedges. The only recent record is for Bradford Dale (SK2063) in 1998, with older ones for Brailsford (SK24) in 1891 and Glapwell (SK46) in 1893. It is mainly a southern species in Britain.

ELAEAGNACEAE

Hippophae rhamnoides L.
Sea-buckthorn

COUNTY STATUS: Casual
CONSERVATION STATUS: None
FIRST YEAR: 1987 **LATEST YEAR:** 2004 **NO OF RECORDS:** 10
RECENT SQUARES: monads 4; tetrads 7; hectads 6
ALL SQUARES: monads 4; tetrads 7; hectads 6

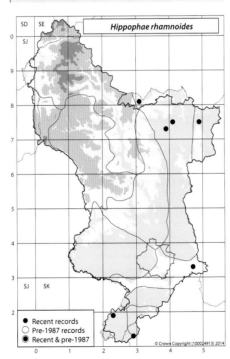

Sea-buckthorn is a very rare, casual shrub reported from eastern and southern parts (Hollingwood SK4074 & Netherseal SK21W). Its vigorous spiny growth makes it suitable for amenity planting but can also make it invasive

and a potential threat to native vegetation. It is indigenous to British coasts.

RHAMNACEAE

Rhamnus cathartica L.
Buckthorn

COUNTY STATUS: Native
CONSERVATION STATUS: None
FIRST YEAR: 1789 **LATEST YEAR:** 2012 **NO OF RECORDS:** 431
RECENT SQUARES: monads 124; tetrads 90; hectads 26
ALL SQUARES: monads 153; tetrads 111; hectads 29

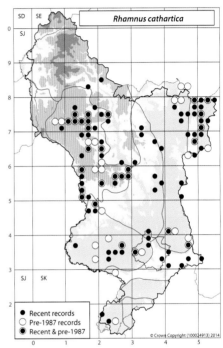

Buckthorn is a spiny native shrub of scrub, hedges and open woods. It is occasional in the White Peak as at Peter Dale (SK1275), Lathkill Dale (SK1765) and Hopton Quarry (SK2656), and on the Magnesian Limestone as at Whitwell Wood (SK5278) and Scarcliffe Park (SK5170). Elsewhere it is rare: Ladybower Dam (SK2085), Sandiacre (SK4636) and Coton in the Elms (SK21H). A specimen with a girth of 0.75m was recently found east of Tideswell Dale (SK1573).

Frangula alnus Mill.
Alder Buckthorn

COUNTY STATUS: Native
CONSERVATION STATUS: B
FIRST YEAR: 1789 **LATEST YEAR:** 2012 **NO OF RECORDS:** 100
RECENT SQUARES: monads 31; tetrads 26; hectads 17
ALL SQUARES: monads 43; tetrads 36; hectads 24

Alder Buckthorn is a rare native shrub of scrub, woods and hedges usually on damp, often peaty, soils. It grows scattered throughout Derbyshire, from Dinting Vale Wood (SK0194) and

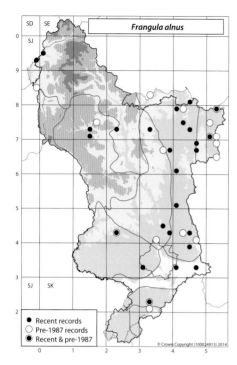

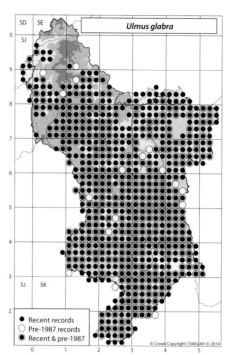

Whitwell Wood (SK5278) in the north, through Bradley Brook Marsh (SK2343), to Carver's Rocks (SK3222) in the south.

ULMACEAE

Ulmus L.
Elms

There has been little work on elms in the area since the Dutch Elm disease outbreak of the 1960s and 1970s severely damaged the local populations. The entries below, except for the easily recognised Wych Elm (*U. glabra*), should therefore be considered as very incomplete. A number of local place names refer to elms, for example Elmton and Coton in the Elms.

Ulmus glabra Huds.
Wych Elm

COUNTY STATUS: Native	
CONSERVATION STATUS: None	
FIRST YEAR: 1789 **LATEST YEAR:** 2013 **NO OF RECORDS:** 3,313	
RECENT SQUARES: monads 1,352; tetrads 618; hectads 42	
ALL SQUARES: monads 1,470; tetrads 635; hectads 42	

Wych Elm is a common native tree of hedgerows and woods, particularly on moist nutrient-rich or base-rich soils. It grows throughout Derbyshire except for the northern moors. It can form a large tree but, although more resistant to Dutch Elm disease than English Elm (*U. procera*), there are still few mature trees left. The largest known specimen is at Little Eaton (SK3542) with a girth of 4.71m. In the few cases where subspecies have been determined, they have been

ssp. *glabra* (Sandiacre SK4736 & Greens Lock SK44Q).

Ulmus × *elegantissima* Horw.
An elm

COUNTY STATUS: Native	
CONSERVATION STATUS: None	
FIRST YEAR: 1950 **LATEST YEAR:** 1969 **NO OF RECORDS:** 5	
RECENT SQUARES: monads 0; tetrads 0; hectads 0	
ALL SQUARES: monads 4; tetrads 4; hectads 3	

Locally extinct, this elm was a very rare native tree of hedgerows but was also often planted. It was recorded for the Ashbourne area (SK1745) and SK17 during middle of last century, but there have been no recent records. It is not known if this means the species has been killed off by Dutch Elm disease or has simply been overlooked.

Ulmus × *vegeta* (Loudon) Ley
Huntingdon Elm

Huntingdon Elm is an established tree, only ever found at Long Eaton (SK4933) in 1999. It is often planted so is probably under-recorded here.

Ulmus × *hollandica* Mill.
Dutch Elm

COUNTY STATUS: Native	
CONSERVATION STATUS: None	
FIRST YEAR: 1968 **LATEST YEAR:** 2010 **NO OF RECORDS:** 6	
RECENT SQUARES: monads 3; tetrads 3; hectads 2	
ALL SQUARES: monads 6; tetrads 6; hectads 5	

Dutch Elm is a native tree of hedgerows. It has been recorded recently around Stoney Clouds (SK4737) and Gallows Inn (SK4740), but was previously noted throughout

central parts (Carsington SK2453 & Barrow Hill SK4175 both for 1969). A hybrid of uncertain origin, it is often planted and is probably under-recorded here.

Ulmus procera Salisb.
English Elm

COUNTY STATUS: Native	
CONSERVATION STATUS: None	
FIRST YEAR: 1789 **LATEST YEAR:** 2012 **NO OF RECORDS:** 350	
RECENT SQUARES: monads 186; tetrads 144; hectads 30	
ALL SQUARES: monads 234; tetrads 180; hectads 33	

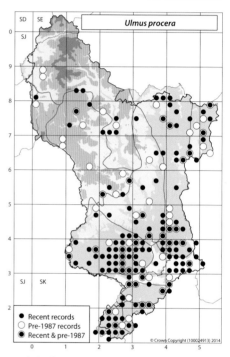

English Elm is an occasional native tree of hedgerows but is also much planted. It occurs throughout the county though is more frequent in the southern half. It proved very susceptible to the outbreak of Dutch Elm disease that began in the 1960s, and all that survives in most hedges now are bushy or sucker growths.

Ulmus minor Mill.
An elm

COUNTY STATUS: Native	
CONSERVATION STATUS: None	
FIRST YEAR: 1998 **LATEST YEAR:** 2000 **NO OF RECORDS:** 11	
RECENT SQUARES: monads 0; tetrads 4; hectads 5	
ALL SQUARES: monads 0; tetrads 4; hectads 5	

Two subspecies have been recorded. **Small-leaved Elm (ssp. *minor*)** is a very rare, native tree of copses and hedgerows. It has been found five times recently (Derbyshire Bridge SK07A, Flagg Moor SK16I, Bradley Old Park SK24L, Horsleygate SK37D and the Derbyshire part of SK06). **Jersey Elm (ssp. *sarniensis*** (C.K. Schneid.) Stace) was noted in 1999 as a planted tree in West Park, Long Eaton (SK4833).

Ulmus plotii Druce
Plot's Elm

COUNTY STATUS: Native
CONSERVATION STATUS: DBRC (Cat 6)
FIRST YEAR: 1969 LATEST YEAR: 1969 NO OF RECORDS: 3
RECENT SQUARES: monads 0; tetrads 0; hectads 0
ALL SQUARES: monads 2; tetrads 2; hectads 3

Locally extinct, Plot's Elm was a very rare, native tree of copses and hedgerows that was also often planted. It was recorded for dales of the Wye Valley (SK17), Cutthorpe (SK3474) and Ford (SK4080) in Clapham's (1969) Flora but there have been no recent records. It is unclear whether the tree was killed off by Dutch Elm disease or has simply been overlooked.

CANNABACEAE

Cannabis sativa L.
Hemp

COUNTY STATUS: Casual
CONSERVATION STATUS: None
FIRST YEAR: 1903 LATEST YEAR: 2008 NO OF RECORDS: 14
RECENT SQUARES: monads 7; tetrads 7; hectads 6
ALL SQUARES: monads 11; tetrads 11; hectads 10

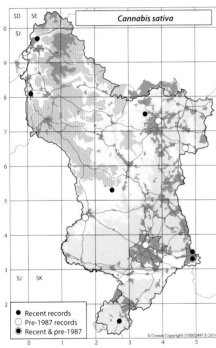

Hemp is a very rare, casual annual of waste places, river banks and parks. There are recent records throughout Derbyshire (Toddbrook Reservoir SK0080, Hadfield SK0296, Long Eaton SK4933 & Linton SK2715). It is grown illegally for drugs, used as bait by anglers and given to birds as feed. Previously Farey (1815) reported small trials of cultivation around Eckington, Mosborough and Overthorpe. It is native to southern and western Asia.

Humulus lupulus L.
Hop

COUNTY STATUS: Native
CONSERVATION STATUS: None
FIRST YEAR: 1789 LATEST YEAR: 2013 NO OF RECORDS: 261
RECENT SQUARES: monads 118; tetrads 99; hectads 27
ALL SQUARES: monads 144; tetrads 118; hectads 32

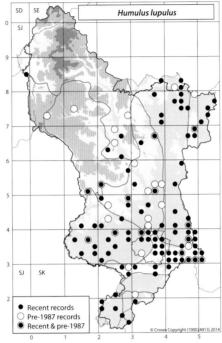

Hop is a scrambling native perennial of hedgerows, scrub and valley-bottom woods. It is also an escapee from cultivation so it is often impossible to say if a particular plant is of native or introduced origin. It is frequent throughout eastern and southern parts, generally avoiding the Dark and White Peak Character Areas, although there were a few scattered records from these areas with one recent record from Mousley Bottom (SJ9985).

MORACEAE

Morus nigra L.
Black Mulberry
Black Mulberry is a small planted tree of parks and gardens which deserves to be more commonly cultivated for its luscious fruits. It is indigenous to central Asia. There are modern records from Overton Hall (SK3462), the home of Sir Joseph Banks, the famous botanist, and also from Darley Park (SK3538), plus Markeaton Park (SK3337) recently removed. Farey (1815) noted it at Eckington (SK47). In southern England it can colonise waste ground from bird-sown seed, but this has not happened here.

Ficus carica L.
Fig
Fig is a small casual tree of walls and waste ground. It is very rare, growing scattered

COUNTY STATUS: Casual
CONSERVATION STATUS: None
FIRST YEAR: 1998 LATEST YEAR: 2010 NO OF RECORDS: 16
RECENT SQUARES: monads 7; tetrads 7; hectads 4
ALL SQUARES: monads 7; tetrads 7; hectads 4

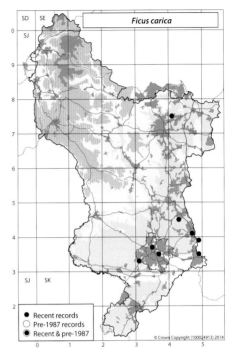

through eastern and southern parts. It is often associated with localised sources of heat such as sewage works (Littleover SK3143), rivers (River Rother SK4175) or city centres (Derby SK3536). It is a native of south-western Asia which is spread by birds or water from sewage or discarded fruit.

URTICACEAE

Urtica dioica L.
Common Nettle

COUNTY STATUS: Native
CONSERVATION STATUS: None
FIRST YEAR: 1789 LATEST YEAR: 2013 NO OF RECORDS: 8,627
RECENT SQUARES: monads 2,436; tetrads 737; hectads 45
ALL SQUARES: monads 2,476; tetrads 739; hectads 45

Common Nettle is a very common and locally abundant, native perennial of a wide range of woody and herbaceous communities. It grows particularly where the soil is enriched by nutrient input from rivers, animal excrement or organic wastes. It occurs throughout the county except for the high moors. It has probably increased in abundance and frequency in recent decades with the widespread use of inorganic fertilisers. It is thus now one of the most often recorded plants in the county. This local increase is mirrored by a similar national one (Braithwaite *et al.* 2006). In Ripley it was celebrated in "Oak

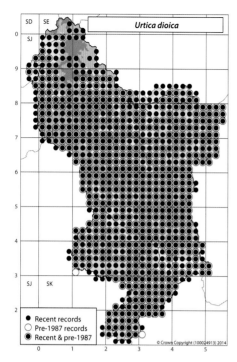

Small Nettle is an anciently established annual of cultivated and waste ground particularly on soils of high fertility. It is occasional in southern and eastern parts of the county, becoming rarer in the more upland White, South West and Dark Peak Character Areas.

Parietaria judaica L.
Pellitory-of-the-Wall

COUNTY STATUS: Native	
CONSERVATION STATUS: None	
FIRST YEAR: 1789 LATEST YEAR: 2013 NO OF RECORDS: 312	
RECENT SQUARES: monads 135; tetrads 109; hectads 28	
ALL SQUARES: monads 150; tetrads 117; hectads 29	

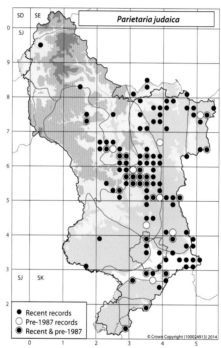

Pellitory-of-the-wall is a native perennial of walls and rock outcrops. It is occasional in the southern and eastern parts of the county becoming rarer in the more upland White, South West and Dark Peak Areas. It is abundant at Derby Museum's Cheapside Annexe (SK3536) where data collation for this Flora took place.

Soleirolia soleirolii (Req.) Dandy
Mind-your-own-business

COUNTY STATUS: Casual	
CONSERVATION STATUS: None	
FIRST YEAR: 1971 LATEST YEAR: 2013 NO OF RECORDS: 52	
RECENT SQUARES: monads 33; tetrads 31; hectads 16	
ALL SQUARES: monads 33; tetrads 31; hectads 16	

Mind-your-own-business is a casual evergreen perennial that grows creeping over damp bare shaded ground. It is rare but widespread through the county, generally never far from houses or gardens (Castleton SK1482, Melbourne SK3825 & Sloade Lane SK3981).

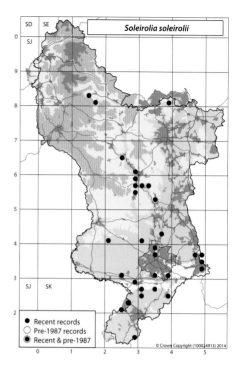

It is a native of western Mediterranean islands.

FAGACEAE

Fagus sylvatica L.
Beech

COUNTY STATUS: Established (Neophyte)	
CONSERVATION STATUS: None	
FIRST YEAR: 1789 LATEST YEAR: 2013 NO OF RECORDS: 2,831	
RECENT SQUARES: monads 1,077; tetrads 557; hectads 40	
ALL SQUARES: monads 1,149; tetrads 578; hectads 40	

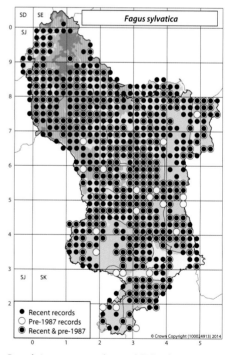

Beech is a commonly established, large tree of woods and parklands. It is often planted in woods, hedges,

and nettle day". Here girls scuttled to school clutching a sprig of oak leaves to protect themselves from gangs of boys who stopped them and demanded "show the oak". Any who could not, had to submit to being slapped with a bunch of nettles.

Urtica urens L.
Small Nettle

COUNTY STATUS: Established (Archaeophyte)	
CONSERVATION STATUS: None	
FIRST YEAR: 1789 LATEST YEAR: 2013 NO OF RECORDS: 203	
RECENT SQUARES: monads 116; tetrads 103; hectads 29	
ALL SQUARES: monads 145; tetrads 129; hectads 34	

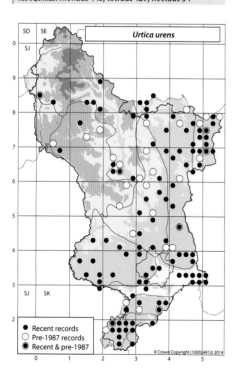

gardens and shelterbelts, particularly at higher altitudes, for timber, amenity and protection. It is known throughout Derbyshire, except for the highest moors and some intensively farmed lowland areas. The largest known tree, with a girth of 8.5m, is at Coombs Road, Bakewell (SK3267). Some considered beech to be native (Clapham 1969), but now it is generally thought to be native only in southern England. Its leaves are frequently used in traditional well dressings.

Castanea sativa Mill.
Sweet Chestnut

COUNTY STATUS: Established (Neophyte)
CONSERVATION STATUS: None
FIRST YEAR: 1815 **LATEST YEAR:** 2013 **NO OF RECORDS:** 659
RECENT SQUARES: monads 300; tetrads 227; hectads 33
ALL SQUARES: monads 327; tetrads 243; hectads 35

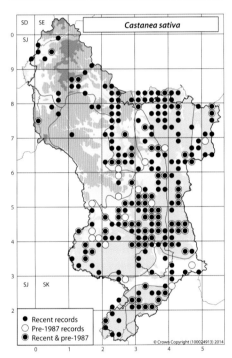

Sweet Chestnut is an established large tree of woods and plantations and a native of southern Europe. It is commonly planted in parks and gardens, and also in woods for timber. Frequent throughout lowland Derbyshire, it is rare in the Dark and South West Peak Character Areas and virtually absent from the White Peak. The largest specimen found in recent years had a girth of 8.04m at Shining Cliff Woods (SK3352).

Quercus cerris L.
Turkey Oak

COUNTY STATUS: Established (Neophyte)
CONSERVATION STATUS: None
FIRST YEAR: 1969 **LATEST YEAR:** 2013 **NO OF RECORDS:** 152
RECENT SQUARES: monads 74; tetrads 62; hectads 26
ALL SQUARES: monads 86; tetrads 67; hectads 27

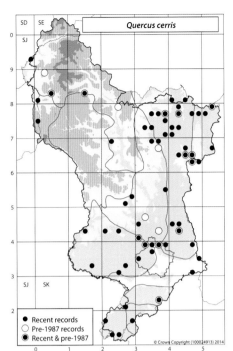

Turkey Oak is a rare established large tree of woods, parks and estates where it is grown as an ornamental. It is scattered throughout the county, avoiding only the White Peak (Chisworth SJ9992, Snelston Estate SK1542, John Wood SK4244 & Pleasley SK4764). A large specimen at Bishops Drive, Oakwood (SK3738) has a girth of 3.88m. It is a native of southern Europe.

Quercus × crenata Lam.
Lucombe Oak

Lucombe Oak is a very rare, casual tree of parks and churchyards where its large size and semi-evergreen nature make it attractive as an ornamental tree. It is recorded for only two sites: Cutthorpe Hall (SK3473) and Sawley Churchyard (SK4731). It is of garden origin from the crossing of Turkey (Q. cerris) with Cork Oak (Q. suber).

Quercus petraea (Matt.) Liebl.
Sessile Oak

COUNTY STATUS: Native
CONSERVATION STATUS: None
FIRST YEAR: 1845 **LATEST YEAR:** 2013 **NO OF RECORDS:** 813
RECENT SQUARES: monads 387; tetrads 264; hectads 31
ALL SQUARES: monads 418; tetrads 282; hectads 34

Sessile Oak is a large native tree of woodlands on dry acid soils (Padley Gorge SK2579). It is often planted in woods, hedges and parks for timber and ornament, so much so that its natural distribution is unclear. Commonly recorded in the South West and Dark Peak, plus the northern sections of the Coal Measures and Peak Fringe Character Areas, it is rare elsewhere. A specimen with a girth of 6.4m

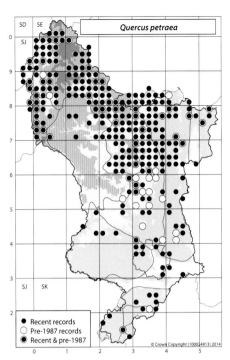

was recently discovered at Chatsworth Park (SK2669). Its stronghold as a native tree is the woodlands of the gritstone cloughs which is reflected in local place names such as Oaken Clough. Regeneration has been poor here during the last 50 years due to overgrazing by sheep, so clough restoration is now one of the priorities of the Peak District Biodiversity Action Plan.

Quercus × rosacea Bechst.
Hybrid Oak

Hybrid Oak is a large native tree of woodlands that is also sometimes planted. It occurs rarely, scattered throughout the northern half of the county (Meadow Farm

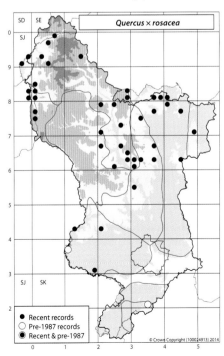

COUNTY STATUS: Native

CONSERVATION STATUS: None

FIRST YEAR: 1891 LATEST YEAR: 2012 NO OF RECORDS: 80

RECENT SQUARES: monads 52; tetrads 43; hectads 19

ALL SQUARES: monads 54; tetrads 45; hectads 20

SK0183, Farley Moor SK3063 & Geer Lane SK3980) with isolated records further south (Shirley Park SK2042). It is the hybrid of the two native oaks, Sessile Oak (*Q. petraea*) and Pedunculate Oak (*Q. robur*). It is often difficult to tell clearly from its parents, and so is probably under-recorded.

Quercus robur L.
Pedunculate Oak

COUNTY STATUS: Native

CONSERVATION STATUS: None

FIRST YEAR: 1789 LATEST YEAR: 2013 NO OF RECORDS: 3,890

RECENT SQUARES: monads 1,515; tetrads 600; hectads 43

ALL SQUARES: monads 1,568; tetrads 608; hectads 43

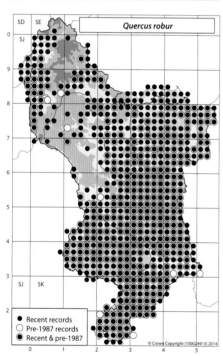

Pedunculate Oak is a large native tree of woodlands, mainly on heavy neutral soils. It is often planted for timber and amenity in woods, hedges and parks so its natural distribution is now uncertain. It occurs very commonly throughout Derbyshire except for the White Peak and the more upland areas of the Dark Peak, where it is rare. Its common occurrence and symbolic significance probably goes a long way to explain its frequency in local place names such as Oakerthorpe, and in local customs such as well dressing and Oak Apple Day, which is still celebrated in Castleton (Mabey 1996). Some huge veteran oaks are known to exist in Calke Abbey (SK3622).

Quercus rubra L.
Red Oak

COUNTY STATUS: Casual

CONSERVATION STATUS: None

FIRST YEAR: 1976 LATEST YEAR: 2013 NO OF RECORDS: 44

RECENT SQUARES: monads 32; tetrads 29; hectads 18

ALL SQUARES: monads 34; tetrads 31; hectads 19

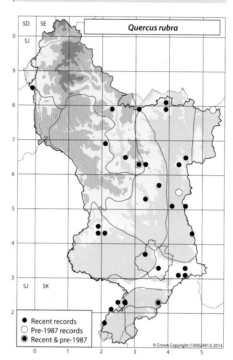

Red Oak is a rare casual tree of woods, hedges and amenity plantings. It occurs throughout the county (Tinker's Inn SK1844, Drakelow Power Station SK2220, Mires Spring Wood SK3880 & St Chad's Water SK4430) but is rarer in the White, Dark and South West Peak Character Areas. It is indigenous to eastern North America.

MYRICACEAE

Myrica gale L.
Bog-myrtle

COUNTY STATUS: Native

CONSERVATION STATUS: DRDB (Cat6)

FIRST YEAR: 1789 LATEST YEAR: 1789 NO OF RECORDS: 1

RECENT SQUARES: monads 0; tetrads 0; hectads 0

ALL SQUARES: monads 0; tetrads 0; hectads 1

Locally extinct, Bog-myrtle was a very rare, native shrub of damp organic soils. It has only ever been recorded at Wingerworth (SK36) in Pilkington (1789). In Britain it has a generally north-western distribution and was on the edge of its range in central England here.

JUGLANDACEAE

Juglans regia L.
Walnut
Walnut is a rare casual or planted tree of

COUNTY STATUS: Casual

CONSERVATION STATUS: None

FIRST YEAR: 1949 LATEST YEAR: 2013 NO OF RECORDS: 57

RECENT SQUARES: monads 29; tetrads 26; hectads 17

ALL SQUARES: monads 39; tetrads 36; hectads 19

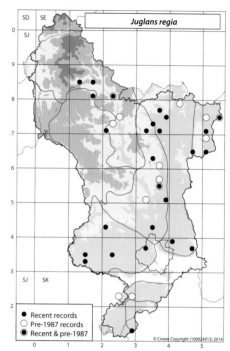

hedgerows and gardens. It grows scattered throughout the area though generally avoids the White Peak and the higher ground of the Dark Peak (Bradwell SK1780, Sutton on the Hill SK2334, Sandiacre SK4736 & Rowthorne SK4764). A specimen at Castleton (SK1285) found recently during a survey of veteran trees had a girth of 2.75m. Walnut is indigenous to south-eastern Europe and Asia.

BETULACEAE

Betula pendula Roth
Silver Birch

COUNTY STATUS: Native

CONSERVATION STATUS: None

FIRST YEAR: 1789 LATEST YEAR: 2013 NO OF RECORDS: 3,522

RECENT SQUARES: monads 1,330; tetrads 605; hectads 42

ALL SQUARES: monads 1,380; tetrads 616; hectads 42

Silver Birch is a native tree of heaths and woods, particularly on light dry acid soils. Its small abundant wind-blown seeds make it a rapid coloniser of any open ground free of grazing. This can make it a problem for the conservation of heaths but conversely heavy grazing can prevent its regeneration even in woods (Piggot 1983). It is often planted in amenity schemes and around buildings, so much so that it seems some architects can conceive of no other tree. It is very common and locally abundant throughout the area except for the White

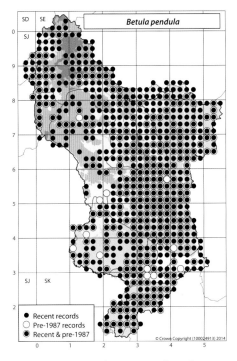

Peak where it is only occasional. It often crops up in local place names such as at Birchen Edge, and in the early 1800s it was grown at Ashover for producing birch wine (Farey 1815). The largest known specimen was found recently with a girth of 3.7m at Yeldwood Farm, Baslow (SK2673).

Betula × *aurata* Borkh.
Hybrid Birch

COUNTY STATUS:	Native
CONSERVATION STATUS:	None

FIRST YEAR: 1997 LATEST YEAR: 2013 NO OF RECORDS: 15
RECENT SQUARES: monads 14; tetrads 12; hectads 11
ALL SQUARES: monads 14; tetrads 12; hectads 11

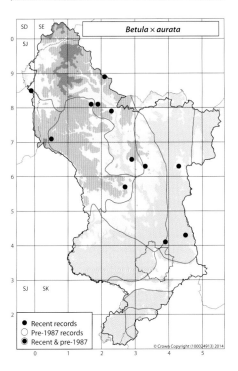

Hybrid Birch is a very rare, native tree. It has been recorded throughout the northern and central parts of the county (Highshaw Clough SK2188, Hopton Quarry SK2656, Wire Stone Plantation SK3263 & Pilsley SK4263). The hybrid of the two native birches, Silver (*B. pendula*) and Downy Birch (*B. pubescens*), it is often difficult to separate from its parents and is probably under-recorded.

Betula pubescens Ehrh.
Downy Birch

COUNTY STATUS:	Native
CONSERVATION STATUS:	None

FIRST YEAR: 1884 LATEST YEAR: 2013 NO OF RECORDS: 879
RECENT SQUARES: monads 438; tetrads 303; hectads 38
ALL SQUARES: monads 481; tetrads 327; hectads 40

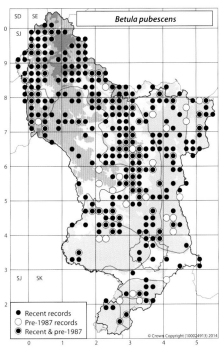

Downy Birch is a native tree of heaths and woods on wet organic soils often at higher altitudes. It can also rapidly colonise areas of moorland, particularly those disturbed by cutting or burning. It is frequent in the Dark Peak but only rare to occasional elsewhere. Our plants are probably all ssp. *pubescens*.

Alnus glutinosa (L.) Gaertn.
Alder

COUNTY STATUS:	Native
CONSERVATION STATUS:	None

FIRST YEAR: 1789 LATEST YEAR: 2013 NO OF RECORDS: 3,723
RECENT SQUARES: monads 1,307; tetrads 625; hectads 45
ALL SQUARES: monads 1,369; tetrads 635; hectads 45

Alder is a native tree of woods on wet soils, often forming pure stands in valley-bottoms, and of the edges of rivers, lakes and fens. Nowadays it is frequently planted

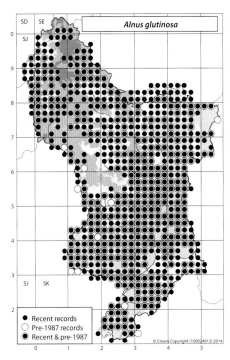

in restoration and amenity schemes. It is very common throughout the area except for the White Peak. The largest tree we know of, with a girth of 6.2 metres, is at Shining Cliff Woods (SK3252). It often crops up in local place names such as Alder Carr, and its cones, known locally as Black Knobs, have been used to outline image borders in well dressings.

Alnus incana (L.) Moench
Grey Alder

Grey Alder is a casual tree of restoration and amenity planting schemes where it can spread by suckers. It is found occasionally throughout the county except for the White

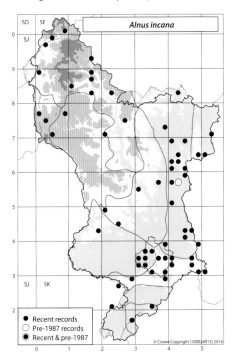

COUNTY STATUS: Casual	
CONSERVATION STATUS: None	
FIRST YEAR: 1983 LATEST YEAR: 2013	NO OF RECORDS: 90
RECENT SQUARES: monads 70; tetrads 63; hectads 24	
ALL SQUARES: monads 71; tetrads 64; hectads 24	

Peak and Magnesian Limestone (Longdendale Trail SK0598, Drakelow Power Station SK2220, Spondon SK4034 & Pilsley SK4263). Its popularity in planting schemes is probably due to its ability to tolerate harsh weather and poor soil conditions. It is a native of continental Europe.

Alnus cordata (Loisel.) Duby
Italian Alder

COUNTY STATUS: Casual	
CONSERVATION STATUS: None	
FIRST YEAR: 1979 LATEST YEAR: 2012	NO OF RECORDS: 31
RECENT SQUARES: monads 21; tetrads 21; hectads 12	
ALL SQUARES: monads 22; tetrads 22; hectads 13	

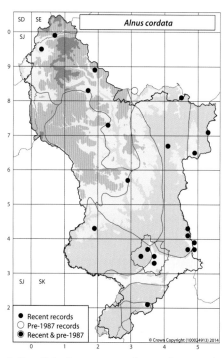

Italian Alder is a rare casual tree of restored land and amenity plantings that can sometimes produce seedlings. It occurs scattered throughout the area (Longdendale Trail SK0698, Wyvern Centre SK3735 & Five Pits Trail SK4166). Unlike other alders it can thrive on dry soils, making it more suitable for the surface materials that are used as soil in many restoration schemes. It is indigenous to Italy and Corsica.

Carpinus betulus L.
Hornbeam

Hornbeam is a casual tree of woodlands, hedges and parks, which is sometimes planted in restoration schemes. It occurs occasionally throughout Derbyshire except for the moors of the Dark Peak, and is a

COUNTY STATUS: Casual	
CONSERVATION STATUS: None	
FIRST YEAR: 1829 LATEST YEAR: 2012	NO OF RECORDS: 241
RECENT SQUARES: monads 113; tetrads 105; hectads 34	
ALL SQUARES: monads 148; tetrads 129; hectads 35	

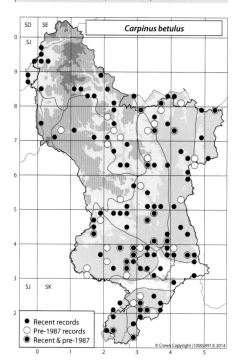

native of south-eastern England. A recent veteran tree survey by Derbyshire Wildlife Trust identified a large specimen with a girth of 2.92m at Calke Park (SK3623).

Corylus avellana L.
Hazel

Hazel is a very common, native shrub of woods, particularly on moist base-rich soils where it is often abundant. It is

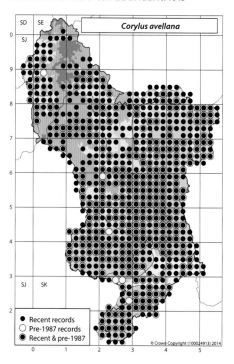

COUNTY STATUS: Native	
CONSERVATION STATUS: None	
FIRST YEAR: 1789 LATEST YEAR: 2013	NO OF RECORDS: 3,910
RECENT SQUARES: monads 1,493; tetrads 636; hectads 41	
ALL SQUARES: monads 1,540; tetrads 641; hectads 41	

frequently the dominant woody plant in scrub on the sides of the limestone dales in the White Peak (Priestcliffe Lees SK1572), and is occasional in species-rich hedges. It is also often planted in parks, hedges and now amenity plantings. In the past it was coppiced for wood but today it is more likely to be cut just to help maintain biodiversity. The largest known specimen, with a girth of 4.35m, was found recently at Millers Dale (SK1573).

CUCURBITACEAE

Bryonia dioica Jacq.
White Bryony

COUNTY STATUS: Native	
CONSERVATION STATUS: None	
FIRST YEAR: 1789 LATEST YEAR: 2013	NO OF RECORDS: 613
RECENT SQUARES: monads 243; tetrads 120; hectads 24	
ALL SQUARES: monads 268; tetrads 134; hectads 26	

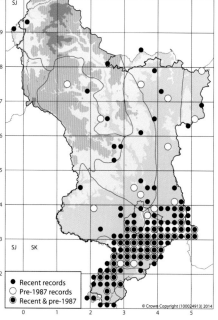

White Bryony is a native scrambling perennial of hedges and scrub. It is very common to the south and east of Derby (Ticknall SK3524 & Stanton-by-Dale SK4638) but very rare elsewhere (Gamesley SK0093 & Back Lane SK3561). Derbyshire is on the north-western edge of its British range.

Cucumis melo L.
Melon

Melon is a casual climbing annual grown for its fruits. Our one record comes from

Heeley (SK3484) where it was found by K. Balkow in 2003 growing on disturbed ground. It is a native of Africa.

Cucurbita pepo L.
Marrow

Marrow is a casual scrambling annual, commonly grown as a vegetable. A single record was made by C. Higginbottom for a muck heap at Brook Farm (SK2843) in 2003. It is native to Central America.

CELASTRACEAE

Euonymus europaeus L.
Spindle

COUNTY STATUS: Native	
CONSERVATION STATUS: None	
FIRST YEAR: 1789 **LATEST YEAR:** 2013 **NO OF RECORDS:** 318	
RECENT SQUARES: monads 106; tetrads 74; hectads 25	
ALL SQUARES: monads 114; tetrads 78; hectads 26	

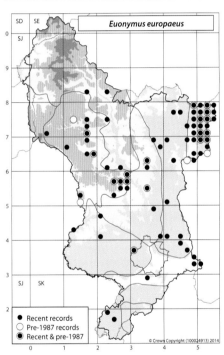

Spindle is a native shrub or small tree of scrub, open woods and hedges, chiefly in limestone areas. It is common on the Magnesian Limestone (Whitwell Wood SK5279 & Langwith Junction SK5269), but only occasional in the White Peak (Deep Dale SK1670 & Slaley SK2757). Elsewhere it is rare (Cliffside Wood SK3455, Trent Meadow SK5032 & Caldwell Hall SK2517). It is sometimes planted in restoration schemes.

PARNASSIACEAE

Parnassia palustris L.
Grass-of-Parnassus

Grass-of-Parnassus is a frequent native perennial of marshy areas and damp grasslands in the White Peak (Coombs

COUNTY STATUS: Native	
CONSERVATION STATUS: ERL, B	
FIRST YEAR: 1789 **LATEST YEAR:** 2013 **NO OF RECORDS:** 391	
RECENT SQUARES: monads 57; tetrads 39; hectads 9	
ALL SQUARES: monads 76; tetrads 47; hectads 15	

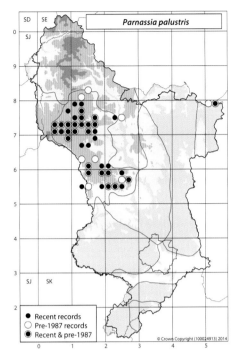

Dale SK2274 & Gratton Dale SK2059). Here its white flowers often form an attractive component of the flora of north-facing slopes (Priestcliffe Lees SK1473). There is also one record for the Magnesian Limestone (Ginney Spring SK5278). Its distribution was previously more widespread off limestone (Copse Hill SK14, Mackworth SK33 & Pinxton SK45 all for 1903). It has also declined nationally, now putting Derbyshire towards the south-eastern limit of its range.

OXALIDACEAE

Oxalis corniculata L.
Procumbent Yellow-sorrel

COUNTY STATUS: Established (Neophyte)	
CONSERVATION STATUS: None	
FIRST YEAR: 1972 **LATEST YEAR:** 2013 **NO OF RECORDS:** 78	
RECENT SQUARES: monads 54; tetrads 49; hectads 23	
ALL SQUARES: monads 57; tetrads 51; hectads 23	

Procumbent Yellow-sorrel is an established annual or short-lived perennial of garden paths, walls and wasteland. It grows occasionally throughout the eastern and southern parts of Derbyshire from Hathersage (SK2381) and Whitwell village (SK5276) in the north, to Croxall (SK1913) and Netherseal (SK2812) in the south. Although widespread in warmer parts of the world, its native range is unclear.

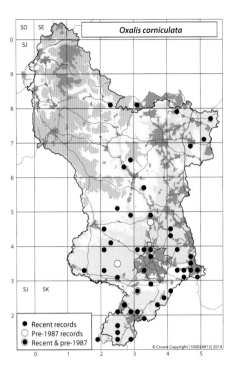

Oxalis exilis A. Cunn.
Least Yellow-sorrel

COUNTY STATUS: Casual	
CONSERVATION STATUS: None	
FIRST YEAR: 1970 **LATEST YEAR:** 2010 **NO OF RECORDS:** 15	
RECENT SQUARES: monads 11; tetrads 10; hectads 7	
ALL SQUARES: monads 13; tetrads 12; hectads 9	

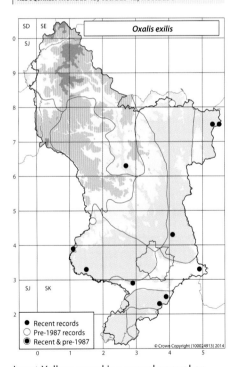

Least Yellow-sorrel is a casual annual or short-lived perennial of gardens, paths, walls and wasteland. It is grown for ornament and occurs scattered throughout southern and eastern parts (Abbotsholme School SK1138, Little Fircliffe SK2663, Melbourne Pool SK3824 & Creswell Village SK5274). It is a native of Australasia.

Oxalis stricta L.
Upright Yellow-sorrel

Upright Yellow-sorrel is a very rare, casual annual of gardens and waste ground. There are recent records from three sites (Great Longstone SK2071, Kedleston Hall SK3140 & Long Eaton SK4832) plus two older ones (Etwall SK22 in 1903 & SK25 in 1873). It is indigenous to North America and eastern Asia.

Oxalis articulata Savigny
Pink-sorrel

COUNTY STATUS: Casual	
CONSERVATION STATUS: None	
FIRST YEAR: 1960 LATEST YEAR: 2010 NO OF RECORDS: 14	
RECENT SQUARES: monads 9; tetrads 8; hectads 7	
ALL SQUARES: monads 11; tetrads 10; hectads 9	

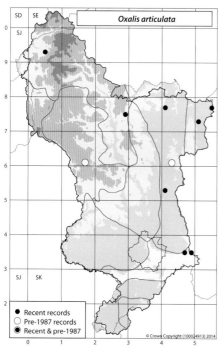

Pink-sorrel is a very rare, casual perennial of waysides, waste ground and flower beds. It is scattered throughout the county from Glossop (SK0492) and Nether Handley Tip (SK4076) in the north, to Long Eaton (SK4934) in the south. Indigenous to eastern South America, it is frequently grown in gardens for ornament.

Oxalis acetosella L.
Wood-sorrel

COUNTY STATUS: Native	
CONSERVATION STATUS: ERL	
FIRST YEAR: 1789 LATEST YEAR: 2013 NO OF RECORDS: 2,237	
RECENT SQUARES: monads 740; tetrads 396; hectads 37	
ALL SQUARES: monads 789; tetrads 421; hectads 39	

Wood-sorrel is a native perennial of woods, hedges and shaded rocks, and also of more open situations such as grassland in the uplands. It is very common throughout

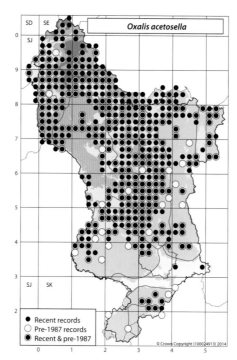

the Peak Fringe, Dark Peak and South West Peak. Elsewhere it is generally occasional but absent from large parts of the White Peak plateau and the Trent Valley. It has a local name of Green Sauce (Grigson 1975).

Oxalis debilis Kunth
Large-flowered Pink-sorrel

Large-flowered Pink-sorrel is an established perennial weed of gardens and waysides. It is widely grown as an ornamental but naturalises itself as an almost ineradicable weed. There are three modern records, all from the Chesterfield area (Barn Road SK3672 in 1998, Birdholme SK3969 in 1997 & West Handley SK3977 in 1999) and an older one for Chatsworth Park (SK2670) in 1981. It is a native of South America.

Oxalis latifolia Kunth
Garden Pink-sorrel

Garden Pink-sorrel is an established, perennial weed of nurseries and waste ground. The only two recent records are for Forbes Hole (SK4932) in 1991 and Golden Valley (SK4250) in 2010. In 1975 it was found in plant pots at Scotland Nursery (SK3359). It is indigenous to Central and South America.

EUPHORBIACEAE

Mercurialis perennis L.
Dog's Mercury

COUNTY STATUS: Native	
CONSERVATION STATUS: None	
FIRST YEAR: 1789 LATEST YEAR: 2013 NO OF RECORDS: 3,856	
RECENT SQUARES: monads 1,194; tetrads 522; hectads 39	
ALL SQUARES: monads 1,261; tetrads 533; hectads 39	

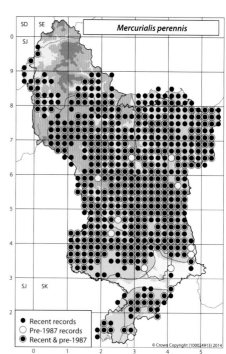

Dog's Mercury is a native perennial of woods, hedges and other shady habitats. It grows best on moist base-rich soils where it can form complete carpets on the floors of woods. In eastern England it is considered an indicator of ancient woods and it often appears to behave as such here. It is very common throughout Derbyshire except for the moors of the Dark and South West Peak, and the intensively farmed Trent Valley.

Mercurialis annua L.
Annual Mercury

Annual Mercury is a very rare, casual annual of cultivated ground and waste places. It

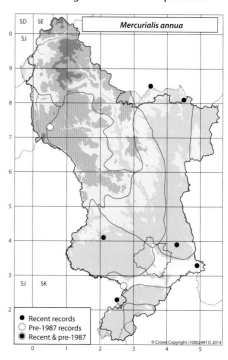

COUNTY STATUS: Casual
CONSERVATION STATUS: None
FIRST YEAR: 1969 LATEST YEAR: 2011 NO OF RECORDS: 11
RECENT SQUARES: monads 7; tetrads 6; hectads 5
ALL SQUARES: monads 9; tetrads 8; hectads 6

occurs scattered through the county from Heeley (SK3484) and Killamarsh (SK4580) in the north, to Stapenhill (SK2522) and Dunshill (SK4238) in the south.

Euphorbia oblongata Griseb.
Balkan Spurge

Balkan Spurge is an established perennial of hedges and waysides. There are two modern records: Hazelbarrow Farm (SK3681) and West Handley (SK3977). It is a native of the Balkans and the Aegean.

Euphorbia platyphyllos L.
Broad-leaved Spurge

Broad-leaved Spurge is a casual annual of cultivated and rough ground in southern England. It is thought to have a long-lived seed bank which might explain our one local record for disturbed ground at Junction 25 of the M1 (SK4735) where it was found as a casual by G. Hirons in 2004.

Euphorbia helioscopia L.
Sun Spurge

COUNTY STATUS: Established (Archaeophyte)
CONSERVATION STATUS: None
FIRST YEAR: 1789 LATEST YEAR: 2013 NO OF RECORDS: 511
RECENT SQUARES: monads 290; tetrads 247; hectads 35
ALL SQUARES: monads 351; tetrads 286; hectads 36

Sun Spurge is an anciently established, annual weed of cultivated and waste ground. It is occasional throughout the county, but is more frequent in the lowland south and east, than in the upland north

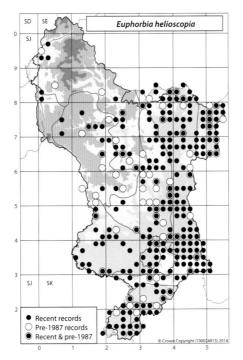

Sun Spurge (*Euphorbia helioscopia*), waste ground near St Alkmund's Way Derby (SK3536), October 2003 (Bill Grange)

and west. It has a local name of Wart-grass as its milk was thought to cure skin ailments (Grigson 1975).

Euphorbia lathyris L.
Caper Spurge

COUNTY STATUS: Casual
CONSERVATION STATUS: None
FIRST YEAR: 1969 LATEST YEAR: 2012 NO OF RECORDS: 45
RECENT SQUARES: monads 26; tetrads 27; hectads 15
ALL SQUARES: monads 35; tetrads 36; hectads 17

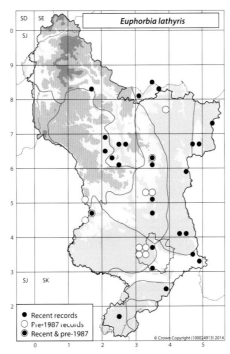

Caper Spurge is a rare casual biennial of waste places and gardens. It is grown for ornament, and is also now a constituent of bird-seed mixes. Recent records exist for

Hope Valley (SK1682) in the north, through Rattle (SK3463), to Melbourne (SK32X) and Rosliston (SK2416) in the south. It is possibly native to southern England.

Euphorbia exigua L.
Dwarf Spurge

COUNTY STATUS: Established (Archaeophyte)
CONSERVATION STATUS: DRDB (Cat2), NT, B
FIRST YEAR: 1789 LATEST YEAR: 2012 NO OF RECORDS: 95
RECENT SQUARES: monads 22; tetrads 20; hectads 13
ALL SQUARES: monads 53; tetrads 46; hectads 18

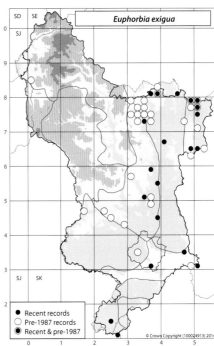

Dwarf Spurge is a rare, anciently established annual of arable fields and waste places. All recent records are for the eastern half of the county from the Moss Valley (SK3880) and Bondhay (SK5078) in the north, to Long Eaton (SK5031) and Seal Fields Farm (SK2611) in the south. It was previously more widespread with records as far west as New Mills (SK0185) in 1980. These losses are probably due to agricultural intensification. It is a plant of central and southern England with Derbyshire on the north-western edge of its range.

Euphorbia peplus L.
Petty Spurge

COUNTY STATUS: Established (Archaeophyte)
CONSERVATION STATUS: None
FIRST YEAR: 1789 LATEST YEAR: 2013 NO OF RECORDS: 747
RECENT SQUARES: monads 446; tetrads 337; hectads 38
ALL SQUARES: monads 468; tetrads 348; hectads 38

Petty Spurge is an anciently established annual of cultivated ground and waste places. It is common throughout lowland parts, becoming rare to absent in the

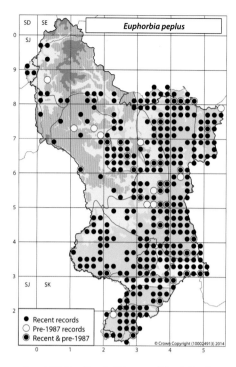

Euphorbia peplus

- Recent records
○ Pre-1987 records
◉ Recent & pre-1987

© Crown Copyright (100024913) 2014

upland White, South West and Dark Peak Character Areas.

Euphorbia × pseudovirgata (Schur) Soo
Twiggy Spurge

Locally extinct, Twiggy Spurge was an established perennial of waste places. The only record is for Little Eaton (SK3641) in 1942. It was previously identified as Leafy Spurge (*E. esula*) but was later redetermined (Clapham 1969). Indigenous to central Europe, it is the hybrid of Waldstein's Spurge (*E. waldsteinii*) and Leafy Spurge (*E. esula*).

Euphorbia cyparissias L.
Cypress Spurge

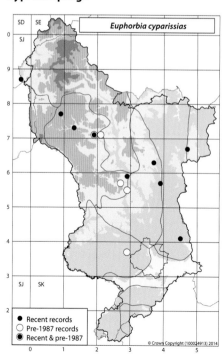

Euphorbia cyparissias

- Recent records
○ Pre-1987 records
◉ Recent & pre-1987

© Crown Copyright (100024913) 2014

| COUNTY STATUS: Established (Neophyte) |
| CONSERVATION STATUS: None |
| FIRST YEAR: 1970 LATEST YEAR: 2009 NO OF RECORDS: 16 |
| RECENT SQUARES: monads 9; tetrads 9; hectads 8 |
| ALL SQUARES: monads 14; tetrads 13; hectads 10 |

Cypress Spurge is an established perennial of rough grassland, waysides and waste places. It is grown as an ornamental in gardens, from where it escapes or is discarded. It occurs very rarely and sporadically across Derbyshire, from Roman Lakes (SJ9687) in the north, through Great Longstone Station (SK1971) and High Tor (SK2958), to West Hallam (SK4441) in the south. It is possibly native to southern England.

Euphorbia amygdaloides L.
Wood Spurge

| COUNTY STATUS: Native |
| CONSERVATION STATUS: DRDB (Cat4) |
| FIRST YEAR: 1789 LATEST YEAR: 2011 NO OF RECORDS: 16 |
| RECENT SQUARES: monads 8; tetrads 7; hectads 7 |
| ALL SQUARES: monads 8; tetrads 7; hectads 10 |

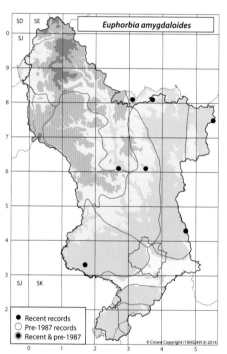

Euphorbia amygdaloides

- Recent records
○ Pre-1987 records
◉ Recent & pre-1987

© Crown Copyright (100024913) 2014

Wood Spurge is represented by two subspecies. **Ssp. *amygdaloides*** is a very rare, native perennial of damp woods and hedgebanks. Recent records are scattered throughout the county from Owler Carr (SK3780) and Belph (SK5475) in the north, through Snitterton (SK2760) and Cocking Tor (SK3461), to Sudbury Hall (SK1632) in the south. Recently **ssp. *robbiae*** has appeared here as an introduced plant, and some records for the native subspecies may well refer to this one. Nationally it has a southern distribution, and is on the northern edge of its native range here.

Ssp. *robbiae* (Turrill) Stace is a recently established perennial, indigenous to south-western Turkey. All three records are recent: Dore (SK3180), Milltown (SK3561) and Heanor Road (SK4642). It is indigenous to south-western Turkey.

Euphorbia falcata L.
Sickle Spurge

Sickle Spurge is a very rare casual. The only record is of a garden weed at Ashbourne (SK1746) in 1982 where it was thought to have originated from bird-seed (Clement & Foster 1994). It occurs naurally in southern Europe.

SALICACEAE

Populus alba L.
White Poplar

| COUNTY STATUS: Established (Neophyte) |
| CONSERVATION STATUS: None |
| FIRST YEAR: 1829 LATEST YEAR: 2013 NO OF RECORDS: 147 |
| RECENT SQUARES: monads 77; tetrads 82; hectads 29 |
| ALL SQUARES: monads 93; tetrads 98; hectads 31 |

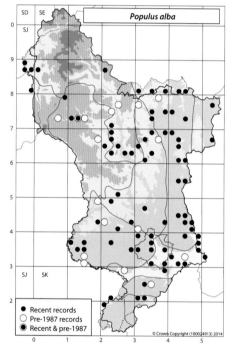

Populus alba

- Recent records
○ Pre-1987 records
◉ Recent & pre-1987

© Crown Copyright (100024913) 2014

White Poplar is an occasional established tree of woods and hedges throughout the county, except for the Dark Peak where it is rare. It is a native of central and southern Europe.

Populus × canescens (Aiton) Sm.
Grey Poplar

| COUNTY STATUS: Established (Neophyte) |
| CONSERVATION STATUS: None |
| FIRST YEAR: 1881 LATEST YEAR: 2013 NO OF RECORDS: 65 |
| RECENT SQUARES: monads 35; tetrads 39; hectads 18 |
| ALL SQUARES: monads 42; tetrads 46; hectads 21 |

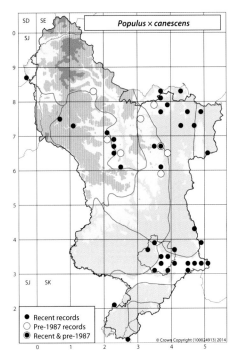

Grey Poplar is a rare established large tree of damp woods, hedges and riversides (Bakewell SK26I, Ogston Reservoir SK3660 & Renishaw SK47N). It was formerly grown for timber, but is increasingly planted for amenity as at St Chads Water (SK4430). It is the hybrid of White Poplar (*P. alba*) and Aspen (*P. tremula*). Although generally planted, some trees may be the result of natural crossings as occurs in continental Europe.

Populus tremula L.
Aspen

Aspen is an occasional native tree of damp woods, hedges and moorland

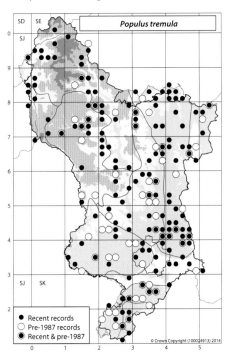

COUNTY STATUS: Native
CONSERVATION STATUS: None
FIRST YEAR: 1789 **LATEST YEAR:** 2013 **NO OF RECORDS:** 393
RECENT SQUARES: monads 175; tetrads 153; hectads 39
ALL SQUARES: monads 223; tetrads 193; hectads 39

flushes. It grows throughout the county, from Longdendale (SK0796) and Mosley Bank (SK1695) in the north, through Crich Chase (SK3452) to Robin Wood (SK3525) and Grange Wood (SK2714) in the south. It usually occurs as individual trees or as dense thickets formed by sucker growths. However, it occasionally occurs as significant stands, as in Cressbrook Dale (SK1773) and Monk's Dale (SK1373) where it forms part of the characteristic daleside vegetation (Mabey 1996).

Populus nigra L.
Black-poplar

COUNTY STATUS: Native
CONSERVATION STATUS: B, C
FIRST YEAR: 1829 **LATEST YEAR:** 2011 **NO OF RECORDS:** 128
RECENT SQUARES: monads 38; tetrads 26; hectads 12
ALL SQUARES: monads 44; tetrads 28; hectads 13

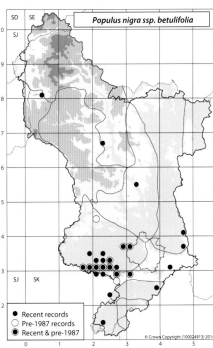

Black-poplar occurs locally in two forms, the native subspecies (map and stats shown), plus a cultivated taxon. **Native Black-poplar** (**ssp. *betulifolia*** (Pursh) Dippel) is a rare native tree of hedges and stream-sides to the west of Derby as at Hatton (SK2230), Hilton (SK2531) and Kirk Langley (SK2937). It was originally thought all our trees were males, but recent surveys found a number of females. It is planted elsewhere in the county for amenity, as at Meaden Bridge (SK2267) and Melbourne (SK3924). **Lombardy-**

poplar ('**Italica**') is a rare casual tree of gardens, parks and windbreaks. It is found mainly in southern and eastern parts (Coton in the Elms SK2314 & Eckington SK47E) but there are also scattered records elsewhere, as at Hope (SK1782). It is of garden origin.

Populus × canadensis Moench
Hybrid Black-poplar

COUNTY STATUS: Casual
CONSERVATION STATUS: None
FIRST YEAR: 1950 **LATEST YEAR:** 2012 **NO OF RECORDS:** 110
RECENT SQUARES: monads 63; tetrads 63; hectads 25
ALL SQUARES: monads 71; tetrads 71; hectads 27

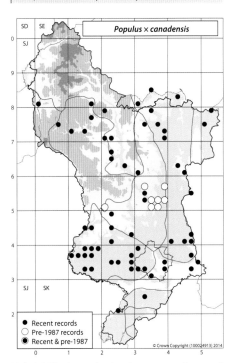

Hybrid Black-poplar is a large casual tree of waysides and woods. It grows occasionally throughout our area except for the Dark Peak where it is very rare. It is the hybrid of Black Poplar (*P. nigra*) and Necklace Poplar (*P. deltoides*) and is of garden origin. Many cultivars are grown for ornament and timber, of which 'Serotina' has been recorded here.

Populus × jackii Sarg.
Balm-of-Gilead

COUNTY STATUS: Casual
CONSERVATION STATUS: None
FIRST YEAR: 1940 **LATEST YEAR:** 2008 **NO OF RECORDS:** 30
RECENT SQUARES: monads 14; tetrads 15; hectads 14
ALL SQUARES: monads 18; tetrads 19; hectads 15

Balm-of-Gilead is a very rare, casual tree of damp woods, stream-sides and amenity plantings. It occurs scattered throughout southern and eastern Derbyshire (Wyaston Brook SK1942, Walton SK2016, Darley Tip SK3538 & Bole Hill SK37H). It is a hybrid of garden origin

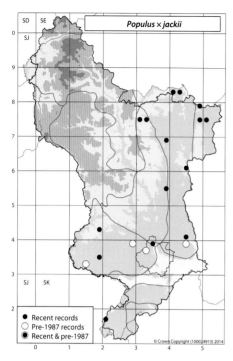

Populus × jackii

Legend:
- Recent records
- Pre-1987 records
- Recent & pre-1987

© Crown Copyright (100024913) 2014

from Necklace Poplar (*P. deltoides*) and Eastern Balsam-poplar (*P. balsamifera*).

Populus trichocarpa Torr. & A.Gray ex Hook.
Western Balsam-poplar

COUNTY STATUS: Casual
CONSERVATION STATUS: None
FIRST YEAR: 1996 LATEST YEAR: 2006 NO OF RECORDS: 11
RECENT SQUARES: monads 8; tetrads 8; hectads 7
ALL SQUARES: monads 8; tetrads 8; hectads 7

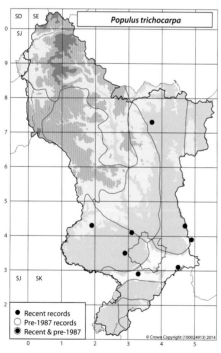

Populus trichocarpa

Legend:
- Recent records
- Pre-1987 records
- Recent & pre-1987

© Crown Copyright (100024913) 2014

Western Balsam-poplar is a very rare, casual tree of southern and eastern parts, where it is planted for ornament and timber (Quilow Lane SK1943, Silverhill Wood SK2935, Holme Brook SK3672 &

Erewash Canal SK4743). It is a native of western North America.

Populus balsamifera L.
Eastern Balsam-poplar

Eastern Balsam-poplar is a very rare, planted tree. It has only been recorded twice. Farey (1815) gave it for Mellor (SJ98), and in 2000 it was found at Kirk Langley (SK2739). It is indigenous to eastern North America.

Salix pentandra L.
Bay Willow

COUNTY STATUS: Native
CONSERVATION STATUS: B
FIRST YEAR: 1903 LATEST YEAR: 2012 NO OF RECORDS: 120
RECENT SQUARES: monads 31; tetrads 32; hectads 16
ALL SQUARES: monads 49; tetrads 46; hectads 23

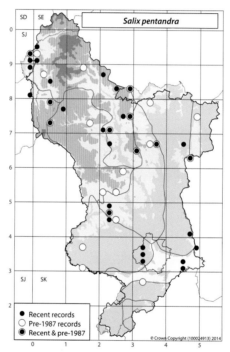

Salix pentandra

Legend:
- Recent records
- Pre-1987 records
- Recent & pre-1987

© Crown Copyright (100024913) 2014

Bay Willow is a rare small native tree of wet woods, hedges, streamsides, fens and marshes that grows throughout the area (Chinley SK0484, Priddock Wood SK2086, Birchill Bank SK2271, Bradley SK2346 & Erewash Canal SK43Y). Its glossy green leaves mean it is occasionally planted for amenity (Derby SK33). It is a northern species towards the southern limit of its native range here.

Salix × meyeriana Rostk. ex Willd.
Shiny-leaved Willow

Locally extinct, Shiny-leaved Willow was a very rare, small casual tree. The only record comes from Derby (SK33) in 1948. It is the hybrid of Bay Willow (*S. pentandra*) with Crack-willow (*S. fragilis*).

Salix fragilis L.
Crack-willow

Crack-willow is an anciently established

COUNTY STATUS: Established (Archaeophyte)
CONSERVATION STATUS: None
FIRST YEAR: 1881 LATEST YEAR: 2012 NO OF RECORDS: 2,198
RECENT SQUARES: monads 980; tetrads 509; hectads 42
ALL SQUARES: monads 1,045; tetrads 525; hectads 42

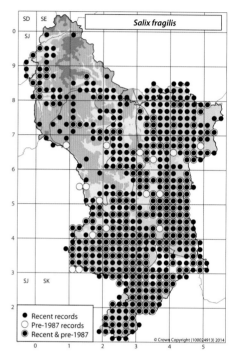

Salix fragilis

Legend:
- Recent records
- Pre-1987 records
- Recent & pre-1987

© Crown Copyright (100024913) 2014

tree of the sides of ponds, streams and rivers that also occurs in hedges, wet woods, fens and marshes. It is very common in southern and eastern Derbyshire where it is often pollarded, but is rarer in the White and Dark Peak Areas. The two largest specimens, with girths of 4.5m are at Catton Hall (SK2015) and Ambaston Farm (SK4232). It is widely planted, often as one of several cultivated varieties, of which the commonest in the area is **Bedford Willow** (**var. russelliana** (Sm.) W.D.J. Koch).

Salix × alopecuroides Tausch ex Opiz
A hybrid willow

Locally extinct, this hybrid of Crack-willow (*S. fragilis*) and Almond Willow (*S. triandra*) was a very rare, native tree. Clapham (1969) listed it for Bentley Brook (SK1646) and Sturston Mill (SK2047), while Linton (1903) also gave it for the former site.

Salix × rubens Schrank
Hybrid Crack-willow

COUNTY STATUS: Established (Archaeophyte)
CONSERVATION STATUS: None
FIRST YEAR: 1903 LATEST YEAR: 2006 NO OF RECORDS: 10
RECENT SQUARES: monads 4; tetrads 4; hectads 4
ALL SQUARES: monads 9; tetrads 8; hectads 9

Hybrid Crack-willow is a very rare, anciently established tree of wet woods and the sides of waterbodies. It was occasionally planted, in previous centuries for basketry, and is now for amenity. It occurs sporadically throughout Derbyshire with only four recent records: Cross Carr (SK1534), Bamford (SK2083), Willington (SK2827) and the River Mease (SK2611 v.c.38). It is the hybrid of White Willow (*S. alba*) and Crack-willow (*S. fragilis*).

Salix × pendulina Wender.
Weeping Crack-willow

Weeping Crack-willow is a very rare, planted small tree. The only records are for Stapenhill (SK2522) in 2000 and Willington (SK2928) in 2007. It is of garden origin from the crossing of Crack-willow (*S. fragilis*) with True Weeping-willow (*S. babylonica*).

Salix alba L.
White Willow

COUNTY STATUS: Established (Archaeophyte)	
CONSERVATION STATUS: None	
FIRST YEAR: 1940 LATEST YEAR: 2013 NO OF RECORDS: 407	
RECENT SQUARES: monads 222; tetrads 175; hectads 37	
ALL SQUARES: monads 246; tetrads 195; hectads 40	

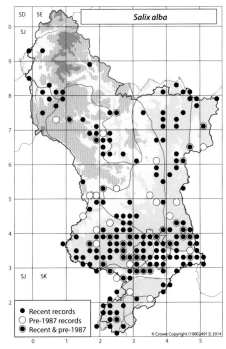

White Willow is an anciently established tree. It occurs occasionally in wet ground by streams and ponds, and in woods and marshy areas. It is also planted for ornament in gardens and elsewhere, sometimes as **Golden Willow** (**var. *vitellina***) as at Dunston Tip (SK3674). It is most frequent in the south of the county, becoming rarer to the north, and almost absent from the Dark Peak. A large specimen found recently at Chaddesden Park (SK3836) was estimated to have a girth of 6m.

Salix × sepulcralis Simonk.
Weeping Willow

Weeping Willow is a very rare, casual tree

COUNTY STATUS: Casual	
CONSERVATION STATUS: None	
FIRST YEAR: 1987 LATEST YEAR: 2012 NO OF RECORDS: 22	
RECENT SQUARES: monads 6; tetrads 7; hectads 7	
ALL SQUARES: monads 6; tetrads 7; hectads 7	

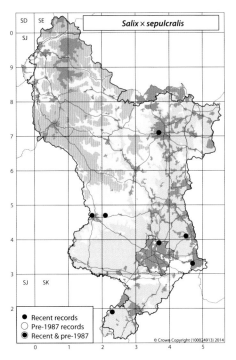

of streamsides, pondsides and ornamental plantings in the south of the county (Breadsall Hilltop SK3738 & Golden Brook Storage Lagoon SK4733). It is of garden origin from the crossing of White Willow (*S. alba*) with True Weeping-willow (*S. babylonica*).

Salix triandra L.
Almond Willow

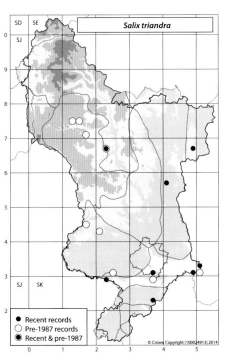

COUNTY STATUS: Established (Archaeophyte)	
CONSERVATION STATUS: A, B	
FIRST YEAR: 1884 LATEST YEAR: 2005 NO OF RECORDS: 32	
RECENT SQUARES: monads 7; tetrads 8; hectads 8	
ALL SQUARES: monads 12; tetrads 15; hectads 14	

Almond Willow is a very rare shrub or small tree found on the margins of waterbodies and marshes. It has often been planted for basketry from whence it spread to become anciently established. Recent records are from central (River Wye SK2267) and southern parts (Calke Park SK3622 & Trent Meadows SK53B).

Salix × mollissima Hoffm. ex Elwert
Sharp-stipuled Willow

COUNTY STATUS: Established (Archaeophyte)	
CONSERVATION STATUS: None	
FIRST YEAR: 1903 LATEST YEAR: 1978 NO OF RECORDS: 9	
RECENT SQUARES: monads 0; tetrads 0; hectads 0	
ALL SQUARES: monads 4; tetrads 3; hectads 8	

Sharp-stipuled Willow is a very rare and anciently established shrub of wet ground by ponds and streams. It occurs throughout the county except for the Dark Peak. It has also been planted for basketry and now nationally for biomass production. There are no recent records, some of the latest being from Chesterfield (SK3872) in 1978, and Bentley Brook (SK1646) and Yeldersley Pond (SK2144) both in 1969. It is the hybrid of Almond Willow (*S. triandra*) and Osier (*S. viminalis*).

Salix purpurea L.
Purple Willow

Purple Willow is a rare native shrub of streamsides, pondsides, marshy areas,

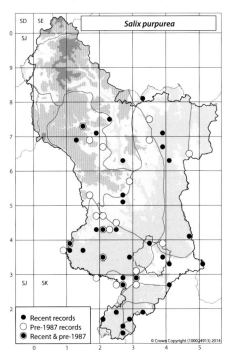

COUNTY STATUS: Native
CONSERVATION STATUS: DRDB (Cat5b)
FIRST YEAR: 1903 LATEST YEAR: 2012 NO OF RECORDS: 80
RECENT SQUARES: monads 33; tetrads 34; hectads 22
ALL SQUARES: monads 51; tetrads 51; hectads 29

hedges and wet woods. It has also been planted for basketry, and occurs throughout Derbyshire except for the moorland areas of the north-western corner (Tideswell Dale SK1573, Eaton SK13D, Netherseal SK2712, Ilkeston SK4741 & Tapton SK3971).

Salix × rubra Huds.
Green-leaved Willow

COUNTY STATUS: Native
CONSERVATION STATUS: None
FIRST YEAR: 1903 LATEST YEAR: 1979 NO OF RECORDS: 9
RECENT SQUARES: monads 0; tetrads 0; hectads 0
ALL SQUARES: monads 6; tetrads 6; hectads 8

Green-leaved Willow is a very rare, native shrub or small tree of wet places that has also been planted for basketry. There are no recent records; some of the latest are from Wye Valley (SK1072) in 1969, Doveridge (SK1134) in 1969, Lathkill Dale (SK2166) in 1979 and Great Wilne (SK43) in 1903. It is the natural hybrid of Purple Willow (*S. purpurea*) and Osier (*S. viminalis*).

Salix × forbyana Sm.
Fine Osier

COUNTY STATUS: Native
CONSERVATION STATUS: None
FIRST YEAR: 1887 LATEST YEAR: 1969 NO OF RECORDS: 11
RECENT SQUARES: monads 0; tetrads 0; hectads 0
ALL SQUARES: monads 0; tetrads 0; hectads 6

Locally extinct, Fine Osier was a very rare, native shrub of wet habitats. Linton (1903) gave a number of records (Brough SK1782 & Trent Lock SK4931). However, there have been no localised reports since then. It is the product of the crossing of three species: Purple Willow (*S. purpurea*), Osier (*S. viminalis*) and Grey Willow (*S. cinerea*).

Salix daphnoides Vill.
European Violet-willow

COUNTY STATUS: Casual
CONSERVATION STATUS: None
FIRST YEAR: 1969 LATEST YEAR: 2000 NO OF RECORDS: 9
RECENT SQUARES: monads 5; tetrads 6; hectads 5
ALL SQUARES: monads 7; tetrads 8; hectads 7

European Violet-willow is a very rare, casual shrub or small tree. It is increasingly being used in the area for amenity plantings because of its attractive twigs.
It occurs scattered through the county from the Limestone Way (SK1367) to

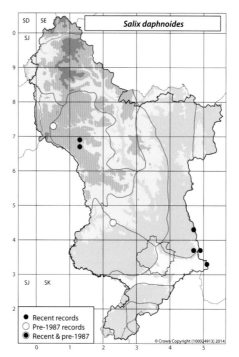

Sandiacre (SK4736) and the old tip at Trent Meadows (SK5032). It is a native of continental Europe.

Salix viminalis L.
Osier

COUNTY STATUS: Established (Archaeophyte)
CONSERVATION STATUS: None
FIRST YEAR: 1829 LATEST YEAR: 2013 NO OF RECORDS: 615
RECENT SQUARES: monads 324; tetrads 244; hectads 40
ALL SQUARES: monads 354; tetrads 265; hectads 40

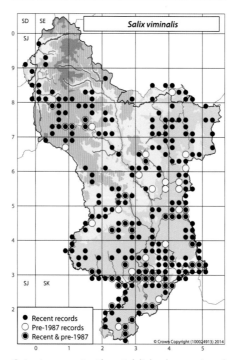

Osier is an anciently established, occasional shrub or small tree. It grows by ponds and streams, and in marshes and wet woods, and is often pollarded. It has also been

planted for basket-making, as around Repton (SK3128). It occurs throughout the area except for most of the Dark Peak.

Salix elaeagnos Scop.
Olive Willow

Olive Willow is a very rare, casual shrub. It occurs as a garden throwout though is also used in amenity plantings. The only record comes from a tip at Butterley (SK3951) in 1998. It is a native of southern-temperate Europe.

Salix × smithiana Willd.
Broad-leaved Osier

COUNTY STATUS: Native
CONSERVATION STATUS: None
FIRST YEAR: 1903 LATEST YEAR: 2013 NO OF RECORDS: 70
RECENT SQUARES: monads 51; tetrads 48; hectads 20
ALL SQUARES: monads 57; tetrads 54; hectads 20

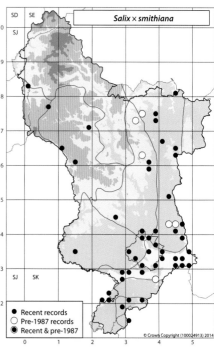

Broad-leaved Osier is a rare native shrub or small tree of streamsides, wet woods and waste ground. It was probably also planted in the past for coarse basketry, and now increasingly in amenity schemes. It occurs sporadically through the county except for the Dark Peak (Crowdecote Bank SK1065, banks of River Trent SK2521, Sawley Oxbow SK4631, Ilkeston SK4642 & Great Pond SK4563). It is the hybrid of Osier (*S. viminalis*) and Goat Willow (*S. caprea*).

Salix × holosericea Willd.
Silky-leaved Osier

COUNTY STATUS: Native
CONSERVATION STATUS: None
FIRST YEAR: 1903 LATEST YEAR: 2012 NO OF RECORDS: 25
RECENT SQUARES: monads 5; tetrads 5; hectads 5
ALL SQUARES: monads 10; tetrads 10; hectads 20

Silky-leaved Osier is a very rare, native shrub or small tree of streamsides, hedges and wet woods. There are only five recent records, all between 1996 and 2012: Derwent Dam (SK1789), Sheepwash (SK2552), Birchwood (SK2645), Via Gellia (SK2957) and St Chads Water (SK4430). Previously it was recorded throughout the county from 1903, but this reduction is probably an artefact of recording. It is the result of the cross between Osier (*S. viminalis*) and Grey Willow (*S. cinerea*).

Salix caprea L.
Goat Willow

COUNTY STATUS: Native

CONSERVATION STATUS: None

FIRST YEAR: 1829 LATEST YEAR: 2013 NO OF RECORDS: 2,424

RECENT SQUARES: monads 1,113; tetrads 596; hectads 42

ALL SQUARES: monads 1,176; tetrads 605; hectads 42

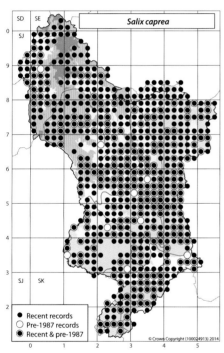

Goat Willow is a common native shrub or small tree of scrub, hedges, open woods and waste ground found throughout the area, generally on damp soils. A large specimen found recently at Leash Fen, Baslow (SK2972) has a girth of 3.5m. Our plant is ssp. *caprea*.

Salix × reichardtii A. Kern.
A hybrid willow

COUNTY STATUS: Native

CONSERVATION STATUS: None

FIRST YEAR: 1969 LATEST YEAR: 2013 NO OF RECORDS: 60

RECENT SQUARES: monads 51; tetrads 47; hectads 25

ALL SQUARES: monads 53; tetrads 49; hectads 25

This hybrid willow is an occasional native shrub or small tree of damp, often

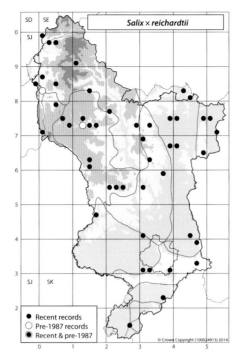

disturbed, ground and the sites of cleared woods. It is recorded sporadically through the area but is probably under-recorded for its parents (Coldwell Clough SK0585, Castleton SK1582, Hollin Hill SK5175, Ashbourne SK1746 & Chellaston Tip SK3830). It is the hybrid of Goat (*S. caprea*) and Grey Willow (*S. cinerea*).

Salix × capreola Jos. Kern. ex Andersson
A hybrid willow

COUNTY STATUS: Native

CONSERVATION STATUS: None

FIRST YEAR: 1890 LATEST YEAR: 2000 NO OF RECORDS: 8

RECENT SQUARES: monads 1; tetrads 1; hectads 1

ALL SQUARES: monads 4; tetrads 4; hectads 5

This hybrid willow is a very rare, native shrub or small tree of scrub and wood margins. The only recent record is from a disused quarry at SJ9887, but there are a few earlier ones from southern Derbyshire (Manystones Quarry SK2355 & Morley SK3841 both from the 1970s). It is the natural hybrid of Goat Willow (*S. caprea*) and Eared Willow (*S. aurita*).

Salix cinerea L.
Grey Willow

COUNTY STATUS: Native

CONSERVATION STATUS: None

FIRST YEAR: 1829 LATEST YEAR: 2013 NO OF RECORDS: 1,852

RECENT SQUARES: monads 978; tetrads 571; hectads 43

ALL SQUARES: monads 1,029; tetrads 590; hectads 43

Grey Willow is a common native shrub or small tree found throughout the county. It grows in a wide range of habitats including woods, moors, marshes and fens. It also occurs by rivers and ponds, and on waste

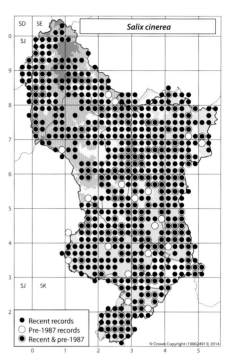

ground. Our plants are all ssp. *oleifolia* Macreight.

Salix × multinervis Doell
A hybrid willow

COUNTY STATUS: Native

CONSERVATION STATUS: None

FIRST YEAR: 1890 LATEST YEAR: 2013 NO OF RECORDS: 22

RECENT SQUARES: monads 17; tetrads 15; hectads 13

ALL SQUARES: monads 18; tetrads 16; hectads 14

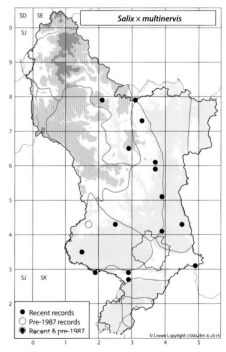

This hybrid willow is a very rare, native shrub or small tree of scrub, wood and hedges. Recent records are scattered throughout the county except for the White Peak and the northern half of the Dark Peak

(Sudbury SK1535, Lock Lane Ash Tip SK4831, Ogston Reservoir SK3760 & Abney Clough SK2079). It is the hybrid of Grey Willow (*S. cinerea*) and Eared Willow (*S. aurita*).

Salix aurita L.
Eared Willow

COUNTY STATUS: Native	
CONSERVATION STATUS: None	
FIRST YEAR: 1890 **LATEST YEAR:** 2012 **NO OF RECORDS:** 85	
RECENT SQUARES: monads 29; tetrads 28; hectads 19	
ALL SQUARES: monads 42; tetrads 40; hectads 29	

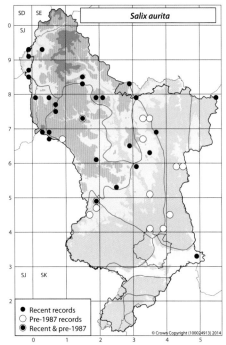

Eared Willow is a rare native shrub of damp woods, scrub on acid soils and moorland flushes. It occurs mainly in the north (Hogshaw SK0675, Priestcliffe Lees SK1472, Lose Hill SK1485, Littlemoor SK3158 & Steetley Quarry SK5478), with isolated records in the south (SK43W), where it was previously more frequent. It has been lost from here, as it has nationally from lowland areas, mostly through agricultural intensification and drainage.

Salix phylicifolia L.
Tea-leaved Willow
Tea-leaved Willow is a very rare, planted shrub or small tree of amenity schemes, but is a native of northern Britain. All records come from the reclaimed Chellaston Tip (SK3829 & SK3830) where it was recorded between 2001 and 2012.

Salix repens L.
Creeping Willow
Creeping Willow is a very rare, native undershrub of damp heaths, moors and disturbed ground. Current records are from northern Derbyshire (Grin Plantation

COUNTY STATUS: Native	
CONSERVATION STATUS: A, B	
FIRST YEAR: 1903 **LATEST YEAR:** 2013 **NO OF RECORDS:** 41	
RECENT SQUARES: monads 11; tetrads 11; hectads 8	
ALL SQUARES: monads 20; tetrads 19; hectads 12	

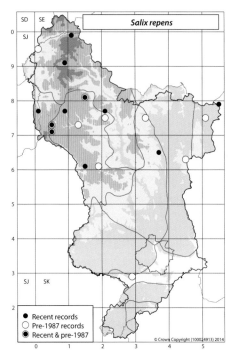

SK0572, Upper Longdendale SK1099 & Alton SK3664). Previously it also grew further south (Spread Eagle Inn SK2939). It occurs throughout the British Isles but has declined recently in central England (Preston *et al.* 2002), probably due to agricultural improvement of marginal land.

VIOLACEAE

Viola odorata L.
Sweet Violet
Sweet Violet is an occasional native perennial of woods, scrub and hedgerows particularly on base-rich soils. It is also a

COUNTY STATUS: Native	
CONSERVATION STATUS: None	
FIRST YEAR: 1789 **LATEST YEAR:** 2013 **NO OF RECORDS:** 297	
RECENT SQUARES: monads 132; tetrads 115; hectads 28	
ALL SQUARES: monads 164; tetrads 140; hectads 33	

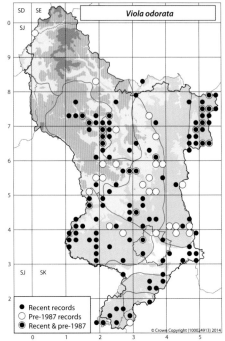

frequent garden escape on verges and waysides, making its native distribution almost impossible to discern. It grows throughout the county except for the high moors of the north-west. It sometimes occurs as a white-flowered form.

Viola hirta L.
Hairy Violet

COUNTY STATUS: Native	
CONSERVATION STATUS: None	
FIRST YEAR: 1801 **LATEST YEAR:** 2013 **NO OF RECORDS:** 247	
RECENT SQUARES: monads 66; tetrads 55; hectads 16	
ALL SQUARES: monads 92; tetrads 73; hectads 21	

Sweet Violet (*Viola odorata*) in grounds of Markeaton Crematorium Derby (SK3237), April 2009 (Peter Smith)

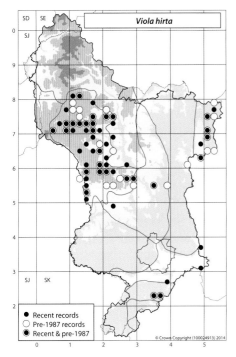

Hairy Violet is a native perennial of limestone grassland and scrub. It is occasional in the White Peak (Cow Dale SK0872 & Via Gellia SK2857) and on the Magnesian Limestone (Whitwell Wood SK5277). It also occurs on the isolated outcrops of limestone at Crich (SK3455) and Ticknall (SK3623).

Viola riviniana Rchb.
Common Dog-violet

COUNTY STATUS: Native
CONSERVATION STATUS: None
FIRST YEAR: 1789 **LATEST YEAR:** 2013 **NO OF RECORDS:** 2,402
RECENT SQUARES: monads 959; tetrads 545; hectads 43
ALL SQUARES: monads 1,030; tetrads 565; hectads 43

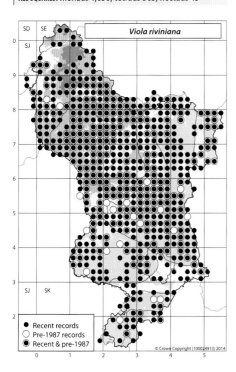

Common Dog-violet is a widespread, and often abundant, native perennial, growing in woods, hedges and moors. It can sometimes become a serious weed of gardens. Two subspecies have been recorded. The usual one is **ssp. *riviniana***, while **ssp. *minor*** (Murb. ex Greg.) has been noted in the past from a few isolated localities (Alkmonton SK1838 in 1968).

Viola × bavarica Schrank
A hybrid dog-violet
Locally extinct, this hybrid of the Common (*V. riviniana*) and the Early Dog-violet (*V. reichenbachiana*) was a very rare, native perennial. The only records are from Hollington (SK2239) in 1891, and Hollinhill and Markland Grips (SK57) in 1949. The frequency of occurrence of its parents suggests it is probably overlooked.

Viola × intersita Beck
A hybrid dog-violet
This hybrid of Common (*V. riviniana*) and Heath Dog-violet (*V. canina*) is a very rare, native perennial. There are only two recorded sites: Shirley Park (SK24) in 1903 and Mill Dale (SK1455) in 1969 and 1978. It is probably under-recorded.

Viola reichenbachiana Jord. ex Boreau
Early Dog-violet

COUNTY STATUS: Native
CONSERVATION STATUS: None
FIRST YEAR: 1887 **LATEST YEAR:** 2012 **NO OF RECORDS:** 226
RECENT SQUARES: monads 83; tetrads 67; hectads 23
ALL SQUARES: monads 114; tetrads 89; hectads 27

Early Dog-violet is an occasional native perennial of woods and scrub (Kinder

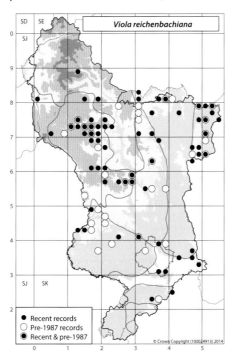

Scout SK1389, Priestcliffe Lees SK1572, Ticknall SK3523 & Whitwell Wood SK5278). Clapham (1969) states it occurs chiefly on calcareous soils but recent records barely support this.

Viola canina L.
Heath Dog-violet

COUNTY STATUS: Native
CONSERVATION STATUS: DRDB (Cat2), NT, B
FIRST YEAR: 1863 **LATEST YEAR:** 2010 **NO OF RECORDS:** 41
RECENT SQUARES: monads 13; tetrads 11; hectads 5
ALL SQUARES: monads 19; tetrads 17; hectads 12

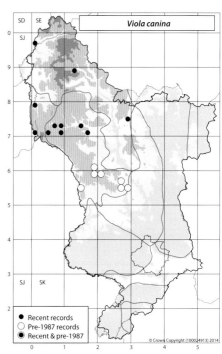

Heath Dog-violet is a very rare, native perennial of grasslands on acid soils. Recent records are from northern Derbyshire (Litton Mill SK17L & the Upper Derwent Valley SK1389). Earlier records show a strange change in distribution due to alterations in what was included under the name *V. canina* over the years. Those made around the start of last century were from the south (Seal Wood SK21 & Ockbrook SK43), whereas those made around the mid-20th century were from central parts (Hopton Quarry SK2656 & Lathkill Dale SK1966). Our plants are all ssp. *canina*.

Viola palustris L.
Marsh Violet

COUNTY STATUS: Native
CONSERVATION STATUS: None
FIRST YEAR: 1829 **LATEST YEAR:** 2013 **NO OF RECORDS:** 577
RECENT SQUARES: monads 229; tetrads 141; hectads 21
ALL SQUARES: monads 268; tetrads 168; hectads 26

Marsh Violet is a native perennial of marshes, fens, bogs and wet woodlands usually on acid substrates. It occurs

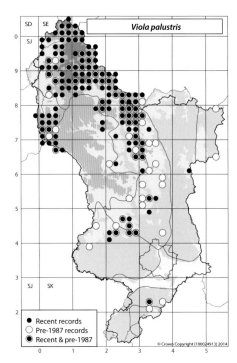

Mountain Pansy (*Viola lutea*) in grassland at Priestcliffe Lees (SK1472), April 2004
(P. & G. Dishart)

frequently in the Dark and South West Peak Areas (Errwood SK0275 & Lady Clough SK1091) but is rare elsewhere (Hulland Moss SK2546 & Carver's Rocks SK3222). Derbyshire plants belong to ssp. *palustris* and are often shy of flowering.

Viola cornuta L.
Horned Pansy

Horned Pansy is a very rare, casual annual or short-lived perennial of waysides. There are only three records: Ferneydale (SK0671) in 2011, Fairfield Common (SK0674) in 2011 and Brierlow Quarry (SK0868) in 1999. A native of the Pyrenees, it is often grown in gardens.

Viola lutea Huds.
Mountain Pansy

COUNTY STATUS: Native
CONSERVATION STATUS: ERL, B
FIRST YEAR: 1650 LATEST YEAR: 2013 NO OF RECORDS: 655
RECENT SQUARES: monads 126; tetrads 72; hectads 11
ALL SQUARES: monads 166; tetrads 91; hectads 15

Mountain Pansy is a frequent, native perennial of slightly acid grasslands over limestone in the White Peak (Tideswell Dale SK1574, High Low SK1767 & Bonsall SK2557). In such habitats it is often associated with old mineral workings due to its tolerance of lead contamination. Such plants are termed "metallophytes". It also occurs in acidic grasslands in the South West Peak (Goyt's Clough SK0173). It was formerly recorded across a wider area (Ollersett Moor SK0585 & Alport Height SK3051). Derbyshire populations generally have yellow flowers. Compared

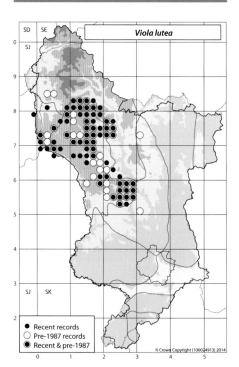

to the northern Pennines, purple or purple/yellow forms are scarce here; if found, they would be worth investigating for hybridity.

Viola lutea × V. tricolor
A hybrid pansy

This hybrid pansy is a very rare, native perennial. It is known only from Derbyshire and Northumberland, but is probably overlooked elsewhere (Stace 1997). The sole record derives from an unconfirmed report by D. Valentine in Stace (1975). A record from Bradford Dale (SK2063) in 1990 is now known to be erroneous.

Viola tricolor L.
Wild Pansy

COUNTY STATUS: Native
CONSERVATION STATUS: DRDB (Cat2), NT, B
FIRST YEAR: 1695 LATEST YEAR: 2012 NO OF RECORDS: 133
RECENT SQUARES: monads 48; tetrads 48; hectads 23
ALL SQUARES: monads 87; tetrads 81; hectads 28

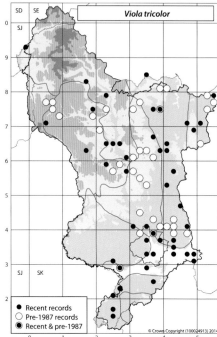

Wild Pansy is a rare native annual or short-lived perennial of grasslands, cultivated ground and waste places. It is recorded throughout the county except for the north-western corner (Stanley Moor SK0470, Rosliston SK2516, Breadsall Hilltop SK3738 & Brearley Hall SK3975). The local plant is ssp. *tricolor* and it has suffered a widespread national decline since 1962 (Preston *et al.* 2002).

Viola × contempta Jord.
A hybrid pansy

Locally extinct, this hybrid between Wild (*V. tricolor*) and Field Pansy (*V. arvensis*) was a very rare, native of cultivated and waste ground. There are only three records, all from Clapham (1969): Ednaston (SK2342), Hulland (SK2546) and above Bradley Wood (SK2046). It is probably under-recorded.

Viola × wittrockiana Gams ex Kappert
Garden Pansy

COUNTY STATUS: Casual
CONSERVATION STATUS: None
FIRST YEAR: 1989 LATEST YEAR: 2012 NO OF RECORDS: 23
RECENT SQUARES: monads 20; tetrads 20; hectads 15
ALL SQUARES: monads 20; tetrads 20; hectads 15

Garden Pansy is a very rare, casual annual or short-lived perennial of waste and

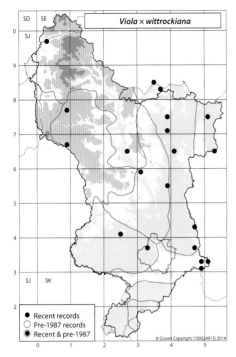

Viola × wittrockiana

disturbed ground throughout the area (Hadfield SK0296, Rowsley Sidings SK2665, Whittington SK3874 & Cotmanhay SK4743). It is commonly grown in gardens, often escaping or being thrown out with waste. It is of garden origin from various crosses of Wild (*V. tricolor*) and Field Pansy (*V. arvensis*).

Viola arvensis Murray
Field Pansy

COUNTY STATUS: Established (Archaeophyte)
CONSERVATION STATUS: None
FIRST YEAR: 1889 LATEST YEAR: 2013 NO OF RECORDS: 616
RECENT SQUARES: monads 353; tetrads 254; hectads 32
ALL SQUARES: monads 389; tetrads 276; hectads 35

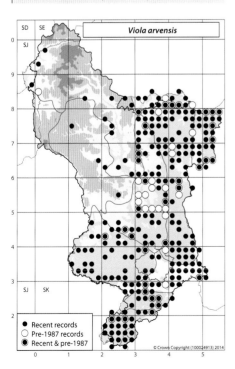

Viola arvensis

Field Pansy is an anciently established, native annual. It occurs occasionally in arable fields and on disturbed ground mostly in the south and east of the county. It persists in intensively cultivated and herbicide-treated fields, where it is often virtually the only arable weed left.

Viola labradorica Schrank
Labrador Violet

Labrador Violet is a casual evergreen perennial native to North America which is often grown in gardens. There are just two records: Great Longstone (SK2071) in 2003 and Old Staveley Works (SK4174) in 2009.

LINACEAE

Linum bienne Mill.
Pale Flax

COUNTY STATUS: Casual
CONSERVATION STATUS: None
FIRST YEAR: 1881 LATEST YEAR: 2009 NO OF RECORDS: 8
RECENT SQUARES: monads 1; tetrads 1; hectads 1
ALL SQUARES: monads 5; tetrads 5; hectads 3

Pale Flax is a very rare, casual annual or short-lived perennial of waysides and waste ground. There is one recent record from Brimington North (SK4074) in 2009. It was previously noted in the south of the county (Sudbury SK1632, Hilton SK2430 & Etwall SK2532 all for 1969), and Renishaw (SK47) in 1899. It is possibly native to southern England.

Linum usitatissimum L.
Flax

Flax is a rare casual annual of waste ground, tips, cultivated land and waysides.

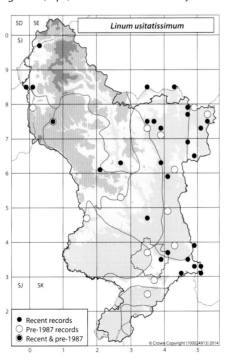

Linum usitatissimum

COUNTY STATUS: Casual
CONSERVATION STATUS: None
FIRST YEAR: 1789 LATEST YEAR: 2012 NO OF RECORDS: 63
RECENT SQUARES: monads 29; tetrads 28; hectads 17
ALL SQUARES: monads 42; tetrads 41; hectads 23

It occurs scattered across Derbyshire, from Hadfield (SK0296) and Beighton Tip (SK4384) in the north, to Derby City (SK33) and Pasture Lane (SK5031) in the south. It was formerly grown for linen (Farey 1815), and is now sown for linseed oil and game food. Of cultivated origin, it is now also a bird-seed alien.

Linum perenne L.
Perennial Flax

Perennial Flax is a very rare, casual perennial, indigenous to eastern England. The only recent record is from Stoney Middleton (SK2275) and there is one other for the Buxton area (Robertson 1854).

Linum catharticum L.
Fairy Flax

COUNTY STATUS: Native
CONSERVATION STATUS: None
FIRST YEAR: 1789 LATEST YEAR: 2013 NO OF RECORDS: 1,638
RECENT SQUARES: monads 483; tetrads 282; hectads 36
ALL SQUARES: monads 533; tetrads 306; hectads 38

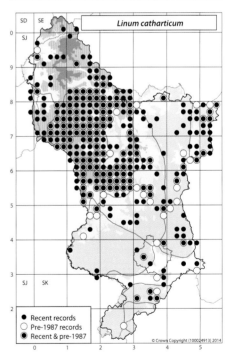

Linum catharticum

Fairy Flax is a native annual or biennial found in a wide range of open habitats. It grows in dry grasslands and woodland rides, on waste ground and quarry spoil, on rock ledges and in moorlands. It is common in the limestone areas of the White Peak and Magnesian Limestone (Laughman Tor SK1077, Lean Low SK1462, Harborough Rocks SK2455, Whitwell Wood

SK3881 & Pleasley SK5064). Elsewhere it is rare (Alport Valley SK1390, Ladywood SK4439 & Ticknall Quarries SK3623).

HYPERICACEAE

Hypericum calycinum L.
Rose-of-Sharon

COUNTY STATUS: Established (Neophyte)	
CONSERVATION STATUS: None	
FIRST YEAR: 1881 LATEST YEAR: 2011 NO OF RECORDS: 10	
RECENT SQUARES: monads 5; tetrads 5; hectads 6	
ALL SQUARES: monads 7; tetrads 7; hectads 8	

Rose-of-Sharon is a very rare, established shrub whose yellow flowers and evergreen foliage make it attractive in gardens and amenity plantings. It may then become naturalized on roadsides, in shrubberies or survive as a relic of cultivation. It occurs scattered throughout the county (Millhouses SK3382, Mapperley SK4342 & Whitwell SK5376). It is indigenous to Turkey and Bulgaria.

Hypericum androsaemum L.
Tutsan

COUNTY STATUS: Established (Neophyte)	
CONSERVATION STATUS: None	
FIRST YEAR: 1829 LATEST YEAR: 2013 NO OF RECORDS: 46	
RECENT SQUARES: monads 30; tetrads 30; hectads 19	
ALL SQUARES: monads 32; tetrads 32; hectads 19	

Tutsan is an established rare undershrub of shaded habitats and waste ground. It occurs sporadically across Derbyshire (Gamesley Woods SK0194, Duffield Station SK3443, Frith Wood SK3678 & Lock Lane Ash Tip SK4831). It is often grown in

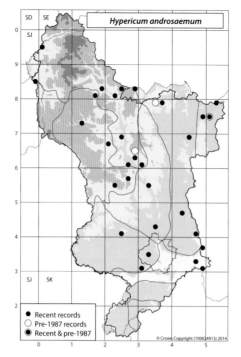

Recent records
Pre-1987 records
Recent & pre-1987

© Crown Copyright (100024913) 2014

gardens from where it is probably spread by birds. It may formerly have been native, as Linton (1903) recorded it at Matlock (SK35), though it has not been seen there since. It is indigenous to western and southern Britain.

Hypericum × inodorum Mill.
Tall Tutsan

COUNTY STATUS: Established (Neophyte)	
CONSERVATION STATUS: None	
FIRST YEAR: 1996 LATEST YEAR: 2007 NO OF RECORDS: 6	
RECENT SQUARES: monads 6; tetrads 5; hectads 4	
ALL SQUARES: monads 6; tetrads 5; hectads 4	

Tall Tutsan is a very rare, established shrub of waste ground and shrubberies which is also planted in gardens and restoration schemes. It is only known from six modern sites including: Fairfield (SK0674), Sheepbridge (SK3675), Stoney Clouds (SK4837), Long Eaton (SK4832) and Cloud Trail (SK4025). It is of English garden origin from its two parents, Tutsan (*H. androsaemum*) and Stinking Tutsan (*H. hircinum*).

Hypericum perforatum L.
Perforate St John's-wort

COUNTY STATUS: Native	
CONSERVATION STATUS: None	
FIRST YEAR: 1789 LATEST YEAR: 2013 NO OF RECORDS: 1,165	
RECENT SQUARES: monads 478; tetrads 329; hectads 38	
ALL SQUARES: monads 502; tetrads 344; hectads 38	

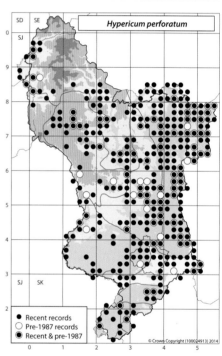

Recent records
Pre-1987 records
Recent & pre-1987

© Crown Copyright (100024913) 2014

Perforate St John's-wort is a frequent native perennial of dry grassland, open woods and waste places. Apparently commoner in eastern parts, it grows throughout the county apart from the high moors of the Dark and South West Peak Character Areas.

Hypericum × desetangsii Lamotte
Des Etangs' St John's-wort

COUNTY STATUS: Native	
CONSERVATION STATUS: None	
FIRST YEAR: 1950 LATEST YEAR: 2011 NO OF RECORDS: 17	
RECENT SQUARES: monads 14; tetrads 12; hectads 8	
ALL SQUARES: monads 14; tetrads 12; hectads 8	

Des Etangs' St John's-wort is a very rare, native perennial of waysides, rough grasslands and waste places, often associated with disused railway lines.

Tutsan (*Hypericum androsaemum*) in Scarcliffe Park (SK5170), July 2012 (Kieron Huston)

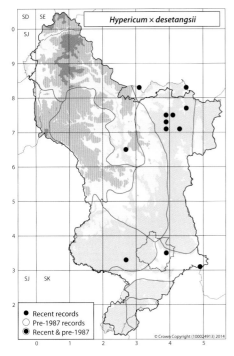

It has been noted mostly through eastern parts, but is probably under-recorded (Etwall SK2733, Tinkersley SK2665 & Lock Lane Ash Tip SK4831). It is the hybrid of Imperforate St John's-wort (*H. maculatum*) and Perforate St John's-wort (*H. perforatum*).

Hypericum maculatum Crantz
Imperforate St John's-wort

COUNTY STATUS: Native
CONSERVATION STATUS: None
FIRST YEAR: 1829 LATEST YEAR: 2012 NO OF RECORDS: 70
RECENT SQUARES: monads 26; tetrads 29; hectads 15
ALL SQUARES: monads 39; tetrads 40; hectads 19

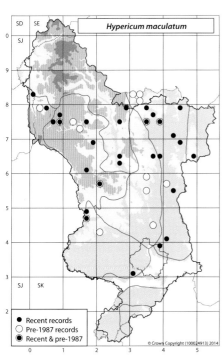

Imperforate St John's-wort is a rare native perennial of damp grasslands, wood edges and waste places. It grows throughout central parts, both on the Coal Measures (Unstone SK3677 & Stanley SK4140) and off them (Buxton Bridge SK0975 & a quarry at SK2057). It no longer appears to have a preference for the former Area, as suggested in Clapham (1969).

Hypericum tetrapterum Fr.
Square-stalked St John's-wort

COUNTY STATUS: Native
CONSERVATION STATUS: None
FIRST YEAR: 1789 LATEST YEAR: 2013 NO OF RECORDS: 600
RECENT SQUARES: monads 262; tetrads 228; hectads 36
ALL SQUARES: monads 310; tetrads 248; hectads 36

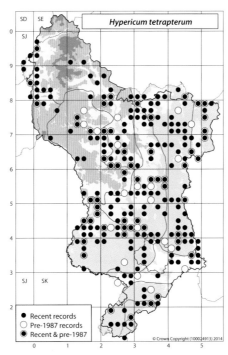

Square-stalked St John's-wort is an occasional native perennial of damp grasslands, marshes and riverbanks. It occurs in all parts of the county except for the high moors of the Dark and South West Peak Areas.

Hypericum humifusum L.
Trailing St John's-wort

COUNTY STATUS: Native
CONSERVATION STATUS: B
FIRST YEAR: 1789 LATEST YEAR: 2012 NO OF RECORDS: 162
RECENT SQUARES: monads 48; tetrads 44; hectads 22
ALL SQUARES: monads 85; tetrads 78; hectads 32

Trailing St John's-wort is a rare native perennial that crawls low over the ground on dry acid soils. It occurs in open grassland, on heaths and in light woods, scattered throughout Derbyshire (Locko Park SK4038, Ashes Farm SK1888 & Moss

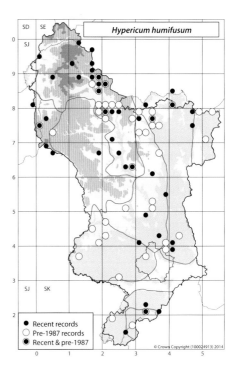

Valley SK4081). It appears to be declining in the south of the county, just as it has done nationally since 1950 (Preston *et al.* 2002).

Hypericum pulchrum L.
Slender St John's-wort

COUNTY STATUS: Native
CONSERVATION STATUS: None
FIRST YEAR: 1789 LATEST YEAR: 2013 NO OF RECORDS: 434
RECENT SQUARES: monads 196; tetrads 157; hectads 29
ALL SQUARES: monads 220; tetrads 175; hectads 37

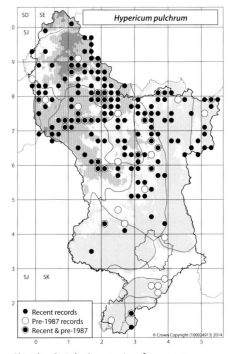

Slender St John's-wort is a frequent native perennial of grasslands, heaths and banks in the northern half of the

county (Monk's Dale SK1373 & Cuckoostone Quarry SK3162). It is rare in the southern half, having decreased since the 1950s (Shirley Park SK2042 & Swainspark SK2916). It has also declined nationally over the same period (Preston *et al.* 2002).

Hypericum hirsutum L.
Hairy St John's-wort

COUNTY STATUS: Native
CONSERVATION STATUS: None
FIRST YEAR: 1789 LATEST YEAR: 2013 NO OF RECORDS: 696
RECENT SQUARES: monads 223; tetrads 152; hectads 29
ALL SQUARES: monads 240; tetrads 162; hectads 32

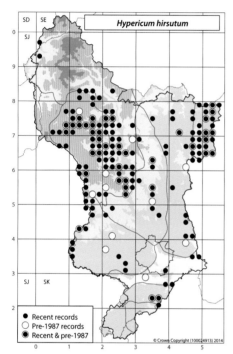

Hairy St John's-wort is a frequent native perennial of grasslands, woods and stabilized screes in the White Peak and Magnesian Limestone Areas. It also occurs, albeit rarely, scattered throughout the other Character Areas though it avoids the moors of the Dark and South West Peak.

Hypericum montanum L.
Pale St John's-wort

COUNTY STATUS: Native
CONSERVATION STATUS: DRDB (Cat2), NT, B
FIRST YEAR: 1811 LATEST YEAR: 2012 NO OF RECORDS: 151
RECENT SQUARES: monads 20; tetrads 19; hectads 6
ALL SQUARES: monads 36; tetrads 28; hectads 12

Pale St John's-wort is a rare native perennial of grasslands, rock outcrops and open woods in the White Peak (Cunning Dale SK0872, Monk's Dale SK1375 & Biggin Dale SK1458) and Magnesian Limestone Areas (Pleasley Vale SK5265). It is also recorded for the

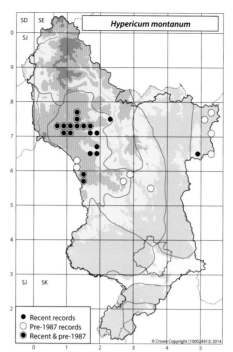

isolated limestone outcrops at Crich (SK3455) in 1968, and Ticknall (SK32) in 1903.

Hypericum elodes L.
Marsh St John's-wort

Locally extinct, Marsh St John's-wort was a very rare, native perennial of bogs and streamsides on acid soils. The most recent report is for Wessington (SK3757) in Clapham (1969), and before that it is only recorded for Tansley Moor (SK36) in Linton (1903) and Glover (1829) for the county in general. Regionally it has been lost from many sites in central England due to drainage (Preston *et al.* 2002).

GERANIACEAE

Geranium endressii J. Gay
French Crane's-bill

COUNTY STATUS: Established (Neophyte)
CONSERVATION STATUS: None
FIRST YEAR: 1969 LATEST YEAR: 2013 NO OF RECORDS: 66
RECENT SQUARES: monads 36; tetrads 43; hectads 20
ALL SQUARES: monads 41; tetrads 48; hectads 23

French Crane's-bill is a rare established perennial of waysides, waste ground and tips. It is much grown in gardens for ornament from where it spreads as a throwout on to roadsides or rubbish dumps. It is scattered through the county, from the flood plain of the River Etherow (SK0196) and Totley Bents (SK3080) in the north, to Shirley Park (SK2042) and the Wyvern Centre (SK3835) in the south. It occurs naturally in the Pyrenees.

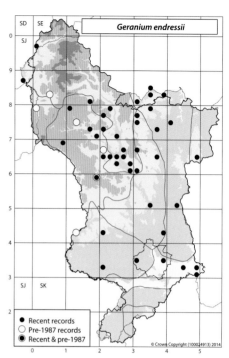

Geranium × oxonianum Yeo
Druce's Crane's-bill

COUNTY STATUS: Established (Neophyte)
CONSERVATION STATUS: None
FIRST YEAR: 1984 LATEST YEAR: 2012 NO OF RECORDS: 41
RECENT SQUARES: monads 33; tetrads 31; hectads 17
ALL SQUARES: monads 35; tetrads 33; hectads 18

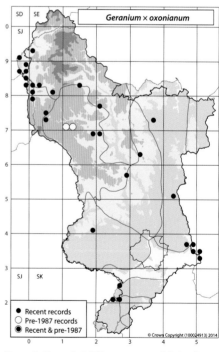

Druce's Crane's-bill is a rare established perennial of waysides and grassy places, generally near houses. It is scattered throughout the county: Marple Bridge (SJ9790), Yeaveley (SK1840) and Sandiacre (SK4837). This garden hybrid originates from the crossing of French (*G. endressii*) and Pencilled Crane's-bill (*G. versicolor*).

It is probably under-recorded in much of Derbyshire.

Geranium versicolor L.
Pencilled Crane's-bill

COUNTY STATUS: Casual
CONSERVATION STATUS: None
FIRST YEAR: 1949 LATEST YEAR: 2011 NO OF RECORDS: 31
RECENT SQUARES: monads 23; tetrads 22; hectads 13
ALL SQUARES: monads 24; tetrads 22; hectads 13

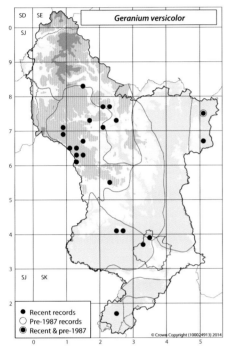

Pencilled Crane's-bill is a rare casual perennial of waysides and grassy places, usually near housing. It is much grown in gardens from where it is spread as a throwout. Sporadic throughout the county (Castleton SK1582, Crowdecote Bank SK1065 & Brailsford SK2641), it grows naturally in the central Mediterranean region.

Geranium nodosum L.
Knotted Crane's-bill
Knotted Crane's-bill is a very rare, casual perennial of waysides. It is grown in gardens, and naturalised plants are probably the result of discarded material. The only records are from Litton Frith Wood (SK1773) in 1997 and Darley Park (SK3538) in 1942. It is native to the mountains of southern Europe.

Geranium rotundifolium L.
Round-leaved Crane's-bill
Round-leaved Crane's-bill is a very rare casual of roadsides and disturbed ground. It had not been reported since 1903, until several sites at Breaston (SK4539) and Long Eaton (SK4933) were discovered in 2006 by R Martin. There is also a recent record from Radbourne (SK2836). It had previously been

COUNTY STATUS: Casual
CONSERVATION STATUS: None
FIRST YEAR: 1789 LATEST YEAR: 2011 NO OF RECORDS: 28
RECENT SQUARES: monads 6; tetrads 6; hectads 3
ALL SQUARES: monads 6; tetrads 6; hectads 9

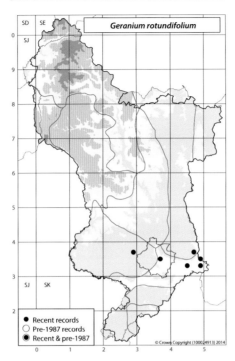

recorded through southern and western parts (Ashwood Dale SK07, Ashbourne SK14 & Repton SK32 all for 1903). It is native to central and southern England.

Geranium sylvaticum L.
Wood Crane's-bill

COUNTY STATUS: Native
CONSERVATION STATUS: DRDB (Cat4), B
FIRST YEAR: 1811 LATEST YEAR: 1982 NO OF RECORDS: 8
RECENT SQUARES: monads 0; tetrads 0; hectads 0
ALL SQUARES: monads 1; tetrads 1; hectads 4

Wood Crane's-bill is a very rare, native perennial of upland woods, though

some authorities have considered it an introduction (Stace *et al.* 2003). The latest record is for woodland at Rainster Rocks (SK2155) in 1980. It was previously recorded at Breadsall (SK33) in 1969 as a probable garden escape, and for Ashwood Dale (SK07), Matlock (SK25) and Chatsworth (SK27) all for 1903. It is a plant of northern Britain that has declined on the edge of its range since 1962 due to agricultural intensification.

Geranium pratense L.
Meadow Crane's-bill

COUNTY STATUS: Native
CONSERVATION STATUS: None
FIRST YEAR: 1789 LATEST YEAR: 2013 NO OF RECORDS: 1,786
RECENT SQUARES: monads 760; tetrads 401; hectads 38
ALL SQUARES: monads 796; tetrads 413; hectads 38

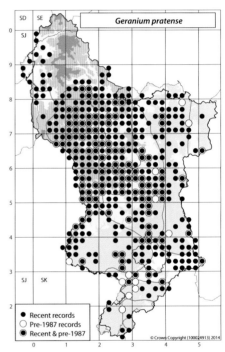

Meadow Crane's-bill is an attractive native perennial of roadsides and meadows.

Meadow Crane's-bill (*Geranium pratense*) surviving on roadside in intensively farmed landscape near Curbar (SK2774), July 2008 (Peter Smith)

Found on damp fertile soils, it is especially common in the White Peak. It is occasional elsewhere, apart from the high moors of the Dark Peak and surprisingly the Magnesian Limestone, where it is rarer. Lost from many meadows due to agricultural intensification, it is increasingly restricted to road verges, particularly in southern and eastern parts. It can nevertheless still make a spectacular sight in early summer, as at Rose End Meadows (SK2956).

Geranium sanguineum L.
Bloody Crane's-bill

COUNTY STATUS: Native	
CONSERVATION STATUS: ERL, B	
FIRST YEAR: 1787 LATEST YEAR: 2013 NO OF RECORDS: 229	
RECENT SQUARES: monads 32; tetrads 21; hectads 12	
ALL SQUARES: monads 48; tetrads 33; hectads 16	

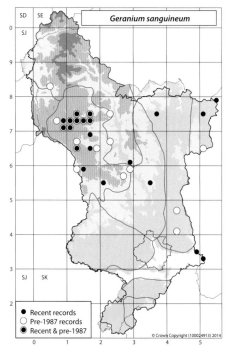

Bloody Crane's-bill is a rare native perennial of grasslands, rock outcrops and open woods in the White Peak (Back Dale SK0970, High Peak Trail SK1365 & Water-cum-Jolly Dale SK1672). It is very rare elsewhere and probably always a throwout from gardens (Sheepbridge SK3674). However, it can persist for many years at some sites (Long Eaton SK4934). This beautiful flower is one of the defining plants of the White Peak, forming attractive stands on many dalesides.

Geranium columbinum L.
Long-stalked Crane's-bill

COUNTY STATUS: Native	
CONSERVATION STATUS: B	
FIRST YEAR: 1789 LATEST YEAR: 2009 NO OF RECORDS: 101	
RECENT SQUARES: monads 22; tetrads 16; hectads 9	
ALL SQUARES: monads 34; tetrads 23; hectads 12	

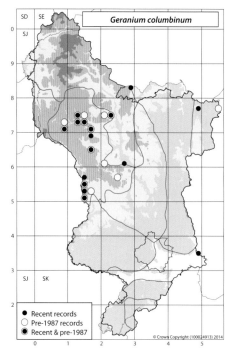

Long-stalked Crane's-bill is a rare native annual of south-facing rocky slopes and quarries in the White Peak (Peter Dale SK1275, One Ash Grange Farm SK1665 & Dove Dale SK1451). Elsewhere it is very rare and probably only casual (Houndkirk Moor SK2982, Sandiacre SK4835 & Clowne SK4876).

Geranium dissectum L.
Cut-leaved Crane's-bill

COUNTY STATUS: Established (Archaeophyte)	
CONSERVATION STATUS: None	
FIRST YEAR: 1789 LATEST YEAR: 2013 NO OF RECORDS: 1,223	
RECENT SQUARES: monads 664; tetrads 415; hectads 41	
ALL SQUARES: monads 718; tetrads 437; hectads 41	

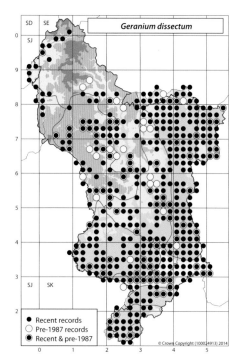

Cut-leaved Crane's-bill is an anciently established annual of disturbed ground, cultivated soils and open grasslands. It is common in the lowland southern and eastern parts of the county but only occasional-to-rare in the more upland north, such as the White and Dark Peak Character Areas.

Geranium ibericum Cav.
Caucasian Crane's-bill

COUNTY STATUS: Casual	
CONSERVATION STATUS: None	
FIRST YEAR: 1993 LATEST YEAR: 2001 NO OF RECORDS: 5	
RECENT SQUARES: monads 5; tetrads 5; hectads 3	
ALL SQUARES: monads 5; tetrads 5; hectads 3	

Bloody Crane's-bill (*Geranium sanguineum*) in limestone grassland Cressbrook Dale (SK1773), June 2008 (Peter Smith)

Caucasian Crane's-bill is a very rare, casual perennial of roadsides and waste ground in the White and Dark Peak Areas (Longstone Moor SK1974, Beeley Moor SK2967 & Owler Bar SK2876). It is sometimes grown in gardens for ornament and is a native of the Caucasus.

Geranium × magnificum Hyl.
Purple Crane's-bill

COUNTY STATUS: Established (Neophyte)
CONSERVATION STATUS: None
FIRST YEAR: 1995 LATEST YEAR: 2012 NO OF RECORDS: 25
RECENT SQUARES: monads 22; tetrads 18; hectads 11
ALL SQUARES: monads 22; tetrads 18; hectads 11

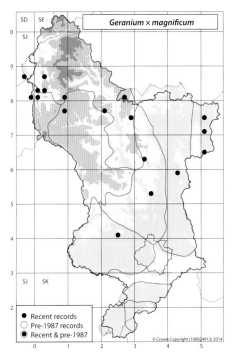

Purple Crane's-bill is an established perennial of grassy waysides and waste ground. It occurs as a rare plant in the northern half of the county (Birch Vale SK0286, Peak Dale SK0876 & Ambergate SK3452). Often grown in gardens for its striking flowers, it is the artificially produced hybrid of Caucasian (*G. ibericum*) with another Crane's-bill (*G. platypetalum*). Growingly vigorously, excess material often gets thrown out as waste.

Geranium pyrenaicum Burm. f.
Hedgerow Crane's-bill

COUNTY STATUS: Established (Neophyte)
CONSERVATION STATUS: B
FIRST YEAR: 1805 LATEST YEAR: 2013 NO OF RECORDS: 150
RECENT SQUARES: monads 71; tetrads 69; hectads 28
ALL SQUARES: monads 82; tetrads 78; hectads 31

Hedgerow Crane's-bill is an established perennial of hedges, waysides and rough grassland. It occurs occasionally throughout the county from Old Glossop

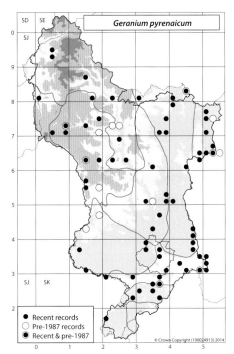

(SK0494) in the north, through Parsley Hay (SK1463) and Cow Dale (SK0872), to Lock Lane (SK4831) and Walton (SK2016) in the south. It is grown in gardens for ornament from where it escapes or is thrown out into more natural situations. It is a native of mountains in southern Europe.

Geranium pusillum L.
Small-flowered Crane's-bill

COUNTY STATUS: Native
CONSERVATION STATUS: None
FIRST YEAR: 1811 LATEST YEAR: 2012 NO OF RECORDS: 132
RECENT SQUARES: monads 63; tetrads 55; hectads 22
ALL SQUARES: monads 89; tetrads 76; hectads 28

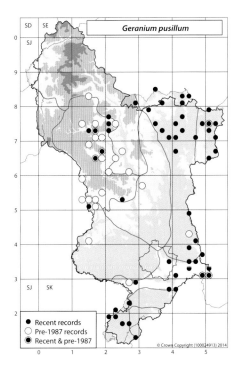

Small-flowered Crane's-bill is an occasional native annual of cultivated ground, waste places and open grasslands, particularly on well-drained soils. It occurs sporadically throughout the county, with clusters of records from the White Peak, the north-east and the south-east (Monsal Trail SK1772, Lathkill Dale SK1665, Hollin Hill SK5175 & Rosliston SK2416). It is probably under-recorded for the superficially similar Dove's-foot Crane's-bill (*G. molle*)

Geranium molle L.
Dove's-foot Crane's-bill

COUNTY STATUS: Native
CONSERVATION STATUS: None
FIRST YEAR: 1789 LATEST YEAR: 2013 NO OF RECORDS: 1,018
RECENT SQUARES: monads 518; tetrads 352; hectads 39
ALL SQUARES: monads 548; tetrads 368; hectads 39

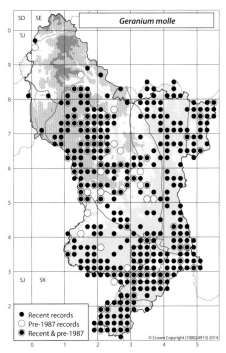

Dove's-foot Crane's-bill is a frequent native annual of open grassland, rock outcrops, cultivated land and waste ground. It occurs commonly throughout the county except for the South West and Dark Peak Areas where it is rare.

Geranium macrorrhizum L.
Rock Crane's-bill

COUNTY STATUS: Casual
CONSERVATION STATUS: None
FIRST YEAR: 1988 LATEST YEAR: 2012 NO OF RECORDS: 10
RECENT SQUARES: monads 10; tetrads 10; hectads 9
ALL SQUARES: monads 10; tetrads 10; hectads 9

Rock Crane's-bill is a very rare, casual perennial of waysides, waste ground and rough grassland. Recent records occur scattered through the county from Furness Vale (SK0083) in the north, to Sunny Hill

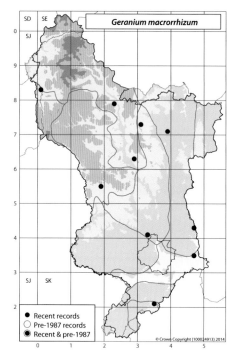

(SK3421) in the south. There are no records prior to 1988. It is commonly grown in gardens from where it is discarded as waste. It grows naturally in the mountains of southern Europe.

Geranium lucidum L.
Shining Crane's-bill

COUNTY STATUS: Native	
CONSERVATION STATUS: None	
FIRST YEAR: 1729 **LATEST YEAR:** 2013 **NO OF RECORDS:** 1,119	
RECENT SQUARES: monads 488; tetrads 315; hectads 37	
ALL SQUARES: monads 502; tetrads 319; hectads 37	

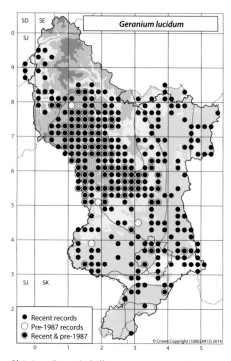

Shining Crane's-bill is a common native annual of screes, walls, banks and rock

outcrops in the White Peak (Brook Bottom SK1476, Cales Farm SK1664 & the High Peak Trail SK2654). Elsewhere it is frequent on cultivated soil, wasteland and disturbed ground except for the Dark and South West Peak (Repton SK3026, Nether Handley SK4076 & between Loscoe and Codnor SK4348). It has shown a marked increase in these latter habitats recently.

Geranium robertianum L.
Herb-Robert

COUNTY STATUS: Native	
CONSERVATION STATUS: None	
FIRST YEAR: 1789 **LATEST YEAR:** 2013 **NO OF RECORDS:** 4,760	
RECENT SQUARES: monads 1,652; tetrads 671; hectads 41	
ALL SQUARES: monads 1,710; tetrads 673; hectads 41	

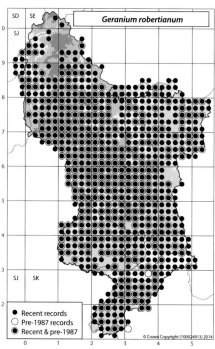

Herb-Robert is a native annual or biennial of woods, hedges and a range of open disturbed habitats, particularly on moist rich soils. It is especially noticeable as a pioneer colonist of limestone screes in the White Peak. It is very common through the county except for the high moors of the Dark Peak. Our plants are ssp. *robertianum*, and may occasionally occur as a white-flowered form (Mabey 1996).

Geranium phaeum L.
Dusky Crane's-bill

COUNTY STATUS: Established (Neophyte)	
CONSERVATION STATUS: None	
FIRST YEAR: 1811 **LATEST YEAR:** 2013 **NO OF RECORDS:** 44	
RECENT SQUARES: monads 12; tetrads 13; hectads 11	
ALL SQUARES: monads 23; tetrads 22; hectads 16	

Dusky Crane's-bill is an established perennial of waysides and open woods. It is found very rarely scattered through the

Dusky Crane's-bill (*Geranium phaeum*) on roadside at Morley (SK3940) where it has been known for many years, June 2008 (Peter Smith)

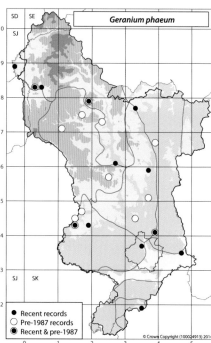

county, from Marple Bridge (SJ9689) in the north, to Smisby (SK3419) in the south. It is often grown in gardens for ornament from where it can escape as seeds or throwouts. It is also sometimes introduced. At Morley it was planted in the 19th century and today still lines the roadside at Church Lane (SK3940). It is a native of central Europe.

Erodium moschatum (L.) L'Her.
Musk Stork's-bill

Musk Stork's-bill is a very rare, casual annual of disturbed ground. There are only three records, all of them recent (Heeley SK3484, Long Eaton SK4833 & Chesterfield SK3870).

Erodium cicutarium (L.) L'Her.
Common Stork's-bill

Common Stork's-bill is an occasional native annual of wasteland, cultivated ground and

COUNTY STATUS: Native	
CONSERVATION STATUS: None	
FIRST YEAR: 1789 **LATEST YEAR:** 2013 **NO OF RECORDS:** 158	
RECENT SQUARES: monads 76; tetrads 69; hectads 25	
ALL SQUARES: monads 96; tetrads 86; hectads 29	

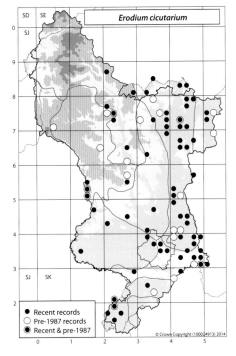

open grassland on well-drained soils. It occurs scattered through the county, from Priddock Wood (SK2086) in the north, through Dove Dale (SK1452) and Craig's Hill (SK4153), to Coton in the Elms (SK2315) in the south.

LYTHRACEAE

Lythrum salicaria L.
Purple-loosestrife

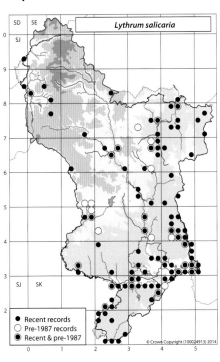

COUNTY STATUS: Native
CONSERVATION STATUS: None
FIRST YEAR: 1789 **LATEST YEAR:** 2013 **NO OF RECORDS:** 333
RECENT SQUARES: monads 127; tetrads 100; hectads 28
ALL SQUARES: monads 141; tetrads 110; hectads 30

Purple-loosestrife is an attractive native perennial found at the edges of waterbodies, and in fens and marshes. It is frequent in the Trent Valley but only rare-to-occasional elsewhere, a pattern that has not changed since Clapham's 1969 Flora. Though it can colonise new sites naturally, it is increasingly being planted in wetland restoration schemes.

Lythrum junceum Banks & Sol.
False Grass-poly
False Grass-poly is a very rare, casual perennial of disturbed and waste ground. All four recent records are from Scarcliffe Park (SK5070 & 5170) in 2000, and it was recorded from Belper (SK3547) in 1971. It is a bird-seed alien from the Mediterranean.

Lythrum hyssopifolia L.
Grass-poly
Grass-poly is a very rare, casual annual of seasonally wet, bare ground. There are two recent records (Hadfield SK0296 in 1989 & Holymoorside SK3469 in 1990) plus an old one from the Calke Abbey-Melbourne area (SK32) in 1837. It grows naturally in southern England.

Lythrum portula (L.) D.A. Webb
Water-purslane
Water-purslane is a very rare, native annual of damp bare ground often by water or in trackways. Recent records occur

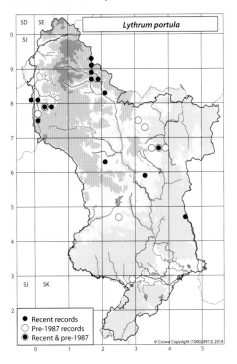

COUNTY STATUS: Native
CONSERVATION STATUS: B
FIRST YEAR: 1829 **LATEST YEAR:** 2012 **NO OF RECORDS:** 60
RECENT SQUARES: monads 17; tetrads 15; hectads 10
ALL SQUARES: monads 24; tetrads 22; hectads 19

sporadically through northern Derbyshire (Nether Ashop SK1786, Combs Reservoir SK0379 & the Great Pond of Stubbing SK3667). It previously occurred sporadically through the south (Hulland Moss SK2546 & Willington SK2928). This local decline is mirrored by its loss from many sites nationally due to drainage and track improvements (Preston *et al.* 2002).

ONAGRACEAE

Epilobium L.
Willowherbs
Willowherbs are a difficult genus to identify, even for experienced field botanists. Many of the rarer species, and all the hybrids, are therefore under-recorded.

Epilobium hirsutum L.
Great Willowherb

COUNTY STATUS: Native
CONSERVATION STATUS: None
FIRST YEAR: 1889 **LATEST YEAR:** 2013 **NO OF RECORDS:** 4,775
RECENT SQUARES: monads 1,781; tetrads 687; hectads 41
ALL SQUARES: monads 1,827; tetrads 690; hectads 41

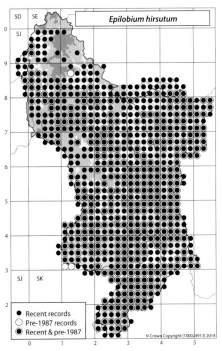

Great Willowherb is a native perennial of damp ground, wet areas beside waterbodies, and of fens and marshes. It is very common and locally abundant throughout the county except for the Dark Peak where it is only frequent. This relative scarcity is probably in part at least, an altitudinal limitation as here in Derbyshire the plant reaches its second highest national locality at 365m (Preston *et al.* 2002).

Epilobium × erroneum Hausskn.
A hybrid willowherb

This hybrid willowherb is a very rare, native perennial of disturbed ground. It was first recorded by Linton (1903) at Bamford (SK18) and Via Gellia (SK25). It was then reported for Chee Dale (SK1273) in 1969, and for SK45 and Eccles House Farm (SK1782) both in 1998. Most recently it has been found at Eyam (SK2376), Middleton (SK2655) and Woodnook (SK3472) all in 2012. It is the hybrid of Great Willowherb (*E. hirsutum*) and Broad-leaved Willowherb (*E. montanum*).

Epilobium × goerzii Rubner
A hybrid willowherb

Locally extinct, this hybrid willowherb was a very rare, native perennial of disturbed ground. The only record is for Hasland (SK36) in 1911. It is the hybrid of Great (*E. hirsutum*) and Pale Willowherb (*E. roseum*).

Epilobium parviflorum Schreb.
Hoary Willowherb

COUNTY STATUS: Native	
CONSERVATION STATUS: None	
FIRST YEAR: 1889 **LATEST YEAR:** 2013 **NO OF RECORDS:** 457	
RECENT SQUARES: monads 236; tetrads 209; hectads 38	
ALL SQUARES: monads 285; tetrads 244; hectads 38	

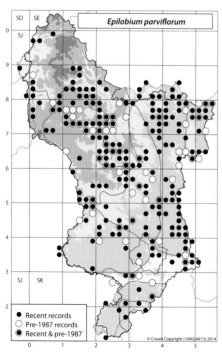

Hoary Willowherb is an occasional native perennial of streamsides, marshes and fens that occurs throughout the county. It is a lowland species, reaching its national altitudinal limit of 365m here in Derbyshire (Preston *et al.* 2002).

Epilobium × limosum Schur
A hybrid willowherb

This hybrid willowherb is a very rare, native perennial of quarries and waste ground. All five recent records are from a small area of the White Peak around Eyam (SK2175/2176) in 2011/2012. It was previously recorded for Chee Dale (SK17), Shirley (SK24) and Hassop (SK27) by Linton (1903), and in the Via Gellia (SK2757) by Clapham (1969). It is the hybrid of Hoary (*E. parviflorum*) and Broad-leaved Willowherb (*E. montanum*).

Epilobium × dacicum Borbas
A hybrid willowherb

Locally extinct, this hybrid willowherb was a very rare, native perennial of wet disturbed ground. It occurred sporadically throughout the county. All five known records are in Linton (1903) including: Edale (SK18), Burnaston (SK23) and Brailsford (SK24). The latter is supported by a voucher in Hull University Herbarium dated 1888. It is the hybrid of Hoary (*E. parviflorum*) and Short-fruited Willowherb (*E. obscurum*).

Epilobium × persicinum Rchb.
A hybrid willowherb

This hybrid willowherb is a very rare, native perennial and the hybrid of Hoary (*E. parviflorum*) and Pale Willowherb (*E. roseum*). It is listed in Stace (1975) for the county, but no other details are known.

Epilobium × floridulum Smejkal
A hybrid willowherb

This hybrid willowherb is a very rare, native perennial of disturbed habitats. There are only three recent records: Haddon Hall (SK2366) in 2011, Willington (SK2927) in 2006 and Matlock (SK2960) in 2012; plus a previous one from Mercaston (SK2742) in 1978. It is the hybrid of Hoary (*E. parviflorum*) and American Willowherb (*E. ciliatum*).

Epilobium × rivulare Wahlenb.
A hybrid willowherb

Locally extinct, this hybrid willowherb was a very rare, native perennial of roadsides and marshy ground. There are just three records. Linton (1903) lists Bradley Brook (SK24) and Robin Hood's Inn (SK27), while Clapham (1969) gives SK57. It is the hybrid of Hoary (*E. parviflorum*) and Marsh Willowherb (*E. palustre*).

Epilobium montanum L.
Broad-leaved Willowherb

COUNTY STATUS: Native	
CONSERVATION STATUS: None	
FIRST YEAR: 1940 **LATEST YEAR:** 2013 **NO OF RECORDS:** 2,748	
RECENT SQUARES: monads 1,289; tetrads 620; hectads 41	
ALL SQUARES: monads 1,337; tetrads 625; hectads 41	

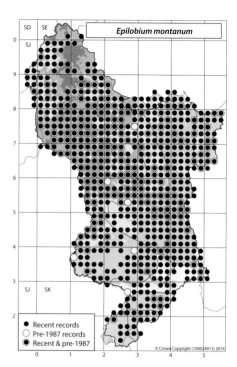

Broad-leaved Willowherb is a native perennial of woods, rocks, walls and cultivated ground. It is very common throughout the county except for the high moors of the Dark Peak.

Epilobium × aggregatum Celak.
A hybrid willowherb

This hybrid willowherb is a very rare, native perennial of damp disturbed ground. It was originally recorded in Linton's 1903 Flora for Brailsford (SK24), Bradley Wood (SK14) and Hassop (SK27). It was recorded at Brockwell (SK37) in 1911 (Clapham 1969), but was not seen for another 100 years until it was found at Haddon Hall (SK2366) in 2011 by G. Kitchener. He also noted it at Youlgrave (SK2164) and Matlock (SK2960) in 2012. It is the hybrid of Broad-leaved (*E. montanum*) and Short-fruited Willowherb (*E. obscurum*).

Epilobium × interjectum Smejkal
A hybrid willowherb

This hybrid willowherb is a very rare, native perennial of disturbed ground. It has been recorded eleven times between 1987 and 2012, mostly for the White Peak Area as at Cressbrook Dale (SK1773) and near Bakewell (SK2267), both in 2011. Elsewhere records are more spread out as at Willington (SK2928) in 2007 and Derwent Dam (SK1789) in 2012. It is the hybrid of Broad-leaved (*E. montanum*) and American Willowherb (*E. ciliatum*).

Epilobium tetragonum L.
Square-stalked Willowherb

Square-stalked Willowherb is a native perennial of damp hedges, open woods,

COUNTY STATUS: Native
CONSERVATION STATUS: None
FIRST YEAR: 1847 LATEST YEAR: 2012 NO OF RECORDS: 99
RECENT SQUARES: monads 59; tetrads 53; hectads 23
ALL SQUARES: monads 72; tetrads 65; hectads 27

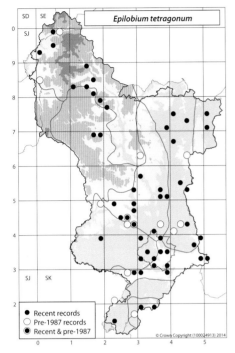

streamsides and ditches. It occurs occasionally throughout the county, growing in small amounts in scattered localities from Mossy Lea (SK0594) in the north to Smisby village (SK3519) in the south.

Epilobium obscurum Schreb.
Short-fruited Willowherb
Short-fruited Willowherb is a native

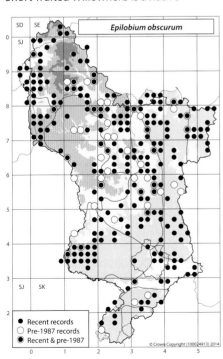

COUNTY STATUS: Native
CONSERVATION STATUS: None
FIRST YEAR: 1889 LATEST YEAR: 2013 NO OF RECORDS: 432
RECENT SQUARES: monads 252; tetrads 231; hectads 39
ALL SQUARES: monads 296; tetrads 259; hectads 40

perennial of marshes, streams and ditches, plus disturbed and cultivated ground. It occurs occasionally throughout Derbyshire, from Long Clough (SK0392) in the north to Caldwell (SK2517) in the south.

Epilobium × brachiatum Celak.
A hybrid willowherb
This hybrid willowherb is a very rare, native perennial. There is an unlocalised record given in Stace (1975), plus one at Chatsworth (SK2670) in 2012. It is the hybrid of Short-fruited (E. obscurum) and Pale Willowherb (E. roseum).

Epilobium × schmidtianum Rostk.
A hybrid willowherb
Locally extinct, this hybrid willowherb was a very rare, native perennial of wet places. It was recorded in Linton's 1903 Flora from near Shirley (SK24) and Malcoff (SK08). It is the hybrid of Short-fruited (E. obscurum) and Marsh Willowherb (E. palustre).

Epilobium roseum Schreb.
Pale Willowherb

COUNTY STATUS: Native
CONSERVATION STATUS: DRDB (Cat5b)
FIRST YEAR: 1903 LATEST YEAR: 2012 NO OF RECORDS: 106
RECENT SQUARES: monads 36; tetrads 35; hectads 18
ALL SQUARES: monads 71; tetrads 69; hectads 29

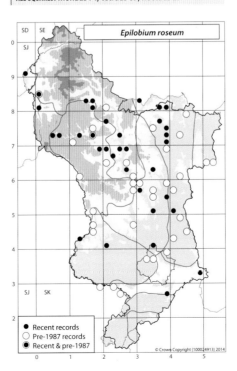

Pale Willowherb is a rare native perennial of damp shaded areas on the sides of ditches, streams and canals, and on disturbed ground. It occurs throughout the county from Hope Valley (SK1682) to Melbourne (SK3926).

Epilobium ciliatum Raf.
American Willowherb

COUNTY STATUS: Established (Neophyte)
CONSERVATION STATUS: None
FIRST YEAR: 1968 LATEST YEAR: 2013 NO OF RECORDS: 776
RECENT SQUARES: monads 435; tetrads 334; hectads 41
ALL SQUARES: monads 504; tetrads 371; hectads 41

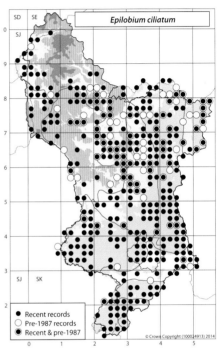

American Willowherb is an established perennial of waste and cultivated ground, roadsides and riverbanks. This North American native is now frequent across Derbyshire except for the high moors of the Dark Peak. Clapham (1969) gives a similar range but notes it as "rare…but increasing". It has clearly done that since then, both here and nationally.

Epilobium palustre L.
Marsh Willowherb

COUNTY STATUS: Native
CONSERVATION STATUS: None
FIRST YEAR: 1889 LATEST YEAR: 2013 NO OF RECORDS: 696
RECENT SQUARES: monads 315; tetrads 228; hectads 36
ALL SQUARES: monads 374; tetrads 272; hectads 38

Marsh Willowherb is a native perennial of marshes, fens and upland flushes. It is common in the Dark and South West Peak Areas, occasional in the Peak Fringe but rare elsewhere. It has been lost from a number of lowland sites due to

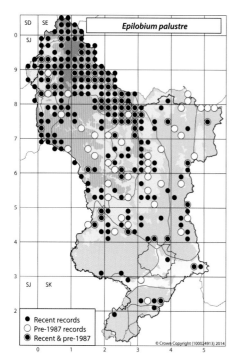

Rosebay Willowherb (*Chamerion angustifolium*) in typical local habitat on roadside at Wardlow (SK1874), July 2008 (Peter Smith)

drainage, a process that has also reduced its frequency nationally (Preston *et al*. 2002).

Epilobium brunnescens (Cockayne) P.H. Raven & Engelhorn
New Zealand Willowherb

COUNTY STATUS: Established (Neophyte)
CONSERVATION STATUS: None
FIRST YEAR: 1969 LATEST YEAR: 2013 NO OF RECORDS: 84
RECENT SQUARES: monads 37; tetrads 28; hectads 11
ALL SQUARES: monads 43; tetrads 33; hectads 14

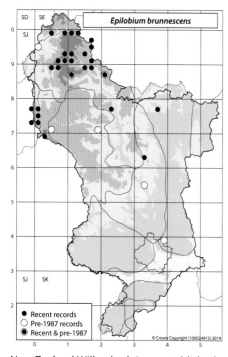

New Zealand Willowherb is an established creeping perennial of damp bare ground on hillsides and waste places. It is occasional in the Dark and South West Peak

Areas (Errwood Hall SK0074 & Woodhead SK0999), and very rare elsewhere in the north (Wire Stone SK3263). Previously it was also recorded from further south (Breadsall SK3939). This apparent local contraction in range contradicts the national spread of the species in the uplands of Britain since 1962 (Preston *et al*. 2002). It is a native of New Zealand.

Epilobium komarovianum H. Lev.
Bronzy Willowherb

Bronzy Willowherb is an established creeping perennial of gardens and disturbed ground. It is only known from two localities. K.M. Hollick recorded it for her garden in Ashbourne (SK1746) in 1971 and said it had been there since 1905. It was also noted for Ladmanlow (SK0471) in 1949. In the past this species has been confused with New Zealand Willowherb (*E. brunnescens*) probably partly because it, too, comes from New Zealand.

Chamerion angustifolium (L.) Holub
Rosebay Willowherb

COUNTY STATUS: Native
CONSERVATION STATUS: None
FIRST YEAR: 1889 LATEST YEAR: 2013 NO OF RECORDS: 6,322
RECENT SQUARES: monads 2,176; tetrads 736; hectads 45
ALL SQUARES: monads 2,237; tetrads 738; hectads 45

Rosebay Willowherb is a very common, native perennial of rocky places, waste ground, waysides and woodland clearings, often in disturbed or burnt areas. It occurs throughout the county except for some of the high moors. It is often locally abundant, forming bold pink stands of flowers in summer which attract many insects. Nationally it was only a species of rocky places and screes in the 1850s. It then underwent

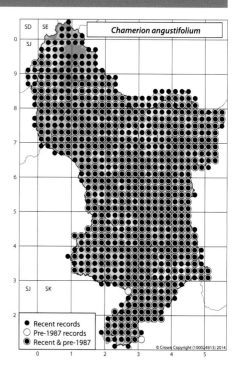

a phenomenal spread through lowland Britain in the mid 20th century. This was probably due to an increase of cleared woodland and disturbed ground (Clapham *et al*. 1987). However it does not seem to have increased as much locally over that time, since Linton (1903) records it as already being abundant throughout Derbyshire at the start of the century.

Oenothera glazioviana P. Micheli
Large-flowered Evening-primrose

COUNTY STATUS: Established (Neophyte)
CONSERVATION STATUS: None
FIRST YEAR: 1969 LATEST YEAR: 2012 NO OF RECORDS: 82
RECENT SQUARES: monads 49; tetrads 52; hectads 25
ALL SQUARES: monads 56; tetrads 58; hectads 25

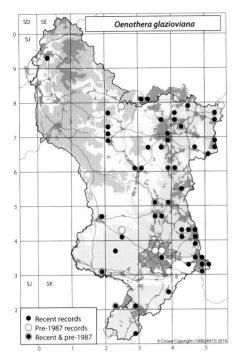

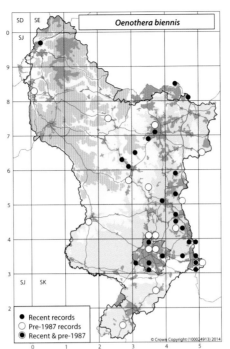

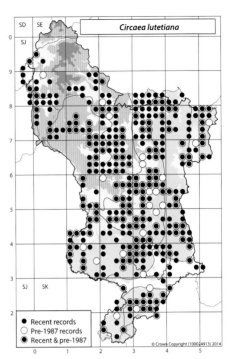

Large-flowered Evening-primrose is an established biennial of open disturbed habitats. It is occasional, and locally abundant, throughout lowland Derbyshire (Lock Lane Ash Tip SK4831, Renishaw SK47P & Stretton SK36V). However, individual populations rapidly decline as sites grow over. It is a native of North America.

Oenothera × *fallax* Renner
Intermediate Evening-primrose
Intermediate Evening-primrose is a very rare, casual biennial of waste ground. It has only been recorded four times, all between 1998 and 2011: Stancliffe Quarries (SK2663), Bowshaw (SK3479), Wyvern Centre (SK3735) and Upper Pleasley (SK4964). It is the hybrid of Large-flowered (*O. glazioviana*) and Common Evening-pimrose (*O. biennis*).

Oenothera biennis L.
Common Evening-primrose

COUNTY STATUS: Established (Neophyte)	
CONSERVATION STATUS: None	
FIRST YEAR: 1854 LATEST YEAR: 2012 NO OF RECORDS: 63	
RECENT SQUARES: monads 25; tetrads 25; hectads 11	
ALL SQUARES: monads 42; tetrads 41; hectads 20	

Common Evening-primrose is a rare established biennial of open waste ground, and is a native of continental Europe. It occurs scattered throughout the eastern half of the county (Sinfin SK3431, Station House SK4359 & Stanton Ironworks SK4639) with only the odd record in the west (Hadfield SK0296). A few records exist for the **Small-flowered Evening-primrose** (*O. cambrica*) in

eastern Derbyshire. However, it is now considered just a segregate of this species.

Oenothera rubricaulis Kleb.
An evening-primrose
This evening-primrose is a very rare, casual biennial, known from just three localities in the centre of the county on old railway land: Clay Cross (SK4064) in 1973, Cromford (SK3056) in 1974 and Parsley Hay (SK1463) in 1974. It is probably a native of Europe.

Fuchsia magellanica Lam.
Fuchsia
Fuchsia is a very rare, casual shrub. It may persist for a while either in abandoned gardens or as a garden throwout. It has been recorded for four sites between 1991 and 2012 (Pin Dale SK1582, Brampton SK3670, Brockwell SK3671 & Tibshelf SK4461). It originated in South America.

Circaea lutetiana L.
Enchanter's-nightshade

COUNTY STATUS: Native	
CONSERVATION STATUS: None	
FIRST YEAR: 1789 LATEST YEAR: 2013 NO OF RECORDS: 1,329	
RECENT SQUARES: monads 525; tetrads 331; hectads 37	
ALL SQUARES: monads 570; tetrads 352; hectads 37	

Enchanter's-nightshade is a frequent native perennial of woods, hedges and shaded riverbanks. It can also grow as a garden weed. It occurs throughout the county except for the uplands of the Dark Peak. It is probably excluded from these by its requirement for soils that are at least moderately base-rich.

Circaea × *intermedia* Ehrh.
Upland Enchanter's-nightshade

COUNTY STATUS: Native	
CONSERVATION STATUS: DRDB (Cat5b), A, B	
FIRST YEAR: 1882 LATEST YEAR: 2009 NO OF RECORDS: 65	
RECENT SQUARES: monads 7; tetrads 6; hectads 4	
ALL SQUARES: monads 27; tetrads 25; hectads 17	

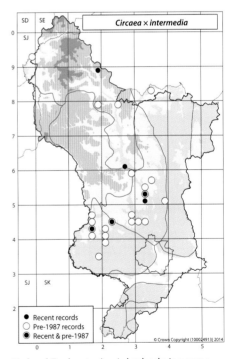

Upland Enchanter's-nightshade is a very rare, native perennial of damp woods. It is recorded recently from only five areas (Holly Wood SK1742, Mill Brook SK1888, Gaskin's Carr SK2244, Millclose Brook SK2661 & Shiningcliff Wood SK3352). It is the hybrid of the common woodland Enchanter's-nightshade (*C. lutetiana*)

and the much rarer Alpine Enchanter's-nightshade (*C. alpina*) which has not been noted in the county. This, coupled with the observation that the hybrid rarely sets seed here, suggests it is a relic of an earlier, colder era.

ANACARDIACEAE

Rhus typhina L.
Stag's-horn Sumach

COUNTY STATUS: Casual	
CONSERVATION STATUS: None	
FIRST YEAR: 1997 **LATEST YEAR:** 2010 **NO OF RECORDS:** 6	
RECENT SQUARES: monads 5; tetrads 5; hectads 4	
ALL SQUARES: monads 5; tetrads 5; hectads 4	

Stag's-horn Sumach is a very rare, casual shrub or small tree of roadsides and waste ground. It is grown in gardens for ornament, and escapes by means of suckers or when discarded as waste. It is recorded from only five sites, all recent, from near Vernon's Oak (SK1536), Mugginton (SK2842), Risley (SK4535), near Sawley Church (SK4731) and Dunston Trading Estate (SK3774). It is a native of eastern North America.

SAPINDACEAE

Aesculus hippocastanum L.
Horse-chestnut

COUNTY STATUS: Established (Neophyte)	
CONSERVATION STATUS: None	
FIRST YEAR: 1949 **LATEST YEAR:** 2013 **NO OF RECORDS:** 1,360	
RECENT SQUARES: monads 677; tetrads 453; hectads 40	
ALL SQUARES: monads 723; tetrads 476; hectads 40	

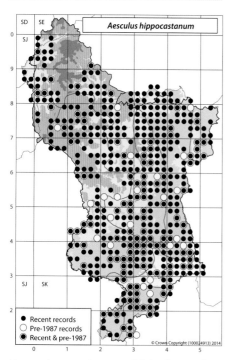

Horse-chestnut is an established tree of copses, waysides and rough ground. It

is widely planted in parks, gardens and streets for ornament, from where it can seed into more natural situations. This native of the Balkans is frequent across Derbyshire, except for the Dark Peak uplands. The largest known tree was found recently at Calke Park (SK3623) with a girth of 5.91m.

Aesculus carnea J. Zeyh.
Red Horse-chestnut

Red Horse-chestnut is a casual tree of waysides and waste places, often planted for ornament in parks and streets. There is a single recent record from Cutthorpe (SK3473) in 2012, and two for 1981, from SK25 and SK26. It is of garden origin from the crossing of Horse-chestnut (*A. hippocastanum*) with Red Buck-eye (*A. pavia*).

Acer platanoides L.
Norway Maple

COUNTY STATUS: Established (Neophyte)	
CONSERVATION STATUS: None	
FIRST YEAR: 1969 **LATEST YEAR:** 2013 **NO OF RECORDS:** 365	
RECENT SQUARES: monads 237; tetrads 192; hectads 37	
ALL SQUARES: monads 248; tetrads 199; hectads 37	

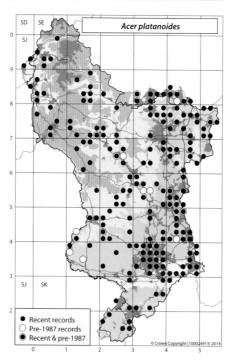

Norway Maple is an established tree of rough grassland, scrub, woods and urban wasteland. It is widely planted in woods, parks, streets and amenity schemes from where seeds spread to more natural situations. Except for the uplands of the Dark Peak, where it is absent, it is occasional throughout the county (Crowden SK0799, Linton SK2715, Normanton Spring SK4084 & Forbes Hole SK4932).

Acer cappadocicum Gled.
Cappadocian Maple

Cappadocian Maple is a very rare, established tree, indigenous to south-western Asia. It is planted in parks and amenity schemes, from where it can naturalise by suckers or seedlings. The only recent records are from Trent Bridge (SK2522) and Foremark (SK32) in 1999; and from Darley Park (SK33) in 1986 (Ellis 1994).

Acer campestre L.
Field Maple

COUNTY STATUS: Native	
CONSERVATION STATUS: None	
FIRST YEAR: 1789 **LATEST YEAR:** 2013 **NO OF RECORDS:** 2,348	
RECENT SQUARES: monads 1,120; tetrads 524; hectads 38	
ALL SQUARES: monads 1,171; tetrads 532; hectads 38	

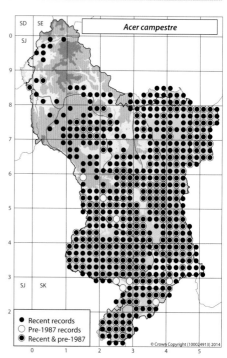

Field Maple is a common native tree or shrub of woods, scrub and hedges on moist calcareous or clay soils. It is increasingly used in amenity plantings and restoration schemes, particularly on opencast coal sites. It occurs throughout the county except for the upland parts of the Dark and South West Peak, and is often considered an indicator of ancient woodlands and old hedges. A large specimen with a girth of 3.52m is known from Creswell Crags Museum (SK5374)

Acer pseudoplatanus L.
Sycamore

Sycamore is an established tree of woods, scrub, hedges and wasteland, and a native of the mountains of central Europe. It is widely planted in woods, parks and streets

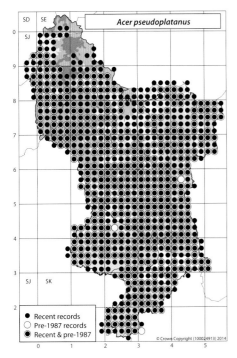

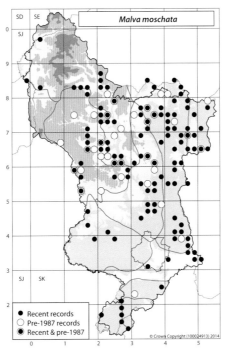

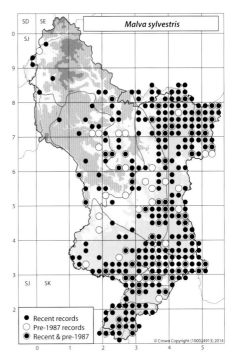

COUNTY STATUS: Established (Neophyte)
CONSERVATION STATUS: None
FIRST YEAR: 1789 **LATEST YEAR:** 2013 **NO OF RECORDS:** 6,567
RECENT SQUARES: monads 2,101; tetrads 709; hectads 42
ALL SQUARES: monads 2,154; tetrads 712; hectads 42

Acer rubrum L.
Red Maple
Red Maple is a small tree, native to eastern North America. It is often planted in parks and on roadsides. Our only record is as a casual at Gorse Bank Lane, Baslow (SK2573) in 1980.

MALVACEAE

Malva moschata L.
Musk-mallow

COUNTY STATUS: Native
CONSERVATION STATUS: None
FIRST YEAR: 1787 **LATEST YEAR:** 2013 **NO OF RECORDS:** 308
RECENT SQUARES: monads 138; tetrads 119; hectads 33
ALL SQUARES: monads 165; tetrads 140; hectads 35

Musk-mallow is an occasional native perennial of grassy banks, woodland edges and waysides (Dove Dale SK1452, Winster SK2460 & Fallgate SK3562). It is now turning up in waste places as a garden escape, and in restoration schemes as a constituent of wild flower seed mixes (Stockley Trail SK4668). It occurs throughout the county except for the high moors of the Dark and South West Peak Character Areas.

Malva alcea L.
Greater Musk-mallow
Greater Musk-mallow is a very rare, casual perennial of waste ground as a garden escape. Both records are for Fairfield (SK0674) in 1996. It is a native of continental Europe.

Malva sylvestris L.
Common Mallow
Common Mallow is a frequent established perennial of waste ground and waysides

for ornament and in upland areas for shelter, particularly around habitations. It is very common throughout the county, except the high moors of the Dark Peak. It is an aggressive invader by seeds of both woods and grassland in lowland areas. When growing in numbers, it can exclude many native species by its dense shade and leaf litter. It is thus actively removed from many conservation areas. However, it can provide food and shelter for some animals, though these are not always ones – such as the Grey Squirrel – that conservationists would like to encourage (Charter 2002). When growing in isolation, as on top of Oker Hill near Matlock, it can form an important element in a landscape. This particular tree is associated with a local story of two brothers who each planted a tree on the hill when young. One tree flourished but the other did not, reflecting their success in life (Mabey 1996). Wordsworth wrote a sonnet about this romantic story. A large specimen found recently at Shining Cliff Woods (SK3352) has a girth of 6.78m.

Acer saccharinum L.
Silver Maple
Silver Maple is a very rare, casual tree of roadsides and amenity plantings. There are only two records, Derby City (SK33) in 1987 and Netherseal (SK2813) in 2003. It grows naturally in North America.

COUNTY STATUS: Established (Neophyte)
CONSERVATION STATUS: None
FIRST YEAR: 1789 **LATEST YEAR:** 2013 **NO OF RECORDS:** 713
RECENT SQUARES: monads 382; tetrads 292; hectads 37
ALL SQUARES: monads 439; tetrads 319; hectads 37

throughout the eastern half of Derbyshire. It also occurs scattered across the rest of the county, albeit not so frequently, where it occurs in similar habitats, as well as in more natural settings such as tall-herb communities in the dales of the White Peak.

Malva nicaeensis All.
French Mallow
French Mallow is very rare, casual annual or biennial of waste ground probably as a contaminant of organic wastes. The sole record is from Bradway (SK3280) in 1973. It is indigenous to southern Europe.

Malva parviflora L.
Least Mallow
Least Mallow is a very rare, casual annual and a native of southern Europe. The only recent record is from near Dore (SK2881) in 2007. There is also one for Pinxton (SK45) in Linton (1903), based on Pilkington (1789). This is a very early record, considering the plant is said to have been first cultivated in Britain only in 1779 (Preston et al. 2002).

Malva neglecta Wallr.
Dwarf Mallow

COUNTY STATUS: Established (Neophyte)
CONSERVATION STATUS: B
FIRST YEAR: 1903 **LATEST YEAR:** 2013 **NO OF RECORDS:** 147
RECENT SQUARES: monads 50; tetrads 40; hectads 14
ALL SQUARES: monads 80; tetrads 65; hectads 25

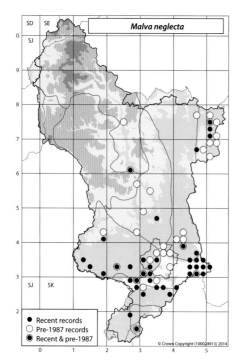

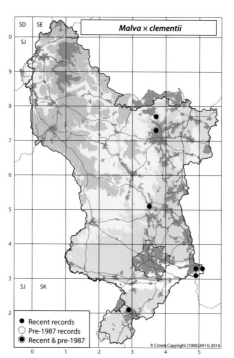

horticultural origin from western Asian parents.

Sidalcea malviflora (DC.) A. Gray ex Benth.
Greek Mallow

Greek Mallow is a very rare, casual perennial of waste ground and a native of North America. It is often grown in gardens for ornament, but the only records are from the Teversal Trail in Pleasley (SK4963), first found by K. Balkow in 2003, and Bradwell (SK1679) in 2009.

Abutilon theophrasti Medik.
Velvetleaf

Velvetleaf is a very rare, casual annual of arable fields, and a native of the eastern Mediterranean. The sole record is from Spath Farm, Longford (SK2235) in 1975, probably as a seed contaminant.

Tilia platyphyllos Scop.
Large-leaved Lime

COUNTY STATUS: Native	
CONSERVATION STATUS: DRDB (Cat3), NS, A, B, C	
FIRST YEAR: 1881 **LATEST YEAR:** 2012 **NO OF RECORDS:** 245	
RECENT SQUARES: monads 65; tetrads 53; hectads 24	
ALL SQUARES: monads 80; tetrads 67; hectads 26	

Dwarf Mallow is a rare established annual of dry open habitats on cultivated land, waste ground and waysides, mostly in the south (Overseal SK2915, Dale SK4338 & Sawley SK4731). It also occurs on the Magnesian Limestone (Hollin Hill SK5175), and there are a few records from the centre of the county (Wensley Dale SK2661).

Malva setigera Schimp. & Spenn.
Rough Mallow

Rough Mallow is a very rare, casual annual of waste ground. The one record at Derby (SK33) in 1987/88 was probably a garden escape. Considered possibly native in southern England, due to its rarity there it is included in various national conservation lists.

Malva × *clementii* (Cheek) Stace
Garden Tree-mallow

COUNTY STATUS: Casual	
CONSERVATION STATUS: None	
FIRST YEAR: 1998 **LATEST YEAR:** 2012 **NO OF RECORDS:** 9	
RECENT SQUARES: monads 7; tetrads 7; hectads 5	
ALL SQUARES: monads 7; tetrads 7; hectads 5	

Garden Tree-mallow is a very rare, casual perennial that can become woody and shrub-like. It is now very popular in gardens from where it escapes, or is thrown out, onto waysides and waste ground. There are only a handful of recent records in southern and eastern parts (Newhall SK2920, Nether Heage SK3550, Chesterfield SK3672 & Ramshaw Wood SK3776). It is the hybrid of *Malva olbia* and *M. thuringiaca*. A number of records were originally recorded as just *M. thuringiaca*.

Alcea rosea L.
Hollyhock

COUNTY STATUS: Casual	
CONSERVATION STATUS: None	
FIRST YEAR: 1994 **LATEST YEAR:** 2010 **NO OF RECORDS:** 7	
RECENT SQUARES: monads 6; tetrads 6; hectads 5	
ALL SQUARES: monads 6; tetrads 6; hectads 5	

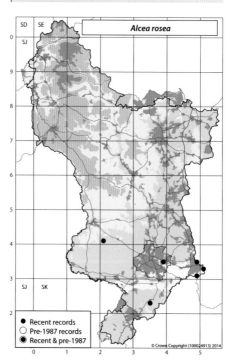

Hollyhock is a very rare, casual biennial or short-lived perennial of waysides. The only records are all recent and from the south of the county (Shirley SK2141, Repton SK3422, Derby SK3835 & Lock Lane SK4831). It is surprising there are so few records for this attractive and popular garden plant. It is of

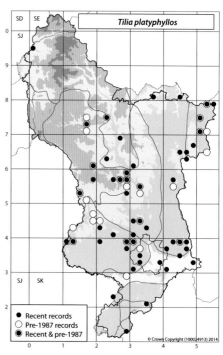

Large-leaved Lime is a rare native tree of the White Peak (Pigott 1969). There it grows on the steeper dalesides in old woods, on cliffs and in screes (Slinter Wood SK2857 & the Matlock Woodlands SK2958). It occurs in similar habitats on the Magnesian Limestone, so is very probably native here, too (Whitwell Wood SK5278 & Markland Grips SK5074). It is also scattered throughout the Peak Fringe, the Coal Measures, and the Claylands. There

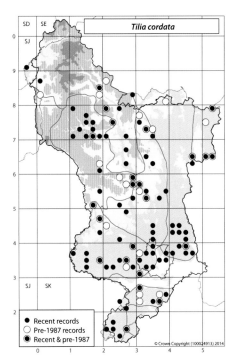

Large-leaved Lime (*Tilia platyphyllos*) growing as a native on Magnesian Limestone crags at Markland Grips, June 2004 (P. & G. Dishart)

its status is more difficult to determine. In some sites it appears to be native as it grows in old woods, as at Dale Hermitage Wood (SK4338), but elsewhere has clearly been planted in hedges and parks (Derby SK3335). In woods on the Carboniferous Limestone it hybridises naturally with the Small-leaved Lime (*T. cordata*). It is very local in woods on base-rich soils in England and Wales and is a Nationally Scarce species. The largest known specimen with a girth of 7.5m was found recently in the Via Gellia (SK2757).

Tilia × europaea L.
Lime

Lime is a very rare, large native tree of ancient woods in the dales of the White

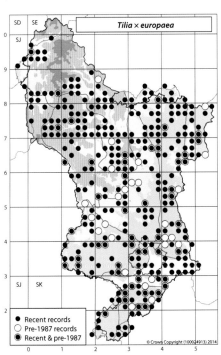

COUNTY STATUS: Native

CONSERVATION STATUS: None

FIRST YEAR: 1789 LATEST YEAR: 2013 NO OF RECORDS: 707

RECENT SQUARES: monads 365; tetrads 318; hectads 38

ALL SQUARES: monads 400; tetrads 344; hectads 38

Peak where its two parents grow together, as at Matlock Dale (SK2958) Mabey (1996). It is extensively planted in gardens, woods and parks, sometimes as magnificent avenues as at Calke Abbey (SK3523). Such plantings are so extensive that its native distribution is obscured. It is the spontaneous hybrid of the Small-leaved Lime (*T. cordata*) and the Large-leaved Lime (*T. platyphyllos*).

Tilia cordata Mill.
Small-leaved Lime

COUNTY STATUS: Native

CONSERVATION STATUS: B

FIRST YEAR: 1835 LATEST YEAR: 2013 NO OF RECORDS: 262

RECENT SQUARES: monads 105; tetrads 93; hectads 27

ALL SQUARES: monads 129; tetrads 109; hectads 29

Small-leaved Lime is a rare native tree of ancient, often rocky, woods in the White Peak (Pigott 1969) as at Matlock Bath (SK2959). In the White Peak it often occurs with Large-leaved Lime (*T. platyphyllos*) and their hybrid. It is native but less frequent in woods on the Magnesian Limestone (Pleasley Vale SK5265) and in some of the gritstone cloughs of the Dark Peak. Elsewhere its status is difficult to decide, but is probably native in a number of ancient woods (Grange Wood SK2714, Linacre Woods SK3272 & Hermit's Wood SK4438). It is also widely but rarely planted throughout the county in parks, gardens and woods. A large specimen at Calke Park (SK3622) has a recorded girth

of 6.81m. It rarely sets seedlings here (Clapham 1969).

THYMELAEACEAE

Daphne mezereum L.
Mezereon

COUNTY STATUS: Native

CONSERVATION STATUS: DRDB (Cat2), VU, NS, A, B

FIRST YEAR: 1789 LATEST YEAR: 2009 NO OF RECORDS: 135

RECENT SQUARES: monads 14; tetrads 10; hectads 4

ALL SQUARES: monads 23; tetrads 16; hectads 12

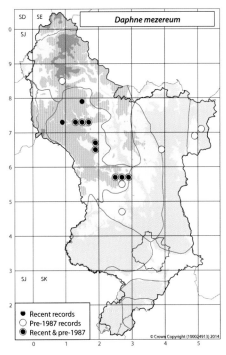

Mezereon is a rare native shrub of the White Peak where it grows in woods on calcareous soils and screes (Via Gellia

SK2556 & Priestcliffe Lees SK1473). In the past it has been recorded from a wider area including the Peak Fringe (Hulland Ward SK2647) and the Magnesian Limestone (Scarcliffe Cutting SK4968). It has been much collected for growing in gardens, so some records, particularly those from near old buildings, may represent relics of cultivation. It is Nationally Scarce.

Daphne laureola L.
Spurge-laurel

COUNTY STATUS: Native	
CONSERVATION STATUS: B	
FIRST YEAR: 1789 LATEST YEAR: 2010 NO OF RECORDS: 105	
RECENT SQUARES: monads 15; tetrads 11; hectads 7	
ALL SQUARES: monads 23; tetrads 15; hectads 12	

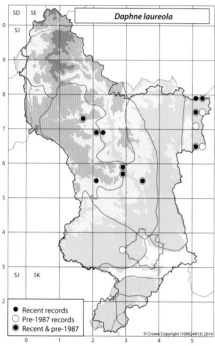

Spurge-laurel is a native evergreen shrub of woods and thickets. It occurs rarely on the Magnesian Limestone (Whitwell Wood SK5278) and in the White Peak (Cressbrook Dale SK1772 & High Tor Woods SK2959). It is also found on the isolated limestone outcrop at Crich (Cliffside Wood SK3455). Previously it occurred in the south of Derbyshire (Radbourne SK2835 in 1969, Foremark SK32 in 1903 & Ockbrook SK43 in 1903). Some of these latter records may be introductions as the plant is occasionally associated with pheasant-rearing. It is towards its northern British limit in the county.

CISTACEAE

Helianthemum nummularium (L.) Mill.
Common Rock-rose

Common Rock-rose is a low-growing native woody perennial of limestone

Common Rock-rose (*Helianthemum nummularium*) in limestone grassland Cressbrook Dale (SK1773), June 2008 (Peter Smith)

COUNTY STATUS: Native	
CONSERVATION STATUS: ERL	
FIRST YEAR: 1789 LATEST YEAR: 2013 NO OF RECORDS: 881	
RECENT SQUARES: monads 176; tetrads 96; hectads 13	
ALL SQUARES: monads 191; tetrads 104; hectads 16	

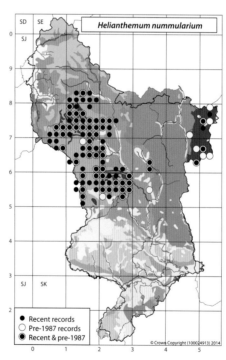

grasslands and outcrops. It is frequent and locally abundant in the White Peak (Tideswell SK1276 & Hopton Quarry SK2656). It also occurs on the Magnesian Limestone (Markland Grips SK5074) but is less abundant there, and on the limestone outcrop at Ashover (SK36L). It was previously recorded for the outcrop at Crich Stand (SK3455).

TROPAEOLACEAE

Tropaeolum majus L.
Nasturtium

Nasturtium is a casual trailing annual. A native of Peru, it is commonly grown in gardens and has been recorded for seven monads locally, all between 2002 and 2012. Examples are: Highcliffe (SK2177), Dore (SK3081), Totley (SK3079), Heeley (SK3484) and Butterley (SK4051).

LIMNANTHACEAE

Limnanthes douglasii R. Br.
Meadow-foam

Meadow-foam is a very rare, casual annual of roadsides and waste ground. The only records are from Owler Bar (SK2977) in 2002 and Heeley (SK3484) in 2004. It is much grown in gardens, and is a native of California.

RESEDACEAE

Reseda luteola L.
Weld

COUNTY STATUS: Established (Neophyte)	
CONSERVATION STATUS: None	
FIRST YEAR: 1789 LATEST YEAR: 2013 NO OF RECORDS: 887	
RECENT SQUARES: monads 390; tetrads 281; hectads 36	
ALL SQUARES: monads 445; tetrads 301; hectads 37	

Weld is an occasional established biennial of waste ground, arable land and waysides. It is found over the entire county but is far more common in the eastern half, probably due to the increased frequency of arable land and rough ground there. It was said

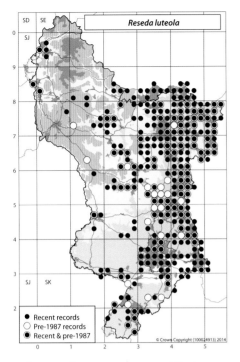

to favour calcareous substrates (Clapham 1969) but its current distribution does not support this.

Reseda lutea L.
Wild Mignonette

COUNTY STATUS: Native
CONSERVATION STATUS: None
FIRST YEAR: 1829 **LATEST YEAR:** 2013 **NO OF RECORDS:** 400
RECENT SQUARES: monads 165; tetrads 120; hectads 31
ALL SQUARES: monads 195; tetrads 140; hectads 34

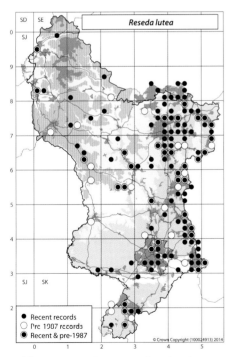

Wild Mignonette is an occasional native biennial or perennial of rough places, arable land and waysides. Found throughout the county, it is more common in eastern parts.

This is probably due to the greater quantity of arable land there. Clapham (1969) suggested it prefers calcareous soils, but our data does not support this.

Reseda odorata L.
Garden Mignonette

Garden Mignonette is a very rare, casual annual or short-lived perennial, and a native of the south-eastern Mediterranean. The only record is for disturbed ground at Heeley (SK3484) in 2003.

BRASSICACEAE

Erysimum cheiranthoides L.
Treacle-mustard

Treacle-mustard is a very rare, established annual of waste ground, arable fields and

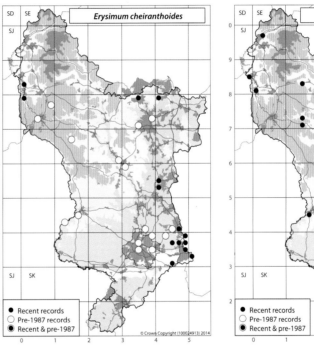

COUNTY STATUS: Established (Neophyte)
CONSERVATION STATUS: None
FIRST YEAR: 1670 **LATEST YEAR:** 2006 **NO OF RECORDS:** 48
RECENT SQUARES: monads 12; tetrads 14; hectads 9
ALL SQUARES: monads 30; tetrads 30; hectads 17

gardens throughout the county (Taxal SK0079, Marsh Lane SK4079, Swanwick SK4053 & Sandiacre SK4736). This is one of the earliest recorded plants in Derbyshire. According to Linton (1903) it was noted in the Peak near Ashbourne by John Ray in his 1670 "*Catalogus Plantarum Angliae*". It is a native of eastern Europe.

Erysimum cheiri (L.) Crantz
Wallflower

Wallflower is a rare established perennial of walls, quarries and limestone cliffs

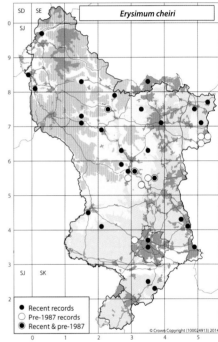

Wallflower (*Erysimum cheiri*) on Carboniferous Limestone outcrop at Stoney Middleton (SK2275), May 2012 (Ken Balkow)

COUNTY STATUS: Established (Neophyte)
CONSERVATION STATUS: None
FIRST YEAR: 1789 LATEST YEAR: 2012 NO OF RECORDS: 69
RECENT SQUARES: monads 31; tetrads 30; hectads 20
ALL SQUARES: monads 40; tetrads 37; hectads 22

throughout the county (Toddbrook Reservoir SK0081 v.c.58, Stoney Middleton SK2275, Cromford SK3057 & Ticknall SK3524). It appears to have increased recently, but this may just be due to greater willingness by today's botanists to record established garden species. It is presumed to be of garden origin as it is not known in the wild.

Arabidopsis thaliana (L.) Heynh.
Thale Cress

COUNTY STATUS: Native
CONSERVATION STATUS: None
FIRST YEAR: 1829 LATEST YEAR: 2013 NO OF RECORDS: 916
RECENT SQUARES: monads 495; tetrads 353; hectads 39
ALL SQUARES: monads 534; tetrads 369; hectads 39

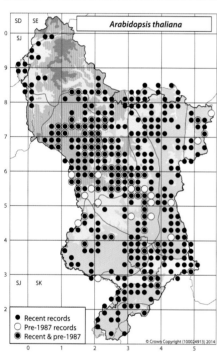

Thale Cress is a native winter annual of dry shallow soils that is intolerant of competition from other plants. It grows on rough ground, cultivated land, walls, rock outcrops and even in the cracks between paving slabs. It is frequent throughout the county except for moorland areas. It is often used for fundamental research into plant genetics due to its short life cycle and plentiful seed production.

Camelina sativa (L.) Crantz
Gold-of-pleasure
Gold-of-pleasure is a casual annual of waste and disturbed ground. The only two recent records are from Clay Cross (SK3962) and

COUNTY STATUS: Casual
CONSERVATION STATUS: None
FIRST YEAR: 1789 LATEST YEAR: 2005 NO OF RECORDS: 13
RECENT SQUARES: monads 2; tetrads 2; hectads 2
ALL SQUARES: monads 9; tetrads 9; hectads 8

Darley Dale (SK2762). Previously it occurred rarely through southern and eastern parts, mostly as a weed of cultivated land (Clifton SK1545, Stanley SK4140 & Chesterfield SK3768). It is indigenous to southern and eastern Europe.

Capsella bursa-pastoris (L.) Medik.
Shepherd's-purse

COUNTY STATUS: Established (Neophyte)
CONSERVATION STATUS: None
FIRST YEAR: 1789 LATEST YEAR: 2013 NO OF RECORDS: 3,191
RECENT SQUARES: monads 1,612; tetrads 672; hectads 43
ALL SQUARES: monads 1,700; tetrads 679; hectads 43

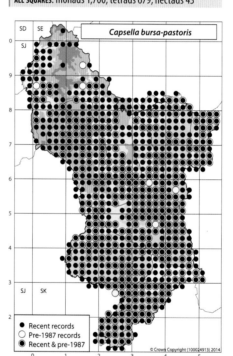

Shepherd's-purse is a very common, established annual of disturbed nutrient-rich habitats such as waste ground, gardens and arable fields. It occurs throughout the county except for the high moors of the Dark Peak Area

Turritis glabra L.
Tower Mustard

COUNTY STATUS: Native
CONSERVATION STATUS: DRDB (Cat2), EN, NS, NERC, B, C
FIRST YEAR: 1787 LATEST YEAR: 1985 NO OF RECORDS: 25
RECENT SQUARES: monads 0; tetrads 0; hectads 0
ALL SQUARES: monads 8; tetrads 7; hectads 11

Tower Mustard is a very rare, native biennial of roadsides and waste ground, with no recent sightings. Previous records occur scattered throughout the county, the latest

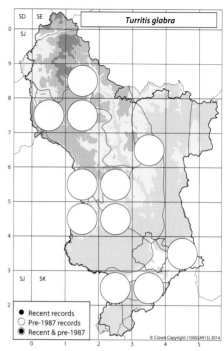

being from the early 1980s in Back Dale (SK0971) and Long Eaton (SK4831). Clapham (1969) gives one record, near Repton (SK3126), and noted it was rare and decreasing even then. It has also declined nationally (Preston et al. 2002) and is given in various lists as Endangered and Nationally Scarce.

Barbarea vulgaris W.T. Aiton
Winter-cress

COUNTY STATUS: Native
CONSERVATION STATUS: None
FIRST YEAR: 1650 LATEST YEAR: 2013 NO OF RECORDS: 519
RECENT SQUARES: monads 309; tetrads 251; hectads 39
ALL SQUARES: monads 344; tetrads 272; hectads 40

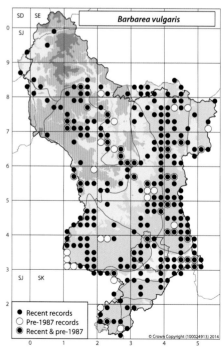

Winter-cress is a native biennial or perennial of roadsides, streamsides and waste ground, often in damp and disturbed ground. It is occasional throughout the county except for the Dark and South West Peak Areas where it is rare.

Barbarea stricta Andrz.
Small-flowered Winter-cress

Small-flowered Winter-cress is a very rare, casual biennial or perennial of roadsides, and a native of southern Europe. All four local records are from Chesterfield town centre (SK3572, SK3771 & SK3871) for 1992 or 1993.

Barbarea intermedia Boreau
Medium-flowered Winter-cress

COUNTY STATUS:	Established (Neophyte)
CONSERVATION STATUS:	None
FIRST YEAR: 1889 LATEST YEAR: 2013 NO OF RECORDS: 14	
RECENT SQUARES:	monads 6; tetrads 6; hectads 4
ALL SQUARES:	monads 9; tetrads 9; hectads 8

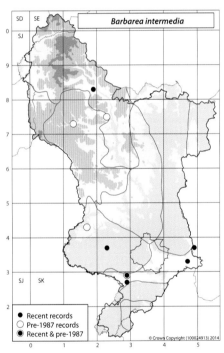

Medium-flowered Winter-cress is a very rare, established biennial of cultivated and waste ground. Recent records are scattered over the county from Hope Station (SK1883) in the north, to Willington (SK2928) and Erewash Canal (SK4837) in the south. It is a native of western Europe.

Barbarea verna (Mill.) Asch.
American Winter-cress

COUNTY STATUS:	Casual
CONSERVATION STATUS:	None
FIRST YEAR: 1863 LATEST YEAR: 2013 NO OF RECORDS: 24	
RECENT SQUARES:	monads 7; tetrads 7; hectads 7
ALL SQUARES:	monads 13; tetrads 13; hectads 14

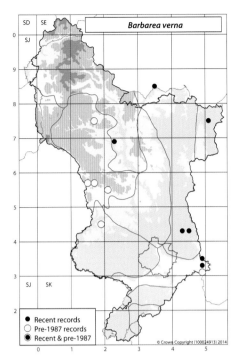

American Winter-cress is a very rare, casual biennial of cultivated and waste ground. Recent records are scattered across Derbyshire from the Sheaf Valley (SK3484) in the north, through Ball Cross (SK2269), to Long Eaton (SK4934) in the south. It is a native of Europe.

Rorippa palustris (L.) Besser
Marsh Yellow-cress

COUNTY STATUS:	Native
CONSERVATION STATUS:	None
FIRST YEAR: 1829 LATEST YEAR: 2012 NO OF RECORDS: 248	
RECENT SQUARES:	monads 110; tetrads 93; hectads 31
ALL SQUARES:	monads 146; tetrads 127; hectads 36

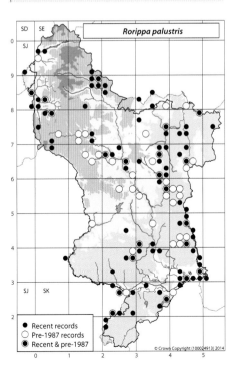

Marsh Yellow-cress is an occasional native annual of damp open habitats, particularly those covered by water in winter. It grows throughout the county, though is commoner at lower elevations. At 320m, Buxton holds the British altitudinal record for this plant (Preston *et al.* 2002). Note that locations given in Clapham (1969) for Marsh Yellow-cress (*R. islandica*) refer to this species.

Rorippa sylvestris (L.) Besser
Creeping Yellow-cress

COUNTY STATUS:	Native
CONSERVATION STATUS:	None
FIRST YEAR: 1829 LATEST YEAR: 2012 NO OF RECORDS: 102	
RECENT SQUARES:	monads 42; tetrads 43; hectads 19
ALL SQUARES:	monads 71; tetrads 63; hectads 27

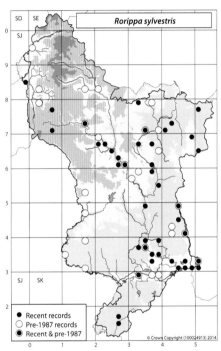

Creeping Yellow-cress is a rare native creeping perennial of damp, often bare, areas on the margins of streams and ponds. It grows throughout Derbyshire, but is very rare in the north-western moorland region (Cressbrook Dale SK17R, Caldwell SK2617, Ashgate SK37K & Larklands SK4741).

Rorippa amphibia (L.) Besser
Great Yellow-cress

COUNTY STATUS:	Native
CONSERVATION STATUS:	None
FIRST YEAR: 1829 LATEST YEAR: 2013 NO OF RECORDS: 175	
RECENT SQUARES:	monads 62; tetrads 52; hectads 19
ALL SQUARES:	monads 80; tetrads 64; hectads 21

Great Yellow-cress is an occasional native creeping perennial that grows in and by the edges of rivers, canals, ponds and reservoirs. It is recorded mostly from the south and east (Cromford Canal SK3056,

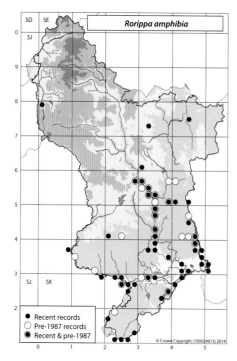

Grange Farm SK3228 & Linacre Woods SK3372). Further north and west there are only isolated records (Taxal Pond SK0079 & Mastin Moor Flash SK4475). It is a species of southern and eastern England, towards the north-western limit of its range here.

Nasturtium W.T. Aiton
Water-cresses

COUNTY STATUS: Native	
CONSERVATION STATUS: None	
FIRST YEAR: 1789 LATEST YEAR: 2013 NO OF RECORDS: 939	
RECENT SQUARES: monads 398; tetrads 316; hectads 37	
ALL SQUARES: monads 480; tetrads 356; hectads 37	

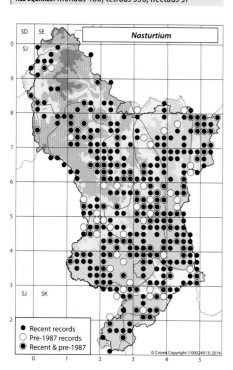

Water-cresses are represented by both native species and their hybrid, but all three are under-recorded due to the difficulty of identification, even when fertile. The accounts below should therefore be considered incomplete.

Nasturtium officinale W.T. Aiton
Water-cress

Water-cress is an occasional native perennial of marshy areas, ditches and slow streams. It has also been cultivated in the past, though Farey (1815) lamented that water-cresses seemed "less well used at the Table here than their pleasant and wholesome nature entitles them".

Nasturtium × *sterile* (Airy Shaw) Oefelein
Hybrid Water-cress

Hybrid Water-cress is a very rare, native perennial of marshy areas, ditches and slow streams throughout central Derbyshire (Tideswell Brook SK1477, Toad's Mouth SK2680, Lees Brook SK4037 & Scarcliffe Park SK57A). This is the most commonly cultivated water-cress and some records probably refer to naturalised colonies.

Nasturtium microphyllum (Boenn.) Rchb.
Narrow-fruited Water-cress

Narrow-fruited Water-cress is a rare native perennial of marshy areas, ditches and slow streams. It is scattered throughout Derbyshire except for extreme northern parts (Conies Dale SK1280, Meadow Place Grange SK2065, Marston Lane SK2330, Ashover SK36L & Markland Grips SK5074).

Armoracia rusticana P. Gaertn., B. Mey. & Scherb.
Horse-radish

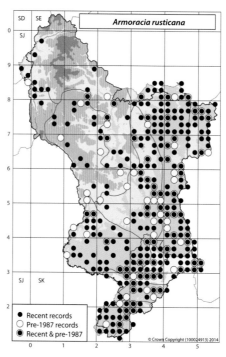

COUNTY STATUS: Established (Neophyte)	
CONSERVATION STATUS: None	
FIRST YEAR: 1847 LATEST YEAR: 2013 NO OF RECORDS: 759	
RECENT SQUARES: monads 367; tetrads 283; hectads 36	
ALL SQUARES: monads 430; tetrads 320; hectads 37	

Horse-radish is an established perennial of overgrown gardens, roadsides, river banks and waste ground. It is frequent in southern and eastern Derbyshire, but rare in the more upland north and west. It was formerly much grown in gardens as a vegetable, but only occurs as a relic of cultivation or garden throwout as it does not set seed in Britain (Preston *et al.* 2002). It is possibly indigenous to western Asia.

Cardamine bulbifera (L.) Crantz
Coralroot

Coralroot is an established rhizomatous perennial with two recent sites: Two Dales (SK2862) in 1997 and Lea Wharf (SK3156) in 2008. There are five older records: Clapham (1969) gives Graves Park (SK3582) and Long Eaton (SK4832), while Linton (1903) gives The Goyt Valley (SJ98). It is a native of southern England, sometimes grown in gardens.

Cardamine amara L.
Large Bitter-cress

COUNTY STATUS: Native	
CONSERVATION STATUS: None	
FIRST YEAR: 1789 LATEST YEAR: 2013 NO OF RECORDS: 656	
RECENT SQUARES: monads 278; tetrads 227; hectads 35	
ALL SQUARES: monads 330; tetrads 257; hectads 37	

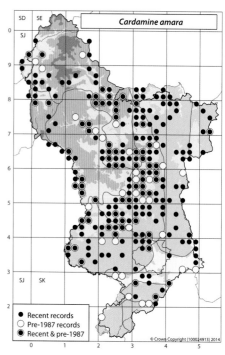

Large Bitter-cress is an occasional native perennial of wet woodlands, marshes, flushes and streamsides. It occurs throughout the county, though is rarer in the White Peak,

Dark Peak and the more intensively farmed lowlands. Thorpe (1984) reported it was an important food resource for adult insects in May and June along the Cromford Canal.

Cardamine raphanifolia Pourr.
Greater Cuckooflower
Greater Cuckooflower is a casual perennial of disturbed ground, first found near Dore (SK2881) in 2007 by K. Balkow. It has since been noted at Shipley (SK4443) in 2009 and Lea Brook (SK3257) in 2011. It is indigenous to southern Europe.

Cardamine pratensis L.
Cuckooflower

COUNTY STATUS: Native
CONSERVATION STATUS: None
FIRST YEAR: 1789 LATEST YEAR: 2013 NO OF RECORDS: 2,749
RECENT SQUARES: monads 1,152; tetrads 608; hectads 43
ALL SQUARES: monads 1,218; tetrads 625; hectads 43

Cuckooflower (*Cardamine pratensis*), Harboro' Rocks (SK2455), May 2008 (Peter Smith)

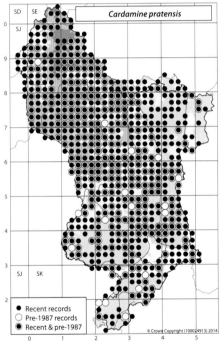

Cuckooflower is a common native perennial of damp grasslands, streamsides, marshes and flushes that sometimes persists in gardens. It grows throughout the county except for some of the more intensively farmed lowland areas. It has the local names of Lady's Smock and Lucy Locket (Grigson 1975), as well as Water Gilleyflower. It is a larval food plant of the Orange-tip Butterfly and can be an important food resource for adult insects in May and early June (Thorpe 1984).

Cardamine × *fringsii* F. Wirtg.
A hybrid bitter-cress
This hybrid bitter-cress is a very rare native, known only from Darley Dale (SK2662 & 2762) where it was discovered by D. Dupree

in 2004 and refound in 2005. It is the hybrid of Cuckooflower (*C. pratensis*) and Wavy Bitter-cress (*C. flexuosa*) and is probably under-recorded.

Cardamine impatiens L.
Narrow-leaved Bitter-cress

COUNTY STATUS: Native
CONSERVATION STATUS: DRDB (Cat2), NT, A, B, C
FIRST YEAR: 1776 LATEST YEAR: 2013 NO OF RECORDS: 212
RECENT SQUARES: monads 33; tetrads 24; hectads 11
ALL SQUARES: monads 62; tetrads 42; hectads 18

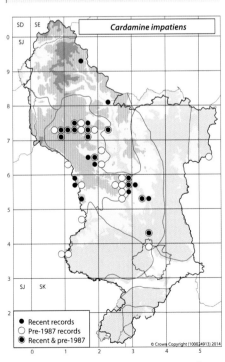

Narrow-leaved Bitter-cress is a rare native annual/biennial of humid woodlands, riverbanks, moist rock outcrops and screes.

It is mainly found in the White Peak Area (Matlock SK2959 & Monks Dale SK1375). It also occurs in the Dark Peak (Hope Forest SK1493) and the Peak Fringe Character Areas (near Duffield Church SK3442). It is scattered through the British Isles and is Nationally Threatened.

Cardamine flexuosa With.
Wavy Bitter-cress

COUNTY STATUS: Native
CONSERVATION STATUS: None
FIRST YEAR: 1789 LATEST YEAR: 2013 NO OF RECORDS: 2,232
RECENT SQUARES: monads 1,052; tetrads 592; hectads 42
ALL SQUARES: monads 1,133; tetrads 615; hectads 42

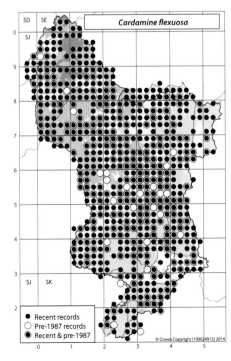

Wavy Bitter-cress is a common native annual of bare damp ground, often in shaded situations such as woods and streamsides. It is also found in more open habitats such as marshes, gardens and cultivated ground, and occurs throughout the county.

Cardamine hirsuta L.
Hairy Bitter-cress

COUNTY STATUS: Native	
CONSERVATION STATUS: None	
FIRST YEAR: 1729 **LATEST YEAR:** 2013 **NO OF RECORDS:** 1,835	
RECENT SQUARES: monads 994; tetrads 543; hectads 40	
ALL SQUARES: monads 1,041; tetrads 554; hectads 40	

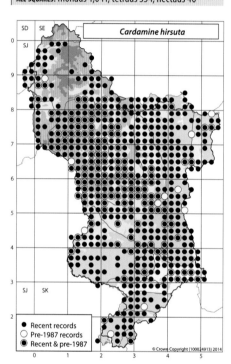

Hairy Bitter-cress is a common native annual or ephemeral of bare ground in gardens, arable fields and waste places. It also grows as a winter annual on shallow soil over rocks and on walls. It is recorded throughout the county except for the high moors of the Dark Peak.

Cardamine corymbosa Hook. f.
New Zealand Bitter-cress
New Zealand Bitter-cress is a very rare, casual annual of gardens and nurseries. It was first discovered at a plant nursery in Calver (SK2374) in 1998 by D. Dupree, and subsequently found at a further five sites up to 2012. It is spreading nationally (Preston *et al.* 2002), so might be expected to occur more often in the future. It is a native of New Zealand.

Lepidium sativum L.
Garden Cress
Garden Cress is a very rare, casual annual of waste ground and waysides, and a native

of Egypt and western Asia. There are only three recent sightings up to 2005 (Hollington Cottage SK2340, Darley Dale SK2762 & Draycott SK4233) plus five older records back to 1969. It was grown as a salad plant and is now included in bird-seed mixes.

Lepidium campestre (L.) W.T. Aiton
Field Pepperwort

COUNTY STATUS: Established (Archaeophyte)	
CONSERVATION STATUS: ERL	
FIRST YEAR: 1829 **LATEST YEAR:** 2012 **NO OF RECORDS:** 47	
RECENT SQUARES: monads 21; tetrads 21; hectads 14	
ALL SQUARES: monads 26; tetrads 26; hectads 20	

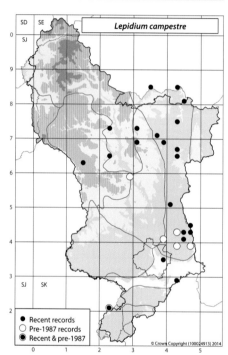

Field Pepperwort is a rare, anciently established annual of open disturbed areas and arable fields. It occurs throughout the county except for the moorlands of the Dark and South West Peak Areas (Pickering Wood SK2365, Drakelow Power Station SK2220, Witches Oak Water SK4329 & Staveley Old Station SK4374). It appears to have declined in arable fields in the south, but increased on waste ground in the east since Clapham (1969).

Lepidium heterophyllum Benth.
Smith's Pepperwort

COUNTY STATUS: Native	
CONSERVATION STATUS: DRDB (Cat5b), A	
FIRST YEAR: 1903 **LATEST YEAR:** 2010 **NO OF RECORDS:** 27	
RECENT SQUARES: monads 7; tetrads 6; hectads 5	
ALL SQUARES: monads 15; tetrads 12; hectads 9	

Smith's Pepperwort is a very rare, native perennial of arable land, waysides and disturbed ground. Recent records are

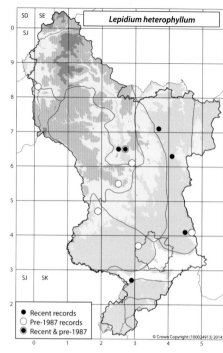

mainly from central Derbyshire (Rowsley Sidings SK2664 & Goyt Side Road SK3670), whilst previously it was recorded across the county (New Mills SK0183, Clifton Goods Yard SK1644 & Ikeston SK44). It occurs throughout the British Isles though is declining in south-eastern England.

Lepidium ruderale L.
Narrow-leaved Pepperwort

COUNTY STATUS: Established (Archaeophyte)	
CONSERVATION STATUS: A	
FIRST YEAR: 1960 **LATEST YEAR:** 2012 **NO OF RECORDS:** 23	
RECENT SQUARES: monads 10; tetrads 10; hectads 9	
ALL SQUARES: monads 19; tetrads 18; hectads 14	

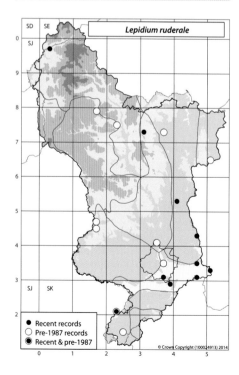

Narrow-leaved Pepperwort is a very rare, anciently established annual of waste ground and waysides. It grows scattered throughout the county (Hadfield SK0296, Drakelow Power Station SK2220, Weston-on-Trent SK3928 & Freebirch Farm SK3072). Nationally it is increasing on salted road verges (Preston *et al.* 2002) but there is little sign of it doing so here, despite a single roadside record at Sawley (SK4631) in 2005. The plant is indigenous to coastal areas of Britain.

Lepidium perfoliatum L.
Perfoliate Pepperwort
Perfoliate Pepperwort is a casual annual of road verges, and a native of continental Europe. The only record is from Matlock Bank (SK3060) in 1977. Nationally it is a rare plant of waste ground and roadsides, introduced as a contaminant of grain and bird-seed mixes.

Lepidium latifolium L.
Dittander

COUNTY STATUS: Established (Neophyte)
CONSERVATION STATUS: None
FIRST YEAR: 1974 LATEST YEAR: 2012 NO OF RECORDS: 30
RECENT SQUARES: monads 11; tetrads 10; hectads 6
ALL SQUARES: monads 11; tetrads 10; hectads 6

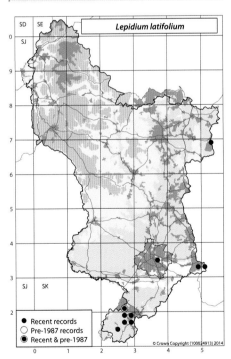

Dittander is a very rare, established perennial of waste ground and waysides, often associated with coal mines or railways (Stanton SK2720, Cadley Hill SK2719, Swadlincote SK2819, Chaddesden SK3635, Long Eaton SK5033 & Shirebrook SK5268). Formerly grown in gardens as a

potherb, it is a native of damp bare ground near the sea in East Anglia.

Lepidium draba L.
Hoary Cress

COUNTY STATUS: Established (Neophyte)
CONSERVATION STATUS: None
FIRST YEAR: 1903 LATEST YEAR: 2012 NO OF RECORDS: 100
RECENT SQUARES: monads 40; tetrads 35; hectads 19
ALL SQUARES: monads 54; tetrads 47; hectads 22

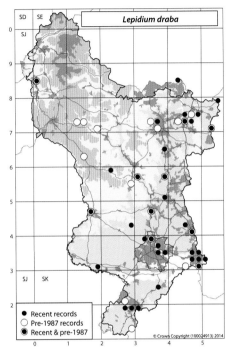

Hoary Cress is a rare established perennial of waste ground and waysides throughout the county. It occurs more frequently in the lowland south and east (Ashbourne SK1746, Swadlincote SK2819, Belper SK3446 & Tupton SK3865), and appears to have been formerly more frequent in the White Peak (Clapham 1969). Our plants are all presumably ssp. *draba*, a native of southern Europe.

Lepidium coronopus (L.) Al-Shehbaz
Swine-cress

COUNTY STATUS: Established (Archaeophyte)
CONSERVATION STATUS: None
FIRST YEAR: 1829 LATEST YEAR: 2013 NO OF RECORDS: 210
RECENT SQUARES: monads 160; tetrads 122; hectads 24
ALL SQUARES: monads 179; tetrads 134; hectads 25

Swine-cress is an occasional, anciently established annual of waysides, waste ground and trampled areas in fields, particularly around gateways. It grows mainly in the south of the county (Cubley SK1738, Coton in the Elms SK2415, Duffield SK3542 & Sawley SK4631) though it has sporadic occurrences in the north (Parkhouse Hill SK0766 & Hope Valley SK1682). At Chester Green, Derby (SK3537)

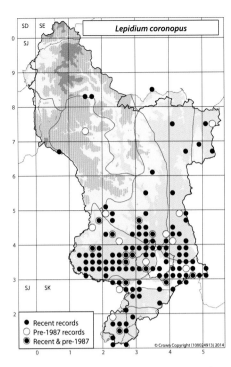

it was particularly found around the goal mouths of football pitches.

Lepidium didymum L.
Lesser Swine-cress

COUNTY STATUS: Established (Neophyte)
CONSERVATION STATUS: None
FIRST YEAR: 1881 LATEST YEAR: 2013 NO OF RECORDS: 88
RECENT SQUARES: monads 64; tetrads 59; hectads 22
ALL SQUARES: monads 70; tetrads 65; hectads 24

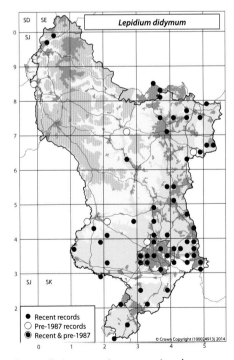

Lesser Swine-cress is an occasional established annual or biennial of disturbed land, cultivated ground and waysides. It occurs mainly in southern and eastern areas (Bog Plantation SK1939, Limehouse

Dam SK3320, Draycott SK4434 & Hollingwood SK4174), with isolated records further north (Hadfield Tip SK0296). It is possibly of South American origin.

Lunaria annua L.
Honesty

COUNTY STATUS: Established (Neophyte)	
CONSERVATION STATUS: None	
FIRST YEAR: 1960 **LATEST YEAR:** 2013 **NO OF RECORDS:** 450	
RECENT SQUARES: monads 282; tetrads 270; hectads 37	
ALL SQUARES: monads 300; tetrads 285; hectads 37	

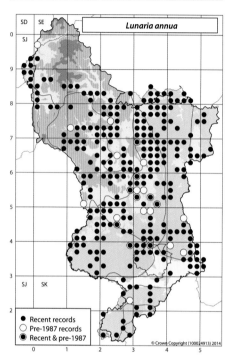

Honesty is an occasional established biennial of roadsides and waste places. Commonly grown in gardens, it escapes to turn up sporadically across the county, except for the north-western moors. The species is a native of south-eastern Europe, but ours is a cultivated subspecies of unknown origin.

Lunaria rediviva L.
Perennial Honesty
Perennial Honesty is a casual perennial of rough ground and waysides. There are only five recent records, all between 1988 and 2011: Monyash (SK1566), Ashford in the Water (SK1969), Minninglow (SK2057), Stoney Middleton (SK2275) and Carrs Wood (SK2362). It is sometimes grown in gardens and is a native of Europe.

Alyssum alyssoides (L.) L.
Small Alison
Locally extinct, Small Alison was a casual annual of farmland. Our only record is from Yeldersley (SK24) given in Linton (1903). It was formerly widespread in southern and eastern Britain but is now virtually confined to Suffolk.

Aurinia saxatilis (L.) Desv.
Golden Alison
Golden Alison is a casual perennial of waste ground and dry banks. There are only two recent records (Peak Dale SK0876 in 1998 & Belper SK3446 in 1994) and two older ones (Alport Heights SK3251 in 1976 & Nether Heage SK3550 in 1977). Commonly grown in gardens, it is indigenous to central and south-eastern Europe.

Berteroa incana (L.) DC.
Hoary Alison
Hoary Alison is a casual biennial of cultivated and waste ground. The only recent record is from Derby (SK3536) in 2009. It was previously recorded from Derby (SK3535) in 1974, Ashbourne (SK1746) in 1946, and near Dale (SK43) in 1903. Occurring naturally in continental Europe, it is generally imported as an impurity of seed or grain.

Lobularia maritima (L.) Desv.
Sweet Alison

COUNTY STATUS: Casual	
CONSERVATION STATUS: None	
FIRST YEAR: 1987 **LATEST YEAR:** 2012 **NO OF RECORDS:** 27	
RECENT SQUARES: monads 22; tetrads 19; hectads 14	
ALL SQUARES: monads 22; tetrads 19; hectads 14	

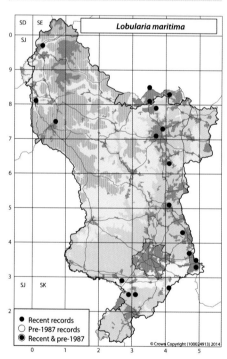

Sweet Alison is a rare casual annual or short-lived perennial of roadsides, waste ground and even cracks in pavements. It occurs scattered through the county usually at lower altitudes (Fairfield Church SK0674, Castle Gresley SK2728, Coal Aston SK3679 & Danesmoor SK4063). Frequently grown in gardens, it is a native of south-western Europe.

Descurainia sophia (L.) Webb ex Prantl
Flixweed
Flixweed is a casual annual or biennial of disturbed ground and cultivated land, with only two recent records: Derby (SK3735) in 1998 and Bolsover (SK4770) in 1987. There are five older ones including: Cromford (SK2957) in 1970 and Ticknall (SK32) in 1903. The earliest is for Markeaton Hill (SK33) in Pilkington (1789). It is a native to arable fields in eastern England.

Hornungia petraea (L.) Rchb.
Hutchinsia

COUNTY STATUS: Native	
CONSERVATION STATUS: DRDB (Cat3), NS, A, B	
FIRST YEAR: 1793 **LATEST YEAR:** 2012 **NO OF RECORDS:** 216	
RECENT SQUARES: monads 25; tetrads 17; hectads 5	
ALL SQUARES: monads 44; tetrads 26; hectads 7	

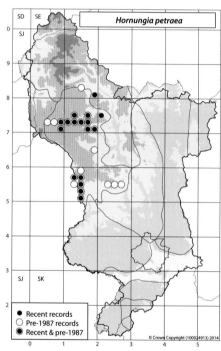

Hutchinsia is a rare native winter annual of the White Peak. It grows in open communities on shallow soil over limestone outcrops, often on slopes with a southerly aspect (Dove Dale SK1451 & Wye Dale SK1871). It was formerly recorded in the Longcliffe area (SK2255) from the 1930s to the 1970s. This Nationally Scarce species is very local in upland England and Wales.

Arabis caucasica Willd. ex Schltdl.
Garden Arabis

COUNTY STATUS: Established (Neophyte)	
CONSERVATION STATUS: None	
FIRST YEAR: 1891 **LATEST YEAR:** 2013 **NO OF RECORDS:** 150	
RECENT SQUARES: monads 54; tetrads 44; hectads 13	
ALL SQUARES: monads 67; tetrads 50; hectads 14	

Garden Arabis is a rare established perennial of rocks, walls and roadside

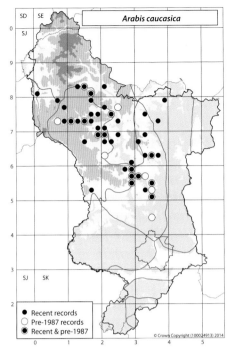

banks. It is grown in gardens and is usually found not far from habitation. It occurs most frequently in the White Peak on limestone outcrops (Chee Dale SK1172, Ashford in the Water SK1969 & Cromford SK2956). Outside this Character Area it grows only sporadically (Bamford SK2083, Ambergate Station SK3451 & Apperknowle SK3878). Linton (1903) stated it had increased enormously over rocks in the Matlock Bath area (SK25) in the twelve years prior to his Flora's publication. It is indigenous to southern Europe.

Arabis hirsuta (L.) Scop.
Hairy Rock-cress

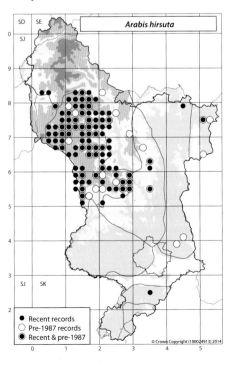

COUNTY STATUS: Native
CONSERVATION STATUS: ERL
FIRST YEAR: 1670 **LATEST YEAR:** 2013 **NO OF RECORDS:** 546
RECENT SQUARES: monads 175; tetrads 99; hectads 15
ALL SQUARES: monads 197; tetrads 114; hectads 20

Hairy Rock-cress is a frequent native biennial or perennial of rock outcrops, grassland and walls in the White Peak (Tideslow Rake SK1577 & Middleton Top SK2754). It also occurs rarely on the Magnesian Limestone (Markland Grips SK5074) and on isolated outcrops of Carboniferous Limestone (Ticknall SK3524 & Ashover SK3562). Other isolated records are probably of casual plants or errors. Its first British record is reputed to be from the walls of Ashbourne Church (SK1746) in 1670 (Clarke 1900).

Aubrieta deltoidea (L.) DC.
Aubretia

COUNTY STATUS: Established (Neophyte)
CONSERVATION STATUS: None
FIRST YEAR: 1968 **LATEST YEAR:** 2012 **NO OF RECORDS:** 20
RECENT SQUARES: monads 11; tetrads 10; hectads 8
ALL SQUARES: monads 15; tetrads 13; hectads 11

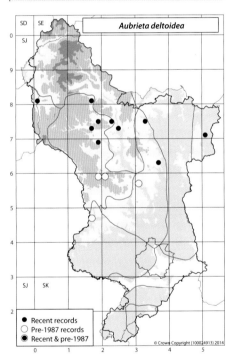

Aubretia is a very rare, established perennial of walls, rock outcrops and roadside banks. It is much grown in gardens and is generally found near habitations, as at Cressbrook Village (SK1772), Middleton Dale (SK2275), Barlow (SK3375) and Littlemoor (SK3662). It is a native of south-eastern Europe.

Draba incana L.
Hoary Whitlowgrass

Hoary Whitlowgrass is a rare native biennial or perennial of rock ledges, open grassland and spoil-heaps in the White Peak Area,

COUNTY STATUS: Native
CONSERVATION STATUS: B
FIRST YEAR: 1821 **LATEST YEAR:** 2010 **NO OF RECORDS:** 86
RECENT SQUARES: monads 13; tetrads 13; hectads 6
ALL SQUARES: monads 18; tetrads 16; hectads 6

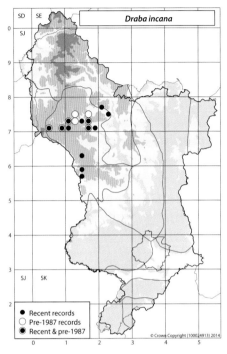

where the majority of the records are from the northern part (Deep Dale SK1072 & Calver Sough SK2374) with outlying records from around Biggin Dale (SK15N) and Hartshead Quarry (SK1462). It has a northern distribution with Derbyshire on the southern edge of its range.

Draba muralis L.
Wall Whitlowgrass

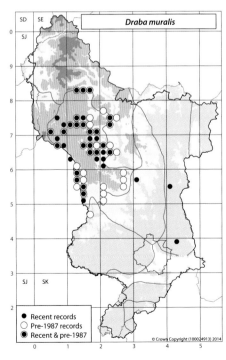

Wall Whitlowgrass (*Draba muralis*) on side of Monsal Trail near Bakewell (SK2268), April 2013 (Kieron Huston)

COUNTY STATUS: Native
CONSERVATION STATUS: DRDB (Cat3), NS, A, B
FIRST YEAR: 1711 LATEST YEAR: 2013 NO OF RECORDS: 305
RECENT SQUARES: monads 52; tetrads 40; hectads 11
ALL SQUARES: monads 87; tetrads 58; hectads 13

Wall Whitlowgrass is a rare native annual of the White Peak. It grows on shallow soils over limestone, on walls and on the ballast of disused railway lines. There are recent records from: Biggin Dale (SK1458), Coombs Dale (SK2274), Deep Dale (SK0971) and Millers Dale (SK1574). There are also scattered records from outside the White Peak, as at Cromford (SK3057) in the Peak Fringe and at Hagg Lane (SK4339) in the Coal Measures. It occurs sporadically throughout Britain and is Nationally Scarce.

Erophila majuscula Jord.
Hairy Whitlowgrass

COUNTY STATUS: Native
CONSERVATION STATUS: None
FIRST YEAR: 1969 LATEST YEAR: 2011 NO OF RECORDS: 22
RECENT SQUARES: monads 15; tetrads 13; hectads 4
ALL SQUARES: monads 16; tetrads 14; hectads 5

Hairy Whitlowgrass is a rare native ephemeral of bare dry ground, rock outcrops and open grassland in the White Peak (Cow Dale SK0872, Cave Dale SK1482 & Long Dale SK1860). It is probably under-recorded due to the problems of separating it from other members of the genus.

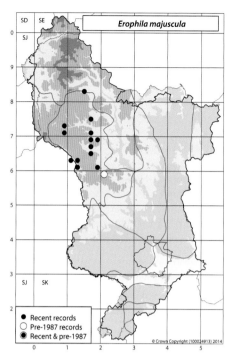

Erophila verna (L.) DC.
Common Whitlowgrass

COUNTY STATUS: Native
CONSERVATION STATUS: None
FIRST YEAR: 1789 LATEST YEAR: 2013 NO OF RECORDS: 239
RECENT SQUARES: monads 158; tetrads 123; hectads 29
ALL SQUARES: monads 162; tetrads 125; hectads 30

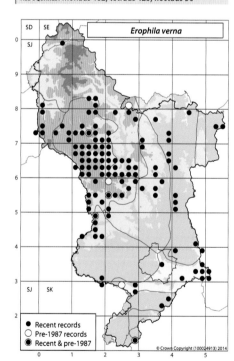

Common Whitlowgrass is an occasional native ephemeral of all types of bare open habitats including limestone outcrops, walls, open grassland, waste ground and even pavement cracks. It is most frequently recorded in the White Peak (Priestcliffe Lees SK1472, Monyash SK1566 & Gratton Grange SK2061). Elsewhere it occurs sporadically,

except for the Dark Peak where it is virtually absent (Netherseal SK2812, Alfreton SK4054 & Hockley SK36Y). It is probably under-recorded due to the difficulty of separating it from related species.

Erophila glabrescens Jord.
Glabrous Whitlowgrass

COUNTY STATUS: Native
CONSERVATION STATUS: None
FIRST YEAR: 1995 LATEST YEAR: 2012 NO OF RECORDS: 22
RECENT SQUARES: monads 16; tetrads 14; hectads 8
ALL SQUARES: monads 16; tetrads 14; hectads 8

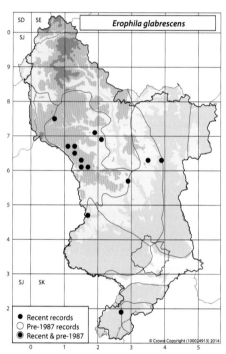

Glabrous Whitlowgrass is a very rare, native ephemeral of a variety of bare dry habitats, mostly on Carboniferous Limestone (Fairfield Church SK0674, Cromford SK2957 & Ashover SK3463). It occurs on shallow soil over limestone outcrops, bare patches in grassland, walls and even pavement cracks. The challenge of separating it from other members of its genus means it is probably under-recorded.

Conringia orientalis (L.) Dumort.
Hare's-ear Mustard

Locally extinct, Hare's-ear Mustard was a very rare, casual annual of rough and cultivated ground. The only two records are from Clapham's 1969 Flora. These are: Clifton (SK1545) in a fowl run, and Ashbourne (SK1746) with parsley seed. Probably introduced as a contaminant of grain or seed, it is indigenous to central and southern Europe.

Diplotaxis tenuifolia (L.) DC.
Perennial Wall-rocket

Perennial Wall-rocket is a very rare, anciently

COUNTY STATUS: Established (Archaeophyte)
CONSERVATION STATUS: None
FIRST YEAR: 1970 LATEST YEAR: 2012 NO OF RECORDS: 41
RECENT SQUARES: monads 12; tetrads 14; hectads 8
ALL SQUARES: monads 18; tetrads 20; hectads 11

COUNTY STATUS: Established (Neophyte)
CONSERVATION STATUS: None
FIRST YEAR: 1863 LATEST YEAR: 2010 NO OF RECORDS: 36
RECENT SQUARES: monads 11; tetrads 11; hectads 8
ALL SQUARES: monads 22; tetrads 23; hectads 15

COUNTY STATUS: Established (Neophyte)
CONSERVATION STATUS: None
FIRST YEAR: 1789 LATEST YEAR: 2013 NO OF RECORDS: 416
RECENT SQUARES: monads 309; tetrads 263; hectads 39
ALL SQUARES: monads 319; tetrads 269; hectads 39

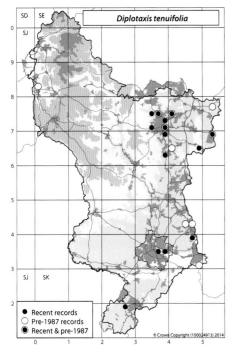

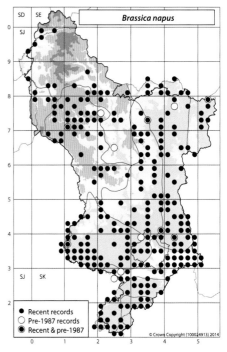

Annual Wall-rocket is a very rare, established annual of waste land, verges and grassland. It is found throughout the county (Over Dale SK1880, Carsington Pasture SK2553, Dimple Dump SK2960, Morley SK3940 & Mortimer Wilson School SK4155). It was probably introduced as a contaminant of seed from central and southern Europe where it is native.

Brassica oleracea L.
Cabbage

COUNTY STATUS: Casual
CONSERVATION STATUS: None
FIRST YEAR: 1969 LATEST YEAR: 2012 NO OF RECORDS: 31
RECENT SQUARES: monads 7; tetrads 22; hectads 10
ALL SQUARES: monads 11; tetrads 26; hectads 12

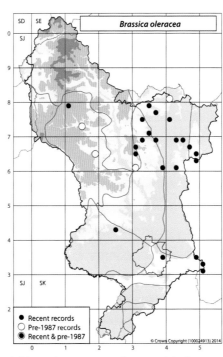

established perennial of waste ground and waysides in southern and eastern parts: (Cadley Hill SK2719, Wyvern Centre SK3735, Sheepbridge SK3774 & Chesterfield SK3871). It was previously found in the north-west at Furness Vale (SK0183) in 1978. It is a native of continental Europe.

Diplotaxis muralis (L.) DC.
Annual Wall-rocket

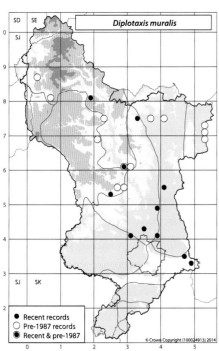

Cabbage is a rare casual perennial of waste ground, verges and abandoned cultivations, found throughout Derbyshire (Dam Dale SK1178, Unstone SK37T & Spondon SK3935). It occurs as several cultivated varieties, each of which is a distinct crop. These include Cabbage, Kale, Cauliflower and Brussels-sprouts. The native variety occurs on sea-cliffs around southern Britain and is Nationally Scarce.

Brassica napus L.
Rape

Rape is an occasional established annual or biennial of waysides, field margins, abandoned cultivations and waste

ground. It is found throughout the county except for the northern moors. Only **ssp. oleifera** (DC.) Metzg. (**Oil-seed Rape**) has been recorded in the wild here. This is the familiar crop plant that turns much of Derbyshire's countryside bright yellow in spring, and is of cultivated origin.

Brassica rapa L.
Turnip

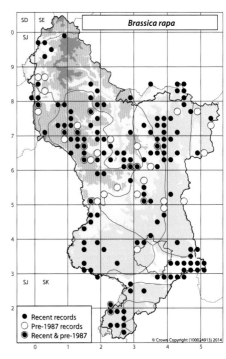

COUNTY STATUS: Established (Neophyte)	
CONSERVATION STATUS: None	
FIRST YEAR: 1789 **LATEST YEAR:** 2012 **NO OF RECORDS:** 263	
RECENT SQUARES: monads 146; tetrads 141; hectads 34	
ALL SQUARES: monads 175; tetrads 165; hectads 37	

Turnip is an occasional established annual or biennial of streamsides, arable fields and waste land. It is found throughout Derbyshire, except for the northern moors. Three subspecies occur. **Wild Turnip (ssp. campestris** (L.) A.R. Clapham) is a plant of semi-natural habitats by streams. **Turnip (ssp. rapa)** is generally a relic of cultivation; and **Turnip-rape (ssp. oleifera** (DC.) Metzg.) is a seed contaminant found mostly on rough ground. The species is a native of Eurasia, and is probably over-recorded for Oil-seed Rape (*B. napus* ssp. *oleifera*).

Brassica juncea (L.) Czern.
Chinese Mustard

Chinese Mustard is a very rare, casual annual of verges and waste ground. It is only recorded from four sites: two recently (Hadfield Tip SK0296 in 1989 & Chesterfield SK3870 in 1996), and two previously (Ford Lane Bridge SK3540 in 1978 & Cathole Tip SK3268 in 1985). Introduced as a bird-seed alien or condiment, it is of hybrid origin from south-eastern Asia.

Brassica nigra (L.) W.D.J. Koch
Black Mustard

COUNTY STATUS: Native	
CONSERVATION STATUS: A	
FIRST YEAR: 1789 **LATEST YEAR:** 2012 **NO OF RECORDS:** 31	
RECENT SQUARES: monads 9; tetrads 9; hectads 6	
ALL SQUARES: monads 15; tetrads 15; hectads 18	

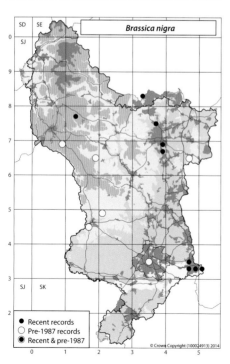

Black Mustard is a very rare, native annual of waysides and waste places. It occurs scattered throughout Derbyshire from Potluck House (SK1377) and Sheffield (SK3383) in the north to Long Eaton in the south (SK4933). Previously it was distributed over much the same parts but grew more often in rural areas where it occurred on stream banks and arable land. Recent records suggest that built-up localities are now its preferred habitat.

Sinapis arvensis L.
Charlock

COUNTY STATUS: Established (Archaeophyte)	
CONSERVATION STATUS: None	
FIRST YEAR: 1789 **LATEST YEAR:** 2013 **NO OF RECORDS:** 616	
RECENT SQUARES: monads 357; tetrads 299; hectads 35	
ALL SQUARES: monads 402; tetrads 319; hectads 35	

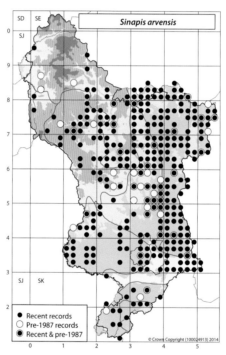

Charlock is an occasional, anciently established annual of waste land, roadsides and arable fields. It occurs throughout the county though becomes rarer in the more intensively farmed parts of the south, in the White Peak and on the northern moors. It has the local name of Cadlock (Grigson 1975).

Sinapis alba L.
White Mustard

COUNTY STATUS: Established (Archaeophyte)	
CONSERVATION STATUS: None	
FIRST YEAR: 1829 **LATEST YEAR:** 2008 **NO OF RECORDS:** 35	
RECENT SQUARES: monads 9; tetrads 11; hectads 8	
ALL SQUARES: monads 20; tetrads 23; hectads 19	

White Mustard is a very rare, anciently established annual of cultivated land, waste ground and waysides. It is recorded

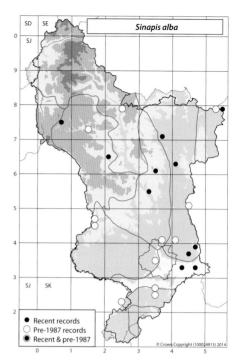

sporadically throughout the county, from Fairfield (SK0674) and Steetley (SK5478) in the north to Draycott (SK4233) in the south. Our plants are presumably ssp. *alba*. This is grown as a crop or is a contaminant of bird-seed, and is native to southern Europe.

Eruca vesicaria (L.) Cav.
Garden Rocket

Locally extinct, Garden Rocket was a casual annual of waste land and tips. There are only four records: Clifton Tip (SK1644) in 1945, Newhaven (SK1660) in 1969, Yeldersley (SK2043) in 1951 & Walton (SK2318) in 1969. It was once grown as a medicinal plant; an aphrodisiac was extracted from the seeds (Preston *et al.* 2002). Nowadays it is a contaminant of seeds, and grown as a salad. It is a native of southern Europe.

Erucastrum gallicum (Willd.) O.E. Schulz
Hairy Rocket

Locally extinct, Hairy Rocket was a casual annual of waste ground, known only from Ashbourne (SK1746) in 1960. It is indigenous to central Europe and the Pyrenees.

Hirschfeldia incana (L.) Lagr.-Foss.
Hoary Mustard

COUNTY STATUS: Casual	
CONSERVATION STATUS: None	
FIRST YEAR: 1970 **LATEST YEAR:** 2011 **NO OF RECORDS:** 17	
RECENT SQUARES: monads 15; tetrads 14; hectads 7	
ALL SQUARES: monads 16; tetrads 15; hectads 7	

Hoary Mustard is a very rare, casual annual or short-lived perennial of waste ground and waysides. It was unknown until 1970 since when it has spread through north-

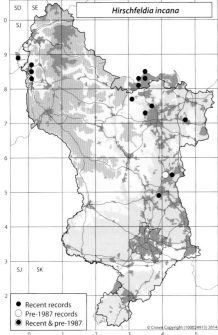

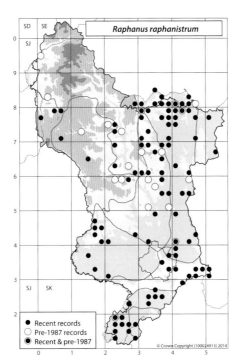

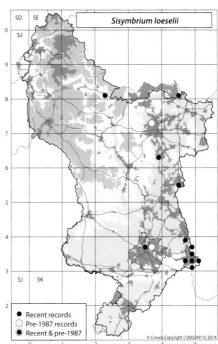

western (Thornsett SK0187) and eastern parts (Millhouses SK3483, Sheepbridge SK3674, Marehay SK3948 & Cotes Park SK4254). It was probably introduced with imported grain or bird-seed from its native range of southern Europe.

Coincya monensis ssp. *cheiranthos*
(Vill.) Aedo, Leadlay & Munoz Garm.
Wallflower Cabbage
Wallflower Cabbage is an established annual or biennial of waste ground. It has only been recorded at one site, an old railway line at Langwith Junction (SK5268), where it was recorded between 1977 and 2003. It is a native of western Europe.

Rapistrum rugosum (L.) Bergeret
Bastard Cabbage
Bastard Cabbage is a casual annual of waste ground and waysides. It is only recorded from two sites: Stoney Middleton (SK2275) in 1975 and Stonegravels (SK3872) in 1979. A native of the Mediterranean, it was probably imported with grain or bird-seed.

Raphanus raphanistrum L.
Wild Radish

COUNTY STATUS: Established (Archaeophyte)	
CONSERVATION STATUS: None	
FIRST YEAR: 1789 **LATEST YEAR:** 2012 **NO OF RECORDS:** 225	
RECENT SQUARES: monads 99; tetrads 102; hectads 30	
ALL SQUARES: monads 117, tetrads 118; hectads 34	

Wild Radish (ssp. *raphanistrum*) is an occasional, anciently established annual of arable land, rough ground and waysides. It is recorded throughout the county but occurs more often in the eastern half.

Its favoured habitat was formerly arable crops but, with the advent of selective herbicides, it is now found most often on rough ground. Both white and yellow flowered forms occur. It is a native of southern Europe.

Raphanus sativus L.
Garden Radish
Garden Radish is a casual annual of rough and cultivated land. There are only three recent records (Stapenhill SK2421, Friar Gate Station SK3436 & Barlow SK3475) and one older one for 1980 (Radbourne SK23X). It is a garden escape or bird-seed alien of cultivated origin.

Sisymbrium irio L.
London-rocket
London-rocket is a casual annual of roadsides and waste places. There have been only three records: Holy Moor (SK3267) in 1985, between Burton and Ashby (SK32) in 1903 and Wingfield Manor (SK35) in 1789. It is a native of continental Europe.

Sisymbrium loeselii L.
False London-rocket

COUNTY STATUS: Casual	
CONSERVATION STATUS: None	
FIRST YEAR: 1971 **LATEST YEAR:** 2010 **NO OF RECORDS:** 25	
RECENT SQUARES: monads 15; tetrads 12; hectads 7	
ALL SQUARES: monads 17; tetrads 14; hectads 8	

False London-rocket is a very rare, casual annual of disturbed and rough ground. It appears to be increasing locally, with records mainly from the eastern half of the county (Hathersage SK2281, Clay Cross SK3862 & Long Eaton SK5032). Probably

introduced with bird-seed mixes, it is a native of central and eastern Europe.

Sisymbrium volgense M. Bieb. ex E. Fourn.
Russian Mustard
Russian Mustard is an established perennial of waysides. The only record is a large colony found by J. Shaw in 1994 on the Erewash Canal towpath (SK4838) at Stanton Gate (Shaw 1995). It is a native of south-western Russia, possibly introduced with grain.

Sisymbrium altissimum L.
Tall Rocket
Tall Rocket is a rare established annual of roadsides and rough ground. Recent

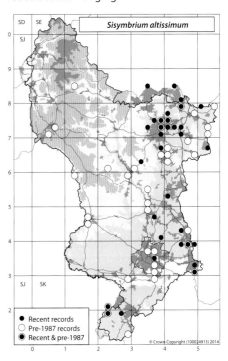

| COUNTY STATUS: Established (Neophyte) |
| CONSERVATION STATUS: None |
| FIRST YEAR: 1907 LATEST YEAR: 2003 NO OF RECORDS: 96 |
| RECENT SQUARES: monads 26; tetrads 32; hectads 14 |
| ALL SQUARES: monads 63; tetrads 62; hectads 24 |

records are from eastern and southern parts (Drakelow Power Station SK2219, Barrow Hill SK4174, Stanton Works SK4738 & Lock Lane Ash Tip SK4831). Previously it was recorded throughout the county. A native of eastern Europe, it was probably introduced as a contaminant of bird-seed or grass-seed mixes.

Sisymbrium orientale L.
Eastern Rocket

| COUNTY STATUS: Established (Neophyte) |
| CONSERVATION STATUS: None |
| FIRST YEAR: 1960 LATEST YEAR: 2013 NO OF RECORDS: 111 |
| RECENT SQUARES: monads 49; tetrads 49; hectads 20 |
| ALL SQUARES: monads 72; tetrads 68; hectads 26 |

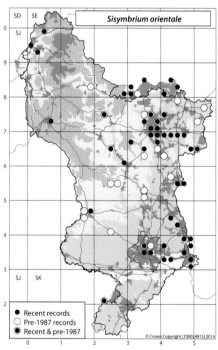

Eastern Rocket is an occasional established annual of roadsides and waste ground throughout the county (Simmondley SK0293, Drakelow Power Station SK2220, Owlthorpe SK4181 & Long Eaton SK4933). It increased locally as a result of bombing during the 1939-45 war (Clapham 1969). It is a native of southern Europe and was cultivated in Britain in the 18th century and more recently has been introduced as a contaminant of grain.

Sisymbrium officinale (L.) Scop.
Hedge Mustard

Hedge Mustard is an anciently established annual or biennial of roadsides, waste ground and cultivated land. It is very

| COUNTY STATUS: Established (Archaeophyte) |
| CONSERVATION STATUS: None |
| FIRST YEAR: 1650 LATEST YEAR: 2013 NO OF RECORDS: 1,717 |
| RECENT SQUARES: monads 921; tetrads 496; hectads 42 |
| ALL SQUARES: monads 965; tetrads 502; hectads 42 |

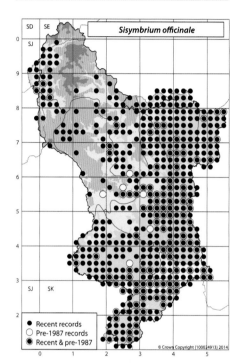

common in the southern and eastern parts of the county but rarer in the White and Dark Peak Areas except for the extreme north-western corner.

Isatis tinctoria L.
Woad

Woad is a casual biennial of waste and cultivated ground. There are only three records: two recent, Kirk Langley (SK2938) in 1998 and Ilkeston (SK4742) in 1998; and one ancient, Willington (SK22) in 1896 (Linton 1903). These probably originated from bird-seed or garden plants. It was previously cultivated as a source of dye, for example around Beighton and Eckington in the early 19th century (Farey 1815).

Alliaria petiolata (M. Bieb.) Cavara & Grande
Garlic Mustard

| COUNTY STATUS: Native |
| CONSERVATION STATUS: None |
| FIRST YEAR: 1789 LATEST YEAR: 2013 NO OF RECORDS: 3,561 |
| RECENT SQUARES: monads 1,569; tetrads 628; hectads 42 |
| ALL SQUARES: monads 1,613; tetrads 633; hectads 42 |

Garlic Mustard is a native biennial of hedges, light woodlands, riverbanks and waste ground. It is very common throughout the county except for the moors of the north-western corner. It favours nutrient-rich soils (Clapham 1969) and is probably increasing due to the intensification of agriculture.

Garlic Mustard (*Alliaria petiolata*), Darley Fields, Derby (SK3537), April 2008 (Peter Smith)

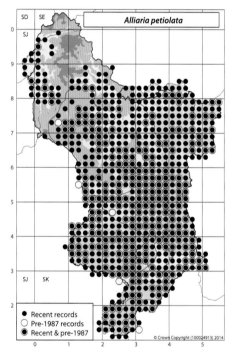

Teesdalia nudicaulis (L.) W.T. Aiton
Shepherd's Cress

| COUNTY STATUS: Native |
| CONSERVATION STATUS: DRDB (Cat2), NT, B |
| FIRST YEAR: 1829 LATEST YEAR: 2009 NO OF RECORDS: 10 |
| RECENT SQUARES: monads 1; tetrads 1; hectads 1 |
| ALL SQUARES: monads 3; tetrads 3; hectads 3 |

Shepherd's Cress is a very rare, native winter annual. The only recent record is at Sir William Hill Road (SK2177). It was previously recorded from Dirtlow Rake

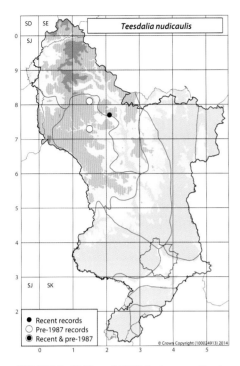

(SK1481) in 1968 and 1983, but was extinct there by 1990. It had only been recorded twice before that: Middleton Dale (SK27) in 1903, and in 1829 for an unspecified locality (Linton 1903).

Thlaspi arvense L.
Field Penny-cress

COUNTY STATUS: Established (Archaeophyte)
CONSERVATION STATUS: None
FIRST YEAR: 1864 LATEST YEAR: 2012 NO OF RECORDS: 109
RECENT SQUARES: monads 57; tetrads 54; hectads 24
ALL SQUARES: monads 84; tetrads 78; hectads 29

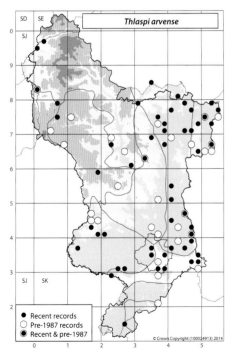

Field Penny-cress is an occasional, anciently established annual of open

disturbed ground that sometimes occurs as a weed of cultivated ground. It is recorded throughout the county except for the moors of the north-western corner (Dinting Vale SK0194, Matlock Bank SK2960, Kirk Hallam SK4640 & Barlborough SK4777).

Noccaea caerulescens (J. & C. Presl) F.K. Mey
Alpine Penny-cress (Leadwort)

COUNTY STATUS: Native
CONSERVATION STATUS: DRDB (Cat3), NS, A, B
FIRST YEAR: 1776 LATEST YEAR: 2012 NO OF RECORDS: 427
RECENT SQUARES: monads 50; tetrads 29; hectads 8
ALL SQUARES: monads 61; tetrads 34; hectads 8

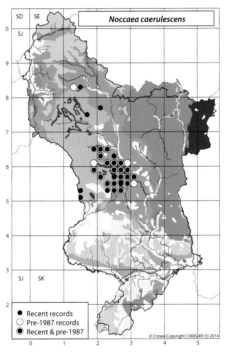

Alpine Penny-cress is a rare native perennial of the White Peak where it is so characteristic of the sparse vegetation on the spoil-heaps of old lead workings that it has acquired the name of **Leadwort**. It often occurs with the equally lead-tolerant Spring Sandwort (Dove Dale SK1453 & Rose End Meadows SK2958), but with few other flowering plants. It can also be found, but much less commonly, on limestone rocks and walls. In the White Peak it exists mostly in the area west of the Matlocks, but there are isolated records further north (Castleton SK1383). Previously it was also recorded for Crich (SK3454) in 1969 where there exists an isolated area of Carboniferous Limestone. Specimens collected from the Matlock area in the 19th century were referred to the continental species *Thlaspi virens* Jord. (Syme 1853). However, such material is now thought to be only a form of the current species. Nationally, it has a local and disjunct distribution throughout Britain, north to Scotland and is Nationally Scarce.

Hesperis matronalis L.
Dame's-violet

COUNTY STATUS: Established (Neophyte)
CONSERVATION STATUS: None
FIRST YEAR: 1805 LATEST YEAR: 2013 NO OF RECORDS: 489
RECENT SQUARES: monads 237; tetrads 175; hectads 34
ALL SQUARES: monads 262; tetrads 190; hectads 34

Dame's-violet is an occasional established perennial of grass verges, streamsides and waste places. It occurs mainly in the centre of the county, being rarer in the southern farmlands and northern moors (Sedsall

Alpine Penny-cress (*Noccaea caerulescens*), Rose End Meadows (SK2956), May 2005 (Nick Moyes)

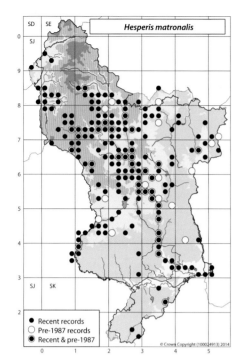

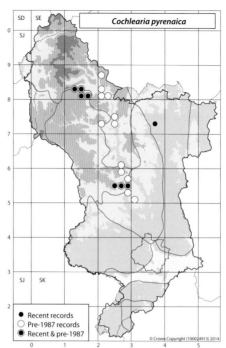

Rough SK1138, Parsley Hay SK1463, Chester Green SK3537 & Bramley Vale SK4666). It is often grown in gardens from where both white- and mauve-flowered forms have escaped into the wild. It is a native of southern Europe.

Matthiola longipetala (Vent.) DC.
Night-scented Stock

Night-scented Stock is a very rare, casual annual of rough places. There are only two records, Hasland Road (SK3869) in 1997 and Holbrook (SK4481) in 2010. Frequently grown in gardens for its scent, it is a native of Greece and North Africa.

Malcolmia maritima (L.) W.T. Aiton
Virginia Stock

Virginia Stock is a very rare, casual annual of tips and waste places. There are only two recent records both from Chesterfield in the 1990s: SK3471 and Saltergate (SK3871). Much grown in gardens, it is a native of Italy and the Balkans.

Cochlearia pyrenaica DC.
Pyrenean Scurvygrass

COUNTY STATUS: Native	
CONSERVATION STATUS: A, B	
FIRST YEAR: 1640 LATEST YEAR: 2012 NO OF RECORDS: 117	
RECENT SQUARES: monads 14; tetrads 8; hectads 3	
ALL SQUARES: monads 30; tetrads 20; hectads 7	

Pyrenean Scurvygrass is a very rare, native biennial of the White Peak. It grows in herbaceous communities on damp limestone outcrops (Castleton SK1582) and on lead mine spoil tips (Carsington Pasture SK2454). It formerly grew over a slightly wider area including High Shaw Clough

(SK2187) in the Dark Peak and Alport (SK3150) in the Peak Fringe. There is also a recent isolated record from Brockwell (SK3672). This was the only member of the genus in the area for a long time but has recently been joined by two others that have spread along roadsides due to winter salting. Nationally it is a northern species on the southern edge of its English distribution here. A record from Parkinson's *Theatrum Britannicum* in 1640 makes this one of the earliest plants to be recorded in Derbyshire.

Cochlearia officinalis L.
Common Scurvygrass

Common Scurvygrass is a very rare, casual annual of roadsides. It is known from only four sites: Alderwasley (SK3053) and Higg

Lane (SK3253) in 2008, Oakerthorpe (SK3853) in 2002 and Wirksworth (SK2854) in 2012. It is undoubtedly spreading due to the increased use of salt on roads in winter. It is native to a range of British coastal habitats. Our plant is presumably ssp. *officinalis*.

Cochlearia danica L.
Danish Scurvygrass

COUNTY STATUS: Established (Neophyte)	
CONSERVATION STATUS: None	
FIRST YEAR: 1972 LATEST YEAR: 2013 NO OF RECORDS: 592	
RECENT SQUARES: monads 324; tetrads 206; hectads 35	
ALL SQUARES: monads 325; tetrads 207; hectads 35	

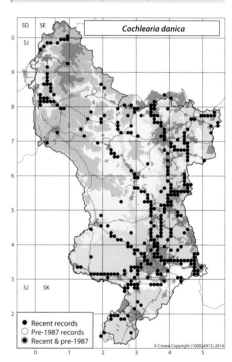

Danish Scurvygrass is a frequent established winter annual of salt-treated roads through the county. In early spring

Danish Scurvygrass (*Cochlearia danica*) beside the A61 in Derby (SK3637), April 2008 (Peter Smith)

it forms linear ribbons of white or lilac along the majority of main roads and some minor ones too (A50 at Foston SK1831, A6 at Ashford SK1869, & A61 at Chesterfield SK3478). Interestingly the first two local records, both in 1972, were not from roadsides but railway ballast (Miller's Dale SK1373 & Butterley SK4051 - specimen in Derby Museum). There were no further records for twenty years until a 1992 record at the side of the A52/M1 in SK43. After that the plant spread explosively along all major routes in just a few years. This local spread has been matched by a national one due to its ability to tolerate the salt used on roads in winter which few other plants can. It is native only to coastal areas of Britain.

Iberis sempervirens L.
Perennial Candytuft

COUNTY STATUS: Established (Neophyte)	
CONSERVATION STATUS: None	
FIRST YEAR: 1968 LATEST YEAR: 2002 NO OF RECORDS: 6	
RECENT SQUARES: monads 4; tetrads 4; hectads 4	
ALL SQUARES: monads 5; tetrads 5; hectads 5	

Perennial Candytuft is a very rare, established undershrub of roadsides and rock outcrops. It is much grown in gardens and occurs sporadically outside them as a garden throwout. There are only five modern records (Marple Bridge SJ9689, Gratton Dale SK2060, Park Head SK3654, Bolsover SK4770 & SK35), and one older one (Long Dale SK1959) for 1968. It is native to mountains in southern Europe.

Iberis amara L.
Wild Candytuft

Wild Candytuft is a very rare, casual annual of short grassland and waste ground. The only recent records are from Miller's Dale (SK1572) in 1988 and Eyam Quarry (SK2175) in 2011. Previously there were two reports in Clapham (1969) including near Tideswell (SK1575), plus five in Linton (1903). The latter include Monsal Dale (SK17) in 1870 and Yeldersley (SK14). There are also a number of specimens in Herb BM(NH) including the earliest record from Breadsall (SK34) in 1844. It is a native of central-southern England and is Nationally Scarce as a native.

Iberis umbellata L.
Garden Candytuft

COUNTY STATUS: Established (Neophyte)	
CONSERVATION STATUS: None	
FIRST YEAR: 1971 LATEST YEAR: 2012 NO OF RECORDS: 19	
RECENT SQUARES: monads 9; tetrads 8; hectads 8	
ALL SQUARES: monads 14; tetrads 14; hectads 11	

Garden Candytuft is a very rare, established annual of waste ground and disturbed land. There are recent

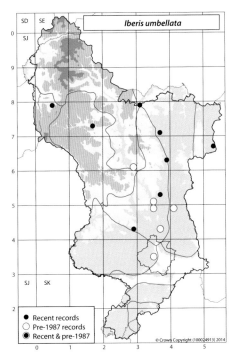

Iberis umbellata

Recent records
Pre-1987 records
Recent & pre-1987

© Crown Copyright (100024913) 2014

records throughout the county (Combs Village SK0478, Cressbrook Mill SK1772, Derby SK33 & Shirebrook SK5366). Often misrecorded as Wild Candytuft (I. amara), it is a native of southern Europe although garden escapees are generally cultivars of horticultural origin.

SANTALACEAE

Viscum album L.
Mistletoe

Mistletoe is a native evergreen that is a partial parasite on the branches of deciduous trees including apples and poplars. It occurs in hedges, copses

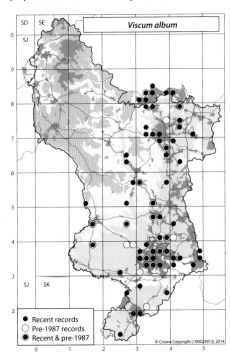

Viscum album

Recent records
Pre-1987 records
Recent & pre-1987

© Crown Copyright (100024913) 2014

COUNTY STATUS: Native	
CONSERVATION STATUS: B	
FIRST YEAR: 1699 LATEST YEAR: 2012 NO OF RECORDS: 217	
RECENT SQUARES: monads 71; tetrads 62; hectads 22	
ALL SQUARES: monads 80; tetrads 68; hectads 24	

and along roadsides, as well as in orchards and gardens, suggesting it is often deliberately introduced. It grows occasionally throughout eastern and southern parts, including Renishaw Park (SK4378), Ridgeway (SK3551), Dobbin Horse Lane (SK1744), Sunny Hill (SK3432) and Lullington Churchyard (SK2513). Having mystical and festive connections, it has often been noted even by non-botanical writers, thus Farey (1815) gives a list of localities. It has sometimes been cultivated for the Christmas market as at Mistletoe Farm, Mercaston (SK2745) in the 1850s.

PLUMBAGINACEAE

Armeria maritima (Mill.) Willd.
Thrift

Thrift is a casual tufted perennial, only recorded at one site in a natural-looking situation. This was on the verge of the A623 near Wall Cliff (SK1377/1477) between 2001 and 2003 where it had the appearance of a roadside halophyte rather than a garden throwout. The plant is a native of British coasts and mountains.

POLYGONACEAE

Persicaria campanulata (Hook. f.) Ronse Decr.
Lesser Knotweed

COUNTY STATUS: Established (Neophyte)	
CONSERVATION STATUS: None	
FIRST YEAR: 1970 LATEST YEAR: 2009 NO OF RECORDS: 15	
RECENT SQUARES: monads 6; tetrads 5; hectads 4	
ALL SQUARES: monads 7; tetrads 6; hectads 5	

Lesser Knotweed is a very rare, established perennial of damp shady places in the north of the county. It has been recorded from four areas: Toddbrook Reservoir (SK0081), Hathersage (SK2380), Whirlow (SK3082) and Stubbing (SK3567 & SK3667). It is sometimes grown in gardens from where it can spread by rhizome fragments. It is a native of the Himalayas.

Persicaria bistorta (L.) Samp.
Common Bistort

COUNTY STATUS: Native	
CONSERVATION STATUS: None	
FIRST YEAR: 1787 LATEST YEAR: 2013 NO OF RECORDS: 411	
RECENT SQUARES: monads 185; tetrads 142; hectads 27	
ALL SQUARES: monads 207; tetrads 159; hectads 35	

Common Bistort is an occasional native perennial of damp grasslands and

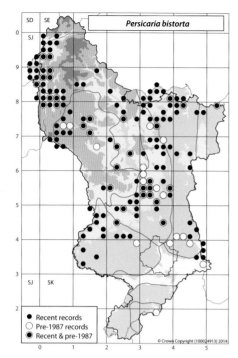

roadsides. It was also commonly grown in gardens as a pot-herb under the local names of Passion or Patience Dock (Grigson 1975). Many colonies are therefore probably garden escapes or throwouts. It occurs throughout Derbyshire, but appears to have been lost recently from areas south of Derby.

Persicaria amplexicaulis (D. Don) Ronse Decr.
Red Bistort

Red Bistort is a casual tufted perennial of roadsides and rough grasslands. It is widely grown in gardens and usually occurs as a throwout or relic of cultivation. There are three recent records: Bamford (SK2082), Hathersage (SK2380) and Alderwasley (SK3253). Previously it was found at Ashbourne (SK1844) in 1953 and Repton (SK3327) in 1958. It is a native of the Himalayas.

Persicaria vivipara (L.) Ronse Decr.
Alpine Bistort

Alpine Bistort is a tufted perennial that grows naturally in upland parts of Britain. In the early 1970s a reservoir was to be built at Cow Green in Teesdale that was to destroy some unique areas of vegetation. Specimens of this and other species were transplanted to Hopton Quarry (SK2656) to preserve them. In the event this plant survived better than most, and was still there in 2008.

Persicaria capitata (Buch.-Ham. ex D. Don) H. Gross
Pink-headed Persicaria

Pink-headed Persicaria is a casual sprawling perennial. There is a single record as a garden escape at Long Eaton (SK5033) in 2010. It is a native of the Himalayas.

Persicaria wallichii Greuter & Burdet
Himalayan Knotweed

Himalayan Knotweed is a casual rhizomatous perennial of roadsides and grassy places. There is a recent record from Duffield (SK3443) in 1996 and an earlier one from the north (SK28) in 1950. Sometimes grown in gardens, it must escape as a throwout since it rarely sets seed. A native of the Himalayas, it has significantly expanded its national range since 1962.

Persicaria amphibia (L.) Delarbre
Amphibious Bistort

COUNTY STATUS: Native	
CONSERVATION STATUS: None	
FIRST YEAR: 1789 LATEST YEAR: 2013 NO OF RECORDS: 525	
RECENT SQUARES: monads 226; tetrads 185; hectads 32	
ALL SQUARES: monads 240; tetrads 197; hectads 35	

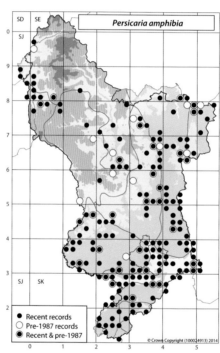

Amphibious Bistort is an occasional native perennial of both aquatic and terrestrial habitats. It grows and flowers in the margins of still and slowly-flowing waterbodies. It also grows more vigorously, but rarely flowers, on banks by water, on rough ground and even as a weed of cultivated land. It is occasional in lowland Derbyshire, but much rarer in upland parts, especially the White and Dark Peak Areas.

Persicaria maculosa Gray
Redshank

Redshank is a native annual of cultivated ground and waste places, especially on nutrient-rich soils or by ponds. It is very common in lowland parts, often becoming a pestilential weed of arable fields. Rarer in the upland areas of the White and Dark Peak because of the shortage of suitable habitats.

COUNTY STATUS: Native	
CONSERVATION STATUS: None	
FIRST YEAR: 1789 LATEST YEAR: 2013 NO OF RECORDS: 1,816	
RECENT SQUARES: monads 951; tetrads 544; hectads 42	
ALL SQUARES: monads 1,095; tetrads 581; hectads 42	

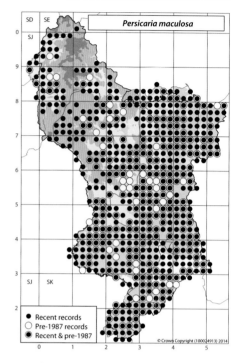

Persicaria × intercedens (Beck) Sojak
A hybrid knotweed

This native hybrid knotweed of Redshank (*P. maculosa*) and Water-pepper (*P. hydropiper*) is only known from an unlocalised listing in Stace (1975).

Persicaria lapathifolia (L.) Delarbre
Pale Persicaria

Pale Persicaria is a native annual of

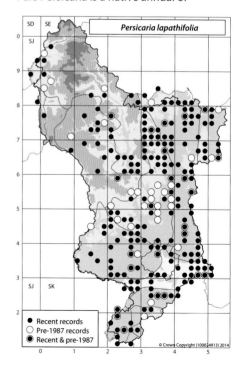

COUNTY STATUS: Native
CONSERVATION STATUS: None
FIRST YEAR: 1873 LATEST YEAR: 2013 NO OF RECORDS: 359
RECENT SQUARES: monads 205; tetrads 207; hectads 36
ALL SQUARES: monads 254; tetrads 238; hectads 37

cultivated, waste and disturbed ground. It is occasional in lowland parts, sometimes becoming abundant in arable fields, particularly on damp ground. It is less frequent in the White Peak and almost absent from the Dark Peak.

Persicaria hydropiper (L.) Delarbre
Water-pepper

COUNTY STATUS: Native
CONSERVATION STATUS: None
FIRST YEAR: 1789 LATEST YEAR: 2013 NO OF RECORDS: 444
RECENT SQUARES: monads 211; tetrads 177; hectads 33
ALL SQUARES: monads 261; tetrads 208; hectads 37

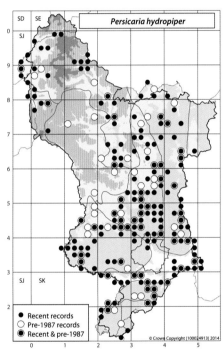

Water-pepper is a native annual of the edges of ponds and ditches, and of damp, often shaded, habitats such as woodland rides. It is frequent throughout Derbyshire, except for the Dark and South West Peak where it is rarer, and the White Peak, where it is virtually absent.

Persicaria minor (Huds.) Opiz
Small Water-pepper

COUNTY STATUS: Native
CONSERVATION STATUS: DRDB (Cat2), VU
FIRST YEAR: 1863 LATEST YEAR: 2012 NO OF RECORDS: 20
RECENT SQUARES: monads 3; tetrads 3; hectads 2
ALL SQUARES: monads 9; tetrads 9; hectads 6

Small Water-pepper is a very rare, native annual of damp ground by fens, rivers and canals. There are three recent records:

Ramsley Pools (SK2874) in 2005, Trentside ponds (SK4228) in 2009 and Leash Fen (SK2972) in 2012. Previously there were a handful of records dating back to 1863, mainly from the south of the area (River Mease SK2711, Repton SK3026, Anchor Church SK3327 and a canal near Chesterfield SK3871). Note that some of these were originally given as **Tasteless Water-pepper** (**P. mitis**) in Clapham (1969).

Fagopyrum esculentum Moench
Buckwheat

COUNTY STATUS: Established (Neophyte)
CONSERVATION STATUS: None
FIRST YEAR: 1789 LATEST YEAR: 2012 NO OF RECORDS: 27
RECENT SQUARES: monads 14; tetrads 14; hectads 11
ALL SQUARES: monads 20; tetrads 20; hectads 16

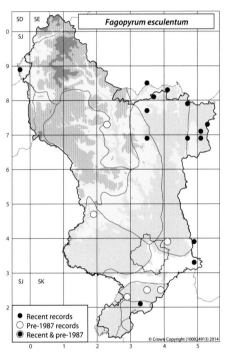

Buckwheat is a very rare, established annual of waste ground, cultivated land and tips (Hartshorne SK3321, Jordanthorpe SK3780, Stanton Gate SK4838 & Creswell SK5273). It was widely cultivated until the 19th century and has since been imported as food or bird-seed, or introduced with Pheasant food. It is a native of Asia.

Polygonum aviculare sensu lato
Knotgrass sensu lato

COUNTY STATUS: Native
CONSERVATION STATUS: None
FIRST YEAR: 1789 LATEST YEAR: 2013 NO OF RECORDS: 3,325
RECENT SQUARES: monads 1,639; tetrads 688; hectads 43
ALL SQUARES: monads 1,746; tetrads 695; hectads 43

Knotgrass sensu lato includes Equal-leaved Knotgrass (P. arenastrum) and Knotgrass (P. aviculare) which have been poorly

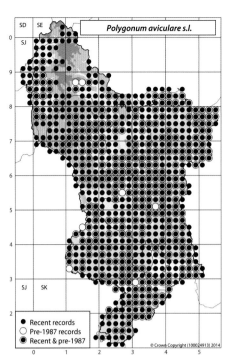

separated in the past by recorders, so are included together here for statistics and mapping.

Polygonum arenastrum Boreau
Equal-leaved Knotgrass

Equal-leaved Knotgrass is a procumbent, anciently established annual found occasionally throughout the area except for the Dark Peak where it is very rare. It grows in all kinds of open ground including arable land and trampled areas. Previously it was recorded with Knotgrass (P. aviculare L.) as an aggregate (P. aviculare s.l.) and is still probably under-recorded. Its true frequency should most likely be "very common".

Polygonum aviculare L.
Knotgrass

Knotgrass is a native annual of disturbed, rough and cultivated ground, where it can become a significant agricultural weed. It is recorded occasionally throughout Derbyshire except for the high moors of the Dark Peak. It was formerly recorded with Equal-leaved Knotgrass (P. arenastrum) as an aggregate (P. aviculare s.l.) and is still probably under-recorded. Its true frequency should probably be "very common".

Fallopia japonica (Houtt.) Ronse Decr.
Japanese Knotweed

COUNTY STATUS: Established (Neophyte)
CONSERVATION STATUS: WCA9
FIRST YEAR: 1949 LATEST YEAR: 2013 NO OF RECORDS: 954
RECENT SQUARES: monads 478; tetrads 333; hectads 38
ALL SQUARES: monads 516; tetrads 349; hectads 38

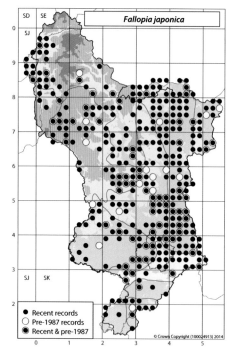

Fallopia japonica

- ● Recent records
- ○ Pre-1987 records
- ◉ Recent & pre-1987

Japanese Knotweed is unfortunately an established perennial of waysides, waste places and tips. It is frequent throughout Derbyshire, except the high moors of the Dark Peak. It was sometimes grown in gardens from where it escaped as a throwout. Once established it forms a troublesome weed, as its dense thickets prevent almost any other plant growing with it (Charter 1997 & 1999). It is so troublesome that it is an offence to plant or otherwise encourage its growth. It is indigenous to eastern Asia.

Fallopia sachalinensis (F. Schmidt) Ronse Decr.
Giant Knotweed

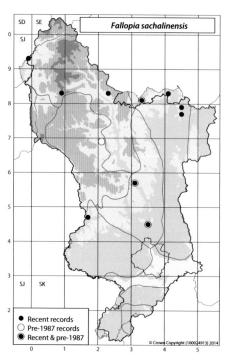

Fallopia sachalinensis

- ● Recent records
- ○ Pre-1987 records
- ◉ Recent & pre-1987

COUNTY STATUS: Established (Neophyte)
CONSERVATION STATUS: WCA9
FIRST YEAR: 1950 LATEST YEAR: 2013 NO OF RECORDS: 29
RECENT SQUARES: monads 10; tetrads 10; hectads 9
ALL SQUARES: monads 12; tetrads 11; hectads 13

Giant Knotweed is a very rare, established perennial of waste ground, roadsides and riverbanks. It occurs scattered through the county from Chisworth (SJ9992) and Beauchief (SK3281) in the north to Cromford (SK3057) and Milford (SK3444) in the south. It is sometimes grown in gardens from where it escapes to form robust rhizomatous thickets. These can be larger than those produced by Japanese Knotweed (*F. japonica*), so it is fortunate the plant does not seem as invasive as its smaller cousin. It is a native of eastern Asia.

Fallopia baldschuanica (Regel) Holub
Russian-vine

COUNTY STATUS: Established (Neophyte)
CONSERVATION STATUS: None
FIRST YEAR: 1971 LATEST YEAR: 2013 NO OF RECORDS: 65
RECENT SQUARES: monads 43; tetrads 39; hectads 22
ALL SQUARES: monads 45; tetrads 40; hectads 22

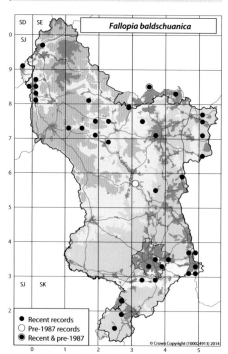

Fallopia baldschuanica

- ● Recent records
- ○ Pre-1987 records
- ◉ Recent & pre-1987

Russian-vine is a rare established woody climber of tips, hedges, walls and abandoned gardens. It grows scattered throughout the county, but it rarely establishes away from habitation (New Mills SK0085, Wingfield Manor SK3754 & Swarkestone Bridge SK3628). It is grown in gardens from where it may escape or get thrown out, although some apparent escapees may still be rooted inside the fence. Indigenous to

central Asia, much of its perceived spread since 1986 is probably due to better recording.

Fallopia convolvulus (L.) A. Love
Black-bindweed

COUNTY STATUS: Established (Archaeophyte)
CONSERVATION STATUS: None
FIRST YEAR: 1789 LATEST YEAR: 2013 NO OF RECORDS: 591
RECENT SQUARES: monads 311; tetrads 263; hectads 35
ALL SQUARES: monads 398; tetrads 315; hectads 36

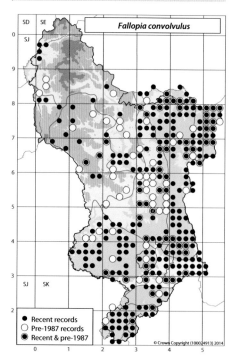

Fallopia convolvulus

- ● Recent records
- ○ Pre-1987 records
- ◉ Recent & pre-1987

Black-bindweed is a scrambling or climbing, anciently established annual of gardens, arable and disturbed land. It is frequent in the lowland southern and eastern parts of the county but rare in the more upland north and west where there is less cultivated land. There are three records for the variety *subalatum* (Ashbourne SK1847 in 1969, Hulland SK24 in 1903 & Beauchief, SK3381 in 1969).

Rheum × rhabarbarum L.
Rhubarb

COUNTY STATUS: Established (Neophyte)
CONSERVATION STATUS: None
FIRST YEAR: 1987 LATEST YEAR: 2012 NO OF RECORDS: 19
RECENT SQUARES: monads 15; tetrads 15; hectads 12
ALL SQUARES: monads 15; tetrads 15; hectads 12

Rhubarb is a very rare, established perennial of waste ground and waysides near habitations. Recent records are scattered across the county but, as it does not set seed, these must be of discarded garden plants or relics of cultivation. It is of garden origin, probably from Siberian parents.

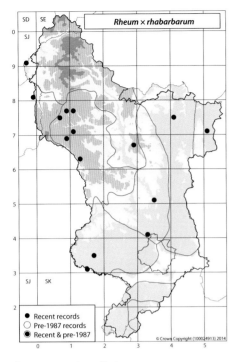

Rumex acetosella L.
Sheep's Sorrel

COUNTY STATUS: Native
CONSERVATION STATUS: None
FIRST YEAR: 1789 **LATEST YEAR:** 2013 **NO OF RECORDS:** 1,915
RECENT SQUARES: monads 849; tetrads 481; hectads 40
ALL SQUARES: monads 940; tetrads 514; hectads 41

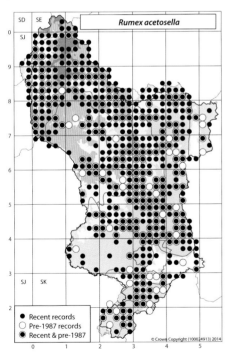

Sheep's Sorrel is a frequent native perennial of bare open ground in heaths, grassland and cultivated land mostly on dry acid soils. It is common throughout Derbyshire, except for the limestone areas and the Claylands where the soils are either too calcareous or heavy respectively for the plant to be common.

The only subspecies recorded is ssp. *acetosella*.

Rumex acetosa L.
Common Sorrel

COUNTY STATUS: Native
CONSERVATION STATUS: None
FIRST YEAR: 1789 **LATEST YEAR:** 2013 **NO OF RECORDS:** 5,330
RECENT SQUARES: monads 1,827; tetrads 714; hectads 45
ALL SQUARES: monads 1,923; tetrads 719; hectads 45

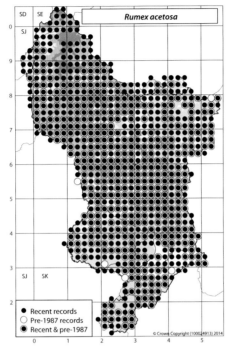

Common Sorrel is a very common, native perennial of grasslands, waysides and open woodlands throughout the county. It occurs most abundantly on damp neutral to calcareous soils. The only subspecies recorded locally is ssp. *acetosa*. It has the local name of Green Sauce (Grigson 1975), no doubt due to a past culinary use.

Rumex alpinus L.
Monk's-rhubarb

COUNTY STATUS: Established (Archaeophyte)
CONSERVATION STATUS: None
FIRST YEAR: 1829 **LATEST YEAR:** 2011 **NO OF RECORDS:** 74
RECENT SQUARES: monads 20; tetrads 19; hectads 9
ALL SQUARES: monads 40; tetrads 33; hectads 17

Monk's-rhubarb is a rare, anciently established perennial of grassy places by roads, streams and habitations. Modern records are virtually confined to the northern part of the Peak Fringe (Holmesfield SK3277, Ashover SK3563 & Highoredish SK3559) with only isolated ones elsewhere (Mellor SJ9988, Cronkston Grange SK1265 & Belper SK3446). It was once grown in gardens and many sightings are probably relics

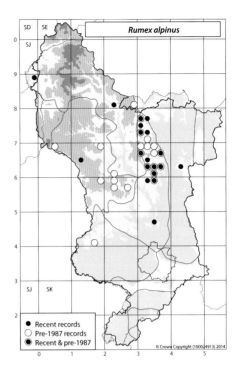

of former cultivation. It is a native of mountains in central and southern Europe.

Rumex longifolius DC.
Northern Dock

COUNTY STATUS: Native
CONSERVATION STATUS: B
FIRST YEAR: 1909 **LATEST YEAR:** 1970 **NO OF RECORDS:** 9
RECENT SQUARES: monads 0; tetrads 0; hectads 0
ALL SQUARES: monads 5; tetrads 5; hectads 5

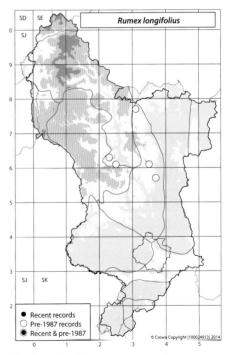

Northern Dock is a very rare, native perennial of damp grassy places in central parts (Birchover SK2362, Winster SK2460, Cordwell Valley SK3176,

Moorwood Moor SK3656 & Milltown SK3561 all for the 1910s). All records were made by E. Drabble, apart from one vague English Nature record for Coombs Dale (SK27) in the 1970s. The plant is a northern species, with Derbyshire on its southern British limit.

Rumex hydrolapathum Huds.
Water Dock

COUNTY STATUS:	Native
CONSERVATION STATUS:	None
FIRST YEAR: 1829	LATEST YEAR: 2013 NO OF RECORDS: 335
RECENT SQUARES:	monads 93; tetrads 55; hectads 14
ALL SQUARES:	monads 107; tetrads 67; hectads 16

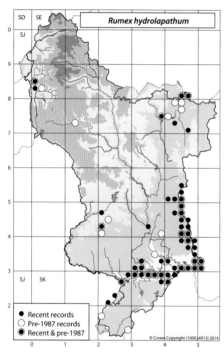

Water Dock is a tufted native perennial of the margins of still or slow-moving waterbodies, and open areas in marshes. Sometimes grown for waterside decoration, this plant is rare in the county but is locally frequent around the Derby area, especially along the Trent and Erewash valleys (Clay Mills SK2626, Barrow on Trent SK3429, Aldercar Flash SK4448 & Nutbrook Canal SK4639).

Rumex crispus L.
Curled Dock

COUNTY STATUS:	Native
CONSERVATION STATUS:	None
FIRST YEAR: 1829	LATEST YEAR: 2013 NO OF RECORDS: 2,531
RECENT SQUARES:	monads 1,257; tetrads 635; hectads 45
ALL SQUARES:	monads 1,337; tetrads 650; hectads 45

Curled Dock is a common native perennial of disturbed ground, roadsides, grasslands and marshy areas. It occurs everywhere except for the high moorlands of the north-west. Our plant is ssp. crispus. It is

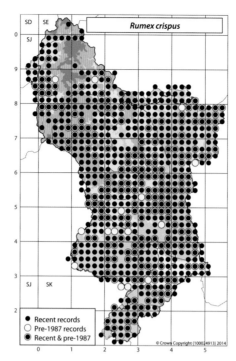

listed as an "injurious weed" under the Weeds Act 1959.

Rumex × pratensis Mert. & W.D.J. Koch
A hybrid dock

COUNTY STATUS:	Native
CONSERVATION STATUS:	None
FIRST YEAR: 1829	LATEST YEAR: 2013 NO OF RECORDS: 23
RECENT SQUARES:	monads 20; tetrads 18; hectads 11
ALL SQUARES:	monads 20; tetrads 18; hectads 11

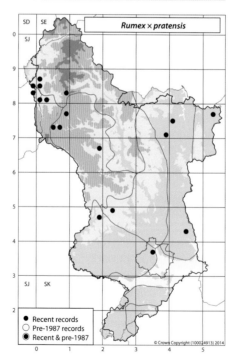

This hybrid dock is a rare native perennial of disturbed ground, grass fields, roadside verges and waste places. Found throughout the county, it probably occurs much more frequently than records show

(New Mills SK0085, Melbourne Farm SK1967 & Ashbourne Green SK1947). It is the hybrid of Curled Dock (R. crispus) and Broad-leaved Dock (R. obtusifolius).

Rumex conglomeratus Murray
Clustered Dock

COUNTY STATUS:	Native
CONSERVATION STATUS:	None
FIRST YEAR: 1873	LATEST YEAR: 2013 NO OF RECORDS: 521
RECENT SQUARES:	monads 269; tetrads 212; hectads 35
ALL SQUARES:	monads 317; tetrads 247; hectads 37

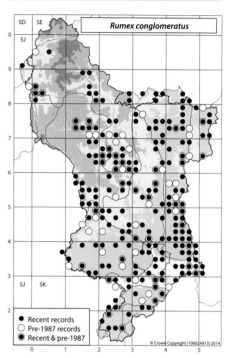

Clustered Dock is an occasional native perennial of damp grassy places, light woods and disturbed ground. It grows throughout Derbyshire except for the higher ground of the Dark, White and South West Peak Areas. It is probably under-recorded due to confusion with other dock species.

Rumex sanguineus L.
Wood Dock

COUNTY STATUS:	Native
CONSERVATION STATUS:	None
FIRST YEAR: 1789	LATEST YEAR: 2013 NO OF RECORDS: 1,248
RECENT SQUARES:	monads 697; tetrads 424; hectads 39
ALL SQUARES:	monads 740; tetrads 439; hectads 39

Wood Dock is a frequent native perennial of roadsides, hedgerows and wood margins. It is found throughout the county except for higher ground of the Dark and White Peak Areas. The common local variety is viridis. The **Bloody Dock (var. sanguineus)**, with red-veined leaves, has only been recorded twice: Newhall (SK22) and the Via Gellia (SK25) both in Linton (1903). Bloody Dock is increasingly being

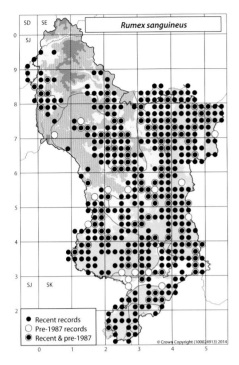

grown as a garden ornamental, and may therefore become more frequent in the wild as a garden escape.

Rumex pulcher L.
Fiddle Dock

Locally extinct, Fiddle Dock was a very rare, casual biennial or short-lived perennial of dry grassy places and disturbed ground. There are only four localised records, dated from 1903 to 1969 (Burton SK22, Repton SK32, Clifton SK1644 & Derby SK3538). It grows as a native in south-eastern Britain.

Rumex obtusifolius L.
Broad-leaved Dock

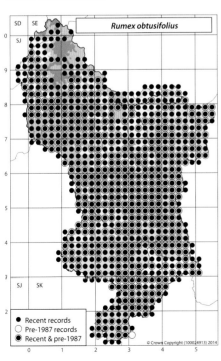

COUNTY STATUS: Native
CONSERVATION STATUS: None
FIRST YEAR: 1789 **LATEST YEAR:** 2013 **NO OF RECORDS:** 5,807
RECENT SQUARES: monads 2,241; tetrads 730; hectads 45
ALL SQUARES: monads 2,289; tetrads 731; hectads 45

Broad-leaved Dock is a very common, native perennial of grass fields, roadside verges, disturbed ground and cultivated land. It is listed as an "injurious weed" under the Weeds Act 1959, and grows throughout the county except for the highest moors of the Dark Peak. Our plants are assumed to be variety *obtusifolius*, though we have only one specific record for it (Hogshaw Wood, SK0674).

Rumex palustris Sm.
Marsh Dock

Marsh Dock is a casual biennial or perennial for which there is just one county record. Seen in Belper (SK3547) in 1976, the recorder noted only one plant, and no obvious source. It is a native of southern and eastern England.

Rumex maritimus L.
Golden Dock

COUNTY STATUS: Native
CONSERVATION STATUS: None
FIRST YEAR: 1670 **LATEST YEAR:** 2011 **NO OF RECORDS:** 34
RECENT SQUARES: monads 16; tetrads 11; hectads 6
ALL SQUARES: monads 22; tetrads 16; hectads 8

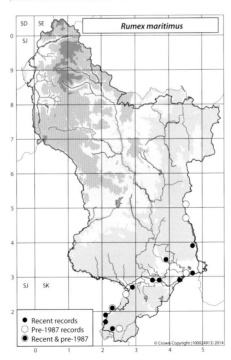

Golden Dock is a very rare, native annual to perennial of marshy areas and bare mud at the edges of still and slowly flowing waterbodies. It grows only in the south-eastern part of the county

(Drakelow Reserve SK2320, Derby Sewage Works SK3834, Aston-on-Trent SK4229 & Ilkeston SK4739). It is one of our oldest known plants, as Ray (1670) gives a record for the River Trent close to Swarkestone Bridge, where it was still known as late as 1995. This early record is also one of the first for the species in Britain (Clarke, 1900).

DROSERACEAE

Drosera rotundifolia L.
Round-leaved Sundew

COUNTY STATUS: Native
CONSERVATION STATUS: ERL, B
FIRST YEAR: 1787 **LATEST YEAR:** 2013 **NO OF RECORDS:** 222
RECENT SQUARES: monads 37; tetrads 31; hectads 9
ALL SQUARES: monads 58; tetrads 40; hectads 15

Round-leaved Sundew is an occasional native insectivorous perennial of open wet peat and Sphagnum moss in the moorlands of the Dark Peak (Kinder Scout SK0488, Jagger's Clough SK1587, Big Moor SK2676 & Beeley Moor SK2868). Previously it also grew in a few places outside the Dark Peak, as at Hulland Moss

Round-leaved Sundew (*Drosera rotundifolia*) amongst Sphagnum moss, Derwent Moors (SK2088), July 2009 (Peter Smith)

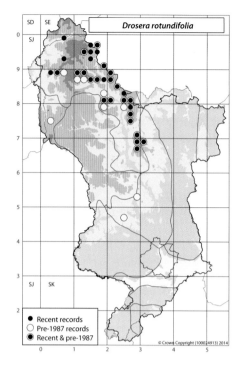

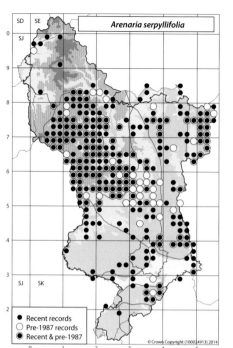

SK2546, Pitty Woods SK2853 and Wild Moor (SK0274).

Drosera anglica Huds.
Great Sundew

COUNTY STATUS: Native	
CONSERVATION STATUS: DRDB (Cat6), NT, A	
FIRST YEAR: 1851 **LATEST YEAR:** 1864 **NO OF RECORDS:** 5	
RECENT SQUARES: monads 0; tetrads 0; hectads 0	
ALL SQUARES: monads 0; tetrads 0; hectads 5	

Locally extinct, Great Sundew was a very rare, native insectivorous perennial of open wet peat and Sphagnum moss lawns. Its first localised records were for moors near Buxton (SK07), Abney Moors (SK18), East Moor (SK27) and SK17 in 1851. It was then recorded from Matlock (SK35) in 1864, but there have been no subsequent records. It was with plants of this species gathered from Derbyshire in 1780 that the insectivorous nature of sundews was first understood (Withering 1796).

CARYOPHYLLACEAE

Arenaria serpyllifolia L.
Thyme-leaved Sandwort

COUNTY STATUS: Native	
CONSERVATION STATUS: None	
FIRST YEAR: 1789 **LATEST YEAR:** 2013 **NO OF RECORDS:** 1,036	
RECENT SQUARES: monads 413; tetrads 255; hectads 35	
ALL SQUARES: monads 497; tetrads 291; hectads 35	

Thyme-leaved Sandwort is a low-growing native winter annual of bare open areas with shallow well-drained soils. It occurs in a range of habitats including rock outcrops, walls and arable fields. It is frequent in central parts, particularly the White Peak,

but is only rare to occasional elsewhere. The map probably contains some records of plants that should have been attributed to the very similar Slender Sandwort (A. leptoclados).

Arenaria leptoclados (Rchb.) Guss.
Slender Sandwort

COUNTY STATUS: Native	
CONSERVATION STATUS: None	
FIRST YEAR: 1903 **LATEST YEAR:** 2006 **NO OF RECORDS:** 31	
RECENT SQUARES: monads 11; tetrads 13; hectads 8	
ALL SQUARES: monads 22; tetrads 23; hectads 17	

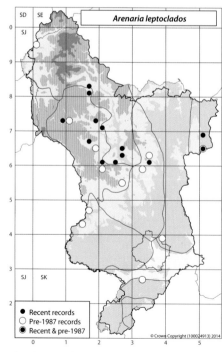

Slender Sandwort is a low-growing native winter annual of bare open areas

with shallow dry soils. It occurs in a range of habitats including rock outcrops and walls. It is rare in central Derbyshire, particularly the White Peak, and is very rare or absent elsewhere. Currently it appears more restricted to limestone areas than the similar Thyme-leaved Sandwort (A. serpyllifolia). Records suggest it has disappeared from the south of the county since 1986, though is under-recorded due to past confusion with Thyme-leaved Sandwort (A. serpyllifolia).

Arenaria balearica L.
Mossy Sandwort

Mossy Sandwort is a very rare, established perennial of walls, and a native of western Mediterranean islands. It was recorded in the 1970s from Calton Lees (SK2568) and Haddon Hall courtyard (SK2366) then re-confirmed at Haddon in 2004 and 2011. These records probably represent escapes from nearby gardens.

Moehringia trinervia (L.) Clairv.
Three-nerved Sandwort

COUNTY STATUS: Native	
CONSERVATION STATUS: None	
FIRST YEAR: 1789 **LATEST YEAR:** 2013 **NO OF RECORDS:** 1,018	
RECENT SQUARES: monads 469; tetrads 341; hectads 39	
ALL SQUARES: monads 537; tetrads 380; hectads 39	

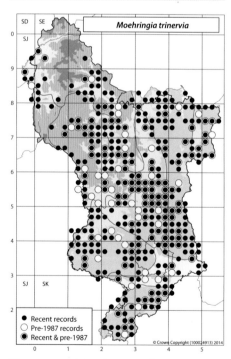

Three-nerved Sandwort is a frequent native annual of open shaded areas in woods and hedgerows, which also occurs on limestone screes and rock ledges. It grows throughout the county, except for areas above 300m in the north-west.

Minuartia verna (L.) Hiern
Spring Sandwort (Leadwort)

COUNTY STATUS: Native
CONSERVATION STATUS: DRDB (Cat2), NT, NS, A, B, C
FIRST YEAR: 1688 **LATEST YEAR:** 2013 **NO OF RECORDS:** 876
RECENT SQUARES: monads 134; tetrads 72; hectads 11
ALL SQUARES: monads 165; tetrads 85; hectads 13

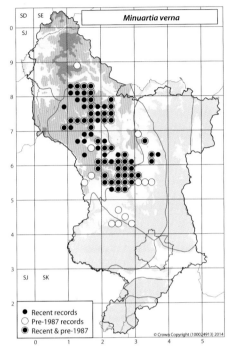

Spring Sandwort is a native loosely-tufted perennial characteristic of lead-mine spoil-heaps, and is better known locally

Spring Sandwort (*Minuartia verna*) amongst remains of Goodluck lead mine at (SK2656), May 2000 (Nick Moyes)

as **Leadwort**. It is often accompanied by the earlier-flowering Alpine Penny-cress (*Noccaea caerulescens*). Few other flowering plants are present in these highly contaminated sites. Due to its strong association with lead workings, Spring Sandwort is virtually confined to the White Peak. Indeed, this Landscape Character Area is one of its main national strongholds, with lead mine spoil-heaps listed in the EU Habitats Directive as of "European importance". Sadly, modern techniques of re-working lead rakes for other minerals leaves the soils depleted of metals, so these specialised metalliferous communities are now under threat. Though only frequent across the White Peak, it can be locally very abundant (Tideslow Rake SK1577 & Rose End Meadows SK2956). It also occurs, but much less often, on limestone ledges and in the Peak Fringe (Ravensnest SK3461). It formerly occurred in the Claylands (Ednaston area SK2442), and at an isolated site in the Dark Peak (Hayridge Farm, Alport SK1389). Elsewhere Spring Sandwort only occurs scattered in upland Britain and is considered Nationally Scarce.

Minuartia hybrida (Vill.) Schischk.
Fine-leaved Sandwort

COUNTY STATUS: Native
CONSERVATION STATUS: DRDB (Cat2), EN, NS, NERC, A
FIRST YEAR: 1877 **LATEST YEAR:** 1997 **NO OF RECORDS:** 36
RECENT SQUARES: monads 5; tetrads 2; hectads 3
ALL SQUARES: monads 13; tetrads 10; hectads 9

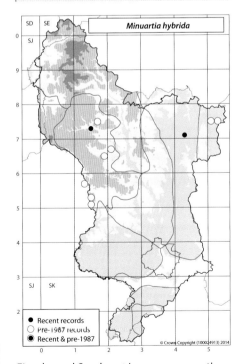

Fine-leaved Sandwort is a very rare, native annual of bare stony ground and walls, generally in limestone areas. It is only

recorded from two modern locations with definite dates: Priestcliffe Lees Reserve (SK1472/SK1473) in 1987 and Arkwright Town (SK4270/4271) in 1990. There are also three records with vaguer dates: SK36 between 1977 and 1997; Coombs Dale (SK27) between 1962 and 1987; and Hollinhill and Markland Grips (SK5175) between 1949 and 1995. Previously it grew over a wider area, including Creswell Crags SK5374 and further south in the White Peak (Lathkill Dale SK1865 & Dove Dale SK15).

Stellaria nemorum L.
Wood Stitchwort

COUNTY STATUS: Native
CONSERVATION STATUS: None
FIRST YEAR: 1829 **LATEST YEAR:** 2006 **NO OF RECORDS:** 64
RECENT SQUARES: monads 14; tetrads 13; hectads 10
ALL SQUARES: monads 22; tetrads 21; hectads 15

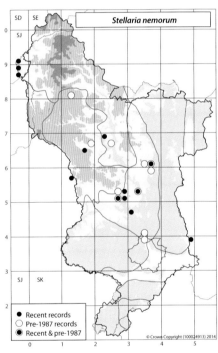

Wood Stitchwort is a very rare, native perennial of damp woods and shady streamsides. It grows scattered across the county (Roman Lakes SJ9687, Cales Dale SK16S, Bottoms Wood SK2750 and Clattercotes & Coalpit Woods SK3660). The local plant is ssp. *nemorum* which is found nationally in upland Britain, with Derbyshire towards the south-eastern limit of its distribution.

Stellaria media (L.) Vill.
Common Chickweed

COUNTY STATUS: Native
CONSERVATION STATUS: None
FIRST YEAR: 1789 **LATEST YEAR:** 2013 **NO OF RECORDS:** 4,355
RECENT SQUARES: monads 1,898; tetrads 716; hectads 45
ALL SQUARES: monads 1,999; tetrads 721; hectads 45

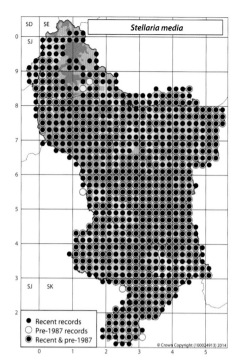

Stellaria media

● Recent records
○ Pre-1987 records
◉ Recent & pre-1987
© Crown Copyright (100024913) 2014

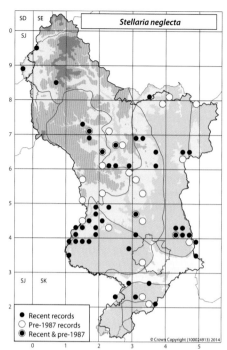

Stellaria neglecta

● Recent records
○ Pre-1987 records
◉ Recent & pre-1987
© Crown Copyright (100024913) 2014

Common Chickweed is a native annual of disturbed ground and cultivated areas particularly on nutrient-enhanced soils. It is very common throughout Derbyshire, avoiding only the high moorland areas of the north-west. The highest known location is around 450m at Snake Pass by Doctors Gate Culvert (SK0992).

Stellaria pallida (Dumort.) Crep.
Lesser Chickweed

COUNTY STATUS: Native	
CONSERVATION STATUS: DRDB (Cat5a)	
FIRST YEAR: 1903 **LATEST YEAR:** 2011 **NO OF RECORDS:** 10	
RECENT SQUARES: monads 1; tetrads 1; hectads 1	
ALL SQUARES: monads 7; tetrads 7; hectads 7	

Lesser Chickweed is a very rare, native annual of bare open habitats, particularly on light, well-drained soils. The only recent record is from Dronfield Hill Top (SK3577) in 2011, though it was recorded in the 1960s and 1970s from various sites across Derbyshire (The Nabs SK1453, Lime Pits SK1541, Drakelow Reserve SK2219, Wigley SK3072 & Pleasley Vale SK5265). The dearth of modern records may be partly due to the problem of distinguishing it from the ubiquitous Common Chickweed (*S. media*).

Stellaria neglecta Weihe
Greater Chickweed

COUNTY STATUS: Native	
CONSERVATION STATUS: None	
FIRST YEAR: 1885 **LATEST YEAR:** 2012 **NO OF RECORDS:** 110	
RECENT SQUARES: monads 60; tetrads 48; hectads 18	
ALL SQUARES: monads 82; tetrads 68; hectads 27	

Greater Chickweed is an occasional native annual or short-lived perennial of damp

shady places. It grows throughout the county in woods and hedges, and on the banks of streams (Southhead Farm SK0685, Snelston SK1443, Meadow Place Grange SK2065, Stapenhill SK2522 & Baldock Mill SK4240). Occurring mainly in the south of England, Derbyshire is towards the north-western edge of its British range.

Stellaria holostea L.
Greater Stitchwort
Greater Stitchwort is a common native perennial that scrambles through the undergrowth of woods and shady hedgerows. It grows throughout Derbyshire, except for

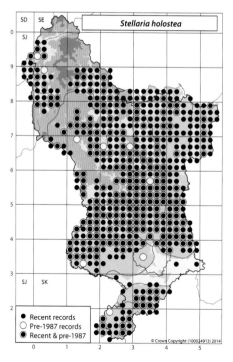

Stellaria holostea

● Recent records
○ Pre-1987 records
◉ Recent & pre-1987
© Crown Copyright (100024913) 2014

COUNTY STATUS: Native	
CONSERVATION STATUS: None	
FIRST YEAR: 1789 **LATEST YEAR:** 2013 **NO OF RECORDS:** 2,533	
RECENT SQUARES: monads 1,033; tetrads 502; hectads 39	
ALL SQUARES: monads 1,084; tetrads 511; hectads 39	

those parts of the White and Dark Peak over 300m, and in a wide band along the valley of the River Trent where the soils are probably too enriched with inorganic fertilisers for the plant to occur. It has the local name of Bird's Eye (Grigson 1975).

Stellaria palustris Ehrh. ex Hoffm.
Marsh Stitchwort

COUNTY STATUS: Native	
CONSERVATION STATUS: DRDB (Cat2), VU, NERC, A, B	
FIRST YEAR: 1829 **LATEST YEAR:** 1998 **NO OF RECORDS:** 45	
RECENT SQUARES: monads 14; tetrads 14; hectads 12	
ALL SQUARES: monads 21; tetrads 20; hectads 19	

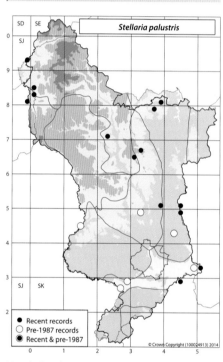

Stellaria palustris

● Recent records
○ Pre-1987 records
◉ Recent & pre-1987
© Crown Copyright (100024913) 2014

Marsh Stitchwort is a very rare, native perennial of marshes and fens. Recent records occur scattered throughout the county (River Goyt SK0183, Pilsley SK2370 & Attenborough SK5133). Previously it was only recorded in the south (Repton SK32, Willington SK2928 & Drakelow SK21, all for 1969). It is difficult to explain this apparent shift in distribution. However, as nationally it favours base-rich sites (Stace, 2010), it may be associated with the increasing eutrophication of the countryside due to fertilisers and pollution.

Stellaria graminea L.
Lesser Stitchwort
Lesser Stitchwort is a common native perennial of grasslands and verges on

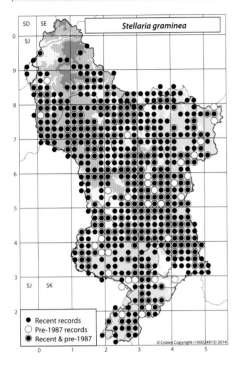

COUNTY STATUS: Native
CONSERVATION STATUS: None
FIRST YEAR: 1789 LATEST YEAR: 2013 NO OF RECORDS: 1,982
RECENT SQUARES: monads 877; tetrads 518; hectads 41
ALL SQUARES: monads 972; tetrads 550; hectads 42

neutral to acidic soils. It often grows in damp conditions and can withstand some nutrient enrichment (Preston *et al.* 2002). It occurs throughout Derbyshire except for the high moorlands of the north-west.

Stellaria alsine Grimm
Bog Stitchwort
Bog Stitchwort is a native perennial of

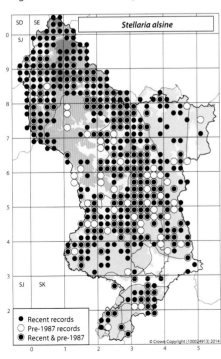

COUNTY STATUS: Native
CONSERVATION STATUS: None
FIRST YEAR: 1795 LATEST YEAR: 2013 NO OF RECORDS: 1,355
RECENT SQUARES: monads 595; tetrads 391; hectads 39
ALL SQUARES: monads 714; tetrads 441; hectads 39

marshes, mires, flushes and wet grasslands. It is frequent throughout the county, reaching up to 500m in flushes around Hern Clough (SK0994). It is rarer in the White Peak, the north-east, and the region south of Derby. Its scarcity in these areas is no doubt owing to the lack of wet habitats in the limestone areas, and to agricultural improvement of marginal areas elsewhere.

Cerastium arvense L.
Field Mouse-ear

COUNTY STATUS: Native
CONSERVATION STATUS: ERL, A, B
FIRST YEAR: 1829 LATEST YEAR: 2011 NO OF RECORDS: 71
RECENT SQUARES: monads 16; tetrads 13; hectads 11
ALL SQUARES: monads 31; tetrads 27; hectads 17

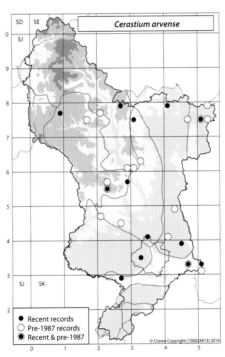

Field Mouse-ear is a very rare, native perennial of dry grasslands on a range of soil types from calcareous to slightly acid. There are recent records from across the county (Longshaw SK2679, Markland Grips SK5074 & Attenborough SK5032), though it has been lost from a number of former sites (Tansley Dale SK1774 & Repton SK32). This is possibly due to agricultural improvement. Nationally it is a species with an eastern distribution that has shown a marked decline in frequency, particularly at the edge of its range (Preston *et al.* 2002).

Cerastium tomentosum L.
Snow-in-summer

COUNTY STATUS: Established (Neophyte)
CONSERVATION STATUS: None
FIRST YEAR: 1941 LATEST YEAR: 2013 NO OF RECORDS: 189
RECENT SQUARES: monads 88; tetrads 102; hectads 30
ALL SQUARES: monads 115; tetrads 118; hectads 31

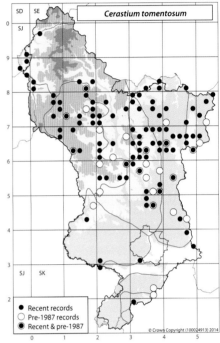

Snow-in-summer is an established mat-forming perennial, frequently found in central Derbyshire on roadsides, waste ground and tips (Hadfield SK0296, Topley Pike SK1172, Hatton SK2130, Matlock Bath SK2958 & Long Eaton SK4934). A native of Italy, it is a common garden plant and often escapes or is thrown out. It appears to be getting more frequent, both locally and nationally. However, this may be partly because botanists are increasingly encouraged to record alien species.

Cerastium fontanum Baumg.
Common Mouse-ear

COUNTY STATUS: Native
CONSERVATION STATUS: None
FIRST YEAR: 1789 LATEST YEAR: 2013 NO OF RECORDS: 5,288
RECENT SQUARES: monads 1,914; tetrads 731; hectads 45
ALL SQUARES: monads 1,996; tetrads 736; hectads 45

Common Mouse-ear is a native perennial, very commonly found throughout Derbyshire, except for the highest moors of the north-west. It grows in most types of grasslands, rough ground and cultivated soils, often where there is some nutrient enrichment (Preston *et al.* 2002). Two subspecies occur here: **ssp. *vulgare*** (Hartm.) Greuter & Burdet is considered to be the commonest, with **ssp. *holosteoides*** (Fr.)

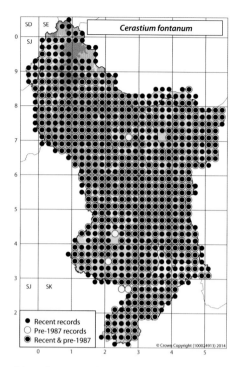

Salman, Ommering & de Voogd only recorded at South Wingfield Sewage Works (SK3853), Trent Meadows (SK5033) and the Creswell/Whitwell region (SK57).

Cerastium glomeratum Thuill.
Sticky Mouse-ear

COUNTY STATUS:	Native
CONSERVATION STATUS:	None
FIRST YEAR: 1829 LATEST YEAR: 2013 NO OF RECORDS: 1,003	
RECENT SQUARES: monads 648; tetrads 454; hectads 41	
ALL SQUARES: monads 679; tetrads 477; hectads 41	

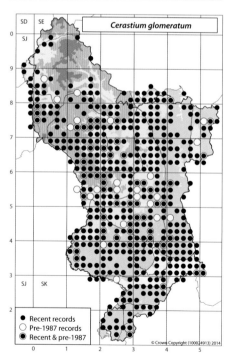

Sticky Mouse-ear is a frequent native annual of open disturbed soils in improved grassland, arable farmland and

waste ground, especially where there is some nutrient enrichment. It occurs throughout Derbyshire, except for upland areas in the Dark Peak. Nationally it has undergone a large increase in frequency since 1962, probably due to an increase in suitable habitats (Preston *et al.* 2002).

Cerastium diffusum Pers.
Sea Mouse-ear

COUNTY STATUS:	Established (Neophyte)
CONSERVATION STATUS:	None
FIRST YEAR: 1970 LATEST YEAR: 2000 NO OF RECORDS: 28	
RECENT SQUARES: monads 3; tetrads 4; hectads 4	
ALL SQUARES: monads 18; tetrads 17; hectads 11	

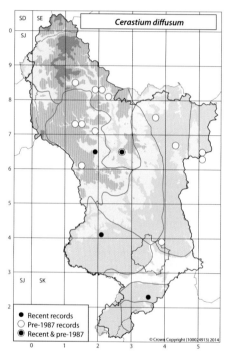

Sea Mouse-ear is a very rare, established annual of dry grassland and road verges which is native to British coastal areas. There are only four recent records: Lathkill Dale (SK1865), Shirley (SK24A), Northwood (SK2664) and Ticknall (SK3523). Nationally it has shown a recent increase along inland salt-treated roads (Preston *et al.* 2002). This may explain its appearance in Derbyshire only since 1970.

Cerastium semidecandrum L.
Little Mouse-ear

COUNTY STATUS:	Native
CONSERVATION STATUS:	None
FIRST YEAR: 1789 LATEST YEAR: 2012 NO OF RECORDS: 64	
RECENT SQUARES: monads 32; tetrads 29; hectads 13	
ALL SQUARES: monads 47; tetrads 42; hectads 18	

Little Mouse-ear is a low-growing native annual of dry open habitats on calcareous or sandy soils. It is occasional in the White Peak (Chrome Hill SK0667, Lathkill Dale

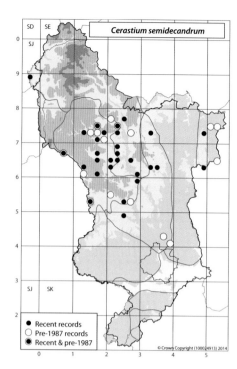

SK1765 & Cressbrook Dale SK1774) but is very rare elsewhere (Rowthorne Trail SK4963). There is some evidence for a local decrease in frequency at the margins of its distribution since 1986. This is probably due to agricultural intensification and land development in general.

Myosoton aquaticum (L.) Moench
Water Chickweed

COUNTY STATUS:	Native
CONSERVATION STATUS:	None
FIRST YEAR: 1789 LATEST YEAR: 2013 NO OF RECORDS: 203	
RECENT SQUARES: monads 86; tetrads 74; hectads 24	
ALL SQUARES: monads 112; tetrads 88; hectads 27	

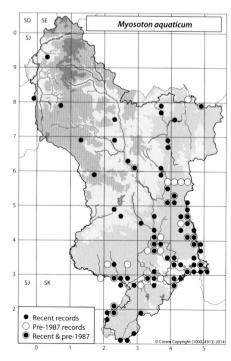

Water Chickweed is a straggling native perennial of damp shaded places, including marshes, ditches and the sides of watercourses. It is occasional in the south-eastern part of the county (Holme Nook SK3539, Weston-on-Trent SK4127, Derwent Mouth SK4530 & the River Erewash SK4741), but very rare elsewhere. Nationally it is a plant of the lowlands, with Derbyshire towards the north-western limit of its range.

Sagina nodosa (L.) Fenzl
Knotted Pearlwort

COUNTY STATUS: Native
CONSERVATION STATUS: ERL, B
FIRST YEAR: 1792 LATEST YEAR: 2012 NO OF RECORDS: 174
RECENT SQUARES: monads 55; tetrads 47; hectads 14
ALL SQUARES: monads 78; tetrads 60; hectads 19

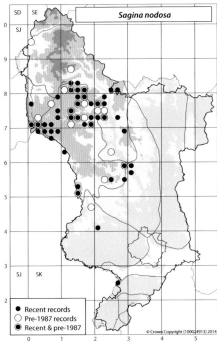

Knotted Pearlwort is a diffuse native perennial found in a range of habitats, including calcareous grassland. It is occasional in northern parts of the White Peak but very rare or absent elsewhere (Chee Dale SK1373, Wall Cliff SK1477 & Monsal Dale SK1871). A plant from Ashbourne Green was used by Keble Martin to illustrate the species in his *Concise British Flora*. He wrote: "While I was working at Ashbourne only a few flowers were actually drawn. These included the strawberry-headed clover and knotted pearlwort" (Keble Martin 1968).

Sagina subulata (Sw.) C. Presl
Heath Pearlwort
Locally extinct, Heath Pearlwort was an established perennial of dry open ground,

known from just one record in Clapham's 1969 Flora (Railway track, Pleasley SK5265). He suggested it might be starting to spread in the county, but clearly this has not happened. It is a native of upland and coastal areas of Britain.

Sagina procumbens L.
Procumbent Pearlwort

COUNTY STATUS: Native
CONSERVATION STATUS: None
FIRST YEAR: 1829 LATEST YEAR: 2013 NO OF RECORDS: 1,337
RECENT SQUARES: monads 780; tetrads 524; hectads 43
ALL SQUARES: monads 827; tetrads 537; hectads 43

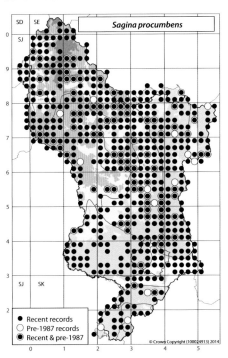

Procumbent Pearlwort is a common native perennial that forms tight mats on soil in a range of artificial and more natural habitats. These include paths, lawns, flower-pots, rocks and riverbanks.

Sagina apetala Ard.
Annual Pearlwort

COUNTY STATUS: Native
CONSERVATION STATUS: None
FIRST YEAR: 1903 LATEST YEAR: 2012 NO OF RECORDS: 138
RECENT SQUARES: monads 46; tetrads 54; hectads 22
ALL SQUARES: monads 84; tetrads 84; hectads 29

Annual Pearlwort is an occasional native annual of dry bare habitats including walls, waste places, paths and rocky outcrops. Except for the high moorland parts of the Dark and South West Peak, it has been recorded throughout the county (Birchover Quarry SK2462, Swadlincote SK2919 & New Whittington SK3975). It is under-recorded due to past confusion with Slender Pearlwort (*S. filicaulis*).

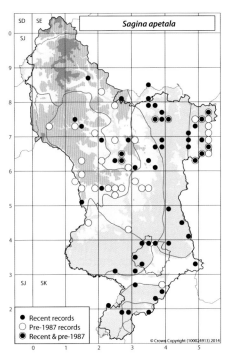

Sagina filicaulis Jord.
Slender Pearlwort

COUNTY STATUS: Native
CONSERVATION STATUS: None
FIRST YEAR: 1903 LATEST YEAR: 2013 NO OF RECORDS: 246
RECENT SQUARES: monads 183; tetrads 160; hectads 36
ALL SQUARES: monads 200; tetrads 173; hectads 37

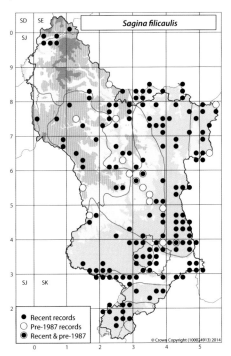

Slender Pearlwort is an occasional native annual of dry bare habitats including walls, paths and cultivated ground. It has been recorded right across Derbyshire, but seems more frequent in the developed south and east than the relatively unspoilt north and west. It is under-recorded due to past confusion with Annual Pearlwort (*S. apetala*).

Scleranthus annuus L.
Annual Knawel

COUNTY STATUS: Native
CONSERVATION STATUS: DRDB (Cat2), EN, NERC, A, B
FIRST YEAR: 1829 LATEST YEAR: 2004 NO OF RECORDS: 25
RECENT SQUARES: monads 2; tetrads 2; hectads 2
ALL SQUARES: monads 11; tetrads 11; hectads 11

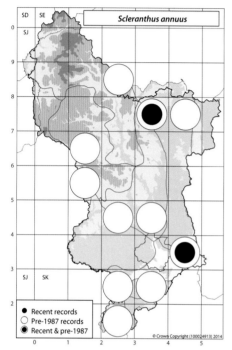

Annual Knawel is now a very rare, native annual or biennial of arable fields and well-drained disturbed ground. There are only two modern records (Locko Park SK4138 & New Whittington SK3976). It formerly occurred throughout Derbyshire (Barlborough Park SK4778, Hulland SK2546 & Overseal SK21). Clapham (1969) noted that it grew on non-calcareous, sandy or gravelly soils.

Corrigiola litoralis L.
Strapwort

Strapwort is a casual annual of open stony ground. It is only known from ashy railway ballast at Ilkeston (SK4743) in 1973. Nationally it is native to south-western England and is Critically Endangered.

Herniaria glabra L.
Smooth Rupturewort

Smooth Rupturewort is a very rare, casual annual or short-lived perennial of waste ground. It was discovered in 1998 by O. Gilbert on the floor of Tunstead Quarry (SK1074), where its origin is unknown. In 1999 it was found at Beauchief (SK3381) on the site of an old nursery, and in 2011 on spoil tips at Dove Holes (SK0877). There are no other records. It is indigenous to eastern England, where it is a Species of Conservation Concern with a status of Near Threatened.

Herniaria hirsuta L.
Hairy Rupturewort

Locally extinct, Hairy Rupturewort was a casual annual of disturbed ground. Our sole record comes from Duffield (SK34) in the eighteenth century (Pilkington 1789). This was also the first British record (Preston et al. 2002). It is a native of central and southern Europe.

Illecebrum verticillatum L.
Coral-necklace

COUNTY STATUS: Casual
CONSERVATION STATUS: None
FIRST YEAR: 1972 LATEST YEAR: 1978 NO OF RECORDS: 6
RECENT SQUARES: monads 0; tetrads 0; hectads 0
ALL SQUARES: monads 3; tetrads 3; hectads 2

Coral-necklace is a very rare, casual annual of bare stony ground with no recent records. It was first discovered in 1972 on railway ballast at Langley Mill (SK4547). The site has been destroyed, but material was translocated to Ironville (SK4450) where it was last recorded in 1978. It was also found at Mapperley (SK4343) in 1976 but that site was also destroyed. It is a native of south-western England.

Spergula arvensis L.
Corn Spurrey

COUNTY STATUS: Established (Archaeophyte)
CONSERVATION STATUS: ERL
FIRST YEAR: 1789 LATEST YEAR: 2013 NO OF RECORDS: 179
RECENT SQUARES: monads 64; tetrads 71; hectads 28
ALL SQUARES: monads 105; tetrads 101; hectads 34

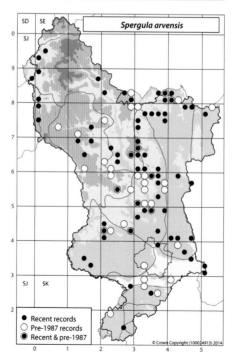

Corn Spurrey is an occasional, anciently established annual of arable farmland,

especially on sandy acidic soil. Scattered across Derbyshire, it avoids only the high moors of the Dark Peak. Two varieties have been recorded, of which var. arvensis is the commonest. Clapham's 1969 Flora notes that var. sativa had been recorded only from Hulland Gravel Pit (SK2645) and Smisby (SK3419). The species is declining nationally due to agricultural intensification (Preston et al. 2002).

Spergularia marina (L.) Besser
Lesser Sea-spurrey

COUNTY STATUS: Casual
CONSERVATION STATUS: None
FIRST YEAR: 1991 LATEST YEAR: 2012 NO OF RECORDS: 46
RECENT SQUARES: monads 30; tetrads 26; hectads 13
ALL SQUARES: monads 30; tetrads 26; hectads 13

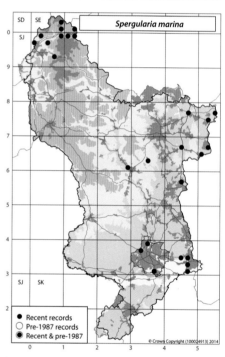

Lesser Sea-spurrey is a rare casual annual of salt-treated road verges. A native of British coastal areas, it has been spreading inland from the east coast since the 1970s. It is thinly scattered locally, occurring wherever either altitude or high traffic flow demands heavy winter gritting (Woodhead Road SK0899, Matlock SK2861, Long Eaton SK4733 & near Creswell SK5275). It first appeared in 1991 on the A6024 road (SE0902 v.c.58). The first record for the Derbyshire vice-county (v.c.57) was made in 1994 at the M1/A617 Junction (SK4566).

Spergularia rubra (L.) J. & C. Presl
Sand Spurrey

Sand Spurrey is a rare native annual or biennial of open, dry acid soils. It occurs in a range of man-made and natural habitats

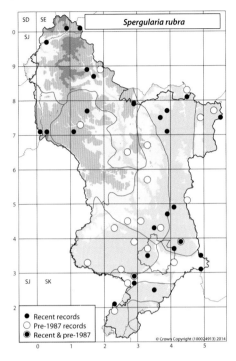

from Tintwistle (v.c.58 SK0397) and Wall Cliff (SK1477) in the north, to Dale Abbey (SK4238) and Willington (SK2927) in the south.

Agrostemma githago L.
Corncockle

Corncockle is a very rare, casual annual of flower beds and newly-sown grass verges, normally arriving as a contaminant

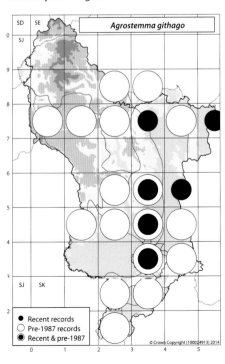

of the soil or the plants used. It has only been recorded from five sites recently (Belper Coppice SK3547, Moorwood Moor SK3556, Derby SK3638, Chesterfield SK3871 & Swanwick SK4053). It is also sown in "farmers' nightmare mixes" to provide colour and interest in restoration schemes. It was once a weed of cornfields but has since been eradicated by improved farming techniques. Farey (1815) mentions it as Corn Rose in barley at Foremark and elsewhere. Linton's 1903 Flora called it "local", whereas Clapham's 1969 Flora said it was "Formerly not infrequent, but now very rare". It has also declined nationally and is now considered extinct in the wild.

Silene nutans L.
Nottingham Catchfly

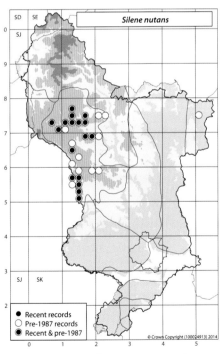

Nottingham Catchfly is an occasional native perennial of the White Peak. It grows in grassland, light woodland and on the ledges of limestone outcrops, often with a southerly aspect. Typical localities include: Deep Dale (SK0971), Chee Dale (SK1273) and Biggin Dale (SK1457). It has also been recorded for the Magnesian Limestone

at Hollinhill and Markland Grips (SK5175) sometime between 1949 and 1995. Nationally it is a southern species with the White Peak forming its northern limit. It is Nationally Scarce.

Silene vulgaris (Monche) Garcke
Bladder Campion

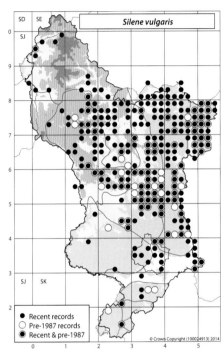

Bladder Campion is an occasional native perennial of grasslands, verges, waste land and cultivated ground. It occurs throughout Derbyshire except for the more upland areas of the Dark Peak, and is less frequent in the south. Only ssp. vulgaris has been recorded here.

Silene uniflora Roth
Sea Campion

Sea Campion is a very rare, casual perennial. There is a recent record from Stockley Pond (SK4666) in 2004, and an earlier one from Little Eaton (SK34) in 1942. Probably a garden escape here, it is a native of coasts and mountains in the British Isles.

Silene armeria L.
Sweet-William Catchfly

Sweet-William Catchfly is a very rare, casual annual of disturbed ground which is sometimes grown in gardens. There are only two records: Shirebrook Tip (SK5268) in 1996 and Heeley (SK3484) in 2003. It is indigenous to southern Europe.

Silene noctiflora L.
Night-flowering Catchfly

COUNTY STATUS: Casual
CONSERVATION STATUS: B
FIRST YEAR: 1863 LATEST YEAR: 2003 NO OF RECORDS: 27
RECENT SQUARES: monads 1; tetrads 2; hectads 2
ALL SQUARES: monads 8; tetrads 9; hectads 11

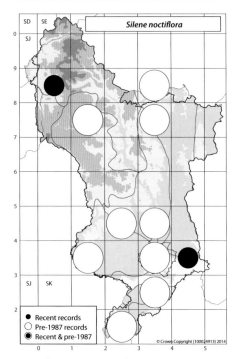

Night-flowering Catchfly is a very rare, casual annual of arable land. There are only two recent records: Sparrowpit (SK08V) in 1991 and Draycott (SK4434) in 2003. Previously it occurred throughout the area but only infrequently (Monsal Dale

SK17, Whirlow SK3182 & Allestree SK33 all for 1969). It appears to have been lost, both locally and nationally, by agricultural intensification (Preston *et al.* 2002). It is an ancient introduction to the British Isles.

Silene latifolia Poir.
White Campion

COUNTY STATUS: Established (Archaeophyte)
CONSERVATION STATUS: None
FIRST YEAR: 1789 LATEST YEAR: 2013 NO OF RECORDS: 692
RECENT SQUARES: monads 297; tetrads 223; hectads 36
ALL SQUARES: monads 364; tetrads 264; hectads 37

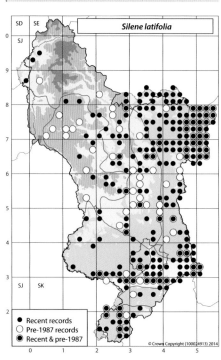

White Campion is an anciently established annual or short-lived perennial of disturbed and cultivated ground plus roadside verges. It is frequent throughout the south and east of the county, becoming rarer in western parts and virtually non-existent in the northern Dark Peak.

Silene × *hampeana* Meusel & K. Werner
Hybrid Campion

COUNTY STATUS: Native
CONSERVATION STATUS: None
FIRST YEAR: 1903 LATEST YEAR: 2012 NO OF RECORDS: 124
RECENT SQUARES: monads 77; tetrads 73; hectads 25
ALL SQUARES: monads 79; tetrads 75; hectads 28

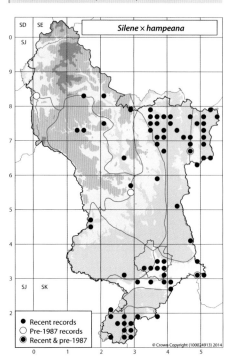

Hybrid Campion is an occasional native perennial of hedgerows and disturbed ground. It occurs throughout the county where the two parents meet, which are Red (*S. dioica*) and White Campion (*S. latifolia*). This hybrid is highly fertile and backcrosses with both its parents.

Silene dioica (L.) Clairv.
Red Campion

COUNTY STATUS: Native
CONSERVATION STATUS: None
FIRST YEAR: 1789 LATEST YEAR: 2013 NO OF RECORDS: 4,875
RECENT SQUARES: monads 1,625; tetrads 649; hectads 42
ALL SQUARES: monads 1,685; tetrads 656; hectads 42

Red Campion is a very common, native perennial of hedgerows and woods on all types of soil except for the most acid and/ or waterlogged. It also occurs on rocks screes and lead mine spoil in the White Peak. It occurs throughout the county except for the higher moors of the Dark and South West Peak.

Red Campion (*Silene dioica*) by Cromford Canal towpath (SK35), May 2008 (Peter Smith)

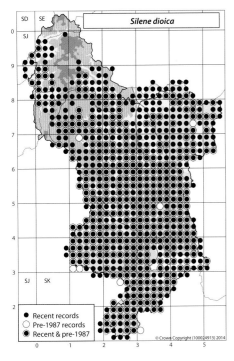

COUNTY STATUS: Established (Neophyte)
CONSERVATION STATUS: None
FIRST YEAR: 1949 **LATEST YEAR:** 2012 **NO OF RECORDS:** 21
RECENT SQUARES: monads 8; tetrads 8; hectads 7
ALL SQUARES: monads 11; tetrads 10; hectads 8

roadsides. It is commonly grown in gardens from where it can escape. It usually appears as a casual, as at New Horwich Road (SK0181), but can become established, as at Lock Lane Ash Tip (SK4831). It is a native of south-eastern Europe.

Silene flos-cuculi (L.) Clairv.
Ragged-Robin

COUNTY STATUS: Native
CONSERVATION STATUS: ERL
FIRST YEAR: 1789 **LATEST YEAR:** 2013 **NO OF RECORDS:** 717
RECENT SQUARES: monads 282; tetrads 222; hectads 37
ALL SQUARES: monads 340; tetrads 259; hectads 39

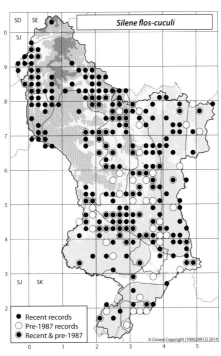

Ragged-Robin is an occasional native perennial from a range of damp habitats, including grasslands, fens, marshes and woodland margins. It grows throughout the county, although it is rare in the White Peak and upland Dark Peak. It has declined nationally due to agricultural improvement (Preston *et al.* 2002). However, there appears to have been little local decline, probably due to more intensive recording recently.

Silene chalcedonica (L.) E.H.L. Krause
Maltese-Cross

Maltese-Cross is a very rare, casual perennial of waysides. Although commonly grown in gardens, it is known from just one roadside locality at Slatepit Lane/Leash Fen

(SK3073). It was first found here in 1998 and then refound in 2008. It is a native of Russia.

Silene viscaria (L.) Jess.
Sticky Catchfly

Sticky Catchfly is a casual perennial, sometimes grown in gardens. The only record is from Lock Lane Ash Tip (SK4831) in 1987. It is a native of upland Britain where it is listed as Nationally Scarce.

Silene baccifera (L.) Roth
Berry Catchfly

Locally extinct, Berry Catchfly was a very rare, casual perennial. The only known record is from western Derbyshire (SK07), published in Clapham (1969). Nationally it is either a bird-seed alien or garden escape, occurring in verges and waste ground. It is a native of south-western Europe.

Saponaria officinalis L.
Soapwort

COUNTY STATUS: Established (Archaeophyte)
CONSERVATION STATUS: None
FIRST YEAR: 1789 **LATEST YEAR:** 2012 **NO OF RECORDS:** 82
RECENT SQUARES: monads 28; tetrads 25; hectads 19
ALL SQUARES: monads 42; tetrads 36; hectads 25

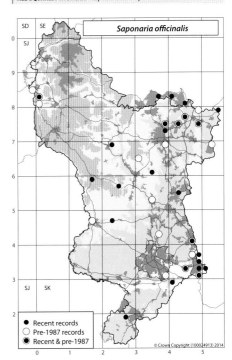

Soapwort is a rare, anciently established perennial of roadsides, waste ground and grassy areas. It grows scattered throughout the county though is commoner in the eastern half (Monsal Trail SK2269, Lock Lane Ash Tip SK4831 & Renishaw SK4477). It is a garden escape or throwout, and is native to continental Europe.

Silene gallica L.
Small-flowered Catchfly

Small-flowered Catchfly is a very rare, casual annual of flower beds. There are only two localised records: Sandybrook Hall (SK1748) in 1969 and Ashbourne (SK1746) in 1982. There are, however, unlocalised earlier records for SK14 in 1942 and 1950. It is a native plant of cultivated land and disturbed ground in the south of the country, where it is regarded as Nationally Scarce.

Silene coronaria (L.) Clairv.
Rose Campion

Rose Campion is a very rare, established perennial found on waste ground and

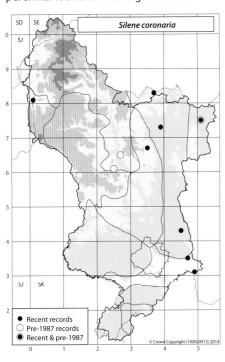

Saponaria ocymoides L.
Rock Soapwort
Rock Soapwort is a very rare, casual perennial of waste ground. Our only record is from Chesterfield (SK3870) in 2010. Often grown in rock-gardens, it is a native of southern Europe.

Vaccaria hispanica (Mill.) Rauschert
Cowherb

COUNTY STATUS: Casual	
CONSERVATION STATUS: None	
FIRST YEAR: 1907 LATEST YEAR: 2004 NO OF RECORDS: 5	
RECENT SQUARES: monads 1; tetrads 1; hectads 1	
ALL SQUARES: monads 4; tetrads 4; hectads 5	

Cowherb is a very rare, casual annual of waste ground and gardens. It is a garden escape or bird-seed alien. There is a single recent record (Elton SK2161 in 2004), and only four previous ones (Ashbourne SK1847, Coombs Dale Tip SK2374 & Ilkeston SK4541 all in the 1970s, plus Wirksworth SK25 in 1907). It is indigenous to southern and central Europe.

Dianthus caryophyllus L.
Clove Pink
Locally extinct, Clove Pink was a very rare, casual perennial. The only record is from near Edensor (SK27), and is given in Pilkington (1789). Nationally it is a garden escape onto walls, rocks and tips, and is native to southern Europe.

Dianthus plumarius L.
Pink
Pink is a very rare, established perennial of roadsides that is sometimes grown in gardens. The only modern record comes from Millers Dale (SK1573) in 1998. There

are also four older records, three from the above site in the 1970s, and one from southern Derbyshire (SK23) in 1950. It is a native of south-eastern Europe.

Dianthus deltoides L.
Maiden Pink

COUNTY STATUS: Native		
CONSERVATION STATUS: DRDB (Cat2), NS, NT, A, B, C		
FIRST YEAR: 1787 LATEST YEAR: 2012 NO OF RECORDS: 191		
RECENT SQUARES: monads 17; tetrads 13; hectads 8		
ALL SQUARES: monads 33; tetrads 25; hectads 12		

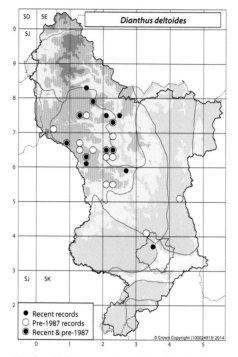

Dianthus deltoides

● Recent records
○ Pre-1987 records
◉ Recent & pre-1987

© Crown Copyright (100024913) 2014

Maiden Pink is a rare, loosely-tufted native perennial of the White Peak. This attractive and delicate plant grows in grassy areas that are sometimes associated with

quarrying and lead-mining (Bradford Dale SK2164, Lathkill Dale SK1765 & Parsley Hay SK1463). Probably the largest colony in the Peak District is now on Bonsall Moor (SK2559) where experimental transplanting took place in 1993. There, in the absence of grazing, it has flourished and spread. One unusual record from Chester Green, Derby (SK3537) refers to a garden escape, at a site now destroyed. Recent research has shown that certain colonies on the Tissington Trail at SK1461/1463 were composed of a garden variety. These were removed in 2012. Outside the county it grows scattered throughout the British Isles. It is Nationally Scarce, and our colonies contribute significantly to the UK population.

Dianthus barbatus L.
Sweet-William

COUNTY STATUS: Casual	
CONSERVATION STATUS: None	
FIRST YEAR: 1971 LATEST YEAR: 2004 NO OF RECORDS: 9	
RECENT SQUARES: monads 5; tetrads 5; hectads 5	
ALL SQUARES: monads 7; tetrads 7; hectads 6	

Sweet-William is a very rare, casual perennial of roadsides, waste ground and tips where it grows as a garden escape or throwout. It is recorded mainly from the north-eastern part of the county (Hucklow Edge SK1877, Milltown SK3561, Barlow SK3575 Doe Lea SK4566 & Barlborough SK4776). It is native to the mountains of southern Europe.

Dianthus armeria L.
Deptford Pink
Deptford Pink is a very rare, casual annual of dry grasslands, roadsides and disturbed ground, but is a native of southern Britain. It has only been recorded from four sites: Ashbourne (SK1746) in 1976 and 1969, SK14 in 1950, Renishaw (SK47) in 1903 and Edensor (SK27) in 1829. It has sometimes been considered native here, but its local habitats indicate otherwise.

AMARANTHACEAE

Chenopodium capitatum (L.) Ambrosi
Strawberry-blight
Strawberry-blight is a very rare, casual annual of abandoned cultivations. The fruits are said to be edible, but promise more than they deliver. Our only record is from Milford Allotments (SK3545) in 2001. It is probably a native of North America.

Chenopodium bonus-henricus L.
Good-King-Henry
Good-King-Henry is an anciently established perennial found on roadsides, abandoned gardens and around old farm

Maiden Pink (*Dianthus deltoides*) colony of garden variety plants, now removed from side of Tissington Trail at Parsley Hay cutting (SK1463), July 2007 (Peter Smith)

COUNTY STATUS: Established (Archaeophyte)
CONSERVATION STATUS: ERL
FIRST YEAR: 1789 LATEST YEAR: 2012 NO OF RECORDS: 176
RECENT SQUARES: monads 74; tetrads 75; hectads 24
ALL SQUARES: monads 107; tetrads 102; hectads 32

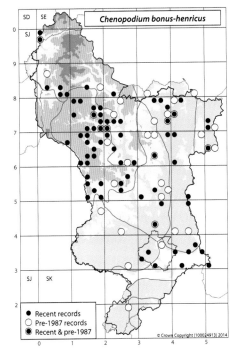

Chenopodium bonus-henricus

buildings. It is occasional throughout the county, becoming rarer in the upland north-west and the intensively farmed south-west. In the latter area it appears to be declining. Its leaves were eaten as a vegetable but most people have forgotten this use. It is a native of central and southern Europe.

Chenopodium glaucum L.
Oak-leaved Goosefoot
Oak-leaved Goosefoot is a very rare, casual annual of manure-enriched disturbed ground. It has only been recorded twice: Hulland (SK2545) in 1949 and Sudbury (SK1532) in 1997. It is native to the mountains of southern and central Europe (Preston et al. 2002).

Chenopodium rubrum L.
Red Goosefoot

COUNTY STATUS: Native
CONSERVATION STATUS: None
FIRST YEAR: 1829 LATEST YEAR: 2013 NO OF RECORDS: 174
RECENT SQUARES: monads 109; tetrads 102; hectads 31
ALL SQUARES: monads 132; tetrads 122; hectads 32

Red Goosefoot is a native annual of tips, manure heaps, disturbed ground and the drawdown zones of waterbodies. Growing occasionally throughout southern and eastern Derbyshire, it appears to have increased both locally and nationally since the 1960s. This is

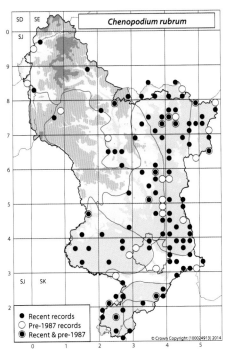

Chenopodium rubrum

probably due to a general increase of soil nutrient levels.

Chenopodium polyspermum L.
Many-seeded Goosefoot

COUNTY STATUS: Established (Archaeophyte)
CONSERVATION STATUS: B
FIRST YEAR: 1789 LATEST YEAR: 2011 NO OF RECORDS: 51
RECENT SQUARES: monads 23; tetrads 22; hectads 12
ALL SQUARES: monads 34; tetrads 33; hectads 17

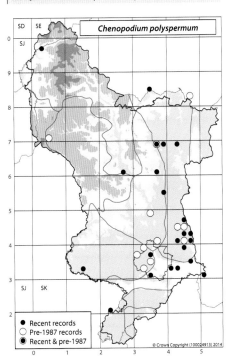

Chenopodium polyspermum

Many-seeded Goosefoot is a rare long-established annual of tips, cultivated ground and disturbed land. It grows mostly in the southern and eastern parts of the county (Sudbury SK1532, Hasland SK36Z

& Shipley SK4443). One isolated northern record comes from Hadfield Tip (SK0296). Derbyshire is towards the north-western limit of its national range.

Chenopodium vulvaria L.
Stinking Goosefoot
Locally extinct, Stinking Goosefoot was a very rare, casual annual of waste ground. It was last recorded in 1969 at Derby (SK3636). Two earlier records are known: Calke Park (SK32) in 1844 and Dethick (SK35) in 1789. Clapham's 1969 Flora suggests that it was possibly native prior to 1930. Nationally its distribution is also reduced, so it is listed in various conservation schedules

Chenopodium hybridum L.
Maple-leaved Goosefoot
Maple-leaved Goosefoot is a very rare, casual annual of wasteland and cultivated ground, and is a native of continental Europe. Only three early records are known: Matlock Moor (SK3266) in 1975; Alderwasley (SK3053) in 1969 and Mickleover (SK33) in 1903.

Chenopodium urbicum L.
Upright Goosefoot
Upright Goosefoot is a very rare, casual annual of disturbed ground. The only recent record comes from a weedy vegetable patch at Rodsley (SK2040), found by G. Hirons in 2003. There are two older records, from Clapham's 1969 Flora: Coton in the Elms (SK2514) and Trent (SK4831). He suggests the species was possibly native prior to 1930.

Chenopodium murale L.
Nettle-leaved Goosefoot
Nettle-leaved Goosefoot is a very rare, casual annual of cultivated ground and tips. It is only recorded for two sites: Sturston Tip (SK1946) in 1935 and as a garden weed at Stonegravels (SK3871) in 1990. It is native to coastal areas in eastern England.

Chenopodium ficifolium Sm.
Fig-leaved Goosefoot

COUNTY STATUS: Casual
CONSERVATION STATUS: None
FIRST YEAR: 1992 LATEST YEAR: 2012 NO OF RECORDS: 15
RECENT SQUARES: monads 11; tetrads 11; hectads 8
ALL SQUARES: monads 11; tetrads 11; hectads 8

Fig-leaved Goosefoot is a very rare, casual annual of disturbed and cultivated ground. It was first discovered as a garden weed at Stonegravels (SK3871) by M. Hewitt in 1992. So far, all other records have been from the eastern side of the county (Melbourne

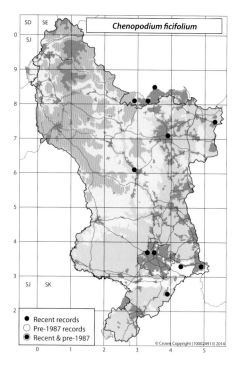

SK3925, near Derby SK4230, Draycott SK4333 & Creswell SK5274). It is anciently established in south-eastern England but is now spreading, with Derbyshire on the north-western edge of its current range.

Chenopodium album L.
Fat-hen

COUNTY STATUS: Native	
CONSERVATION STATUS: None	
FIRST YEAR: 1789 **LATEST YEAR:** 2013 **NO OF RECORDS:** 1,252	
RECENT SQUARES: monads 763; tetrads 487; hectads 42	
ALL SQUARES: monads 827; tetrads 511; hectads 42	

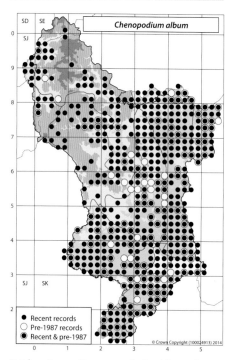

Fat-hen is a native annual of cultivated and disturbed habitats on nutrient-rich

soils. It often appears in quantity on land disturbed by house-building or on verges of new roads. It is very common throughout lowland parts, but is only occasional in the more upland areas of the Dark and White Peak. It is absent from land over 500m.

Chenopodium suecicum Murr
Swedish Goosefoot

Swedish Goosefoot is a very rare, casual annual of waste ground. Only two sites are known: Beighton (SK48) in 1897 and a Long Eaton car park (SK4933), found by D. Bryce in 2002. It is very similar to Fat-hen (C. album), so is probably under-recorded. It is native to northern Europe, and is likely to arrive as a seed contaminant.

Bassia scoparia (L.) Voss
Summer-cypress

Summer-cypress is a very rare, casual annual of rubbish tips and waysides, and a native of temperate Asia. The first record is from Hadfield (SK0296), found by J. Guest in 1989 and thought to be of bird-seed origin. More recently it was recorded from Junction 25 of the M1 (SK4735) in 2004. Nationally it appears to have extended its range in recent years (Preston et al. 2002).

Spinacia oleracea L.
Spinach

Spinach is a very rare, casual annual of disturbed ground. It has only been recorded once in the wild (Harehill SK1734 in 2000), although it is widely grown as a garden plant and arable crop. It is probably a native of south-western Asia.

Atriplex hortensis L.
Garden Orache

Garden Orache is a very rare, casual annual of waste ground. The only record is for two plants found in 1997 by D. Dupree at a fishing club car park near Press Farm (SK3665). It is now grown for ornament in gardens but also turns up as a bird-seed alien. It is probably a native of central Asia.

Atriplex prostrata Boucher ex DC.
Spear-leaved Orache

COUNTY STATUS: Native	
CONSERVATION STATUS: None	
FIRST YEAR: 1789 **LATEST YEAR:** 2013 **NO OF RECORDS:** 724	
RECENT SQUARES: monads 489; tetrads 364; hectads 36	
ALL SQUARES: monads 510; tetrads 375; hectads 37	

Spear-leaved Orache is a native annual of cultivated ground and waste places. It grows particularly on the bare margins of salt-treated roads. Common throughout lowland Derbyshire, it is rare in the more upland parts of the Dark and White Peak.

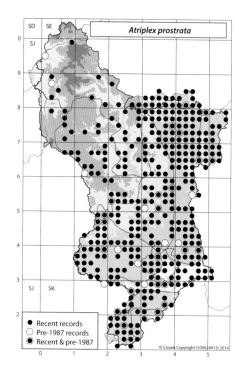

It is the commonest of the group of salt-tolerant plants that have been spreading inland along major roads, both locally and nationally, over the last twenty or so years.

Atriplex littoralis L.
Grass-leaved Orache

COUNTY STATUS: Casual	
CONSERVATION STATUS: None	
FIRST YEAR: 1994 **LATEST YEAR:** 2011 **NO OF RECORDS:** 11	
RECENT SQUARES: monads 7; tetrads 7; hectads 7	
ALL SQUARES: monads 7; tetrads 7; hectads 7	

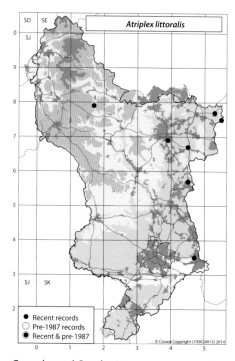

Grass-leaved Orache is a very rare, casual annual of disturbed ground and the margins of salt-treated roads. The few records we have are all very recent, mostly from eastern Derbyshire (Birdholme SK3869, central reservation A38 SK4556, M1 Junction-29 SK4566 & Whitwell SK5377). Indigenous to coastal areas of Britain, it has spread rapidly along inland roads since the 1980s, particularly those in eastern England (Braithwaite *et al.* 2006).

Atriplex patula L.
Common Orache

COUNTY STATUS:	Native
CONSERVATION STATUS:	None
FIRST YEAR: 1789	LATEST YEAR: 2013 NO OF RECORDS: 1,097
RECENT SQUARES:	monads 682; tetrads 473; hectads 42
ALL SQUARES:	monads 784; tetrads 508; hectads 43

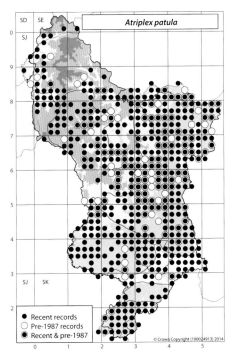

Common Orache is a native annual of cultivated disturbed and waste ground. It grows commonly throughout Derbyshire, except in the upland moors of the north, where it is rare or absent.

Beta vulgaris L.
Beet

COUNTY STATUS:	Casual
CONSERVATION STATUS:	None
FIRST YEAR: 1970	LATEST YEAR: 2008 NO OF RECORDS: 17
RECENT SQUARES:	monads 9; tetrads 14; hectads 12
ALL SQUARES:	monads 9; tetrads 14; hectads 12

Beet is a very rare, casual annual or biennial plant of rough ground and cultivated land. Records are thinly scattered across Derbyshire, except for the upland north and west where it is absent (Walton SK2016, Beeley SK2667 & Melbourne SK3923). Most records should probably refer to ssp. *vulgaris*, grown

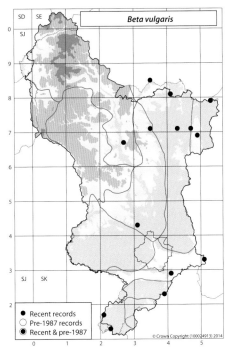

as **Sugar Beet** or **Fodder Beet**. It is of cultivated origin.

Salsola kali ssp. *tragus* (L.) Celak.
Spineless Saltwort

Spineless Saltwort is a very rare, casual annual of rubbish tips. The only record was made by G. Kay at Hadfield (SK0296) in 1989, where it probably originated from bird-seed. It is a native of continental Europe.

Amaranthus retroflexus L.
Common Amaranth

Common Amaranth is a very rare, established annual of nutrient-rich farmland and disturbed ground. It is either

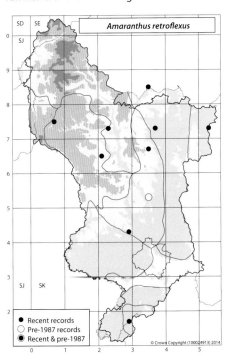

COUNTY STATUS:	Established (Neophyte)
CONSERVATION STATUS:	None
FIRST YEAR: 1903	LATEST YEAR: 2012 NO OF RECORDS: 16
RECENT SQUARES:	monads 9; tetrads 9; hectads 9
ALL SQUARES:	monads 10; tetrads 10; hectads 11

grown as Pheasant food, or appears as a contaminant in imported grain and seed. Records are widely scattered across the county: Fairfield (SK0674), near Raper Mine (SK2165), Linton (SK2816) and Creswell (SK5273). It appears to be increasing locally, but this may just reflect better recent recording of aliens. It is a native of North America.

Amaranthus hybridus L.
Green Amaranth

Green Amaranth is a very rare, casual annual of disturbed nutrient-rich soil. The only records are from Long Eaton (SK4833) in 2003 and 2008, and a Nether Heage roadside (SK3550 & 3650) in 1976. It is a native of central America.

Amaranthus cruentus L.
Purple Amaranth

Purple Amaranth is a casual annual of disturbed nutrient-rich soil. The sole record is from Melandra Tip (SK0095) in 1976. It was probably imported as a contaminant of grain or oil seeds, and originated in central America, possibly of cultivated origin.

Amaranthus deflexus L.
Perennial Pigweed

Perennial Pigweed is a casual annual of waste ground. The only record comes from a car park at Spondon (SK3935) where it was known from 1995 to 1997. A native of South America, it was discovered by A. Loy (Voucher at Derby Museum).

Amaranthus albus L.
White Pigweed

White Pigweed is a very rare, casual annual of disturbed, nutrient-rich ground. Our only records are from Heeley (SK3484) and Weston Underwood (SK2842) both in 2003 and from Derby (SK3833) in 1983. It is a native of North America.

MONTIACEAE

Claytonia perfoliata Donn ex Willd.
Spring Beauty

COUNTY STATUS:	Established (Neophyte)
CONSERVATION STATUS:	None
FIRST YEAR: 1930	LATEST YEAR: 2012 NO OF RECORDS: 71
RECENT SQUARES:	monads 30; tetrads 30; hectads 18
ALL SQUARES:	monads 48; tetrads 46; hectads 21

Spring Beauty is a rare established annual of cultivated and waste ground,

Spring Beauty (*Claytonia perfoliata*), base of wall at East Mill, Belper (SK3448), April 2004 (Philip Precey)

acquaintance in 1837 (Clapham 1969). It has spread greatly in the UK since the 1930s, and is a native of western North America.

Montia fontana L.
Blinks

COUNTY STATUS: Native
CONSERVATION STATUS: None
FIRST YEAR: 1789 LATEST YEAR: 2013 NO OF RECORDS: 340
RECENT SQUARES: monads 172; tetrads 125; hectads 23
ALL SQUARES: monads 207; tetrads 154; hectads 30

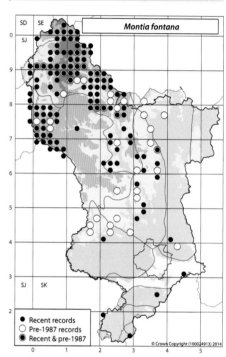

Blinks is a low-growing native perennial, found in a range of damp, unshaded habitats including streams, flushes and pastures. It is frequent through the Dark and South West Peak Character Areas, but is rare elsewhere. It is a variable plant with four subspecies found locally, though few separate them. **Ssp. *variabilis*** Walters is probably the most widespread, covering 22 monads. **Ssp. *chondrosperma*** (Fenzl) Walters has only been recorded four times: Brackenfield SK3758 in 1998, with Edlaston SK1742, Edensor SK2469 and Beauchief SK3381 all in the 1970s. **Ssp. *fontana*** has been recorded twice: Buxton SK07 in 1950 and Pikenaze Moor SE1000 (v.c.58) in 1999. **Ssp. *amporitana*** Sennen was recorded in SK18 in 1911.

CORNACEAE

Cornus sanguinea L.
Dogwood

COUNTY STATUS: Native
CONSERVATION STATUS: None
FIRST YEAR: 1789 LATEST YEAR: 2013 NO OF RECORDS: 892
RECENT SQUARES: monads 388; tetrads 266; hectads 36
ALL SQUARES: monads 423; tetrads 289; hectads 36

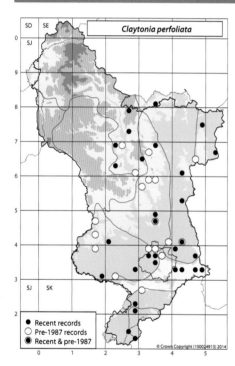

COUNTY STATUS: Established (Neophyte)
CONSERVATION STATUS: None
FIRST YEAR: 1837 LATEST YEAR: 2013 NO OF RECORDS: 221
RECENT SQUARES: monads 97; tetrads 69; hectads 24
ALL SQUARES: monads 115; tetrads 82; hectads 27

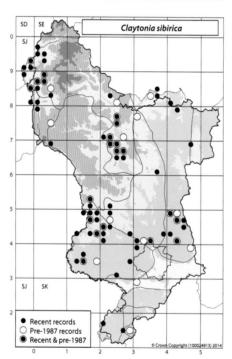

particularly on lighter soils. It was not known in Derbyshire before 1930 (Clapham 1969). Since then it has spread throughout lowland parts, probably due to the movement of plants and soil by gardeners (Rodsley SK2040, Grange Wood SK2714, West Hallam churchyard SK4341 & Derby city centre SK3436, 3536). There has been a similar national spread over the same time span. It is indigenous to western North America.

Claytonia sibirica L.
Pink Purslane

Pink Purslane is an occasional established annual or short-lived perennial, of damp shaded places in woods, hedges and

by streamsides. It occurs sporadically, being absent from some parts, yet locally frequent in others (Sett Valley Trail SK0287, Mapleton SK1648, Bailey Brook marsh SK4447 & Calton Lees Wood SK2568). In the Long Walk at Kedleston Park (SK3040) it forms drifts of pink flowers which smother the other plants. It was first discovered locally in Edensor Woods near Chatsworth (SK26/27) by Sir Joseph Paxton or an

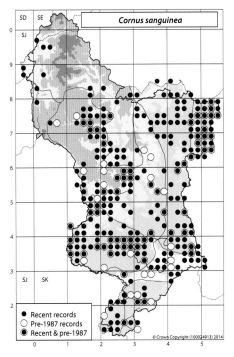

Cornus sanguinea

- Recent records
- ○ Pre-1987 records
- ◉ Recent & pre-1987

© Crown Copyright (100024913) 2014

Two subspecies occur. **Dogwood (ssp. sanguinea)** is an occasional native shrub of scrub, hedges and woods, often on base-rich soils. Also it is increasingly being used in amenity plantings and restoration schemes. It occurs throughout the area but is commonest on the Magnesian Limestone (Whitwell Wood SK5278), and parts of the White Peak and Claylands Areas. It is rare elsewhere (Dinting SK0294, Linton SK2614 & Lower Midway SK3021). **Southern Dogwood (ssp. australis** (C.A. Mey.) Jav.) is a very rare, casual shrub. It is increasingly being used in amenity plantings and restoration schemes, often in error for the native plant. It was not recorded until 2007 but was clearly used

earlier. There are scattered records from Derwent Dam (SK1789) in the north to Drakelow Reserve (SK2220) in the south.

Cornus sericea L.
Red-osier Dogwood

COUNTY STATUS: Casual
CONSERVATION STATUS: None
FIRST YEAR: 1997 LATEST YEAR: 2013 NO OF RECORDS: 18
RECENT SQUARES: monads 12; tetrads 12; hectads 10
ALL SQUARES: monads 12; tetrads 12; hectads 10

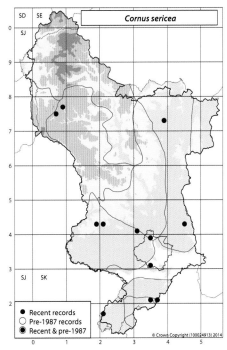

Cornus sericea

- Recent records
- ○ Pre-1987 records
- ◉ Recent & pre-1987

© Crown Copyright (100024913) 2014

Red-osier Dogwood is a very rare, casual shrub of waysides, riverbanks and parks. It is frequently grown in ornamental and amenity plantings from where it naturalises by means of suckers. It is found scattered

throughout the county as at Hogshaw Wood (SK0674), Shirley Park (SK2042) and the banks of the River Rother at Chesterfield (SK3872). It is a native of North America.

Cornus alba L.
White Dogwood

COUNTY STATUS: Casual
CONSERVATION STATUS: None
FIRST YEAR: 1996 LATEST YEAR: 2007 NO OF RECORDS: 5
RECENT SQUARES: monads 5; tetrads 5; hectads 5
ALL SQUARES: monads 5; tetrads 5; hectads 5

White Dogwood is a very rare, casual shrub of waysides and parkland. It is grown for ornament in parks and amenity plantings, from where it can naturalise by means of suckers. There are only five records, all recent: (Fairfield SK0674, Quilow Lane SK1943, Drakelow Power Station SK2220, Chesterfield SK3868 & Hallam Lock SK4839). It is native to eastern Asia.

Cornus mas L.
Cornelian-cherry

Cornelian-cherry is a very rare, casual shrub or small tree, indigenous to central Europe. The only modern record is from an old hedge at Unthank (SK3176) in 1991. An earlier one in Clapham (1969) from the Cordwell Valley (SK3170) is probably an error for SK3176.

HYDRANGEACEAE

Philadelphus coronarius L.
Mock-orange

Mock-orange is a very rare, established shrub of waste ground, usually a relic of cultivation.

Dogwood (*Cornus sanguinea*) in limestone scrub Markland Grips (SK5175), June 2004 (P. & G. Dishart)

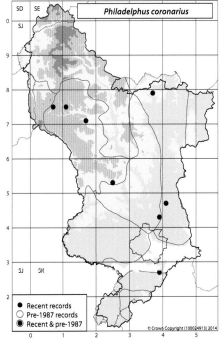

Philadelphus coronarius

- Recent records
- ○ Pre-1987 records
- ◉ Recent & pre-1987

© Crown Copyright (100024913) 2014

COUNTY STATUS: Established (Neophyte)
CONSERVATION STATUS: None
FIRST YEAR: 1988 **LATEST YEAR:** 2012 **NO OF RECORDS:** 8
RECENT SQUARES: monads 8; tetrads 8; hectads 7
ALL SQUARES: monads 8; tetrads 8; hectads 7

Records are scattered from Fairfield (SK0674) in the north to Melbourne (SK3926) in the south. It grows naturally in southern Europe. Some records are possibly errors for Hairy Mock-orange (*P.* × *virginalis*).

BALSAMINACEAE

Impatiens noli-tangere L.
Touch-me-not Balsam

Locally extinct, Touch-me-not Balsam was a very rare, casual annual. There are only three records: Matlock Bath (SK2958) in Clapham (1969), and two records in Linton (1903), Osmaston Park (SK14) in 1881 and a first record for 1874. Occasionally grown in gardens for ornament, it is native to western Britain.

Impatiens capensis Meerb.
Orange Balsam

COUNTY STATUS: Established (Neophyte)
CONSERVATION STATUS: None
FIRST YEAR: 1867 **LATEST YEAR:** 2013 **NO OF RECORDS:** 90
RECENT SQUARES: monads 42; tetrads 26; hectads 7
ALL SQUARES: monads 45; tetrads 27; hectads 8

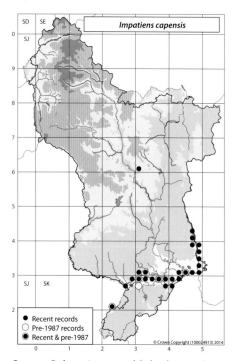

Orange Balsam is an established annual found amongst waterside vegetation. It is frequent in the Trent Valley along the Trent and Mersey Canal, and in the River Trent (Willington SK2928, Shardlow SK4430 & Sawley SK4731). It is also recorded for a

marsh at Drakelow Power Station (SK2220) and for Lumsdale (SK3161). This North American native is currently expanding its UK range (Preston *et al.* 2002) and may be expected to do so here, too.

Impatiens parviflora DC.
Small Balsam

COUNTY STATUS: Established (Neophyte)
CONSERVATION STATUS: None
FIRST YEAR: 1874 **LATEST YEAR:** 2012 **NO OF RECORDS:** 153
RECENT SQUARES: monads 52; tetrads 44; hectads 20
ALL SQUARES: monads 89; tetrads 67; hectads 26

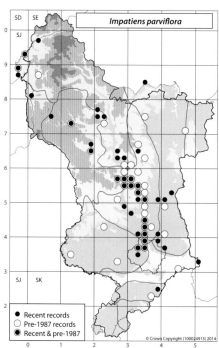

Small Balsam is a rare, established annual of damp shady places in woods, on riverbanks and in disturbed areas. It has been found from Chisworth (SJ9992) and Meersbrook Park (SK3584) in the north, through Lathkill Dale (SK1865) and Ambergate Station (SK3451), to Melbourne Pool (SK3824) and Attenborough (SK5033) in the south. It appears to be particularly associated with the corridor of the River Derwent near Derby (Markeaton Park SK3337). Clapham (1969) said it was increasing, but there seems little evidence of any spread since then, though it does appear to move around from site to site.

Impatiens glandulifera Royle
Himalayan Balsam

COUNTY STATUS: Established (Neophyte)
CONSERVATION STATUS: WCA9
FIRST YEAR: 1948 **LATEST YEAR:** 2013 **NO OF RECORDS:** 1,306
RECENT SQUARES: monads 512; tetrads 318; hectads 37
ALL SQUARES: monads 538; tetrads 329; hectads 38

Himalayan Balsam is an established annual of river banks, canal sides, wet woods and

Himalayan Balsam (*Impatiens glandulifera*), margin of damp grassland, August 2008
(Kieron Huston)

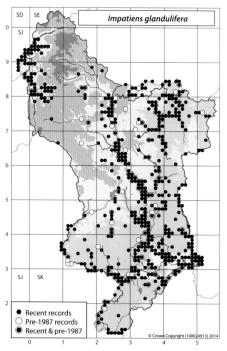

damp disturbed ground. It is frequent and locally abundant throughout lowland Derbyshire (Robin Wood SK0094, River Rother Beighton SK4483, Trent Lock SK5031 & Drakelow Reserve SK2220), but thankfully only rare in upland parts. Also known as Policeman's Helmet, it was originally introduced from the Himalayas as a garden ornamental but escaped by means of its copious seed production into more natural settings. It soon became a pernicious weed of wetlands, and the bane of conservationists, swamping out and replacing natural communities over large areas (Charter 1997 & 1999). In recent years removal efforts have become more coordinated, involving working downstream from the headwaters of various rivers. During a five year period, over 2,600 tons were removed from one watercourse by the Moss Valley Wildlife Group.

POLEMONIACEAE

Polemonium caeruleum L.
Jacob's-ladder

COUNTY STATUS: Native
CONSERVATION STATUS: DRDB (Cat3), NR, A, B, C
FIRST YEAR: 1787 LATEST YEAR: 2013 NO OF RECORDS: 376
RECENT SQUARES: monads 58; tetrads 46; hectads 18
ALL SQUARES: monads 83; tetrads 62; hectads 26

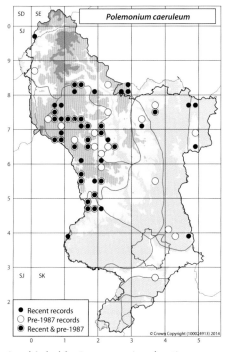

Jacob's-ladder is an occasional native perennial of the White Peak where it is

one of the most characteristic and showy plants of the dalesides. It grows naturally here in a range of habitats including grassland, light woods, screes, rock ledges and streamsides (Parkhouse Hill SK0767, Lathkill Dale SK1665, Wolfscote Dale SK1456, Taddington Dale SK1671 & Wye Dale SK1473). Owing to its attractive blue flowers, it has been much planted in gardens from where it has established itself in other parts of the county. Pollen evidence from peat bogs indicates it was widespread throughout Britain just after the last ice-age. However as a native it is now restricted to Derbyshire's White Peak and the Yorkshire Dales, and is Nationally Rare. It appeared on the cover of the last Flora of Derbyshire (Clapham 1969), and a plant collected from Bentley Brook was illustrated in the *Concise British Flora in Colour* (Keble Martin 1965). In 2004 it was voted as Derbyshire's "county plant" in a nationwide survey run by Plantlife.

PRIMULACEAE

Primula vulgaris Huds.
Primrose

COUNTY STATUS: Native
CONSERVATION STATUS: None
FIRST YEAR: 1789 LATEST YEAR: 2013 NO OF RECORDS: 681
RECENT SQUARES: monads 288; tetrads 219; hectads 37
ALL SQUARES: monads 329; tetrads 244; hectads 37

Primrose is an occasional native perennial of woods, hedgebanks and rarely grasslands on heavier soils. It is also frequently cultivated and readily establishes itself in lawns, churchyards and on roadsides. It grows throughout the county except for the upland moors of the extreme north and west. Clapham

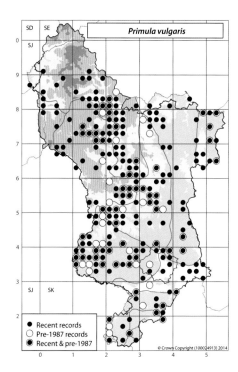

(1969) states that it had declined greatly since the early years of the 20th century but there is no evidence here for this trend continuing.

Primula × *polyantha* Mill.
False Oxlip

COUNTY STATUS: Native
CONSERVATION STATUS: None
FIRST YEAR: 1789 LATEST YEAR: 2013 NO OF RECORDS: 90
RECENT SQUARES: monads 27; tetrads 25; hectads 16
ALL SQUARES: monads 50; tetrads 38; hectads 22

False Oxlip is a native hybrid perennial of lightly wooded areas where the distributions of its parents meet. Occasional in the White Peak, it is very rare elsewhere in the lowlands of the county. As the hybrid of Primrose (*P. vulgaris*) and

Jacob's-ladder (*Polemonium caeruleum*) at Hobs House, Monsal Dale (SK1771), June 2011 (Ken Balkow)

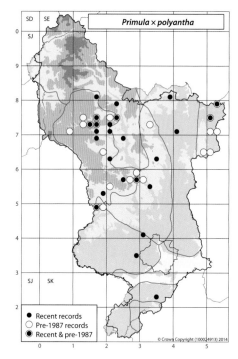

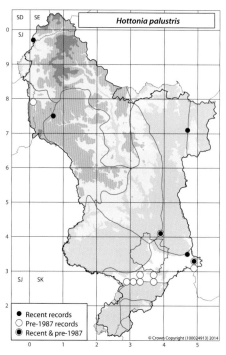

Cowslip (*P. veris*), it is probably the origin of the garden Polyanthus and some records may be garden escapes or throwouts.

Primula veris L.
Cowslip

COUNTY STATUS: Native
CONSERVATION STATUS: None
FIRST YEAR: 1789 LATEST YEAR: 2013 NO OF RECORDS: 1,580
RECENT SQUARES: monads 478; tetrads 295; hectads 36
ALL SQUARES: monads 531; tetrads 317; hectads 36

Cowslip is a native perennial of unimproved grasslands and light woods. It is common in the White Peak and Magnesian Limestone Areas but only rare to frequent elsewhere. It has declined greatly over the years with agricultural improvement. Farey (1815)

almost laments its abundance, saying drainage and liming could often remove it. Clapham (1969) said it was decreasing, a decline that continued into the 1980s and 1990s by which time it had been lost from 85% of the hay meadows in the Peak District (Buckingham *et al.* 1997). This decline has been partly reversed by new planting since the 1990s for road building and land restoration schemes.

Primula farinosa L.
Bird's-eye Primrose

Bird's-eye Primrose is a very rare, introduced perennial. It is included on the basis of records from Hopton Quarry (SK2656). Plants that were to be destroyed with the construction of Cow Green

Reservoir in Teesdale were transplanted there in 1971. They flowered for many years and were last recorded in 2011. However, it may once have been a native in the county, as there is a vague reference in Raven (1947) to its occurrence here in the 16th century. The plant grows naturally in open vegetation over limestone in northern England.

Hottonia palustris L.
Water-violet

COUNTY STATUS: Native
CONSERVATION STATUS: DRDB (Cat5b), A, B
FIRST YEAR: 1789 LATEST YEAR: 2013 NO OF RECORDS: 115
RECENT SQUARES: monads 6; tetrads 6; hectads 6
ALL SQUARES: monads 15; tetrads 14; hectads 9

Water-violet is a very rare, native perennial of standing and gently flowing waterbodies. Recent records are scattered throughout the county (Morley Brickyards SK3841, Snipe Bog SK4671 & Arnfield Tower SK0097 v.c.58). Previous records are mostly from the south of the county. Locally the plant is considered native, though its attractive flowers make it of interest to gardeners and it may have been introduced at some sites. Nationally the plant has declined due to drainage, nutrient enrichment and disturbance of waterbodies.

Lysimachia nemorum L.
Yellow Pimpernel

COUNTY STATUS: Native
CONSERVATION STATUS: None
FIRST YEAR: 1789 LATEST YEAR: 2013 NO OF RECORDS: 990
RECENT SQUARES: monads 388; tetrads 265; hectads 36
ALL SQUARES: monads 421; tetrads 283; hectads 38

Cowslip (*Primula veris*) in unimproved neutral grassland at Calke Abbey (SK3622), April 2008 (Malcolm Neal)

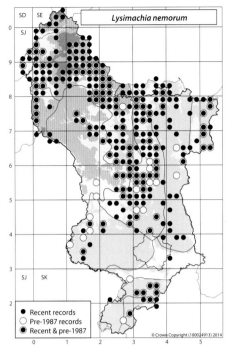

Yellow Pimpernel is a native evergreen and creeping perennial of damp woods, hedges, flushes and stream banks. It is common in the Dark Peak (Fair Brook SK1089 & Clough Wood SK2561) and the Peak Fringe (Birkinshaw Wood SK3269), but only occasional elsewhere. It has declined nationally due to the felling of deciduous woods or their replanting with conifers (Preston *et al.* 2002), but there is little sign of such a decline locally.

Lysimachia nummularia L.
Creeping-Jenny

Creeping-Jenny is an occasional native plant of damp shaded places where it

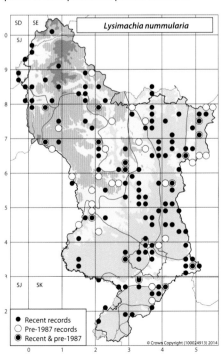

COUNTY STATUS:	Native
CONSERVATION STATUS:	None
FIRST YEAR: 1789	LATEST YEAR: 2013	NO OF RECORDS: 264
RECENT SQUARES:	monads 129; tetrads 129; hectads 37
ALL SQUARES:	monads 161; tetrads 156; hectads 37

grows as an evergreen perennial, sprawling over the soil surface. It occurs throughout the county with its altitude record in Britain just south of Buxton at 365m. It is often grown in gardens from where it regularly escapes into the wild. Some of the records mapped here are therefore probably of introduced plants.

Lysimachia vulgaris L.
Yellow Loosestrife

COUNTY STATUS:	Native
CONSERVATION STATUS:	B
FIRST YEAR: 1829	LATEST YEAR: 2011	NO OF RECORDS: 144
RECENT SQUARES:	monads 66; tetrads 66; hectads 25
ALL SQUARES:	monads 81; tetrads 77; hectads 28

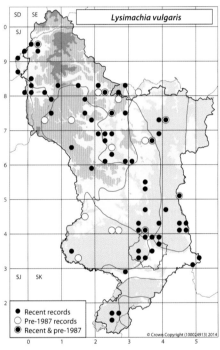

Yellow Loosestrife is a native perennial of damp woods, streamsides and fens, though it can occur in drier areas such as the roadside south of Litton village (SK1674). It is occasional in all areas (Glossop SK0294, Lumsdale SK3160 & Linton SK2716) except for the Magnesian Limestone and upland moors. It has declined nationally in the last 30 years due to watercourse maintenance, but there is no sign of such a decline here.

Lysimachia punctata L.
Dotted Loosestrife

Dotted Loosestrife is an occasional established perennial of waste ground and waysides throughout the county. It is

COUNTY STATUS:	Established (Neophyte)
CONSERVATION STATUS:	None
FIRST YEAR: 1903	LATEST YEAR: 2013	NO OF RECORDS: 281
RECENT SQUARES:	monads 180; tetrads 161; hectads 33
ALL SQUARES:	monads 194; tetrads 170; hectads 34

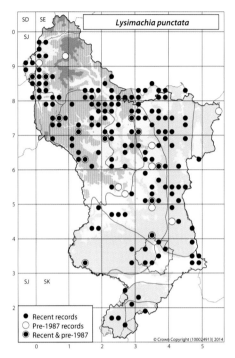

much grown in gardens where its vigorous growth means that excess plants are often discarded into the wild (Preston *et al.* 2002). It is a native of south-eastern Europe.

Anagallis tenella (L.) L.
Bog Pimpernel

Bog Pimpernel is a rare native species of the Dark Peak (Hollingworth Clough SK0489, Ladybower SK1985 & Brampton

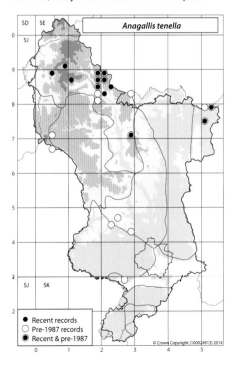

Bog Pimpernel (*Anagallis tenella*), Derwent Moors (SK2088), July 2009 (Peter Smith)

COUNTY STATUS: Native	
CONSERVATION STATUS: DRDB (Cat5b), B	
FIRST YEAR: 1789 **LATEST YEAR:** 2011 **NO OF RECORDS:** 95	
RECENT SQUARES: monads 14; tetrads 13; hectads 6	
ALL SQUARES: monads 32; tetrads 23; hectads 17	

Moor SK2970) and Magnesian Limestone Areas (Markland Grips SK5074) where it grows as a creeping evergreen perennial of boggy areas and fens. It was previously recorded from central and southern Derbyshire (Hulland Moss SK2546 & Egginton Sewage Farm SK2729). Its distribution has been similarly reduced nationally due to the agricultural improvement of marginal land (Preston *et al.* 2002).

Anagallis arvensis L.
A pimpernel

Two subspecies occur here. **Scarlet Pimpernel (ssp. *arvensis*)** is a frequent

COUNTY STATUS: Native	
CONSERVATION STATUS: None	
FIRST YEAR: 1789 **LATEST YEAR:** 2013 **NO OF RECORDS:** 455	
RECENT SQUARES: monads 259; tetrads 200; hectads 33	
ALL SQUARES: monads 297; tetrads 226; hectads 35	

native plant of lowland Derbyshire. It grows as a winter annual in bare areas amongst arable crops, on waste ground and on wall tops. It also occurs in the uplands in similar habitats, but is rare there. **Blue Pimpernel (ssp. *foemina*** (Mill.) Schinz & Thell.) is a very rare, long-established annual of arable land throughout the area (Ashbourne SK1746, Buxton SK0673 & Little Chester SK3537). It was last recorded in 1968 and, according to Clapham's 1969 Flora some older records may well be errors for the blue-flowered form of Scarlet Pimpernel. This subspecies is regarded as Nationally Scarce.

Trientalis europaea L.
Chickweed-wintergreen

COUNTY STATUS: Native	
CONSERVATION STATUS: DRDB (Cat4), A, B	
FIRST YEAR: 1969 **LATEST YEAR:** 2009 **NO OF RECORDS:** 16	
RECENT SQUARES: monads 1; tetrads 1; hectads 1	
ALL SQUARES: monads 1; tetrads 1; hectads 1	

Chickweed-wintergreen is a very rare, native perennial, only ever recorded in one moorland flush on Houndkirk Moor near Sheffield (SK2882). Clapham's 1969 Flora noted it as a recent discovery. Subsequently it has been recorded there on several occasions up to 2009. In June 2001 over 80 delicate plants with 30 attractive white flowers were counted. The site no longer falls within modern Derbyshire, but remains within v.c.57. It

is a plant of northern British moors, with Houndkirk Moor its most southerly locality in England (Stace 2010).

Centunculus minimus L.
Chaffweed

COUNTY STATUS: Native	
CONSERVATION STATUS: DRDB (Cat2), NT, B	
FIRST YEAR: 1969 **LATEST YEAR:** 1969 **NO OF RECORDS:** 1	
RECENT SQUARES: monads 0; tetrads 0; hectads 0	
ALL SQUARES: monads 0; tetrads 0; hectads 1	

Locally extinct, Chaffweed was a very rare, native annual of damp sandy ground on heaths. Its occurrence in the county is based on a single record for SK07 in Clapham (1969).

Cyclamen hederifolium Aiton
Sowbread

Sowbread is a very rare, established perennial of waysides. The first record was made in 2006 by R. Martin in Long Eaton (SK4832). It has since been recorded for three further sites: Church Broughton (SK2033) in 2011, and High Peak Trail (SK2855) and Black Rocks (SK2955) both in 2012. A garden escape or throwout, it is a native of southern Europe.

Samolus valerandi L.
Brookweed

COUNTY STATUS: Native	
CONSERVATION STATUS: DRDB (Cat4)	
FIRST YEAR: 1864 **LATEST YEAR:** 2005 **NO OF RECORDS:** 5	
RECENT SQUARES: monads 1; tetrads 1; hectads 1	
ALL SQUARES: monads 1; tetrads 1; hectads 5	

Brookweed is a very rare, native perennial of wet mineral soil especially by streams

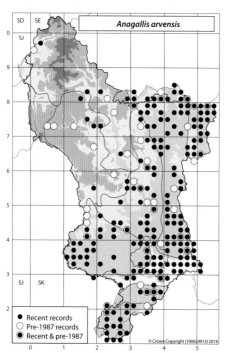

Anagallis arvensis

● Recent records
○ Pre-1987 records
◉ Recent & pre-1987

© Crown Copyright (100024913) 2014

Chickweed-wintergreen (*Trientalis europaea*) at its sole local site, Houndkirk Moor (SK2882), June 1995 (Ken Balkow)

and flushes. The only modern record was made by R. Frost in 2005 at Steetley Quarry (SK5478). It had previously been recorded only four times. Linton (1903) listed it for Tansley Moor (SK36) in 1864 and Swarkestone Bridge (SK32). Later there are two rather vague records, one for SK35 in 1903 and one for SK28 around 1950. This loss mirrors the national situation where the plant has disappeared from many inland sites since 1950 due to drainage (Preston *et al.* 2002).

SARRACENIACEAE

Sarracenia purpurea L.
Pitcherplant
Pitcherplant is a very rare, established perennial of wet peat-bogs. It is only known from Stoke Flat (SK2576), where a strong population was discovered by T. Lewis in 2010. A native of North America, it is grown in gardens as a novelty plant because of its insectivorous habit. Natural England has been considering whether efforts should be made to remove it from this site.

ERICACEAE

Arctostaphylos uva-ursi (L.) Spreng.
Bearberry

COUNTY STATUS: Native	
CONSERVATION STATUS: DRDB (Cat5a), CitesD, A, B	
FIRST YEAR: 1799 **LATEST YEAR:** 2012 **NO OF RECORDS:** 45	
RECENT SQUARES: monads 8; tetrads 7; hectads 3	
ALL SQUARES: monads 9; tetrads 8; hectads 5	

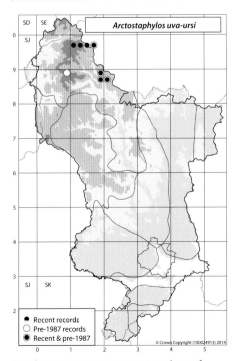

Bearberry is a very rare, native plant of gritstone rocks and banks, where it grows as an evergreen, procumbent undershrub.

It has and still does occur exclusively in the Dark Peak (Bleaklow Moors SK1096 & Ladybower Tor SK1986, plus Kinder Scout SK0889 in 1969). It is a northern species, on the southern edge of its range in Derbyshire, and is thought to be nationally declining due to moor-burning (Preston *et al.* 2002).

Empetrum nigrum L.
Crowberry

COUNTY STATUS: Native	
CONSERVATION STATUS: None	
FIRST YEAR: 1658 **LATEST YEAR:** 2013 **NO OF RECORDS:** 1,063	
RECENT SQUARES: monads 382; tetrads 142; hectads 17	
ALL SQUARES: monads 393; tetrads 147; hectads 19	

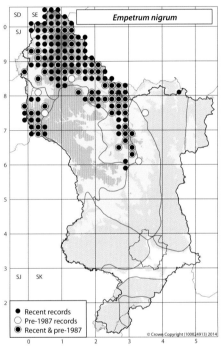

Crowberry is a native evergreen undershrub of moors, hillsides and blanket bogs, though in the latter habitat it only grows in drier parts (Tallis 1997). It occurs commonly throughout the Dark and South West Peak Areas. There are only two records outside these Character Areas: Cobnor Wood (SK3575) from 1973 and coal mine waste tips at Holbrook Meadows (SK4480) in 1993. Our plant is ssp. *nigrum*, and is sometimes known as Heath (Grigson 1975). Recently there has been some dieback of plants in the Dark Peak; the reason for this is as yet unknown.

Rhododendron ponticum L.
Rhododendron

COUNTY STATUS: Established (Neophyte)	
CONSERVATION STATUS: WCA9	
FIRST YEAR: 1968 **LATEST YEAR:** 2013 **NO OF RECORDS:** 1,005	
RECENT SQUARES: monads 392; tetrads 268; hectads 35	
ALL SQUARES: monads 428; tetrads 281; hectads 38	

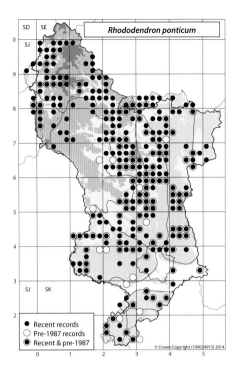

Rhododendron is an established evergreen shrub of acidic soils in woods and more open heathy areas. It is frequent throughout the county except for the White Peak and the highest moorland areas. It can be locally abundant, and its profusion of pink flowers in spring can make an attractive sight. However, the dense shade it casts prevents plant growth beneath it, so making it unwelcome to conservationists, many of whom expend much effort in trying to eradicate it from sensitive areas. Its spread in the Peak District and Sheffield area has been studied by I. Rotherham (1986a, b & c). Recently found to be a hybrid of garden origin from a number of Rhododendron species, it should now more correctly be known as *R.* × *superponticum*.

Rhododendron luteum Sweet
Yellow Azalea
Yellow Azalea is a casual deciduous shrub of woodlands and a native of eastern Europe and western Asia. It has been recorded from only four sites, all between 1998 and 2012: Errwood Hall (SK0074 v.c.58), Shooter's Clough (SK0175), Beeley Moor (SK2966) and the site of Siberia nursery (SK3065). It is far less of a conservation problem than Rhododendron (*R. ponticum*), partly due to its deciduous habit.

Rhododendron groenlandicum (Oeder)
Kron & Judd
Labrador-tea
Labrador-tea is a very rare, established shrub of high moorland and is a native of northern Europe and North America. All current records are scattered across the

COUNTY STATUS: Established (Neophyte)

CONSERVATION STATUS: None

FIRST YEAR: 1949 LATEST YEAR: 2008 NO OF RECORDS: 46

RECENT SQUARES: monads 6; tetrads 5; hectads 2

ALL SQUARES: monads 7; tetrads 6; hectads 3

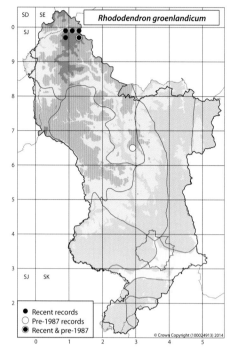

Bleaklow Moors in the Dark Peak (Torside Grain SK0897 & Barrow Stones SK1396). Until 1981 it was also known at Old Rowsley (Whitesprings SK2865) as a survivor from a nursery. The origin of the Bleaklow plants has been much debated (Yalden 1996)

Labrador-tea (*Rhododendron groenlandicum*), Barrow Stones (SK1396), September 2005 (Nick Moyes)

and some even considered them native. However, our plants are not the central European species (*R. tomentosum*), which would be expected if they were native. They may have originated from bird-sown seed or be the relics of planting for game cover around 1900 (Capper 2001). Whatever their origins, they have survived here since at least the middle of last century. It can regenerate after severe fires and in recent years the Barrow Stones plant was found to have small daughter plants to the north-east, suggesting self-seeding down-wind.

Kalmia angustifolia L.
Sheep-laurel

Sheep-laurel is an established evergreen shrub, known from just two old plant nursery sites: Farley Moor (SK2962 & 3063) between 1950 and 2010, and Whitesprings Nurseries (SK2865) in the 1970s. It is indigenous to eastern North America.

Calluna vulgaris (L.) Hull
Heather

COUNTY STATUS: Native

CONSERVATION STATUS: ERL

FIRST YEAR: 1789 LATEST YEAR: 2013 NO OF RECORDS: 2,327

RECENT SQUARES: monads 682; tetrads 288; hectads 30

ALL SQUARES: monads 729; tetrads 311; hectads 38

Heather, also known as Ling, is a native evergreen undershrub of heaths, moors and open woods on acid soils. It is still very common in the South West and Dark Peak

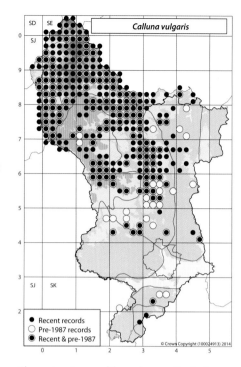

Character Areas, although over the last half century its abundance in the uplands has been reduced due to overgrazing by sheep (Anderson & Yalden 1981). However, it is still possible to find places where its purple flowers form vast sheets of colour over Derbyshire's uplands in autumn. It is occasional in the Peak Fringe, and White Peak Areas; in the latter it occurs mostly as scattered bushes on the edges of dales. These plants are relics of a once extensive coverage of heath over the limestone plateau, long since removed by agricultural improvement at the start of the 19th century (Farey 1815). A few more extensive remnants of this limestone heath still survive, as at Longstone Moor (SK1973) and Elton Common (SK2059). Heather is rare outside these Areas as most sites have been lost to agriculture. To some extent this has been counteracted by the gain of new sites on coalmine waste tips (Albert Village SK3018).

Erica tetralix L.
Cross-leaved Heath

COUNTY STATUS: Native

CONSERVATION STATUS: ERL

FIRST YEAR: 1789 LATEST YEAR: 2013 NO OF RECORDS: 651

RECENT SQUARES: monads 279; tetrads 130; hectads 18

ALL SQUARES: monads 289; tetrads 136; hectads 19

Cross-leaved Heath is a frequent native plant of the South West and Dark Peak Character Areas, where it grows as an evergreen undershrub on bogs, wet heaths and moors. Outside these Areas it is very rare, occurring at only a few scattered localities (Blake Moor SK1562 in the White Peak & Mugginton Bottoms SK2843 in the

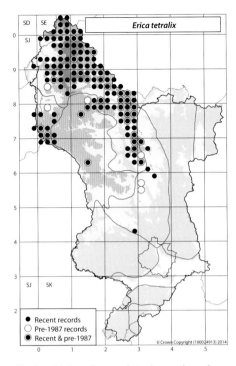

Claylands). Local records indicate there has been little change in its distribution over the last fifty years.

Erica cinerea L.
Bell Heather

COUNTY STATUS: Native	
CONSERVATION STATUS: ERL	
FIRST YEAR: 1729 **LATEST YEAR:** 2013 **NO OF RECORDS:** 386	
RECENT SQUARES: monads 168; tetrads 112; hectads 19	
ALL SQUARES: monads 187; tetrads 123; hectads 24	

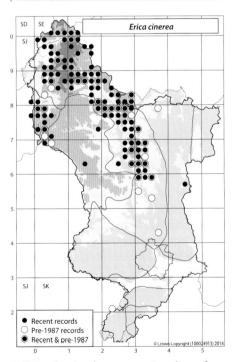

Bell Heather is a frequent native plant of the South West, Dark Peak and Peak Fringe Areas where it grows as an evergreen undershrub of dry heath and moorland. It

is very rare elsewhere, occurring as isolated records in the White Peak (Tissington Trail SK1462) and Coal Measures (Fordbridge Lane SK4457). There is also an unusual 1970s record from Drakelow Reserve (SK2220) in the south. Nationally it grows throughout the country including chalk heaths, though is absent from the ecologically similar limestone heaths of Derbyshire.

Erica vagans L.
Cornish Heath

Cornish Heath is an established, evergreen undershrub of heathy and scrubby areas. Both modern records are from the Edale area (SK1186) in 2011/2012. Older records all came from around the Matlock area (Whitesprings Nursery SK2865 in 1972, Matlock Moor Farm SK3162 in 1969 & Tansley SK35 in 1942), where it was probably a relic of nursery cultivation. As a native of western Cornwall it is Nationally Rare.

Andromeda polifolia L.
Bog-rosemary

COUNTY STATUS: Native	
CONSERVATION STATUS: ERL, A, B	
FIRST YEAR: 1829 **LATEST YEAR:** 2007 **NO OF RECORDS:** 35	
RECENT SQUARES: monads 10; tetrads 9; hectads 5	
ALL SQUARES: monads 13; tetrads 10; hectads 6	

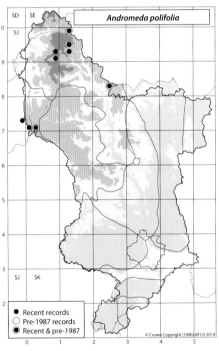

Bog-rosemary is a very rare, native undershrub of boggy areas and wet moorland in the Dark and the South West Peak Areas (Featherbed Moss SK0892, Far Black Clough SK1298, Goyt Valley SK0271 & White Path Moss SK2583). It can be very diminutive and hard to locate. It was recorded for the Peak Fringe at Poorlots Quarry (SK3360) in 1975, but could not be

relocated just five years later. Nationally it is a northern plant, with Derbyshire on the south-eastern limit of its range.

Gaultheria shallon Pursh
Shallon

Shallon is a very rare, established evergreen shrub of woods and shrubberies on acid soils. All recent records come from a small area of central Derbyshire (Whitesprings Plantation SK2865 in 1992, Farley Moor SK3064 in 2010 and Sydnope Brook SK2963 in 2011). Older records cover the same area and slightly further south (Tansley SK3160 in 1973). It comes from western North America, occurring here as a relic of gardens, nurseries or planting for game birds. In parts of the UK it is becoming a nuisance, but there is no sign of this here yet.

Gaultheria mucronata (L. f.) Hook. & Arn.
Prickly Heath

Prickly Heath is a very rare, established evergreen shrub of open woods and shrubby areas on sandy soils. All records are from the north-eastern corner of the county. There are recent records from four tetrads: Whitesprings (SK2865) in 2002, Darley Moor (SK3065), Wirestone Plantation (SK3263) in 1999 and Leveret Croft (SK2482) in 2011. Older records come from: Nether Padley (SK2578), Blacka Moor (SK2880) and Dore (SK2980) all for 1969. It is a relic of plantings or a bird-seed escapee (Preston *et al.* 2002). It occurs naturally in Chile.

Vaccinium oxycoccos L.
Cranberry

Cranberry is a locally frequent, native plant of the South West and Dark Peak

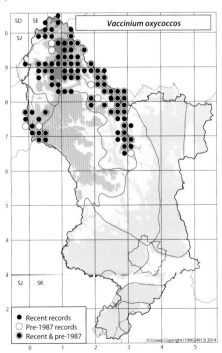

COUNTY STATUS: Native
CONSERVATION STATUS: None
FIRST YEAR: 1658 LATEST YEAR: 2013 NO OF RECORDS: 504
RECENT SQUARES: monads 152; tetrads 92; hectads 16
ALL SQUARES: monads 175; tetrads 99; hectads 19

Areas (Goyt Valley SK0076, Alport SK1293 & Ramsley Moor SK2976) where it grows as an evergreen, procumbent undershrub on wet heaths and bogs. It is most often seen trailing over lawns of Bog Moss (*Sphagnum* spp.). Its edible berries have been eaten locally, particularly by "the Poor" (Farey 1815). It features in a number of places-names in the uplands, for example Cranberry Ness, Upper Derwent. There has been little change in its distribution over the last 50 years, whilst nationally it is a plant of the upland north and west, with Derbyshire on its eastern limits.

Vaccinium vitis-idaea L.
Cowberry

COUNTY STATUS: Native
CONSERVATION STATUS: None
FIRST YEAR: 1658 LATEST YEAR: 2013 NO OF RECORDS: 534
RECENT SQUARES: monads 213; tetrads 107; hectads 16
ALL SQUARES: monads 227; tetrads 113; hectads 16

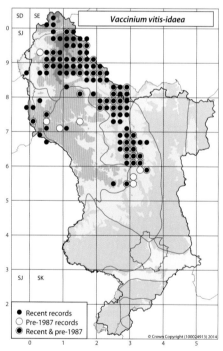

Cowberry is an occasional native plant of the South West Peak (Hogshaw Brook SK0575), Dark Peak (Ashop Clough SK1090) and Peak Fringe (Stone Edge SK36I) where it grows as an evergreen undershrub in open woods and moors. Its only current records away from these areas are the White Peak (Bradwell Moor SK1480 & Deep Dale SK1071). There has been no recorded change in its distribution over the last 50 years. Locally it has been known as

Clusterberry (Grigson 1975). Nationally it is a plant of upland areas, on the eastern limit of its distribution here.

Vaccinium × intermedium Ruthe
Hybrid Bilberry

COUNTY STATUS: Native
CONSERVATION STATUS: B
FIRST YEAR: 1947 LATEST YEAR: 2010 NO OF RECORDS: 139
RECENT SQUARES: monads 36; tetrads 27; hectads 8
ALL SQUARES: monads 44; tetrads 32; hectads 9

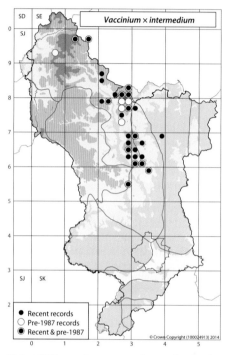

Hybrid Bilberry is a rare native undershrub of moors and heathy areas in the Dark

Peak (Priddock Wood SK2085 & Swains Greave SK1397) and Peak Fringe (Bottom Moor Plantation SK3263). It is the hybrid between Bilberry (*V. myrtillus*) and Cowberry (*V. vitis-idaea*) with both of which it generally occurs. It grows particularly where the ground has recently been disturbed, sometimes displaying hybrid vigour (Clapham 1969). As it is a particularly Derbyshire plant, growing only in two other counties - Staffordshire and Yorkshire - it has engendered a lot of local interest. It has been the subject of numerous investigations (Waite 1974 & Cavalot 2005). Many specimens and photos collected by K. Cavalot in the late 1990s are held at Derby Museum.

Vaccinium uliginosum L.
Bog Bilberry

COUNTY STATUS: Native
CONSERVATION STATUS: DRDB (Cat4)
FIRST YEAR: 2004 LATEST YEAR: 2008 NO OF RECORDS: 5
RECENT SQUARES: monads 1; tetrads 1; hectads 1
ALL SQUARES: monads 1; tetrads 1; hectads 1

Bog Bilberry is a very rare, native undershrub of blanket bogs. It was discovered at its only location by D. Yalden in 2004 at the top of Far Small Clough (SK131983). It was growing in a shallow peaty gully amongst Crowberry (*Empetrum nigrum*), Heather (*Calluna vulgaris*) and Hare's-tail Cottongrass (*Eriophorum vaginatum*). It is a plant of northern England and Scotland, with just two outlying sites: Exmoor and Derbyshire. The reason for its sudden appearance here

Bog Bilberry (*Vaccinium uliginosum*), Far Small Clough (SK1398), September 2005 (Nick Moyes)

is a mystery. Is it a new colonist, or was it simply overlooked for decades on such open moorland? It might even have been present for a while as buried seed as they are known to survive for a long time (Hill & Kloet 2005). The final possibility is it was planted as an experimental source of food for grouse, as it is known to have been available from local nurseries in the 1790s at least.

Vaccinium myrtillus L.
Bilberry

COUNTY STATUS: Native
CONSERVATION STATUS: None
FIRST YEAR: 1789 **LATEST YEAR:** 2013 **NO OF RECORDS:** 2,445
RECENT SQUARES: monads 745; tetrads 289; hectads 27
ALL SQUARES: monads 788; tetrads 304; hectads 29

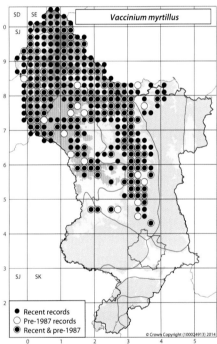

Bilberry is native deciduous undershrub of moors, heaths and woods. It is very common and locally abundant in the South West Peak and Dark Peak, but only common in the Peak Fringe. It is occasional in the White Peak, where it occurs in grasslands over acid loams on the edge of some dales (Deep Dale SK1669). There has been little change in distribution over the last 50 years. However, it is less abundant in some areas now due to its sensitivity to increased sheep grazing (Welch 1998). Farey (1815) noted its fruit is "gathered by the Poor; and used for Puddings and Pies, and ... served up in Desserts at the Tables of the more wealthy". This led to a number of local names including Black Whorts and Wimberry (Grigson 1975). It occurs throughout the country except for central and eastern England, with Derbyshire at its eastern limits in the Midlands.

Pyrola minor L.
Common Wintergreen

COUNTY STATUS: Native
CONSERVATION STATUS: ERL, A, B
FIRST YEAR: 1889 **LATEST YEAR:** 2013 **NO OF RECORDS:** 68
RECENT SQUARES: monads 10; tetrads 7; hectads 4
ALL SQUARES: monads 14; tetrads 9; hectads 4

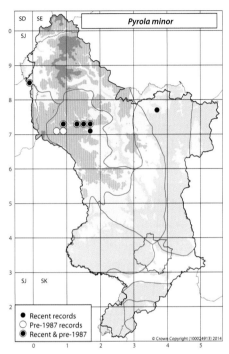

Common Wintergreen is a very rare, native evergreen perennial of wooded and heathy areas. It is found in north Derbyshire (Disley SJ9885 & Unstone SK3777), with the majority of records from the Miller's Dale/Monsal Dale area (SK17). Previously it grew over a similar range, but has not shown the same decline as seen nationally through changes in land use and management (Preston *et al.* 2002).

Pyrola rotundifolia L.
Round-leaved Wintergreen

COUNTY STATUS: Native
CONSERVATION STATUS: DRDB (Cat2), NS, NT
FIRST YEAR: 1981 **LATEST YEAR:** 2011 **NO OF RECORDS:** 5
RECENT SQUARES: monads 1; tetrads 1; hectads 1
ALL SQUARES: monads 2; tetrads 2; hectads 2

Round-leaved Wintergreen is a very rare, native evergreen perennial of light woods. Our only recent record is for Gamesley Sidings (SK0093) in 2011. Previously it was recorded from near Bradwell (SK1782) by H. Smith in 1981. Two others are mentioned in Clapham (1969), but are based on records in Linton's Flora of 1903. Both authors consider them as probably erroneous. Derbyshire plants are referable to ssp. *rotundifolia*.

Yellow Bird's-nest (*Hypopitys monotropa*) in Brierley Wood (SK3775), July 2013 (Ken Balkow)

Hypopitys monotropa Crantz
Yellow Bird's-nest

COUNTY STATUS: Native
CONSERVATION STATUS: DRDB (Cat2), EN, NS, NERC, A, B
FIRST YEAR: 1809 **LATEST YEAR:** 2013 **NO OF RECORDS:** 49
RECENT SQUARES: monads 7; tetrads 4; hectads 3
ALL SQUARES: monads 10; tetrads 7; hectads 5

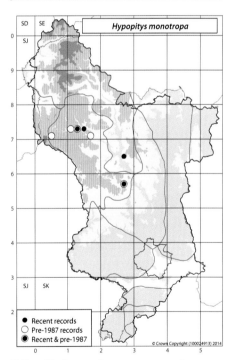

Yellow Bird's-nest is a very rare, native perennial of woods. All records are from the White Peak (Priestcliffe Lees SK1572 & Hopton Quarry SK2656) except for modern records at Rowsley Sidings (SK2665) and Kirk Hallam (SK4541), and an old report from Ashover (SK36) in 1903. Preston *et al.* (2002) note the highest record for the species in Britain is here at Buxton. They also note an association with Hazel (*Corylus avellana*), but Clapham (1969) associates it locally with Beech (*Fagus sylvatica*). As it is one of the rare flowering plants that feeds off decaying plant material, it only appears above ground to flower. This means it is probably under-recorded. Where identified to subspecies, they have always been recorded as ssp. *hypophegea* (Wallr.) Tzvelev.

GARRYACEAE

Aucuba japonica Thunb.
Spotted-laurel

Spotted-laurel is a casual evergreen shrub of shrubberies and waysides. It is generally a relic of cultivation but can sometimes be self-sown. It has been recorded from five areas: Acresford (SK2812), Calver Weir (SK2475), Carr Wood (SK4051), Cutthorpe (SK3473) and Drakelow (SK21J), all between 1988 and 2012. It is a native of eastern Asia.

RUBIACEAE

Sherardia arvensis L.
Field Madder

COUNTY STATUS: Native
CONSERVATION STATUS: None
FIRST YEAR: 1789 LATEST YEAR: 2012 NO OF RECORDS: 140
RECENT SQUARES: monads 49; tetrads 41; hectads 18
ALL SQUARES: monads 73; tetrads 60; hectads 26

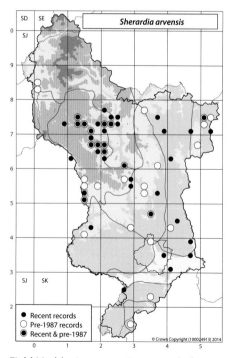

Field Madder is a rare native annual of open grasslands, waste ground and arable land. It occurs scattered throughout the county from Monk's Dale (SK1473) and

Sheepbridge (SK3675) in the north, to Thulston (SK4031) and Winshill (SK2624) in the south. It has declined in frequency, both locally and nationally, since the 1950s due to agricultural intensification (Preston *et al.* 2002).

Asperula cynanchica L.
Squinancywort

COUNTY STATUS: Native
CONSERVATION STATUS: DRDB (Cat6)
FIRST YEAR: 1789 LATEST YEAR: 1903 NO OF RECORDS: 4
RECENT SQUARES: monads 0; tetrads 0; hectads 0
ALL SQUARES: monads 0; tetrads 0; hectads 4

Locally extinct, Squinancywort was a very rare, native perennial of dry base-rich grasslands. We know of only four records, scattered through the southern half of the county (Ashford SK16, Bonsall SK25 & Normanton SK33, all for 1903, and Pinxton SK45 for 1789). Nationally it has been lost from many areas due to agricultural improvement or neglect of marginal land (Preston *et al.* 2002). The local plant was ssp. *cynanchica*.

Asperula arvensis L.
Blue Woodruff

Locally extinct, Blue Woodruff was a very rare, casual annual of cultivated and waste ground. The only records are Clifton SK1545 in 1941, Beauchief SK3381 in 1940 & near Darley Abbey SK3538 in 1969. It is indigenous to southern Europe and a constituent of bird-seed mixes.

Galium odoratum (L.) Scop.
Woodruff

COUNTY STATUS: Native
CONSERVATION STATUS: None
FIRST YEAR: 1789 LATEST YEAR: 2013 NO OF RECORDS: 431
RECENT SQUARES: monads 135; tetrads 102; hectads 30
ALL SQUARES: monads 149; tetrads 110; hectads 32

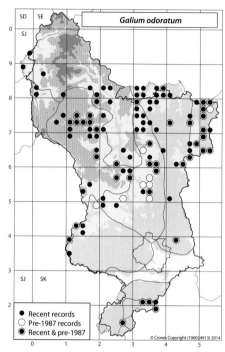

Woodruff is an occasional native perennial of damp areas in ancient woods and hedges, generally on base-rich soils. It is also commonly grown in gardens so

Woodruff (*Galium odoratum*) in limestone scrub Rose End Meadows (SK2956), April 2011 (Peter Smith)

some records, particularly those near habitations, may be garden escapes. It has been recorded across Derbyshire, from Woodseats (SJ9992) and Bondhay Plantation (SK5078) in the north, to Grange Wood (SK2714) and Wicket Nook (SK3619) in the south.

Galium uliginosum L.
Fen Bedstraw

COUNTY STATUS:	Native
CONSERVATION STATUS:	DRDB (Cat5b)
FIRST YEAR: 1789	LATEST YEAR: 2013 NO OF RECORDS: 120
RECENT SQUARES:	monads 26; tetrads 25; hectads 14
ALL SQUARES:	monads 71; tetrads 59; hectads 30

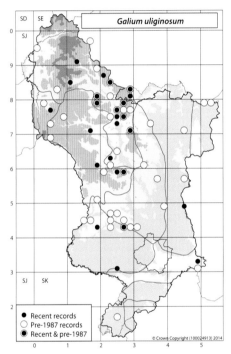

Fen Bedstraw is a rare scrambling native perennial of fens and base-rich marshy areas. It occurs throughout the county, with records from Houndkirk Moor (SK2882), Sandyford Brook (SK2674), Taylor's Field (SK4448), Mercaston Marsh (SK2643) and Hilton Gravel Pits (SK2431). It has declined in frequency since 1950, both locally and nationally (Preston *et al.* 2002).

Galium palustre L.
Common Marsh-bedstraw

COUNTY STATUS:	Native
CONSERVATION STATUS:	None
FIRST YEAR: 1789	LATEST YEAR: 2013 NO OF RECORDS: 1,597
RECENT SQUARES:	monads 616; tetrads 406; hectads 41
ALL SQUARES:	monads 710; tetrads 442; hectads 42

Common Marsh-bedstraw is a scrambling native perennial of marshes, damp meadows, fens, flushes and streamsides. It is frequent throughout the county wherever suitable habitats occur. Two forms occur locally. **Ssp. *palustre*** has been

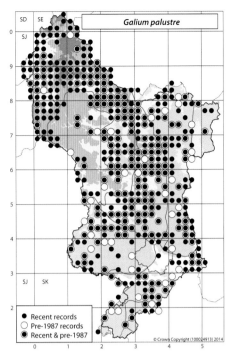

more frequently recorded, and occurs throughout the area. **Ssp. *elongatum*** (C. Presl) Arcang. is less frequent, occurring mostly in eastern and southern parts.

Galium verum L.
Lady's Bedstraw

COUNTY STATUS:	Native
CONSERVATION STATUS:	None
FIRST YEAR: 1789	LATEST YEAR: 2013 NO OF RECORDS: 2,186
RECENT SQUARES:	monads 721; tetrads 359; hectads 37
ALL SQUARES:	monads 770; tetrads 383; hectads 39

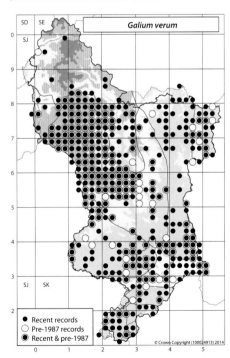

Lady's Bedstraw is a native perennial of dry unimproved grassland, and waysides on all but the most acid soils. It is now also a

frequent constituent of wild-flower seed mixes. It is very common throughout the White Peak and frequent elsewhere, except for the high moors of the Peak District where it is virtually absent. It has declined due to agricultural improvement of grasslands. Even in the White Peak, although still widespread, it was lost from 94% of hay meadows between the mid-1980s and mid-1990s (Buckingham *et al.* 1997).

Galium × pomeranicum Retz.
Hybrid Yellow Bedstraw

Locally extinct, Hybrid Yellow Bedstraw was a very rare, native perennial. Our only record comes from a roadside near Whitwell (SK5277) in 1969, but it is probably under-recorded. It is the hybrid of Lady's (*G. verum*) and Hedge Bedstraw (*G. album*).

Galium album Mill.
Hedge Bedstraw

COUNTY STATUS:	Native
CONSERVATION STATUS:	None
FIRST YEAR: 1789	LATEST YEAR: 2013 NO OF RECORDS: 307
RECENT SQUARES:	monads 124; tetrads 106; hectads 27
ALL SQUARES:	monads 154; tetrads 125; hectads 31

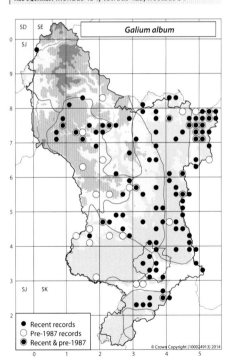

Hedge Bedstraw is a scrambling native perennial of waysides, hedges and open woods, generally found on well-drained calcareous soils. It occurs throughout the county apart from the high moors of the Dark and South West Peak Areas. Two subspecies are occasionally noted. **Ssp. *mollugo*** L. is more commonly reported, for example, from Forty Foot Lane (SK4025), near Cotmanhay (SK4743)

and Whaley Bridge (SK5171). **Ssp. *erectum*** Syme is rarer, with examples of modern records from Taddington By-pass (SK1471), Calver (SK2375) and Whitwell Wood (SK5277).

Galium sterneri Ehrend.
Limestone Bedstraw

COUNTY STATUS: Native
CONSERVATION STATUS: None
FIRST YEAR: 1789 LATEST YEAR: 2013 NO OF RECORDS: 851
RECENT SQUARES: monads 218; tetrads 105; hectads 10
ALL SQUARES: monads 240; tetrads 114; hectads 11

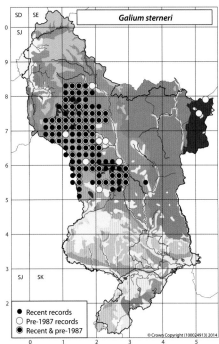

Limestone Bedstraw is a scrambling native perennial of short calcareous grasslands and rock outcrops. All recent records are from Carboniferous Limestone. It is very common throughout the White Peak (Wheston SK1277, Lathkill Dale SK1666 & Harborough Rocks SK2455), and is also known from the limestone outlier at Crich (SK3455). These and many other sites in the White Peak form an important national stronghold. It was previously recorded for the Magnesian Limestone (Markland Grips SK5074 & Whitwell Woods SK5278) in 1969. Where patches of acid soil overlay Carboniferous Limestone, it may occur with the very similar, but acid-loving Heath Bedstraw (*G. saxatile*), as near Fairthorn (SK0469). A useful aide-memoire for distinguishing them is that hairs along the leaf edges of Limestone Bedstraw point backwards – towards the "stern". Our plants are on the south-eastern edge of its British range (Preston *et al.* 2002). Note: All records of *G. pumilum* given by Linton (1903) and other early authors are now assumed to be *G. sterneri*,

as the species were not separated at that time.

Galium saxatile L.
Heath Bedstraw

COUNTY STATUS: Native
CONSERVATION STATUS: None
FIRST YEAR: 1789 LATEST YEAR: 2013 NO OF RECORDS: 2,537
RECENT SQUARES: monads 901; tetrads 416; hectads 37
ALL SQUARES: monads 967; tetrads 443; hectads 39

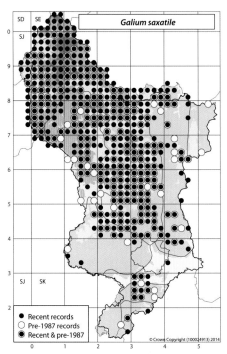

Heath Bedstraw is a low-growing native perennial of moors, heaths, dry grasslands, rocky places and open woods, on infertile acid soils. It is very common throughout the Dark Peak, South West and Peak Fringe Areas. It is frequent in the White Peak where acid soils overlay the limestone, and in such localities can grow side-by-side with the lime-loving Limestone Bedstraw (*G. sterneri*), as at Grin Low (SK0571). Elsewhere, in the lowlands it is only occasional, as at Swainspark (SK2917), Brimington Common (SK4172) and Dale Hills (SK4338).

Galium aparine L.
Cleavers

COUNTY STATUS: Native
CONSERVATION STATUS: None
FIRST YEAR: 1789 LATEST YEAR: 2013 NO OF RECORDS: 6,508
RECENT SQUARES: monads 2,187; tetrads 698; hectads 42
ALL SQUARES: monads 2,229; tetrads 700; hectads 42

Cleavers is a scrambling native annual of scrub, hedges, waste ground, cultivated land, riverbanks and waysides, generally on highly fertile soils. It is very common throughout Derbyshire, except for the high moors of the Dark Peak. It has a local name

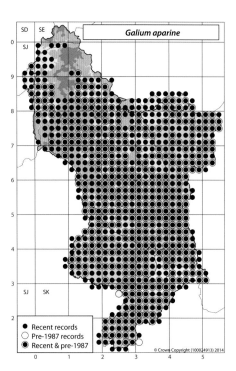

of Erif or Herath, possibly a corruption of Hay Ruff.

Galium spurium L.
False Cleavers

Locally extinct, False Cleavers was a scrambling casual annual of cultivated land. A native of continental Europe, it has only been found once: K.M. Hollick noted it as a garden weed at Longford Hall (SK2138) in 1938.

Galium tricornutum Dandy
Corn Cleavers

Locally extinct, Corn Cleavers was a very rare, casual annual. It is known from only four localities. Clapham (1969) gives: Stores Road Derby (SK3537) and from canary-seed in a garden at Clifton (SK1545) in 1941. Linton (1903) gives a cornfield at Bolsover (SK47) and an unlocalised cornfield in 1870.

Galium parisiense L.
Wall Bedstraw

Wall Bedstraw is a very rare, casual annual of waste ground. The only record is from the old Staveley Works (SK4174), discovered by A. Willmot in 2009. It is native to south-eastern England.

Cruciata laevipes Opiz
Crosswort

COUNTY STATUS: Native
CONSERVATION STATUS: ERL
FIRST YEAR: 1789 LATEST YEAR: 2013 NO OF RECORDS: 1,684
RECENT SQUARES: monads 566; tetrads 269; hectads 29
ALL SQUARES: monads 609; tetrads 288; hectads 33

Crosswort is a sprawling native perennial of grasslands, waysides, scrub and open

Crosswort (*Cruciata laevipes*) in limestone grassland Cressbrook Dale (SK1773), June 2008 (Peter Smith)

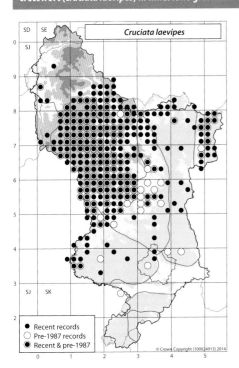

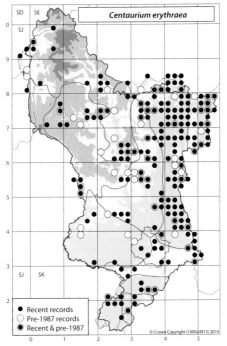

woodland, generally on well-drained calcareous soils. It is common in the White Peak, the southern part of the Dark Peak and on the Magnesian Limestone. Elsewhere it is rare, as near Somersal Herbert (SK1235), on the Sett Valley Trail (SK0086) and near Crich (SK3455).

GENTIANACEAE

Centaurium erythraea Rafn
Common Centaury

COUNTY STATUS: Native
CONSERVATION STATUS: None
FIRST YEAR: 1789 LATEST YEAR: 2013 NO OF RECORDS: 565
RECENT SQUARES: monads 250; tetrads 190; hectads 35
ALL SQUARES: monads 291; tetrads 216; hectads 35

Common Centaury is an attractive native biennial of dry open grasslands, heaths, woodland margins, spoil tips and waste places. It is occasional in eastern parts, where it can be locally abundant on areas disturbed for mining or restoration. Example localities are Swainspark (SK2916), Lock Lane Ash Tip (SK4831), The Sanctuary, Derby (SK3735), Holloway (SK3255) and Steetley Quarry (SK5478). It is rare elsewhere (Dinting Reserve SK0194).

Centaurium pulchellum (Sw.) Druce
Lesser Centaury
Lesser Centaury is a casual annual with only one old record for Linacre (SK3372) in 1981, at a site now destroyed. Native around the coasts of England and Wales

in damp open habitats, it occasionally spreads inland in southern Britain.

Blackstonia perfoliata (L.) Huds.
Yellow-wort

COUNTY STATUS: Native
CONSERVATION STATUS: B
FIRST YEAR: 1789 LATEST YEAR: 2012 NO OF RECORDS: 216
RECENT SQUARES: monads 61; tetrads 42; hectads 13
ALL SQUARES: monads 68; tetrads 44; hectads 14

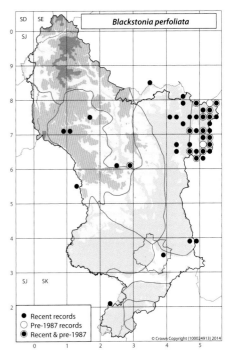

Yellow-wort is an attractive native annual of dry stony, often disturbed, areas of grassland, waste places and disused quarries. It is almost confined to the Magnesian Limestone, where it is occasional (Pleasley SK4863, Bolsover Moor SK5077 & Steetley Quarry SK5478). Elsewhere it is very rare and only occurs in isolated locations (Heeley Sidings SK3484, Cawdor Quarry SK2860, Drakelow Reserve SK2220 & Stanton Ironworks SK4739).

Gentianella campestris (L.) Boerner
Field Gentian

COUNTY STATUS: Native
CONSERVATION STATUS: DRDB (Cat2), VU, NERC, A, B
FIRST YEAR: 1805 LATEST YEAR: 2012 NO OF RECORDS: 41
RECENT SQUARES: monads 2; tetrads 3; hectads 3
ALL SQUARES: monads 9; tetrads 10; hectads 14

Field Gentian is now a very rare, native annual or biennial of unimproved grasslands. There are only three modern records, all from the White Peak: Brand Top (SK0468), High Rake (SK17) and Sir William Hill (SK2177). Recent attempts failed to relocate it at these sites, except for the latter where just one flower was found in 2012. It was formerly recorded scattered

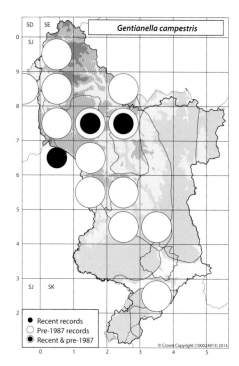

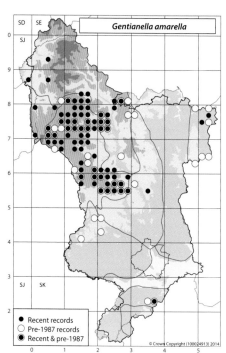

over a wider area, from Glossop (SK09) in the Dark Peak to Repton Shrubs (SK32) in the south. Nationally it is a northern species on the southern edge of its range here.

Gentianella germanica (Willd.) Boerner
Chiltern Gentian

An unconfirmed taxon, Chiltern Gentian was recorded by E. Drabble for Castleton and Fallgate (SK18) in 1911. As this is far north of other English localities, and there have been no other records, this sighting is treated as unconfirmed. It may even have been an error for Autumn Gentian (*G. amarella*).

Gentianella amarella (L.) Boerner
Autumn Gentian

COUNTY STATUS: Native
CONSERVATION STATUS: ERL
FIRST YEAR: 1789 LATEST YEAR: 2012 NO OF RECORDS: 403
RECENT SQUARES: monads 132; tetrads 81; hectads 16
ALL SQUARES: monads 164; tetrads 104; hectads 23

Autumn Gentian is an attractive native biennial of well-drained calcareous grasslands and the spoil tips of limestone quarries. It is occasional in the White Peak as at Eldon Hill (SK1181), Monyash (SK1466) and Redhill Quarry (SK2755). Elsewhere it is very rare, occurring on isolated outcrops of Carboniferous Limestone as at Ticknall Quarries (SK3623) and Crich Cliff (SK3455); Magnesian Limestone at Whitwell Wood (SK5277); and in non-limestone areas as at Moorfield (SK0492). Previously it was more frequent outside the White Peak as at Pleasley Vale (SK5265) and Ashbourne Green (SK1847). Our plant is ssp. *amarella*. An important but unconfirmed 1911 record for Chiltern Gentian (*G. germanica*)

by E. Drabble in SK18 is probably an error for this species.

Gentianella uliginosa (Willd.) Boerner
Dune Gentian

COUNTY STATUS: Native
CONSERVATION STATUS: DRDB (Cat6), WCA8, VU, NR, NERC
FIRST YEAR: 1898 LATEST YEAR: 1898 NO OF RECORDS: 4
RECENT SQUARES: monads 0; tetrads 0; hectads 0
ALL SQUARES: monads 1; tetrads 1; hectads 2

Locally extinct, Dune Gentian has been recorded here twice: Miller's Dale (SK17) in 1899 and Buxton (SK07) in 1898. The former is unconfirmed but the latter is supported by a well-labelled specimen in the National Museum of Wales, confirmed by H. Tingnong. This record has previously been considered erroneous by Lousley (1950) and Clapham (1969), no doubt because all other UK localities are coastal dunes in western Britain. However, current experts regard it as valid, and hence native, in the broader European context as the plant is widespread in damp meadows across northern Europe as in Poland (pers. comm. T. Rich 2003).

Gentiana pneumonanthe L.
Marsh Gentian

COUNTY STATUS: Native
CONSERVATION STATUS: DRDB (Cat6), NS
FIRST YEAR: 1789 LATEST YEAR: 1789 NO OF RECORDS: 1
RECENT SQUARES: monads 0; tetrads 0; hectads 0
ALL SQUARES: monads 0; tetrads 0; hectads 1

Locally extinct, Marsh Gentian was a very rare, native perennial. The only record is for Egginton Heath (SK22) by Pilkington (1789), and was noted as "Long extinct" by Linton

in 1903. It declined nationally before the 1930s due to drainage and development (Preston *et al.* 2002).

Gentiana verna L.
Spring Gentian

Spring Gentian is a very rare, planted perennial. In March 1971 it was transplanted from Cow Green in Teesdale to Nimblejack Quarry Reserve (SK2656), now known as Hopton Quarry Reserve. The Teesdale site was to be destroyed by reservoir construction, and although many other plants transplanted at the same time failed to survive, this gentian has grown well and was still flowering there over 40 years later in 2012.

APOCYNACEAE

Vinca minor L.
Lesser Periwinkle

COUNTY STATUS: Established (Archaeophyte)
CONSERVATION STATUS: None
FIRST YEAR: 1789 LATEST YEAR: 2013 NO OF RECORDS: 108
RECENT SQUARES: monads 42; tetrads 48; hectads 21
ALL SQUARES: monads 63; tetrads 65; hectads 26

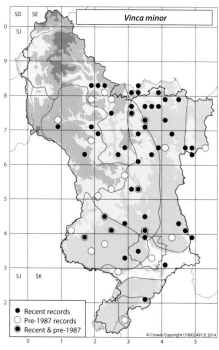

Lesser Periwinkle is an anciently established, creeping perennial of waysides, woods and waste places. It occurs rarely throughout the county from Lower Shatton (SK1982) and Millhouses (SK3383) in the north, through Alderwasley (SK3253), to Thulston (SK4031) and Pistern Hill (SK3520) in the south. It is widely grown in gardens for ornament, and often grows out into surrounding areas or is discarded with garden waste. It is a native of central and south-western Europe.

Vinca major L.
Greater Periwinkle

COUNTY STATUS: Established (Neophyte)
CONSERVATION STATUS: None
FIRST YEAR: 1789 LATEST YEAR: 2013 NO OF RECORDS: 92
RECENT SQUARES: monads 49; tetrads 58; hectads 25
ALL SQUARES: monads 57; tetrads 66; hectads 27

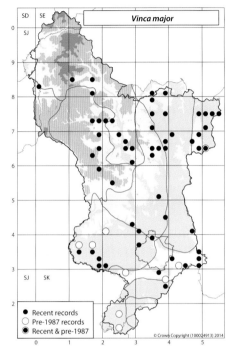

Greater Periwinkle is an established creeping perennial of waysides, shrubberies, scrub and rough places. It occurs rarely throughout the area from Barber Booth (SK1184) and Pleasley Vale (SK56C) in the north, through Pentrich Lane End (SK3751), to Doveridge (SK1234) and Melbourne Town (SK3825) in the south. It is widely grown for ground cover, and, being a vigorous grower, it often scrambles out of gardens or is discarded with garden waste. It is indigenous to the Mediterranean.

BORAGINACEAE

Lithospermum officinale L.
Common Gromwell

COUNTY STATUS: Native
CONSERVATION STATUS: DRDB (Cat5b), A, B
FIRST YEAR: 1789 LATEST YEAR: 2012 NO OF RECORDS: 96
RECENT SQUARES: monads 8; tetrads 6; hectads 2
ALL SQUARES: monads 15; tetrads 12; hectads 6

Common Gromwell is a very rare, native perennial of scrub on limestone. Current records are mainly from the Magnesian Limestone (Scarcliffe Park SK5270 & Whitwell Wood SK5278) with an isolated record from a long-known site on the Carboniferous Limestone (Cotterhole Quarry SK2656). Older records cover the same

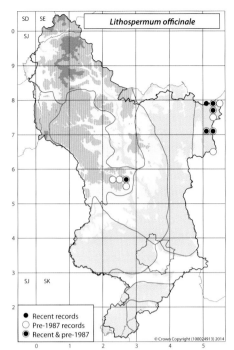

areas, plus the southern part of the county (Calke SK32 & Drakelow SK22, both for 1903).

Lithospermum arvense L.
Field Gromwell

COUNTY STATUS: Established (Archaeophyte)
CONSERVATION STATUS: DRDB (Cat2), EN, A, B, C
FIRST YEAR: 1789 LATEST YEAR: 2001 NO OF RECORDS: 20
RECENT SQUARES: monads 2; tetrads 2; hectads 2
ALL SQUARES: monads 7; tetrads 7; hectads 12

Field Gromwell is a very rare, anciently established annual of open ground and arable land on lighter soils. There are only two modern records, both from the north-east of the county: Scarcliffe Park (SK5170) and Stonegravels (SK3872). It was previously more widely spread, being scattered from Charlesworth (SK09) in the

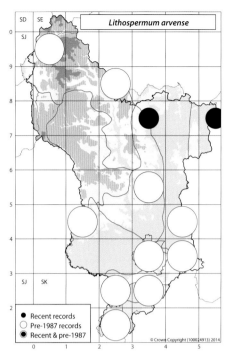

north, through Matlock (SK35) and Allestree (SK33), to Caldwell (SK21) in the south.

Echium vulgare L.
Viper's-bugloss

COUNTY STATUS: Native
CONSERVATION STATUS: None
FIRST YEAR: 1789 LATEST YEAR: 2012 NO OF RECORDS: 108
RECENT SQUARES: monads 33; tetrads 28; hectads 18
ALL SQUARES: monads 47; tetrads 40; hectads 21

Viper's-bugloss is a rare native biennial of open grasslands, disturbed areas and cultivated ground, on light well-drained soils. It occurs scattered throughout Derbyshire from near Torside Bridge (SK0698) and Ridgeway Moor (SK4080) in the north, through Minninglow (SK2057), to Carver's Rocks (SK3222) in the south. It is

Viper's-bugloss (*Echium vulgare*) on floor of Longsidings Quarry (SK0975), June 2011 (Kieron Huston)

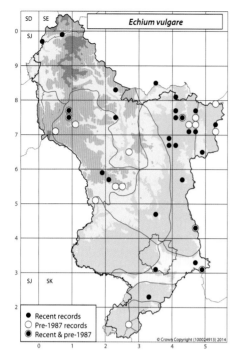

also sometimes planted in wild flower seed mixes, when it can persist, as it did through the 1990s at Sinfin Moor (SK3431).

Echium plantagineum L.
Purple Viper's-bugloss

Purple Viper's-bugloss is a casual biennial of waste ground. The only record was made by K. Balkow on imported soil at Heeley (SK3484) in 2003. It is considered native in Cornwall but casual over most of southern Britain.

Pulmonaria officinalis L.
Lungwort

Lungwort is a rare established perennial of waysides, wood margins and waste

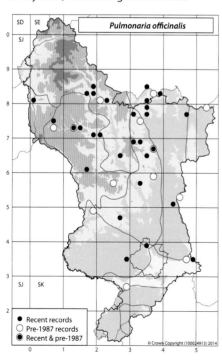

COUNTY STATUS: Established (Neophyte)	
CONSERVATION STATUS: None	
FIRST YEAR: 1847 **LATEST YEAR:** 2012 **NO OF RECORDS:** 59	
RECENT SQUARES: monads 25; tetrads 29; hectads 18	
ALL SQUARES: monads 39; tetrads 40; hectads 24	

ground. It occurs scattered throughout the county (Yorkshire Bridge SK1984, Chee Dale SK1273, Wren Park Wood SK3667, Golden Valley SK4251 & Slade Plantation SK2935). Much grown in gardens for ornament, it occurs naturally in continental Europe.

Symphytum officinale L.
Common Comfrey

COUNTY STATUS: Native	
CONSERVATION STATUS: None	
FIRST YEAR: 1789 **LATEST YEAR:** 2012 **NO OF RECORDS:** 273	
RECENT SQUARES: monads 87; tetrads 83; hectads 29	
ALL SQUARES: monads 156; tetrads 140; hectads 35	

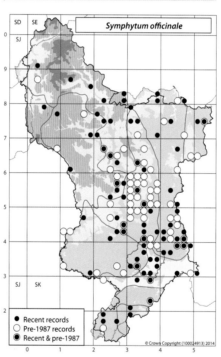

Common Comfrey is an occasional native perennial on the sides of streams and ditches. It is scattered throughout the county, but has been so confused in the past with Russian Comfrey (S. × uplandicum) that its correct distribution is unclear. Nationally it is a plant of the lowlands that reaches its British altitudinal limit of 320m near Buxton (Preston et al. 2002).

Symphytum × uplandicum Nyman
Russian Comfrey

COUNTY STATUS: Established (Neophyte)	
CONSERVATION STATUS: None	
FIRST YEAR: 1903 **LATEST YEAR:** 2013 **NO OF RECORDS:** 903	
RECENT SQUARES: monads 574; tetrads 411; hectads 40	
ALL SQUARES: monads 587; tetrads 415; hectads 40	

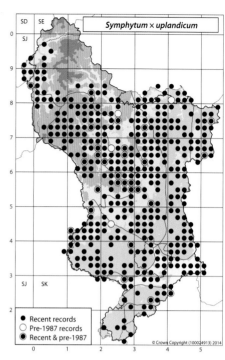

Russian Comfrey is an established perennial of waysides, rough grassland and wasteland. It occurs frequently throughout Derbyshire except for the high moors of the Peak District. It is the hybrid of Common (S. officinale) and Rough Comfrey (S. asperum) and was introduced into Britain at the end of the 19th century as a fodder crop, but is little used now. Its origin is uncertain.

Symphytum asperum Lepech.
Rough Comfrey

COUNTY STATUS: Casual	
CONSERVATION STATUS: None	
FIRST YEAR: 1987 **LATEST YEAR:** 2008 **NO OF RECORDS:** 5	
RECENT SQUARES: monads 5; tetrads 5; hectads 3	
ALL SQUARES: monads 5; tetrads 5; hectads 3	

Rough Comfrey is a very rare, casual perennial. There are only five records, all recent. Four are for the White Peak (SK1760, 1767, 2556 & 2656) and the fifth for the Dark Peak (Curbar Gap SK2574). Nationally it is a lowland plant that reaches its British altitudinal limit of 315m here at Sheldon (Preston et al. 2002). A native of south-western Asia, it was once grown as an ornamental, but is little used today.

Symphytum tuberosum L.
Tuberous Comfrey

COUNTY STATUS: Casual	
CONSERVATION STATUS: None	
FIRST YEAR: 1969 **LATEST YEAR:** 2003 **NO OF RECORDS:** 9	
RECENT SQUARES: monads 6; tetrads 5; hectads 5	
ALL SQUARES: monads 7; tetrads 6; hectads 7	

Tuberous Comfrey is a very rare, casual perennial of waysides and rough ground.

There are seven recent records scattered through the area including: Great Longstone (SK2071), Allen Wood (SK3175), Scarcliffe (SK4968), Brook Farm (SK3027) and near Caldwell (SK2618). Older records from Crich (SK35) in 1913 and Gannabrig Wood (SK5474) in the 1970s have been taken to suggest the plant was once native here (Clapham 1969). It is indigenous to northern Britain.

Symphytum × hidcotense P.D. Sell
Hidcote Comfrey
Hidcote Comfrey is an ornamental garden plant and an established perennial of waysides and waste ground. There are only two records, both since 2000: Linnet Clough (SJ9788) and Stanton Bridge (SK4639). It is a hybrid of garden origin, possibly between Creeping (*S. grandiflorum*) and Russian Comfrey (*S. × uplandicum*).

Symphytum grandiflorum DC.
Creeping Comfrey
Creeping Comfrey is an established perennial of waysides and waste ground, and a native of the Caucasus. There are fourteen records scattered through the county, all between 2001 and 2013. Example sites are: Norbury Hall (SK1242), Dale Brook (SK2624), Blacka Moor (SK2980), Monk Wood (SK3576) and Ecclesall Wood (SK3181). Planted for ornament, its vigorous growth often leads to its escape or disposal over the garden wall.

Symphytum orientale L.
White Comfrey
White Comfrey is an established perennial of waysides, woods and waste ground. There are recent records from just three sites (Ladies Spring Wood SK3281 in 2007, Risley SK4635 in 2011 & Long Eaton SK4934 in 2009), plus two earlier ones from Bramley Vale (SK4566) in 1969, and Totley Wood (SK3281) in 1951. Grown in gardens, it is indigenous to western Russia and Turkey.

Brunnera macrophylla (Adams) I.M. Johnst.
Great Forget-me-not
Great Forget-me-not is a herbaceous perennial, widely grown in gardens. Our one record is a casual at Hazelbarrow Farm (SK3681), reported as a throwout on a lane by K. Balkow in 2006. It occurs naturally in the Caucasus.

Anchusa azurea Mill.
Garden Anchusa
Garden Anchusa is an attractive casual perennial, grown in gardens for ornament. The only record is from Rowsley Sidings (SK2564) in 1996 where it may have been a garden escape or a bird-seed alien. It grows naturally in southern Europe.

Anchusa arvensis (L.) M. Bieb.
Bugloss

COUNTY STATUS: Established (Archaeophyte)
CONSERVATION STATUS: None
FIRST YEAR: 1789 LATEST YEAR: 2011 NO OF RECORDS: 68
RECENT SQUARES: monads 26; tetrads 27; hectads 16
ALL SQUARES: monads 45; tetrads 44; hectads 21

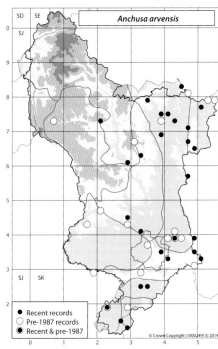

Bugloss is a rare, anciently established annual of open disturbed areas and arable fields, particularly on lighter soils. It occurs scattered from Dronfield (SK3578) and Beighton (SK4483) in the north, through Mugginton Pit (SK2845) and Locko Park (SK4238), to Drakelow Power Station (SK2219) and Mount Pleasant Barn (SK2913) in the south. It appears to have become less frequent on arable sites since 1969, no doubt due to agricultural intensification, but more frequent on disturbed ground.

Pentaglottis sempervirens (L.) Tausch ex L.H. Bailey
Green Alkanet

COUNTY STATUS: Established (Neophyte)
CONSERVATION STATUS: None
FIRST YEAR: 1903 LATEST YEAR: 2013 NO OF RECORDS: 276
RECENT SQUARES: monads 161; tetrads 146; hectads 33
ALL SQUARES: monads 174; tetrads 154; hectads 34

Green Alkanet is an established perennial of waysides and waste ground, generally near habitation. Except for the high moors and limestone plateau of the Peak District, it is found occasionally across the county. A native of south-western Europe, it is often grown in gardens and spreads so

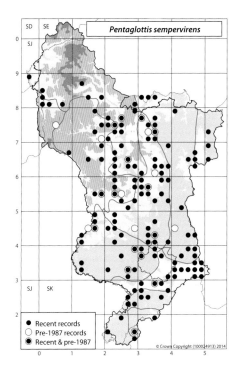

vigorously that it easily escapes or gets thrown out.

Borago officinalis L.
Borage

COUNTY STATUS: Casual
CONSERVATION STATUS: None
FIRST YEAR: 1829 LATEST YEAR: 2012 NO OF RECORDS: 40
RECENT SQUARES: monads 21; tetrads 23; hectads 16
ALL SQUARES: monads 24; tetrads 26; hectads 18

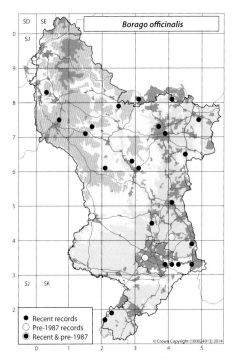

Borage is a rare casual annual of rough ground and waysides, often near houses. It is found throughout the county, from Brierley Green (SK0282) and Ridgeway (SK4081) in the north, to Long Eaton (SK4733) and

Walton (SK2017) in the south. Indigenous to southern Europe, it is often grown in gardens and also occurs in bird-seed.

Trachystemon orientalis (L.) G. Don
Abraham-Isaac-Jacob

COUNTY STATUS: Established (Neophyte)
CONSERVATION STATUS: None
FIRST YEAR: 1977 LATEST YEAR: 2004 NO OF RECORDS: 8
RECENT SQUARES: monads 4; tetrads 4; hectads 3
ALL SQUARES: monads 4; tetrads 4; hectads 3

Abraham-Isaac-Jacob is an established perennial of waysides, grasslands and disturbed habitats. There are four recent records: Buxton (SK0671 & 0672), the Monsal Trail (SK1373) and at Norton (SK3582) where it was first found in 1977. A popular ornamental garden plant, it is a native of eastern Europe.

Amsinckia lycopsoides Lehm.
Scarce Fiddleneck

Locally extinct, Scarce Fiddleneck was a very rare, casual annual of waysides. There are only two records both in Linton (1903): Miller's Dale (SK17) and Hilton (SK23). Clapham (1969) gave a record for near Castle Donington (SK4428), but this is in v.c.55 Leicestershire. It is a native of western North America.

Amsinckia micrantha Suksd.
Common Fiddleneck

COUNTY STATUS: Casual
CONSERVATION STATUS: None
FIRST YEAR: 1973 LATEST YEAR: 2012 NO OF RECORDS: 10
RECENT SQUARES: monads 9; tetrads 8; hectads 7
ALL SQUARES: monads 10; tetrads 9; hectads 7

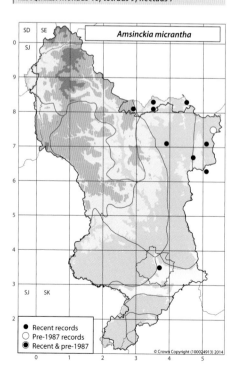

Common Fiddleneck is a very rare, casual annual of waysides and rough ground, particularly on light disturbed soils. Most locations are in the north-eastern corner of the county (Dyche Lane SK3580, Beighton SK4483 & Pleasley SK5063) but it is increasingly being recorded in the south as at Derby (SK3635) in 2012. Originating from western North America, it is a seed contaminant of grain that is spreading nationally (Stace 2010).

Myosotis scorpioides L.
Water Forget-me-not

COUNTY STATUS: Native
CONSERVATION STATUS: None
FIRST YEAR: 1789 LATEST YEAR: 2013 NO OF RECORDS: 1,064
RECENT SQUARES: monads 422; tetrads 307; hectads 40
ALL SQUARES: monads 458; tetrads 324; hectads 40

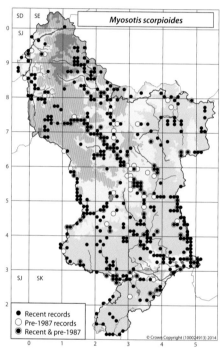

Water Forget-me-not is an occasional native perennial. It grows in and by the edges of ponds, rivers and canals, and in marshes and fens. It occurs throughout the county particularly at lower altitudes along river valleys.

Myosotis secunda Al. Murray
Creeping Forget-me-not

COUNTY STATUS: Native
CONSERVATION STATUS: B
FIRST YEAR: 1878 LATEST YEAR: 2012 NO OF RECORDS: 302
RECENT SQUARES: monads 155; tetrads 116; hectads 20
ALL SQUARES: monads 174; tetrads 132; hectads 28

Creeping Forget-me-not is an attractive native annual or short-lived perennial. It is frequent in the Dark and South West Peak Areas by upland streams, springs and flushes, generally on peaty soils. Elsewhere it is very

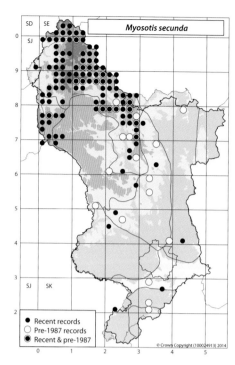

rare, with isolated occurrences at Baldock Mill (SK4240), Ashbourne Airfield (SK2045), Atlow (SK2248) and in the Via Gellia (SK2857). Previously it was more frequently recorded outside the upland Peak with sites as far south as Twyford Greens (SK3228) and Repton Rocks (SK3222) both in 1973.

Myosotis laxa Lehm.
Tufted Forget-me-not

COUNTY STATUS: Native
CONSERVATION STATUS: None
FIRST YEAR: 1837 LATEST YEAR: 2012 NO OF RECORDS: 362
RECENT SQUARES: monads 174; tetrads 155; hectads 35
ALL SQUARES: monads 234; tetrads 201; hectads 36

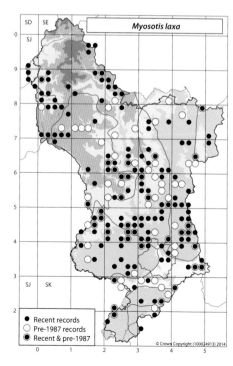

Tufted Forget-me-not is an occasional native annual or biennial. It occurs throughout the area in and by the edges of ponds and streams, and in marshes and fens (Birch Vale Mill Ponds SK0186, Ashes Farm SK1888, Peat Brooks SK3252, Golden Brook Storage Lagoon SK4633 & Drakelow Power Station SK2219).

Myosotis sylvatica Ehrh. ex Hoffm.
Wood Forget-me-not

COUNTY STATUS: Native
CONSERVATION STATUS: None
FIRST YEAR: 1789 **LATEST YEAR:** 2013 **NO OF RECORDS:** 1,589
RECENT SQUARES: monads 762; tetrads 480; hectads 42
ALL SQUARES: monads 811; tetrads 501; hectads 42

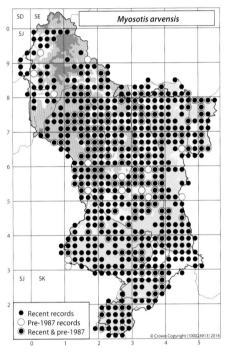

Wood Forget-me-not is a frequent native perennial of woods, hedges and other

damp shaded habitats. It is also often grown in gardens, and many lowland occurrences probably represent escapes from cultivation. Flowers of forget-me-nots are often represented in traditional Ashford Black Marble inlay work, though they are not necessarily of this particular species.

Myosotis arvensis (L.) Hill
Field Forget-me-not

COUNTY STATUS: Established (Archaeophyte)
CONSERVATION STATUS: None
FIRST YEAR: 1789 **LATEST YEAR:** 2013 **NO OF RECORDS:** 1,599
RECENT SQUARES: monads 880; tetrads 542; hectads 42
ALL SQUARES: monads 939; tetrads 556; hectads 42

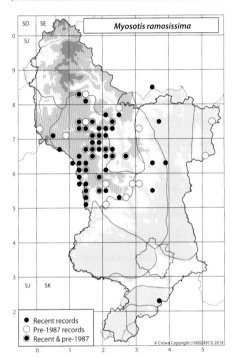

Field Forget-me-not is a dainty annual or short-lived perennial of dry bare habitats

such as arable fields, open grassland, disturbed ground, gardens, walls and quarries. It occurs commonly through the county except for the high moors of the Peak District. Once thought of as native, it is now considered to be an ancient introduction.

Myosotis ramosissima Rochel
Early Forget-me-not

COUNTY STATUS: Native
CONSERVATION STATUS: None
FIRST YEAR: 1837 **LATEST YEAR:** 2012 **NO OF RECORDS:** 164
RECENT SQUARES: monads 53; tetrads 51; hectads 14
ALL SQUARES: monads 64; tetrads 64; hectads 17

Early Forget-me-not is an occasional native annual of dry open habitats such as bare grassland, rock outcrops and walls in the White Peak (Winnats Pass SK18G, Monyash SK16N & Parwich Village SK15X). It is very rare elsewhere in similar habitats (Ticknall Quarries SK3623 & Chesterfield SK3675).

Myosotis discolor Pers.
Changing Forget-me-not

COUNTY STATUS: Native
CONSERVATION STATUS: None
FIRST YEAR: 1829 **LATEST YEAR:** 2012 **NO OF RECORDS:** 96
RECENT SQUARES: monads 44; tetrads 41; hectads 20
ALL SQUARES: monads 63; tetrads 59; hectads 27

Changing Forget-me-not is a rare native annual of dry bare habitats such as in open grassland and disturbed ground. It occurs from Torside Reservoir (SK0698) and Parson's Piece (SK2288) in the north, through Over Haddon (SK2066), to Hulland Hollow (SK2445) and Hagg Lane (SK4339) in the south. Previously it also occurred

Wood Forget-me-not (*Myosotis sylvatica*), Darley Fields Derby (SK3538), May 2003 (Bill Grange)

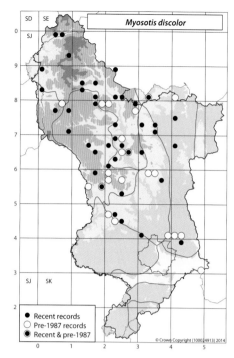

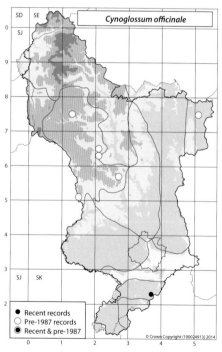

further south as at Calke and Repton (SK22) in 1903, and Drakelow (SK21) in 1969.

Cynoglossum officinale L.
Hound's-tongue

| COUNTY STATUS: Native |
| CONSERVATION STATUS: DRDB (Cat2), NT, A, B |
| FIRST YEAR: 1789 LATEST YEAR: 2013 NO OF RECORDS: 32 |
| RECENT SQUARES: monads 2; tetrads 1; hectads 1 |
| ALL SQUARES: monads 11; tetrads 7; hectads 8 |

Hound's-tongue is a very rare, native biennial of disturbed ground and grassland in the south of the county. All recent records have been from Calke Park (SK3622 & 3722). In the past it was scattered widely

over Derbyshire's limestone landscapes, including Markland Grips (SK5074) in the Magnesian Limestone, plus Buxton (SK07), Dove Dale (SK1451) and Via Gellia (SK2656) in the White Peak Character Area. Reasons for this contraction of range are uncertain, but it is on its northern British limits here.

Phacelia tanacetifolia Benth.
Phacelia

| COUNTY STATUS: Casual |
| CONSERVATION STATUS: None |
| FIRST YEAR: 1999 LATEST YEAR: 2012 NO OF RECORDS: 9 |
| RECENT SQUARES: monads 9; tetrads 9; hectads 8 |
| ALL SQUARES: monads 9; tetrads 9; hectads 8 |

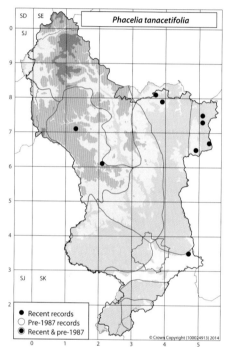

Phacelia is a very rare, casual annual of arable land, disturbed ground and restored grasslands. Records are scattered over central parts (Taddington SK1371, South-eastern Sheffield SK3781, M1 Junction 25 SK4735 & Shirebrook Colliery SK5366). A native of California, it is increasingly being planted for ornament or as a nectar source for insects, so may be expected to occur more frequently in the future.

Cerinthe major L.
Greater Honeywort

Greater Honeywort is an annual herb grown in gardens for its attractive flowers and foliage. There is one record found as a casual at Station Road, Sandiacre (SK4836) by R. Martin in 2005. It is native to southern Europe.

CONVOLVULACEAE

Convolvulus arvensis L.
Field Bindweed

Field Bindweed is a climbing native

| COUNTY STATUS: Native |
| CONSERVATION STATUS: None |
| FIRST YEAR: 1789 LATEST YEAR: 2013 NO OF RECORDS: 1,019 |
| RECENT SQUARES: monads 512; tetrads 329; hectads 37 |
| ALL SQUARES: monads 569; tetrads 356; hectads 37 |

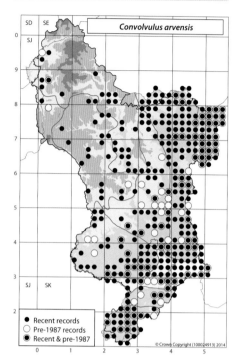

perennial of wasteland, cultivated ground, waysides and grasslands. It is common in the southern and eastern parts of the county, becoming rarer in more upland parts of the Peak District.

Calystegia sepium (L.) R. Br.
Hedge Bindweed

Hedge Bindweed is a native climbing perennial of hedges, fens, marshes,

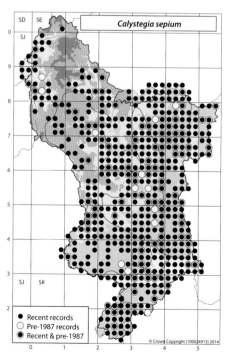

COUNTY STATUS: Native
CONSERVATION STATUS: None
FIRST YEAR: 1789 LATEST YEAR: 2013 NO OF RECORDS: 1,494
RECENT SQUARES: monads 824; tetrads 495; hectads 40
ALL SQUARES: monads 870; tetrads 508; hectads 40

gardens and rough ground. It is common everywhere except for the high moors of the Peak District, where it is rare. It reaches its national altitudinal limit (365m) near Buxton (Preston *et al.* 2002). The local plant is ssp. *sepium* and there is one record for its forma *schizoflora* (Druce) Stace on the Erewash Canal (SK4644).

Calystegia × lucana (Ten.) G. Don
A hybrid bindweed
This hybrid bindweed is a native climbing perennial of hedges and rough ground. There are only three local records, all recent: Ashbourne (SK1846), Peak Forest (SK1179) and Killingley's Farm (SK3469). It is the hybrid of the native Hedge (*C. sepium*) and the introduced Large Bindweed (*C. silvatica*).

Calystegia pulchra Brummitt & Heywood
Hairy Bindweed

COUNTY STATUS: Established (Neophyte)
CONSERVATION STATUS: None
FIRST YEAR: 1947 LATEST YEAR: 2012 NO OF RECORDS: 50
RECENT SQUARES: monads 21; tetrads 20; hectads 13
ALL SQUARES: monads 38; tetrads 35; hectads 19

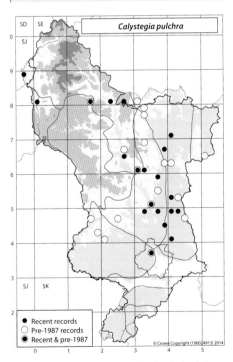

Hairy Bindweed is an established climbing perennial of hedges and rough ground. It occurs rarely scattered throughout the county from Start Lane (SK0081 v.c.58) and Stony Ridge (SK2780) in the north, through Matlock (SK36A), to King Street Derby

(SK3436) and Stanley (SK4140) in the south. It is of uncertain, possibly hybrid, origin.

Calystegia silvatica (Kit.) Griseb.
Large Bindweed

COUNTY STATUS: Established (Neophyte)
CONSERVATION STATUS: None
FIRST YEAR: 1950 LATEST YEAR: 2013 NO OF RECORDS: 559
RECENT SQUARES: monads 335; tetrads 270; hectads 38
ALL SQUARES: monads 369; tetrads 290; hectads 39

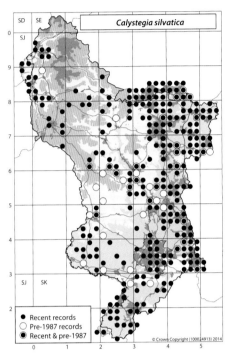

Large Bindweed is an established climbing perennial of hedges and waste ground. It is frequent in the lowland south and east, but is rare in the more upland parts of the Peak District. It is a native of southern Europe.

Cuscuta europaea L.
Greater Dodder
Locally extinct, Greater Dodder was a rootless parasitic perennial, recorded just once as casual in Glover (1829). There have been no further records despite the plant occurring naturally in central and southern England, and the abundance of its usual host, Common Nettle (*Urtica dioica*).

Cuscuta epithymum (L.) L.
Dodder
Locally extinct, Dodder was a very rare, rootless parasitic perennial on gorse (*Ulex* species), Heather (*Calluna vulgaris*) and clovers (*Trifolium* species). All records were from southern Derbyshire: Repton (SK32) and Bretby (SK22) both for 1881, and Osmaston (SK24), Yeldersley (SK24) and Ockbrook (SK43) all for 1903. When on clovers, it was probably a casual introduced with the crop, but it may have been native on the other hosts mentioned.

SOLANACEAE

Lycium barbarum L.
Duke of Argyll's Teaplant

COUNTY STATUS: Established (Neophyte)
CONSERVATION STATUS: None
FIRST YEAR: 1903 LATEST YEAR: 2012 NO OF RECORDS: 90
RECENT SQUARES: monads 32; tetrads 39; hectads 21
ALL SQUARES: monads 50; tetrads 57; hectads 28

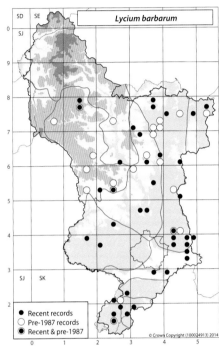

Duke of Argyll's Teaplant is an established spiny shrub of hedges, walls and waste places. It occurs rarely throughout Derbyshire from Clowne (SK47X) and near White Rake (SK1477) in the north, through Hopton Village (SK2553) and Stanley (SK4240), to Coton in the Elms (SK2415) in the south. It is planted to form hedges, and can spread from these by suckers or bird-sown seed to more natural settings. Much confused with the Chinese Teaplant (*L. chinense*), it is a native of China.

Lycium chinense Mill.
Chinese Teaplant

COUNTY STATUS: Established (Neophyte)
CONSERVATION STATUS: None
FIRST YEAR: 1950 LATEST YEAR: 2000 NO OF RECORDS: 27
RECENT SQUARES: monads 6; tetrads 5; hectads 4
ALL SQUARES: monads 15; tetrads 15; hectads 20

Chinese Teaplant is an established spiny shrub of hedges, walls and waste ground. It has only been recorded from five tetrads recently: Ivy House (SK1659), Bradford Dale (SK2063), Youlgrave (SK2064), Hallam Lock (SK4839) and Creswell Crags (SK5374). Previously it was found more frequently and over a wider area. However, this apparent contraction is probably due to

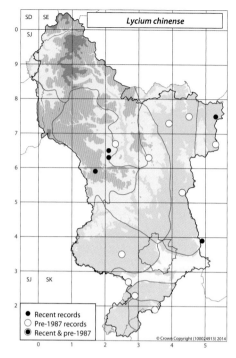

over-recording in the past for Duke of Argyll's Teaplant (*L. barbarum*). It is planted to form hedges, and can spread from these by suckers or bird-sown seed. It is indigenous to China.

Atropa belladonna L.
Deadly Nightshade

COUNTY STATUS:	Casual
CONSERVATION STATUS:	B
FIRST YEAR: 1787	LATEST YEAR: 2006 NO OF RECORDS: 28
RECENT SQUARES:	monads 6; tetrads 6; hectads 6
ALL SQUARES:	monads 12; tetrads 9; hectads 11

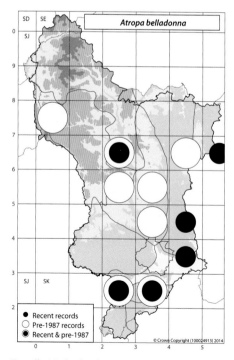

Deadly Nightshade is a very rare perennial of scrub, waysides and waste ground,

that occurs scattered throughout the county. It is possibly native at some sites, such as Conksbury Bridge (SK2165) but only casual elsewhere, as on waste ground at Ilkeston (SK4642). At other sites, such as at Pleasley Vale (SK5265), Erewash Canal bank (SK4836) and Winshill (SK2623), it is impossible to decide on its status. It was grown as a medicinal herb, and occurs naturally elsewhere in central Britain.

Hyoscyamus niger L.
Henbane

COUNTY STATUS:	Established (Archaeophyte)
CONSERVATION STATUS:	DRDB (Cat2), VU, A, B
FIRST YEAR: 1789	LATEST YEAR: 2006 NO OF RECORDS: 30
RECENT SQUARES:	monads 3; tetrads 3; hectads 2
ALL SQUARES:	monads 10; tetrads 10; hectads 11

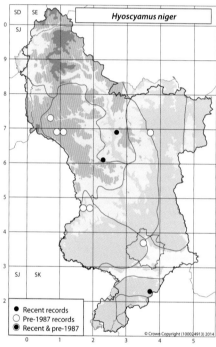

Henbane is a very rare, long-established annual or biennial of open disturbed areas especially where there are light soils. Recent records are scattered through the centre and south of the county: Winster (SK2360), Chatsworth (SK2669) and Calke Park (SK3622). Older records are scattered over a wider area and include Standen (SK0772), Pinxton (SK45) and Stapenhill (SK22). Derbyshire is towards the northern limit of its British range.

Nicandra physalodes (L.) Gaertn.
Apple-of-Peru

COUNTY STATUS:	Casual
CONSERVATION STATUS:	None
FIRST YEAR: 1980	LATEST YEAR: 2007 NO OF RECORDS: 10
RECENT SQUARES:	monads 7; tetrads 7; hectads 6
ALL SQUARES:	monads 8; tetrads 8; hectads 7

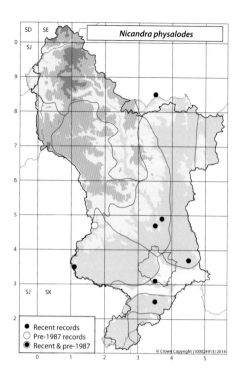

Apple-of-Peru is a very rare, casual annual of waysides, waste places and cultivated ground. There are several recent records scattered over the county including: Doveridge (SK1134), Heeley (SK3484), Ticknall (SK3524) and Sandiacre Lodge Farm (SK4437); plus an earlier one from Ashbourne (SK1746) in 1980. Grown in gardens for ornament, it is also a bird-seed alien and a native of South America.

Datura stramonium L.
Thorn-apple

Thorn-apple is a very rare, casual annual of waste land and cultivated ground. It was more common and widespread in the past,

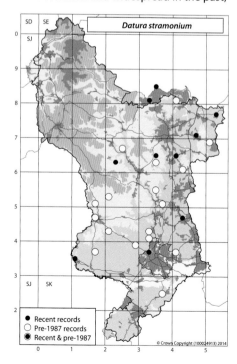

COUNTY STATUS: Casual
CONSERVATION STATUS: None
FIRST YEAR: 1789 LATEST YEAR: 2011 NO OF RECORDS: 45
RECENT SQUARES: monads 10; tetrads 10; hectads 9
ALL SQUARES: monads 28; tetrads 27; hectads 20

with recent records scattered throughout central and southern Derbyshire: Whitwell (SK5376), Birchover (SK2362) and Markeaton Park (SK3337). Arising as a contaminant of bird feed and other seeds, it probably originates from the Americas.

Physalis alkekengi L.
Japanese-lantern

Japanese-lantern is a very rare, casual perennial of waste land and tips. The only records are from Manners Industrial Estate (SK4542) in 1998 and Long Eaton Station (SK4832) in 2001. A native of central and southern Europe, it is grown in gardens for ornament and fruit, and generally escapes as a throwout.

Solanum nigrum L.
Black Nightshade

COUNTY STATUS: Native
CONSERVATION STATUS: None
FIRST YEAR: 1789 LATEST YEAR: 2013 NO OF RECORDS: 168
RECENT SQUARES: monads 103; tetrads 82; hectads 23
ALL SQUARES: monads 122; tetrads 96; hectads 25

Black Nightshade is a native annual weed of arable crops, gardens and waste ground. In the 2000s it became particularly noticeable as a weed of fodder maize in the Derby area. It occurs occasionally throughout eastern and southern parts (Fanshawe Gate SK3178, Grange Park

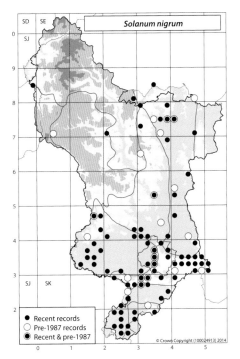

SK53B & Lullington SK2413), but is very rare elsewhere. Our plants are generally referable to ssp. nigrum.

Solanum physalifolium Rusby
Green Nightshade

Green Nightshade is a very rare, casual annual of disturbed land and is a native of South America. The only recent record is from Heeley (SK3484) in 2003. Before that it was known between 1971 and 1976 from a garden in Ashbourne (SK1746), but was originally misidentified as **Leafy-fruited Nightshade (S. sarachoides)** in Patrick & Hollick (1974).

Black Nightshade (*Solanum nigrum*), Allestree/Quarndon (SK3340), September 2008 (Bill Grange)

Bittersweet (*Solanum dulcamara*), Allestree/ Quarndon (SK3340), August 2013 (Bill Grange)

Solanum dulcamara L.
Bittersweet

COUNTY STATUS: Native
CONSERVATION STATUS: None
FIRST YEAR: 1789 LATEST YEAR: 2013 NO OF RECORDS: 2,910
RECENT SQUARES: monads 1,164; tetrads 502; hectads 40
ALL SQUARES: monads 1,232; tetrads 509; hectads 40

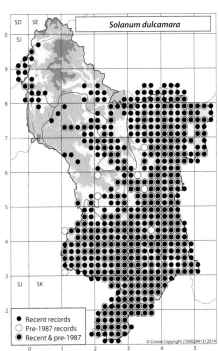

Bittersweet is a scrambling native perennial of waysides, riverbanks, woods, fens and waste ground. It is very common throughout southern and eastern parts, but in the north and west is much rarer, being confined to lower-lying areas such as the valley of the River Derwent.

Solanum tuberosum L.
Potato

COUNTY STATUS: Casual
CONSERVATION STATUS: None
FIRST YEAR: 1970 LATEST YEAR: 2013 NO OF RECORDS: 45
RECENT SQUARES: monads 36; tetrads 34; hectads 19
ALL SQUARES: monads 41; tetrads 40; hectads 21

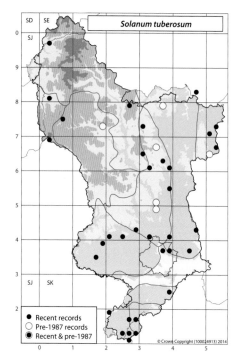

Potato is a rare casual perennial of waysides, tips and waste ground. It is widely cultivated, and readily regenerates from discarded waste. It also occurs in fields and gardens as a relic of cultivation. Probably under-recorded, it originates from South America.

Solanum lycopersicum L.
Tomato

COUNTY STATUS: Casual		
CONSERVATION STATUS: None		
FIRST YEAR: 1970 LATEST YEAR: 2011 NO OF RECORDS: 34		
RECENT SQUARES: monads 29; tetrads 27; hectads 19		
ALL SQUARES: monads 32; tetrads 30; hectads 21		

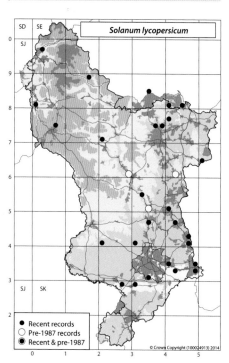

Tomato is a scrambling casual annual of waste ground, sewage works, tips and waysides. It occurs very rarely scattered throughout the area but is under-recorded as many botanists do not bother to note its presence. Grown in gardens as a salad or vegetable, it finds its way into more natural settings by being discarded in waste either before or after being eaten. It is indigenous to central and southern America.

Solanum rostratum Dunal
Buffalo-bur
Buffalo-bur is a very rare, casual annual of cultivated and disturbed ground where it originates as a contaminant of bird feed or other seeds. The only recent record is from Heeley (SK3484) in 2003. Previously it was noted from Boythorpe (SK3870) in 1983 and Cornhill (SK3439) in 1976. It is a native of North America.

Nicotiana × sanderae W. Watson
A hybrid tobacco
This hybrid tobacco is a casual annual, grown in gardens for ornament. The sole record is from Fairfield Tip (SK0674) in 1996. It is a hybrid of garden origin from Sweet (*N. alata* Link & Otto) and Red Tobacco (*N. forgetiana* Hemsl.) both of which originate from South America.

Petunia × hybrida (Hook.) Vilm.
Petunia
Petunia is a very rare, casual annual of disturbed ground and waste land. It is recorded from only three sites, all between 2003 and 2010: Heeley (SK3484), Sheepbridge (SK3775) and Lock Lane (SK4831). It is a hybrid of garden origin, much grown for ornament.

OLEACEAE

Forsythia × intermedia Zabel
Forsythia
Forsythia is an established shrub of waste ground. There are five records from between 1987 and 2011: Sides Lane (SK1544), Church Gresley (SK2918), Derby City (SK33), Oak Hurst (SK3452) and Barlow Brook (SK3575). Much grown in gardens, it is either a relic of cultivation or throwout but is of uncertain origin.

Forsythia suspensa (Thunb.) Vahl
Golden-bell
Golden-bell is an established shrub of waste ground, only known from Fallgate (SK3562) in 1994. It is a commonly grown garden ornamental that is native to China.

Fraxinus excelsior L.
Ash

COUNTY STATUS: Native		
CONSERVATION STATUS: None		
FIRST YEAR: 1789 LATEST YEAR: 2013 NO OF RECORDS: 7,260		
RECENT SQUARES: monads 2,214; tetrads 712; hectads 42		
ALL SQUARES: monads 2,253; tetrads 715; hectads 42		

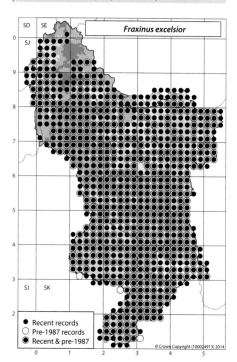

Ash is a very common, native tree of woods, rough ground and hedges, particularly on damp base-rich soils in valley bottoms. It also forms almost pure woods on scree-slopes in the dales of the White Peak, and is an early coloniser of waste ground and abandoned quarries. It occurs throughout the county except for the high moors of the Dark and South West Peak. The largest known tree, with a girth of 8m, is at Allestree Park (SK3440). As an important component of daleside vegetation of the White Peak, its status there has attracted much research (Merton 1970 & Scurfield 1959). The general consensus is that these woods are not ancient, but the result of relatively recent colonisation after a reduction in grazing pressure. As a common tree, it has lent itself to many local place names such as Ashbourne, Ashford and Ashwood Dale. It also figures in local legends such as the Sheldon Duck. Here in 1610 a duck was seen to fly into an Ash tree but not to fly out again. It was thus known as the Duck Tree for nearly three centuries. When finally felled, the image of a duck was found in its grain. Unfortunately in 2012 it seemed the continued existence of this important species in the county could be seriously threatened by the arrival of a violent fungal disease new to the country – **Ash Dieback (*Chalara fraxinea*)**.

Fraxinus ornus L.
Manna Ash

Manna Ash is a very rare, planted tree of hedges and waysides, indigenous to southern Europe. There are records from only two sites: Radbourne Lane (SK2935) in 2011 and Erewash Canal (SK4741) in 1999. It is virtually indistinguishable from Ash (F. excelsior) except when flowering, so is probably under-recorded.

Syringa vulgaris L.
Lilac

COUNTY STATUS:	Casual
CONSERVATION STATUS:	None
FIRST YEAR: 1969	LATEST YEAR: 2012 NO OF RECORDS: 239
RECENT SQUARES:	monads 135; tetrads 136; hectads 34
ALL SQUARES:	monads 145; tetrads 144; hectads 34

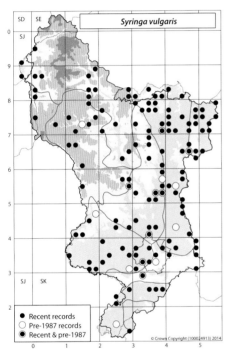

Lilac is a casual shrub of hedges and waysides, generally near habitations, and of waste ground. It occurs occasionally from Compstall (SJ9690) and Ladybower Reservoir (SK1888) in the north, through Middleton Cross (SK2855), to Netherseal (SK2813) and Lock Lane Ash Tip (SK4831) in the south. It is much grown in gardens and hedges for its fragrant flowers, and spreads to more natural situations by suckers, throwouts and, rarely, by seeds. It is a native of south-eastern Europe.

Ligustrum vulgare L.
Wild Privet

COUNTY STATUS:	Native
CONSERVATION STATUS:	None
FIRST YEAR: 1789	LATEST YEAR: 2013 NO OF RECORDS: 647
RECENT SQUARES:	monads 265; tetrads 224; hectads 32
ALL SQUARES:	monads 304; tetrads 265; hectads 34

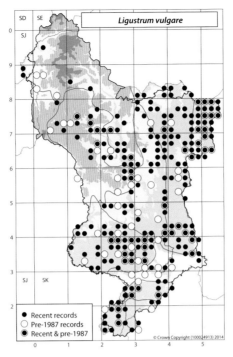

Wild Privet is a native shrub of woods, hedges and scrub, particularly on base-rich soils. It is also widely planted in hedges near houses and gardens. It is very common on the Magnesian Limestone, as at Pebley (SK4878) and Pleasley Park (SK5165). Elsewhere it is occasional throughout the area from Marple Bridge (SJ9688) in the north, through the Via Gellia (SK2857), to Westbrook Farm (SK2312) in the south.

Ligustrum ovalifolium Hassk.
Garden Privet

Garden Privet is a casual evergreen shrub of waste ground, waysides tips and

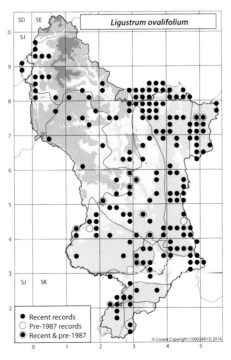

COUNTY STATUS:	Casual
CONSERVATION STATUS:	None
FIRST YEAR: 1949	LATEST YEAR: 2013 NO OF RECORDS: 316
RECENT SQUARES:	monads 219; tetrads 180; hectads 35
ALL SQUARES:	monads 226; tetrads 183; hectads 35

hedges. It grows occasionally throughout Derbyshire from the River Etherow (SK0196) and Birley Vale (SK3984) in the north, through Lea Bridge (SK3156), to Netherseal (SK2812) and Sawley (SK4631) in the south. It is commonly planted near houses and in gardens for hedging and, as it is rarely self-sown, it is generally a relic of cultivation or a garden throwout. It is indigenous to Japan.

VERONICACEAE

Digitalis purpurea L.
Foxglove

COUNTY STATUS:	Native
CONSERVATION STATUS:	None
FIRST YEAR: 1789	LATEST YEAR: 2013 NO OF RECORDS: 3,743
RECENT SQUARES:	monads 1,498; tetrads 626; hectads 42
ALL SQUARES:	monads 1,547; tetrads 636; hectads 42

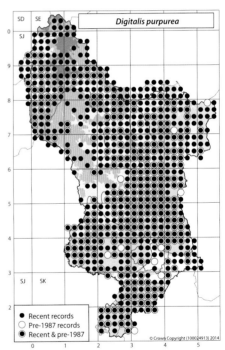

Foxglove is a native biennial or short-lived perennial of open habitats on well-drained acid soils, including wood margins, heaths, moors and waste ground. It is often grown in gardens, and some populations probably represent escapes. It occurs very commonly throughout the county except for the limestone areas and the high moors of the Dark Peak.

Erinus alpinus L.
Fairy Foxglove

Fairy Foxglove is an established semi-evergreen perennial of walls. Clapham

(1969) also records it as growing in rocky woods. There are nine recent records between 1999 and 2012, mostly for the White Peak Area, as at Stoney Middleton (SK2375), Steeple Grange (SK2855) and Repton (SK3027). There are three older ones: Longcliffe (SK2355) in 1969 and Longshaw House (SK2679) for both 1934 and 1969. It is indigenous to the mountains of south-western Europe.

Veronica officinalis L.
Heath Speedwell

COUNTY STATUS: Native	
CONSERVATION STATUS: ERL	
FIRST YEAR: 1789 LATEST YEAR: 2013 NO OF RECORDS: 526	
RECENT SQUARES: monads 265; tetrads 193; hectads 34	
ALL SQUARES: monads 286; tetrads 208; hectads 39	

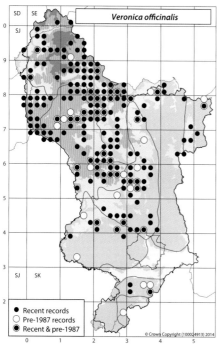

Heath Speedwell is an occasional native perennial of grasslands, heaths and open woods, on well-drained moderately acidic soils. It occurs throughout the area from Heyden Bridge (SE0900 v.c.58) and Mosborough (SK4182) in the north, through Biggin Dale (SK1458), to Woodlands Field (SK3440) and Calke Park (SK3622) in the south. It was previously more widespread in the south and east, from where it has probably been lost due to the agricultural improvement of marginal land.

Veronica montana L.
Wood Speedwell

COUNTY STATUS: Native	
CONSERVATION STATUS: None	
FIRST YEAR: 1789 LATEST YEAR: 2013 NO OF RECORDS: 903	
RECENT SQUARES: monads 391; tetrads 277; hectads 39	
ALL SQUARES: monads 425; tetrads 294; hectads 39	

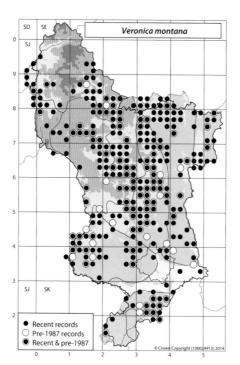

Wood Speedwell is an occasional native perennial of damp woods, scrub and shaded streamsides. It occurs scattered throughout the county as at Swallowhouse Mill Pond (SK0387), Miller's Dale (SK1573), Hob Hill Rough (SK3246), Robin Wood (SK3525) and Markland Grips (SK5074).

Veronica scutellata L.
Marsh Speedwell

COUNTY STATUS: Native	
CONSERVATION STATUS: DRDB (Cat5b), A	
FIRST YEAR: 1789 LATEST YEAR: 2010 NO OF RECORDS: 68	
RECENT SQUARES: monads 13; tetrads 17; hectads 11	
ALL SQUARES: monads 27; tetrads 26; hectads 18	

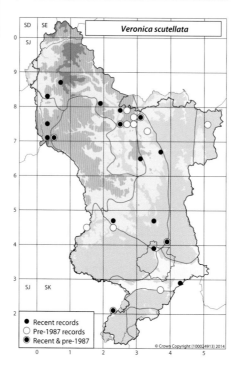

Marsh Speedwell is a very rare, native perennial of ponds, streamsides, marshes and ditches. It is currently recorded throughout the county except for limestone areas (Laneside Farm SK0283, Bradley Nook Farm SK2347 & Witches Oak Water SK4329). Older records cover a similar area with the occasional record on the limestone as at Chee Dale (SK17) in the White Peak. Nationally it is declining in central England (Stace 2010).

Veronica beccabunga L.
Brooklime

COUNTY STATUS: Native	
CONSERVATION STATUS: None	
FIRST YEAR: 1789 LATEST YEAR: 2013 NO OF RECORDS: 1,823	
RECENT SQUARES: monads 765; tetrads 480; hectads 40	
ALL SQUARES: monads 839; tetrads 499; hectads 40	

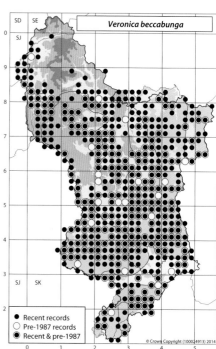

Brooklime is a frequent native perennial of the margins of ponds and streams, as well as ditches, marshes, flushes and wet woodland rides. It is intolerant of competition and thus generally occurs in rather open habitats. It has been recorded for all Derbyshire's Character Areas, though it is absent from the limestone plateau of the White Peak and the high moors of the Dark Peak.

Veronica anagallis-aquatica L.
Blue Water-speedwell

COUNTY STATUS: Native	
CONSERVATION STATUS: None	
FIRST YEAR: 1789 LATEST YEAR: 2011 NO OF RECORDS: 131	
RECENT SQUARES: monads 49; tetrads 42; hectads 14	
ALL SQUARES: monads 65; tetrads 55; hectads 25	

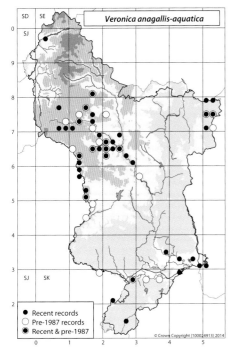

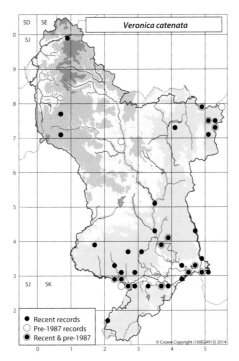

Blue Water-speedwell is a rare native perennial that grows in or at the margins of ponds and streams, as well as in marshes and wet meadows. Most records are from limestone areas: Monk's Dale (SK1373) and Lud Well (SK1262) in the White Peak, and Markland Grips (SK5074) in the Magnesian Limestone. It also occurs in the Trent Valley as at Trent Lock (SK43V). Previous records come from a wider area including Scropton (SK1829) and Anchor Church (SK3327) for 1969, and South Normanton (SK45) for 1903.

Veronica × *lackschewitzii* J.B. Keller
Hybrid Water-speedwell

Hybrid Water-speedwell is a very rare, native annual. The only record for Derbyshire (v.c.57) is dated pre-1970 and is listed in Stace (1975). It is the hybrid of Blue (*V. anagallis-aquatica*) and Pink Water-speedwell (*V. catenata*).

Veronica catenata Pennell
Pink Water-speedwell

COUNTY STATUS: Native
CONSERVATION STATUS: B
FIRST YEAR: 1949 LATEST YEAR: 2011 NO OF RECORDS: 92
RECENT SQUARES: monads 38; tetrads 35; hectads 16
ALL SQUARES: monads 48; tetrads 39; hectads 17

Pink Water-speedwell is a rare native annual, found on the muddy margins of waterbodies with little or no water movement. The majority of records are for the south, particularly the Trent Valley (Marston on Dove SK2328, Swarkestone SK3627 & Trent Lock SK4931). There is also a cluster of records for the Magnesian Limestone (Fox Green SK5273) plus

isolated records elsewhere (Woodhead Reservoir SK0899).

Veronica serpyllifolia L.
Thyme-leaved Speedwell

COUNTY STATUS: Native
CONSERVATION STATUS: None
FIRST YEAR: 1789 LATEST YEAR: 2013 NO OF RECORDS: 1,085
RECENT SQUARES: monads 647; tetrads 451; hectads 42
ALL SQUARES: monads 685; tetrads 464; hectads 42

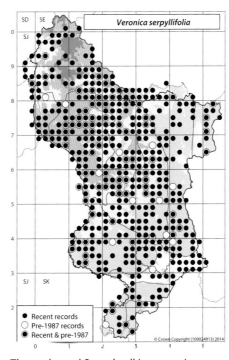

Thyme-leaved Speedwell is a creeping native perennial that grows in a range of natural and artificial habitats, including open grasslands, heaths, woodland rides, lawns, waste ground and cultivated land. It

grows frequently throughout the county. Our plant is ssp. *serpyllifolia*.

Veronica repens Clarion ex DC.
Corsican Speedwell

Locally extinct, Corsican Speedwell was a very rare, casual perennial. The only record is of a lawn weed in some quantity at Alrewas House, Clifton (SK1545) in the 1930s. It is indigenous to Corsica and southern Spain.

Veronica longifolia L.
Garden Speedwell

COUNTY STATUS: Established (Neophyte)
CONSERVATION STATUS: None
FIRST YEAR: 1969 LATEST YEAR: 2010 NO OF RECORDS: 16
RECENT SQUARES: monads 8; tetrads 8; hectads 6
ALL SQUARES: monads 11; tetrads 11; hectads 9

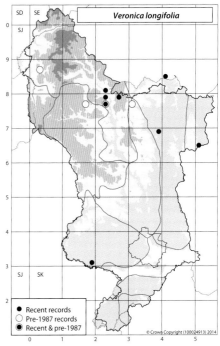

Garden Speedwell is a very rare, established perennial of waste ground and waysides. Recent records are scattered throughout the county, but mainly from northern parts (Hathersage SK2281, Totley SK2778, Birdholme SK3869 & Normanton Springs SK4084). A garden ornamental, it is native to northern and central Europe.

Veronica spicata L.
Spiked Speedwell

Spiked Speedwell is a very rare, casual perennial of waysides. Our only record is for Hallowes Lane (SK3577) in 1984, where it was a garden escape.

Veronica hederifolia L.
Ivy-leaved Speedwell

Ivy-leaved Speedwell is an anciently established, scrambling annual of

COUNTY STATUS: Established (Archaeophyte)
CONSERVATION STATUS: None
FIRST YEAR: 1789 **LATEST YEAR:** 2013 **NO OF RECORDS:** 766
RECENT SQUARES: monads 424; tetrads 312; hectads 41
ALL SQUARES: monads 472; tetrads 338; hectads 41

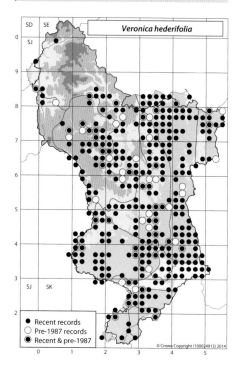

cultivated ground, wasteland, hedges and banks. It occurs occasionally throughout the county, only avoiding the high moors of the Peak District. Two subspecies occur: **ssp. hederifolia** is a plant of more open habitats such as arable fields while **ssp. lucorum** (Klett & Richt.) Hartl occurs in more

Slender Speedwell (*Veronica filiformis*) in typical lawn habitat, Hardwick Hall (SK4663), April 2008 (Nick Moyes)

shaded habitats such as hedges, and is less commonly recorded.

Veronica filiformis Sm.
Slender Speedwell

COUNTY STATUS: Established (Neophyte)
CONSERVATION STATUS: None
FIRST YEAR: 1960 **LATEST YEAR:** 2013 **NO OF RECORDS:** 449
RECENT SQUARES: monads 269; tetrads 212; hectads 34
ALL SQUARES: monads 290; tetrads 224; hectads 34

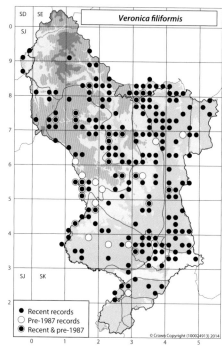

Slender Speedwell is an established perennial of lawns, grassy paths, waysides and the margins of streams. It occurs occasionally throughout the county (Wormhill SK1274, Dove Dale SK1452, Markeaton Lane SK3237 & St Andrew's Churchyard SK4053). It has spread, even into parts well away from built-up areas, since Clapham (1969) recorded it as "still uncommon in Derbyshire". It is indigenous to northern Turkey and the Caucasus.

Veronica agrestis L.
Green Field-speedwell

COUNTY STATUS: Established (Archaeophyte)
CONSERVATION STATUS: None
FIRST YEAR: 1789 **LATEST YEAR:** 2013 **NO OF RECORDS:** 121
RECENT SQUARES: monads 52; tetrads 55; hectads 24
ALL SQUARES: monads 85; tetrads 88; hectads 30

Green Field-speedwell is an anciently established annual of cultivated land and waste places, generally on well-drained acidic soils. It occurs occasionally throughout the county from Audenshaw Clough (SE1100 v.c.58) and Hutcliffe Cemetery (SK3382) in the north, through Cromford (SK2956) and Hill Top Farm

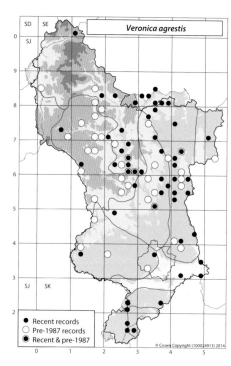

(SK4266), to Overseal (SK2815) and Ticknall (SK3623) in the south.

Veronica polita Fr.
Grey Field-speedwell

COUNTY STATUS: Established (Neophyte)
CONSERVATION STATUS: A
FIRST YEAR: 1847 **LATEST YEAR:** 2013 **NO OF RECORDS:** 38
RECENT SQUARES: monads 11; tetrads 12; hectads 10
ALL SQUARES: monads 29; tetrads 30; hectads 21

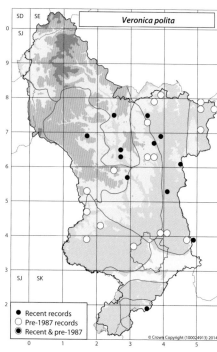

Grey Field–speedwell is a very rare, established annual of cultivated and disturbed ground. It occurs throughout the county except for the upland north-western part of the area (Calver SK27M,

Germander Speedwell (*Veronica chamaedrys*) by side of the path in Markland Grips (SK5175), May 2008 (Peter Smith)

Rowsley Sidings SK2664 & Smisby SK3518). It previously had much the same distribution, though was more frequently recorded in the south than today.

Veronica persica Poir.
Common Field-speedwell

COUNTY STATUS: Established (Neophyte)
CONSERVATION STATUS: None
FIRST YEAR: 1881 LATEST YEAR: 2013 NO OF RECORDS: 1,147
RECENT SQUARES: monads 686; tetrads 431; hectads 40
ALL SQUARES: monads 742; tetrads 447; hectads 40

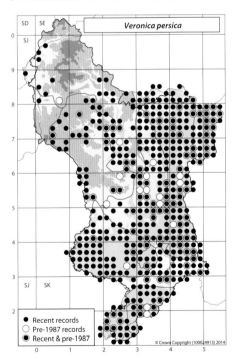

Common Field-speedwell is an established annual of cultivated land, gardens and waste ground, generally on the more fertile soils. It is common throughout the lowland

south and east, becoming rarer in the more upland Peak District. It is a native of the Caucasus and northern Iran.

Veronica chamaedrys L.
Germander Speedwell

COUNTY STATUS: Native
CONSERVATION STATUS: None
FIRST YEAR: 1789 LATEST YEAR: 2013 NO OF RECORDS: 3,747
RECENT SQUARES: monads 1,348; tetrads 614; hectads 43
ALL SQUARES: monads 1,423; tetrads 625; hectads 43

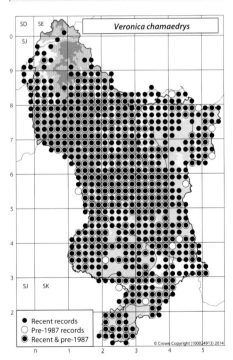

Germander Speedwell is a very common, native perennial of grasslands, open woods, waysides and waste ground. It has been recorded from all of Derbyshire except for the high moors of the Dark Peak.

Veronica arvensis L.
Wall Speedwell

COUNTY STATUS: Native
CONSERVATION STATUS: None
FIRST YEAR: 1789 LATEST YEAR: 2013 NO OF RECORDS: 1,192
RECENT SQUARES: monads 698; tetrads 460; hectads 42
ALL SQUARES: monads 744; tetrads 476; hectads 43

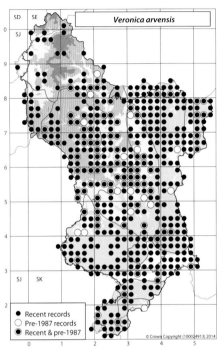

Wall Speedwell is a frequent native annual of cultivated ground, wasteland, grasslands and heaths, generally in open areas on dry soils, plus walls and rock ledges. It occurs throughout the county except for the high moors of the Dark Peak and some of the intensively farmed areas of the lowlands.

Veronica salicifolia G. Forst.
Koromiko

Koromiko is a casual evergreen shrub of waste ground, and is a native of New Zealand and Chile. Our only record was made by K. Balkow in 2008 at Abbeydale (SK3281).

Antirrhinum majus L.
Snapdragon

COUNTY STATUS: Established (Neophyte)
CONSERVATION STATUS: None
FIRST YEAR: 1789 LATEST YEAR: 2013 NO OF RECORDS: 261
RECENT SQUARES: monads 165; tetrads 155; hectads 35
ALL SQUARES: monads 180; tetrads 164; hectads 35

Snapdragon is an established annual or short-lived perennial of walls, waste ground, tips and rock outcrops. It is occasional in the eastern half of the county (Hasland SK36Z, Ridgeway SK3551 & Melbourne Hall SK3924) but only rare in the west (Hadfield SK0296 & Flagg SK16J). A native of south-western Europe, it is very popular in gardens for

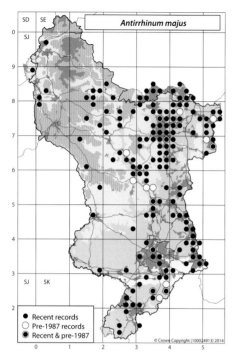

Antirrhinum majus

● Recent records
○ Pre-1987 records
◉ Recent & pre-1987

© Crown Copyright (100024913) 2014

its showy flowers from where it readily escapes as seeds or throwouts.

Chaenorhinum minus (L.) Lange
Small Toadflax

COUNTY STATUS: Established (Archaeophyte)
CONSERVATION STATUS: None
FIRST YEAR: 1801 LATEST YEAR: 2013 NO OF RECORDS: 214
RECENT SQUARES: monads 82; tetrads 72; hectads 26
ALL SQUARES: monads 129; tetrads 108; hectads 32

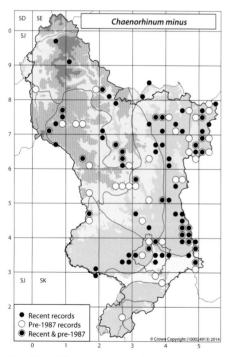

Chaenorhinum minus

● Recent records
○ Pre-1987 records
◉ Recent & pre-1987

© Crown Copyright (100024913) 2014

Small Toadflax is an anciently established annual of dry open habitats on waste ground, particularly on railway land. It occurs throughout the area from Torside Clough (SK0697) and the Snake Inn (SK19A)

in the north, through Northwood (SK2664) and Butterley Reservoir (SK4051), to Scropton (SK1930) and Forbes Hole (SK4932) in the south. Previously it also occurred as a weed of arable land but appears to have been mostly lost from this habitat.

Misopates orontium (L.) Raf.
Weasel's-snout

COUNTY STATUS: Casual
CONSERVATION STATUS: None
FIRST YEAR: 1789 LATEST YEAR: 1976 NO OF RECORDS: 5
RECENT SQUARES: monads 0; tetrads 0; hectads 0
ALL SQUARES: monads 2; tetrads 2; hectads 5

Weasel's-snout is a very rare, casual annual of cultivated ground. There are no recent records, the latest being from Ashbourne (SK1746) in 1976 as a garden weed. There was an earlier record from a cornfield at Beauchief (SK3381) in 1934, and records for Matlock (SK25), Breadsall (SK33) and Pinxton (SK45) in Linton (1903). Its loss from the county has no doubt been due to agricultural intensification. It is perhaps anciently established elsewhere in the Midlands.

Asarina procumbens Mill.
Trailing Snapdragon

Trailing Snapdragon is an established creeping perennial of cultivated ground in gardens. The only recent record is from Chesterfield (SK3671) in 1997, with one older one from Hardwick Hall (SK4663) in 1977. It is a garden ornamental that comes from southern France and north-eastern Spain.

Cymbalaria muralis P. Gaertn., B. Mey. & Scherb.
Ivy-leaved Toadflax

Ivy-leaved Toadflax is an established perennial of walls and sometimes rock outcrops. It is occasional throughout the

COUNTY STATUS: Established (Neophyte)
CONSERVATION STATUS: None
FIRST YEAR: 1789 LATEST YEAR: 2013 NO OF RECORDS: 857
RECENT SQUARES: monads 360; tetrads 281; hectads 38
ALL SQUARES: monads 390; tetrads 295; hectads 38

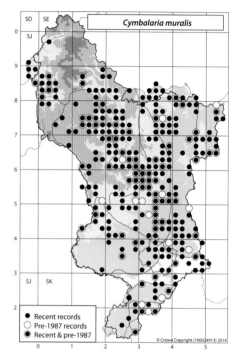

Cymbalaria muralis

● Recent records
○ Pre-1987 records
◉ Recent & pre-1987

© Crown Copyright (100024913) 2014

county from Hadfield (SK0296) and Ashes Farm (SK1888) in the north, through Bonsall (SK2857), to Smisby Village (SK3419) and Coton in the Elms (SK2415) in the south. The local plant is ssp. *muralis*. It is a garden species, originating from central southern Europe.

Cymbalaria pallida (Ten.) Wettst.
Italian Toadflax

Italian Toadflax is a very rare, casual perennial of walls and pavements. All records are from

Ivy-leaved Toadflax (*Cymbalaria muralis*) on a wall by Cromford Canal (SK35), May 2008 (Peter Smith)

COUNTY STATUS: Casual	
CONSERVATION STATUS: None	
FIRST YEAR: 1999 **LATEST YEAR:** 2013 **NO OF RECORDS:** 6	
RECENT SQUARES: monads 6; tetrads 6; hectads 5	
ALL SQUARES: monads 6; tetrads 6; hectads 5	

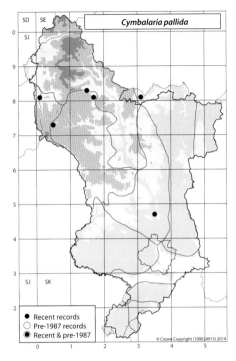

1999 and 2013. They come from ten sites throughout the county for example: Buxton (SK0573), Whaley Bridge (SK0181), Bradwell (SK1681), Belper (SK3447) and Dore (SK3081). Previously it may have been overlooked for Ivy-leaved Toadflax (*C. muralis*). It is indigenous to the mountains of central Italy.

Kickxia elatine (L.) Dumort.
Sharp-leaved Fluellen

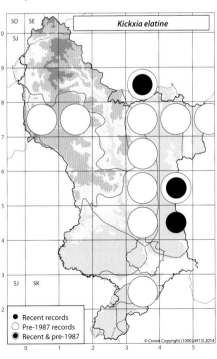

COUNTY STATUS: Established (Archaeophyte)	
CONSERVATION STATUS: DRDB (Cat5a), A, B	
FIRST YEAR: 1789 **LATEST YEAR:** 2010 **NO OF RECORDS:** 29	
RECENT SQUARES: monads 3; tetrads 3; hectads 3	
ALL SQUARES: monads 7; tetrads 6; hectads 12	

Sharp-leaved Fluellen is an anciently established annual of arable land particularly on lighter soils. There are only three recent records: Moss Valley (SK3980), Swanwick (SK4152) and West Hallam (SK4241), all in eastern Derbyshire. This coincides with most of the earlier records, though these are scattered over a slightly wider area, ranging from Whitwell (SK5278) to Calke (SK32). There are also a few old records in the west, such as Ladmanlow Tip (SK0471). Clapham (1969) noted that it was decreasing and this appears to have continued to the present day, most probably due to arable intensification. The county is on the northern limit of its British distribution (Stace 2010).

Linaria vulgaris Mill.
Common Toadflax

COUNTY STATUS: Native	
CONSERVATION STATUS: None	
FIRST YEAR: 1789 **LATEST YEAR:** 2013 **NO OF RECORDS:** 953	
RECENT SQUARES: monads 340; tetrads 226; hectads 35	
ALL SQUARES: monads 383; tetrads 244; hectads 37	

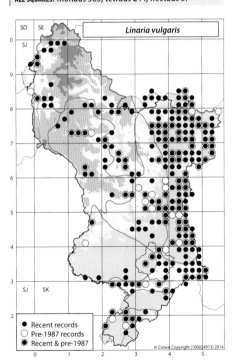

Common Toadflax is a native perennial of open grassland, waysides, waste places and rough ground, particularly on railway land. It is frequent throughout lowland eastern parts (Eckington SK47J, Lower Hartshay SK3851 & King's Newton SK3827). In more upland western parts, it is only

occasional (Gamesley Sidings SK0093 & Parsley Hay SK1463).

Linaria × *sepium* G.J. Allman
A hybrid toadflax

This hybrid toadflax is a very rare, native perennial. The only recent records, both from railway tracks, are for the Monsal Trail (SK2268) in 2000 and Matlock (SK2861) in 1996. There is also a previous record from the Monsal Trail (SK2368) in 1986. It is the hybrid of Common (*L. vulgaris*) and Pale Toadflax (*L. repens*).

Linaria purpurea (L.) Mill.
Purple Toadflax

COUNTY STATUS: Established (Neophyte)	
CONSERVATION STATUS: None	
FIRST YEAR: 1960 **LATEST YEAR:** 2013 **NO OF RECORDS:** 331	
RECENT SQUARES: monads 201; tetrads 189; hectads 35	
ALL SQUARES: monads 217; tetrads 199; hectads 36	

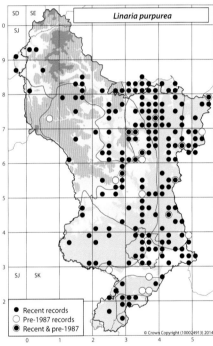

Purple Toadflax is an established perennial of rough ground, wasteland, waysides, tips and sometimes walls. It occurs occasionally throughout the area from Charlesworth (SK0092) and Meersbrook Bank (SK3484) in the north, through Bonsall (SK2857), to Long Eaton (SK4832) and Rosliston (SK2416) in the south. It is a popular garden flower that escapes as seed or discarded with waste It is indigenous to central and southern Italy.

Linaria × *dominii* Druce
A hybrid toadflax

This hybrid toadflax is a very rare, native perennial. There are only two recent records: Monsal Dale (SK2367) and Jodrell

Meadow (SK0081 v.c.58). Previous reports are mentioned in Stace (1982) and Stace (1975) as on "waste ground and railways". It is the hybrid of Purple (*L. purpurea*) and Pale Toadflax (*L. repens*).

Linaria repens (L.) Mill.
Pale Toadflax

COUNTY STATUS: Casual	
CONSERVATION STATUS: None	
FIRST YEAR: 1847 **LATEST YEAR:** 2011 **NO OF RECORDS:** 61	
RECENT SQUARES: monads 15; tetrads 15; hectads 9	
ALL SQUARES: monads 30; tetrads 29; hectads 17	

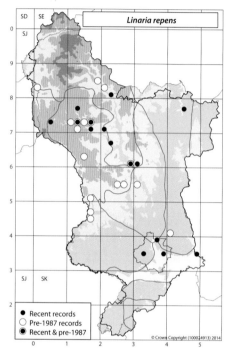

Pale Toadflax is a very rare, casual perennial of rough ground, often along railway lines, and waysides. Recent records are scattered throughout central and southern parts (Miller's Dale Station SK1373, Renishaw SK4477 & the A38 roundabout in Derby SK3235). Nationally it is a lowland species that reaches its highest British altitude of 335m near Brassington (SK2554) Preston *et al.* (2002). It is possibly native to southern and western Britain.

Linaria supina (L.) Chaz.
Prostrate Toadflax
Prostrate Toadflax is a casual annual. The only record was made by G. Kay in 1989 on a rubbish dump at Hadfield (SK0296). It is indigenous to south-western Europe.

Linaria pelisseriana (L.) Mill.
Jersey Toadflax
Jersey Toadflax is a very rare, casual annual, known only from one sighting at Dunston Tip, Chesterfield (SK3674) in 1984. It is a native of south-western Europe.

Sea Plantain (*Plantago maritima*) on a roadside at Doe Lea (SK4566), June 2001 (Ken Balkow)

Linaria maroccana Hook. f.
Annual Toadflax
Annual Toadflax is a casual of waste ground and pavements. There are only two records: Brockwell (SK3672) in 1996 and Long Eaton (SK4832) in 2010. It is a garden escape that originates from North Africa.

PLANTAGINACEAE

Plantago coronopus L.
Buck's-horn Plantain

COUNTY STATUS: Native	
CONSERVATION STATUS: A, B	
FIRST YEAR: 1789 **LATEST YEAR:** 2013 **NO OF RECORDS:** 37	
RECENT SQUARES: monads 18; tetrads 17; hectads 12	
ALL SQUARES: monads 21; tetrads 19; hectads 16	

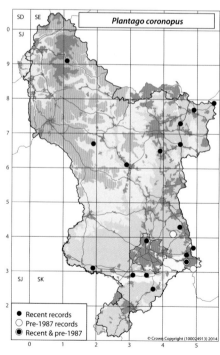

Buck's-horn Plantain is a very rare, native annual or perennial of dry disturbed areas on roadsides and waste ground. Current records come from across Derbyshire (Snake Inn SK1190 & Staunton Harold SK3724), including the limestone areas (Steetley SK5478 & Melbourne Farm SK1967). Older records are only from southern parts. This local expansion reflects the national inland spread along salt-treated roads (Preston *et al.* 2002).

Plantago maritima L.
Sea Plantain
Sea Plantain is a casual perennial, known only from the verge of the A617 at Doe Lea (SK4566) in 2001. It is a native of coastal salt marshes that has been spreading inland along salt-treated roads since the 1960s (Preston *et al.* 2002).

Plantago major L.
Greater Plantain

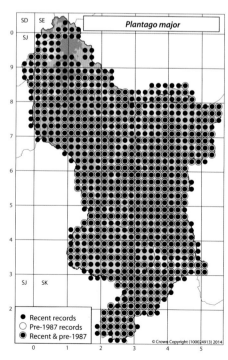

COUNTY STATUS: Native
CONSERVATION STATUS: None
FIRST YEAR: 1789 LATEST YEAR: 2013 NO OF RECORDS: 5,962
RECENT SQUARES: monads 2,253; tetrads 739; hectads 44
ALL SQUARES: monads 2,304; tetrads 739; hectads 44

Greater Plantain is a very common, native perennial of disturbed ground, cultivated land, waysides and grassy habitats, particularly where there is heavy trampling as along paths and around gateways. It grows throughout the county except for the high moors of the Dark Peak. The local plant is **ssp. major**, though there are two records for **ssp. intermedia** (Gilib.) Lange on the shore of the Toddbrook Reservoir (SK0080 v.c.58) in 1994 and the Accordis Lagoons (SK3934) in 2009.

Plantago media L.
Hoary Plantain

COUNTY STATUS: Native
CONSERVATION STATUS: ERL
FIRST YEAR: 1789 LATEST YEAR: 2013 NO OF RECORDS: 1,139
RECENT SQUARES: monads 398; tetrads 227; hectads 36
ALL SQUARES: monads 431; tetrads 244; hectads 36

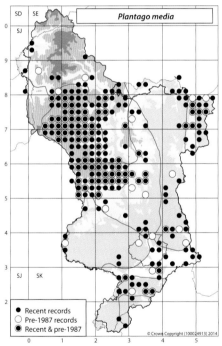

Hoary Plantain is a native perennial of neutral to basic grasslands. It is common in the White Peak as at Peter Dale (SK1276) and Bonsall (SK2556), and frequent on the Magnesian Limestone as at Creswell Crags (SK5374) and Bolsover Moor (SK4971). Elsewhere it occurs rarely scattered throughout the area as at Dinting Vale Wood (SK0194), Crich Cliff (SK3455) and Ticknall Village (SK3523). It has been lost from many sites in both the lowlands and the Peak District (Buckingham et al. 1997) since the 1980s due to agricultural

improvement of pastures and hay meadows. However, its decline in the Peak District has been masked by its continued presence in marginal areas and on roadsides.

Plantago lanceolata L.
Ribwort Plantain

COUNTY STATUS: Native
CONSERVATION STATUS: None
FIRST YEAR: 1789 LATEST YEAR: 2013 NO OF RECORDS: 7,162
RECENT SQUARES: monads 2,166; tetrads 719; hectads 44
ALL SQUARES: monads 2,232; tetrads 723; hectads 44

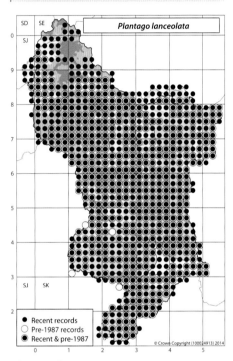

Ribwort Plantain is a very common, native perennial of grass fields, waysides and waste places. It has been recorded throughout the county except for the high moors of the Dark Peak. Its local name in the Peak District of Chimney Sweep or Sweepers no doubt alludes to the appearance of its flower head.

Littorella uniflora (L.) Asch.
Shoreweed

COUNTY STATUS: Native
CONSERVATION STATUS: B
FIRST YEAR: 1903 LATEST YEAR: 2012 NO OF RECORDS: 65
RECENT SQUARES: monads 18; tetrads 14; hectads 7
ALL SQUARES: monads 22; tetrads 18; hectads 10

Shoreweed is a very rare, native perennial of shallow water at the margins of waterbodies, typically the drawdown zones of reservoirs. It occurs in northern Derbyshire, for example at the following reservoirs: Combs (SK0379), Ladybower (SK1789), Linacre (SK3272) and Ogston (SK3760). When Ramsley Reservoir (SK2874) was decommissioned in 2002,

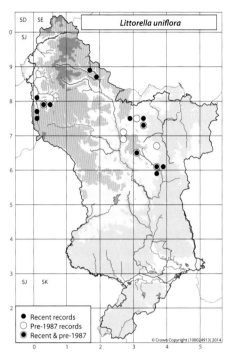

good populations of the plant were found and attempts made to retain its habitat in the restoration scheme. It was previously recorded further south in SK44 during the 1950s.

HIPPURIDACEAE

Hippuris vulgaris L.
Mare's-tail

COUNTY STATUS: Native
CONSERVATION STATUS: B
FIRST YEAR: 1829 LATEST YEAR: 2011 NO OF RECORDS: 104
RECENT SQUARES: monads 30; tetrads 28; hectads 12
ALL SQUARES: monads 44; tetrads 39; hectads 18

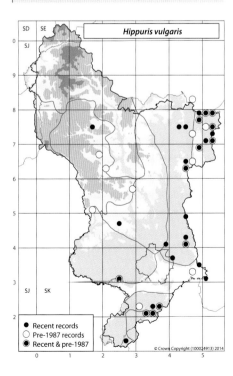

Mare's-tail is an emergent native perennial of pond margins, flooded gravel pits and slow streams. It is occasional on the Magnesian Limestone as at Scarcliffe Pond (SK4968), Castle Hill Farm (SK5078) and Creswell Crags (SK5374). Elsewhere it is very rare and mostly in the southern part of the county, as at Hilton Gravel Pits (SK2431), near Several Wood (SK3320) and Straw's Bridge (SK4541). There is also a single record from the White Peak in Cressbrook Dale (SK1774). Previously there were a few more records from the White Peak, as at Lathkill Dale (SK1966) in 1955 and 1969.

CALLITRICHACEAE

Callitriche hermaphroditica L.
Autumnal Water-starwort

COUNTY STATUS: Native	
CONSERVATION STATUS: DRDB (Cat4)	
FIRST YEAR: 2002 LATEST YEAR: 2002 NO OF RECORDS: 2	
RECENT SQUARES: monads 2; tetrads 2; hectads 2	
ALL SQUARES: monads 2; tetrads 2; hectads 2	

Autumnal Water-starwort is a submerged native annual of ponds. It was first discovered in 2002 by N. Law at Miller's Pond (SK4564) then found the same year at Grange Farm (SK3228). It is a plant of upland Britain, towards the southern edge of its range here. It has recently been spreading elsewhere in the Midlands, too (Preston *et al.* 2002).

Callitriche truncata Guss.
Short-leaved Water-starwort
Short-leaved Water-starwort is a submerged native annual of lakes and flooded gravel pits. It occurs rarely in the Trent Valley with records from Willington

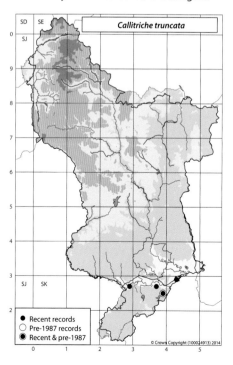

Callitriche truncata

Recent records
Pre-1987 records
Recent & pre-1987

COUNTY STATUS: Native	
CONSERVATION STATUS: DRDB (Cat3), NS	
FIRST YEAR: 1978 LATEST YEAR: 2002 NO OF RECORDS: 16	
RECENT SQUARES: monads 4; tetrads 4; hectads 3	
ALL SQUARES: monads 5; tetrads 4; hectads 3	

Gravel Pits (SK2827), Swarkestone Gravel Pits (SK3627), Witches' Oak Water (SK4329) and Melbourne Pool (SK3824). There is also an old record from Melbourne Pool (SK3924) in 1978. It is a lowland species with Derbyshire at the northern edge of its range, but has recently been increasing and spreading northwards in Britain (Preston *et al.* 2002).

Callitriche stagnalis Scop.
Common Water-starwort

COUNTY STATUS: Native	
CONSERVATION STATUS: None	
FIRST YEAR: 1969 LATEST YEAR: 2011 NO OF RECORDS: 120	
RECENT SQUARES: monads 42; tetrads 59; hectads 24	
ALL SQUARES: monads 52; tetrads 68; hectads 37	

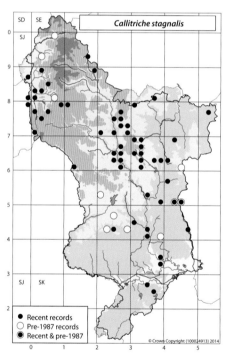

Callitriche stagnalis

Recent records
Pre-1987 records
Recent & pre-1987

Common Water-starwort is a native annual or perennial that grows in the margins of shallow ponds and streams, and on bare wet mud often in woodland rides. It occurs occasionally throughout the area from Lantern Pike (SK0288) and Nether Wood Plantation (SK1693) in the north, through Exhibition Plantation (SK4250), to Robin Wood (SK3526 & SK3625) in the south. It is probably under-recorded due to the problems of identification to species level.

Callitriche platycarpa Kuetz.
Various-leaved Water-starwort
Various-leaved Water-starwort is a rare native annual or perennial of ponds, ditches and streams. It occurs scattered

---

COUNTY STATUS: Native	
CONSERVATION STATUS: DRDB (Cat5b), A	
FIRST YEAR: 1903 LATEST YEAR: 2011 NO OF RECORDS: 65	
RECENT SQUARES: monads 15; tetrads 21; hectads 15	
ALL SQUARES: monads 42; tetrads 47; hectads 23	

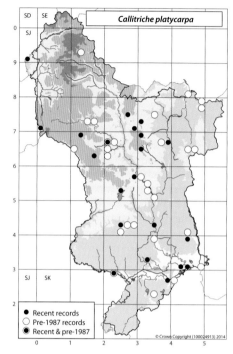

Callitriche platycarpa

Recent records
Pre-1987 records
Recent & pre-1987

throughout the county avoiding only the higher parts of the Peak District (Etherow SJ9791, Bradley Old Park SK24L, Hipper Sick SK3168 & Black Pool SK3927). Nationally it is considered to be spreading, probably due to the increased eutrophication of waters (Preston *et al.* 2002).

Callitriche obtusangula Le Gall
Blunt-fruited Water-starwort

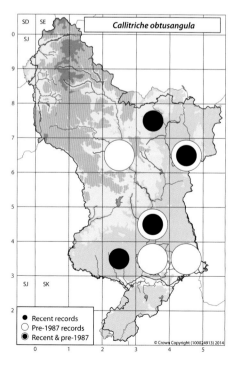

Callitriche obtusangula

Recent records
Pre-1987 records
Recent & pre-1987

COUNTY STATUS:	Native
CONSERVATION STATUS:	DRDB (Cat5a), A
FIRST YEAR: 1903	LATEST YEAR: 2010 NO OF RECORDS: 17
RECENT SQUARES:	monads 5; tetrads 6; hectads 4
ALL SQUARES:	monads 6; tetrads 7; hectads 7

Blunt-fruited Water-starwort is a very rare, native perennial of ponds. Currently scattered over central parts of the county (Burnaston SK2830, Wyver Lane SK3449, Chesterfield area SK3971 & SK37W and Hardwick Park SK4563 & SK4564), it was previously recorded for a greater range of habitats including streams and ditches (Clapham, 1969). It is probably under-recorded due to difficulties of identification.

Callitriche brutia ssp. *hamulata* (Kuetz. ex W.D.J. Koch) O. Bolos & Vigo
Intermediate Water-Starwort

COUNTY STATUS:	Native
CONSERVATION STATUS:	DRDB (Cat5b), A
FIRST YEAR: 1889	LATEST YEAR: 2003 NO OF RECORDS: 72
RECENT SQUARES:	monads 15; tetrads 15; hectads 13
ALL SQUARES:	monads 46; tetrads 45; hectads 26

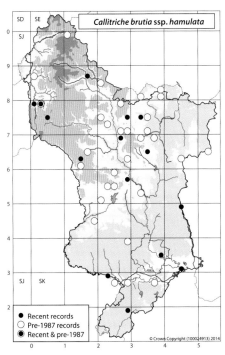

Intermediate Water-starwort is a rare native annual or perennial of ponds and small streams. It is recorded sparsely through the county (Combs Reservoir SK0379, Ladybower SK1786, Hall Wood SK2818 & Evans Pond SK4448). It is probably under-recorded due to the difficulties of identification.

SCROPHULARIACEAE

Verbascum blattaria L.
Moth Mullein
Moth Mullein is a very rare, casual annual of waste ground in central parts. There

are only three recent records: Tansley (SK3159), Lock Lane Ash Tip (SK4831) and Pleasley (SK4964). It is a southern species, with Derbyshire on the northern edge of its current British range. It is native to southern Europe.

Verbascum virgatum Stokes
Twiggy Mullein

COUNTY STATUS:	Casual
CONSERVATION STATUS:	None
FIRST YEAR: 1899	LATEST YEAR: 1979 NO OF RECORDS: 13
RECENT SQUARES:	monads 0; tetrads 0; hectads 0
ALL SQUARES:	monads 6; tetrads 5; hectads 6

Twiggy Mullein is a very rare, casual biennial of tips and waste ground. The only records are a series of county-wide sightings for the 1960s and 1970s. These include: Piper House (SK2880), Grindleford Tip (SK2478), Denby Tip (SK3947) and near Breadsall (SK3639). It is sometimes considered native to south-western England.

Verbascum phoeniceum L.
Purple Mullein
Purple Mullein is a very rare, casual perennial of waste ground. The sole record is from Pleasley Mine (SK4964) in 1999. Indigenous to south-eastern Europe, it is grown in gardens for ornament but can also be a bird-seed alien.

Verbascum phlomoides L.
Orange Mullein

COUNTY STATUS:	Established (Neophyte)
CONSERVATION STATUS:	None
FIRST YEAR: 1870	LATEST YEAR: 2003 NO OF RECORDS: 10
RECENT SQUARES:	monads 4; tetrads 4; hectads 4
ALL SQUARES:	monads 7; tetrads 7; hectads 6

Orange Mullein is an established biennial of waysides and waste ground in central parts. There are just four recent records: Ashbourne (SK1746), Hopton Tunnel (SK2654), Darley Dale (SK2664) and Clowne (SK4875). A native of continental Europe, it was formerly cultivated in gardens.

Verbascum densiflorum Bertol.
Dense-flowered Mullein
Dense-flowered Mullein is a very rare, casual biennial. It has been recorded twice: a roadside near Cliff College (SK2473) in 1997, and restored land at Alvaston (SK3933 & 3934) in 2011. It is a garden escape, indigenous to continental Europe.

Verbascum thapsus l
Great Mullein
Great Mullein is an occasional native biennial of grassy places, waysides and quarries, mostly on well-drained soils. It is also grown in gardens for ornament from

COUNTY STATUS:	Native
CONSERVATION STATUS:	None
FIRST YEAR: 1789	LATEST YEAR: 2013 NO OF RECORDS: 443
RECENT SQUARES:	monads 206; tetrads 181; hectads 37
ALL SQUARES:	monads 249; tetrads 207; hectads 37

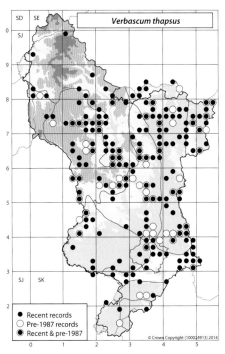

where it escapes as seed or throwouts onto tips and waste ground. It occurs throughout Derbyshire but generally avoids the high ground of the Dark and South West Peak Character Areas. Specimen localities are Gamesley Sidings (SK0093), Miller's Dale Quarry (SK1473), Dove Dale (SK1456), Smisby Village (SK3419) and Creswell Crags (SK5274).

Verbascum × *semialbum* Chaub.
A hybrid mullein
This hybrid mullein is a very rare, native of waysides and rough ground with only four known sites. There are recent reports from Losehill Hall (SK1581) and the High Peak Trail (SK2654) plus others for Alport Mill (SK26) and west of Whatstandwell (SK35), both in 1884. It is the spontaneous hybrid of Great (*V. thapsus*) and Dark Mullein (*V. nigrum*).

Verbascum nigrum L.
Dark Mullein

COUNTY STATUS:	Native
CONSERVATION STATUS:	DRDB (Cat5b), B
FIRST YEAR: 1789	LATEST YEAR: 2008 NO OF RECORDS: 102
RECENT SQUARES:	monads 19; tetrads 12; hectads 7
ALL SQUARES:	monads 31; tetrads 22; hectads 12

Dark Mullein is a very rare, native perennial of waysides, wasteland and rough ground. It occurs chiefly in, or around the edges of, the White Peak in areas of disturbed

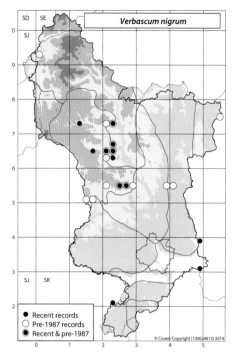

calcareous soils, as at Miller's Dale Station (SK1373), Alport and Shiningbank Quarry (SK2264), and the High Peak Trail (SK2554). There are also isolated recent records from Drakelow Power Station (SK2220), Lock Lane Ash Tip (SK4831) and Stanton Gate (SK4838). Previous records cover a wider area but similar habitats (Gamesley Sidings SK0093 in 1985 & Gannabrig Wood SK5474 in 1975).

Hoary Mullein (*Verbascum pulverulentum*) in the upper reaches of Lathkill Dale (SK1666), August 2004 (Nick Moyes)

Verbascum pulverulentum Vill.
Hoary Mullein

Hoary Mullein is a very rare and established biennial. All records bar one for this attractive plant come from the upper reaches of Lathkill Dale (SK1665, SK1666 & SK1765) where it has been recorded on several occasions between 1975 and 2012. It was considered for some time to be native here but is now known to have originated from East Anglia. The other record is from Meaden Bridge, Bakewell (SK2267) in 1999/2000 where it is a known introduction of seed collected from Lathkill Dale.

Verbascum lychnitis L.
White Mullein

White Mullein is an established biennial, and a native of southern England. It was first recorded in Derbyshire in 1829, at an unspecified location. Afterwards it has only ever been recorded from walls at Haddon Hall (SK2366) on five occasions between 1873 and 2013, probably as a garden escape.

Scrophularia nodosa L.
Common Figwort

COUNTY STATUS:	Native
CONSERVATION STATUS:	None
FIRST YEAR: 1789	LATEST YEAR: 2013 NO OF RECORDS: 1,468
RECENT SQUARES:	monads 678; tetrads 442; hectads 37
ALL SQUARES:	monads 742; tetrads 460; hectads 38

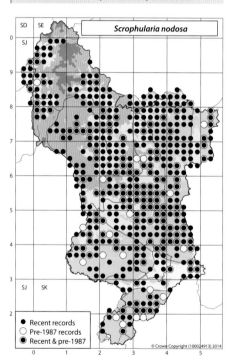

Common Figwort is a frequent native perennial of waysides, hedges and open woods, often on damp and or fertile soils. It also occurs as a colonist of disturbed ground in drier situations. It is recorded right across the county apart from some of the higher ground of the Peak District.

Scrophularia auriculata L.
Water Figwort

COUNTY STATUS:	Native
CONSERVATION STATUS:	None
FIRST YEAR: 1789	LATEST YEAR: 2013 NO OF RECORDS: 1,125
RECENT SQUARES:	monads 445; tetrads 289; hectads 38
ALL SQUARES:	monads 482; tetrads 309; hectads 39

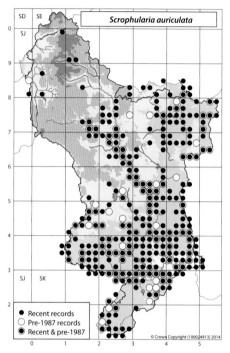

Water Figwort is a native perennial that grows on the margins of ponds, lakes, rivers and canals, and in wet grasslands, woodlands and marshes. It is frequent in the southern and eastern lowlands, but rare in the uplands of the Peak District.

Scrophularia umbrosa Dumort.
Green Figwort

COUNTY STATUS:	Native
CONSERVATION STATUS:	DRDB (Cat5a), A, B
FIRST YEAR: 1858	LATEST YEAR: 1998 NO OF RECORDS: 12
RECENT SQUARES:	monads 1; tetrads 1; hectads 1
ALL SQUARES:	monads 4; tetrads 4; hectads 5

Green Figwort is a very rare, native perennial of damp shady places. The only recent sighting is from Whitwell Wood (SK5277), found on a BSBI survey weekend. Previously it was recorded thinly scattered over a wide area of eastern (Pleasley Vale SK5265), central (Cromford Canal SK3156) and southern Derbyshire (Burton SK22). The Pleasley record in 1966 was also made during a BSBI meeting.

Scrophularia vernalis L.
Yellow Figwort

Yellow Figwort is a very rare, casual biennial or short-lived perennial. The sole record is from Crich (SK3453) in 1987. It is indigenous to the mountains of central and southern Europe.

Limosella aquatica L.
Mudwort

COUNTY STATUS: Native

CONSERVATION STATUS: DRDB (Cat3), NS, A, B, C

FIRST YEAR: 1835 LATEST YEAR: 2011 NO OF RECORDS: 26

RECENT SQUARES: monads 6; tetrads 4; hectads 3

ALL SQUARES: monads 7; tetrads 5; hectads 7

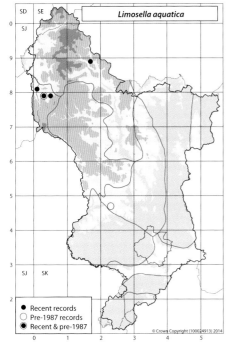

Mudwort is a very rare, native annual of upland areas. It occurs on the muddy margins of waterbodies, especially where new ground is exposed by the drawing-down of the water level. Recently it has been recorded from three reservoirs: Toddbrook (SK0080), Combs (SK0379 & SK0479) and Ladybower (SK1789). It was previously recorded for the same area and further south: Bradley Pastures (SK2246) in 1981, Shipley Reservoir (SK44) in 1837, Willington (SK22) in 1903 and Repton (SK32) in 1903. It occurs very scattered throughout Britain and is Nationally Scarce.

Buddleja davidii Franch.
Butterfly-bush

COUNTY STATUS: Established (Neophyte)

CONSERVATION STATUS: None

FIRST YEAR: 1970 LATEST YEAR: 2013 NO OF RECORDS: 456

RECENT SQUARES: monads 248; tetrads 183; hectads 34

ALL SQUARES: monads 252; tetrads 186; hectads 34

Butterfly-bush is an established shrub of waste ground, walls, scrub and waysides. It occurs occasionally throughout Derbyshire from the Longdendale Trail (SK0598) and Birley Vale (SK3984) in the north, to Drakelow Power Station (SK21J) and Church Gresley (SK2919) in the south. It generally grows as scattered bushes but can form dense stands as at the old Friar

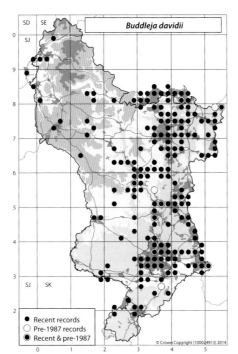

Gate Station in Derby (SK3436) where it forms an important habitat for butterflies. It is much grown in gardens from where seeds are readily dispersed by the wind. It is indigenous to China.

Buddleja globosa Hope
Orange-ball-tree

Orange-ball-tree is very rare, planted shrub originating from South America. Known only from a road junction south of Tansley (SK3259) in 1999, it is increasingly grown in gardens and may be expected to spread as a casual.

Buddleja × *weyeriana* Weyer
Weyer's Butterfly-bush

Weyer's Butterfly-bush is a very rare, casual shrub of waysides. Our sole record is from Erewash Meadows (SK4450) in 2010. It is of garden origin from the cross of Butterfly-bush (*B. davidii*) and Orange-ball-tree (*B. globosa*).

LAMIACEAE

Stachys byzantina K. Koch
Lamb's-ear

COUNTY STATUS: Established (Neophyte)

CONSERVATION STATUS: None

FIRST YEAR: 1993 LATEST YEAR: 2011 NO OF RECORDS: 8

RECENT SQUARES: monads 7; tetrads 7; hectads 6

ALL SQUARES: monads 7; tetrads 7; hectads 6

Lamb's-ear is a very rare, established perennial. It has been recorded from only seven sites, between 1993 and 2011: Moss Rake (SK1480), Monsal Trail (SK2269); Mugginton (SK2842); Chesterfield (SK3870); Herdings Park (SK3783); Heeley (SK3488);

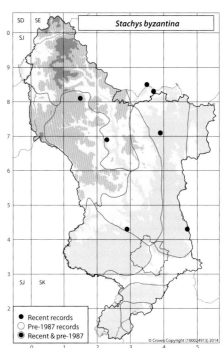

and Cotmanhay (SK4743). Indigenous to south-western Asia, and often grown in UK gardens, these reports are probably all escapes or throwouts.

Stachys sylvatica L.
Hedge Woundwort

COUNTY STATUS: Native

CONSERVATION STATUS: None

FIRST YEAR: 1789 LATEST YEAR: 2013 NO OF RECORDS: 4,587

RECENT SQUARES: monads 1,808; tetrads 697; hectads 42

ALL SQUARES: monads 1,885; tetrads 700; hectads 42

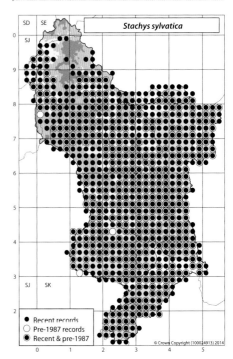

Hedge Woundwort is a very common, native perennial of woods, hedges, riverbanks and disturbed ground, generally on moist fertile soils. It can be found occasionally as a garden weed and has been noted throughout the county, except for the high moors of the Dark Peak.

Stachys × ambigua Sm.
Hybrid Woundwort

COUNTY STATUS: Native	
CONSERVATION STATUS: None	
FIRST YEAR: 1863 **LATEST YEAR:** 2012 **NO OF RECORDS:** 43	
RECENT SQUARES: monads 13; tetrads 13; hectads 9	
ALL SQUARES: monads 24; tetrads 21; hectads 16	

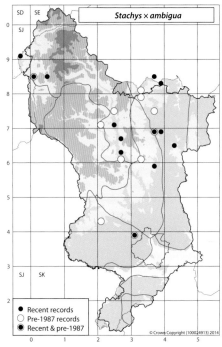

Hybrid Woundwort is a very rare, native perennial of damp woods and the edges of waterbodies. Most recent records are from northern and central Derbyshire (Etherow SJ9791, Rollestone SK3684, Smelting Mill Wood SK2666 & Timber Lane Farm SK4264). Clapham's 1969 Flora recorded it more frequently from southern parts (Calke SK32, Willington and Stapenhill SK22). It is the hybrid of Hedge (*S. sylvatica*) and Marsh Woundwort (*S. palustris*).

Stachys palustris L.
Marsh Woundwort

COUNTY STATUS: Native	
CONSERVATION STATUS: None	
FIRST YEAR: 1811 **LATEST YEAR:** 2013 **NO OF RECORDS:** 406	
RECENT SQUARES: monads 176; tetrads 130; hectads 32	
ALL SQUARES: monads 194; tetrads 141; hectads 34	

Marsh Woundwort is a native perennial that grows by the edges of rivers, canals and ponds, and in swamps, fens and marshes. It is frequent along river corridors in the south of the county (Stenson SK3229, Shardlow SK4430 & Crich SK3452 but rare elsewhere (Hadfield

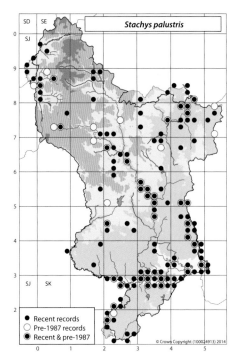

SK0196, Beighton SK4484 & Noton Barn Farm SK2166).

Stachys arvensis (L.) L.
Field Woundwort

COUNTY STATUS: Established (Archaeophyte)	
CONSERVATION STATUS: DRDB (Cat2), NT, B	
FIRST YEAR: 1789 **LATEST YEAR:** 2010 **NO OF RECORDS:** 99	
RECENT SQUARES: monads 28; tetrads 25; hectads 13	
ALL SQUARES: monads 55; tetrads 51; hectads 24	

Field Woundwort is an anciently established annual of arable fields and waste ground, generally on non-calcareous soils. It occurs rarely in eastern and southern areas (Sothall SK4482, Avenue Farm SK3967, Wilsthorpe School SK4733 & Linton SK2614) with an

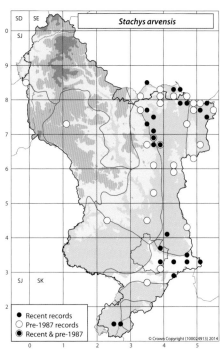

isolated record in the extreme north-west (SK09). It appears to have declined in arable situations since Clapham (1969) but increased on waste ground.

Betonica officinalis L.
Betony

COUNTY STATUS: Native	
CONSERVATION STATUS: None	
FIRST YEAR: 1789 **LATEST YEAR:** 2013 **NO OF RECORDS:** 1,047	
RECENT SQUARES: monads 416; tetrads 279; hectads 37	
ALL SQUARES: monads 467; tetrads 310; hectads 38	

Betony is an occasional native perennial of unimproved grasslands, heaths and open woodlands. It is found across Derbyshire, except for the high moors of the Peak

Betony (*Betonica officinalis*) in unimproved grassland at Holmesfield (SK3176), July 2009 (Ken Balkow)

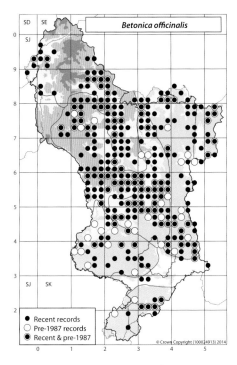

District and some intensively farmed areas of the lowlands. There have been a few local losses since the 1980s due to agricultural improvement.

Ballota nigra L.
Black Horehound

COUNTY STATUS: Established (Archaeophyte)
CONSERVATION STATUS: None
FIRST YEAR: 1789 **LATEST YEAR:** 2013 **NO OF RECORDS:** 286
RECENT SQUARES: monads 106; tetrads 98; hectads 25
ALL SQUARES: monads 143; tetrads 126; hectads 28

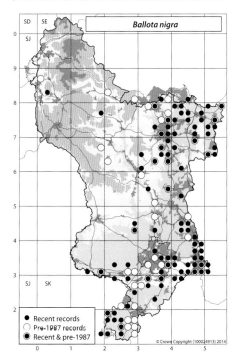

Black Horehound is an anciently established perennial of waste ground and waysides, generally on nutrient-rich

soils near habitations. It is occasional throughout eastern and southern Derbyshire from Jordanthorpe (SK38Q) and Steetley Quarry (SK5478) in the north, through Oakerthorpe (SK3854) and Shipley (SK4444), to Ticknall (SK3523) and Lullington (SK2513) in the south. Elsewhere it is very rare: Brierley Green (SK0282) and Grindlow (SK1877).

Leonurus cardiaca L.
Motherwort

Motherwort is an established perennial of waysides and disturbed ground, often near dwellings. There are four recent records between 1992 and 2011: Fairfield (SK0674), Rodsley (SK2040), Ashgate (SK3671) and Palterton (SK4768). Previously it was recorded from a wider area extending as far south as Kirk Ireton (SK2649) in 1969, and Derby (SK3535) in 1980. The first record is in Pilkington (1789). Indigenous to continental Europe, it was formerly grown as a medicinal herb, but was also a contaminant of imported grain.

Lamiastrum galeobdolon (L.) Ehrend. & Polatschek
Yellow Archangel

COUNTY STATUS: Native
CONSERVATION STATUS: None
FIRST YEAR: 1789 **LATEST YEAR:** 2013 **NO OF RECORDS:** 1,557
RECENT SQUARES: monads 513; tetrads 317; hectads 35
ALL SQUARES: monads 586; tetrads 342; hectads 37

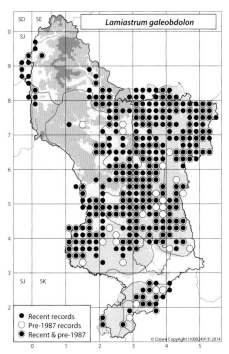

Two subspecies occur in the county.
Yellow Archangel (ssp. *montanum* (Pers.) Ehrend. & Polatschek) is a sprawling native perennial. It is frequent in ancient woods and hedgerows in lowland Derbyshire

(South Normanton SK4455 & Grange Wood SK2714). It is rare elsewhere, almost entirely avoiding the higher ground of the Peak District (Chisworth SJ9891, Yorkshire Bridge SK1984, Over Haddon SK2066 & Hollowchurch Way SK2656). **Garden Yellow Archangel (ssp. *argentatum* (Smejkal) Stace)** is a newly established, sprawling perennial of shrubberies, waysides and waste ground. It occurs occasionally scattered throughout the county (Longdendale Trail SK0798, Beighton SK4484, Stanton Woodhouse SK2564, Pentrich SK3852, Melbourne SK3924 & Hatton SK2131). It is much grown in gardens for ornament and, being a vigorous grower, often escapes or is discarded into the wild. It is of uncertain origin.

Lamium album L.
White Dead-nettle

COUNTY STATUS: Established (Archaeophyte)
CONSERVATION STATUS: None
FIRST YEAR: 1789 **LATEST YEAR:** 2013 **NO OF RECORDS:** 3,124
RECENT SQUARES: monads 1,370; tetrads 561; hectads 39
ALL SQUARES: monads 1,429; tetrads 573; hectads 40

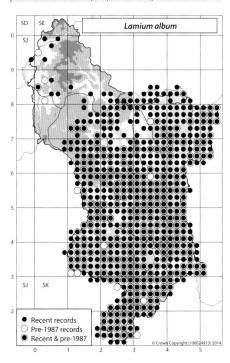

White Dead-nettle is an anciently established perennial of waysides, disturbed ground and waste places, particularly on fertile soils near habitations. It is very common throughout the county except for the high moors of the Dark and South West Peak, and north-western part of the White Peak.

Lamium maculatum (L.) L.
Spotted Dead-nettle

Spotted Dead-nettle is an established perennial of waysides, waste ground and tips, often near habitations. It occurs

The Flora of Derbyshire 225

COUNTY STATUS: Established (Neophyte)
CONSERVATION STATUS: None
FIRST YEAR: 1837 LATEST YEAR: 2013 NO OF RECORDS: 145
RECENT SQUARES: monads 72; tetrads 76; hectads 29
ALL SQUARES: monads 96; tetrads 98; hectads 33

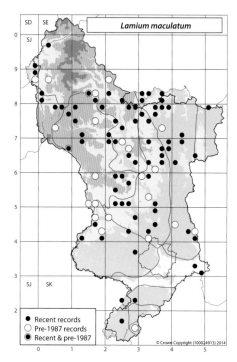

scattered occasionally throughout the county from Hadfield (SK0296) and the Gleadless Valley (SK3782) in the north, to Lock Lane Ash Tip (SK4831) and Caldwell Village (SK2517) in the south. It is often grown in gardens for ornament, and is a native of continental Europe.

Lamium purpureum L.
Red Dead-nettle

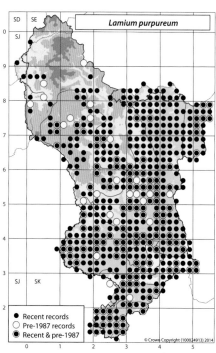

Red Dead-nettle is an anciently established annual of arable land, gardens, disturbed ground and waysides, generally on fertile soils. It occurs very commonly throughout the lowland, southern and eastern parts of Derbyshire, becoming less frequent in the more upland Peak District.

Lamium hybridum Vill.
Cut-leaved Dead-nettle

COUNTY STATUS: Established (Archaeophyte)
CONSERVATION STATUS: B
FIRST YEAR: 1866 LATEST YEAR: 2012 NO OF RECORDS: 45
RECENT SQUARES: monads 26; tetrads 25; hectads 15
ALL SQUARES: monads 30; tetrads 29; hectads 15

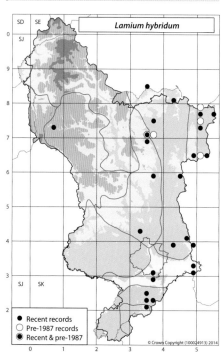

Cut-leaved Dead-nettle is an anciently established annual of cultivated and waste ground. It occurs occasionally through the eastern half of the county from Mosborough (SK4281) and Brookside (SK3470) in the north, to Trent Lock (SK4831) and Calke Park (SK3523) in the south. There is also an isolated record from Buxton (SK0672). It is probably under-recorded for Red Dead-nettle (*L. purpureum*). It is a lowland species, reaching its British altitudinal limit of 320m here in Derbyshire (Preston *et al.* 2002).

Lamium confertum Fr.
Northern Dead-nettle

Northern Dead-nettle is a very rare, casual annual of cultivated and disturbed ground.

COUNTY STATUS: Established (Archaeophyte)
CONSERVATION STATUS: None
FIRST YEAR: 1829 LATEST YEAR: 2013 NO OF RECORDS: 1,451
RECENT SQUARES: monads 805; tetrads 466; hectads 41
ALL SQUARES: monads 866; tetrads 488; hectads 42

COUNTY STATUS: Casual
CONSERVATION STATUS: None
FIRST YEAR: 1847 LATEST YEAR: 1978 NO OF RECORDS: 5
RECENT SQUARES: monads 0; tetrads 0; hectads 0
ALL SQUARES: monads 2; tetrads 2; hectads 5

There are no recent records and only four earlier ones, all from the south: (Ashbourne SK1746 in 1978, Derby SK3536 in 1978, Drakelow SK21 in 1903, Bonsall SK25 in 1847 & SK22 in 1889). It is a plant of lowland northern England, reaching its national altitudinal limit of 320m in Derbyshire as a casual (Preston *et al.* 2002).

Lamium amplexicaule L.
Henbit Dead-nettle

COUNTY STATUS: Established (Archaeophyte)
CONSERVATION STATUS: None
FIRST YEAR: 1829 LATEST YEAR: 2012 NO OF RECORDS: 96
RECENT SQUARES: monads 44; tetrads 41; hectads 18
ALL SQUARES: monads 62; tetrads 56; hectads 26

Henbit Dead-nettle is an anciently established annual of gardens, arable fields, waste land and walls. It is recorded occasionally throughout eastern and southern parts, as at Proctor's Nursery (SK3470), between Lea and Holloway (SK3356), Fields Farm Road (SK4932) and Lullington Village (SK2413). Elsewhere there is only the odd record in the north-west as at Charlesworth (SK0093). Many local plants set seed without opening their flowers. Clapham (1969) notes it is "now decreasing" but, apart from some losses between Derby and

Henbit Dead-nettle (*Lamium amplexicaule*), Witches Oak Waters (SK4329), April 2004 (Philip Precey)

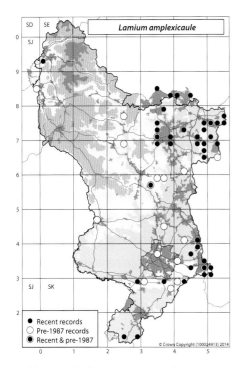

Ashbourne, it does not seem to have declined further.

Galeopsis angustifolia Ehrh. ex Hoffm.
Red Hemp-nettle

COUNTY STATUS: Established (Archaeophyte)
CONSERVATION STATUS: DRDB (Cat2), CR, NS, NERC, A, B, C
FIRST YEAR: 1789 LATEST YEAR: 2007 NO OF RECORDS: 67
RECENT SQUARES: monads 9; tetrads 8; hectads 7
ALL SQUARES: monads 17; tetrads 16; hectads 12

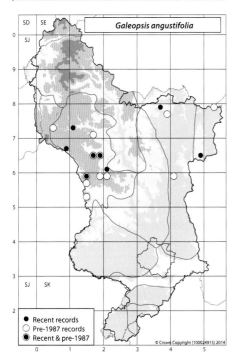

Red Hemp-nettle is an anciently established annual of the White Peak. It occurs rarely in unshaded, limestone screes in Biggin Dale (SK1458), Lathkill Dale (SK1765) and Gratton Dale (SK2060). There

Red Hemp-nettle (*Galeopsis angustifolia*), Biggin Dale (SK1458), June 2002 (Ken Balkow)

are isolated casual records away from the White Peak, as at Frith Wood (SK3678) and Pleasley Pit (SK4964). Previously it occurred in a greater range of habitats. Both Clapham (1969) and Linton (1903) mention it as a plant of arable land though it is not known from that habitat today. Found sporadically throughout England and Wales, it is a Nationally Scarce species.

Galeopsis speciosa Mill.
Large-flowered Hemp-nettle

COUNTY STATUS: Established (Archaeophyte)
CONSERVATION STATUS: DRDB (Cat2), VU
FIRST YEAR: 1805 LATEST YEAR: 2011 NO OF RECORDS: 82
RECENT SQUARES: monads 17; tetrads 17; hectads 16
ALL SQUARES: monads 40; tetrads 38; hectads 29

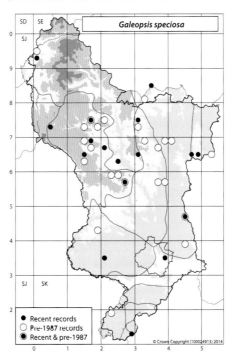

Large-flowered Hemp-nettle is an anciently established annual of cultivated land, waste ground and wood edges. It

occurs rarely throughout the area from Charlesworth (SK0093) in the north, through Litton Dale (SK1675), and Bonsall Moor (SK2657), to Barton Fields (SK2135) and Netherseal (SK21W) in the south. It appears to have declined since Clapham (1969), probably due to changes in arable farming techniques.

Galeopsis tetrahit L.
Common Hemp-nettle

COUNTY STATUS: Native
CONSERVATION STATUS: None
FIRST YEAR: 1789 LATEST YEAR: 2013 NO OF RECORDS: 576
RECENT SQUARES: monads 329; tetrads 268; hectads 36
ALL SQUARES: monads 366; tetrads 293; hectads 37

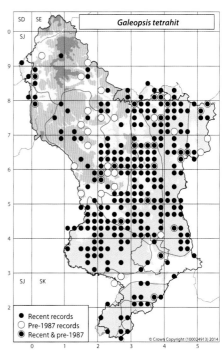

Common Hemp-nettle is an occasional native annual of arable land, rough ground, wood edges and heathlands. It occurs scattered throughout the county (Watford Lodge SK0086, Clough Wood SK2561, Black Brook Sand Pit SK2744, Courtauld's Lagoon SK3934 & Spring Wood SK3722). Recorders have not always separated it from Bifid Hemp-nettle (*G. bifida*) so it is probably under-recorded. Variety *nigricans* Breb. was noted by (Clapham 1969) but there are no recent records.

Galeopsis bifida Boenn.
Bifid Hemp-nettle

COUNTY STATUS: Native
CONSERVATION STATUS: None
FIRST YEAR: 1950 LATEST YEAR: 2013 NO OF RECORDS: 122
RECENT SQUARES: monads 84; tetrads 90; hectads 27
ALL SQUARES: monads 85; tetrads 91; hectads 28

Bifid Hemp-nettle is an occasional native annual of arable land and rough ground.

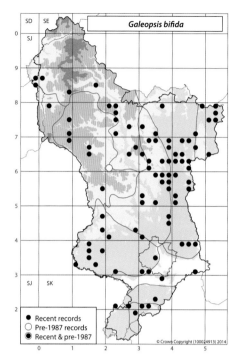

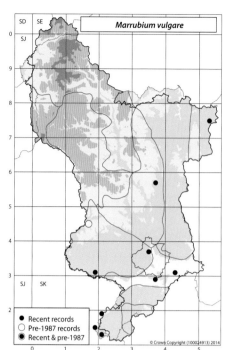

It is scattered throughout the area from New Mills (SK0086) and Pebley (SK4878) in the north, to Drakelow Power Station (SK2220) and Hartshorne Village (SK3220) in the south. It has not always been clearly separated from Common Hemp-nettle (*G. tetrahit*) so is probably under-recorded.

Galeopsis ladanum L.
Broad-leaved Hemp-nettle
Broad-leaved Hemp-nettle is a very rare, casual annual of cultivated land. The last known location was Cowley (SK3477) in 1970 earlier records come from Biggin Dale (SK1458) in 1969 and Elmton (SK57) in 1895. It is a native of continental Europe.

Melittis melissophyllum L.
Bastard Balm
Locally extinct, Bastard Balm was a very rare, casual perennial of hedgebanks. The only record came from between Barrow and Sinfin (SK33/32) in 1829. Sometimes grown in gardens, it is a native of southern and western Britain.

Marrubium vulgare L.
White Horehound

COUNTY STATUS: Casual	
CONSERVATION STATUS: None	
FIRST YEAR: 1789 **LATEST YEAR:** 2009 **NO OF RECORDS:** 13	
RECENT SQUARES: monads 9; tetrads 9; hectads 8	
ALL SQUARES: monads 10; tetrads 10; hectads 10	

White Horehound is a very rare, casual perennial of waste ground and waysides. There are recent records from the southern and eastern parts of the county (Scropton SK1930, The Grange SK2013, Shardlow SK4330 & Creswell Crags SK5374). Previous

records cover a similar but wider area (Middleton Dale SK27 in 1789, Clifton Tip SK1644 in 1969 & Repton SK32 in 1903). It is sometimes grown in gardens as an herb, and is native to parts of southern Britain.

Scutellaria altissima L.
Somerset Skullcap
Somerset Skullcap is a perennial herb which is established at just one site. It was first seen by B. Gough in Ilkeston (SK4642) in 2002 and was known there until at least 2005. It is a native of south-eastern Europe.

Scutellaria galericulata L.
Skullcap

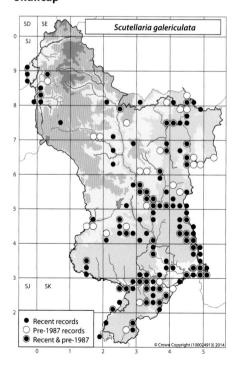

COUNTY STATUS: Native	
CONSERVATION STATUS: None	
FIRST YEAR: 1789 **LATEST YEAR:** 2013 **NO OF RECORDS:** 475	
RECENT SQUARES: monads 153; tetrads 118; hectads 29	
ALL SQUARES: monads 199; tetrads 144; hectads 33	

Skullcap is an occasional native perennial that grows in and by the edges of ponds, canals and streams, and in marshes, fens and wet grasslands. It is found mainly in the southern and eastern lowlands (Hollingwood SK4174, Cromford Canal SK3353, River Trent SK5031 & Willington Grasslands SK3029). It is rarely scattered elsewhere, including the north-west (Etherow SJ9791 & Furness Vale SK0083).

Scutellaria minor Huds.
Lesser Skullcap

COUNTY STATUS: Native	
CONSERVATION STATUS: A, B	
FIRST YEAR: 1789 **LATEST YEAR:** 2012 **NO OF RECORDS:** 38	
RECENT SQUARES: monads 8; tetrads 8; hectads 6	
ALL SQUARES: monads 13; tetrads 11; hectads 10	

Lesser Skullcap is a very rare, native perennial of acid mires and wet heaths. All current records, except one, are from the Dark Peak (Heyden Brook SE0903 v.c.58, Hope Forest SK1590 & Harland Sick SK2968). The exception is from Wessington Green (SK3757) in the Peak Fringe. It was previously found further south (Hulland Moss SK2446 in 1968 & Repton Shrubs

Lesser Skullcap (*Scutellaria minor*), Upper Derwent Valley (SK19), September 2012 (David Blowers)

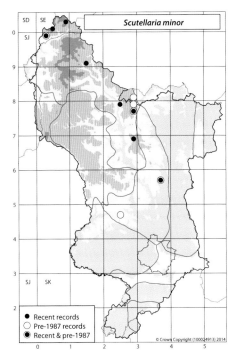

SK32 in 1903). Nationally it has shown a similar contraction in range, probably due to drainage and habitat destruction (Preston *et al.* 2002).

Teucrium scorodonia L.
Wood Sage

COUNTY STATUS: Native
CONSERVATION STATUS: None
FIRST YEAR: 1789 LATEST YEAR: 2013 NO OF RECORDS: 1,712
RECENT SQUARES: monads 574; tetrads 346; hectads 34
ALL SQUARES: monads 633; tetrads 369; hectads 37

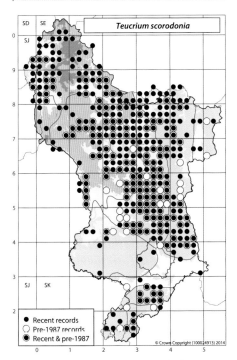

Wood Sage is a native perennial of woods, waysides, scrub, heaths and rough grasslands, on dry soils that are usually

at least slightly acidic. It is common throughout the Peak Fringe, Dark Peak and the Coal Measures Character Areas, but is rare elsewhere.

Ajuga reptans L.
Bugle

COUNTY STATUS: Native
CONSERVATION STATUS: None
FIRST YEAR: 1789 LATEST YEAR: 2013 NO OF RECORDS: 1,410
RECENT SQUARES: monads 518; tetrads 345; hectads 39
ALL SQUARES: monads 577; tetrads 370; hectads 39

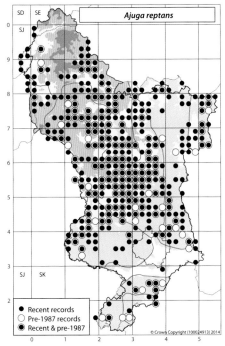

Bugle is a creeping native perennial of damp woods, wet grasslands and flushed ground throughout the county (Swallowhouse SK0387, Markland Grips SK5074, Hopton Quarry SK2656, Sudbury Coppice SK1535 & Mere Pond SK3622). It is common in central parts, but rarer in the Peak District and some of the intensively farmed lowland areas.

Nepeta cataria L.
Cat-mint

COUNTY STATUS: Established (Archaeophyte)
CONSERVATION STATUS: DRDB (Cat2), VU, A, B
FIRST YEAR: 1829 LATEST YEAR: 2003 NO OF RECORDS: 26
RECENT SQUARES: monads 6; tetrads 6; hectads 4
ALL SQUARES: monads 8; tetrads 8; hectads 11

Cat-mint is an anciently established perennial of waysides and rough ground. Current records are almost exclusively from the Magnesian Limestone (Scarcliffe Park SK5170 & Hollinhill SK5175), though it is rare even there. Elsewhere there are only isolated records, as at Kirk Hallam (SK4639) and Churchdale Hall (SK2070). It previously occurred throughout the

county, from Whaley (SK08 in 1986) in the north to Linton (SK21 in 1903) in the south. Nationally it has shown a similar contraction of range due to agricultural intensification and the growth of scrub (Preston *et al.* 2002).

Nepeta × *faassenii* Bergmans ex Stearn
Garden Cat-mint

COUNTY STATUS: Casual
CONSERVATION STATUS: None
FIRST YEAR: 1973 LATEST YEAR: 2004 NO OF RECORDS: 6
RECENT SQUARES: monads 5; tetrads 5; hectads 5
ALL SQUARES: monads 6; tetrads 6; hectads 6

Garden Cat-mint is a very rare, casual perennial of roadsides, tips and waste ground. There are recent records from Perryfoot (SK1081), Hartington Meadows (SK1561), Freebirch Farm (SK3072), Ashbourne (SK1746) and Melbourne (SK3925), plus an earlier one from Coombs Dale (SK2274) in 1973. It is grown in gardens from where it is often discarded with waste. It is of horticultural origin from the hybridisation of two foreign cat-mints (*N. racemosa* Lam. and *N. nepetella* L.).

Glechoma hederacea L.
Ground-ivy

COUNTY STATUS: Native
CONSERVATION STATUS: None
FIRST YEAR: 1789 LATEST YEAR: 2013 NO OF RECORDS: 3,096
RECENT SQUARES: monads 1,237; tetrads 588; hectads 42
ALL SQUARES: monads 1,308; tetrads 601; hectads 42

Ground-ivy is a creeping native perennial of woods, hedges, grasslands and rough ground, usually on heavy fertile soils. It occurs very commonly throughout the

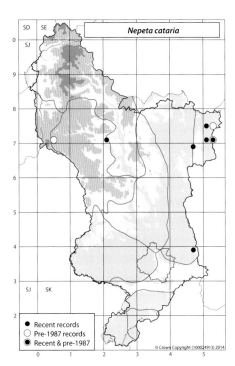

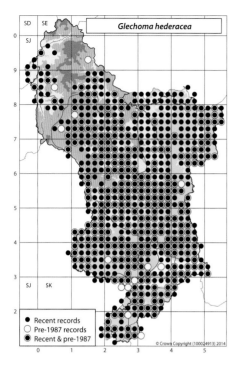

county except for the high moors of the Dark and South West Peak Areas where it is generally absent. It has a local name of Robin-run-in-the-hedge (Grigson 1975).

Prunella vulgaris L.
Selfheal

COUNTY STATUS: Native

CONSERVATION STATUS: None

FIRST YEAR: 1789 LATEST YEAR: 2013 NO OF RECORDS: 3,810

RECENT SQUARES: monads 1,462; tetrads 676; hectads 43

ALL SQUARES: monads 1,542; tetrads 690; hectads 43

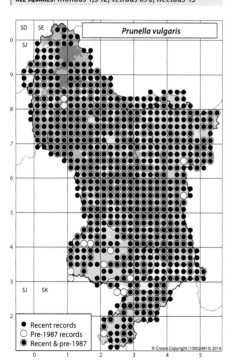

Selfheal is a patch-forming native perennial of grasslands, lawns, woodland clearings and waste places, typically on moist fertile

soils. It grows very commonly throughout Derbyshire, avoiding only some of the higher moors of the Peak District. White flowered forms sometimes arise.

Melissa officinalis L.
Balm

COUNTY STATUS: Established (Neophyte)

CONSERVATION STATUS: None

FIRST YEAR: 1969 LATEST YEAR: 2013 NO OF RECORDS: 36

RECENT SQUARES: monads 23; tetrads 22; hectads 16

ALL SQUARES: monads 27; tetrads 26; hectads 18

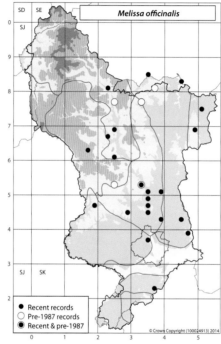

Balm is an established perennial of waysides and waste ground. It occurs rarely throughout the area from Meersbrook Bank (SK3484) and Sothall (SK4482) in the north, through Alderwasley (SK3253), to Kirk Hallam (SK4639) and Home Farm (SK3722) in the south. It is grown in gardens for its fragrant foliage, from where it often spreads by seeds or discarded waste. It is a native of southern Europe.

Clinopodium ascendens (Jord.) Samp.
Common Calamint

COUNTY STATUS: Native

CONSERVATION STATUS: DRDB (Cat5b), A, B

FIRST YEAR: 1859 LATEST YEAR: 2010 NO OF RECORDS: 32

RECENT SQUARES: monads 5; tetrads 5; hectads 5

ALL SQUARES: monads 12; tetrads 11; hectads 13

Common Calamint is a very rare, native perennial of dry banks and rough grassland, generally on calcareous soils. It has only been recorded recently from six areas: Ravenstor (SK1573); Hucklow (SK1878); Mickleover (SK3035); Long Eaton (SK43); Pleasley Park (SK56); and Creswell

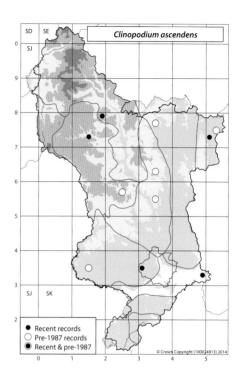

(SK5173). It was formerly scattered more frequently through the same parts of the county.

Clinopodium vulgare L.
Wild Basil

COUNTY STATUS: Native

CONSERVATION STATUS: None

FIRST YEAR: 1789 LATEST YEAR: 2012 NO OF RECORDS: 211

RECENT SQUARES: monads 70; tetrads 60; hectads 18

ALL SQUARES: monads 101; tetrads 80; hectads 26

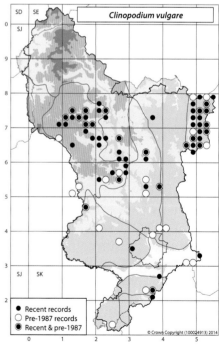

Wild Basil is a clump-forming native perennial of hedges, scrub and wood margins, generally on dry calcareous soils. It is frequent on the Magnesian Limestone as

at Whitwell (SK5377), Poulter Park Reserve (SK5271) and Pleasley Vale (SK5064). It is occasional in the White Peak for example in Monk's Dale (SK1375) and the Via Gellia (SK2556). Elsewhere it is rare as at Brockwell (SK3672) and Ticknall Quarries (SK3623).

Clinopodium acinos (L.) Kuntze
Basil Thyme

COUNTY STATUS: Native
CONSERVATION STATUS: DRDB (Cat2), VU, NERC, A
FIRST YEAR: 1789 LATEST YEAR: 2006 NO OF RECORDS: 57
RECENT SQUARES: monads 11; tetrads 8; hectads 5
ALL SQUARES: monads 24; tetrads 18; hectads 14

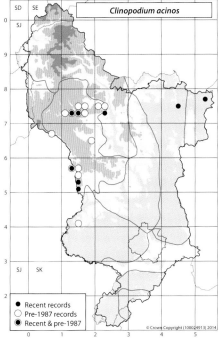

Wild Marjoram (*Origanum vulgare*) on floor of Chee Dale Quarry (SK1373), July 2008 (Peter Smith)

Basil Thyme is a very rare, native annual of dry sunny banks and rocky outcrops. The majority of recent records are for the White Peak (Priestcliffe Lees SK1472 & Dove Dale SK1451). There is a single record for the Magnesian Limestone (Whitwell SK5376) and another for the Coal Measures (Mastin Moor SK4475). Previously it occurred over a wider area including Birchwood Quarry (SK1541 in 1969), Foremark (SK32 in 1903) and Holbrook (SK34 in 1903). A number of these earlier records refer to it as a weed of arable land. It has been lost from this habitat due to herbicide use, which also accounts for much of its national decline (Preston *et al.* 2002).

Origanum vulgare L.
Wild Marjoram

COUNTY STATUS: Native
CONSERVATION STATUS: None
FIRST YEAR: 1789 LATEST YEAR: 2013 NO OF RECORDS: 625
RECENT SQUARES: monads 193; tetrads 134; hectads 30
ALL SQUARES: monads 208; tetrads 147; hectads 32

Wild Marjoram is a clump-forming native perennial of dry grasslands, scrub and disturbed ground, generally on infertile calcareous soils. It is frequent in the White Peak (Hay Dale SK1176, Over Haddon SK2066 & Middleton Top SK2755), but rare elsewhere (Fairholmes SK1789, Markland Grips SK5074 & King's Newton SK3827). It is sometimes grown as the culinary herb Oregano, so a few records may represent garden escapes.

Thymus pulegioides L.
Large Thyme
Large Thyme is an established prostrate perennial of open or waste ground. There

are only two records: Grassmoor Old Colliery (SK4167) in 2001 and Pin Dale (SK1682) in 2010. An old record, for Miller's Dale (SK1573) in Clapham (1969), is now considered an error. It is native elsewhere in southern Britain.

Thymus polytrichus A. Kern. ex Borbas
Wild Thyme

COUNTY STATUS: Native
CONSERVATION STATUS: None
FIRST YEAR: 1789 LATEST YEAR: 2013 NO OF RECORDS: 1,379
RECENT SQUARES: monads 301; tetrads 134; hectads 17
ALL SQUARES: monads 319; tetrads 142; hectads 25

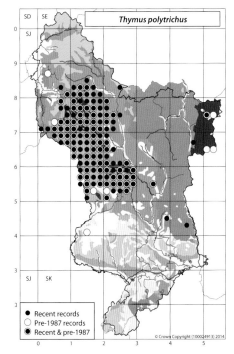

Wild Thyme is a prostrate native perennial of short dry grassland and rocky outcrops.

Wild Thyme (*Thymus polytrichus*) on Carboniferous Limestone outcrops near Hartington (SK1260), July 2008 (Malcolm Neal)

It is very common throughout the White Peak (Dam Dale SK1178, Over Haddon SK2066 & Parwich SK1854), but very rare elsewhere (Markland Grips SK5074, Crich Cliff SK3455 & Horeston Cottages SK3845). Previously it was more frequent in the south (Turnditch SK24, Radbourne SK23, Littleover SK33, Burton SK22 & Calke SK32 all for 1903) but it has been lost from here, probably due to the agricultural improvement of marginal land.

Lycopus europaeus L.
Gypsywort

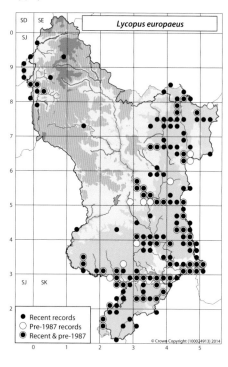

| COUNTY STATUS: Native |
| CONSERVATION STATUS: None |
| FIRST YEAR: 1789 LATEST YEAR: 2013 NO OF RECORDS: 747 |
| RECENT SQUARES: monads 243; tetrads 151; hectads 30 |
| ALL SQUARES: monads 258; tetrads 161; hectads 31 |

Gypsywort is a native perennial of marshes, fens, canals, riversides and the margins of ponds. It is occasional in the lowland southern and eastern parts (Renishaw Lake SK4378, Cromford Canal SK3452 & Drakelow Reserve SK2220). It also occurs in the extreme north-west (Arnfield SK0097 v.c.58 & Brierley Green SK0282), but otherwise generally avoids the upland areas of the Peak District.

Mentha arvensis L.
Corn Mint

| COUNTY STATUS: Native |
| CONSERVATION STATUS: ERL |
| FIRST YEAR: 1789 LATEST YEAR: 2012 NO OF RECORDS: 329 |
| RECENT SQUARES: monads 128; tetrads 123; hectads 30 |
| ALL SQUARES: monads 179; tetrads 159; hectads 34 |

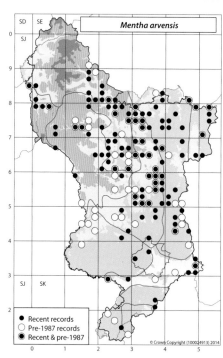

Corn Mint is an occasional native perennial of damp areas at the margins of woods, ponds and arable fields, though is less common in the latter habitat than previously. It occurs sporadically from Furness Vale (SK0084) and Stoneley Wood (SK3882) in the north, through Wessington Green (SK3757), to South Wood (SK3620) and Linton (SK2614) in the south.

Mentha × verticillata L.
Whorled Mint

Whorled Mint is a rare native perennial found in damp grassland at the edges of ponds, reservoirs, canals and streams.

| COUNTY STATUS: Native |
| CONSERVATION STATUS: None |
| FIRST YEAR: 1789 LATEST YEAR: 2003 NO OF RECORDS: 68 |
| RECENT SQUARES: monads 15; tetrads 16; hectads 12 |
| ALL SQUARES: monads 46; tetrads 46; hectads 26 |

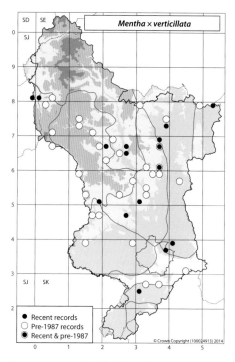

It grows sporadically throughout Derbyshire from Toddbrook Reservoir (SJ9980 v.c.58) and Chesterfield Canal (SK3872) in the north, through Ogston Reservoir (SK3760), to Locko Park (SK4038) and Lawn Bridge (SK3125) in the south. It appears to have declined both locally and nationally (Preston *et al.* 2002). It is the hybrid of Corn (*M. arvensis*) and Water Mint (*M. aquatica*).

Mentha × smithiana R.A. Graham
Tall Mint

| COUNTY STATUS: Established (Neophyte) |
| CONSERVATION STATUS: None |
| FIRST YEAR: 1829 LATEST YEAR: 2009 NO OF RECORDS: 46 |
| RECENT SQUARES: monads 8; tetrads 8; hectads 5 |
| ALL SQUARES: monads 28; tetrads 27; hectads 19 |

Tall Mint is a very rare, established perennial of the edges of waterbodies, waysides and waste ground. It is recorded sporadically throughout central Derbyshire: Ogston Reservoir (SK3759) and Lawn Farm (SK3050). It used to occur over a wider area: Whaley Bridge (SK08 in 1903), Clarion Hut (SK2981 in 1969), Ockbrook (SK43 in 1903) and Ticknall (SK32 in 1903). It has also declined nationally (Preston *et al.* 2002) but it is not clear if this is a real decline or just a change in recording. It is the hybrid of Corn (*M. arvensis*), Water (*M. aquatica*) and Spear Mint (*M. spicata*). Probably of

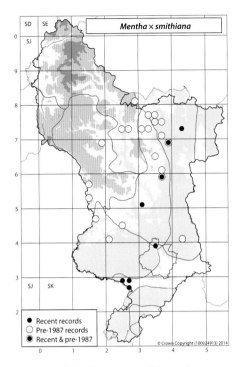

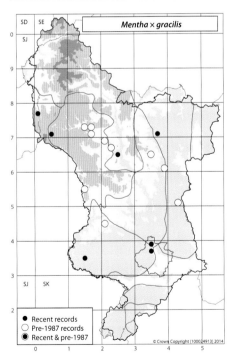

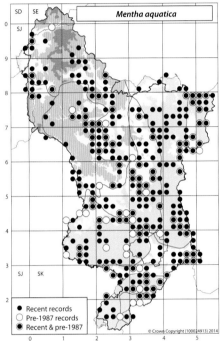

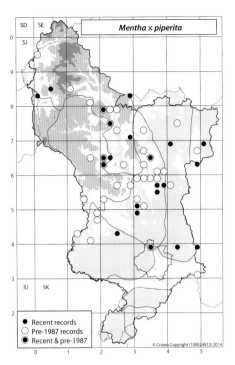

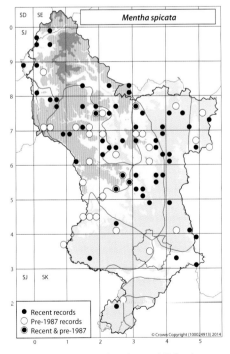

the River Wye (SK2565). It is the cultivated hybrid of Corn (*M. arvensis*) and Spear Mint (*M. spicata*). However, it can arise spontaneously so some records may be of native rather than cultivated origin.

Mentha aquatica L.
Water Mint

COUNTY STATUS: Native

CONSERVATION STATUS: None

FIRST YEAR: 1789 **LATEST YEAR:** 2013 **NO OF RECORDS:** 905

RECENT SQUARES: monads 358; tetrads 289; hectads 39

ALL SQUARES: monads 398; tetrads 312; hectads 39

Water Mint is a native perennial of marshes, fens and carrs, plus the sides of waterbodies. It is frequent in lowland parts of southern and eastern Derbyshire but rare in the more upland Peak District.

Mentha × *piperita* L.
Peppermint

COUNTY STATUS: Established (Neophyte)

CONSERVATION STATUS: None

FIRST YEAR: 1789 **LATEST YEAR:** 2011 **NO OF RECORDS:** 82

RECENT SQUARES: monads 20; tetrads 22; hectads 13

ALL SQUARES: monads 60; tetrads 53; hectads 23

Peppermint is an established perennial of damp waysides, streamsides and waste places. It occurs rarely from Chinley Head (SK0484) and Lady Canning's Plantation (SK2883) in the north, through Meadow Place Grange (SK2065), to Darley Abbey (SK3539) and Erewash Canal (SK4839) in the south. It is the cultivated hybrid of Water (*M. aquatica*) and Spear Mint (*M. spicata*). It can also arise spontaneously so some records may be of native material, not garden escapes. It has been cultivated

garden origin, it may sometimes arise spontaneously in the wild.

Mentha × *gracilis* Sole
Bushy Mint

COUNTY STATUS: Established (Neophyte)

CONSERVATION STATUS: None

FIRST YEAR: 1789 **LATEST YEAR:** 2011 **NO OF RECORDS:** 27

RECENT SQUARES: monads 7; tetrads 7; hectads 5

ALL SQUARES: monads 18; tetrads 17; hectads 13

Bushy Mint is an established perennial of watersides and damp waste places. Recent records are spread over the central parts of the county: Fernilee Reservoir (SK0177 v.c.58), Solomon's Temple (SK0571) and

commercially in the past at Litton in Cressbrook Dale (Farey 1815). **Eau de Cologne Mint** (**variety *citrata*** (Ehrh.) Briq.) has been recorded once at Norbury (SK1242) in 1972.

Mentha spicata L.
Spear Mint

COUNTY STATUS: Established (Archaeophyte)

CONSERVATION STATUS: None

FIRST YEAR: 1789 **LATEST YEAR:** 2012 **NO OF RECORDS:** 136

RECENT SQUARES: monads 53; tetrads 63; hectads 26

ALL SQUARES: monads 88; tetrads 91; hectads 32

Spear Mint is an anciently established perennial of the sides of waterbodies, damp roadsides and waste ground. It occurs occasionally throughout the county from Torside Reservoir (SK0598) and Lady Canning's Plantation (SK2883) in the north, through Via Gellia (SK2656), to Caldwell (SK2518) and Trent Lock (SK4831) in the south. It is a culinary herb, probably of horticultural origin, and is often discarded with garden rubbish.

Mentha × *villosonervata* Opiz
Sharp-toothed Mint

Sharp-toothed Mint is an established perennial of waysides, riverbanks and waste ground. It occurs scattered throughout the county. There are only four recent records, between 1997 and 2011. These include: Glossop (SK0493), Snelston (SK1443) and Poolsbrook (SK4373). Four earlier records only extend back to Chelmorton (SK1170) in 1977. Cultivated as a herb, it generally escapes as a throwout and is the hybrid of Spear (*M. spicata*) and Horse Mint (*M. longifolia*), probably of garden origin.

Mentha × *villosa* Huds.
Apple-mint

COUNTY STATUS: Established (Neophyte)	
CONSERVATION STATUS: None	
FIRST YEAR: 1903 LATEST YEAR: 2012 NO OF RECORDS: 69	
RECENT SQUARES: monads 23; tetrads 25; hectads 16	
ALL SQUARES: monads 53; tetrads 53; hectads 24	

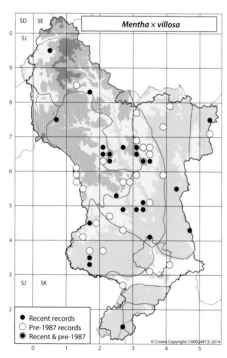

Apple-mint is an established perennial of waysides and waste ground. It occurs rarely throughout the county from Mossy Lea (SK0594) and Creswell Crags (SK5374) in the north, through Wire Stone (SK3263), to Sudbury Park (SK1633) and Grange Wood

(SK2714 v.c.55) in the south. It is grown as a garden herb from where it often escapes as a throwout. It is the hybrid of Spear (*M. spicata*) and Round-leaved Mint (*M. suaveolens*), probably of garden origin. Two varieties have been recorded. **Garden Apple-mint (var. *alopecuroides* (Hull) Briq.)** has a recent record from Clifton (SK1644), plus others from Alport (SK2264) and Belper (SK34) in the 1970s. **Variety *villosa*** was recorded in the 1970s from Owler Bar (SK3077) and Spitewinter (SK3466).

Mentha × *rotundifolia* (L.) Huds.
False Apple-mint

False Apple-mint is an established perennial. The only record is from 1999 near Hope Valley Cement Works (SK1682), and was probably a garden escape or throwout. It is the hybrid of Horse (*M. longifolia* (L.) Huds.) and Round-leaved Mint (*M. suaveolens*) that grows naturally in continental Europe.

Mentha suaveolens Ehrh.
Round-leaved Mint

Round-leaved Mint is an established perennial of waysides and waste ground, often in damp areas. There are seven recent records between 1989 and 2012 scattered through the county. These include: Bradwell (SK1681), Ramsley Moor (SK2876) and Brockwell Reservoir (SK3771). Previous records cover the same area and extend back to the first record in Glover (1829). It is a garden escape, native to parts of south-western Britain.

Mentha pulegium L.
Pennyroyal

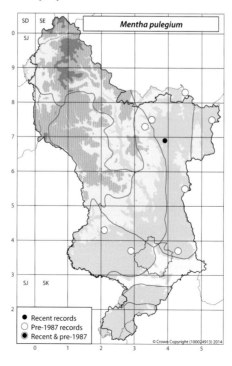

COUNTY STATUS: Native	
CONSERVATION STATUS: DRDB (Cat2), WCA8, EN, NS, NERC, B, C	
FIRST YEAR: 1789 LATEST YEAR: 1997 NO OF RECORDS: 23	
RECENT SQUARES: monads 1; tetrads 1; hectads 1	
ALL SQUARES: monads 9; tetrads 8; hectads 7	

Pennyroyal is a very rare, native perennial found on the margins of waterbodies and wet heaths. The only recent record, from the St Augustine's and Hasland area (SK3868), is undoubtedly for planted specimens. There are earlier records for Linacre Reservoir (SK3272) in 1981, Sheepbridge Ponds (SK3575) in 1980, and a roadside at Creswell Crags (SK5374) in 1968. All others are much earlier: Beighton (SK48) in 1800, plus Pinxton (SK45), Ockbrook Common (SK43), and Radbourne and Langley Commons (SK23) all for 1789. This decline mirrors a national one due to habitat loss (Preston *et al.* 2002).

Salvia pratensis L.
Meadow Clary

Locally extinct, Meadow Clary was a very rare, casual perennial of waste places. The only records are from Swarkestone (SK32) in 1866 and Crich (SK35) in 1789. It is a native of southern England.

Salvia reflexa Hornem.
Mintweed

Mintweed is a casual annual of waste ground, known only from old railway sidings near Fairfield Church (SK0674) in 1996. A contaminant of imported seed and grain, it is native to North America.

Salvia verticillata L.
Whorled Clary

Whorled Clary is a very rare, casual perennial of waste ground. Both recent records are from Longsidings Quarry (SK0976) in 1998 and 2011. There are records from the same site in the 1970s and Clay Mills (SK2726) in 1970. A garden escape or grain contaminant, it grows naturally in southern Europe.

PHRYMACEAE

Mimulus moschatus Douglas ex Lindl.
Musk

COUNTY STATUS: Established (Neophyte)	
CONSERVATION STATUS: None	
FIRST YEAR: 1934 LATEST YEAR: 2013 NO OF RECORDS: 31	
RECENT SQUARES: monads 7; tetrads 7; hectads 6	
ALL SQUARES: monads 21; tetrads 20; hectads 12	

Musk is a very rare, established perennial of pond margins, waysides, damp walls and flushes. It now occurs scattered throughout the county from Kinder Scout (SK1389) in the north, through Old Brampton (SK3371),

Musk (*Mimulus moschatus*) on base of walls at Calke Abbey (SK3622), September 2007 (Nick Moyes)

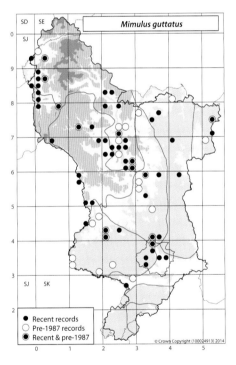

Mimulus × robertsii Silverside
Hybrid Monkeyflower

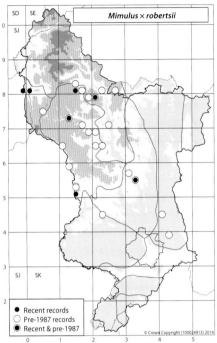

COUNTY STATUS: Established (Neophyte)

CONSERVATION STATUS: None

FIRST YEAR: 1969 **LATEST YEAR:** 2012 **NO OF RECORDS:** 42

RECENT SQUARES: monads 7; tetrads 7; hectads 7

ALL SQUARES: monads 31; tetrads 26; hectads 14

Hybrid Monkeyflower is an established perennial of the margins of waterbodies, damp grasslands and marshes. It is recorded rarely through the northern and central parts of the county, as at Toddbrook Reservoir (SK0081 v.c.58), Lindale (SK1551) and Watergate Farm (SK3254). It was previously recorded more widely, including near Dale (SK4238) in 1973. It is of garden origin from the crossing of Monkeyflower (*M. guttatus*) and Blood-drop-emlets (*M. luteus*), and is probably under-recorded for its two parents.

Mimulus luteus L.
Blood-drop-emlets

COUNTY STATUS: Established (Neophyte)

CONSERVATION STATUS: None

FIRST YEAR: 1881 **LATEST YEAR:** 2005 **NO OF RECORDS:** 23

RECENT SQUARES: monads 5; tetrads 5; hectads 5

ALL SQUARES: monads 13; tetrads 13; hectads 15

Blood-drop-emlets is an established perennial of damp open habitats. It occurs very rarely scattered throughout the county: Bretton Clough (SK1978), Lawrence Field (SK2680), Littlemoor House (SK3662), Mickleover Railway Cutting (SK3236) and Long Eaton (SK5033). It was previously recorded more frequently, but some records were probably errors for the Hybrid Monkeyflower (*M. × robertsii*). Cultivated in gardens for its flowers, it grows naturally in the Andes.

Cow Close Farm (SK2363) and Shirley Park (SK2042), to Calke Abbey (SK3622) in the south. At Calke it is abundant around the base of the National Trust property itself. A native of western North America, it is grown in gardens for ornament.

Mimulus guttatus DC.
Monkeyflower

COUNTY STATUS: Established (Neophyte)

CONSERVATION STATUS: None

FIRST YEAR: 1969 **LATEST YEAR:** 2011 **NO OF RECORDS:** 140

RECENT SQUARES: monads 63; tetrads 57; hectads 22

ALL SQUARES: monads 89; tetrads 75; hectads 27

Monkeyflower is an established perennial of marshes, damp grasslands and wet places by streams and ponds. It occurs rarely throughout the county from Long Clough (SK0392) and Sheffield Road Grassland (SK5274) in the north, through the Holt Wood area (SK2862) and Shirley Park (SK2042), to the River Derwent (SK3834) and the Trent and Mersey Canal (SK2626) in the south. It is probably over-recorded for the Hybrid Monkeyflower (*M. × robertsii*), particularly in the uplands. Grown in gardens for ornament, it is a native of western North America.

OROBANCHACEAE

Melampyrum pratense L.
Common Cow-wheat

COUNTY STATUS: Native	
CONSERVATION STATUS: ERL	
FIRST YEAR: 1789 LATEST YEAR: 2011 NO OF RECORDS: 185	
RECENT SQUARES: monads 56; tetrads 39; hectads 12	
ALL SQUARES: monads 85; tetrads 59; hectads 21	

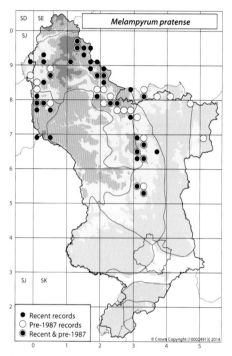

Common Cow-wheat is a semi-parasitic native annual. It grows on the roots of other plants in scrub, open woods and moors, on well-drained acidic soils. It occurs occasionally in the Dark Peak, South West Peak and Peak Fringe Areas: Ludworth Moor (SJ9990), Upper Derwent (SK1397), Priddock Wood (SK2086), Cathole (SK3367) and Shining Cliff Woods (SK3352). It was previously recorded from a wider area, including Langwith Wood (SK5068) in 1978 on the Magnesian Limestone, and Calke and Repton (SK32) in southern Derbyshire in 1903. This local loss mirrors a national decline from much of central and eastern England due to habitat destruction (Preston *et al.* 2002). Despite a wide range of colour forms, for example white, cream, yellow and gold flowers at Eyam Moor (SK2378), all our plants appear referable to ssp. *pratense*.

Euphrasia L.
Eyebrights

COUNTY STATUS: Native	
CONSERVATION STATUS: None	
FIRST YEAR: 1789 LATEST YEAR: 2013 NO OF RECORDS: 1,256	
RECENT SQUARES: monads 411; tetrads 221; hectads 28	
ALL SQUARES: monads 439; tetrads 232; hectads 33	

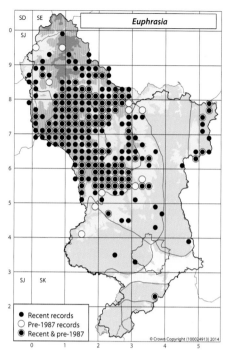

This entry includes all Eyebrights together, as few recorders distinguish the various species that occur here. These are noted individually below, but all are probably very under-recorded. Taken together, Eyebrights are a native annual semi-parasitic herb that grows on the roots of a wide range of plants and small shrubs, mainly in unimproved permanent grassland. They are common in the White

Eyebright (*Euphrasia* sp.), Goytside Meadows (SK0084), July 2012 (David Blowers)

Peak and some adjacent areas, occasional on the Magnesian Limestone as at Whitwell Wood (SK5277), and rare elsewhere as at Ticknall Quarries (SK3623). They were previously more frequent outside their current core area of the White Peak.

Euphrasia officinalis L.
An eyebright

This eyebright is represented by two subspecies, both of which have a national conservation status. **Rostkov's Eyebright** (**ssp. *pratensis***) Schuebl. & G. Martens is a very rare, native annual of damp grasslands. The only recent record is from Stanton Moor (SK2563), but it was previously recorded across the Peak District and Magnesian Limestone: Kinder (SK08 in 1947), Chatsworth Park (SK26 in 1903) and Whitwell (SK57 in 1903). **English Eyebright** (**ssp. *anglica***) (Pugsley) Silverside is a very rare, native annual of damp grassland and heathland. The only two recent records are from the north-western part of modern Derbyshire, in v.c.58: Taxal Moor (SK0079) and Hoo Moor (SK0176). Older records exist for a wider area in western Derbyshire, from (SK08) in the north, through Gib Hill (SK1563) and Coombs Dale (SK2274) in the White Peak, to Clifton (SK1743) in the Claylands. The number of early records on limestone may seem surprising, considering its preference for acid areas, but this is probably explained by the existence of large amounts of limestone heath at that time.

Euphrasia officinalis × *E. confusa*
A hybrid eyebright

Locally extinct, this hybrid eyebright was a very rare, native annual, known only from Thorpe (SK1550) prior to 1956 (Yeo 1956).

Euphrasia arctica Lange ex Rostrup
Arctic Eyebright

Arctic Eyebright is a very rare, native annual of damp rough grasslands. The only recent record is from near Buxton (SK06). It was previously found scattered through the Peak District including: Black Rocks (SK2955) in 1978, Stoney Middleton Dale (SK2175) in 1969, and Combs Moss (SK07), The Winnats (SK18) and near the Snake Inn (SK19), all for 1903. Our plant is ssp. *borealis* (F. Towns.) Yeo. It has disappeared from many sites in central England since 1970 (Preston *et al.* 2002), so our loss may well be real and not just due to under-recording. It is an English Red List species.

Euphrasia nemorosa (Pers.) Wallr.
Common Eyebright

Common Eyebright is a native annual of grasslands and heaths. It occurs rarely in the

COUNTY STATUS: Native
CONSERVATION STATUS: ERL, A
FIRST YEAR: 1903 LATEST YEAR: 2013 NO OF RECORDS: 82
RECENT SQUARES: monads 22; tetrads 19; hectads 8
ALL SQUARES: monads 47; tetrads 42; hectads 18

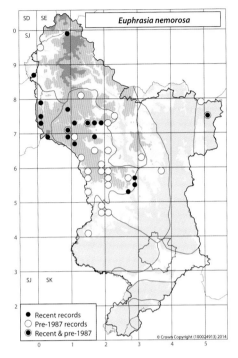

White and South West Peak Areas: Miller's Dale (SK1472) and the Goyt Valley (SK0173 v.c.58). There are also isolated records at Longdendale (SK0999) and Markland (SK5075). Previously it occurred occasionally over a wider area including Pebley Sand Quarry (SK4978), Ogston (SK3759) and Snelston (SK1541). Much of this decrease is probably due to under-recording.

Euphrasia nemorosa × E. confusa
A hybrid eyebright
This hybrid eyebright is a very rare, native annual of grasslands, known only from an unlocalised pre-1970 listing in Stace *et al.* (2003).

Euphrasia confusa Pugsley
Confused Eyebright

COUNTY STATUS: Native
CONSERVATION STATUS: ERL
FIRST YEAR: 1956 LATEST YEAR: 2011 NO OF RECORDS: 32
RECENT SQUARES: monads 12; tetrads 11; hectads 7
ALL SQUARES: monads 20; tetrads 19; hectads 11

Confused Eyebright is a rare native annual of short grasslands in the White and Dark Peak Areas. There are recent records from Mellor Moor (SJ9887) and Peter Dale (SK1176) in the north, to Long Dale (SK1860), Bonsall Mines (SK2657) and Sydnope Hill (SK2863) in the south. It was formerly known further south at

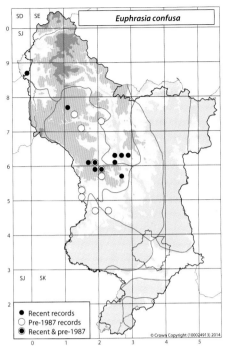

Ashbourne Green (SK1847) and Atlow Rough (SK2247), both in 1969.

Odontites vernus (Bellardi) Dumort.
Red Bartsia

COUNTY STATUS: Native
CONSERVATION STATUS: None
FIRST YEAR: 1789 LATEST YEAR: 2013 NO OF RECORDS: 442
RECENT SQUARES: monads 212; tetrads 175; hectads 33
ALL SQUARES: monads 253; tetrads 203; hectads 36

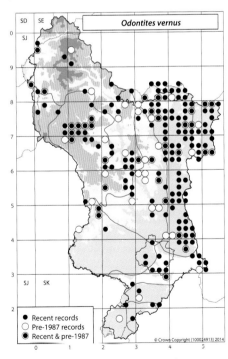

Red Bartsia is a semi-parasitic native annual that grows on the roots of other plants in waste places, short grassland and arable fields. It occurs occasionally throughout the county, though is rarer

in the intensively farmed south and in the upland moors of the north. There are recent records from Dinting Vale (SK0194) and Beauchief (SK3280) in the north, through Deep Dale (SK1069) and Farley Moor (SK3063), to Chellaston (SK3829) and Pistern Hill (SK3421) in the south. Two subspecies occur. There are recent records for **ssp. serotinus** (Syme) Corb. from Mousley Bottom (SJ9985) and Roseland Wood (SK4967), plus older ones for **ssp. vernus** from Buxworth Basin (SK0282) in 1977, Norbury (SK1242) in 1970, and near Poolsbrook (SK4473) in 1969.

Parentucellia viscosa (L.) Caruel
Yellow Bartsia
Yellow Bartsia is a semi-parasitic casual annual of reclaimed land. There are only two recent localities: restored opencast land at Denby (SK3847/3947) and Whaley Bridge (SJ9981). There is also an unlocalised record for the county in 1970. It is native to coastal areas of England and Wales.

Rhinanthus minor L.
Yellow-rattle

COUNTY STATUS: Native
CONSERVATION STATUS: None
FIRST YEAR: 1789 LATEST YEAR: 2013 NO OF RECORDS: 1,159
RECENT SQUARES: monads 457; tetrads 297; hectads 35
ALL SQUARES: monads 504; tetrads 324; hectads 38

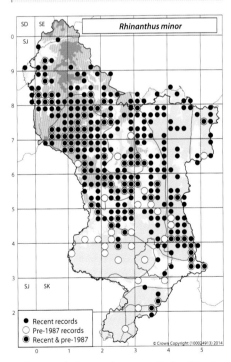

Yellow-rattle is a native annual of nutrient-poor, sometimes damp, grasslands where it is a semi-parasite on the roots of grasses. It is increasingly being included in wild-flower seed mixes used in restoration schemes. It occurs occasionally throughout the county, though is rare in the intensively farmed south and the high moors of the north (Long Clough SK0392, Centenary Pools SK4184, Parsley Hay SK1463, Bottom Moor SK3262, Grange Park SK5033 & Tadsor Farm SK3421). It was lost from 68% of its Peak District hay meadow sites between the mid-1980s and mid-1990s (Buckingham *et al.* 1997). It has a local name of Horse-pennies (Grigson 1975). Two subspecies have been recorded recently: **ssp. *stenophyllus*** O. Schwarz is known from the Peak District (Hollingworth SK0097 v.c.58 & the Tissington Trail at SK1461) and from the Magnesian Limestone (Markland Grips SK5074). **Ssp. *minor*** has only been recorded from the Peak District (Goyt Meadows SK0084 v.c.58 & Moneystones SK1561), but was previously found across the county.

Pedicularis palustris L.
Marsh Lousewort

COUNTY STATUS: Native	
CONSERVATION STATUS: DRDB (Cat4), B	
FIRST YEAR: 1789 **LATEST YEAR:** 1986 **NO OF RECORDS:** 18	
RECENT SQUARES: monads 0; tetrads 0; hectads 0	
ALL SQUARES: monads 2; tetrads 2; hectads 10	

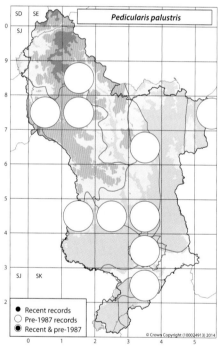

Marsh Lousewort is a very rare, native annual or biennial that grows as a semi-parasite on the roots of other plants in wet meadows, fens and marshes. The latest records are from Monk's Dale (SK1375) in 1986 and Hulland Moss (SK2546) in 1954. Earlier ones are scattered throughout the county, including Woodseats (SK18), Scarcliffe Park Wood (SK57), Tansley Moor (SK36), Foremark (SK32) and Repton (SK32), all for 1903. This decline replicates a regional loss in central and southern England during the 20th century due to

drainage and agricultural improvement (Preston *et al.* 2002).

Pedicularis sylvatica L.
Lousewort

COUNTY STATUS: Native	
CONSERVATION STATUS: ERL	
FIRST YEAR: 1789 **LATEST YEAR:** 2013 **NO OF RECORDS:** 222	
RECENT SQUARES: monads 58; tetrads 50; hectads 20	
ALL SQUARES: monads 99; tetrads 82; hectads 30	

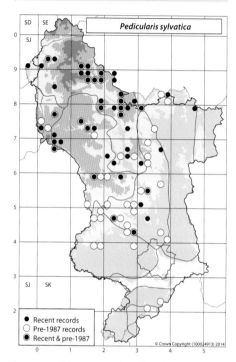

Lousewort is an occasional native perennial that is semi-parasitic on the roots of other plants in moorlands, dry bogs and damp grasslands on acid soils. It occurs throughout the Peak District and adjacent areas from Long Clough (SK0392) and Ladybower (SK1889) in the north, through Priestcliffe Lees (SK1473) and Bigginmoor (SK1758), to Agnes Meadow (SK2247) and Mugginton Bottoms (SK2843) in the south. It previously occurred further south to Repton Rocks (SK3221) in 1969 and Spring Wood (SK3722) in 1977. Ssp. *sylvatica* is recorded from Backside Wood (SK1587), but all records probably refer to this plant.

Lathraea squamaria L.
Toothwort

COUNTY STATUS: Native	
CONSERVATION STATUS: None	
FIRST YEAR: 1787 **LATEST YEAR:** 2013 **NO OF RECORDS:** 151	
RECENT SQUARES: monads 42; tetrads 32; hectads 19	
ALL SQUARES: monads 60; tetrads 48; hectads 27	

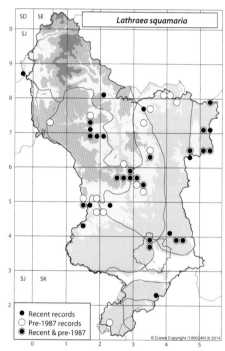

Toothwort (*Lathraea squamaria*) on banks of the River Derwent at Darley Park (SK3537), April 2009 (Peter Smith)

Toothwort is a rare native annual or perennial that grows as a total root parasite on woody plants in hedges, scrub and woodlands. It typically grows on Hazel (*Corylus avellana*) but has also been recorded here on poplar (*Populus* species) and Beech (*Fagus sylvatica*). It occurs throughout the county from Brook Bottom (SJ9786) and Offerton Stepping Stones (SK2181) in the north, through Shacklow Wood (SK1769) and Rose End Meadows (SK2956), to Hermit's Wood (SK4438) and Mere Pond (SK3622) in the south.

Lathraea clandestina L.
Purple Toothwort

Purple Toothwort is an established perennial that grows as a total parasite on the roots of willow trees and bushes (*Salix* species) in damp places. It is known from only two localities: Hilton Gravel Pits (SK2431) between 1980 and 2011, and Egginton (SK2628) between 1974 and 2001. A native of western or south-western Europe, it is grown in gardens as a curiosity and may be dispersed by floodwaters or on the roots of nursery stock.

Orobanche purpurea Jacq.
Yarrow Broomrape

COUNTY STATUS: Native
CONSERVATION STATUS: DRDB (Cat6), VU, NR, B, C
FIRST YEAR: 1969 LATEST YEAR: 1969 NO OF RECORDS: 1
RECENT SQUARES: monads 0; tetrads 0; hectads 0
ALL SQUARES: monads 1; tetrads 1; hectads 1

Locally extinct, Yarrow Broomrape was a very rare, native perennial that occurred as a total root parasite on Yarrow (*Achillea millefolium*) and other members of the Daisy family. Our only record is from Ilkeston Station (SK4642). It was published in Clapham's 1969 Flora, but probably dates from much earlier. Derbyshire is on the northern limits of its British range.

Orobanche rapum-genistae Thuill.
Greater Broomrape

COUNTY STATUS: Native
CONSERVATION STATUS: DRDB (Cat6), NT, NS, B, C
FIRST YEAR: 1789 LATEST YEAR: 1903 NO OF RECORDS: 15
RECENT SQUARES: monads 0; tetrads 0; hectads 0
ALL SQUARES: monads 4; tetrads 4; hectads 7

Locally extinct, Greater Broomrape was a very rare, native perennial, which grew as a total root parasite on Broom (*Cytisus scoparius*) and Gorse (*Ulex europaeus*). It formerly occurred in the south of the county from Stanton Moor (SK26) in 1889 and Alfreton-Holbrook (SK45) in 1789, to Repton Rocks (SK32) and Dale Hills (SK43) both 1903. This loss mirrors a more widespread regional decline, the cause

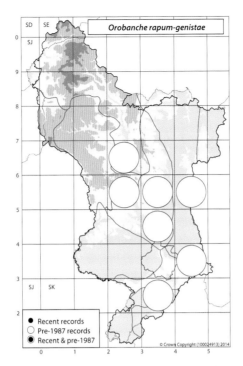

of which is not understood (Preston *et al.* 2002).

Orobanche minor Sm.
Common Broomrape

COUNTY STATUS: Native
CONSERVATION STATUS: DRDB (Cat5a), A, B
FIRST YEAR: 1864 LATEST YEAR: 2013 NO OF RECORDS: 35
RECENT SQUARES: monads 4; tetrads 4; hectads 3
ALL SQUARES: monads 8; tetrads 8; hectads 5

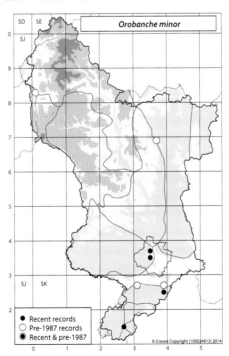

Common Broomrape is a very rare, native perennial which grows as a root parasite on a range of herbaceous perennials in rough grassland. It has been recorded recently at just four sites: the disused railway station

Common Broomrape (*Orobanche minor*), Friar Gate Station, Derby (SK3436), June 2005 (Bill Grange)

at Friar Gate, Derby (SK3436), Derby city centre (SK3535), Woodside Farm (SK2715) and the Cloud Trail (SK3927). It grows in abundance only at the Friar Gate Station site, where it has been known since at least 1987, but now faces destruction from development. Older records exist for three other scattered sites: New Mills (SK0183) in 1985, Chesterfield (SK3768) in 1968 and Repton (SK3026) in 1942. The oldest is an unlocalised 1864 record in Linton's 1903 Flora. Our plant is probably ssp. *minor*.

LENTIBULARIACEAE

Pinguicula vulgaris L.
Common Butterwort

COUNTY STATUS: Native
CONSERVATION STATUS: DRDB (Cat5b)
FIRST YEAR: 1789 LATEST YEAR: 2012 NO OF RECORDS: 156
RECENT SQUARES: monads 29; tetrads 25; hectads 8
ALL SQUARES: monads 48; tetrads 37; hectads 11

Common Butterwort is an insect-eating native perennial of damp nutrient-poor soils in fens, bogs and flushes. It occurs occasionally in the northern part of the White Peak on volcanic rocks (Monk's Dale SK1373) and in the Dark Peak (Grinds Brook SK1187, Linch Clough SK1594 & Hathersage Dale Bottom SK2481). There is an isolated occurrence at Whitwell Wood (SK5278) on the Magnesian Limestone. It was also previously known in the south of the county at Mugginton Bottoms (SK2843) in

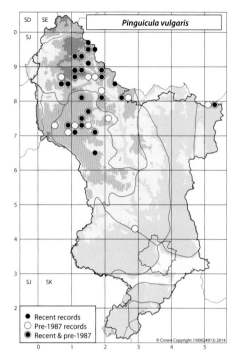

Pinguicula vulgaris

Recent records
Pre-1987 records
Recent & pre-1987

1969, and near Mackworth, Derby (SK33) in 1789.

Pinguicula grandiflora Lam.
Large-flowered Butterwort
Large-flowered Butterwort is an established insect-eating perennial and a native of south-western Ireland. It has been known from its only site on the banks of Grindsbrook Clough (SK1187) for many years, where it grows amongst moss on damp shaded rocks. It was apparently

Large-flowered Butterwort (*Pinguicula grandiflora*), Grindsbrook (SK1187), June 2009 (Peter Smith)

introduced there before the First World War, though formal recording only began in the early 1960s. Subsequently it has been recorded at least 8 times up until 2013. It is so well established that in some years there are over 200 flowers.

Utricularia vulgaris L.
Greater Bladderwort

COUNTY STATUS: Native	
CONSERVATION STATUS: DRDB (Cat6)	
FIRST YEAR: 1829 **LATEST YEAR:** 1889 **NO OF RECORDS:** 4	
RECENT SQUARES: monads 0; tetrads 0; hectads 0	
ALL SQUARES: monads 0; tetrads 0; hectads 1	

Locally extinct, Greater Bladderwort was a very rare, native submerged perennial of nutrient-poor still waters. All three localised records are from pools near the Trent in the Swarkestone/Repton area (SK32) between 1845 and 1889. There is also an unlocalised one for 1829 in Linton's 1903 Flora. It can grow where other water plants cannot as it supplements a meagre nutrient supply by trapping and digesting small aquatic animals. However, increased nutrient supply from agricultural runoff allows other plants to grow and exclude it.

ACANTHACEAE

Acanthus spinosus L.
Spiny Bear's-breech
Spiny Bear's-breech is a very rare, casual perennial. The only record is from near Hassop Church (SK2272) in 1989. Indigenous to the central Mediterranean, it is grown as a garden ornamental for its flowers and foliage.

VERBENACEAE

Verbena officinalis L.
Vervain

COUNTY STATUS: Established (Archaeophyte)	
CONSERVATION STATUS: DRDB (Cat5a), A, B	
FIRST YEAR: 1789 **LATEST YEAR:** 2012 **NO OF RECORDS:** 25	
RECENT SQUARES: monads 5; tetrads 4; hectads 4	
ALL SQUARES: monads 9; tetrads 8; hectads 13	

Vervain is a very rare, anciently established perennial of grassy and waste places. There are only five recent records: Bradwell Moor (SK1480), Hope Station (SK1883), Calver Low Quarry (SK2374), Elvaston Castle (SK4033) and Williamthorpe (SK4266). It was previously more widespread, records coming from scattered locations in central and southern parts. These include Monsal Dale (SK1772) plus others south to Shardlow (SK4429) and Linton (SK21). It is locally common in southern England but only scattered in the north (Stace, 1997).

Verbena bonariensis L.
Argentinian Vervain
Argentinian Vervain is a very rare, casual perennial of rough and disturbed ground. It is only recorded from three sites, all recent: Chaddesden Sidings (SK3635), Belper (SK3448) and Upper Pleasley (SK4964). Indigenous to South America, it is increasingly being grown in gardens and may be expected to increase in the wild.

AQUIFOLIACEAE

Ilex aquifolium L.
Holly

COUNTY STATUS: Native	
CONSERVATION STATUS: None	
FIRST YEAR: 1789 **LATEST YEAR:** 2013 **NO OF RECORDS:** 4,417	
RECENT SQUARES: monads 1,720; tetrads 663; hectads 43	
ALL SQUARES: monads 1,765; tetrads 674; hectads 43	

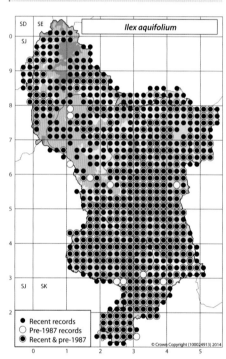

Ilex aquifolium

Recent records
Pre-1987 records
Recent & pre-1987

Holly is a spiny evergreen native shrub of hedges, woods and scrub. It can occur as a tree – sometimes a large ancient one – as at Hathersage (SK231814). It was also cultivated in times past as winter browse for stock (Spray 1981), and is now planted for amenity and as a source of food for wildlife. It is very common throughout the county, only becoming rare in the uplands of the Dark and White Peak. It has a local name of Hollin (Grigson 1975) and often forms part of Derbyshire place names, such as at Hollin Clough and Hollinhill Grips. This is thought to refer to stands of trees, hollins or holly hags, that were maintained in the past as a source of winter-feed for farm animals. Nowadays holly berries are used to form the patterns in some traditional well-dressing images.

Ilex × altaclerensis (Loudon) Dallim.
Highclere Holly

COUNTY STATUS: Casual
CONSERVATION STATUS: None
FIRST YEAR: 1999 LATEST YEAR: 2013 NO OF RECORDS: 15
RECENT SQUARES: monads 11; tetrads 10; hectads 7
ALL SQUARES: monads 11; tetrads 10; hectads 7

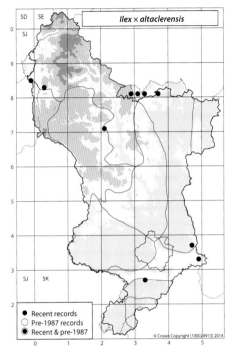

Highclere Holly is a casual evergreen shrub or small tree of woods, scrub, hedges and rough ground. It occurs very rarely scattered across the county (Mousley Bottom SJ9985, Milton SK3226, Ecclesall Woods SK3281 & Forbes Hole SK4932). It is much planted in gardens from whence it can be bird-sown into more natural situations. It is of garden origin from the crossing of Holly (*I. aquifolium*) with Canary Holly (*I. perado* Aiton).

CAMPANULACEAE

Campanula patula L.
Spreading Bellflower

COUNTY STATUS: Native
CONSERVATION STATUS: DRDB (Cat6), EN, NS, NERC
FIRST YEAR: 1903 LATEST YEAR: 1930 NO OF RECORDS: 6
RECENT SQUARES: monads 0; tetrads 0; hectads 0
ALL SQUARES: monads 1; tetrads 1; hectads 5

Locally extinct, Spreading Bellflower was a very rare, native biennial of open woods, hedges and arable fields, known only from southern Derbyshire. The latest record is for Melbourne (SK4026) around the 1930s, whilst Linton (1903) gave Osmaston (SK14), Stapenhill (SK22), Darley (SK33) and Morleymoor (SK34). All were on the north-eastern limit of the species in Britain. Their loss is probably part of a general

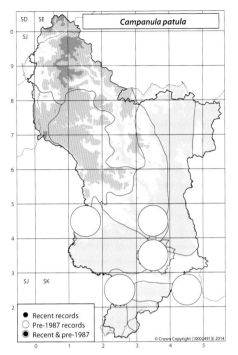

decrease due to cessation of coppicing and increased use of herbicides on roadsides (Preston *et al.* 2002).

Campanula persicifolia L.
Peach-leaved Bellflower

COUNTY STATUS: Established (Neophyte)
CONSERVATION STATUS: None
FIRST YEAR: 1949 LATEST YEAR: 2009 NO OF RECORDS: 25
RECENT SQUARES: monads 18; tetrads 17; hectads 13
ALL SQUARES: monads 19; tetrads 18; hectads 13

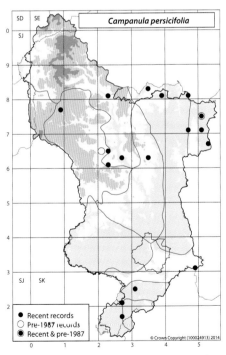

Peach-leaved Bellflower is an established perennial of waste ground and waysides. It occurs scattered rarely throughout the county from Longsidings Quarry (SK0976)

and Norton Hammer (SK3483) in the north, to Lock Lane Ash Tip (SK4831) and Coton Park (SK2717) in the south. It is a garden ornamental originating from continental Europe.

Campanula medium L.
Canterbury-bells

Canterbury-bells is a very rare, casual perennial. The only record is from a railway cutting at Shirebrook (SK5166) in 1970. It is much grown in gardens for its flowers, and is native to Italy and south-eastern France.

Campanula glomerata L.
Clustered Bellflower

COUNTY STATUS: Native
CONSERVATION STATUS: DRDB (Cat5b), B
FIRST YEAR: 1811 LATEST YEAR: 2011 NO OF RECORDS: 93
RECENT SQUARES: monads 16; tetrads 17; hectads 9
ALL SQUARES: monads 28; tetrads 19; hectads 13

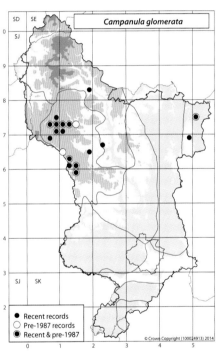

Clustered Bellflower is a rare native perennial of grassland and scrub on base-rich soils. All recent native records are from the limestone areas, as at Cow Dale (SK0872), Long Dale (SK1363) and Biggin Dale (SK1459) in the White Peak, and Markland Grips (SK5074) on the Magnesian Limestone. Also grown in gardens, some may be of escapes, as at Hope Road (SK1882). There are also records from SK36 in 1963 and from Stanton-by-Dale and Spondon (SK43) in 1903.

Campanula portenschlagiana Schult.
Adria Bellflower

Adria Bellflower is an established sprawling perennial of waste ground and walls. It is recorded at only five sites, all between 1996 and 2011 (Pin Dale SK1582, Hathersage SK2381, Ballcross Farm SK2269, Duffield SK3443 & West Handley SK3977). It is a native of the western Balkans, much grown as an ornamental in gardens.

Campanula poscharskyana Degen
Trailing Bellflower

COUNTY STATUS: Established (Neophyte)	
CONSERVATION STATUS: None	
FIRST YEAR: 1992 **LATEST YEAR:** 2012 **NO OF RECORDS:** 13	
RECENT SQUARES: monads 12; tetrads 11; hectads 7	
ALL SQUARES: monads 12; tetrads 11; hectads 7	

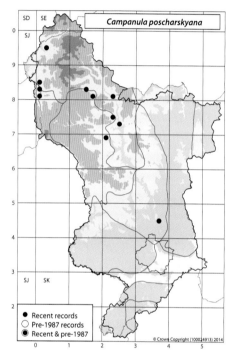

Trailing Bellflower is an established sprawling perennial of waysides and walls. It has been recorded rarely throughout the county, but mostly in north-western parts (New Mills SK0085 & Castleton SK1582). Originating from the Balkans, it is often grown in gardens.

Campanula latifolia L.
Giant Bellflower

COUNTY STATUS: Native	
CONSERVATION STATUS: None	
FIRST YEAR: 1670 **LATEST YEAR:** 2013 **NO OF RECORDS:** 409	
RECENT SQUARES: monads 154; tetrads 122; hectads 30	
ALL SQUARES: monads 201; tetrads 149; hectads 35	

Giant Bellflower is an occasional native perennial of damp shaded habitats, generally on nutrient-rich calcareous or mildly acid soils. It occurs frequently through central Derbyshire, particularly on limestone areas (Wormhill SK1274 & Via Gellia SK2656 in the White Peak, and Pleasley Vale SK5064 on the Magnesian Limestone). Elsewhere it is rare in southern

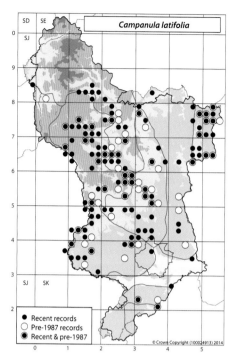

parts (Repton Shrubs SK3123 & Cubley Church SK1637) and virtually absent from the north (Mousley Bottom SJ9985).

Campanula trachelium L.
Nettle-leaved Bellflower

COUNTY STATUS: Native	
CONSERVATION STATUS: None	
FIRST YEAR: 1789 **LATEST YEAR:** 2012 **NO OF RECORDS:** 226	
RECENT SQUARES: monads 54; tetrads 48; hectads 21	
ALL SQUARES: monads 74; tetrads 63; hectads 22	

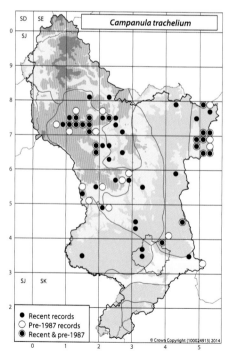

Nettle-leaved Bellflower is a native perennial of woods, scrub and hedges, generally on base-rich soils. It is occasional in the limestone areas, as at Monk's

Dale (SK1374), Lathkill Dale (SK1966) and Cromford (SK2957) in the White Peak, and at Whitwell Wood (SK5178) and Scarcliffe Park (SK5070) on the Magnesian Limestone. Elsewhere it is very rare (Breadsall Railway Cutting SK3839 & Shipley Country Park SK4444) and never beyond suspicion of being a garden escape. Our records are on the northern limit of its natural distribution, and Monk's Dale holds its altitudinal record in the British Isles at 320m (Preston *et al.* 2002).

Campanula rapunculoides L.
Creeping Bellflower

COUNTY STATUS: Established (Neophyte)	
CONSERVATION STATUS: None	
FIRST YEAR: 1965 **LATEST YEAR:** 2009 **NO OF RECORDS:** 13	
RECENT SQUARES: monads 3; tetrads 3; hectads 4	
ALL SQUARES: monads 10; tetrads 10; hectads 9	

Creeping Bellflower is an established perennial of waysides, wasteland and cultivated ground. There are four recent records (Darley Bridge SK2762, Derby SK33, Kedleston Park SK3040 & Hallam Fields SK4739), plus a scatter of older records from across the county (Creswell Crags SK5374 in 1979, Mackworth Vicarage SK3137 & Clay Mills Tip SK2626 in 1969). It is a garden ornamental, indigenous to continental Europe.

Campanula rotundifolia L.
Harebell

COUNTY STATUS: Native	
CONSERVATION STATUS: ERL	
FIRST YEAR: 1789 **LATEST YEAR:** 2013 **NO OF RECORDS:** 2,894	
RECENT SQUARES: monads 970; tetrads 476; hectads 39	
ALL SQUARES: monads 1,052; tetrads 505; hectads 39	

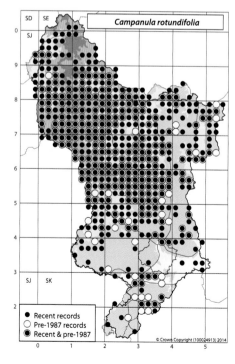

Harebell (*Campanula rotundifolia*) in limestone grassland Lathkill Dale (SK1765), August 2004 (Nick Moyes)

COUNTY STATUS: Native
CONSERVATION STATUS: DRDB (Cat2), NT, B
FIRST YEAR: 1889 LATEST YEAR: 2012 NO OF RECORDS: 88
RECENT SQUARES: monads 15; tetrads 10; hectads 6
ALL SQUARES: monads 20; tetrads 13; hectads 8

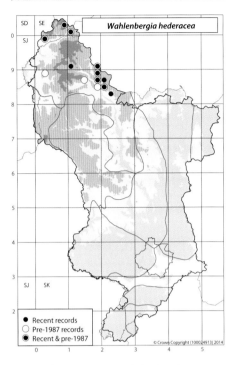

Harebell is a native perennial of unimproved grasslands, waysides and rock ledges on mildly acidic to calcareous soils. This attractive plant is very common northwards from Derby, but is only occasional to the south (Willington Grasslands SK3029, Repton Road Field SK3121 & Calke Park SK3622). As in Scotland, it has sometimes acquired the local name of Bluebell (Grigson 1975). It has also been one of the plants recently studied by the Buxton Climate Change Impacts Laboratory Group (Fridley *et al.* 2007).

Legousia hybrida (L.) Delarbre
Venus's-looking-glass

COUNTY STATUS: Established (Archaeophyte)
CONSERVATION STATUS: DRDB (Cat5a), A
FIRST YEAR: 1829 LATEST YEAR: 1998 NO OF RECORDS: 12
RECENT SQUARES: monads 1; tetrads 1; hectads 1
ALL SQUARES: monads 5; tetrads 5; hectads 7

Venus's-looking-glass is an anciently established annual of arable fields on lighter soils. There has been only one recent sighting, at Creswell Crags (SK5374). There are earlier records for this area, but others are mostly for southern Derbyshire e.g. Hulland (SK2546), Dale (SK4338) and Caldwell (SK21). It is scattered across southern, central and eastern England where, as here, it is decreasing

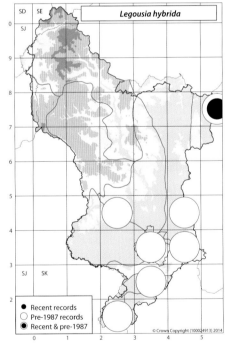

due to the intensification of arable farming (Stace, 1997).

Wahlenbergia hederacea (L.) Rchb.
Ivy-leaved Bellflower

Ivy-leaved Bellflower is a low-growing native perennial of open damp areas of peat on moors. It is entirely confined to northern parts of the Dark Peak, as at

Tintwistle (SK0398 v.c.58), Audenshaw Clough (SE1100 v.c.58), Mill Brook (SK1889), Ladybower Tor (SK1987) and Outseats (SK2383). However, there is an undated earlier record for SK38 on the southern outskirts of Sheffield, and Linton's 1903 Flora lists Repton Rocks (SK3322) in south Derbyshire.

Phyteuma spicatum L.
Spiked Rampion

Spiked Rampion is an established perennial. The sole record was made at St Mary's Nursing Home, Ednaston (SK2342) in 1975 by K.M. Hollick and is reputed to have been present there for the previous 40 years. It occurs naturally in southern England but has been grown widely elsewhere for centuries as a medicinal plant.

Jasione montana L.
Sheep's-bit

COUNTY STATUS: Native
CONSERVATION STATUS: DRDB (Cat5b), A, B
FIRST YEAR: 1789 LATEST YEAR: 2008 NO OF RECORDS: 69
RECENT SQUARES: monads 8; tetrads 8; hectads 8
ALL SQUARES: monads 27; tetrads 27; hectads 22

Sheep's-bit is a very rare, native annual or short-lived perennial of grassy places and rocky areas on well-drained acid soils. It is rare in upland northern parts (Upper Derwent SK1594 & Hare Knoll

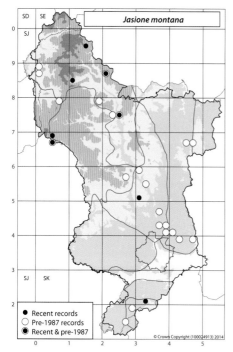

Jasione montana

Recent records
Pre-1987 records
Recent & pre-1987

© Crown Copyright (100024913) 2014

SK2474) and virtually absent from lowland southern parts (Alport Heights SK3051 & Hartshorne SK3221). Older records came from across the county (Dale SK4388 & Netherseal SK2715), though still avoiding limestone areas. Regionally it has declined greatly since 1962 due to agricultural improvement and competition from coarser vegetation (Preston *et al.* 2002). It is still locally common in the west of Britain.

Lobelia erinus L.
Garden Lobelia
Garden Lobelia is a very rare, casual annual of waysides and waste ground. It has been recorded throughout the county, as at

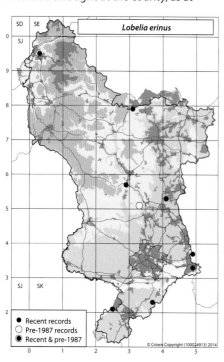

Lobelia erinus

Recent records
Pre-1987 records
Recent & pre-1987

© Crown Copyright (100024913) 2014

COUNTY STATUS:	Casual

CONSERVATION STATUS: None

FIRST YEAR: 1977 LATEST YEAR: 2012 NO OF RECORDS: 14

RECENT SQUARES: monads 8; tetrads 8; hectads 7

ALL SQUARES: monads 9; tetrads 9; hectads 8

Manor Park (SK0394), Totley (SK3079) and Hickton Road (SK4052). It is widely grown in gardens for its attractive flowers, from where it escapes into more natural settings. It is indigenous to southern Africa.

Pratia angulata (G. Forst.) Hook. f.
Lawn Lobelia
Lawn Lobelia is a creeping casual perennial of cultivated areas and lawns. There are only four records, all made between 1994 and 2012: Allestree (SK3439), Newbold (SK3772 & SK3872) and Swanwick (SK4052). It is an increasingly popular plant in rock gardens, originating from New Zealand.

MENYANTHACEAE

Menyanthes trifoliata L.
Bogbean

COUNTY STATUS: Native

CONSERVATION STATUS: DRDB (Cat5b), CitesD, B

FIRST YEAR: 1789 LATEST YEAR: 2013 NO OF RECORDS: 160

RECENT SQUARES: monads 29; tetrads 24; hectads 14

ALL SQUARES: monads 51; tetrads 40; hectads 20

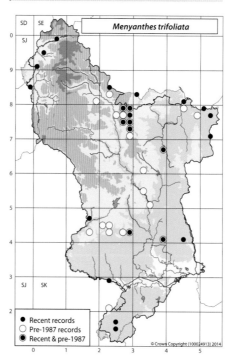

Menyanthes trifoliata

Recent records
Pre-1987 records
Recent & pre-1987

© Crown Copyright (100024913) 2014

Bogbean is a rare native perennial of bogs, fens and shallow waters in the Dark Peak as at Big Moor (SK2674) and Leash Fen (SK2873). Elsewhere it is very rare, occurring in widely scattered localities as at Bettenhill Pond (SK0395), Whitwell Wood (SK5277), Morley Brickyards

---

(SK3841) and Marston on Dove (SK2328). It is often planted for ornament in lowland waters, so some sites outside the Dark Peak may be the result of introductions. However early records at sites like Repton Rocks (SK32) and Newhall (SK21) both for 1903 suggest that it is, or was, native in some places.

Nymphoides peltata Kuntze
Fringed Water-lily

COUNTY STATUS: Established (Neophyte)

CONSERVATION STATUS: None

FIRST YEAR: 1970 LATEST YEAR: 2012 NO OF RECORDS: 41

RECENT SQUARES: monads 20; tetrads 19; hectads 12

ALL SQUARES: monads 24; tetrads 22; hectads 13

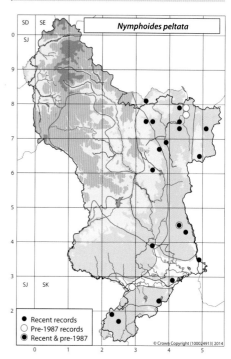

Nymphoides peltata

Recent records
Pre-1987 records
Recent & pre-1987

© Crown Copyright (100024913) 2014

Fringed Water-lily is an established perennial of ponds and lakes. It occurs rarely throughout southern and eastern parts, from Beauchief Hall (SK3281) and Renishaw (SK4378) in the north, through Shipley Wood (SK4543), to Drakelow Power Station (SK2219) and Ticknall Quarries (SK3623) in the south. It is often planted for ornament but can easily spread to nearby waterbodies. It is indigenous to parts of southern and eastern England.

ASTERACEAE

Echinops sphaerocephalus L.
Glandular Globe-thistle

COUNTY STATUS: Established (Neophyte)

CONSERVATION STATUS: None

FIRST YEAR: 1980 LATEST YEAR: 1999 NO OF RECORDS: 4

RECENT SQUARES: monads 3; tetrads 3; hectads 3

ALL SQUARES: monads 3; tetrads 3; hectads 3

Glandular Globe-thistle is a very rare, established perennial of waysides and rough ground. Only three sites are known: near Blackwell (SK1271) in 1980 and 1990, found by M. Hewitt, plus Rowsley Sidings (SK2663) and Poolsbrook Country Park (SK4373). Native to central France, it is grown in gardens for ornament.

Echinops exaltatus Schrad.
Globe-thistle

COUNTY STATUS: Established (Neophyte)
CONSERVATION STATUS: None
FIRST YEAR: 1995 LATEST YEAR: 2010 NO OF RECORDS: 9
RECENT SQUARES: monads 7; tetrads 7; hectads 6
ALL SQUARES: monads 7; tetrads 7; hectads 6

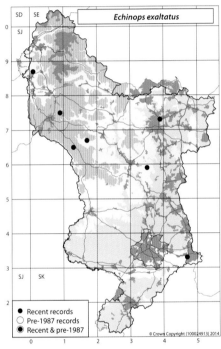

Globe-thistle is a very rare, established perennial of roadsides and waste ground. It occurs scattered throughout the county: Watford Bridge (SK0086), Hardybarn (SK0875), End Moor (SK1365), Blores Barn Farm (SK1767) and Lindway Lane Farm (SK3558). A garden ornamental, it is indigenous to central and southern Europe.

Echinops bannaticus Rochel ex Schrad.
Blue Globe-thistle
Blue Globe-thistle is a very rare, casual perennial. There are three recent records (Pin Dale SK1582, Tinkers Barn SK2612 & Draycott SK4434) and one from Lindway Lane (SK3558) in the 1970s. It is a garden ornamental that escapes as a throwout and originates from south-eastern Europe.

Carlina vulgaris L.
Carline Thistle
Carline Thistle is a spiny native biennial of short dry grassland, generally on

COUNTY STATUS: Native
CONSERVATION STATUS: ERL
FIRST YEAR: 1789 LATEST YEAR: 2013 NO OF RECORDS: 300
RECENT SQUARES: monads 73; tetrads 53; hectads 15
ALL SQUARES: monads 85; tetrads 65; hectads 20

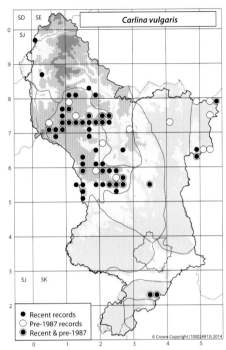

calcareous soils. It is occasional in the White Peak, often in association with the remains of lead workings (Hay Dale SK1177, Lathkill Dale SK1865 & Harborough Rocks SK2455). It also occurs on the Magnesian Limestone at Steetley Quarry (SK5478), and on the isolated limestone outcrops at Crich (SK3455) and Ticknall (SK3523). There are only three recent records from non-limestone sites: Hollingworth Wood (SK0097), Ollersett Reservoir (SK0286) and Rowsley Sidings (SK2665).

Arctium lappa L.
Greater Burdock

COUNTY STATUS: Native
CONSERVATION STATUS: A, B
FIRST YEAR: 1864 LATEST YEAR: 2010 NO OF RECORDS: 52
RECENT SQUARES: monads 17; tetrads 18; hectads 12
ALL SQUARES: monads 27; tetrads 28; hectads 16

Greater Burdock is a rare biennial of wood-clearings, field margins and waste places. It is treated here as native but considered by some as an ancient introduction (Preston *et al.* 2002). It has only been recorded recently from central and southern parts: from Hollinhill (SK5075) and Tupton (SK3966) in the north, to Lullington (SK2311) and the Trent Ox-bow (SK4631) in the south. Earlier records occurred in the same area, with an isolated report from Mellor (SJ98). It is probably

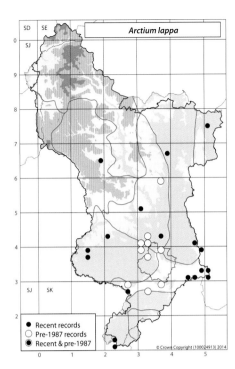

under-recorded due to confusion with the much commoner Lesser Burdock (*A. minus*).

Arctium minus (Hill) Bernh.
Lesser Burdock

COUNTY STATUS: Native
CONSERVATION STATUS: None
FIRST YEAR: 1789 LATEST YEAR: 2013 NO OF RECORDS: 2,698
RECENT SQUARES: monads 1,277; tetrads 603; hectads 43
ALL SQUARES: monads 1,322; tetrads 609; hectads 43

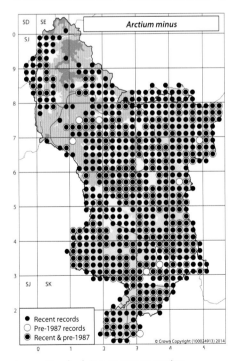

Lesser Burdock is a common native biennial of waysides, woodland edges and waste ground. It occurs throughout Derbyshire except for the high moors of the Dark and South West Peak Character

Areas. It is probably over-recorded due to imprecise separation from other members of its genus. Two subspecies occur locally: **ssp. minus** and **ssp. pubens** (Bab.) P. Fourn. The latter has only been recorded at Markland Grips (SK5074).

Arctium nemorosum Lej.
Wood Burdock

COUNTY STATUS: Native	
CONSERVATION STATUS: A	
FIRST YEAR: 1866 LATEST YEAR: 1998 NO OF RECORDS: 22	
RECENT SQUARES: monads 1; tetrads 1; hectads 2	
ALL SQUARES: monads 13; tetrads 12; hectads 16	

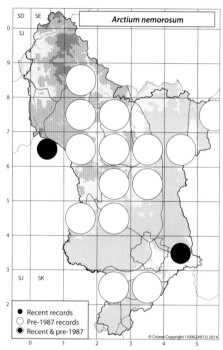

Wood Burdock is a very rare, native biennial of open woods and semi-shaded disturbed ground, generally on calcareous soil. There are two recent records: Hermit's Wood (SK4338) plus an unlocalised one in SK06. It is probably under-recorded, being overlooked for the much commoner Lesser Burdock (*A. minus*). Previously it grew scattered throughout the county from Hope (SK18 in 1903) and Steetley (SK5478 in 1969) in the north, to Bretby (SK2922 in 1969) and Ticknall (SK3623 in 1973) in the south.

Carduus tenuiflorus Curtis
Slender Thistle

Slender Thistle is a casual spiny annual of waysides and waste places. It is a very rare plant with only two recent records (near Cambridge Wood SK2561 & The Long Walk at Kedleston Hall SK3040), and two earlier ones (Via Gellia SK25 in 1909 & Castleton SK18 in 1801). It was previously considered native here (Clapham 1969) but it is now only thought to be so in coastal England and Wales.

Carduus crispus L.
Welted Thistle

COUNTY STATUS: Native	
CONSERVATION STATUS: None	
FIRST YEAR: 1789 LATEST YEAR: 2013 NO OF RECORDS: 684	
RECENT SQUARES: monads 347; tetrads 244; hectads 36	
ALL SQUARES: monads 385; tetrads 263; hectads 37	

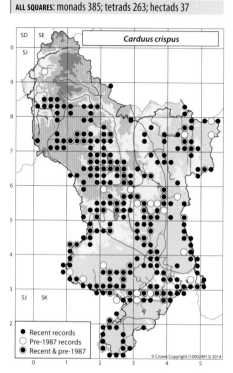

Welted Thistle is a native biennial of rough grassland, waysides, riverbanks and waste ground, generally on moist soils. It occurs occasionally throughout Derbyshire from Bole Hill (SK0584) and Parsons Piece (SK2288) in the north, to Haunton (SK2411) and Trent Lock (SK5031) in the south. It is a lowland species, with Castleton at 365m being its highest known UK location (Preston *et al.* 2002). Our plant is ssp. *multiflorus* (Gaudin) Gremli.

Carduus × stangii H. Buek ex Nyman
A hybrid thistle

This hybrid thistle is a spiny native biennial of disturbed ground and grasslands. The only recent records are from adjacent tetrads at Sawley Cut (SK4730/4731) and Trent Lock (SK4830/4831), plus Longstone Edge (SK2373). There are older records from Middleton Top (SK2754) in 1974, plus the Via Gellia (SK25) and Cressbrook Dale (SK17) both for 1903. It is the hybrid of Welted (*C. crispus*) and Musk Thistle (*C. nutans*) and is probably under-recorded.

Carduus nutans L.
Musk Thistle

Musk Thistle is a native biennial of grassland, disturbed ground and waste places, particularly over limestone. This handsome plant is frequent in the White

COUNTY STATUS: Native	
CONSERVATION STATUS: None	
FIRST YEAR: 1789 LATEST YEAR: 2013 NO OF RECORDS: 534	
RECENT SQUARES: monads 222; tetrads 144; hectads 26	
ALL SQUARES: monads 254; tetrads 164; hectads 31	

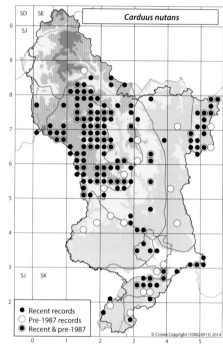

Peak (Winnats Pass SK1382, Glutton Bridge SK0866 & Carsington Pastures SK2354) and on the Magnesian Limestone (Pleasley Vale SK5165 & Firbeck Common SK5378). Elsewhere it is generally rare (Chaneyfield Wood SK3172, Belper SK3447 & Hill Farm SK3024). There have been some recent losses outside the limestone Character Areas, probably due to agricultural

Musk Thistle (*Carduus nutans*), Derbyshire, 2004 (Stephen Trotter)

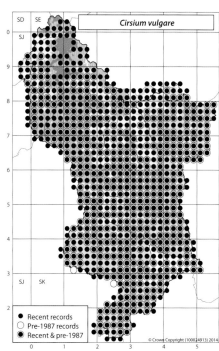

is very common throughout Derbyshire, only being absent from some areas of high moorland. It is a specified injurious weed under the Weeds Act 1959.

Cirsium dissectum (L.) Hill
Meadow Thistle

COUNTY STATUS: Native
CONSERVATION STATUS: DRDB (Cat5a), A, B
FIRST YEAR: 1829 **LATEST YEAR:** 2006 **NO OF RECORDS:** 17
RECENT SQUARES: monads 5; tetrads 2; hectads 2
ALL SQUARES: monads 8; tetrads 4; hectads 8

Woolly Thistle (*Cirsium eriophorum*) by path in centre of Coombs Dale (SK2274) (Ken Balkow)

improvement, but it is still common on the Trentside banks, including the location in Linton's (1903) Flora at Thrumpton Ferry (SK5031).

Cirsium eriophorum (L.) Scop.
Woolly Thistle

COUNTY STATUS: Native
CONSERVATION STATUS: A, B
FIRST YEAR: 1805 **LATEST YEAR:** 2013 **NO OF RECORDS:** 121
RECENT SQUARES: monads 15; tetrads 12; hectads 6
ALL SQUARES: monads 24; tetrads 19; hectads 10

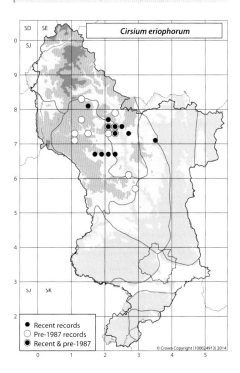

Woolly Thistle is a very rare, native biennial of pastures and open scrub, generally on calcareous soils. All modern records bar one are from the White Peak and adjacent parts of the Dark Peak (Ricklow Quarry SK1666, Coombs Dale SK2374 & Dirtlow Rake SK1581). The exception is Oakfield Meadow (SK3570) in the Peak Fringe. Previously it was recorded over the same area and further south (Via Gellia SK2857 in 1968 & Calke SK32 in 1903). Surprisingly, despite its preference for limestone, it has never been recorded on the Magnesian Limestone. It occurs in central and eastern England, with Derbyshire on the western edge of its range.

Cirsium × grandiflorum Kitt.
A hybrid thistle
This hybrid thistle is a spiny native perennial. It has only been recorded at two sites: Johnnygate Farm (SK3275) found in 1988 by L. Storer and Coombs Dale (SK2174) in 2008. It is the hybrid of Woolly (*C. eriophorum*) and Spear Thistle (*C. vulgare*).

Cirsium vulgare (Savi) Ten.
Spear Thistle

COUNTY STATUS: Native
CONSERVATION STATUS: None
FIRST YEAR: 1789 **LATEST YEAR:** 2013 **NO OF RECORDS:** 5,354
RECENT SQUARES: monads 2,142; tetrads 743; hectads 45
ALL SQUARES: monads 2,218; tetrads 745; hectads 45

Spear Thistle is a spiny native perennial of grass fields, waysides and waste ground, generally on well-drained fertile soils. It

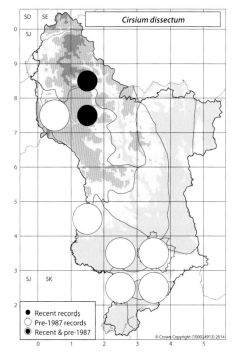

Meadow Thistle is a very rare, native perennial of wet fields. The only recent records are from the Ox Low/Old Moor

area (SK18F) and Monsal Dale (SK1771). Previously it grew in fens scattered throughout the county from Buxton (SK07) in the north to Willington (SK2928) in the south (Clapham 1969). It is on the north-western edge of its national distribution here, but it has been lost from many former sites due to either drainage or shading by scrub development (Preston *et al.* 2002).

Cirsium heterophyllum (L.) Hill
Melancholy Thistle

COUNTY STATUS:	Native
CONSERVATION STATUS:	ERL, B
FIRST YEAR: 1811	LATEST YEAR: 2012 NO OF RECORDS: 259
RECENT SQUARES:	monads 50; tetrads 33; hectads 10
ALL SQUARES:	monads 72; tetrads 46; hectads 13

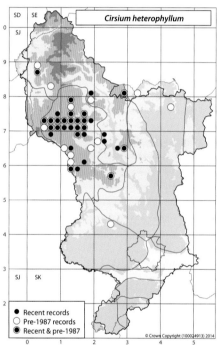

Melancholy Thistle is an occasional native perennial of damp grasslands, scrub and open woods in the dales of the White Peak, as at Peak Forest (SK1279), Deepdale (SK1568) and Bruns Wood (SK2456). It also occurs rarely in the Dark Peak as at Hayfield (SK0387), Blacka Moor (SK2880) and Whitesprings (SK2965). It was previously recorded further afield at Breck Farm (SK4276) in 1970 on the Coal Measures, and Ednaston (SK2442) in 1969 in the Claylands. It is on the south-eastern edge of its British range here (Preston *et al.* 2002) with reduced seed production compared to the bulk of its distribution further north (Jump & Woodward 2003).

Cirsium acaule Scop.
Dwarf Thistle

Dwarf Thistle is a spiny native perennial of short dry grassland, generally on lime-rich

COUNTY STATUS:	Native
CONSERVATION STATUS:	B
FIRST YEAR: 1829	LATEST YEAR: 2013 NO OF RECORDS: 222
RECENT SQUARES:	monads 54; tetrads 41; hectads 13
ALL SQUARES:	monads 73; tetrads 54; hectads 16

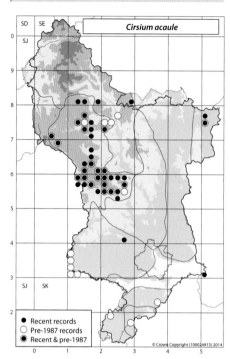

soils. It is virtually confined to south-west facing slopes of dales in the White Peak where it is occasional but locally abundant (Wall Cliff SK1475, Dowel Dale SK0768 & Hopton Quarry SK2656). It also occurs on the Magnesian Limestone, but is much less frequent and abundant there (Markland Grips SK5074). Elsewhere it is very rare with isolated records at Mercaston (SK2741), Trent Lock (SK5031) and Totley Bents (SK2980). Previously it was recorded for the same area but with more localities in the south including: Sedsall Fields (SK1137) in 1983, Swainspark (SK2917) in 1983 and Ticknall Quarries (SK3623) in 1971. Derbyshire is on the north-western edge of its British range (Preston *et al.* 2002) with reduced seed production compared to populations further south (Jump & Woodward 2003).

Cirsium palustre (L.) Scop.
Marsh Thistle

COUNTY STATUS:	Native
CONSERVATION STATUS:	None
FIRST YEAR: 1789	LATEST YEAR: 2013 NO OF RECORDS: 3,723
RECENT SQUARES:	monads 1,295; tetrads 609; hectads 43
ALL SQUARES:	monads 1,397; tetrads 639; hectads 43

Marsh Thistle is a native perennial of marshes, fens, flushes, wet woods and damp grasslands. Although very common throughout most of the county, it is less

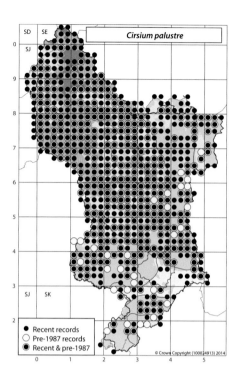

so in the more intensively farmed south and east.

Cirsium arvense (L.) Scop.
Creeping Thistle

COUNTY STATUS:	Native
CONSERVATION STATUS:	None
FIRST YEAR: 1829	LATEST YEAR: 2013 NO OF RECORDS: 6,709
RECENT SQUARES:	monads 2,284; tetrads 736; hectads 45
ALL SQUARES:	monads 2,341; tetrads 738; hectads 45

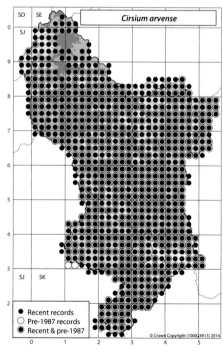

Creeping Thistle is a spiny native perennial of grass fields, cultivated land, waysides and rough ground. It is very common throughout Derbyshire except for some areas of high moors in the Dark Peak, and is listed as an injurious weed under the Weeds Act 1959.

Onopordum acanthium L.
Cotton Thistle

COUNTY STATUS: Casual	
CONSERVATION STATUS: None	
FIRST YEAR: 1829 **LATEST YEAR:** 2010 **NO OF RECORDS:** 36	
RECENT SQUARES: monads 16; tetrads 15; hectads 8	
ALL SQUARES: monads 26; tetrads 24; hectads 17	

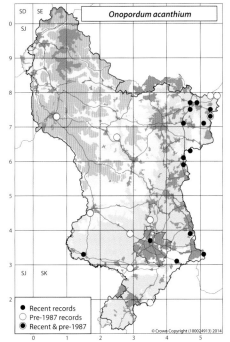

Cotton Thistle is a casual spiny biennial of rubbish tips, wasteland and roadsides, but is considered by some authorities as anciently established (Stace *et al.* 2003). It occurs rarely through lowland eastern and southern parts, from Barlborough (SK4776) and Whaley (SK5171) in the north, to Sudbury (SK1532) and Trent Meadows (SK5032) in the south. Previously it grew in more upland areas, as at Staden (SK0772 in 1969) and Rowsley (SK2566 in 1969). It is frequently grown in gardens, and is a native of continental Europe.

Silybum marianum (L.) Gaertn.
Milk Thistle

Milk Thistle is a casual spiny annual of waysides and disturbed ground that may have been established in the past due to its use by herbalists. There are six recent records spread through southern and eastern parts for example: Steeple Grange (SK2855), Derby (SK3633), Trent Lock (SK4831) and Whaley Common (SK5171). It was previously recorded from Trent Lock (SK4831) in 1969, SK32 in 1889 and SK21 in 1863, with the earliest record being in Glover (1829). It is sometimes grown in gardens for ornament but is also found in

bird-seed mixes, and is indigenous to the Mediterranean.

Serratula tinctoria L.
Saw-wort

COUNTY STATUS: Native	
CONSERVATION STATUS: DRDB (Cat5b)	
FIRST YEAR: 1789 **LATEST YEAR:** 2012 **NO OF RECORDS:** 222	
RECENT SQUARES: monads 30; tetrads 22; hectads 11	
ALL SQUARES: monads 64; tetrads 49; hectads 23	

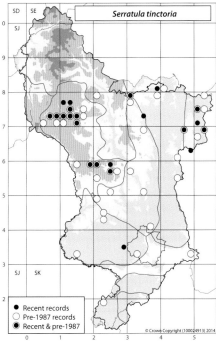

Saw-wort is a native perennial of unimproved grasslands and open woods. It occurs mostly in the limestone Character Areas, but even here is rare. Avoiding drier lime-rich soils, it prefers those that are damper, surface-leached, or derived from igneous rocks. Sites in the White Peak include Peter Dale (SK1275), and Grange Mill (SK2457); and on the Magnesian Limestone, Markland Grips (SK5074). Elsewhere it has now become very rare, occurring mainly in unimproved grasslands (Mickleover SK2935). This local loss mirrors a sad national decline in grassland floras due to the agricultural "improvement" of many sites (Preston *et al.* 2002).

Centaurea scabiosa L.
Greater Knapweed

COUNTY STATUS: Native	
CONSERVATION STATUS: None	
FIRST YEAR: 1789 **LATEST YEAR:** 2013 **NO OF RECORDS:** 481	
RECENT SQUARES: monads 166; tetrads 114; hectads 26	
ALL SQUARES: monads 190; tetrads 132; hectads 31	

Greater Knapweed is a native perennial. In limestone areas it is frequent on rocky grassland slopes, rock outcrops and cliff-ledges (Peter Dale SK1275 & Long Dale

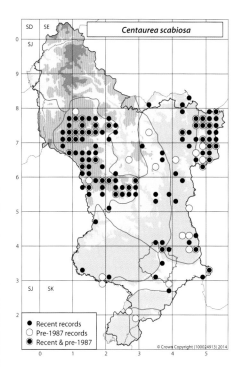

SK1959 in the White Peak and Barlborough SK4877 & Pleasley Vale SK5064 on the Magnesian Limestone). Elsewhere it is a rare plant of rough grasslands, waysides and waste ground from Bradway (SK3380) and Beighton (SK4483) in the north, to Doveridge (SK1233) and Attenborough Junction Tip (SK5033) in the south. It was previously more widespread in these other areas, having been recorded at Bretby Colliery (SK2720) in 1974, and Church Gresley (SK2819) in 1969. It is a lowland species, reaching its national altitudinal limit of 320m at Matlock (Preston *et al.* 2002).

Greater Knapweed (*Centaurea scabiosa*) in limestone grassland, Deep Dale near Buxton (SK0971), July 2003 (Ken Balkow)

Centaurea montana L.
Perennial Cornflower

COUNTY STATUS: Established (Neophyte)
CONSERVATION STATUS: None
FIRST YEAR: 1969 LATEST YEAR: 2013 NO OF RECORDS: 201
RECENT SQUARES: monads 117; tetrads 132; hectads 32
ALL SQUARES: monads 126; tetrads 140; hectads 32

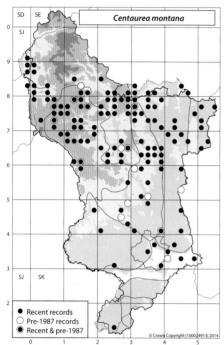

Perennial Cornflower is an established perennial of rough grassland, waysides and waste places. It occurs occasionally throughout the county from Gird Lane (SJ9990) and Beighton (SK4483) in the north, through Sydnope Hall (SK2964), to Chellaston (SK3830) and SK22 in the south. It is much grown in gardens for its attractive flowers from where it escapes as seed or gets thrown out. Probably spreading, it is indigenous to the mountains of central and southern Europe.

Centaurea cyanus L.
Cornflower

COUNTY STATUS: Casual
CONSERVATION STATUS: B
FIRST YEAR: 1789 LATEST YEAR: 2012 NO OF RECORDS: 83
RECENT SQUARES: monads 23; tetrads 23; hectads 16
ALL SQUARES: monads 40; tetrads 40; hectads 22

Cornflower is a rare casual annual of waste places, waysides and rubbish tips. There are records from Long Line (SK2982) and Mosborough (SK4281) in the north, through Black Rocks (SK2855), to Drakelow Power Station (SK2220) and Long Eaton (SK5032) in the south. These plants are probably bird-seed aliens or the result of wild-flower seed mixes. Previously it was a not infrequent weed of cornfields, as at Ashbourne (SK1646) in 1969 and between

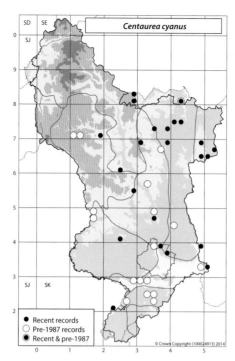

Twyford and Findern (SK3229) in 1944. However, it has been lost from this habitat due to improved farming techniques and once had the local name of Bachelor's Buttons (Grigson 1975). It is a lowland species, reaching its British altitudinal limit of 350m at Bakewell (Preston *et al.* 2002).

Centaurea calcitrapa L.
Red Star-thistle

Locally extinct, Red Star-thistle was a casual spiny biennial of rough ground. Our only record is from "near a fowl-pen" at Hanging Bridge (SK1545) in 1944. It is a native of the Mediterranean.

Centaurea solstitialis L.
Yellow Star-thistle

Yellow Star-thistle is a casual annual herb. The only record is from Barlow (SK3475) where it was found in 2003 by K. Balkow. It was growing on the banks of a new pond where aviary sweepings had been deliberately spread. It is indigenous to southern Europe.

Centaurea diluta Aiton
Lesser Star-thistle

Lesser Star-thistle is a very rare casual of waste ground and tips. It is recorded only from Bamford (SK2082) in 1977 and Rowthorne Tip (SK4764) in both 1966 and 1968. Probably introduced as a contaminant of bird-seed or grain, it is indigenous to south-western Spain.

Centaurea nigra L.
Common Knapweed

Common Knapweed is a very common, native perennial of unimproved grasslands,

COUNTY STATUS: Native
CONSERVATION STATUS: None
FIRST YEAR: 1789 LATEST YEAR: 2013 NO OF RECORDS: 5,772
RECENT SQUARES: monads 1,799; tetrads 667; hectads 41
ALL SQUARES: monads 1,858; tetrads 675; hectads 41

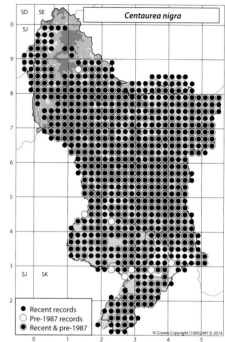

waysides, rock outcrops and rough ground. It occurs throughout the county apart from the high moors of the north-western corner. As early as 1815 Farey was lamenting it as a rough unsightly weed of dairy pastures. More recently it has proved possible to remove it from many grassland sites by agricultural improvement. It was lost from 62% of its hay meadow sites in the Peak District between the mid-1980s and the mid-1990s (Buckingham *et al.* 1997). However, it is still widespread due to its occurrence on waysides and rough ground. In the past both ssp. *nigra* and *nemoralis* have been recorded (Clapham 1969). They have not been separated recently due to the high number of intermediate forms. Being a common plant of agricultural grasslands it has attracted a number of local names including Hard Irone and Clob-heads (Farey 1815), and Sweps (Grigson 1975).

Centaurea paniculata L.
Jersey Knapweed

Locally extinct, Jersey Knapweed was a very rare casual, known only from one site at Buxton (SK07) in 1969. It is a native plant of south-western Europe.

Carthamus tinctorius L.
Safflower

Safflower is a spiny casual annual of tips and disturbed ground, and is possibly native to south-western Asia. There are two modern records (Barlow SK3473 & Heeley SK3484 both in 2003) plus two earlier ones (Melandra Tip SK0095 in 1977 & Dimple Tip SK2656 in 1969). They probably all originated from bird-seed, although it has been cultivated as a crop.

Cichorium intybus L.
Chicory

COUNTY STATUS: Established (Archaeophyte)
CONSERVATION STATUS: None
FIRST YEAR: 1789 **LATEST YEAR:** 2013 **NO OF RECORDS:** 75
RECENT SQUARES: monads 25; tetrads 23; hectads 13
ALL SQUARES: monads 49; tetrads 48; hectads 24

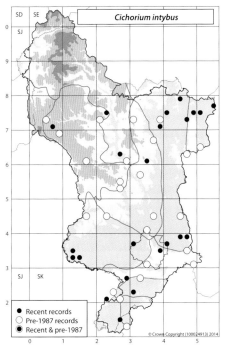

Chicory is an anciently established perennial of waysides, waste ground and fields. It occurs rarely throughout central and southern parts, from Ferneydale Avenue (SK0671) and Hodthorpe (SK5476) in the north, to Drakelow Power Station (SK2220) and Linton (SK2715) in the south. It has been cultivated commercially in small amounts (Farey 1815), and is still widely grown in gardens as a salad crop.

Lapsana communis L.
Nipplewort

COUNTY STATUS: Native
CONSERVATION STATUS: None
FIRST YEAR: 1789 **LATEST YEAR:** 2013 **NO OF RECORDS:** 3,145
RECENT SQUARES: monads 1,486; tetrads 655; hectads 42
ALL SQUARES: monads 1,536; tetrads 660; hectads 42

Nipplewort is a very common, native annual of hedges, open woods, waysides and waste ground. It is found everywhere except for the high moors of the Dark

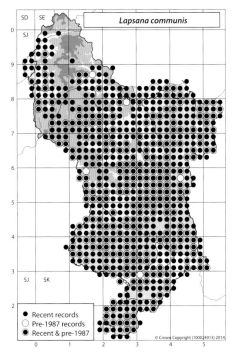

Peak. Our plant is the common British ssp. *communis.*

Hypochaeris radicata L.
Cat's-ear

COUNTY STATUS: Native
CONSERVATION STATUS: None
FIRST YEAR: 1829 **LATEST YEAR:** 2013 **NO OF RECORDS:** 3,016
RECENT SQUARES: monads 1,390; tetrads 672; hectads 44
ALL SQUARES: monads 1,449; tetrads 679; hectads 44

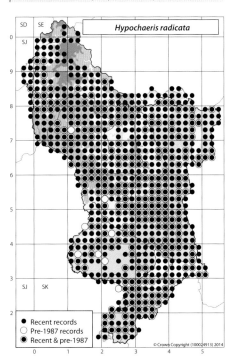

Cat's-ear is a native perennial of grasslands, waysides and waste ground. It is very common throughout Derbyshire except for some of the high moors in the Dark Peak.

Scorzoneroides autumnalis (L.) Moench
Autumnal Hawkbit

COUNTY STATUS: Native
CONSERVATION STATUS: None
FIRST YEAR: 1829 **LATEST YEAR:** 2013 **NO OF RECORDS:** 2,265
RECENT SQUARES: monads 1,200; tetrads 626; hectads 43
ALL SQUARES: monads 1,303; tetrads 651; hectads 43

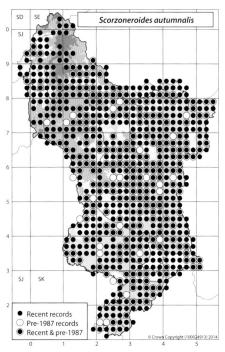

Autumnal Hawkbit is a native perennial of grasslands, waysides and moors. It is common throughout the county.

Leontodon hispidus L.
Rough Hawkbit

Rough Hawkbit is a native perennial of dry grasslands, waysides and rocky outcrops,

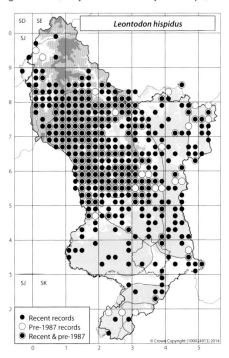

COUNTY STATUS: Native
CONSERVATION STATUS: None
FIRST YEAR: 1789 LATEST YEAR: 2013 NO OF RECORDS: 1,797
RECENT SQUARES: monads 640; tetrads 355; hectads 36
ALL SQUARES: monads 712; tetrads 377; hectads 38

especially on calcareous substrates. It is very common throughout the White Peak, but rare-to-occasional elsewhere. Formerly more frequent, it has now been lost from many sites due to agricultural improvement of pastures and hay meadows. Variety *glabratus* (W.D.J.Koch) Bisch. has been determined once, at Chee Dale (SK1172) in 1985.

Leontodon saxatilis Lam.
Lesser Hawkbit

COUNTY STATUS: Native
CONSERVATION STATUS: DRDB (Cat5b)
FIRST YEAR: 1829 LATEST YEAR: 2011 NO OF RECORDS: 177
RECENT SQUARES: monads 60; tetrads 61; hectads 25
ALL SQUARES: monads 108; tetrads 101; hectads 34

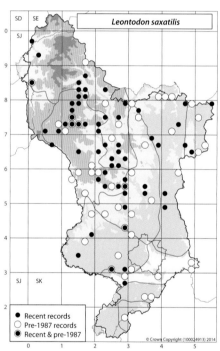

Lesser Hawkbit is an occasional native perennial of dry grasslands, waysides and waste ground. It occurs scattered throughout the county from Hollingworth Wood (SK0097) and Steetley Quarry (SK5478) in the north, through Peak Forest Canal (SK0084) and Miller's Dale (SK1473), to Alder Moor (SK1535) and Willington (SK2827) in the south. It was previously more frequent in the south, as at Ticknall Quarries (SK3523) and Weston-on-Trent (SK3828), both in 1969.

Picris hieracioides L.
Hawkweed Oxtongue

Hawkweed Oxtongue is a rare native biennial or perennial of grassland, waste ground and rock outcrops, generally

COUNTY STATUS: Native
CONSERVATION STATUS: None
FIRST YEAR: 1829 LATEST YEAR: 2013 NO OF RECORDS: 148
RECENT SQUARES: monads 44; tetrads 36; hectads 18
ALL SQUARES: monads 64; tetrads 51; hectads 24

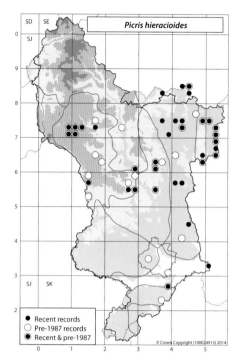

on calcareous soils. It occurs mainly throughout central parts, as at Cow Dale (SK0872), Alsop Moor (SK1556), Crich Museum (SK3454) and Markland Grips (SK5074).

Helminthotheca echioides (L.) Holub
Bristly Oxtongue

Bristly Oxtongue is a casual annual or biennial of waste and disturbed ground. It occurs occasionally through southern

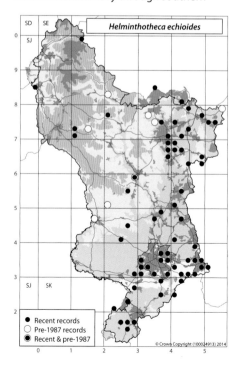

COUNTY STATUS: Casual
CONSERVATION STATUS: B
FIRST YEAR: 1847 LATEST YEAR: 2012 NO OF RECORDS: 123
RECENT SQUARES: monads 72; tetrads 67; hectads 24
ALL SQUARES: monads 79; tetrads 74; hectads 27

and eastern parts, as at Sheepbridge Tip (SK3674), Trent Meadows (SK53B) and near Linton (SK2614). Previously it was anciently established in central Derbyshire, as at Miller's Dale (SK1473) and Kniveton Churchyard (SK2050) both for 1969. However, it appears to have died out here in the 1980s and then reappeared in southern and eastern parts in the late 1990s.

Tragopogon pratensis L.
Goat's-beard

COUNTY STATUS: Native
CONSERVATION STATUS: None
FIRST YEAR: 1789 LATEST YEAR: 2013 NO OF RECORDS: 1,524
RECENT SQUARES: monads 752; tetrads 483; hectads 39
ALL SQUARES: monads 808; tetrads 495; hectads 39

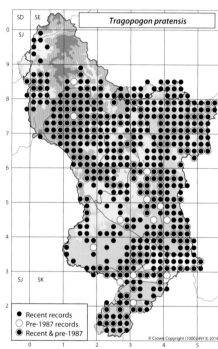

Two subspecies of Goat's-beard occur here. **Ssp. *minor*** (Mill.) Wahlenb. is a native annual or perennial of hay meadows, grasslands, waysides and rough ground. It is occasional throughout Derbyshire except for the high moors of the Dark Peak. **Ssp. *pratensis*** is an established annual or perennial of grassy habitats and waste ground. The only records are for: west Derbyshire (SK06), Whitwell Wood (SK5278) and Pleasley Vale (SK5265) all in 1969. It is native to continental Europe.

Tragopogon porrifolius L.
Salsify

Salsify is a casual biennial of rough ground and waysides. It occurs very

COUNTY STATUS: Casual	
CONSERVATION STATUS: None	
FIRST YEAR: 1829 LATEST YEAR: 2011 NO OF RECORDS: 16	
RECENT SQUARES: monads 5; tetrads 5; hectads 4	
ALL SQUARES: monads 8; tetrads 8; hectads 8	

rarely scattered throughout southern and eastern Derbyshire (Scropton SK1931, Long Eaton SK4934, Butterley Reservoir SK4051, Swanwick SK4053 & Grassmoor SK4166). Grown occasionally as a garden vegetable, it is indigenous to the Mediterranean area.

Geropogon glaber L.
Slender Salsify

Slender Salsify is a casual annual of roadsides and flower beds. Our only records are for Bamford (SK2083) and Scarcliffe (SK4968), both in 1974. It is a bird-seed alien originating from southern Europe.

Sonchus arvensis L.
Perennial Sowthistle

COUNTY STATUS: Native
CONSERVATION STATUS: None
FIRST YEAR: 1789 LATEST YEAR: 2013 NO OF RECORDS: 1,358
RECENT SQUARES: monads 773; tetrads 479; hectads 40
ALL SQUARES: monads 830; tetrads 496; hectads 40

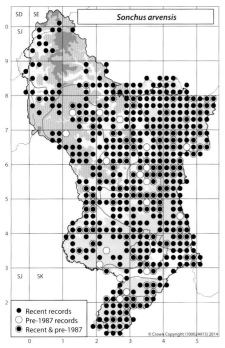

Perennial Sowthistle is a frequent native perennial of waysides, riverbanks, cultivated land and waste ground, generally on nutrient-enriched soils. It is common everywhere, except for the high moors of the Dark Peak, where it is virtually absent. Its tall stems with large yellow flower heads are a characteristic feature of Derbyshire roadsides in summer.

Sonchus oleraceus L.
Smooth Sowthistle

COUNTY STATUS: Native
CONSERVATION STATUS: None
FIRST YEAR: 1789 LATEST YEAR: 2013 NO OF RECORDS: 2,217
RECENT SQUARES: monads 1,175; tetrads 602; hectads 42
ALL SQUARES: monads 1,242; tetrads 610; hectads 42

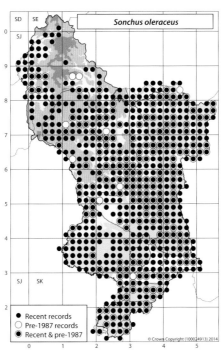

Smooth Sowthistle is a common native annual or biennial of cultivated ground, waste land, waysides and walls. It grows throughout Derbyshire, except for the high moors of the Peak District.

Sonchus asper (L.) Hill
Prickly Sowthistle

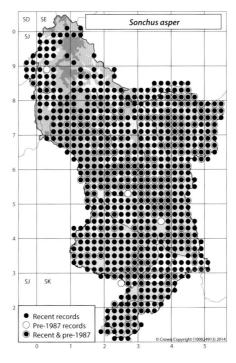

COUNTY STATUS: Native
CONSERVATION STATUS: None
FIRST YEAR: 1881 LATEST YEAR: 2013 NO OF RECORDS: 2,950
RECENT SQUARES: monads 1,564; tetrads 676; hectads 43
ALL SQUARES: monads 1,622; tetrads 680; hectads 43

Prickly Sowthistle is a very common native annual or biennial of cultivated land, waste ground, waysides and rock outcrops, generally on dry disturbed soils. It is found throughout the county, except for the high moors of the Peak District, where it is virtually absent.

Lactuca serriola L.
Prickly Lettuce

COUNTY STATUS: Established (Archaeophyte)
CONSERVATION STATUS: None
FIRST YEAR: 1975 LATEST YEAR: 2013 NO OF RECORDS: 699
RECENT SQUARES: monads 425; tetrads 274; hectads 36
ALL SQUARES: monads 428; tetrads 277; hectads 36

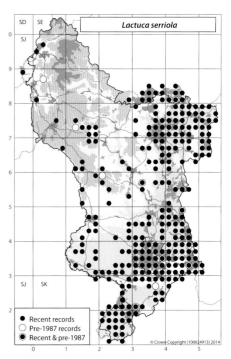

Prickly Lettuce is an anciently established annual or biennial of wasteland, rough ground and waysides. It is frequent throughout southern and eastern parts. Elsewhere it is rare as at Tintwistle (SK0397 v.c.58), Peter Dale (SK1275) and Brassington (SK2354). Records suggest it has become much commoner since the 1980s. This increase mirrors a general national increase which is thought, at least in part, to be due to climate change (Braithwaite *et al.* 2006).

Lactuca sativa L.
Garden Lettuce

Garden Lettuce is a casual annual or biennial of waste ground and tips. The only records are from Hadfield Tip (SK0296) in 1989 and Melbourne (SK3925) in 2002.

Widely grown as a salad vegetable in gardens, it is probably of cultivated origin from the eastern Mediterranean.

Lactuca virosa L.
Great Lettuce

COUNTY STATUS: Established (Neophyte)
CONSERVATION STATUS: None
FIRST YEAR: 1789 **LATEST YEAR:** 2013 **NO OF RECORDS:** 120
RECENT SQUARES: monads 82; tetrads 67; hectads 22
ALL SQUARES: monads 84; tetrads 68; hectads 23

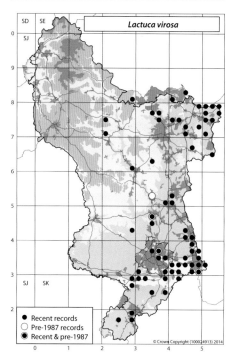

Great Lettuce is an established annual or biennial of waysides and rough ground, though may be native on rock outcrops in some localities. It occurs occasionally throughout eastern and southern parts, from Hassop Station (SK2170) and Sothall (SK4482) in the north, through Belper Station (SK3446), to Blakenhall Farm (SK2516) and Lock Lane Ash Tip (SK4831) in the south. It appears to have become more frequent throughout its range since the 1980s. This increase is matched by a national one which is thought to have been favoured by higher summer temperatures (Braithwaite *et al.* 2006).

Cicerbita macrophylla (Willd.) Wallr.
Common Blue-sowthistle

COUNTY STATUS: Established (Neophyte)
CONSERVATION STATUS: None
FIRST YEAR: 1954 **LATEST YEAR:** 2013 **NO OF RECORDS:** 103
RECENT SQUARES: monads 52; tetrads 37; hectads 16
ALL SQUARES: monads 68; tetrads 46; hectads 19

Common Blue-sowthistle is an established perennial of waysides and waste ground. It grows rarely throughout northern and eastern Derbyshire, from Rowarth (SK0189)

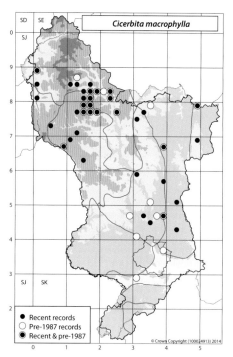

and Outlane Farm (SK2282) in the north, through Aldery Cliff (SK0966), to Denby (SK3847) and Chevinend (SK3445) in the south. Surprisingly for such a rare recent introduction, it has already attracted local names: Eyam Churchyard Weed and Bradda Weed in Bradwell. It is sometimes grown in gardens, and our plant is ssp. *uralensis* (Rouy) P.D. Sell, which is indigenous to the Urals.

Mycelis muralis (L.) Dumort.
Wall Lettuce

Wall Lettuce is a native perennial of walls, rocks and woodland edges, often on calcareous substrates. It is common throughout the Peak District apart from

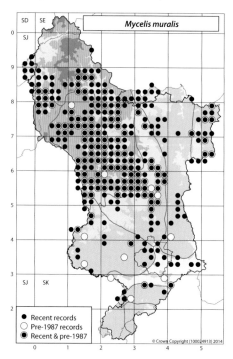

COUNTY STATUS: Native
CONSERVATION STATUS: None
FIRST YEAR: 1729 **LATEST YEAR:** 2013 **NO OF RECORDS:** 1,187
RECENT SQUARES: monads 468; tetrads 285; hectads 35
ALL SQUARES: monads 510; tetrads 296; hectads 36

the high moors. Elsewhere it only occurs sporadically as at Norbury (SK1242) and Anchor Church (SK3327).

Taraxacum F.H. Wigg.
Dandelions

COUNTY STATUS: Native
CONSERVATION STATUS: None
FIRST YEAR: 1789 **LATEST YEAR:** 2013 **NO OF RECORDS:** 7,576
RECENT SQUARES: monads 2,371; tetrads 741; hectads 45
ALL SQUARES: monads 2,409; tetrads 743; hectads 45

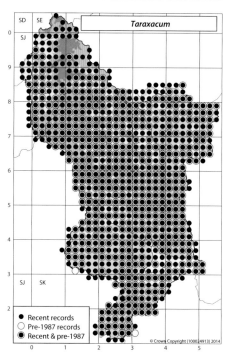

As an aggregate, ***Taraxacum officinale*** (**Dandelion**) is a native rosette-forming perennial found in a wide range of semi-natural and man-made habitats, such as cliffs, mires, woods and grasslands as well as arable fields, lawns, waysides and waste ground. It is very common, only being absent from the highest parts of the upland Dark Peak. Nationally, dandelions form a critical group of around 230 microspecies. Each generally self-pollinates and all are herbaceous perennials that look very similar to one another. Few botanists have attempted to separate them in Derbyshire, so all are grossly under-recorded. Most simply lump them together as the "aggregate" species *Taraxacum officinale* (Dandelion). No systematic attempt has been made therefore to judge relative frequencies, or to provide statistics or distribution maps. Most details on the distribution and

Dandelion (*Taraxacum* sp.), long expanses of flowers such as this roadside show at Wessington (SK3757) are common sights in spring, May 2008 (Peter Smith)

ecologies of each microspecies given are taken from Dudman & Richards (1997), including species arrangement, as so little is known about the plants locally. The bulk of the following records come from just two sources: collections made by R. Smith in the late 1970s and early 1980s (specimens determined by A.J. Richards), and from a Botanical Society of the British Isles "*Taraxacum* meeting" held at Dove Dale, Thorpe and Fenny Bentley in 1993, led by A.J. Richards. Other records were made by J.N. Mills and D. Stewart.

Taraxacum lacistophyllum (Dahlst.) Raunk.
A dandelion
This is a native plant of grasslands on light well-drained neutral to calcareous soils, and of walls and cliffs. There are nine old records from central parts all from 1979/1980 including: Cressbrook Dale (SK1774), Lin Dale (SK1551), Breadsall Cutting (SK3839) and Markland Grips (SK5174).

Taraxacum brachyglossum (Dahlst.) Raunk.
A dandelion
This is a native dandelion of well-drained neutral to calcareous soils. There are four localised records, all for 1979/1980, Woo Dale (SK0972), Monsal Dale (SK1771), Rainster Rocks (SK2254) and Markland Grips (SK5174).

Taraxacum argutum Dahlst.
A dandelion
This native dandelion is generally a plant of limestone areas in western Britain. The only record is from Dove Dale (SK1450) in 1993.

Taraxacum rubicundum (Dahlst.) Dahlst.
A dandelion
This is a native dandelion of dry areas mostly in calcareous grasslands. There are only two localised records for the county: High Edge (SK0668) and Rainster Rocks (SK2254) both for 1979.

Taraxacum parnassicum Dahlst.
A dandelion
This native dandelion of dry calcareous grasslands is only known from Bradwell (SK1682), where it was discovered by R. Smith in 1980.

Taraxacum haworthianum Dudman & A.J. Richards
A dandelion
This is a native species of dry grasslands. There are only four localised records: Monsal Dale (SK16 in 1971), Shirley (SK24 in 1895), Harborough Rocks (SK25 in 1895) and Markland Grips (SK57 in 1899).

Taraxacum oxoniense Dahlst.
A dandelion
This is a native dandelion of dry neutral or calcareous grasslands. There are only three localised records: Lin Dale (SK1551 in 1980), Via Gellia area (SK2656 in 1979) and Wirksworth (SK2753 in 1980).

Taraxacum fulviforme Dahlst.
A dandelion
This native dandelion is a plant of dry habitats such as cliff tops and calcareous grasslands. There is one localised record from the Monsal Dale area (SK1771) in

1980, plus an unlocalised one made in 1885.

Taraxacum fulvum Raunk.
A dandelion
This native dandelion usually occurs on light well-drained neutral to calcareous soils. It is known from just one unprovenanced record from SK17 in 1895.

Taraxacum glauciniforme Dahlst.
A dandelion
This native dandelion mostly grows on light well-drained soils that are neutral to calcareous. The only recent record is from Dove Dale (SK1450) but there are earlier records from Woo Dale (SK0972 in 1980), Lin Dale (SK1551 in 1980) and Markland Grips (SK5074 in 1980 & 1899).

Taraxacum acutum A.J. Richards
A dandelion
This native dandelion is a plant of base-rich grasslands in southern Britain. A single unlocalised post-1970 report for SK15 (Dudman & Richards 1997) represents its northern limit in England.

Taraxacum faeroense (Dahlst.) Dahlst.
A dandelion
This is a native plant of wet places in hilly districts and of roadsides. There are four localised records, all for 1980: Ashbourne (SK1848), Thorpe Marsh (SK1650), Alderwasley (SK3054) and Pebley Sand Quarry (SK4978). It is mainly a plant of upland Britain though also occurs in the lowlands, so is probably the most widespread dandelion in Britain.

Taraxacum naevosum Dahlst.
A dandelion
This is a native plant of damp hay meadows in upland Britain. Our sole record was discovered in 1980 by R. Smith near Alderwasley (SK3053). This is on the south-eastern limit of its English distribution.

Taraxacum naevosiforme Dahlst.
A dandelion
This native dandelion is a plant of wet grasslands and cliffs amongst other habitats. It is known from only four records: Ashwood Dale (SK0972 in 1980), Glossop (SK0294 in 1979), Long Dale (SK1860 in 1974) and Cressbrook Dale (SK1774 in 1980). It is a plant of upland Britain with Derbyshire close to its south-eastern limit in England.

Taraxacum euryphyllum (Dahlst.) Hjelt
A dandelion
This native dandelion is a plant of wet sheltered and base-rich sites. There are

ten records, all from central Derbyshire between 1970 and 1980. Examples are: Ashwood Dale (SK0972), Ashbourne Green (SK1947), Mercaston (SK2743), Shining Cliff Woods (SK3352) and Pebley Sand Quarry (SK4978), all for 1980.

Taraxacum maculosum A.J. Richards
A dandelion

This is a native dandelion of wet areas on wood margins and cliff-faces, mainly in the north of Britain. There are only four records: Ashbourne Green (SK1847), Monk's Dale (SK1375), Wirksworth (SK2753) and Alderwasley (SK3054) all for 1980.

Taraxacum pseudolarssonii A.J. Richards
A dandelion

This is a native plant of meadows and waysides in upland Britain with just a single unlocalised record from SK17 in 1981.

Taraxacum subnaevosum A.J. Richards
A dandelion

This is a native plant of upland Britain, known only from three localised records: Rainster Rocks (SK2254 in 1979), near Wirksworth (SK2753 in 1980) and Tansley (SK3160 in 1980). Derbyshire is on the south-eastern limit of its range.

Taraxacum stictophyllum Dahlst.
A dandelion

This is a native dandelion of moist grasslands in southern Britain. The only records are from Fenny Bentley (SK1650), found by A.J. Richards and party in 1993, and from Hulland (SK2448) in 1979.

Taraxacum richardsianum C.C. Haw.
A dandelion

This is a native dandelion of moist grasslands. The only record is from Fenny Bentley (SK1650) where it was discovered by A.J. Richards and others in 1993.

Taraxacum gelertii Raunk.
A dandelion

Locally extinct, the only records for this native dandelion of grassy habitats and bare ground are two unlocalised ones for 1904 and 1918.

Taraxacum bracteatum Dahlst.
A dandelion

This native dandelion usually grows in damp habitats. The only localised records are from near Monyash (SK1365 in 1979), Nether Heage (SK3651 in 1980), Crich (SK3454 in 1980) and Stanton-by-Dale (SK4636 in 1979).

Taraxacum subbracteatum A.J. Richards
A dandelion

The only record for this native dandelion is

from Fenny Bentley (SK1650) in 1993, found by A.J. Richards and others. Nationally it is a plant of the Atlantic seaboard.

Taraxacum duplidentifrons Dahlst.
A dandelion

This is a native plant of grassy areas, especially on well-drained base-rich soils. It grows throughout Britain, where it is one of the commonest dandelions. However, our only records are from: Clay Mills (SK2627 in 1979), Carver's Rocks (SK3322 in 1979) and Heage Firs (SK3551 in 1980).

Taraxacum excellens Dahlst.
A dandelion

This native dandelion occurs throughout Britain. Here it is known from a single record at Thorpe (SK1650) in 1993.

Taraxacum landmarkii Dahlst.
A dandelion

This native dandelion of stream and pathsides was discovered here by R. Smith in Ashwood Dale (SK0972) in 1980. Nationally it is a plant of upland areas.

Taraxacum nordstedtii Dahlst.
A dandelion

This native dandelion is a plant of wet habitats including meadows, cliffs and wasteland. All four of our original records are from 1980: Dowel Dale (SK0767), Ashbourne Green (SK1947), Ashbourne (SK1848) and Pebley Sand Quarry (SK4978).

Taraxacum fulvicarpum Dahlst.
A dandelion

This native dandelion occurs in wet grasslands, wood borders and other habitats. The sole record is for the Breck Edge area (SK0882) in 1975, discovered by J.N. Mills. It is a plant of upland Britain with Derbyshire on the south-eastern limit of its distribution.

Taraxacum unguilobum Dahlst.
A dandelion

This native dandelion is a plant of wet ground and flushes in upland parts of Britain. Our only record is from near New Mills (SK0678) in 1977.

Taraxacum hamatum Raunk.
A dandelion

This is a native dandelion of woods, grassland and open ground. Only five localised records exist, all for 1979/1980: Shirley Mill (SK2141), Via Gellia area (SK2656), Nether Heage (SK3550), Heage Firs (SK3551) and Common Side (SK3375). There is also an unlocalised record for 1904.

Taraxacum subhamatum M.C. Christ.
A dandelion

This is a native species of grassy places, open habitats and scrub. It was discovered in 1979 by R. Smith at Hathersage (SK2281) and near Catton (SK2214). There are no other localised records.

Taraxacum marklundii Palmgr.
A dandelion

This native dandelion of grassy places and wasteland was found by A.J. Richards at Dove Dale (SK1450) in 1993. There are no other records.

Taraxacum hamiferum Dahlst.
A dandelion

This is a native species of dandelion known only from six field records all for 1979. Examples are: near Calver (SK2377), near Coal Aston (SK3580), Mastin Moor (SK4574) and Whitwell Wood (SK5277).

Taraxacum quadrans H. Oellg.
A dandelion

This is a native species of dandelion, discovered by R. Smith at its sole county site of Alfreton (SK4154) in 1979.

Taraxacum pseudohamatum Dahlst.
A dandelion

This is a native plant of grassy places, rocky areas and disturbed ground. There are no recent localised records but ten older ones from central and northern Derbyshire for between 1979 and 1980. Examples are: near Newhaven (SK1657 in 1979), Edale (SK1586 in 1979), Heage Firs (SK3550 in 1980) and Whitwell Wood (SK5277 in 1979).

Taraxacum fusciflorum H. Oellg.
A dandelion

The only record for this nationally uncommon, established dandelion was made in 1979 by R. Smith for SK47.

Taraxacum boekmanii Borgv.
A dandelion

This native dandelion is a plant of woods, grassy places and open ground. There are just four localised records: Ashbourne Green (SK1746), Clay Mills (SK2627), Alfreton (SK4154) and Killamarsh (SK4481) all for 1979.

Taraxacum atactum Sahlin & Soest
A dandelion

This is a native dandelion of grassy places and wasteland. The sole localised record is from Edale (SK1586) in 1979.

Taraxacum sahlinianum Dudman & A.J. Richards
A dandelion

A native species, its sole local record is

from Dove Dale (SK1450) where it was discovered by A.J. Richards in 1993.

Taraxacum hamatiforme Dahlst.
A dandelion

This is a native dandelion of grassy places and hedge banks. There are only five field records: Ashbourne (SK1746 in 1979), Rowsley (SK2665 in 1979), Hathersage (SK2281 in 1979), Dethick Common (SK3358 in 1980) and near Kelstedge (SK3362 in 1979).

Taraxacum lamprophyllum M.P. Christ.
A dandelion

This is an established species with no modern records, and only four others: near Whaley Bridge (SK0280 in 1979), Heage Firs (SK3550 in 1980), near Kelstedge (SK3362 in 1979) and Alfreton (SK4154 in 1979).

Taraxacum laeticolor Dahlst.
A dandelion

This is an established dandelion of grassy situations and roadsides. Our only field record is for Stainsby Common (SK4365) in 1979, found by R. Smith.

Taraxacum pannucium Dahlst.
A dandelion

An established plant of grassy habitats, scrub and wasteland, this dandelion was recorded in 1979 by R. Smith at Clay Mills (SK2627), Heage Firs (SK3550) and near Newhaven (SK1657). There have been no other records.

Taraxacum subexpallidum Dahlst.
A dandelion

This dandelion is an established plant of grassy places, scrub and wasteland. Our only localised records are from High Edge (SK0669) in 1973 and Hathersage (SK2281) in 1979.

Taraxacum corynodes G.E. Haglund
A dandelion

This established species was found locally by A.J. Richards at the Dog and Partridge, Thorpe (SK1650) in 1993. There have been no further records. Nationally it is a plant of grassy places and wasteland, mainly in Wales and the Welsh borders.

Taraxacum undulatum H. Lindb. & Markl.
A dandelion

This is a native dandelion of grassy situations and wasteland. There are no localised records but it is listed for Derbyshire in Dudman & Richards (1997).

Taraxacum dilaceratum M.Christ.
A dandelion

This is an established dandelion of grassy situations and roadsides. It was found in

1979 by R. Smith in Ashwood Dale (SK0772), Ashbourne (SK1746) and Mastin Moor (SK4574). There have been no further field records.

Taraxacum alatum H. Lindb.
A dandelion

This is a native dandelion of grassy places and wastelands. The sole field record is for Catton (SK2215) in 1979.

Taraxacum insigne Ekman ex M.P. Christ. & Wiinst.
A dandelion

This is a native dandelion of dry open grassy places and wasteland, recorded only from Mastin Moor (SK4574) by R. Smith in 1979.

Taraxacum pannulatiforme Dahlst.
A dandelion

This is a native dandelion of grassy situations and wastelands, found in 1979 by R. Smith near Quarndon (SK3441). There have been no subsequent field records.

Taraxacum expallidiforme Dahlst.
A dandelion

This is a native plant of grassy places and wasteland. R. Smith found it in Whitwell Wood (SK5277) in 1979. There have been no further field records.

Taraxacum subcyanolepis M.P. Christ.
A dandelion

The only local record for this native dandelion of old grasslands is from the Dog and Partridge, Thorpe (SK1650) in 1993 by A.J. Richards.

Taraxacum croceiflorum Dahlst.
A dandelion

This native dandelion was found in SK34 by R. Smith in 1981, there have been no further records. Nationally it is a plant of grassy places and wasteland.

Taraxacum stenacrum Dahlst.
A dandelion

This dandelion is a native of grassy habitats and waste ground. The only field records are: Heage Firs (SK3551 for 1980) and Stanton-by-Dale (SK4636 for 1979).

Taraxacum broddesonii G.E.Haglund ined.
A dandelion

An established plant of waste places such as pub car parks, this is probably the largest dandelion found in Britain. Our only record is from the Dog and Partridge at Thorpe (SK1650) in 1993.

Taraxacum undulatiflorum M.P. Christ.
A dandelion

This is an established dandelion of roadsides and wasteland. Only three

localised records are known, all made in 1979: Catton (SK2315), Clay Mills (SK2627) and Etwall (SK2632).

Taraxacum piceatum Dahlst.
A dandelion

This is an established dandelion of roadsides and rough ground. The only two records are both from 1979: Glossop (SK0294) and the Via Gellia area (SK2656).

Taraxacum cyanolepis Dahlst.
A dandelion

This is a native dandelion of humid grasslands, walls and cliffs. Our only field record was made in 1974 by J.N. Mills in Chee Dale (SK1373).

Taraxacum tumentilobum Markl. ex Puol.
A dandelion

The only record for this established dandelion of grassy habitats and waste ground is from the Dog and Partridge, Thorpe (SK1650) by A.J. Richards in 1993.

Taraxacum intumescens G.E. Haglund
A dandelion

This is an established dandelion of roadsides and wasteland. The one local record from Fenny Bentley (SK1650) was discovered in 1993 by A.J. Richards.

Taraxacum ancistrolobum Dahlst.
A dandelion

This is a native dandelion of grassy places and wasteland. There are only four field records all from 1979. These are: Marston Montgomery (SK1337), Hathersage (SK2281), Slack (SK3362) and Common Side (SK3375).

Taraxacum sellandi Dahlst.
A dandelion

This is a native species of grassy places and wasteland. There are only four localised records all for 1979/1980. These are: Biggin Moor (SK1657), Via Gellia (SK2656), Calver (SK2373) and Heage Firs (SK3551).

Taraxacum stereodes Ekman ex G.E. Haglund
A dandelion

The only record for this established roadside dandelion is from the Dog and Partridge, Thorpe (SK1650) in 1993 by A.J. Richards. It is chiefly a plant of southern Britain.

Taraxacum aequilobum Dahlst.
A dandelion

This established dandelion of grassy places, wasteland and gardens was discovered at the Dog and Partridge, Thorpe (SK1650) by A.J. Richards in 1993. There have been no further records.

Taraxacum acroglossum Dahlst.
A dandelion

This is an established dandelion of grassy places, roadsides and wastelands. It was discovered in Derbyshire by R. Smith in 1979 at Stanton-by-Dale (SK4636) and Mastin Moor (SK4574). There have been no subsequent field records.

Taraxacum exsertum Hagend., Soest & Zevenb.
A dandelion

The only field record for this established dandelion was made in 1980 by R. Smith at Peak Forest (SK1179).

Taraxacum exacutum Markl.
A dandelion

This is an established dandelion of wasteland and rubbish dumps. Found by R. Smith in the Via Gellia (SK2656) in 1979, there have been no subsequent localised records.

Taraxacum pannulatum Dahlst.
A dandelion

This established dandelion of grassy places and waste ground was recorded in 1993 at the Dog and Partridge, Thorpe (SK1650) by A.J. Richards. There are no other records.

Taraxacum lingulatum Markl.
A dandelion

This is a native dandelion of grassy habitats and wasteland. The only four field records are: Topley Pike (SK1072 in 1979), Heage Firs (SK3550 in 1980), Crich (SK3454 in 1980) and Alfreton (SK4154 in 1979).

Taraxacum macranthoides G.E. Haglund
A dandelion

This established dandelion is listed for Derbyshire in Dudman & Richards (1997) but there are no localised records.

Taraxacum cordatum Palmgr.
A dandelion

This is a native plant of cliffs, roadsides and wasteland. Only four records are known: Edale (SK1586 in 1979), Etwall (SK2632 in 1979), Swarkestone (SK3628 in 1979) and Heage Firs (SK3550 in 1980).

Taraxacum sagittipotens Dahlst. & R.Ohlsen ex G.E. Haglund
A dandelion

This is a native dandelion of grassy situations and waste ground. There are just five localised records, all from 1979. These are: Catton (SK2215), Quarndon (SK3441), Common Side (SK3375), Killamarsh (SK4481) and Pleasley Vale (SK5265).

Taraxacum ekmanii Dahlst.
A dandelion

This is a native dandelion of grassy habitats, roadsides and wasteland. There are only five field records: near Whaley Bridge (SK0280 in 1979), Cadley Hill (SK2719 in 1979), Heage Firs (SK3551 in 1980), Nether Heage (SK3651 in 1980) and Killamarsh (SK4481 in 1979).

Taraxacum ochrochlorum G.E. Haglund ex Rail.
A dandelion

The only record for this established dandelion of woods and shaded verges is from the Dog and Partridge, Thorpe (SK1650), made by A.J. Richards in 1993.

Taraxacum aurosulum H. Lindb.
A dandelion

This established dandelion of shady road verges was discovered by R. Smith in 1979 at Marston Montgomery (SK1337), Ashbourne (SK1746) and Stanton-by-Dale (SK4636). It has not been recorded in the field again.

Taraxacum oblongatum Dahlst.
A dandelion

This native dandelion is a plant of grassy habitats, particularly damp fertile pastures. There are only two localised records, both for 1979: Hulland (SK2448) and Carver's Rocks (SK3322).

Taraxacum cophocentrum Dahlst.
A dandelion

This native species of wood margins, scrub and grassy places was first found in 1979 at Shipley (SK4345). There have been no further records.

Taraxacum pachymerum G.E. Haglund
A dandelion

This is an established dandelion of grassy places and waste ground. The only localised record is from Stainsby Common (SK4365), discovered in 1979 by R. Smith.

Taraxacum dilatatum H. Lindb.
A dandelion

This native dandelion, of grassy places and roadsides mainly in western Britain, was discovered by A.J. Richards in 1993 at Fenny Bentley (SK1650). There are no other records.

Taraxacum tanyphyllum Dahlst.
A dandelion

This dandelion is an established species of roadsides. Our only localised record is from Rowsley (SK2665) in 1979.

Taraxacum laciniosifrons Wiinst.
A dandelion

This native dandelion of grassy habitats and roadsides is mainly a plant of southern Britain. It has been recorded only once, for SK24 by R. Smith in 1979.

Taraxacum dahlstedtii H. Lindb.
A dandelion

This is a native dandelion of grassy places, roadsides and wasteland, known in the field only from Derby (SK3535) in 1979.

Taraxacum obliquilobum Dahlst.
A dandelion

This is an established plant of roadside verges. There are two reports for 1979: Stanton-by-Dale (SK4636) and Killamarsh (SK4481). There are no other field records.

Taraxacum huelphersianum G.E. Haglund
A dandelion

This is an established dandelion of grassy places and wasteland. It was discovered at Heanor (SK4345) in 1979 by R. Smith. There are no other localised records.

Taraxacum fagerstroemii Saltin
A dandelion

This established dandelion of grassy habitats was recorded at the Dog and Partridge, Thorpe (SK1650) in 1993 by A.J. Richards. There are no other records.

Taraxacum pectinatiforme H. Lindb.
A dandelion

This is an established dandelion of grassy situations and rough ground. It was discovered at Heanor (SK4345) in 1979 by R. Smith and has not been recorded since.

Taraxacum polyodon Dahlst.
A dandelion

This is a native plant of grassy habitats and wastelands, known from nine field records made between 1974 and 1980. These are scattered from Peak Forest (SK1179) and Whitwell Wood (SK5277) in the north, to Cadley Hill (SK2719) in the south.

Taraxacum incisum H. Oellg.
A dandelion

An established dandelion of grassy situations and wasteland, it was found in 1993 by A.J. Richards at the Dog and Partridge, Thorpe (SK1650). No other records are known.

Taraxacum xanthostigma H. Lindb.
A dandelion

The sole record for this native dandelion of grassy situations and wasteland is one for west of Peak Forest (SK1079) in 1989 by D. Stewart.

Taraxacum longisquameum H. Lindb.
A dandelion

This is a native dandelion of grassy places. It was discovered at Heanor (SK4345) in 1979 by R. Smith. There have been no further field records.

Taraxacum fasciatum Dahlst.
A dandelion
This is a native dandelion of grassy roadsides. There are just seven localised old records scattered throughout the county, from Glossop (SK0294 in 1979) and Whitwell Wood (SK5277 in 1979) in the north, to Cadley Hill (SK2719 in 1979) in the south.

Crepis paludosa (L.) Moench
Marsh Hawk's-beard

COUNTY STATUS: Native

CONSERVATION STATUS: None

FIRST YEAR: 1805 LATEST YEAR: 2013 NO OF RECORDS: 126

RECENT SQUARES: monads 42; tetrads 32; hectads 11

ALL SQUARES: monads 65; tetrads 52; hectads 17

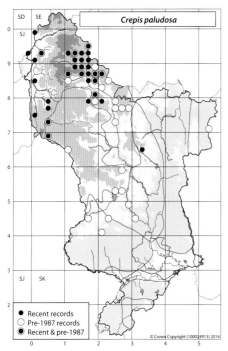

Marsh Hawk's-beard is a native perennial of wet rocky woods, streamsides, marshes and flushes. It is occasional in the Dark and South West Peak Areas (Arnfield SK0098 v.c.58, Linch Clough SK1694 & Shatton SK1880). Elsewhere it is very rare (Grin Low SK0472 & Hodgelane Brook SK3364). Previously it was also found in southern Derbyshire (Shirley Wood SK2141 in 1969 & Breward's Carr SK3044 in 1976). Nationally it is a northern species on its south-eastern limit here.

Crepis biennis L.
Rough Hawk's-beard

COUNTY STATUS: Casual

CONSERVATION STATUS: None

FIRST YEAR: 1854 LATEST YEAR: 2012 NO OF RECORDS: 34

RECENT SQUARES: monads 17; tetrads 17; hectads 12

ALL SQUARES: monads 22; tetrads 21; hectads 19

Rough Hawk's-beard is a casual biennial of rough grassy places, waste ground and wood margins. It is recorded very rarely throughout

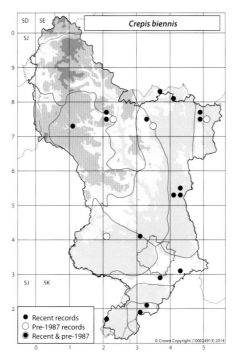

the county, from Blackwell Mill (SK1172) and the Gleadless Valley (SK3782) in the north, through Larkhill (SK4053), to between Catton and Walton-on-Trent (SK2016) in the south. It is often introduced with grass seed, but may also be native as it does occur naturally further south in central England.

Crepis capillaris (L.) Wallr.
Smooth Hawk's-beard

COUNTY STATUS: Native

CONSERVATION STATUS: None

FIRST YEAR: 1789 LATEST YEAR: 2013 NO OF RECORDS: 1,643

RECENT SQUARES: monads 761; tetrads 454; hectads 40

ALL SQUARES: monads 837; tetrads 474; hectads 40

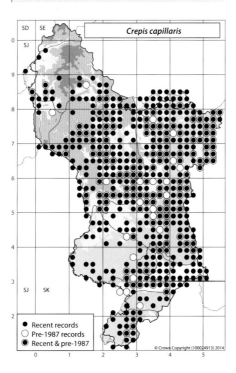

Smooth Hawk's-beard is a native annual or biennial of grassland, waste places and rough ground. It occurs frequently throughout the county, apart from some areas of moorland, and some intensively farmed southern regions.

Crepis vesicaria L.
Beaked Hawk's-beard

COUNTY STATUS: Established (Neophyte)

CONSERVATION STATUS: None

FIRST YEAR: 1867 LATEST YEAR: 2012 NO OF RECORDS: 163

RECENT SQUARES: monads 95; tetrads 85; hectads 29

ALL SQUARES: monads 100; tetrads 88; hectads 29

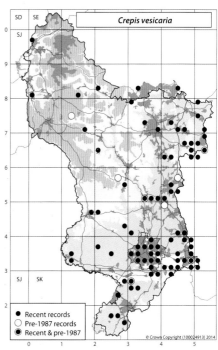

Beaked Hawk's-beard is an established biennial of waysides, walls and rough ground. It occurs occasionally throughout eastern and southern regions of the county. There are records from Millhouses (SK3383) and Sothall (SK4482) in the north, through Pentrichlane-end (SK3751), to Rosliston Village (SK2516) in the south. It is rare elsewhere (Hollingworth Wood SK0097), but appears to have become more frequent since the 1980s. The local plant is ssp. *taraxacifolia* (Thuill.) Thell. ex Schinz & R. Keller, a native of continental Europe.

Crepis setosa Haller f.
Bristly Hawk's-beard
Bristly Hawk's-beard is a very rare, casual annual of newly sown grasslands and disturbed ground. It has been recorded from only five sites: two recent ones (Chesterfield SK3872 in 1992 & Derby SK3635 in 2004), and three earlier ones (Ashbourne SK1746 in 1977, Taddington Dale SK1670 in 1976 & Dronfield SK3578 in 1975). It is a native of southern Europe.

Pilosella peleteriana (Merat) F.W.Schultz & Sch. Bip.
Shaggy Mouse-ear-hawkweed

COUNTY STATUS: Native
CONSERVATION STATUS: DRDB (Cat6), NR, NT, A
FIRST YEAR: 1968 LATEST YEAR: 1968 NO OF RECORDS: 2
RECENT SQUARES: monads 0; tetrads 0; hectads 0
ALL SQUARES: monads 0; tetrads 0; hectads 1

Locally extinct, Shaggy Mouse-ear-hawkweed was a very rare, native perennial of short dry grasslands. It is noted from SK15 in Perring (1968) and is probably repeated as a Dove Dale record in Sell & Murrell (2006). Our plant is ssp. *tenuiscapa* (Pugsley) P.D. Sell & C. West.

Pilosella officinarum F.W. Schultz & Sch. Bip.
Mouse-ear-hawkweed

COUNTY STATUS: Native
CONSERVATION STATUS: None
FIRST YEAR: 1789 LATEST YEAR: 2013 NO OF RECORDS: 2,811
RECENT SQUARES: monads 983; tetrads 516; hectads 40
ALL SQUARES: monads 1,055; tetrads 541; hectads 40

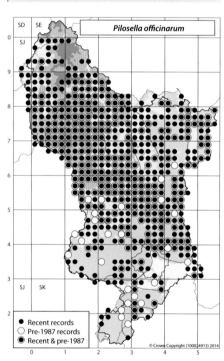

Mouse-ear-hawkweed is a native perennial of open short grasslands and heaths on well-drained soils, plus rock outcrops and walls. It is very common in central Derbyshire, particularly the White Peak, but becomes rare on the northern moors and in the intensively-farmed southern parts. The following subspecies have all recently been recorded for Monsal Dale (SK1771): **ssp. *euronota*** (Naegeli & Peter) P.D. Sell & C. West, **ssp. *officinarum*** and **ssp. *trichosoma*** (Peter) P.D. Sell & C. West.

Pilosella flagellaris (Willd.) P.D. Sell & C. West
A Mouse-ear-hawkweed
This mouse-ear-hawkweed is a very rare,

casual perennial. The only record is from the site of a demolished bridge at Pleasley (SK5064) in 1977. It was probably ssp. *flagellaris*, a garden escape from central Europe.

Pilosella aurantiaca (L.) F.W. Schultz & Sch. Bip.
Fox-and-cubs

COUNTY STATUS: Established (Neophyte)
CONSERVATION STATUS: None
FIRST YEAR: 1969 LATEST YEAR: 2013 NO OF RECORDS: 329
RECENT SQUARES: monads 188; tetrads 173; hectads 36
ALL SQUARES: monads 222; tetrads 196; hectads 36

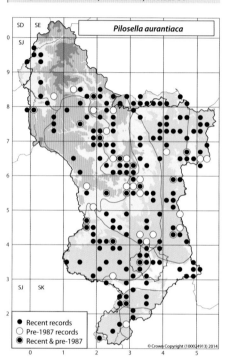

Fox-and-cubs is an established perennial of waysides, churchyards, walls and rough ground. A garden escape from northern and central Europe, it occurs occasionally throughout Derbyshire from the River Etherow (SK0196) and Beighton (SK4483) in the north, through Holloway Village (SK3256), to Edingale (SK2112) and Trent Lock (SK4831) in the south. Whenever plants have been critically examined, they have been found to be ssp. *carpathicola* (Naegeli & Peter) Sojak.

Hieracium L.
Hawkweeds

COUNTY STATUS: Native
CONSERVATION STATUS: None
FIRST YEAR: 1898 LATEST YEAR: 2013 NO OF RECORDS: 1,837
RECENT SQUARES: monads 784; tetrads 468; hectads 41
ALL SQUARES: monads 834; tetrads 477; hectads 41

Nationally, hawkweeds form a critical group of some 400 species. They are all tap-rooted herbaceous perennials which generally set seed without cross-fertilization. As the differences between

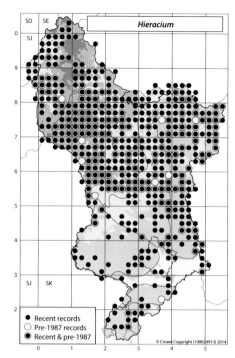

them are small, they are often referred to as "microspecies", and generally regarded as difficult to identify. This means they are all seriously under-recorded, though the group as an aggregate (as mapped here) is well known and common throughout the northern half of Derbyshire, but only occasional in the south. Most species are native, but there are a few introduced ones. They occur in a wide range of dry, infertile habitats where grazing is restricted, but are not heavily shaded. These include rough grasslands, as on railway embankments, light woods, rock outcrops, walls, quarries and heaths amongst others. It was not the intention of this Flora to make special efforts to record the Hawkweeds. However, since Clapham's previous Flora in 1969, progress has been made in our knowledge of these difficult, but attractive plants. From 1982 to 1990 the *Hieracia* Study Group of the Botanical Society of the British Isles made several visits to the county, adding records and helping solve the mystery of plants previously called *Hieracium caledonicum*. The publication of a revision of the British hawkweeds by Sell & Murrell (2006), along with the *Atlas of British and Irish Hawkweeds* by McCosh & Rich (2011), enabled more species to be recognised locally. The following accounts, which include 48 species, are based on local records and we are also indebted to T. Rich and D. McCosh for supplying further details of Derbyshire species.

Hieracium vagum Jord.
Glabrous-headed Hawkweed
Glabrous-headed Hawkweed is a native perennial of rough grasslands, rocky places

COUNTY STATUS: Native
CONSERVATION STATUS: None
FIRST YEAR: 1971 LATEST YEAR: 2008 NO OF RECORDS: 52
RECENT SQUARES: monads 42; tetrads 28; hectads 11
ALL SQUARES: monads 44; tetrads 30; hectads 12

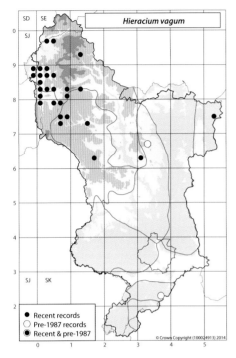

and open woods. Recent records suggest it is occasional in the north-western (Rowarth SK0189 & South Buxton SK0672) and rare in north-eastern parts (Creswell Village SK5274 & Cuckoostone Lane SK3162). It was previously noted further south from Ticknall Quarries (SK3623) in 1971, whilst Clapham (1969) recorded it as widespread and locally common.

Hieracium salticola (Sudre) P.D. Sell & C. West
Bluish-leaved Hawkweed
Bluish-leaved Hawkweed is an established perennial, only ever found at old mine workings at Masson Hill (SK2858) in 1990 by R. Smith and J. Bevan. It is possibly native in Scotland.

Hieracium sabaudum L.
Autumn Hawkweed

COUNTY STATUS: Native
CONSERVATION STATUS: None
FIRST YEAR: 1940 LATEST YEAR: 2013 NO OF RECORDS: 53
RECENT SQUARES: monads 23; tetrads 22; hectads 13
ALL SQUARES: monads 32; tetrads 31; hectads 18

Autumn Hawkweed is a native perennial of rough ground, roadsides, heaths and open woodland. There are scattered records throughout the county from Rowarth (SK0189) in the north, through Clifton (SK1644) and Bailey Brook Marsh (SK4447), to South Street (SK3118) in the south. Clapham (1969) recorded it as

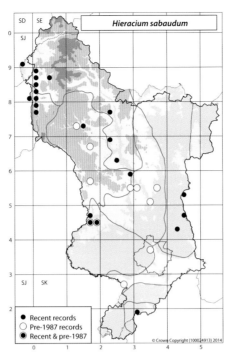

frequent. Nationally it is the commonest lowland hawkweed (McCosh & Rich 2011).

Hieracium umbellatum L.
Umbellate Hawkweed

COUNTY STATUS: Native
CONSERVATION STATUS: None
FIRST YEAR: 1984 LATEST YEAR: 2002 NO OF RECORDS: 14
RECENT SQUARES: monads 10; tetrads 9; hectads 7
ALL SQUARES: monads 11; tetrads 10; hectads 8

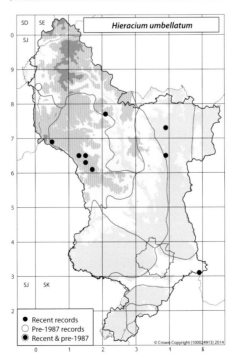

Umbellate Hawkweed is a native perennial of grasslands, quarries, tips and heaths. It is widely scattered from Furness Quarry (SK2076) in the north, through Cotesfield Farm (SK1364) and Old Tupton (SK3865), to

Lock Lane Ash Tip (SK4831) in the south. Clapham (1969) regarded it as occasional. Our plant is ssp. *umbellatum*.

Hieracium subcrocatum (E.F. Linton) Roffey
Dark-styled Hawkweed
Locally extinct, Dark-styled Hawkweed was a native perennial, known from only one field record (Chapel-en-le-Frith SK0579) listed in Clapham (1969).

Hieracium eboracense Pugsley
Northern Hawkweed
Locally extinct, Northern Hawkweed was a native perennial of grassy places and open woods. Clapham (1969) gives it for Eyam (SK2176), and there are specimens in Liverpool Museum collected by W.R. Linton in 1890 for Dog Lane, Atlow (SK2448), Sturston (SK2046) and Edlaston (SK1742).

Hieracium scabrisetum (Zahn) Roffey
Scabrous Hawkweed

COUNTY STATUS: Native
CONSERVATION STATUS: DRDB (Cat6)
FIRST YEAR: 1898 LATEST YEAR: 1898 NO OF RECORDS: 1
RECENT SQUARES: monads 0; tetrads 0; hectads 0
ALL SQUARES: monads 0; tetrads 0; hectads 1

Locally extinct, a native perennial, Scabrous Hawkweed has only ever been recorded at Malcoff, near Chapel-en-le-Frith (SK08) by W.R. Linton in 1898. It is endemic to Wales, with isolated records in Derbyshire and the Isle of Man (McCosh & Rich 2011).

Hieracium placerophylloides Pugsley
Purplish-leaved Hawkweed

COUNTY STATUS: Native
CONSERVATION STATUS: DRDB (Cat6)
FIRST YEAR: 1896 LATEST YEAR: 1903 NO OF RECORDS: 7
RECENT SQUARES: monads 0; tetrads 0; hectads 0
ALL SQUARES: monads 1; tetrads 1; hectads 1

Locally extinct, Purplish-leaved Hawkweed was a native perennial, only ever recorded at Harborough Rocks (SK2455), where W.R. Linton collected it in 1896. It was known until 1903, but has not been seen since. Specimens are in Liverpool Museum and were originally determined as **Toothed Hawkweed** (*H. calcaricola*), but have now been reassigned to this species.

Hieracium prenanthoides Vill.
Rough-leaved Hawkweed
Rough-leaved Hawkweed is a native perennial of coarse grassland over limestone. It has only ever been recorded from the Tideswell Dale/Miller's Dale area (SK1473 & 1573), where it has been known since its 1879 discovery by T. Whitelegg. Subsequently it has been recorded on at least five occasions,

the last being in 2000. It is a plant of upland Britain on the edge of its distribution in the Peak District (McCosh & Rich 2011).

Hieracium mirandum P.D. Sell & C. West
Remote Hawkweed

COUNTY STATUS: Native	
CONSERVATION STATUS: DRDB (Cat6), NR, A	
FIRST YEAR: 1946 LATEST YEAR: 1946 NO OF RECORDS: 1	
RECENT SQUARES: monads 0; tetrads 0; hectads 0	
ALL SQUARES: monads 1; tetrads 1; hectads 1	

Locally extinct, Remote Hawkweed was a native perennial of limestone outcrops, and only ever recorded from Masson Hill (SK2858) in 1946 by E C. Wallace. It was looked for in 1967 but not refound (Mills & Mills, 1970) and again by R. Smith in 1990 and 2011. It is endemic to northern England with Derbyshire at its southern limit (Rich & Scott 2011).

Hieracium angustisquamum (Pugsley) Pugsley
Red-tinted Hawkweed

Red-tinted Hawkweed is a native perennial known from only one locality, Rowsley Sidings (SK2664), where it was discovered on a bridge by R. Smith in 1985 (Akeroyd *et al.* 1986). It was still there in 2010, but in danger from encroaching shrubs.

Hieracium dentulum (E.F. Linton) P.D. Sell
Thick-leaved Hawkweed

COUNTY STATUS: Native	
CONSERVATION STATUS: None	
FIRST YEAR: 1898 LATEST YEAR: 1986 NO OF RECORDS: 16	
RECENT SQUARES: monads 0; tetrads 0; hectads 0	
ALL SQUARES: monads 5; tetrads 4; hectads 3	

Thick-leaved Hawkweed is a rare native perennial of grassy banks and cliff ledges in the White Peak, known from a number of 1980s field records including Lathkill Dale (SK1666), Deep Dale (SK0970), Hartington (SK1460) and Dove Dale (SK1452). Records in Clapham (1969) for **Caledonian Hawkweed** (*H. caledonicum*) are errors for this plant. Note: it was originally described by E.F. Linton as a variety of **Undivided Hawkweed** (*H. holophyllum* W.R. Linton). The closely related **Boswell's Hawkweed** (*H. boswellii*) was also originally described by E.F. Linton, and there is a single pre-1960 record for it in SK17 (McCosh & Rich 2011).

Hieracium holophyllum W.R. Linton
Undivided-leaved Hawkweed

COUNTY STATUS: Native	
CONSERVATION STATUS: None	
FIRST YEAR: 1887 LATEST YEAR: 2006 NO OF RECORDS: 23	
RECENT SQUARES: monads 1; tetrads 1; hectads 1	
ALL SQUARES: monads 11; tetrads 9; hectads 6	

Undivided-leaved Hawkweed was discovered, and described as new to science, in 1887 by W.R. Linton from Dove Dale (SK15). It has since been found as native in a few other White Peak locations (Tansley Dale SK1774 in 1983; Hay Dale SK1276 in 1903; Conies Dale SK1280 in 1896 & Harborough Rocks SK2455 in 1896). The only recent record is from Back Dale (SK0970 in 2006). This attractive species comes into flower three weeks later than the closely-related Thick-leaved Hawkweed (*H. dentulum*). Beyond Derbyshire it only occurs in North Wales and the Staffordshire Dales.

Hieracium vagense (F. Hanb.) Ley
Wye Hawkweed

Plants referable to the Wye Hawkweed were discovered in Coombes Clough (SK0599 v.c.58) by O. Gilbert in 1980. They were refound there by G. Kay in the 1990s, who also found similar plants in Arnfield Brook (SK0298 v.c.58) in 1999. As this is a species of limestone, and neither of the above sites are on such rock, all records are currently considered unverified.

Hieracium decolor (W.R. Linton) Ley
Shade Hawkweed

Shade Hawkweed is a native perennial of the White Peak. The only field records are from three dales (Deep Dale SK0971 in 1984, Cales Dale SK1765 in 1975 & Chee Dale SK1172 in 1951). It is a plant of northern England, with Derbyshire on the southern limit of its range. Some records may be errors for the similar **Porrect-bracted Hawkweed** (*H. subcyaneum* (W.R. Linton) Pugsley), known from Great Rocks Dale (SK1172) in 1961 and Back Dale (SK0870) in 1962 (McCosh & Rich 2011).

Hieracium saxorum (F. Hanb.) P.D. Sell & C. West
Rock Hawkweed

Rock Hawkweed is a native perennial of the White Peak. There are localised records from Hay Dale (SK1177) in 1982 and 1985 plus Miller's Dale Quarry (SK1473) in 1980. While Clapham (1969) mentions old specimens from Tideswell (SK17) and Hay Dale (SK07).

Hieracium dalense P.D. Sell
Dales Hawkweed

COUNTY STATUS: Native	
CONSERVATION STATUS: None	
FIRST YEAR: 1898 LATEST YEAR: 2013 NO OF RECORDS: 14	
RECENT SQUARES: monads 1; tetrads 1; hectads 1	
ALL SQUARES: monads 6; tetrads 5; hectads 2	

Dales Hawkweed is a native perennial of the White Peak. The only recent record is from Tideswell Dale (SK1574) in 2013. Older ones are all from SK07 and SK17, including

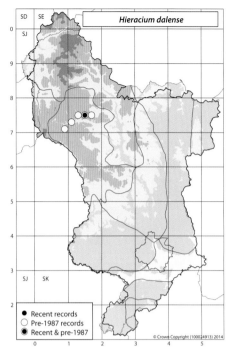

Hieracium dalense

● Recent records
○ Pre-1987 records
◉ Recent & pre-1987

© Crown Copyright (100024913) 2014

Deep Dale (SK0970) in 1984, Tideswell Dale (SK1574) in 1986 and Chee Dale (SK1072) in 1903. The species is known only from Derbyshire and Staffordshire, including its type locality of the Derbyshire Dales. Records of **Flat-leaved Hawkweed** (*H. subplanifolium*) in Clapham (1969) are errors for this species.

Dales Hawkweed (*Hieracium dalense*), Carboniferous Limestone outcrops, Tideswell Dale (SK1574), June 2013 (Roy & Ruth Smith)

Hieracium dicella P.D. Sell & C. West
Forked Hawkweed

Forked Hawkweed is a native perennial of the White Peak. The only recent record is for Tansley Dale (SK1774) in 1988, and there is an earlier record from scree in Deep Dale (SK0971) in 1984. Clapham (1969) regarded it as frequent in the limestone dales, and gave a further 15 records including: Hitter Hill (SK0867), Cow Dale (SK0872) and Bradwell Dale (SK1780), however, the *Hieracia* Study Group did not find it to be common here. It occurs in upland Britain, and is on its southern limit in the Peak District.

Hieracium britannicum F. Hanb.
British Hawkweed

COUNTY STATUS: Native
CONSERVATION STATUS: ERL
FIRST YEAR: 1889 LATEST YEAR: 1994 NO OF RECORDS: 64
RECENT SQUARES: monads 2; tetrads 2; hectads 2
ALL SQUARES: monads 30; tetrads 20; hectads 8

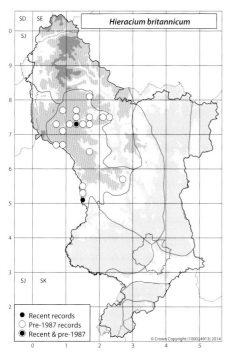

British Hawkweed is a native perennial of limestone outcrops and rocks in the White Peak. There are only two recent records: Dove Dale (SK1451) and Monk's Dale (SK1373). However, there are many older records from across the White Peak (Great Rocks Dale SK1073, Lathkill Dale SK1765 & Alsop SK1554). Clapham (1969) recorded it as locally abundant, and gave over 20 monads where it had been noted. Nationally it is only known from Derbyshire and Staffordshire (McCosh & Rich 2011).

Hieracium naviense J.N. Mills
Derby Hawkweed

Derby Hawkweed is a native perennial of limestone cliffs, first discovered in the

Derby Hawkweed (*Hieracium naviense*) at its classic locality on Carboniferous Limestone outcrops in Winnats Pass (SK1382), July 2013 (Roy & Ruth Smith)

COUNTY STATUS: Native
CONSERVATION STATUS: DRDB (Cat2), CR, NR
FIRST YEAR: 1966 LATEST YEAR: 2013 NO OF RECORDS: 8
RECENT SQUARES: monads 1; tetrads 1; hectads 1
ALL SQUARES: monads 1; tetrads 1; hectads 1

Winnats Pass (SK1382) by J.N. Mills in 1966. It has been refound there on a number of occasions since, up until 2013, including in 1981 by P.D. Sell who declared it "a good species". It has never been recorded anywhere else in the country, or indeed the world.

Hieracium stenopholidium (Dahlst.) Omang
Western Hawkweed

Western Hawkweed is a native perennial of the Dark Peak, known only from one site: Alport Castles (SK1491). Specimens in Liverpool Museum show it was first found by W.R. Linton in 1893, but was seen there again in 1981 by R. Smith. It occurs on the western side of Britain, with Derbyshire at its eastern limit (McCosh & Rich 2011).

Hieracium vulgatum Fr.
Common Hawkweed

COUNTY STATUS: Native
CONSERVATION STATUS: None
FIRST YEAR: 1887 LATEST YEAR: 2002 NO OF RECORDS: 121
RECENT SQUARES: monads 36; tetrads 39; hectads 13
ALL SQUARES: monads 62; tetrads 57; hectads 19

Common Hawkweed is a native perennial of rough grassland, waste ground and rocky habitats, including both sandstone and limestone. It is occasional in north-western parts (Goytside SK0084, Combs Village SK0478, Peter Dale SK17I & Hand Dale SK16K). There are also odd scattered records in central Derbyshire (Cromford Canal SK3056). Clapham (1969) described it as common over these areas, while Linton

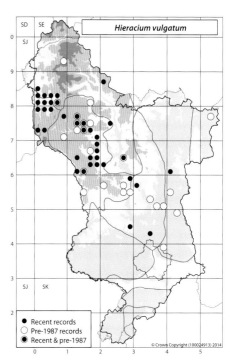

(1903) noted it further south (Mickleover SK33 & Anchor Church SK32). The similar **Grey-haired Hawkweed** (*H. coniops* Norrl.) was found in Tideswell Dale (SK1574) in 2001 by V. Jones (McCosh & Rich 2011)

Hieracium peccense (W.R. Linton) P.D. Sell
Peak Hawkweed

COUNTY STATUS: Native
CONSERVATION STATUS: None
FIRST YEAR: 1893 LATEST YEAR: 2000 NO OF RECORDS: 37
RECENT SQUARES: monads 1; tetrads 1; hectads 1
ALL SQUARES: monads 9; tetrads 9; hectads 5

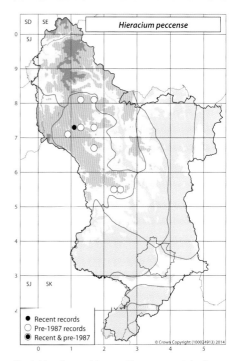

Peak Hawkweed is a native perennial of grassy and rocky places in the White Peak.

The sole recent record is from Topley Pike (SK1172) in 2000. Earlier records exist from across the White Peak (Back Dale SK0870 in 1984, Lathkill Dale SK1666 in 1980, Ravensdale SK1773 in 1898, Conies Dale SK1280 in 1903 & Brassington SK2354 in 1979). This is another plant originally described by W.R. Linton who knew it as a variety of **Rusty-red Hawkweed** (*H. rubiginosum*).

Hieracium spilophaeum Jord. ex Boreau
Spotted Hawkweed

COUNTY STATUS: Established (Neophyte)	
CONSERVATION STATUS: None	
FIRST YEAR: 1959 **LATEST YEAR:** 2008 **NO OF RECORDS:** 11	
RECENT SQUARES: monads 4; tetrads 4; hectads 4	
ALL SQUARES: monads 6; tetrads 6; hectads 6	

Spotted Hawkweed is an introduction on railway embankments, quarries, mine waste and other rough ground. There are recent records from Hopton Quarry (SK2656), Miller's Dale (SK1373) and Scropton (SK1929 & SK1930). There are earlier records from Clay Mills (SK2726) and Jackson's Bank (SK3827), both from the 1970s. Its native distribution is unknown but it is widespread in Southern England. Note: there is more than one spotted hawkweed, so caution must be exercised with these records. Some in urban areas may prove to be **Dappled Hawkweed** (*H. scotostictum* Hyl.). Also with heavily blotched leaves, **Lacerate-leaved Hawkweed** (*H. fictum* Jord. ex Boreau) was recorded by McCosh and Rich (2011) at Ashwood Dale (SK0772) in 1961.

Hieracium anglorum (Ley) Pugsley
Anglian Hawkweed

COUNTY STATUS: Native	
CONSERVATION STATUS: None	
FIRST YEAR: 1890 **LATEST YEAR:** 1996 **NO OF RECORDS:** 37	
RECENT SQUARES: monads 5; tetrads 5; hectads 5	
ALL SQUARES: monads 22; tetrads 21; hectads 18	

Anglian Hawkweed is a native perennial from a range of habitats including roadsides, quarries and sandpits, on calcareous to more acid substrates. Recent records are scattered throughout central Derbyshire (Combs village SK0478, Common Farm SK2845, Masson Hill SK2858, Watts Cliff Quarry SK2262 & Grindleford SK2478). Previous records cover the entire county, from Black Tor (SE0600 v.c.58 in 1896) in the north, to Swain's Park (SK2917 in 1979) in the south. Plants included here were previously determined in Clapham (1969) as **Dark-veined Hawkweed** (*H. diaphanum* Fr.) but it is not entirely clear how many should actually be included. A related species, **Petite-leaved**

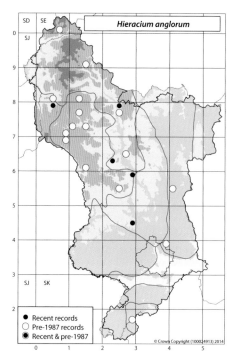

Hawkweed (*H. daedalolepioides* (Zahn) Roffey) listed for Derbyshire in McCosh & Rich (2011), was reported from Gardom's Edge (SK2773) by J.N. Mills in 1959.

Hieracium diaphanoides Lindeb.
Diaphanous Hawkweed

COUNTY STATUS: Native	
CONSERVATION STATUS: None	
FIRST YEAR: 1898 **LATEST YEAR:** 1988 **NO OF RECORDS:** 23	
RECENT SQUARES: monads 1; tetrads 1; hectads 1	
ALL SQUARES: monads 9; tetrads 8; hectads 5	

Diaphanous Hawkweed is a native perennial of central and northern Derbyshire. The only modern record is from Brassington Sand Quarry (SK2454), but there are others from Chapel-en-le-Frith (SK0680 in 1906), Chee Dale (SK1172 in 1954), Winnats Pass (SK1382 in 1982), Common Farm (SK2845 in 1979) and Wirksworth (SK2854 in 1906). **Distinguished Hawkweed** (*H. praesigne* (Zahn) Roffey), recorded by McCosh & Rich (2011) for Derbyshire would probably have formerly been included in this species. Its two most recent records are Chee Dale (SK1172) and Millers Dale (SK1473) in 1954 (McCosh *Hieracium* database). **Skipton Hawkweed** (*H. lepidiceps* (Dahlst.) Prain) similarly listed by McCosh & Rich (2011) was recorded at Mottram (SJ99) in 1894, and without date from Chatsworth (SK27) in Sell & Murrell (2006).

Hieracium acuminatum Jord.
Tall Hawkweed
Many of the specimens, until lately named as Tall Hawkweed, have now been redetermined as belonging to five

species listed below. However there are still specimens referable to this established species, but only from before 1960 (McCosh & Rich 2011), and so it should really be regarded as Locally Extinct. Nationally it is a native plant of rocky limestone woods and streamsides in Wales (Sell & Murrell 2006). **Sociable Hawkweed** (*H. consociatum* Jord. ex Boreau) has been recorded from Lathkill Dale (SK16), Rodsley (SK24), Wirksworth (SK25) and Baslow Edge (SK27), all before 1906. **Southern Hawkweed** (*H. argillaceum* Jord.) is a more common plant with records made between 1960-63 from Chapel-en-le-Frith (SK0680), Glossop (SK09), Bradwell Dale (SK1780), Alport Dale (SK1292) and Stoney Middleton (SK2175). **Grassland Hawkweed** (*H. nemophilum* Jord. ex Boreau) has been found once, at Bradwell (SK1780) in 1960. **Many-toothed Hawkweed** (*H. aviicola* Jord. ex Boreau) has old records for Ashbourne (SK14) and Dove Dale (SK15), but none since 1890. **Cher Hawkweed** (*H. cheriense* Jord. ex Boreau) is represented by a single record from Ashop Valley (SK09) in 1926.

Hieracium cymbifolium Purchas
Boat-leaved Hawkweed

COUNTY STATUS: Native	
CONSERVATION STATUS: None	
FIRST YEAR: 1890 **LATEST YEAR:** 1995 **NO OF RECORDS:** 19	
RECENT SQUARES: monads 2; tetrads 2; hectads 2	
ALL SQUARES: monads 10; tetrads 6; hectads 3	

Boat-leaved Hawkweed is a native perennial of the White Peak. There are two recent records from Priestcliffe Lees (SK1572) and Mam Tor (SK1383). Previously it was more commonly recorded: Back Dale (SK0970) in 1984; Topley Pike (SK1072) in 1981 and Miller's Dale Quarry (SK1373) in Davis (1977). Clapham (1969) noted it as being frequent in the limestone dales, giving 16 localities including Ashwood Dale (SK0772), Deep Dale (SK1072) and Bradwell (SK1780).

Hieracium subprasinifolium Pugsley
Leek-coloured Hawkweed

COUNTY STATUS: Native	
CONSERVATION STATUS: DRDB (Cat6), NR, A	
FIRST YEAR: 1898 **LATEST YEAR:** 1954 **NO OF RECORDS:** 8	
RECENT SQUARES: monads 0; tetrads 0; hectads 0	
ALL SQUARES: monads 1; tetrads 1; hectads 1	

Locally extinct, Leek-coloured Hawkweed was a native perennial of the White Peak. All records were from Chee Dale (SK1172 in 1954) and the Great Rocks Dale area (SK17 in 1898 & 1903). Nationally it is only known from Staffordshire and Derbyshire (McCosh & Rich 2011), with specimens at Liverpool and Birmingham Museums. Sell and

Murrell (2006) describe it as common on "ledges, rock scree and banks throughout the Derbyshire Dales", but others do not find it is.

Hieracium grandidens Dahlst.
Grand-toothed Hawkweed

COUNTY STATUS: Established (Neophyte)
CONSERVATION STATUS: None
FIRST YEAR: 1954 LATEST YEAR: 2001 NO OF RECORDS: 35
RECENT SQUARES: monads 13; tetrads 10; hectads 6
ALL SQUARES: monads 20; tetrads 16; hectads 10

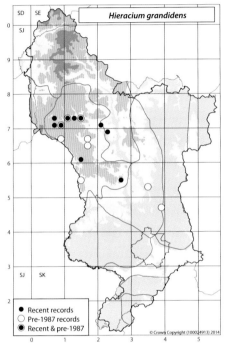

Grand-toothed Hawkweed is a rare, established perennial of the White Peak (High Peak College SK0670, Biggin SK1561, Miller's Dale Station SK1373, Hopton Incline SK2654 & Great Longstone SK2071). It was previously recorded from the Peak Fringe (Denby SK3847 in 1978 and Bullbridge SK3552 in 1985). It occurs throughout continental Europe, though its native distribution is unclear. **Trackway Hawkweed** (**H. subcrassum** (Almq. ex Dahlst.) Johanss.) a close relative, was found in Ashwood Dale (SK0772) in 1981 (McCosh & Rich 2011).

Hieracium sublepistoides (Zahn) Druce
Grey-bracted Hawkweed

COUNTY STATUS: Native
CONSERVATION STATUS: None
FIRST YEAR: 1919 LATEST YEAR: 2003 NO OF RECORDS: 22
RECENT SQUARES: monads 2; tetrads 2; hectads 2
ALL SQUARES: monads 10; tetrads 9; hectads 7

Grey-bracted Hawkweed is a native perennial of central parts of the county. There are only two recent records, both from the White Peak (Tideswell Dale SK1574 & Shining Bank Quarry SK2265). It was previously recorded further south (Alsop Cutting SK1555, Hopton Quarry SK2656 & Butterley SK3951, all in 1978). It occurs naturally in Europe. The plant previously called "dark-headed *sublepistoides*" in Clapham (1969) equates to **Black-bracted Hawkweed** (**H. subaequialtum** Hyl.) in Sell & Murrell (2006). Post-1960 records are: Taddington Dale (SK1571) in 1961, Via Gellia (SK25) in 1964 and Chapel-en-le-Frith (SK0682) in 1968 (McCosh *Hieracium* database).

Hieracium sericeps Wiinst.
Strict-headed Hawkweed
Locally extinct, Strict-headed Hawkweed was an established perennial, known only from two poorly-dated records in the Peak District. McCosh & Rich (2011) list it from SK18 sometime after 1959, whilst Clapham (1969) refers to "an old specimen from Ashwood Dale 37" which is an error for SK07. It occurs in Scotland and Scandinavia, but its native distribution is unclear.

Hieracium pellucidum Laest.
Pellucid-leaved Hawkweed

COUNTY STATUS: Native
CONSERVATION STATUS: None
FIRST YEAR: 1898 LATEST YEAR: 2000 NO OF RECORDS: 26
RECENT SQUARES: monads 8; tetrads 5; hectads 3
ALL SQUARES: monads 16; tetrads 11; hectads 4

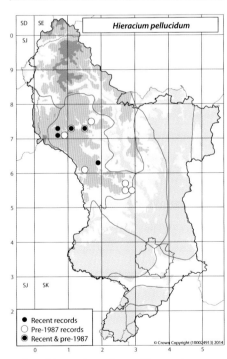

Pellucid-leaved Hawkweed is a native perennial of limestone outcrops and spoil-heaps in the White Peak. There are several recent field records including: High Peak College (SK0670), South Buxton (SK0672), Bradford Dale (SK1963), Wye Dale (SK1072) and Topley Pike (SK1072). Previously it was also known from the Hopton Quarry area (SK2656 in 1978), while Clapham (1969) referred to it as frequent in the Dales.

Hieracium exotericum Jord. ex Boreau
Jordan's Hawkweed

COUNTY STATUS: Established (Neophyte)
CONSERVATION STATUS: None
FIRST YEAR: 1892 LATEST YEAR: 2001 NO OF RECORDS: 34
RECENT SQUARES: monads 8; tetrads 8; hectads 6
ALL SQUARES: monads 28; tetrads 22; hectads 9

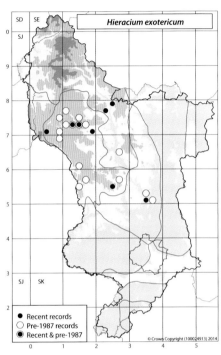

Jordan's Hawkweed is an established perennial found in central parts (Grin Low SK0471, Tideswell Dale SK1573, Brassington SK2454, Stoke Wood SK2376 & Ambergate SK3451). It occurs scattered in Britain and central Europe, but its native distribution is unclear. Note: this has previously been used as an aggregate name by Clapham (1969), so some records may refer to the closely related Grand-toothed (*H. grandidens*), Strict-headed (*H. sericeps*) or Grey-bracted Hawkweed (*H. sublepistoides*).

Filago vulgaris Lam.
Common Cudweed

COUNTY STATUS: Native
CONSERVATION STATUS: DRDB (Cat2), NT, A
FIRST YEAR: 1789 LATEST YEAR: 2012 NO OF RECORDS: 98
RECENT SQUARES: monads 50; tetrads 44; hectads 20
ALL SQUARES: monads 62; tetrads 55; hectads 25

Common Cudweed is a rare native annual of dry bare patches in grasslands, heaths, waste ground and arable land. It occurs scattered throughout the county except for the high moors of the Dark Peak (Beighton SK4484, Steetley Quarry SK5478, Parsley Hay SK1463, Stancliffe Quarry

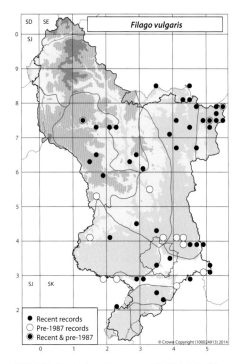

SK2663, Drakelow Reserve SK2320 & Robin Wood SK3622). It was previously more frequent in the south as at Birchwood Quarry (SK1541) and West Hallam (SK4240), both records being for 1969.

Filago minima (Sm.) Pers.
Small Cudweed

COUNTY STATUS: Native	
CONSERVATION STATUS: DRDB (Cat5a)	
FIRST YEAR: 1829 **LATEST YEAR:** 2009 **NO OF RECORDS:** 17	
RECENT SQUARES: monads 6; tetrads 6; hectads 5	
ALL SQUARES: monads 7; tetrads 7; hectads 7	

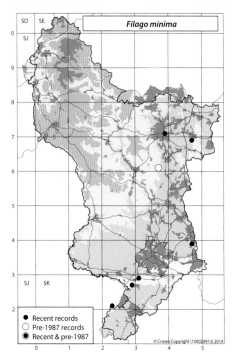

Small Cudweed is a very rare, native annual of bare areas in grasslands, waste ground

and waysides, especially on sandy or stony ground. It previously also occurred as a weed on arable land. It was recorded at Ogston (SK3760) in 1973, near Repton Rocks (SK32) in 1903, and at Findern (SK33) in 1829. In 2002 it was rediscovered at Willington Power Station (SK3029) by P. Precey then found at Drakelow Reserve (SK2220) and Carr Vale (SK4669).

Antennaria dioica (L.) Gaertn.
Mountain Everlasting

COUNTY STATUS: Native	
CONSERVATION STATUS: DRDB (Cat5b), A, B	
FIRST YEAR: 1795 **LATEST YEAR:** 2013 **NO OF RECORDS:** 73	
RECENT SQUARES: monads 14; tetrads 12; hectads 6	
ALL SQUARES: monads 21; tetrads 18; hectads 9	

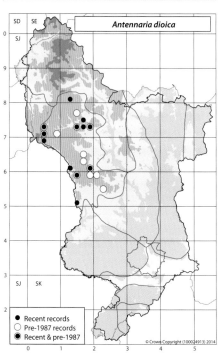

Mountain Everlasting is a rare native perennial of short leached calcareous grassland. Recent records are exclusively from the White Peak (Solomon's Temple SK0571, Priestcliffe Lee's SK1472 & Long Dale SK1860). However, there are older records for the Dark Peak (Glossop SK09 & Axe Edge SK06) and the Coal Measures (SK38). In these areas it grew on more acidic but still nutrient-rich soils. It is now almost confined to upland Britain, with Derbyshire virtually on its south-eastern limit.

Anaphalis margaritacea (L.) Benth.
Pearly Everlasting

COUNTY STATUS: Established (Neophyte)	
CONSERVATION STATUS: None	
FIRST YEAR: 1969 **LATEST YEAR:** 1997 **NO OF RECORDS:** 11	
RECENT SQUARES: monads 2; tetrads 2; hectads 2	
ALL SQUARES: monads 7; tetrads 7; hectads 4	

Pearly Everlasting is an established perennial of waysides, waste ground and walls. The only two recent records are from Friden Picnic Site (SK1760) and Coldwell Hill (SK3771). Previously it was noted further north at Cunning Dale (SK0773) in 1980 and Birch Vale (SK0386) in 1974. It is grown in gardens for its attractive foliage, and originates from North America and north-eastern Asia.

Gnaphalium sylvaticum L.
Heath Cudweed

COUNTY STATUS: Native	
CONSERVATION STATUS: DRDB (Cat2), EN, A, B, C	
FIRST YEAR: 1847 **LATEST YEAR:** 1994 **NO OF RECORDS:** 33	
RECENT SQUARES: monads 2; tetrads 2; hectads 2	
ALL SQUARES: monads 11; tetrads 10; hectads 11	

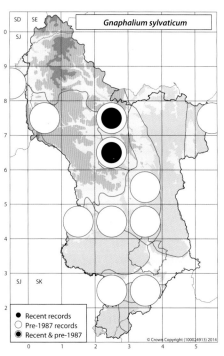

Heath Cudweed is a very rare, native perennial of dry open woods, heaths and grasslands in the southern part of the Dark Peak. In the past it occurred more widely across the county from Charlesworth (SK0092 in 1903) in the north-west, to Edlaston Coppice (SK1743 in 1968) and Bretby (SK2923 in 1968) in the south. This contraction of range is mirrored over much of Britain, particularly in the west (Stace 2010).

Gnaphalium uliginosum L.
Marsh Cudweed

COUNTY STATUS: Native	
CONSERVATION STATUS: None	
FIRST YEAR: 1789 **LATEST YEAR:** 2013 **NO OF RECORDS:** 421	
RECENT SQUARES: monads 233; tetrads 200; hectads 34	
ALL SQUARES: monads 292; tetrads 239; hectads 37	

Marsh Cudweed is a native annual of bare damp areas in grassland, arable

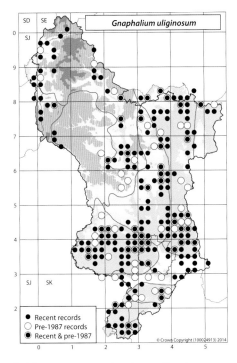

fields, waste ground and woodland rides, generally on acid soils. It occurs occasionally throughout the county, except for the White Peak and the high moors of the Dark Peak, where it is very rare or absent.

Inula helenium L.
Elecampane

COUNTY STATUS: Established (Archaeophyte)
CONSERVATION STATUS: ERL
FIRST YEAR: 1969 LATEST YEAR: 2012 NO OF RECORDS: 21
RECENT SQUARES: monads 8; tetrads 8; hectads 6
ALL SQUARES: monads 12; tetrads 12; hectads 10

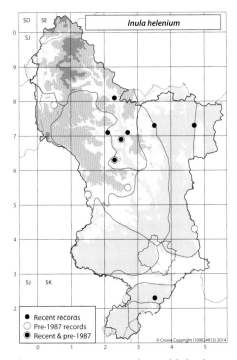

Elecampane is an anciently established perennial of waysides and riverbanks. It

is recorded very rarely from Hathersage (SK2281) and Shuttlewood (SK4772) in the north, through Youlgrave (SK2263), to Ticknall (SK3422) in the south. It is occasionally grown in gardens for medicinal use or ornamental value, and in the past has been cultivated on a small scale, as at Milltown in Ashover (Farey 1815). It is a native of western and central Asia.

Inula conyzae (Griess.) Meikle
Ploughman's-spikenard

COUNTY STATUS: Native
CONSERVATION STATUS: None
FIRST YEAR: 1829 LATEST YEAR: 2013 NO OF RECORDS: 374
RECENT SQUARES: monads 114; tetrads 84; hectads 21
ALL SQUARES: monads 131; tetrads 94; hectads 22

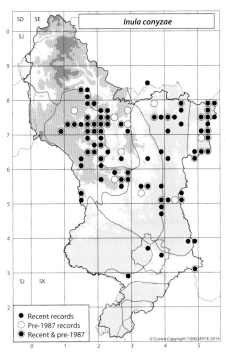

Ploughman's-spikenard is a native perennial of rock outcrops, open grassland, scrub, railway ballast and walls, generally on base-rich substrates. It is occasional in the limestone areas, both in the White Peak (Miller's Dale SK1373 & Cotterhole Quarry SK2656) and on the Magnesian Limestone (Whitwell Wood SK5278 & Pleasley SK5064). It is rare elsewhere (Robin Wood SK2772, Ironville SK4450 & Lock Lane Ash Tip SK4831).

Pulicaria dysenterica (L.) Bernh.
Common Fleabane

COUNTY STATUS: Native
CONSERVATION STATUS: None
FIRST YEAR: 1789 LATEST YEAR: 2012 NO OF RECORDS: 219
RECENT SQUARES: monads 73; tetrads 69; hectads 28
ALL SQUARES: monads 103; tetrads 88; hectads 35

Common Fleabane is an occasional native perennial of wet grasslands, marshes and streamsides. It is found scattered

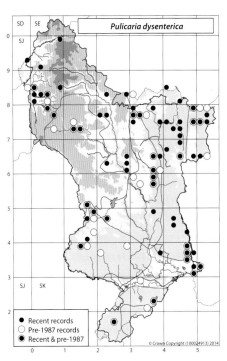

throughout the county from Woodhead Reservoir (SK0899) and Centenary Pond (SK4184) in the north, through Moorwood Moor (SK3656), to Long Eaton (SK43W) and Staunton Harold Reservoir (SK3623) in the south. Previously it was more frequent, probably having been lost due to agricultural improvement of marginal land.

Telekia speciosa (Schreb.) Baumg.
Yellow Oxeye

Yellow Oxeye is a very rare, casual perennial of roadside grasslands. All three recent records are from the Chatsworth area at Calton Lees (SK2568), near Beeley (SK2566) and Chatsworth itself (SK27). It was previously recorded in the same area (SK2670) and at Radbourne Churchyard (SK2836) both in 1978. A garden ornamental, it is native to eastern-central Europe.

Solidago virgaurea L.
Goldenrod

COUNTY STATUS: Native
CONSERVATION STATUS: ERL
FIRST YEAR: 1789 LATEST YEAR: 2013 NO OF RECORDS: 408
RECENT SQUARES: monads 126; tetrads 99; hectads 26
ALL SQUARES: monads 158; tetrads 112; hectads 31

Goldenrod is a native perennial of open woods, grasslands, moorlands and rock outcrops, generally on well-drained nutrient-poor soils. It is frequent throughout the Dark Peak, and locally frequent in the White Peak as at Miller's Dale Quarry (SK1372) and Hopton Quarry Reserve (SK2656). Elsewhere it is rare: Hollinhill (SK5175), Carnfield Hall (SK4256) and Friar Gate Station (SK3436) where it may have been introduced. Previously it

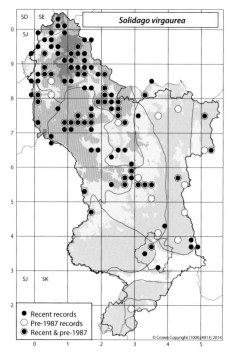

(SK0296) and Beighton (SK4384) in the north, through Ashbourne (SK1746) and Belper (SK3446), to Lock Lane Ash Tip (SK4831) and Netherseal (SK2812) in the south. Widely grown in gardens as an ornamental, it originates from North America.

Solidago gigantea Aiton
Early Goldenrod

COUNTY STATUS: Established (Neophyte)	
CONSERVATION STATUS: None	
FIRST YEAR: 1966 LATEST YEAR: 2013 NO OF RECORDS: 112	
RECENT SQUARES: monads 70; tetrads 70; hectads 29	
ALL SQUARES: monads 82; tetrads 80; hectads 30	

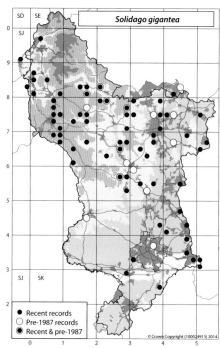

Early Goldenrod is an established perennial of rough ground, coarse grassland and waysides. It is found occasionally scattered throughout Derbyshire from Etherow Reserve (SJ9791) and Apperknowle (SK3978) in the north, through Whatstandwell (SK3354), to Melbourne (SK3925) and near Trent Lock (SK5031) in the south. It is a commonly grown ornamental, generally escaping by the dumping of garden rubbish. It is indigenous to North America.

Aster × *versicolor* Willd.
Late Michaelmas-daisy

COUNTY STATUS: Established (Neophyte)	
CONSERVATION STATUS: None	
FIRST YEAR: 1987 LATEST YEAR: 2009 NO OF RECORDS: 9	
RECENT SQUARES: monads 9; tetrads 9; hectads 7	
ALL SQUARES: monads 9; tetrads 9; hectads 7	

Late Michaelmas-daisy is an established perennial of rough ground and tips. It occurs very rarely throughout the county (Marple Bridge SJ9890, Dove Holes SK0777, Ashbourne SK1746 & Trent Meadows

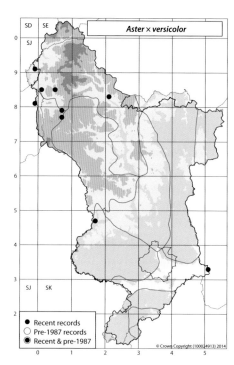

SK5033). A garden ornamental, it generally escapes by being thrown out with waste. It is of horticultural origin from the crossing of Glaucous (*A. laevis* L.) with Confused Michaelmas-daisy (*A. novi-belgii*).

Aster novi-belgii L.
Confused Michaelmas-daisy

COUNTY STATUS: Established (Neophyte)	
CONSERVATION STATUS: None	
FIRST YEAR: 1969 LATEST YEAR: 2005 NO OF RECORDS: 23	
RECENT SQUARES: monads 7; tetrads 7; hectads 5	
ALL SQUARES: monads 16; tetrads 15; hectads 10	

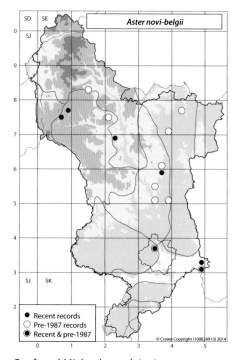

Confused Michaelmas-daisy is an established perennial of waysides

was more frequent in southern and eastern parts, as at Swadlincote (SK2819) in 1969, and near Langley Mill (SK4547) in 1969.

Solidago canadensis L.
Canadian Goldenrod

COUNTY STATUS: Established (Neophyte)	
CONSERVATION STATUS: None	
FIRST YEAR: 1970 LATEST YEAR: 2013 NO OF RECORDS: 177	
RECENT SQUARES: monads 106; tetrads 93; hectads 31	
ALL SQUARES: monads 113; tetrads 97; hectads 31	

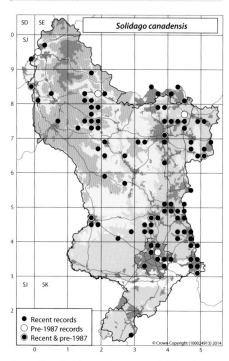

Canadian Goldenrod is an established perennial of rough grassland, waysides and wasteland. It is recorded occasionally throughout the county from Hadfield

and waste ground, found very rarely throughout the county. There are recent records are from, amongst others, Doveholes Dale (SK0877), Ogston Reservoir (SK3759) and New Sawley (SK4832). A garden ornamental, it originates from North America.

Aster × salignus Willd.
Common Michaelmas-daisy

COUNTY STATUS: Established (Neophyte)
CONSERVATION STATUS: None
FIRST YEAR: 1987 LATEST YEAR: 2011 NO OF RECORDS: 15
RECENT SQUARES: monads 12; tetrads 11; hectads 7
ALL SQUARES: monads 12; tetrads 11; hectads 7

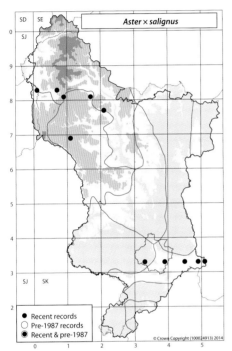

Common Michaelmas-daisy is an established perennial of waste ground, watersides and waysides, often on damp soils. It grows very rarely throughout Derbyshire from New Mills (SK0183) in the north, through Sterndale Moor (SK1068), to Normanton Pond (SK3333) in the south. A garden ornamental of horticultural origin, it resulted from the hybridisation of Narrow-leaved (*A. lanceolatus*) with Confused Michaelmas-daisy (*A. novi-belgii*).

Aster lanceolatus Willd.
Narrow-leaved Michaelmas-daisy

COUNTY STATUS: Established (Neophyte)
CONSERVATION STATUS: None
FIRST YEAR: 1953 LATEST YEAR: 2001 NO OF RECORDS: 13
RECENT SQUARES: monads 5; tetrads 5; hectads 4
ALL SQUARES: monads 10; tetrads 10; hectads 8

Narrow-leaved Michaelmas-daisy is an established perennial of waysides and rough ground. All recent records are from western Derbyshire (Marple Bridge SJ9689,

Darley Moor SK1742, Pomeroy SK1167, Ashbourne SK1746 & Coton Park SK2717). It was previously only recorded from the eastern half (Cathole SK3368 in 1978 & Erewash Canal SK4740 in 1953). A garden ornamental, it originates from eastern North America.

Aster tripolium L.
Sea Aster

Locally extinct, Sea Aster was a very rare, casual perennial. Our sole record is from "mudflats of coal waste" at Killamarsh Colliery (SK4481), found in 1946 by J. Brown. It is native to British coastal mudflats and salt marshes.

Erigeron annuus (L.) Pers.
Tall Fleabane

Locally extinct, Tall Fleabane was a very rare, casual annual of waste places. The only record is from Ashbourne (SK2046) in 1948. Sometimes grown as a garden plant, it is native to North America.

Erigeron acris L.
Blue Fleabane

COUNTY STATUS: Native
CONSERVATION STATUS: None
FIRST YEAR: 1829 LATEST YEAR: 2012 NO OF RECORDS: 259
RECENT SQUARES: monads 89; tetrads 69; hectads 29
ALL SQUARES: monads 114; tetrads 87; hectads 33

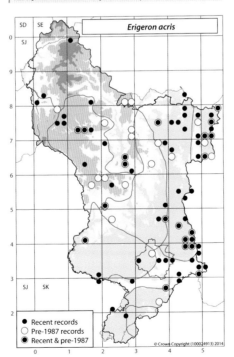

Blue Fleabane is an occasional native annual or perennial. In the Peak District it occurs mainly on walls, rock outcrops and in dry open grassland, especially over limestone (Stancliffe Hall SK2663, Miller's Dale Station SK1373 & Upper Longdendale SK1099). Elsewhere it occurs mainly on

rough ground, on industrial waste and in disused quarries (Steetley Quarry SK5478, Oakwell Brickworks SK4541 & Melbourne Cycleway SK3827).

Conyza canadensis (L.) Cronquist
Canadian Fleabane

COUNTY STATUS: Established (Neophyte)
CONSERVATION STATUS: None
FIRST YEAR: 1969 LATEST YEAR: 2013 NO OF RECORDS: 297
RECENT SQUARES: monads 162; tetrads 140; hectads 32
ALL SQUARES: monads 175; tetrads 149; hectads 33

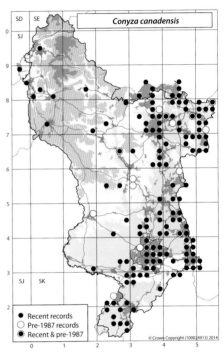

Canadian Fleabane is an established annual of disturbed habitats, waste land and cultivated ground, especially on well-drained soils. It is occasional throughout eastern and southern parts (Meersbrook Bank SK3484, Cotespark SK4254, Long Eaton SK5131 & Netherseal SK2812). It is rare elsewhere (Monsal Head SK1871 & Manor Park SK0394). It is a native of North America.

Conyza sumatrensis (Retz.) E.Walker
Guernsey Fleabane

Guernsey Fleabane is a casual annual or biennial of waste land and rough ground. It is currently only known from the Long Eaton area (Long Eaton SK4932 & SK4934 and Trent Meadows Tip SK5032). However, it is still spreading nationally (Stace 2010) and may well do so here.

Bellis perennis L.
Daisy

Daisy is a native evergreen perennial of all types of short grassland including those which are mown, grazed or trampled. It is very common in all parts except for the

Daisy (*Bellis perennis*) in Racecourse Park, Derby (SK3637), May 2008 (Peter Smith)

COUNTY STATUS: Native

CONSERVATION STATUS: None

FIRST YEAR: 1789 LATEST YEAR: 2013 NO OF RECORDS: 5,350

RECENT SQUARES: monads 1,988; tetrads 716; hectads 44

ALL SQUARES: monads 2,039; tetrads 721; hectads 44

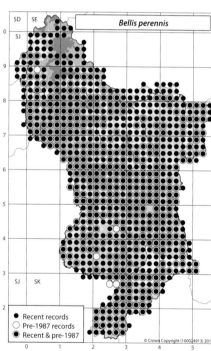

high moors of the Dark Peak. It has a local name of Golland (Grigson 1975).

Tanacetum parthenium (L.) Sch. Bip.
Feverfew

COUNTY STATUS: Established (Archaeophyte)

CONSERVATION STATUS: None

FIRST YEAR: 1789 LATEST YEAR: 2013 NO OF RECORDS: 1,090

RECENT SQUARES: monads 587; tetrads 431; hectads 38

ALL SQUARES: monads 630; tetrads 445; hectads 38

Feverfew is an anciently established perennial of waysides, rough ground and

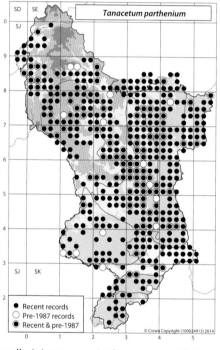

walls. It is common in the eastern half of the county, but only occasional in the west, becoming virtually absent from large areas of the Peak District. Commonly cultivated as an ornamental plant, a medicinal herb or for use in well-dressings, it is a native of the Balkans.

Tanacetum vulgare L.
Tansy

COUNTY STATUS: Native

CONSERVATION STATUS: None

FIRST YEAR: 1789 LATEST YEAR: 2013 NO OF RECORDS: 1,054

RECENT SQUARES: monads 429; tetrads 270; hectads 36

ALL SQUARES: monads 466; tetrads 290; hectads 37

Tansy is an aromatic perennial of tall grasslands, waysides, watersides and waste ground. It is considered native but

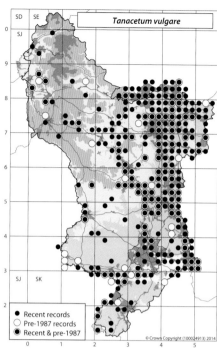

has often been grown in gardens as a culinary or medicinal herb. It is thus impossible to distinguish now between native and anciently established populations. Frequent in the lowland east and south, it is rare in the more upland north and west.

Artemisia vulgaris L.
Mugwort

COUNTY STATUS: Established (Archaeophyte)

CONSERVATION STATUS: None

FIRST YEAR: 1789 LATEST YEAR: 2013 NO OF RECORDS: 2,697

RECENT SQUARES: monads 1,162; tetrads 581; hectads 44

ALL SQUARES: monads 1,228; tetrads 597; hectads 44

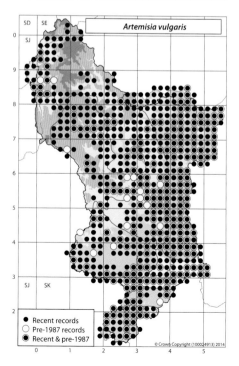

Mugwort is an anciently established perennial of waysides, watersides, rough ground and waste places, generally on fertile soils. It is very common in lowland Derbyshire, but less so in the upland parts, particularly the Dark and South West Peak Character Areas.

Artemisia verlotiorum Lamotte
Chinese Mugwort

Chinese Mugwort is a very rare, casual perennial whose only record is from a roadside at Danesmoor (SK4063) in 1999. It is indigenous to south-western China.

Artemisia absinthium L.
Wormwood

COUNTY STATUS:	Established (Archaeophyte)
CONSERVATION STATUS:	None
FIRST YEAR: 1789 **LATEST YEAR:** 2013 **NO OF RECORDS:** 876	
RECENT SQUARES: monads 354; tetrads 248; hectads 34	
ALL SQUARES: monads 428; tetrads 291; hectads 37	

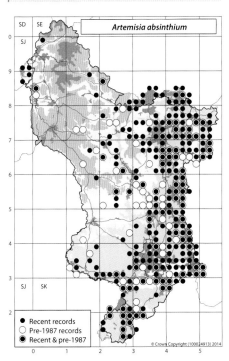

Wormwood is an aromatic, anciently established perennial of waysides, watersides, rough and disturbed ground. It is occasional in eastern and southern parts, but only rare in the north and west.

Achillea ptarmica L.
Sneezewort

COUNTY STATUS:	Native
CONSERVATION STATUS:	None
FIRST YEAR: 1789 **LATEST YEAR:** 2012 **NO OF RECORDS:** 508	
RECENT SQUARES: monads 224; tetrads 185; hectads 38	
ALL SQUARES: monads 279; tetrads 221; hectads 39	

Sneezewort is a native perennial of marshes, fens, flushes, damp grasslands and wet heaths. It is found throughout the

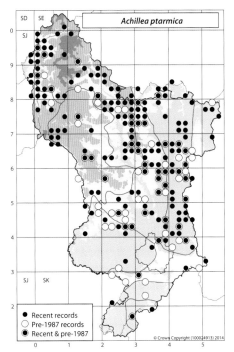

county (Long Clough SK0392, Mercaston Marsh SK2743, Swainspark SK2917, Willington Junction SK3029 & Dowey Lumb SK3780). It is locally frequent in the Peak District but rare elsewhere.

Achillea millefolium L.
Yarrow

COUNTY STATUS:	Native
CONSERVATION STATUS:	None
FIRST YEAR: 1789 **LATEST YEAR:** 2013 **NO OF RECORDS:** 5,571	
RECENT SQUARES: monads 1,954; tetrads 708; hectads 44	
ALL SQUARES: monads 2,026; tetrads 713; hectads 44	

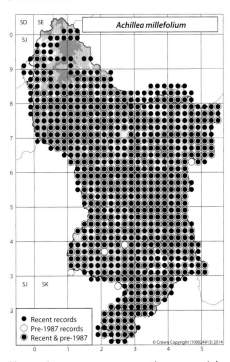

Yarrow is a very common, native perennial of a wide range of short grasslands

including pastures, rough grazings and lawns. It grows throughout the county except for the high moors of the Dark Peak. In the past it was used locally in the dying of cloth (Farey 1815).

Achillea distans Waldst. & Kit. ex Willd.
Tall Yarrow

Tall Yarrow is a very rare, casual perennial of grasslands. The only three recent records are from: Bubnell (SK2471 & SK2472) and Dronfield (SK3477) in 2012. There are earlier ones from Matlock (SK25) in 1864, and Cromford Moor (SK35) in 1843. Presumably a garden escape, it grows naturally in central Europe. The local plant is ssp. *tanacetifolia* Janch.

Chamaemelum nobile (L.) All.
Chamomile

COUNTY STATUS:	Native
CONSERVATION STATUS:	DRDB (Cat2), VU, NERC, B, C
FIRST YEAR: 1829 **LATEST YEAR:** 1977 **NO OF RECORDS:** 21	
RECENT SQUARES: monads 0; tetrads 0; hectads 0	
ALL SQUARES: monads 7; tetrads 7; hectads 7	

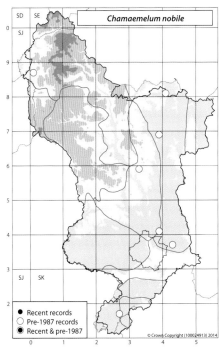

Chamomile is a very rare, native perennial of grasslands and heaths, generally on sandy soils. There are no recent records while earlier ones are scattered across the county (Sett Valley SK0086 in 1977, Ford SK4180 in 1970, & Boythorpe SK3869 in 1969). At the time of Linton's 1903 Flora it was known at a handful of sites in central and southern Derbyshire. It was once cultivated for medicinal use (Davis 1811) particularly around Ashover (Farey 1815), and has been used to create lawns. Its decline here mirrors a national decrease due to changes in farming practices (Preston *et al.* 2002).

Anthemis punctata Vahl
Sicilian Chamomile

Sicilian Chamomile is a very rare, casual perennial, whose only record is for Wadshelf near Puddingpie (SK3171) in 1982. Grown in gardens, it can also be a contaminant of grain. It is a native of Sicily.

Anthemis arvensis L.
Corn Chamomile

COUNTY STATUS: Casual	
CONSERVATION STATUS: None	
FIRST YEAR: 1789 **LATEST YEAR:** 2011 **NO OF RECORDS:** 16	
RECENT SQUARES: monads 1; tetrads 1; hectads 1	
ALL SQUARES: monads 5; tetrads 5; hectads 10	

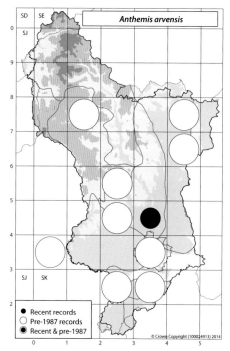

Corn Chamomile is a very rare, casual annual. All modern records are from Belper Coppice (SK3547). Previously it was recorded as a roadside casual (Taddington SK1471 in 1968 & Carsington SK2653 in 1982). Even earlier it was noted as a rare weed of arable fields (Newhall SK22, Repton SK32 & Renishaw SK47, all for 1903). Its loss from arable fields reflects a national decline due to increased herbicide use (Preston *et al.* 2002).

Anthemis cotula L.
Stinking Chamomile

COUNTY STATUS: Established (Archaeophyte)	
CONSERVATION STATUS: DRDB (Cat2), VU	
FIRST YEAR: 1789 **LATEST YEAR:** 1979 **NO OF RECORDS:** 24	
RECENT SQUARES: monads 0; tetrads 0; hectads 0	
ALL SQUARES: monads 12; tetrads 12; hectads 18	

Stinking Chamomile is an anciently established annual of arable land and waste ground. There are no recent records, though previously it was recorded across

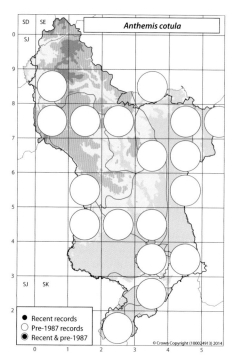

the county (High Rake SK1677, Beauchief SK3381, Yeldersley SK2144, Hartington SK1259 & Overseal SK2915, all for 1969). This loss mirrors a national decline since 1962 due to use of more effective herbicides (Preston *et al.* 2002).

Anthemis tinctoria L.
Yellow Chamomile

COUNTY STATUS: Casual	
CONSERVATION STATUS: None	
FIRST YEAR: 1903 **LATEST YEAR:** 2009 **NO OF RECORDS:** 6	
RECENT SQUARES: monads 1; tetrads 1; hectads 1	
ALL SQUARES: monads 4; tetrads 4; hectads 5	

Yellow Chamomile is a very rare, casual perennial of waste ground and roadsides, which is indigenous to continental Europe. The only recent record is from Chesterfield (SK3870). There are earlier records from Dimple Tip (SK2960) in 1971, Peasunhurst Quarry (SK3166) in 1972, Renishaw (SK47) in 1903 and for SK57 in 1941. It was formerly cultivated for its yellow dye. Now it is occasionally grown in gardens for ornament, and is probably a bird-seed alien too.

Glebionis segetum (L.) Fourr.
Corn Marigold

COUNTY STATUS: Established (Archaeophyte)	
CONSERVATION STATUS: VU, ERL	
FIRST YEAR: 1789 **LATEST YEAR:** 2011 **NO OF RECORDS:** 53	
RECENT SQUARES: monads 12; tetrads 14; hectads 11	
ALL SQUARES: monads 34; tetrads 34; hectads 24	

Corn Marigold is an anciently established, annual weed of arable fields and a recent introduction in restoration schemes. As a cornfield weed it occurred occasionally throughout eastern and southern

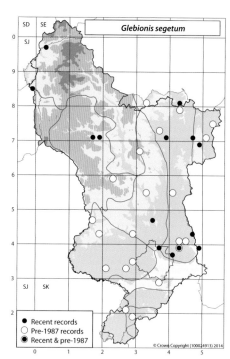

Derbyshire (Beauchief SK3381, Creswell SK5274, Ashbourne SK1746 & Swarkestone SK3628 all for 1969). Recently it has occurred solely as a short-lived introduction with wild-flower seed mixes in restoration and planting schemes (Longdendale SK0397 & the Meteor Centre Derby SK3638). Its local loss from arable fields reflects a national decline due to improved crop husbandry (Preston *et al.* 2002).

Leucanthemum vulgare Lam.
Oxeye Daisy

Oxeye Daisy is a widespread native perennial of unimproved grasslands, waysides and rough ground. It is very

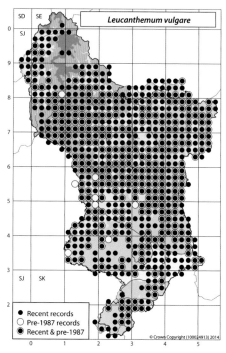

COUNTY STATUS: Native	COUNTY STATUS: Established (Archaeophyte)	COUNTY STATUS: Established (Neophyte)
CONSERVATION STATUS: None	CONSERVATION STATUS: None	CONSERVATION STATUS: None
FIRST YEAR: 1789 LATEST YEAR: 2013 NO OF RECORDS: 3,794	FIRST YEAR: 1789 LATEST YEAR: 2013 NO OF RECORDS: 787	FIRST YEAR: 1897 LATEST YEAR: 2013 NO OF RECORDS: 3,176
RECENT SQUARES: monads 1,360; tetrads 617; hectads 42	RECENT SQUARES: monads 532; tetrads 356; hectads 39	RECENT SQUARES: monads 1,620; tetrads 691; hectads 43
ALL SQUARES: monads 1,427; tetrads 625; hectads 42	ALL SQUARES: monads 560; tetrads 372; hectads 39	ALL SQUARES: monads 1,721; tetrads 697; hectads 43

common throughout most of the county, becoming less frequent in the more intensively farmed south and virtually absent from the high moors of the Dark Peak. Recently it has declined in agricultural grasslands, for example in the White Peak (Buckingham *et al.* 1997), due to agricultural improvement. However, this decline has been partly offset by its increasing use in restoration schemes. It has a local name of Horse Pennies (Grigson 1975).

Leucanthemum × *superbum* (Bergmans ex J.W. Ingram) D.H. Kent
Shasta Daisy

COUNTY STATUS: Established (Neophyte)
CONSERVATION STATUS: None
FIRST YEAR: 1970 LATEST YEAR: 2013 NO OF RECORDS: 45
RECENT SQUARES: monads 23; tetrads 29; hectads 18
ALL SQUARES: monads 28; tetrads 34; hectads 20

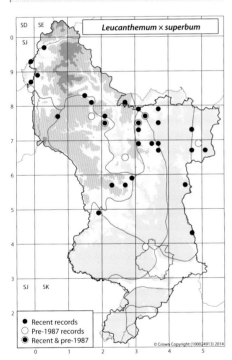

Shasta Daisy is an established perennial of waysides and waste ground. It is found rarely throughout the county (Rowarth SK0089, Longcliffe SK2256, Grange Lumb SK3174, Derby City SK33 & Ilkeston SK4642). Commonly grown in gardens for its showy flowers, its origin is uncertain.

Matricaria chamomilla L.
Scented Mayweed

Scented Mayweed is an anciently established annual of arable land and waste places, generally on lighter soils. It is

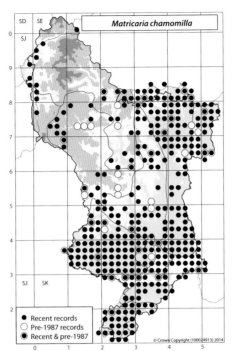

common throughout eastern and southern parts, occasional in the Peak District, and virtually absent from the Dark Peak moors. It appears to have increased since 1986, most probably on rough ground.

Matricaria discoidea DC.
Pineappleweed

Pineappleweed is an established annual of bare trampled areas, arable fields and

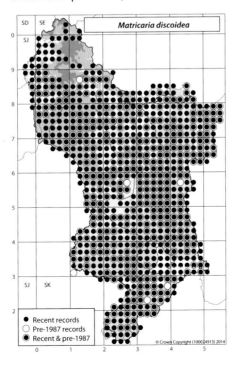

waste ground, generally on fertile soils. It is very common throughout the county, apart from the Dark Peak moors. It is a native of northern and southern Asia.

Tripleurospermum inodorum (L.) Sch. Bip.
Scentless Mayweed

COUNTY STATUS: Established (Archaeophyte)
CONSERVATION STATUS: None
FIRST YEAR: 1789 LATEST YEAR: 2013 NO OF RECORDS: 1,466
RECENT SQUARES: monads 747; tetrads 471; hectads 41
ALL SQUARES: monads 854; tetrads 512; hectads 41

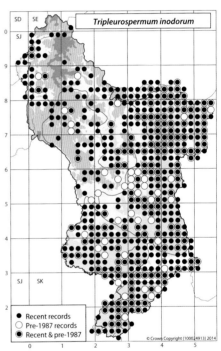

Scentless Mayweed is an anciently established annual of cultivated land, rough ground and waste places. It is common throughout southern and eastern parts, but only occasional in the Peak District.

Cotula coronopifolia L.
Buttonweed

Buttonweed is a very rare, established annual of open wet habitats, and a native of South Africa. It was first discovered in 2004 at Ilkeston (SK4541) by A. Willmot. In 2009 it was seen at Swanwick (SK4053) and refound at Ilkeston. It often grows in saline conditions but we do not know if this is the case here.

Senecio cineraria DC.
Silver Ragwort

Silver Ragwort is a casual evergreen shrub of waysides, and a garden ornamental originating from the Mediterranean area.

Our only records are from Kedleston Road, Derby (SK3437) in 1999 and Hucklow (SK1680) in 1993.

Senecio jacobaea L.
Common Ragwort

COUNTY STATUS: Native
CONSERVATION STATUS: None
FIRST YEAR: 1789 LATEST YEAR: 2013 NO OF RECORDS: 5,648
RECENT SQUARES: monads 1,983; tetrads 713; hectads 44
ALL SQUARES: monads 2,028; tetrads 718; hectads 44

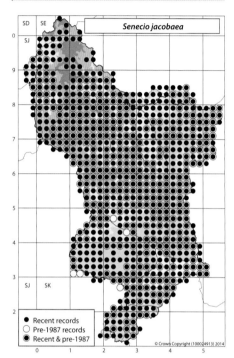

Common Ragwort is a native perennial of grasslands, waysides, waste places, open woods and rock outcrops. It occurs very commonly throughout the county except for the high moors of the Dark Peak. It was classified as an injurious weed under the

Common Ragwort (*Senecio jacobaea*) in the White Peak near High Peak Trail, August 2011 (Nick Moyes)

Weeds Act 1959 due to its toxicity to stock if eaten, and is the subject of the Ragwort Control Act 2003. It is nevertheless regarded as a valuable resource for insects, especially in intensively farmed places where other flowers are lacking.

Senecio × ostenfeldii Druce
A hybrid ragwort

This hybrid ragwort is a native perennial of damp grasslands. There are two recent records (Etherow Reserve SJ9791 in 2002 & New Mills SK0085 in 1988), plus one from New Mills (SJ9885) in 1980. It is the spontaneous hybrid of Common (*S. jacobaea*) and Marsh Ragwort (*S. aquaticus*).

Senecio aquaticus Hill
Marsh Ragwort

COUNTY STATUS: Native
CONSERVATION STATUS: ERL
FIRST YEAR: 1789 LATEST YEAR: 2012 NO OF RECORDS: 366
RECENT SQUARES: monads 144; tetrads 133; hectads 33
ALL SQUARES: monads 184; tetrads 165; hectads 37

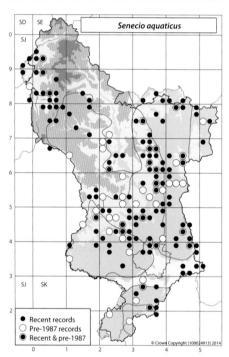

Marsh Ragwort is an occasional native perennial of damp grasslands, marshes and watersides. It is found throughout the county, for example Chinley Village (SK0482), Eckington (SK4379), Ashbourne Pond (SK1846), Kirk Hallam (SK4639) and Southwood House Fields (SK3521). It has been lost from a number of sites since 1986, no doubt due to agricultural "improvement" of marginal land.

Senecio erucifolius L.
Hoary Ragwort

Hoary Ragwort is a native perennial of grassy waysides, waste places and wood-

COUNTY STATUS: Native
CONSERVATION STATUS: None
FIRST YEAR: 1789 LATEST YEAR: 2013 NO OF RECORDS: 292
RECENT SQUARES: monads 131; tetrads 109; hectads 25
ALL SQUARES: monads 159; tetrads 123; hectads 31

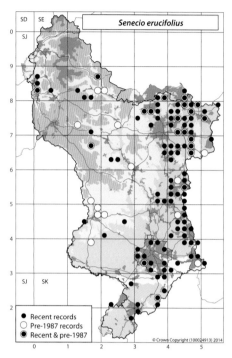

margins, generally on clay soils. It is frequent in the Coal Measures Area, as in the Moss Valley (SK3880), Pinxton Wharf (SK4554) and Stanton Ironworks (SK4738), but rare elsewhere for example Lodge Cote (SK1987) and Stanton Moor (SK2463).

Senecio inaequidens DC.
Narrow-leaved Ragwort

Narrow-leaved Ragwort is a casual annual of waste ground, generally near roads or car parks. It was discovered in 2008 at Black Hole Mine (SK2077) by J. Middleton, and was still there in 2009 and 2010. It has since been reported from four other sites between 2009 and 2012: Derby (SK3437 & 3535), Heeley (SK3484) and Stonegravels (SK3871). This spread is mirrored by a national one and is expected to continue. It is indigenous to South Africa.

Senecio sarracenicus L.
Broad-leaved Ragwort

Locally extinct, Broad-leaved Ragwort was an established perennial of streamsides, fens and damp woods. Only four records are known: Moscar Lodge (SK2387) in 1969, for SK27 and SK37 in 1903, and near Chatsworth (SK26) in 1835. A native of continental Europe, it is sometimes grown as a garden ornamental, and was once cultivated for medicinal use.

Senecio squalidus L.
Oxford Ragwort

COUNTY STATUS: Established (Neophyte)
CONSERVATION STATUS: None
FIRST YEAR: 1941 **LATEST YEAR:** 2013 **NO OF RECORDS:** 1,133
RECENT SQUARES: monads 442; tetrads 296; hectads 38
ALL SQUARES: monads 545; tetrads 344; hectads 39

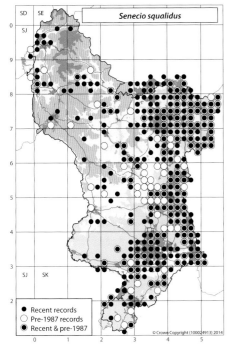

Oxford Ragwort is an established annual or perennial of waysides, waste ground and walls, particularly on well-drained soils. It has become frequent throughout the eastern half of the county since its discovery near Chesterfield in 1941 (Clapham 1969). It has also spread through the western half, though is still only rare there. It is native to southern Europe.

Senecio × *subnebrodensis* Simonk.
A hybrid ragwort

COUNTY STATUS: Native
CONSERVATION STATUS: None
FIRST YEAR: 1949 **LATEST YEAR:** 2000 **NO OF RECORDS:** 6
RECENT SQUARES: monads 3; tetrads 3; hectads 3
ALL SQUARES: monads 6; tetrads 5; hectads 5

This hybrid ragwort is a very rare, native annual or perennial of waste ground and waysides. There are only three recent records: Belper (SK3446), North Alfreton (SK4156) and Birdholme (SK3869). It had previously been found at Barlborough Common (SK4875) in the 1970s and Markland Grips (SK5075) in 1949. It is the spontaneous hybrid of Oxford Ragwort (*S. squalidus*) and Sticky Groundsel (*S. viscosus*).

Senecio vulgaris L.
Groundsel

Groundsel is a very common, native annual

COUNTY STATUS: Native
CONSERVATION STATUS: None
FIRST YEAR: 1789 **LATEST YEAR:** 2013 **NO OF RECORDS:** 3,210
RECENT SQUARES: monads 1,504; tetrads 657; hectads 43
ALL SQUARES: monads 1,602; tetrads 663; hectads 43

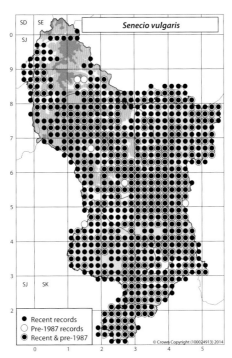

of cultivated land and open disturbed ground, found throughout Derbyshire except for the high moors of the Dark Peak. The non-rayed variety *vulgaris* is the common form, but the rayed var. *hibernicus* Syme is also found, albeit rarely across the county.

Senecio sylvaticus L.
Heath Groundsel

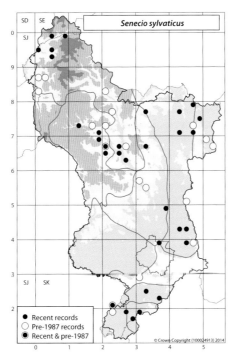

COUNTY STATUS: Native
CONSERVATION STATUS: None
FIRST YEAR: 1829 **LATEST YEAR:** 2012 **NO OF RECORDS:** 91
RECENT SQUARES: monads 33; tetrads 31; hectads 15
ALL SQUARES: monads 47; tetrads 48; hectads 29

Heath Groundsel is a rare native annual of open disturbed ground, generally on light-textured non-basic soils. It is scattered throughout the county, from the Longdendale Trail (SK0598) and Foxstone Wood (SK4277) in the north, through Over Haddon (SK2066), to Drakelow Power Station (SK2220) and near Swainspark (SK2916) in the south. Previously it was more frequent in southern and eastern parts, as at SK14, SK23 and SK46, all for 1969.

Senecio viscosus L.
Sticky Groundsel

COUNTY STATUS: Established (Neophyte)
CONSERVATION STATUS: None
FIRST YEAR: 1829 **LATEST YEAR:** 2013 **NO OF RECORDS:** 399
RECENT SQUARES: monads 190; tetrads 169; hectads 35
ALL SQUARES: monads 239; tetrads 208; hectads 38

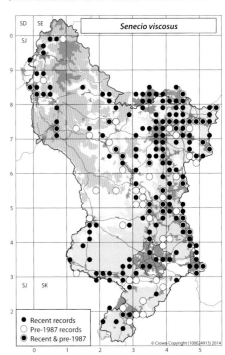

Sticky Groundsel is an established annual of waste ground and waysides, particularly railway lines. It is occasional throughout the county. It occurs on the continent, and possibly in southern Britain, as a native.

Doronicum pardalianches L.
Leopard's-bane

COUNTY STATUS: Established (Neophyte)
CONSERVATION STATUS: None
FIRST YEAR: 1829 **LATEST YEAR:** 2013 **NO OF RECORDS:** 115
RECENT SQUARES: monads 41; tetrads 36; hectads 17
ALL SQUARES: monads 57; tetrads 47; hectads 22

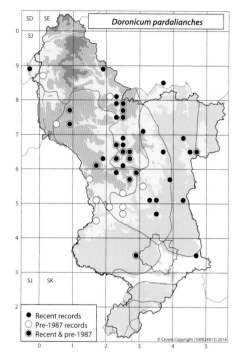

Leopard's-bane is a rare established perennial of open woods, waysides and walls. It occurs sporadically throughout Derbyshire, as at Peak Dale (SK0876), Rowthorne Trail (SK4764), Via Gellia (SK2657) and Radbourne Park (SK2835). Indigenous to western Europe, it is now grown widely in gardens for ornament, and was once cultivated for medicinal use.

Doronicum × excelsum (N.E. Br.) Stace
Harpur-Crewe's Leopard's-bane
Harpur-Crewe's Leopard's-bane is a very rare, casual perennial. The sole record is from a hedge at Moorwood Moor (SK3655) in 1998. It is of garden origin

from the crossing of Leopard's-bane (*D. pardalianches*), Plantain-leaved Leopard's-bane (*D. plantagineum* L.) and Eastern Leopard's-bane (*D. columnae* Ten.).

Tussilago farfara L.
Colt's-foot

COUNTY STATUS: Native
CONSERVATION STATUS: None
FIRST YEAR: 1789 LATEST YEAR: 2013 NO OF RECORDS: 3,931
RECENT SQUARES: monads 1,495; tetrads 682; hectads 43
ALL SQUARES: monads 1,620; tetrads 696; hectads 43

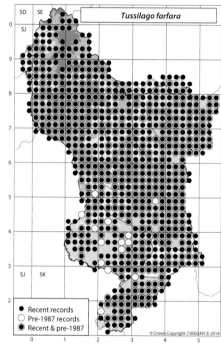

Colt's-foot is a very common, native perennial of cultivated land, waysides and disturbed ground, especially on clay soils.

It occurs throughout the county, though is less common in upland areas and some intensively farmed regions. It has the local names of Foal's Foot or Foal-foot (Grigson 1975).

Petasites hybridus (L.) P. Gaertn., Mey. & Scherb.
Butterbur

COUNTY STATUS: Native
CONSERVATION STATUS: None
FIRST YEAR: 1789 LATEST YEAR: 2013 NO OF RECORDS: 1,212
RECENT SQUARES: monads 452; tetrads 290; hectads 37
ALL SQUARES: monads 479; tetrads 306; hectads 39

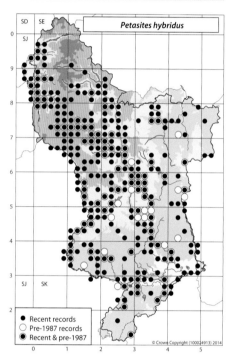

Butterbur is an occasional native perennial of damp shaded habitats on fertile soils, such as streamsides, marshes and waysides. While locally abundant throughout Derbyshire, it is most frequent in the Peak District, particularly at the bottom of wet limestone dales (Chee Dale area SK1072/1172). Separate male and female plants occur, and both form extensive stands due to underground stems. Whilst male plants are more frequent in the UK, our county has many locations where females are commoner, as near Froggatt and Ashbourne.

Petasites japonicus (Siebold & Zucc.) Maxim.
Giant Butterbur

Giant Butterbur is an established perennial of damp shaded habitats. The only recent record is from Egginton (SK2628) in 2001; there are older records from the same site and from Idridgehay (SK2949) in the 1970s, plus Hazelwood (SK3145) in 1980. A native of Japan and Sakhalin, it is grown in gardens but also planted in semi-wild situations for landscaping.

Butterbur (*Petasites hybridus*) beside the River Wye in Chee Dale (SK1273), April 2008 (Peter Smith)

Petasites albus (L.) Gaertn.
White Butterbur

COUNTY STATUS: Established (Neophyte)
CONSERVATION STATUS: None
FIRST YEAR: 1971 LATEST YEAR: 2009 NO OF RECORDS: 13
RECENT SQUARES: monads 5; tetrads 5; hectads 4
ALL SQUARES: monads 6; tetrads 6; hectads 4

White Butterbur is an established perennial of rough ground, waysides and woods. There are five recent records: Fairfield Golf Course (SK0674), Taxal (SK0080 v.c.58), Goytside (SK0084), Repton (SK3026) and Whatstandwell (SK3354). There is also a 1971 record from near Taxal (SK0079). It is indigenous to European mountains.

Petasites fragrans (Vill.) C. Presl
Winter Heliotrope

COUNTY STATUS: Established (Neophyte)
CONSERVATION STATUS: None
FIRST YEAR: 1903 LATEST YEAR: 2013 NO OF RECORDS: 65
RECENT SQUARES: monads 25; tetrads 26; hectads 17
ALL SQUARES: monads 34; tetrads 33; hectads 20

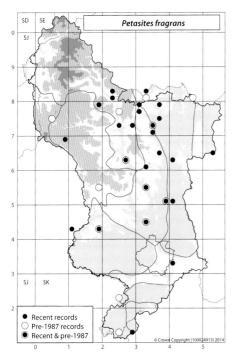

Petasites fragrans

Winter Heliotrope is a rare established perennial of rough ground, waste places and waysides, often on damp soils. Except for the high moors of the Dark Peak, it is scattered throughout the county (Holmesfield SK37E, Whatstandwell SK3354, Butterley SK3951, Sicklebrook Lane SK3779 & Netherseal SK2812). A garden ornamental, it originates from the central Mediterranean.

Calendula officinalis L.
Pot Marigold

Pot Marigold is a rare casual annual of waste ground and waysides, generally near habitations. It is scattered throughout the

COUNTY STATUS: Casual
CONSERVATION STATUS: None
FIRST YEAR: 1987 LATEST YEAR: 2012 NO OF RECORDS: 27
RECENT SQUARES: monads 18; tetrads 21; hectads 14
ALL SQUARES: monads 18; tetrads 21; hectads 14

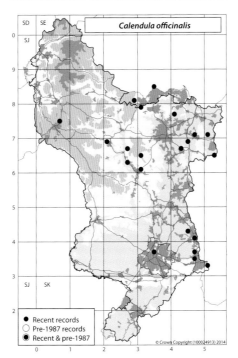

Calendula officinalis

Recent records
Pre-1987 records
Recent & pre-1987

county from Fairfield Church (SK0674) and Blacka Plantation (SK2881) in the north, through Matlock (SK36A), to Ashbourne Road, Derby (SK3437) and Ilkeston (SK44Q) in the south. Widely grown in gardens either as an ornamental, a pot herb or a medicinal plant, it is of unknown, possibly cultivated, origin.

Ambrosia artemisiifolia L.
Ragweed

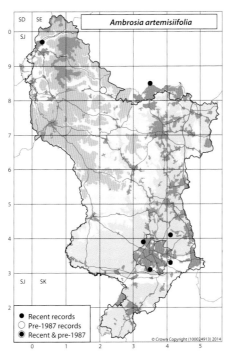

Ambrosia artemisiifolia

Recent records
Pre-1987 records
Recent & pre-1987

COUNTY STATUS: Casual
CONSERVATION STATUS: None
FIRST YEAR: 1974 LATEST YEAR: 2012 NO OF RECORDS: 9
RECENT SQUARES: monads 6; tetrads 6; hectads 5
ALL SQUARES: monads 7; tetrads 7; hectads 6

Ragweed is a very rare, casual annual of tips and waysides. There are scattered records from Hadfield (SK0296) and Heeley (SK3484) in the north to Sinfin Moor (SK3431) and Elvaston (SK4132) in the south. A single record from Bamford (SK2083) in 1974 emphasises the fact that this plant appears to be spreading locally, just as it is nationally (Groom 2006) and across Europe. Probably introduced via bird-seed, it is a native of North America, and is expected to be subject to new EU legislation in 2016 to control invasive alien species.

Ambrosia trifida L.
Giant Ragweed

Giant Ragweed is a very rare, casual annual of roadsides, known only from Bamford (SK2082) in 1974. Probably a bird-seed alien, it originates from North America.

Rudbeckia hirta L.
Black-eyed-Susan

Black-eyed-Susan is a very rare, casual perennial of rough ground. There are only two recent records: West Park (SK4833) in 2009 and Staveley (SK4374) in 2012. There is also one from the aerodrome above Bradley Wood (SK2046) in 1948. A garden ornamental, it originates from North America.

Helianthus annuus L.
Sunflower

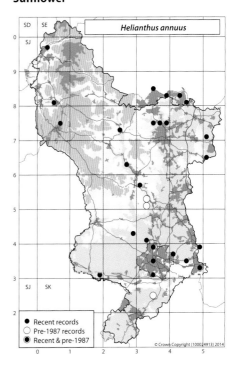

Helianthus annuus

Recent records
Pre-1987 records
Recent & pre-1987

Sunflower is a very rare, casual annual of rough ground, waste land and tips. It has been recorded scattered throughout the county from Hadfield (SK0296) and Heeley (SK3484) in the north, through Stancliffe Quarry (SK26R) to Derby city centre (SK3435) and Draycott (SK4434) in the south. It is widely grown as a garden ornamental but is also often a relic of bird feeding. It is native to North America.

Helianthus tuberosus L.
Jerusalem Artichoke
Jerusalem Artichoke is a casual perennial. The only record is from Hadfield Tip (SK0296) in 1989. Occasionally grown as a root-crop in gardens, it originates from North America.

Guizotia abyssinica (L. f.) Cass.
Niger
Niger is a very rare, casual annual of rubbish tips. There are four recent records between 1989 and 2003: Hadfield (SK0296), Ticknall (SK3424), Barlow (SK3475) and Heeley (SK3484). The only previous record is from Hady Tip (SK3971) in 1975. A bird-seed alien, it is indigenous to East Africa.

Galinsoga parviflora Cav.
Gallant-soldier
Gallant-soldier is a very rare, casual annual of cultivated ground and waste land. It is recorded from Whitwell village (SK5276) and

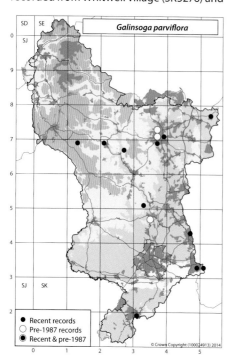

Flagg (SK1369) southward to Woodville (SK3119) and Long Eaton (SK4933). It is sometimes grown as a garden ornamental. Clapham (1969) suggested the plant was spreading in the county but it does not seem to have done so.

Galinsoga quadriradiata Ruiz & Pav.
Shaggy-soldier

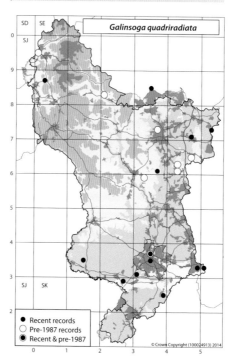

Shaggy-soldier is a very rare, casual annual of waysides, waste places and cultivated ground. It is found sporadically through Derbyshire from Hayfield (SK0387) and Heeley (SK3484) in the north, through St Werburgh's Churchyard, Derby (SK3436), to Melbourne (SK3925) and Long Eaton (SK4933) in the south. Probably introduced via soil from nursery plants, it is indigenous to South America.

Bidens cernua L.
Nodding Bur-marigold

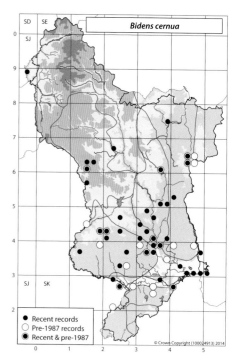

Nodding Bur-marigold is a native annual of marshy areas, wet ditches and the sides of lakes, pits, rivers and canals. Very rare in the Peak District, it is occasional in the central and southern parts of Derbyshire (Heathcote Mere SK1460, Miller's Pond SK4564, Allestree Park SK3440, Marston on Dove SK2328 & Weston-on-Trent SK4127). Nationally it is a lowland plant that reaches its British altitudinal record of 310m locally at Heathcote (Preston *et al.* 2002).

Bidens tripartita L.
Trifid Bur-marigold
Trifid Bur-marigold is a native annual of marshy areas by the sides of lakes, ponds,

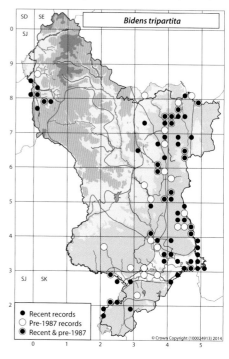

COUNTY STATUS: Native
CONSERVATION STATUS: None
FIRST YEAR: 1789 LATEST YEAR: 2013 NO OF RECORDS: 196
RECENT SQUARES: monads 75; tetrads 64; hectads 18
ALL SQUARES: monads 101; tetrads 85; hectads 22

pits, rivers and canals. It is occasional throughout southern and eastern parts of the county, from Nether Moor (SK4481) in the north, through Ogston Reservoir (SK3760), to Swadlincote (SK2819) and Walton-on-Trent (SK2119) in the south. It is generally absent from the northern and western parts of the county except for a cluster of records around Toddbrook (SK0080 v.c.58) and Combs Reservoirs (SK0379).

Bidens frondosa L.
Beggarticks

COUNTY STATUS: Casual
CONSERVATION STATUS: None
FIRST YEAR: 1998 LATEST YEAR: 2012 NO OF RECORDS: 11
RECENT SQUARES: monads 10; tetrads 9; hectads 5
ALL SQUARES: monads 10; tetrads 9; hectads 5

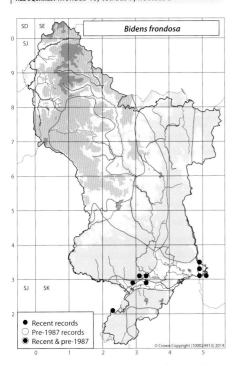

Beggarticks is a very rare, casual annual of the sides of slow-moving waterbodies, particularly canals. It was first recorded in 1998 at Trent Lock (SK5031), and has since been found on the Erewash Canal (SK4832), the Trent and Mersey Canal (SK2828) and at Drakelow (SK2220). Possibly a wool alien, it is native to the Americas.

Bidens ferulifolia (Jacq.) Sweet
Fern-leaved Beggarticks
Fern-leaved Beggarticks is a very rare, casual annual of waste ground and disturbed land, known from just two sites recently: a pavement at New Mills (SK0085)

in 1997 and allotments at Holbrook (SK3645) in 2006. This increase is part of a more general national spread (Groom 2006). Commonly grown in gardens and hanging baskets, it is a native of Mexico.

Coreopsis grandiflora Hogg ex Sweet
Large-flowered Tickseed
Large-flowered Tickseed is a very rare, established perennial of waste ground. Our only site is at Sandiacre (SK4836), discovered by R. Martin in 2007. A garden escape or throwout, it grows naturally in North America.

Cosmos bipinnatus Cav.
Mexican Aster
Mexican Aster is a very rare, casual annual of waste ground. Our only site is Killamarsh (SK4481), found in 2010 by K. Balkow. Much grown in gardens, it is a native of southern North America.

Eupatorium cannabinum L.
Hemp-agrimony

COUNTY STATUS: Native
CONSERVATION STATUS: None
FIRST YEAR: 1789 LATEST YEAR: 2013 NO OF RECORDS: 681
RECENT SQUARES: monads 222; tetrads 142; hectads 33
ALL SQUARES: monads 241; tetrads 153; hectads 34

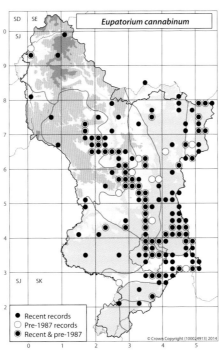

Hemp-agrimony is an occasional native perennial of damp grasslands, ditches, wet woods, waysides and the edges of waterbodies. It occurs mainly along river and canal corridors in central and southern parts (Derby SK3536, Whatstandwell SK3354, Derby Canal SK3729 & Lock Lane Ash Tip SK4831). There are scattered records elsewhere (Charlesworth Village SK0092, Bondhay SK5078 & near Stanton SK2720).

ESCALLONIACEAE
Escallonia macrantha Hook. & Arn.
Escallonia
Escallonia is a very rare, casual evergreen shrub of hedges. It has only been recorded twice between 1998 and 2006: Unstone (SK3777) and Sloade Lane (SK3980). It occurs in south-western Britain as a relic of planting in gardens and hedges, and is a native of Chile.

ADOXACEAE
Adoxa moschatellina L.
Moschatel

COUNTY STATUS: Native
CONSERVATION STATUS: None
FIRST YEAR: 1789 LATEST YEAR: 2013 NO OF RECORDS: 640
RECENT SQUARES: monads 275; tetrads 183; hectads 31
ALL SQUARES: monads 316; tetrads 211; hectads 36

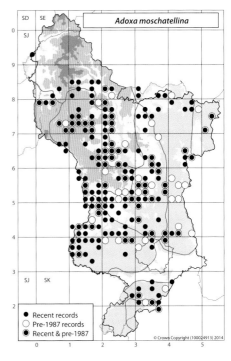

Moschatel (*Adoxa moschatellina*) in spring woodland near Bretby (SK3023), April 2008 (Peter Smith)

Moschatel is an occasional native perennial of woods, hedges and shaded limestone outcrops, generally on damp humus-rich soil. It occurs throughout the county (Combs Reservoir SK0479, Gratton Dale SK2060, Pistern Hill SK3421, Darley Park SK3537, Stanley Grange Farm SK4240 & Creswell Crags SK5374). It flowers early in spring, and even then is inconspicuous, so is probably under-recorded.

CAPRIFOLIACEAE

Sambucus racemosa L.
Red-berried Elder

Red-berried Elder is an established shrub of grassland, waste ground and waysides. Recent records, covering 1989 to 2011, come from only four tetrads: Deep Dale (SK0971), Hallmoor Wood (SK2863), Darley Hillside (SK2763) and the site of Siberia Nursery (SK3065). Older records, dating from 1960, cover a wider area from Edale (SK1286) in the north, to Alsop en le Dale (SK1555) in the south, both for the 1980s. It is a native of continental Europe.

Sambucus nigra L.
Elder

COUNTY STATUS: Native	
CONSERVATION STATUS: None	
FIRST YEAR: 1789 **LATEST YEAR:** 2013 **NO OF RECORDS:** 6,590	
RECENT SQUARES: monads 2,179; tetrads 692; hectads 42	
ALL SQUARES: monads 2,212; tetrads 696; hectads 42	

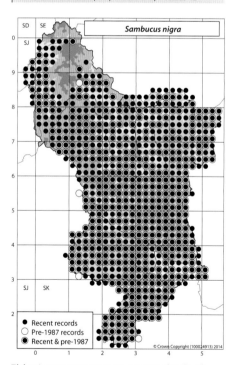

Elder is a very common, native shrub of hedges, wasteland, scrub and woods, particularly in areas with disturbed nutrient-rich soil. It occurs throughout

the county, only avoiding the high moors of the Peak District. It is a variable plant. Variety *laciniata* has been recorded previously for Grindsbrook Booth (SK1286), Jagger's Clough (SK1587) and Knockerdown (SK2351), while yellow or green-fruited forms have been noted for Old Brampton (SK37), Roston Common (SK14) and Sinfin (SK33). All were for the 1960/1970s. A large specimen, with a girth of 3.82m, was recorded recently at Markeaton Park (SK3333). It has local names of Eller and Devil's Wood (Grigson 1975), while the drawing of green branches over young turnips was reputed to prevent damage by Turnip Beetle (Pilkington 1789).

Sambucus canadensis L.
American Elder

American Elder is a very rare, casual shrub of waste ground and waysides, often on railway lines. The only recent record is from Chee Dale (SK1373) in 1992, while there are others from Ashwood Dale (SK0872) in 1970, Alsop Station (SK1554) in 1969, and Ashbourne (SK1746) in 1975. It is indigenous to eastern North America.

Sambucus ebulus L.
Dwarf Elder

COUNTY STATUS: Established (Archaeophyte)	
CONSERVATION STATUS: B	
FIRST YEAR: 1789 **LATEST YEAR:** 2007 **NO OF RECORDS:** 47	
RECENT SQUARES: monads 10; tetrads 8; hectads 7	
ALL SQUARES: monads 15; tetrads 13; hectads 15	

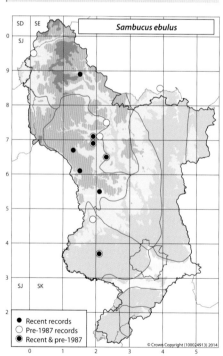

Dwarf Elder is an anciently established perennial of waysides and waste ground. It occurs very rarely from the Upper

Derwent area (SK1489) in the north, through Ashford in the Water (SK1969), to West Mammerton (SK2136) and SK45 in the south. It was previously widely cultivated as a medicinal herb.

Viburnum opulus L.
Guelder-rose

COUNTY STATUS: Native	
CONSERVATION STATUS: None	
FIRST YEAR: 1789 **LATEST YEAR:** 2013 **NO OF RECORDS:** 1,272	
RECENT SQUARES: monads 506; tetrads 359; hectads 38	
ALL SQUARES: monads 578; tetrads 391; hectads 38	

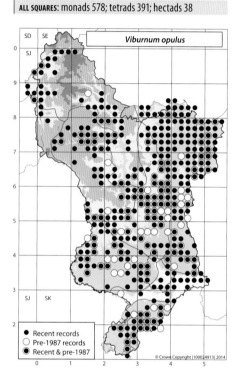

Guelder-rose is a frequent native shrub of woods, scrub and hedges, particularly on damp neutral to calcareous soils. It is increasingly being planted in restoration and amenity schemes, and occurs throughout the county except for the more upland parts of the Peak District.

Viburnum lantana L.
Wayfaring-tree

COUNTY STATUS: Casual	
CONSERVATION STATUS: None	
FIRST YEAR: 1789 **LATEST YEAR:** 2012 **NO OF RECORDS:** 57	
RECENT SQUARES: monads 20; tetrads 23; hectads 15	
ALL SQUARES: monads 26; tetrads 28; hectads 19	

Wayfaring-tree is a rare casual shrub of waysides and amenity areas, now often included in restoration and enhancement schemes. It is sometimes considered native (Clapham 1969) but there are no sites where it is above suspicion of having been planted or spread from planted specimens. It occurs scattered through the county from Hope Valley (SK1782)

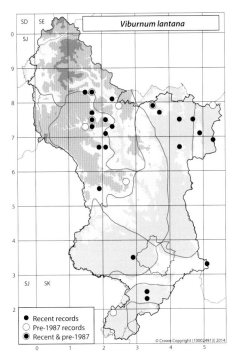

and Dronfield (SK37P) in the north, to Foremark Reservoir (SK3324 & 3323) in the south. It is native to England south of Derbyshire.

Symphoricarpos albus (L.) S.F. Blake
Snowberry

COUNTY STATUS: Established (Neophyte)	
CONSERVATION STATUS: None	
FIRST YEAR: 1940 LATEST YEAR: 2013 NO OF RECORDS: 1,113	
RECENT SQUARES: monads 571; tetrads 406; hectads 38	
ALL SQUARES: monads 622; tetrads 426; hectads 38	

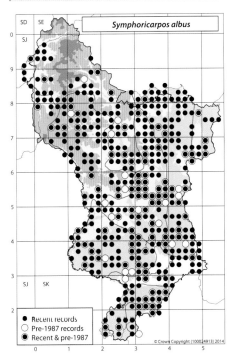

Snowberry is an established shrub of woods, scrub, hedges and waste ground. It occurs frequently throughout the

county except for the high moors of the Peak District. It is grown in gardens for its white berries, and was also widely planted for game-cover in woods. It originates from western North America.

Symphoricarpos × *chenaultii* Rehder
Chenault's Coralberry

Chenault's Coralberry is an established shrub of waste ground and waysides, and is increasingly being planted in enhancement schemes. There are only nine records, all from between 1998 and 2012. Example sites are: Eccles House Farm (SK1782), Bottom Moor (SK3263), Trent Lane (SK4932), Staveley Works (SK4174) and Holbrook Heath (SK4481) It is of garden origin from the crossing of Coralberry (*S. orbiculatus* Moench) with another North American member of the genus (*S. microphyllus* Kunth).

Leycesteria formosa Wall.
Himalayan Honeysuckle

Himalayan Honeysuckle is a casual semi-herbaceous shrub of waste ground and waysides. It is recorded from only nine sites, between 2001 and 2012, for example: Toddbrook Reservoir (SK0080), Long Eaton (SK5032), Pleasley (SK5064) and Clowne (SK5075). It is grown in gardens for ornament, and in woods for pheasant cover. It is native to the Himalayas.

Weigela florida (Bunge) A. DC.
Weigelia

Weigelia is a casual shrub of waste ground and waysides. It is recorded from only four sites between 1996 and 2012: Roman Lakes (SJ9687), Fairfield Church (SK0674), Sturgess Field (SK3337) and Long Eaton (SK4833). Much grown in gardens as an ornamental, it is indigenous to China.

Lonicera pileata Oliv.
Box-leaved Honeysuckle

Box-leaved Honeysuckle is a casual evergreen shrub, which is increasingly being planted on roadsides and in shrubberies for ground cover. The sole two records are for Millhouses (SK3382) in 2001 and Pleasley (SK5064) in 2008. It is a native of China.

Lonicera nitida E.H. Wilson
Wilson's Honeysuckle

Wilson's Honeysuckle is a casual evergreen shrub of waysides, hedges and waste ground, originating from China. It is very rarely scattered throughout the county from Marple

COUNTY STATUS: Casual	
CONSERVATION STATUS: None	
FIRST YEAR: 1999 LATEST YEAR: 2012 NO OF RECORDS: 12	
RECENT SQUARES: monads 11; tetrads 12; hectads 10	
ALL SQUARES: monads 11; tetrads 12; hectads 10	

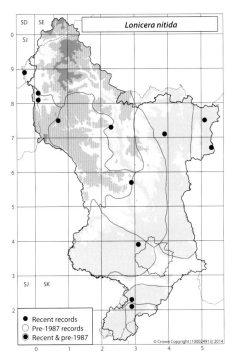

Bridge (SJ9689) and Clowne (SK5075) in the north, to Newhall (SK2920) and Bretby Woods (SK22W) in the south. Frequently planted in gardens for hedging, its seeds can be spread by birds (Preston *et al.* 2002).

Lonicera involucrata (Richardson) Banks ex Spreng.
Californian Honeysuckle

Californian Honeysuckle is a very rare, established shrub of roadsides and waste ground. It is known from only two recent localities: Derby (SK3834) in 1995 and by the A6, Wye Dale (SK0872) in 2003, where it was also noted in 1985 and 1966. It is a garden ornamental originating from western North America.

Lonicera xylosteum L.
Fly Honeysuckle

COUNTY STATUS: Casual	
CONSERVATION STATUS: None	
FIRST YEAR: 1884 LATEST YEAR: 2011 NO OF RECORDS: 44	
RECENT SQUARES: monads 14; tetrads 13; hectads 7	
ALL SQUARES: monads 18; tetrads 17; hectads 9	

Fly Honeysuckle is a very rare, casual shrub of woods, hedges and waysides. It is known scattered throughout the county from Wormhill (SK1273) and Hassop (SK2271) in the north, through Butterley (SK3951), to Sharp's Bottom (SK3320) and Ticknall (SK3523) in the

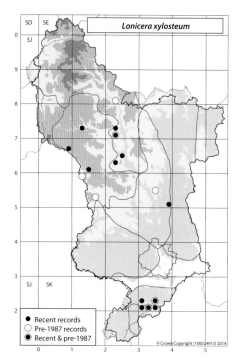

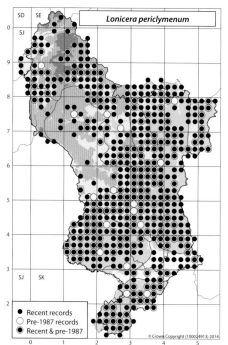

COUNTY STATUS: Native

CONSERVATION STATUS: None

FIRST YEAR: 1789 LATEST YEAR: 2012 NO OF RECORDS: 149

RECENT SQUARES: monads 54; tetrads 47; hectads 17

ALL SQUARES: monads 67; tetrads 54; hectads 22

walls and rocky outcrops. It is occasional in the White Peak: Chee Dale (SK1373), Lathkill Dale (SK16S) and Middleton Cross (SK2855). Elsewhere it is very rare: Bretby Village (SK2923), Stanley Methodist Church (SK4140) and Nether Handley (SK4076). At 365m, Wormhill (SK17) holds the UK altitude record for this species.

Valerianella carinata Loisel.
Keeled-fruited Cornsalad

COUNTY STATUS: Established (Archaeophyte)

CONSERVATION STATUS: None

FIRST YEAR: 1858 LATEST YEAR: 2013 NO OF RECORDS: 55

RECENT SQUARES: monads 25; tetrads 23; hectads 12

ALL SQUARES: monads 34; tetrads 31; hectads 14

south. It is possibly native to southern England.

Lonicera tatarica L.
Tartarian Honeysuckle

Tartarian Honeysuckle is a very rare, casual shrub. The only record is from Hartington Station Quarry (SK1561) in 1996. Grown in gardens, it originates from western and central Asia.

Lonicera japonica Thunb.
Japanese Honeysuckle

Japanese Honeysuckle is a casual semi-evergreen climber of woodland and waste ground. There are only three recent records: Wingerworth (SK3666) in 1988, Fox Covert (SK4834) in 2013 and Erewash Canal (SK4835) in 2006. Previously it was recorded from Derby (SK3637) in 1976 and from an unlocalised site in SK28 around 1950. It is a garden plant that originates from eastern Asia.

Lonicera periclymenum L.
Honeysuckle

COUNTY STATUS: Native

CONSERVATION STATUS: None

FIRST YEAR: 1789 LATEST YEAR: 2013 NO OF RECORDS: 2,009

RECENT SQUARES: monads 908; tetrads 493; hectads 42

ALL SQUARES: monads 963; tetrads 508; hectads 42

Honeysuckle is a native woody climber of hedges, scrub, woods and rocky outcrops. It is common throughout the lowlands of Derbyshire, but is only occasional in the more upland Peak District. Some records may refer to garden escapees.

Lonicera caprifolium L.
Perfoliate Honeysuckle

Perfoliate Honeysuckle is an established woody climber of waste ground. Our only two records are from the Monsal Trail (SK2169) in 1993 and Monsal Dale (SK1772) in 2008. Grown as a garden ornamental, it is a native of southern Europe.

VALERIANACEAE

Valerianella locusta (L.) Laterr.
Common Cornsalad

Common Cornsalad is a native winter annual of open ground, generally on thin dry soils, including cultivated land,

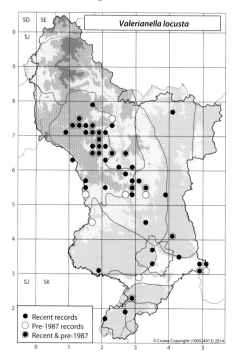

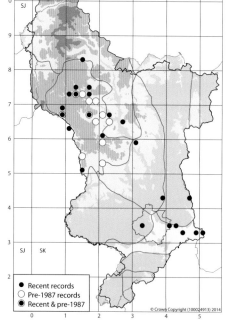

Keeled-fruited Cornsalad is an anciently established annual. It is recorded rarely for rock outcrops in the White Peak: Wormhill (SK1273), Castleton (SK1482), Glutton Dale (SK0867) and Thorpe Cloud (SK1451). Elsewhere it has also been noted very rarely for waysides and waste ground: Darley Dale (SK2664), Crich Avenue (SK3334), Cloves Wood (SK3942) and Cotmanhay (SK4743).

Valerianella rimosa Bastard
Broad-fruited Cornsalad

Locally extinct, Broad-fruited Cornsalad was an anciently established annual of arable fields. The latest record is for Dove Dale (SK15) in 1903. Earlier it was recorded

COUNTY STATUS: Established (Archaeophyte)
CONSERVATION STATUS: DRDB (Cat6), EN, NS, NERC
FIRST YEAR: 1864 LATEST YEAR: 1903 NO OF RECORDS: 6
RECENT SQUARES: monads 0; tetrads 0; hectads 0
ALL SQUARES: monads 1; tetrads 1; hectads 5

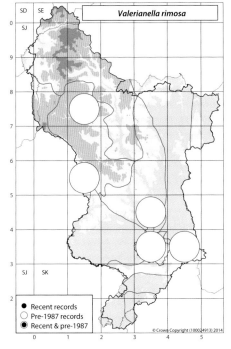

Valerianella rimosa

● Recent records
○ Pre-1987 records
◉ Recent & pre-1987

© Crown Copyright (100024913) 2014

for Monsal Dale (SK17), Breadsall (SK33 & 34) and Locko Park (SK43) in the second half of the 19th century. This mirrors a national decline due to agricultural intensification (Preston *et al.* 2002).

Valerianella dentata (L.) Pollich
Narrow-fruited Cornsalad
Narrow-fruited Cornsalad is an anciently established annual of arable fields. The

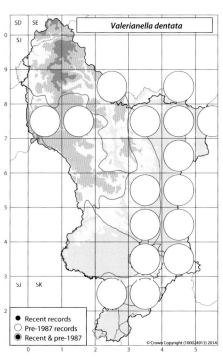

Valerianella dentata

● Recent records
○ Pre-1987 records
◉ Recent & pre-1987

© Crown Copyright (100024913) 2014

COUNTY STATUS: Established (Archaeophyte)
CONSERVATION STATUS: DRDB (Cat2), EN, C
FIRST YEAR: 1829 LATEST YEAR: 1977 NO OF RECORDS: 29
RECENT SQUARES: monads 0; tetrads 0; hectads 0
ALL SQUARES: monads 6; tetrads 6; hectads 16

latest known record is from Upper Pleasley (SK4963) in 1977. There were others from Deep Dale (SK0971), Stanley (SK4143), Oxcroft Colliery (SK4673) and fields near Whitwell Wood (SK5178 & 5278) in the 1960s and 1970s. Before that it was scattered throughout the county: Newhall (SK22), Calke (SK32) and Repton (SK32), all for 1903. This decline reflects a national decrease through intensification of arable farming (Preston *et al.* 2002).

Valerianella eriocarpa Desv.
Hairy-fruited Cornsalad
Locally extinct, Hairy-fruited Cornsalad was a casual winter annual of arable fields and waste ground. The only two records are from between Miller's Dale and Litton Mill (SK1673) in 1969, and Dove Dale (SK15) in 1837. It is a native of southern Europe.

Valeriana officinalis L.
Common Valerian

COUNTY STATUS: Native
CONSERVATION STATUS: ERL
FIRST YEAR: 1724 LATEST YEAR: 2013 NO OF RECORDS: 1,405
RECENT SQUARES: monads 467; tetrads 304; hectads 37
ALL SQUARES: monads 530; tetrads 345; hectads 38

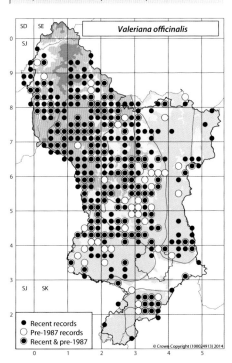

Valeriana officinalis

● Recent records
○ Pre-1987 records
◉ Recent & pre-1987

© Crown Copyright (100024913) 2014

Common Valerian is an occasional native perennial of dry or damp grassy places, marshes, fens, water margins and wet woods throughout the county. Some authorities recognise two subspecies, one

of dry calcareous grassland and the other of wetter habitats (Stace 2010). However, it is often not possible to separate the two forms clearly. It has been grown for medicinal purposes, including the cure of hysteria and nervous complaints. Farey (1815) notes it was cultivated at Milltown and Ashover; Mabey (1996) describes its planting near Clay Cross in the 1860s; and Grigson (1975) mentions it was grown in several parishes.

Valeriana pyrenaica L.
Pyrenean Valerian
Pyrenean Valerian is an established perennial of waysides and woods. All recent records are from two monads in the north-west: Reservoir Road (SK0081 v.c.58) in 2001 and Furness Vale (SK0084 v.c.58) between 1994 and 2002. The one other record is from Clapham's 1969 Flora at Hopton Hall (SK2552) in mid-Derbyshire. Sometimes grown in gardens, it is a native of the Pyrenees.

Valeriana dioica L.
Marsh Valerian

COUNTY STATUS: Native
CONSERVATION STATUS: DRDB (Cat5b)
FIRST YEAR: 1789 LATEST YEAR: 2013 NO OF RECORDS: 180
RECENT SQUARES: monads 43; tetrads 37; hectads 18
ALL SQUARES: monads 82; tetrads 67; hectads 29

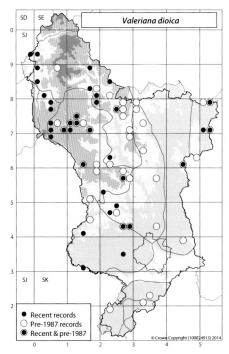

Valeriana dioica

● Recent records
○ Pre-1987 records
◉ Recent & pre-1987

© Crown Copyright (100024913) 2014

Marsh Valerian is a rare native perennial of wet grasslands, marshes, fens and flushes. It grows scattered throughout northern and central parts: Gamesley (SK0093), Ginny Springs (SK5278), Hartington (SK1461), Hopton Quarry (SK2656), Anacrehill Farm (SK1541) and Mugginton

Bottoms (SK2743). It was previously more frequent, and also occurred in the south: Drakelow Reserve (SK2219) in 1973 and Ticknall (SK3523) in 1969. This matches a national decline due to habitat degradation and loss (Preston *et al.* 2002).

Centranthus ruber (L.) DC.
Red Valerian

COUNTY STATUS: Established (Neophyte)	
CONSERVATION STATUS: None	
FIRST YEAR: 1889 **LATEST YEAR:** 2013 **NO OF RECORDS:** 277	
RECENT SQUARES: monads 161; tetrads 157; hectads 29	
ALL SQUARES: monads 175; tetrads 166; hectads 31	

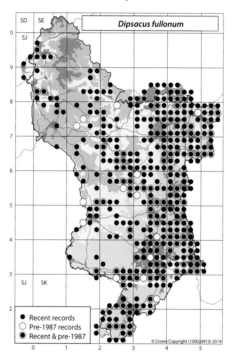

Red Valerian is an established perennial of walls, rock outcrops, waste ground and waysides. It occurs occasionally throughout the county, though is more frequently recorded in the eastern half. Records range from Brierley Green (SK0282), Longway Bank (SK3254), Heage Village (SK3750), Chellaston (SK3830) and Shirebrook (SK56I). It is a popular garden ornamental originating from the Mediterranean.

DIPSACACEAE

Dipsacus fullonum L.
Wild Teasel

Wild Teasel is a robust native biennial of waysides, waste ground, stream banks and wood-margins, particularly on heavy disturbed soils. It is frequent in the eastern

Red Valerian (*Centranthus ruber*) on reclaimed colliery site at Pleasley Pit Country Park (SK4964), June 2009 (Peter Smith)

COUNTY STATUS: Native	
CONSERVATION STATUS: None	
FIRST YEAR: 1889 **LATEST YEAR:** 2013 **NO OF RECORDS:** 1,075	
RECENT SQUARES: monads 523; tetrads 366; hectads 40	
ALL SQUARES: monads 565; tetrads 380; hectads 40	

half of the county becoming rarer in the western half, especially the Peak District.

Dipsacus pilosus L.
Small Teasel

COUNTY STATUS: Native	
CONSERVATION STATUS: DRDB (Cat5b), B	
FIRST YEAR: 1789 **LATEST YEAR:** 2012 **NO OF RECORDS:** 144	
RECENT SQUARES: monads 21; tetrads 17; hectads 12	
ALL SQUARES: monads 27; tetrads 22; hectads 15	

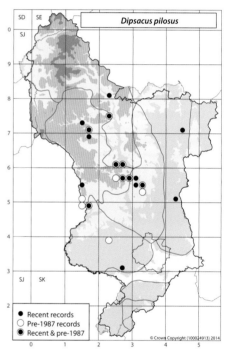

Small Teasel is a native biennial of waysides and woodlands where it is taken to be an indicator of ancient woods. It is rare in the White Peak: Coombs Dale (SK2274), Alsop Station (SK1554) and in the Via Gellia (SK2857). Elsewhere it is very rare: High Low (SK28F), Cromford Canal (SK3255) and Egginton (SK2630). It was previously more frequent in the south of the county: Bretby Mill (SK22) and Repton Shrubs (SK32), both in 1903.

Cephalaria gigantea (Ledeb.) Bobrov
Giant Scabious

Giant Scabious is a very rare, casual perennial of waysides and rough ground. It is been found recently at Quilow (SK1943) in 1997 and 2001, Butts Ashover (SK3463) in 1996, Highfield Road (SK3771) in 1992 and Pleasley Pit (SK5064) in 2010. There is one earlier record from Ilkeston (SK4542) in 1973. A popular garden ornamental, it originates from the Caucasus.

Knautia arvensis (L.) Coult.
Field Scabious

COUNTY STATUS: Native

CONSERVATION STATUS: ERL

FIRST YEAR: 1789 LATEST YEAR: 2013 NO OF RECORDS: 1,531

RECENT SQUARES: monads 583; tetrads 328; hectads 32

ALL SQUARES: monads 633; tetrads 348; hectads 34

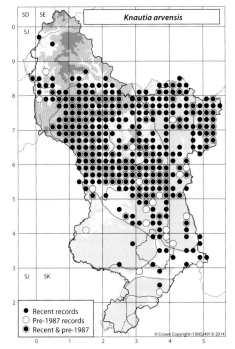

Field Scabious is an attractive native
perennial of unshaded limestone crags,
unimproved grasslands and waysides,
particularly on well-drained neutral to
calcareous soils. Nowadays included in
some wild flower mixes in restoration
schemes, it is frequent throughout central
parts, but rare elsewhere (West Hallam
SK4442 & Ticknall SK3624). It was formerly
more frequent, and even in the Peak
District has been lost from 94% of its hay
meadow sites between the mid-1980s
and mid-1990s (Buckingham *et al.* 1997).
At 365m, Derbyshire holds the UK altitude
record (Preston *et al.* 2002).

Succisa pratensis Moench
Devil's-bit Scabious

COUNTY STATUS: Native

CONSERVATION STATUS: ERL

FIRST YEAR: 1789 LATEST YEAR: 2013 NO OF RECORDS: 1,222

RECENT SQUARES: monads 415; tetrads 280; hectads 35

ALL SQUARES: monads 474; tetrads 315; hectads 37

Devil's-bit Scabious is an occasional native
perennial of unimproved grasslands,
moors, marshes, waysides and open
woods, especially on damp, mildly acid
soils. It occurs throughout the county from
Dinting (SK0194) and the Upper Derwent
area (SK1596) in the north, through Biggin
Dale (SK1458) and Wingfield Manor

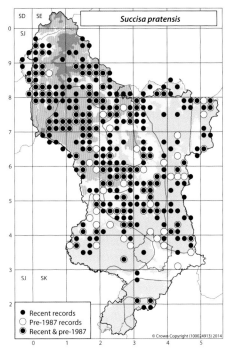

(SK3754), to Nether Hall (SK3121) and
Bryan's Coppice (SK3519) in the south.

Scabiosa columbaria L.
Small Scabious

COUNTY STATUS: Native

CONSERVATION STATUS: None

FIRST YEAR: 1789 LATEST YEAR: 2013 NO OF RECORDS: 804

RECENT SQUARES: monads 227; tetrads 122; hectads 21

ALL SQUARES: monads 238; tetrads 130; hectads 25

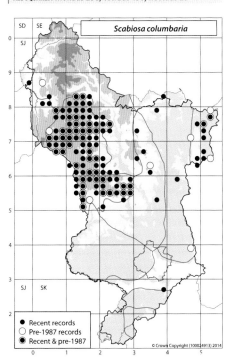

Small Scabious is an attractive native
perennial of dry unimproved grasslands
and unshaded rocky outcrops, generally
on calcareous substrates. It is common in
the White Peak: Hay Dale (SK1177), Lathkill

Dale (SK16S) and Gang Mine (SK2855). It is
occasional on the Magnesian Limestone:
Mason Street Field (SK5276) and Snake
Field (SK5064). Elsewhere it is very rare:
Tithe Farm meadows (SK3653) and along
the Trent and Mersey Canal (SK3827).

ARALIACEAE

Hedera colchica (K. Koch) K. Koch
Persian Ivy

COUNTY STATUS: Established (Neophyte)

CONSERVATION STATUS: None

FIRST YEAR: 1977 LATEST YEAR: 2012 NO OF RECORDS: 17

RECENT SQUARES: monads 13; tetrads 12; hectads 11

ALL SQUARES: monads 13; tetrads 12; hectads 11

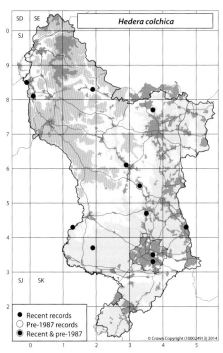

Persian Ivy is an established woody
evergreen of scrub, woods, walls, waysides
and waste places. It is a climber like the
native ivy (*H. helix*), albeit weaker, often just
sprawling over the ground. It is very rare
throughout the county: Mousley Bottom
(SJ9985), Lower Shatton (SK1982), Awdishaw
Lane (SK1836) and Derby City (SK33). It is
widely grown in gardens and shrubberies
for ground cover, and is probably under-
recorded. It is native to the Caucasus.

Hedera helix L.
Common Ivy

COUNTY STATUS: Native

CONSERVATION STATUS: None

FIRST YEAR: 1789 LATEST YEAR: 2013 NO OF RECORDS: 5,179

RECENT SQUARES: monads 1,801; tetrads 660; hectads 42

ALL SQUARES: monads 1,851; tetrads 664; hectads 42

Common Ivy is a native woody evergreen
that climbs up trees in woods and hedges,
and over rock outcrops and walls. It also

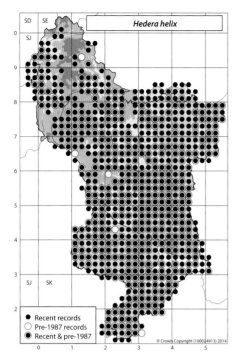

occurs on the ground, even in deep shade. As it tolerates all but the driest, wettest or most acidic situations, it is very common throughout Derbyshire, apart from the high moors of the South West and Dark Peak. It features in a number of place names such as Ivyhouse and Ivyspring Wood, and has the local name of Ivin (Grigson 1975). Until very recently Atlantic Ivy (*H. hibernica*) was considered to be a subspecies, so our map may well contain a very small number of incorrect records.

Common Ivy (*Hedera helix*) on hedgerow tree in Allestree (SK3240), March 2008 (Nick Moyes)

Hedera hibernica (G. Kirchn.) Bean
Atlantic Ivy

COUNTY STATUS:	Established (Neophyte)
CONSERVATION STATUS:	None
FIRST YEAR: 1983	LATEST YEAR: 2013 NO OF RECORDS: 89
RECENT SQUARES:	monads 77; tetrads 66; hectads 27
ALL SQUARES:	monads 78; tetrads 67; hectads 27

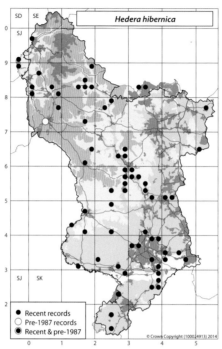

Atlantic Ivy is a woody evergreen climber of copses, plantations and rocks. It is less of a climber than Common Ivy, more often sprawling over the ground. A native of western Britain, it is considered established here through being planted for ornament and ground cover. It is occasional throughout the county: River Etherow (SK0196), Whitwell Village (SK5276), Willersley Castle (SK2957), Golden Valley (SK4251), Winshill (SK2623) and Melbourne (SK3824). Our plant is generally the cultivar *Hibernica*.

HYDROCOTYLACEAE

Hydrocotyle vulgaris L.
Marsh Pennywort

COUNTY STATUS:	Native
CONSERVATION STATUS:	ERL
FIRST YEAR: 1789	LATEST YEAR: 2013 NO OF RECORDS: 397
RECENT SQUARES:	monads 122; tetrads 87; hectads 18
ALL SQUARES:	monads 152; tetrads 104; hectads 25

Marsh Pennywort is a native perennial of marshes, fens and flushes. It is frequent in the Dark Peak: Upper Longdendale (SK1099), Nether Moor (SK1487) and Bucka Hill (SK2877). Elsewhere it is absent or rare, occurring only in isolated locations: Merrill Sick Meadow (SK4864), Morley Brickpits (SK3841) and Mercaston Marsh (SK2643). Previously it was more frequent outside the

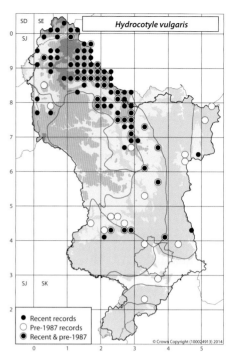

Dark Peak with records, for example, from Carver's Rocks (SK3222) and Swarkestone (SK3628) both for 1969. This local loss matches a general decline in south-eastern England since 1950 due to drainage and development (Preston *et al.* 2002).

Hydrocotyle ranunculoides L. f.
Floating Pennywort

Floating Pennywort is a newly established, invasive perennial of ponds and rivers. It is recorded from only two sites: Etherow Reserve (SJ9791) in 2002 and Sunnydale Park, Derby (SK3333) in 2005 and 2006, but has since been removed from the latter. Introduced from North America as an ornamental aquatic, it soon spread to more natural situations where it forms dense floating colonies on the edges of slow-moving streams and ponds (Preston *et al.* 2002).These exclude native species, so vigorous efforts are needed to eradicate it. In 2013 its sale in England was banned.

APIACEAE

Sanicula europaea L.
Sanicle

COUNTY STATUS:	Native
CONSERVATION STATUS:	ERL
FIRST YEAR: 1789	LATEST YEAR: 2013 NO OF RECORDS: 491
RECENT SQUARES:	monads 128; tetrads 100; hectads 28
ALL SQUARES:	monads 168; tetrads 125; hectads 35

Sanicle is an occasional native perennial of deciduous woods and damp shaded localities. It is frequent on the Magnesian Limestone: Bondhay Plantation (SK5078) and Pleasley Vale (SK5164). Elsewhere it is only occasional from Tom Wood (SJ9993)

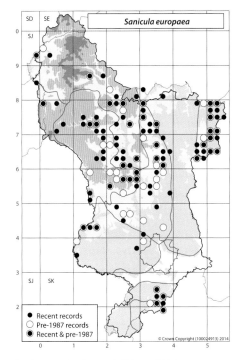

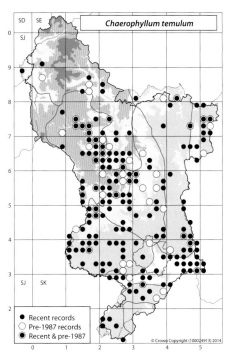

in the north, through Priestcliffe Lees (SK1572), to Seven Spouts Plantation (SK3525) and Wicket Nook (SK3619) in the south. Previously it appears to have been more frequent in lowland Derbyshire.

Astrantia major L.
Astrantia

COUNTY STATUS: Casual	
CONSERVATION STATUS: None	
FIRST YEAR: 1969 **LATEST YEAR:** 2003 **NO OF RECORDS:** 5	
RECENT SQUARES: monads 1; tetrads 1; hectads 2	
ALL SQUARES: monads 4; tetrads 4; hectads 4	

Astrantia is a casual perennial of waysides and old gardens, indigenous to central Europe. There are two recent records: Derby City (SK33) and The Kennels Meadow (SK3253). Previously it was recorded from Breadsall (SK3839), Beauchief (SK3381) and Yeld Wood (SK2672), all for 1969. Widely grown in gardens for ornament, it often escapes into more natural settings.

Eryngium planum L.
Blue Eryngo

Blue Eryngo is a spiny casual perennial. The only record is from waste ground on Sinfin Moor Lane (SK3431), found by N. Moyes in 1998. A garden ornamental, it grows naturally in central and south-eastern Europe.

Chaerophyllum temulum L.
Rough Chervil

COUNTY STATUS: Native	
CONSERVATION STATUS: None	
FIRST YEAR: 1829 **LATEST YEAR:** 2013 **NO OF RECORDS:** 420	
RECENT SQUARES: monads 222; tetrads 173; hectads 35	
ALL SQUARES: monads 258; tetrads 201; hectads 36	

Rough Chervil is an occasional native biennial of hedges, waysides and wood borders, generally on moist base-rich soils. It is found scattered throughout the county from Chunal (SK0391) and Bondhay (SK5178) in the north, through Snitterton (SK2760) and Carsington Water (SK2452), to Coton in the Elms (SK2414) and Lock Lane Ash Tip (SK4831) in the south. It is a lowland species that reaches its British altitudinal limit of 365m in Derbyshire.

Anthriscus sylvestris (L.) Hoffm.
Cow Parsley

Cow Parsley is a very common, native perennial of waysides, wood margins

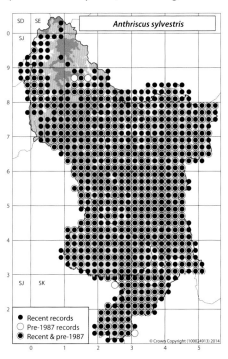

COUNTY STATUS: Native	
CONSERVATION STATUS: None	
FIRST YEAR: 1789 **LATEST YEAR:** 2013 **NO OF RECORDS:** 5,693	
RECENT SQUARES: monads 2,061; tetrads 698; hectads 44	
ALL SQUARES: monads 2,134; tetrads 702; hectads 44	

and unimproved grasslands. It is locally abundant throughout the county, particularly on roadsides, except for the highest parts of the Dark and South West Peak Areas where it is virtually absent. It is possibly becoming more frequent along road verges now, due to less regular mowing. It has various local names including Cicely and Kedlock (Grigson 1975).

Anthriscus cerefolium (L.) Hoffm.
Garden Chervil

Locally extinct, Garden Chervil was a very rare, casual annual, formerly cultivated in gardens as a herb. Our only record is for Buxton (SK07) in 1811; one given for SK28 in Clapham (1969) is an error. It is a native of south-eastern Europe.

Anthriscus caucalis M. Bieb.
Bur Chervil

COUNTY STATUS: Native	
CONSERVATION STATUS: DRDB (Cat5a), A, B	
FIRST YEAR: 1829 **LATEST YEAR:** 1995 **NO OF RECORDS:** 12	
RECENT SQUARES: monads 1; tetrads 1; hectads 1	
ALL SQUARES: monads 5; tetrads 4; hectads 5	

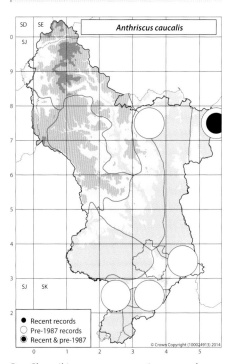

Bur Chervil is a very rare, native annual of open disturbed and dry areas. The only recent record is from the Magnesian Limestone at Markland Grips (SK5074) in 1990. It was previously known from Willington (SK2929), Milton (SK3226) and

Spital (SK3871) in the 1960s, and Derwent Mouth (SK43) in 1903.

Scandix pecten-veneris L.
Shepherd's-needle

COUNTY STATUS: Established (Archaeophyte)
CONSERVATION STATUS: DRDB (Cat2), CR, NERC, A, B, C
FIRST YEAR: 1789 LATEST YEAR: 1996 NO OF RECORDS: 66
RECENT SQUARES: monads 1; tetrads 1; hectads 1
ALL SQUARES: monads 23; tetrads 20; hectads 22

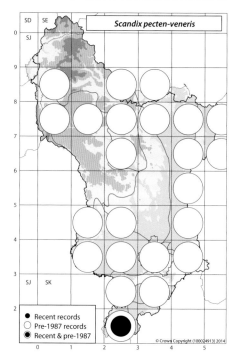

Shepherd's-needle is a very rare, anciently established annual of arable land on fertile soil. The only recent record is for Linton (SK2616), where it was found by C. & M. Smith in 1996. It was previously more frequent and widespread, with Clapham's 1969 Flora noting 13 localities. It occurs scattered throughout central and southern England, but is declining due to agricultural "improvement". It is listed as Critically Endangered and a UK Biodiversity Action Plan priority species.

Myrrhis odorata (L.) Scop.
Sweet Cicely

COUNTY STATUS: Established (Neophyte)
CONSERVATION STATUS: None
FIRST YEAR: 1789 LATEST YEAR: 2013 NO OF RECORDS: 1,096
RECENT SQUARES: monads 470; tetrads 276; hectads 33
ALL SQUARES: monads 499; tetrads 284; hectads 34

Sweet Cicely is an established perennial of waysides, riverbanks and field borders, and is native to the mountains of central and southern Europe. It is frequent in the White Peak and parts of adjacent areas from Gamesley (SK0194) in the north, through Tideswell (SK1474) and Parwich (SK1854), to Cubley (SK1637) and Derby City (SK3834)

Sweet Cicely (*Myrrhis odorata*) at Middleton (SK2756), roadside above the Via Gellia, May 2008 (Peter Smith)

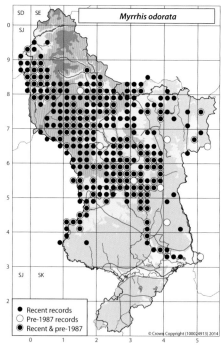

in the south. Elsewhere it is only rare, as at Draycott (SK4233) and Romeley (SK4675). Plants around Derby (SK3536/3834) probably derive from seeds washed down-river. It is a plant of north-western Britain with Derbyshire on the south-eastern edge of its main distribution (Preston *et al.* 2002).

Coriandrum sativum L.
Coriander

Coriander is a casual annual of cultivated land and waste ground. There are only two recent records: Stonegravels (SK3871

in 1997) and Heeley (SK3484 in 2003). Older records are from Ripley (SK3950) and Weston-on-Trent (SK3827) in the 1980s, and Windmill Tip (SK1677) and Dimple Dump (SK2960) in the 1960s. Introduced as culinary waste or a bird-seed alien, it is indigenous to the Mediterranean.

Smyrnium olusatrum L.
Alexanders

Alexanders is an anciently established perennial of roadsides and railway verges. It occurs very rarely scattered throughout

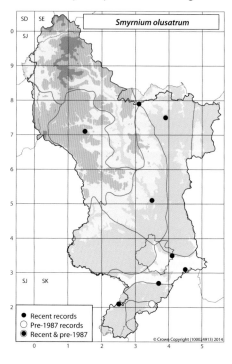

COUNTY STATUS: Established (Archaeophyte)
CONSERVATION STATUS: None
FIRST YEAR: 1969 LATEST YEAR: 2008 NO OF RECORDS: 13
RECENT SQUARES: monads 8; tetrads 8; hectads 6
ALL SQUARES: monads 9; tetrads 9; hectads 7

the county from Taddington (SK1470) and Totley (SK3179) in the north, to Borrowash (SK4134), Ingleby (SK3627) and Stapenhill (SK2520) in the south. It was cultivated up until the 15th century as a vegetable (Preston *et al.* 2002), but it is uncertain if local plants are descendants of this cultivation or are more recent introductions. It is a native of southern Europe.

Conopodium majus (Gouan) Loret
Pignut

COUNTY STATUS: Native
CONSERVATION STATUS: None
FIRST YEAR: 1789 LATEST YEAR: 2013 NO OF RECORDS: 2,430
RECENT SQUARES: monads 934; tetrads 501; hectads 41
ALL SQUARES: monads 1,020; tetrads 534; hectads 41

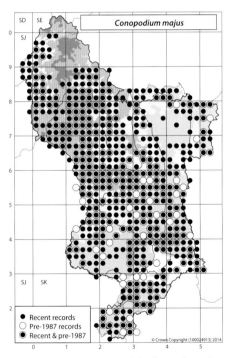

Pignut is a native perennial of woods and unimproved grasslands. It is frequent throughout the county except for the high moors of the Dark Peak and some areas of intensive farming where it is virtually absent. It has been lost from a number of grassland sites in the latter half of last century due to agricultural "improvements".

Pimpinella major (L.) Huds.
Greater Burnet-saxifrage
Greater Burnet-saxifrage is a native perennial of grasslands, hedge-banks and woodland margins, particularly on base-

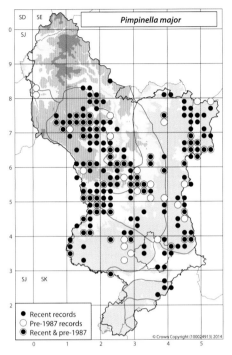

rich soils. It is frequent in the White Peak (Monk's Dale SK1375, High Low SK1568 & Black Rocks SK2154) and Magnesian Limestone Areas (Roseland Wood SK4967 & Pleasley Vale SK5265). Elsewhere it is rare (Dennis Knowle SK2284, Langley Mill SK4446 & Marston on Dove SK2329), and is almost absent from the Dark and South West Peak Areas. A lowland species, it reaches its national altitudinal limit of 320m in Derbyshire (Preston *et al.* 2002).

Pimpinella saxifraga L.
Burnet-saxifrage

COUNTY STATUS: Native
CONSERVATION STATUS: None
FIRST YEAR: 1829 LATEST YEAR: 2013 NO OF RECORDS: 1,097
RECENT SQUARES: monads 395; tetrads 267; hectads 35
ALL SQUARES: monads 447; tetrads 297; hectads 36

Burnet-saxifrage is a native perennial of unimproved grasslands, particularly on well-drained calcareous soils. It is frequent in the White Peak (Peter Dale SK1275, Over Haddon SK2066 & Hopton Quarry SK2656) and the Magnesian Limestone areas (Markland Grips SK5074 & Upper Langwith SK5169). Elsewhere it is rare (Warhurst Fold Bridge SJ9993, Bretby SK2619 & between Kirk and Little Hallam SK4640), and is virtually absent from the South West and Dark Peak. It has been lost from some sites in the latter

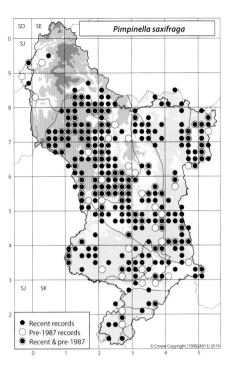

half of last century due to agricultural intensification.

Aegopodium podagraria L.
Ground-elder

COUNTY STATUS: Established (Archaeophyte)
CONSERVATION STATUS: None
FIRST YEAR: 1789 LATEST YEAR: 2013 NO OF RECORDS: 1,527
RECENT SQUARES: monads 818; tetrads 503; hectads 41
ALL SQUARES: monads 858; tetrads 511; hectads 41

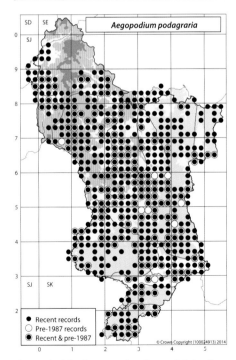

Ground-elder is an anciently established perennial of cultivated ground and waste places, and originates from central Europe. It is common throughout the county except for the high moors of the Dark Peak.

It typically occurs near habitations where it is a pernicious garden weed, though was originally introduced as a culinary or medicinal herb.

Sium latifolium L.
Greater Water-parsnip

COUNTY STATUS: Native
CONSERVATION STATUS: DRDB (Cat6), EN, NS, NERC
FIRST YEAR: 1923 LATEST YEAR: 1923 NO OF RECORDS: 1
RECENT SQUARES: monads 0; tetrads 0; hectads 0
ALL SQUARES: monads 1; tetrads 1; hectads 1

Locally extinct, Greater Water-parsnip was a very rare, native perennial. The only record is from Forbes Pond (SK4932), where it was discovered by Professor Sir Harry Godwin, as a young student in 1923.

Berula erecta (Huds.) Coville
Lesser Water-parsnip

COUNTY STATUS: Native
CONSERVATION STATUS: None
FIRST YEAR: 1801 LATEST YEAR: 2012 NO OF RECORDS: 134
RECENT SQUARES: monads 47; tetrads 38; hectads 16
ALL SQUARES: monads 77; tetrads 61; hectads 25

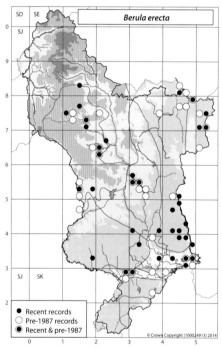

Lesser Water-parsnip is an emergent native perennial that grows in or by the margins of ditches, canals and rivers. It occurs occasionally throughout the county, avoiding only the South West Peak and Dark Peak Areas. Example localities are Cressbrook Dale (SK1773), Bradford Dale (SK2063), the River Poulter (SK5270), Whatstandwell (SK3354) and Forbes Pond (SK4932). It appears to have been lost from some sites, probably due to habitat destruction or pollution.

Oenanthe fistulosa L.
Tubular Water-dropwort

COUNTY STATUS: Native
CONSERVATION STATUS: DRDB (Cat2), VU, NERC, ERL, B
FIRST YEAR: 1789 LATEST YEAR: 2009 NO OF RECORDS: 71
RECENT SQUARES: monads 14; tetrads 12; hectads 6
ALL SQUARES: monads 19; tetrads 17; hectads 11

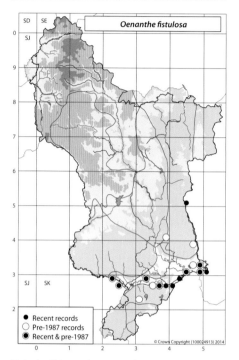

Tubular Water-dropwort is a very rare, native perennial on the margins of ponds and rivers. Recent records are confined to the corridors of the Rivers

Erewash, Dove and Trent south of Derby (Marston on Dove SK2328, Stanton by Bridge SK3627 & Trent Lock SK4931). It previously grew further north with records for Sterndale (SK06), Renishaw (SK47) and Pinxton (SK45), all for 1903. It is a lowland species with Derbyshire on the north-western margin of its national distribution.

Oenanthe silaifolia M. Bieb.
Narrow-leaved Water-dropwort

Narrow-leaved Water-dropwort is a very rare, established perennial. The only recent records are from Priestcliffe Lees (SK1572) in 2001 and Long Eaton (SK43W) in 2000. It was also recorded for the former site in 1985. The origin of these records is uncertain and puzzling since the plant is decreasing elsewhere (Stace 2010). It is a native of southern and eastern England, with the Derbyshire localities on the north-western margin of its range (Preston *et al.* 2002).

Oenanthe crocata L.
Hemlock Water-dropwort

COUNTY STATUS: Native
CONSERVATION STATUS: B
FIRST YEAR: 1866 LATEST YEAR: 2012 NO OF RECORDS: 66
RECENT SQUARES: monads 31; tetrads 24; hectads 8
ALL SQUARES: monads 32; tetrads 24; hectads 8

Hemlock Water-dropwort is a rare native perennial of marshy areas at the margins of rivers and canals, and in wet woods. It is

Hemlock Water-dropwort (*Oenanthe crocata*), Swarkestone (SK3628), July 2004 (Philip Precey)

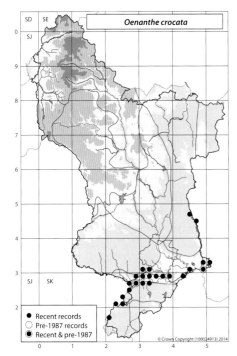

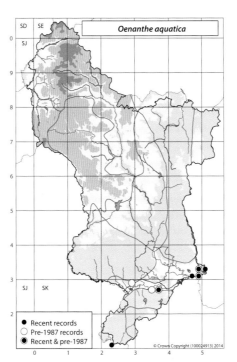

north and west (New Mills SK0085 & Darley Bridge SK2661). Our plant is ssp. *cynapium*.

Foeniculum vulgare Mill.
Fennel

COUNTY STATUS: Established (Archaeophyte)
CONSERVATION STATUS: None
FIRST YEAR: 1903 LATEST YEAR: 2012 NO OF RECORDS: 124
RECENT SQUARES: monads 55; tetrads 52; hectads 22
ALL SQUARES: monads 68; tetrads 64; hectads 23

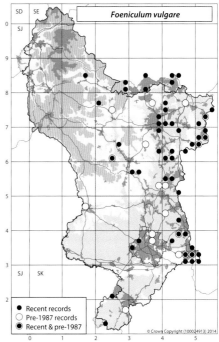

virtually confined locally to the corridor of the River Trent, from Borough Hill Wetland (SK2017), through Newton Solney (SK2826) and Swarkestone (SK3728), to Trent Lock (SK4831). It appears to have spread in recent years as Clapham (1969) records it only for "near Repton" (SK32).

Oenanthe fluviatilis (Bab.) Coleman
River Water-dropwort

COUNTY STATUS: Native
CONSERVATION STATUS: DRDB (Cat4)
FIRST YEAR: 1863 LATEST YEAR: 2006 NO OF RECORDS: 3
RECENT SQUARES: monads 1; tetrads 1; hectads 1
ALL SQUARES: monads 1; tetrads 1; hectads 2

River Water-dropwort is a very rare, native perennial of slow rivers. Our one recent record is for the River Mease at Haunton (SK2311), found by D. Broughton in 2006. It was previously recorded at Tutbury (SK22) in 1863 and Burton-on-Trent (SK22) in 1889. Nationally it is a plant of southern and eastern England, and is on the north-western limit of its distribution here.

Oenanthe aquatica (L.) Poir.
Fine-leaved Water-dropwort

COUNTY STATUS: Native
CONSERVATION STATUS: DRDB (Cat5a), A, B
FIRST YEAR: 1837 LATEST YEAR: 2011 NO OF RECORDS: 36
RECENT SQUARES: monads 8; tetrads 6; hectads 4
ALL SQUARES: monads 10; tetrads 8; hectads 5

Fine-leaved Water-dropwort is a very rare native and short-lived perennial of still or slow-flowing waters and marshes. All current records (Stanton by Bridge SK3727 & Forbes Hole SK4932) and past ones

(Willington Bridge SK2928 in 1949) are from the Trent Valley bar one (SK2311).

Aethusa cynapium L.
Fool's Parsley

COUNTY STATUS: Native
CONSERVATION STATUS: None
FIRST YEAR: 1789 LATEST YEAR: 2013 NO OF RECORDS: 485
RECENT SQUARES: monads 281; tetrads 244; hectads 31
ALL SQUARES: monads 324; tetrads 264; hectads 33

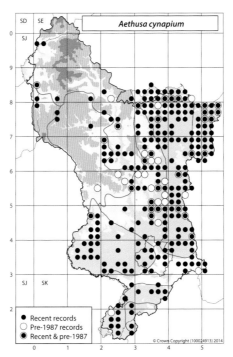

Fool's Parsley is a native annual of cultivated land and waste ground. It is frequent in southern and eastern parts (Ashbourne SK1746, Larklands SK4741 & Glapwell SK4765) but only rare in the

Fennel is an anciently established perennial of waste ground and waysides, though some recent records probably refer to casual plants. It occurs occasionally through eastern and southern parts, from Beighton (SK4384) and Creswell (SK5273) in the north, through Ironville (SK4451), to Long Eaton (SK4832) and Westbrook Farm (SK2312) in the south. A native to continental Europe, it was and still is grown as an attractive culinary garden herb.

Anethum graveolens L.
Dill

Dill is a casual annual of disturbed ground and waste land. There are only two records, Hadfield Tip (SK0296) in 1989 and Chesterfield (SK3870) in 2009. A culinary herb and a constituent of bird-seed, it is native to western and central Asia.

Silaum silaus (L.) Schinz & Thell.
Pepper-saxifrage

COUNTY STATUS: Native
CONSERVATION STATUS: DRDB (Cat5b), A, B
FIRST YEAR: 1789 LATEST YEAR: 2012 NO OF RECORDS: 85
RECENT SQUARES: monads 13; tetrads 11; hectads 9
ALL SQUARES: monads 32; tetrads 27; hectads 20

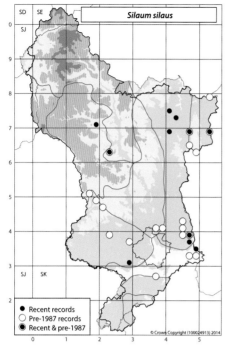

Pepper-saxifrage is a very rare, native perennial of unimproved meadows and pastures on neutral soils. Recent records are scattered throughout the county except for the upland northern and western parts (Ivy Bar Brook SK2263, Poolsbrook Reserve SK4372 & Nutbrook Canal SK4639). Previous records came from the same area but were more frequent, particularly in the south (Fenny Bentley SK1750 & Swarkestone Bridge SK3627). Its decline has been caused by agricultural "improvement" of grasslands.

Conium maculatum L.
Hemlock

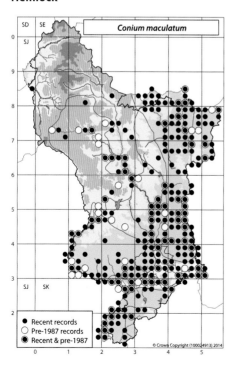

COUNTY STATUS: Established (Archaeophyte)
CONSERVATION STATUS: None
FIRST YEAR: 1789 LATEST YEAR: 2013 NO OF RECORDS: 803
RECENT SQUARES: monads 366; tetrads 255; hectads 34
ALL SQUARES: monads 406; tetrads 279; hectads 36

Hemlock is a poisonous and anciently established biennial of streamsides, waysides, waste ground and wet open woods. It is frequent throughout eastern and southern Derbyshire (Ashbourne SK1746, Catton SK2014, Darley Abbey SK3538, Weston-on-Trent SK4127, Steetley Quarry SK5476 & Killamarsh SK4480). Elsewhere it is rare or virtually absent, as in the Dark Peak. Clapham (1969) lists it as "Locally frequent, especially in the south of the county" and it thus appears to have spread through the north-eastern corner in the last 50 years.

Bupleurum rotundifolium L.
Thorow-wax

Thorow-wax is a very rare, casual annual of gardens and arable land, and a native of continental Europe. The most recent records are for Little Chester (SK3537) and Brackenfield (SK3658), both in 1969. There are earlier ones for Dale Road (SK4036) in 1967 and Hanging Bridge (SK1545) in 1944. These probably all resulted from bird-seed or the contamination of imported seed. Some records for this species may be errors for the next.

Bupleurum subovatum Link ex Spreng.
False Thorow-wax

False Thorow-wax is a very rare, casual annual of gardens. All nine records date between 1967 and 1977, and are scattered throughout the county from Aston Lane (SK1783) in the north, to Willington (SK2928) and Ockbrook (SK4236) in the south. Generally associated with garden bird-seed, it is native to the Mediterranean.

Apium graveolens L.
Wild Celery

Wild Celery is a casual biennial of damp, often waste, ground. It is recorded from only five sites recently: Ambaston (SK4132), Ambaston Lane (SK4232), Bradway Grange Farm (SK3380), Elvaston (SK4132) and Golden Valley (SK4251), all dated between 2000 and 2009. There are older ones for Dimple (SK2960) in 1969, Matlock (SK26) in 1903 and Pinxton (SK45) in 1789. It is unknown whether these records refer to the native form that occurs wild near British coasts or to cultivated forms.

Apium nodiflorum (L.) Lag.
Fool's-water-cress

Fool's-water-cress is an emergent native perennial found at the edges of

COUNTY STATUS: Native
CONSERVATION STATUS: None
FIRST YEAR: 1789 LATEST YEAR: 2013 NO OF RECORDS: 847
RECENT SQUARES: monads 356; tetrads 241; hectads 31
ALL SQUARES: monads 409; tetrads 269; hectads 35

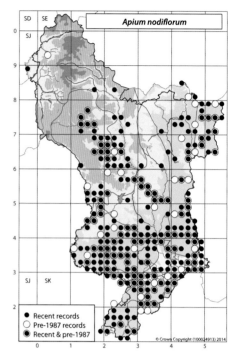

ponds, ditches, streams and sometimes in marshes. It is frequent in southern Derbyshire from Bradbourne (SK2052) and Cromford Canal (SK3851), south to Coton in the Elms (SK2414) and Netherseal (SK2812). Further north it is occasional on the Magnesian Limestone as at Markland Grips (SK5074) and parts of the White Peak as at Brook Bottom (SK1476), but is rare elsewhere. Previously it appears to have been more frequent in the Dark Peak.

Apium × moorei (Syme) Druce
A hybrid marshwort

Locally extinct, this native hybrid of Fool's-water-cress (A. nodiflorum) and Lesser Marshwort (A. inundatum) was discovered in the Renishaw Canal (SK47) by G.C. Druce in 1911. There have been no further records.

Apium inundatum (L.) Rchb. f.
Lesser Marshwort

COUNTY STATUS: Native
CONSERVATION STATUS: DRDB (Cat5b), A, B
FIRST YEAR: 1864 LATEST YEAR: 2011 NO OF RECORDS: 49
RECENT SQUARES: monads 5; tetrads 5; hectads 5
ALL SQUARES: monads 15; tetrads 14; hectads 12

Lesser Marshwort is a very rare, native perennial of shallow water and bare mud. There are recent records from only four areas: Combs Reservoir (SK0379), Chatsworth Park (SK2670), Morley Brickyards (SK3841) and Trent Rifle Range

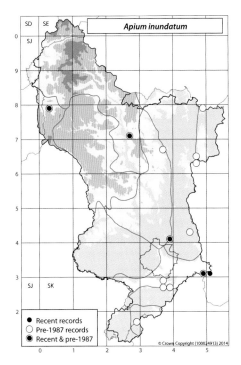

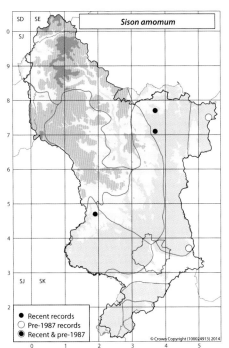

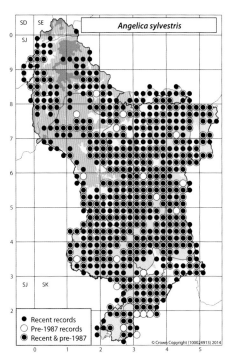

(SK4931 and 5031). Previously it occurred scattered throughout eastern Derbyshire. Nationally its decline has been attributed to the destruction of shallow waterbodies by drainage and eutrophication.

Petroselinum crispum (Mill.) Fuss
Garden Parsley

COUNTY STATUS: Casual	
CONSERVATION STATUS: None	
FIRST YEAR: 1889 LATEST YEAR: 1998 NO OF RECORDS: 9	
RECENT SQUARES: monads 1; tetrads 1; hectads 2	
ALL SQUARES: monads 4; tetrads 4; hectads 6	

Garden Parsley is a very rare, casual biennial of waste grassland and rocky places, often near habitations or gardens. There are only two recent records: Erewash Valley (SK43) and Bakewell (SK2267). Previous records are from Bolsover Castle (SK4770) in 1983, Langwith (SK5270) in 1977, Crich Quarry (SK3454) in 1969, and Horsley Castle (SK34) in 1889. Grown in gardens as a culinary herb, it is native to the eastern Mediterranean.

Sison amomum L.
Stone Parsley

COUNTY STATUS: Native	
CONSERVATION STATUS: DRDB (Cat5a), A, B	
FIRST YEAR: 1789 LATEST YEAR: 2003 NO OF RECORDS: 16	
RECENT SQUARES: monads 3; tetrads 3; hectads 2	
ALL SQUARES: monads 5; tetrads 5; hectads 7	

Stone Parsley is a very rare, native biennial of hedgebanks and roadsides. The only recent records are from Chesterfield (SK3771 & 3776) and Ashbourne (SK1846). Previously it occurred scattered across lowland parts (Lullington SK21 in 1903,

Stanton-by-Dale SK4637 in 1968 & Creswell Crags SK5374 in 1955). It is a southern species in Britain, on the northern edge of its range here in Derbyshire.

Ammi majus L.
Bullwort

Bullwort is a very rare, casual annual of roadsides, gardens, tips and waste ground. It is a bird-seed alien from southern Europe. There are four recent records between 1989 and 2003: Hadfield Tip (SK0296), Chinley (SK0482), Hollis Lane (SK3870) and Westhorpe Hills (SK4579), plus an earlier one for Bamford (SK2083) in 1974.

Carum carvi L.
Caraway

Caraway is a casual biennial or short-lived perennial of waysides. The only recent record is from Derby City (SK33) in 1988. Previous ones are from Breadsall Cutting (SK3839 & SK3940) for the 1970s, Stores Road Derby (SK3537) for 1969, and Ashby Road Calke (SK32) for 1881 in Linton (1903). It was formerly cultivated in Britain but local records are probably the result of "seeds" imported for flavouring. It is a native of continental Europe.

Angelica sylvestris L.
Wild Angelica

COUNTY STATUS: Native	
CONSERVATION STATUS: None	
FIRST YEAR: 1789 LATEST YEAR: 2013 NO OF RECORDS: 3,237	
RECENT SQUARES: monads 986; tetrads 551; hectads 41	
ALL SQUARES: monads 1,073; tetrads 571; hectads 41	

Wild Angelica is a common native perennial of wet grasslands, marshes, fens,

stream-sides and wet open woods. It grows widely throughout the county except for the drier parts of the White Peak, and the high moors of the Dark Peak.

Angelica archangelica L.
Garden Angelica

Garden Angelica is a very rare, casual perennial. Our only record is for Tideswell Rake (SK1478) in 1996. However, it is common on some Nottinghamshire rivers just to the east, so could well spread here in the future. It is sometimes grown in gardens for ornament or culinary use.

Levisticum officinale W.D.J. Koch
Lovage

Lovage is a very rare, casual perennial of waste ground and waysides, sometimes as a relic of cultivation. There are two recent records: Chesterfield (SK3771) in 1988 and Atlow (SK2348) 2004. Previously there are records for Buckland Hollow (SK3752) in 1985 and for Sheepbridge (SK3774) in 1973. Grown as a culinary herb, it is a native of Iran and Afghanistan.

Imperatoria ostruthium L.
Masterwort

Masterwort is an anciently established perennial of roadsides, indigenous to central and south-western Europe. The sole recent record is from Staden (SK0772) in 1993. Earlier ones are from Deepdale (SK1568) in 1985, Staden (SK0772) in 1969, Axe Edge (SK06) in 1903 and Buxton (SK07) in 1800. It was formerly cultivated as a pot-herb or for veterinary purposes. It is a plant of northern Britain with

Derbyshire at the south-eastern limit of
its range.

Pastinaca sativa L.
Wild Parsnip

COUNTY STATUS: Native
CONSERVATION STATUS: None
FIRST YEAR: 1863 LATEST YEAR: 2012 NO OF RECORDS: 112
RECENT SQUARES: monads 38; tetrads 35; hectads 15
ALL SQUARES: monads 59; tetrads 53; hectads 21

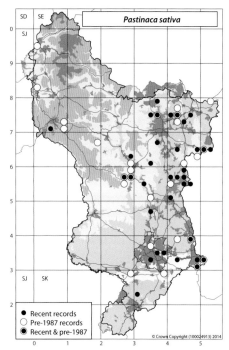

Wild Parsnip is a rare native biennial
of grassland, waysides and waste
ground, especially on dry base-rich soils.
It occurs mainly in the east: Staveley
(SK4374), Alfreton Station (SK4256),
Swanwick Junction (SK4151) and Lock
Lane Ash Tip (SK4831). There are also a
few records in the White Peak to the
west: Dean Hollow (SK2856) and Grin
Low (SK0571). Our plant is ssp. *sylvestris*
(Mill.) Rouy & E.G. Camus but many records,
particularly on waste ground, may
be escaped plants of the cultivated
ssp. *sativa*.

Heracleum sphondylium L.
Hogweed

COUNTY STATUS: Native
CONSERVATION STATUS: None
FIRST YEAR: 1789 LATEST YEAR: 2013 NO OF RECORDS: 7,243
RECENT SQUARES: monads 2,213; tetrads 718; hectads 44
ALL SQUARES: monads 2,271; tetrads 722; hectads 44

Hogweed is a very common, native
perennial of grassland, waysides, open
woods and waste ground. It grows
throughout Derbyshire, except for the
high Dark Peak moors. The local plant is
ssp. *sphondylium*, and variety *angustifolium*

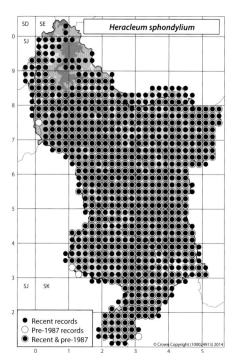

occurs sporadically, as at Taxal (SK0079)
and Grin Low (SK0472).

Heracleum mantegazzianum Sommier
& Levier
Giant Hogweed

COUNTY STATUS: Established (Neophyte)
CONSERVATION STATUS: WCA9
FIRST YEAR: 1969 LATEST YEAR: 2013 NO OF RECORDS: 89
RECENT SQUARES: monads 48; tetrads 42; hectads 23
ALL SQUARES: monads 55; tetrads 48; hectads 26

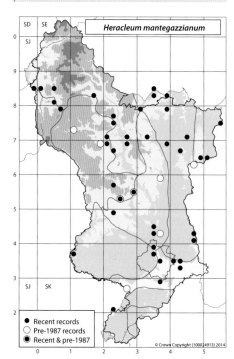

Giant Hogweed is an established perennial
of waysides, riverbanks and waste ground.
It grows scattered through the county
from the Goyt Meadows (SJ9984) and

Meersbrook Bank (SK3484) in the north,
through Hopton Village (SK2553) and
Darley Park (SK3538), to Drakelow Power
Station (SK2220) and Draycott Road (SK4233)
in the south. A native of south-western Asia,
it was originally cultivated as an ornamental,
but soon spread by seed to more natural
situations and became a nuisance, as in
Chesterfield (Charter 2003). It can invade
and swamp out native plants, also causing
dermatitis if touched, particularly in
sunlight. It was previously more restricted
in distribution, and its spread has mirrored
a national one since 1962, despite efforts to
control it (Preston *et al.* 2002).

Torilis japonica (Houtt.) DC.
Upright Hedge-parsley

COUNTY STATUS: Native
CONSERVATION STATUS: None
FIRST YEAR: 1829 LATEST YEAR: 2013 NO OF RECORDS: 1,427
RECENT SQUARES: monads 678; tetrads 419; hectads 40
ALL SQUARES: monads 726; tetrads 439; hectads 40

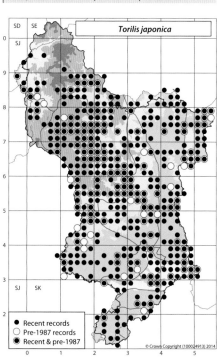

Upright Hedge-parsley is a frequent native
annual of waysides, wood borders and
grassy places, particularly on dry fertile
soils. It is found throughout the county
except for the high moors of the Dark and
South West Peak Areas.

Torilis arvensis (Huds.) Link
Spreading Hedge-parsley

Locally extinct, Spreading Hedge-parsley
was a casual annual weed of arable fields
and gardens in the south of the county. All
nine records date between 1829 and 1903,
for example: Dove Dale (SK15), Drakelow
(SK21), Repton (SK32) and Shipley (SK44). Its
local loss mirrors a national decline due

to intensive crop management as it is particularly vulnerable to herbicides and competition from other plants (Preston *et al.* 2002). It is indigenous to continental Europe.

Torilis nodosa (L.) Gaertn.
Knotted Hedge-parsley

COUNTY STATUS: Native
CONSERVATION STATUS: A, B
FIRST YEAR: 1829 LATEST YEAR: 2008 NO OF RECORDS: 26
RECENT SQUARES: monads 9; tetrads 9; hectads 7
ALL SQUARES: monads 14; tetrads 15; hectads 15

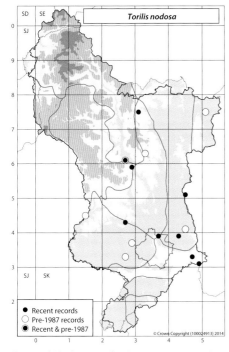

Knotted Hedge-parsley is a very rare, native annual of dry disturbed ground. It is currently

only known from the more lowland central and southern parts of the county: Dale (SK4339), Wensley Dale (SK2661) and Barlow (SK3174). It previously occurred over much the same area, albeit more frequently: Markland Grips (SK57), Clifton (SK1545) and Repton (SK32). It has shown a similar decline nationally since 1962, particularly in inland areas (Preston *et al.* 2002).

Daucus carota L.
Wild Carrot

Wild Carrot is a native biennial of waysides, waste places and grasslands, on well-drained, often base-rich soils. It

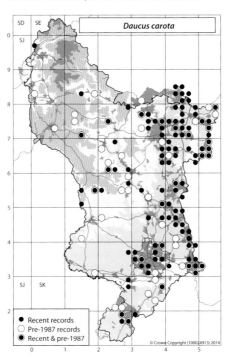

COUNTY STATUS: Native
CONSERVATION STATUS: None
FIRST YEAR: 1789 LATEST YEAR: 2013 NO OF RECORDS: 364
RECENT SQUARES: monads 137; tetrads 111; hectads 27
ALL SQUARES: monads 178; tetrads 143; hectads 35

is occasional throughout the eastern part of the county, as near Caldwell (SK2618), Derby City (SK3635), Erewash Meadows (SK5033) and Beighton (SK4484). Elsewhere it is rare, as at Parwich (SK1954) and Hollingworth (SK0097). The wild plant is ssp. *carota*, but some records, particularly those from waste places probably relate to escapes of the cultivated vegetable, ssp. *sativus* (Hoffm.) Arcang.

Turgenia latifolia (L.) Hoffm.
Greater Bur-parsley

Locally extinct, Greater Bur-parsley was a very rare, casual annual of waste ground. The only two records are: one from Gib Yard allotments (SK0672) in 1969 and an unconfirmed one from Stores Road, Derby (SK3537) in 1969. It has declined in frequency both locally and nationally over recent years, and is a native of southern Europe.

ACORACEAE

Acorus calamus L.
Sweet-flag

COUNTY STATUS: Established (Neophyte)
CONSERVATION STATUS: None
FIRST YEAR: 1789 LATEST YEAR: 2013 NO OF RECORDS: 223
RECENT SQUARES: monads 83; tetrads 60; hectads 23
ALL SQUARES: monads 103; tetrads 76; hectads 25

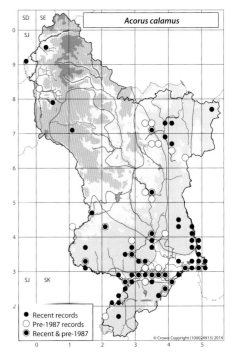

Sweet-flag is an established emergent perennial on the margins of lakes, ponds,

Knotted Hedge-parsley (*Torilis nodosa*) on open ground at Wensley Dale (SK2661), June 2004 (Philip Precey)

rivers and canals. It is occasional in south Derbyshire: Sudbury Hall (SK1532), Melbourne Pool (SK3924) and Trent Lock (SK4831). It is rarer further north: Cromford Canal (SK3452), Whitwell Wood (SK5277) and Glossop (SK0395). It is native to Asia and North America.

ARACEAE

Lysichiton americanus Hulten & H. St. John
American Skunk-cabbage

American Skunk-cabbage is an established perennial of swampy ground beside ponds and streams. It is indigenous to western North America. Planted occasionally for

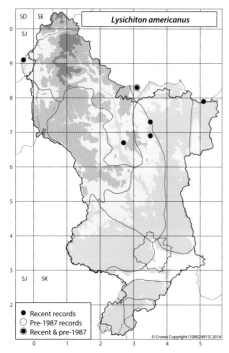

COUNTY STATUS: Established (Neophyte)	
CONSERVATION STATUS: None	
FIRST YEAR: 1980 LATEST YEAR: 2006 NO OF RECORDS: 10	
RECENT SQUARES: monads 6; tetrads 6; hectads 6	
ALL SQUARES: monads 6; tetrads 6; hectads 6	

ornament in parks and gardens, it can be persistent in natural-looking situations. It is only recorded for a few sites, all in the north: Etherow Reserve (SJ99Q), Whirlow Park Ponds (SK3082) and Walton Lodge (SK3568).

Calla palustris L.
Bog Arum

Bog Arum is an established perennial of marshy ground, and a native of continental Europe. It is grown for ornament, but has only ever been recorded locally from the lake in Allestree Park (SK3440 & 3540) between 1952 (Caulton 1961) and 1997, and Stenson Junction (SK3129) in 2007.

Zantedeschia aethiopica (L.) Spreng.
Altar-lily

Altar-lily is a very rare, casual perennial that is grown for ornament in damp areas. It is known from only one site, a stream-fed pond near Totley (SK3079), found by K. Balkow in 2007 and refound in 2011.

Arum maculatum L.
Lords-and-Ladies

COUNTY STATUS: Native	
CONSERVATION STATUS: None	
FIRST YEAR: 1789 LATEST YEAR: 2013 NO OF RECORDS: 2,398	
RECENT SQUARES: monads 940; tetrads 462; hectads 38	
ALL SQUARES: monads 993; tetrads 479; hectads 38	

Lords-and-Ladies is a common native perennial of woods, hedges and

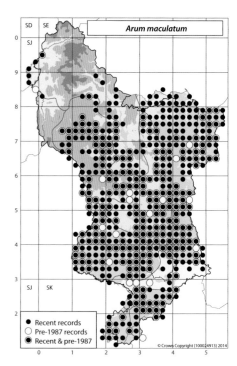

plantations. It is widespread throughout the county except for the Dark and South West Peak Areas. It has the local name of Priest's Pintle (Grigson 1975). There have been recent incidents of mass thefts from Dove Dale, possibly associated with its suggested use in fighting cancer. Plantlife's recent Common Plant Survey showed a national increase in frequency in hedges.

Arum italicum Mill.
Italian Lords-and-Ladies

Italian Lords-and-Ladies is an established perennial of waysides and waste places. Grown in gardens for ornament, it can persist after being thrown out. It is recorded recently from only Beeley Village (SK2667) in 2006, Chesterfield (SK3571) in 2009, Middle Moor (SK3163) in 2006, Stony Clouds (SK4737) in 2008 and 2009, and Linacre Woods (SK3372) in 2012. There are older records from Whirlow Park (SK3283) in 1969 and New Mills (SJ9885) in the 1980s. Our plants are probably all ssp. *italicum* – a native to Atlantic Europe.

Pistia stratiotes L.
Water-lettuce

Water-lettuce is a very rare, casual floating plant, increasingly being used as an ornamental in Britain. Found as casual on the Old Hay Brook (SK3080) by K. Balkow in 2006, it is a native of Africa.

LEMNACEAE

Spirodela polyrhiza (L.) Schleid.
Greater Duckweed

Greater Duckweed is a very rare, native aquatic that grows floating on still and

American Skunk-cabbage (*Lysichiton americanus*) by the Limb Brook in Whirlow Park (SK3082), May 2001 (Ken Balkow)

COUNTY STATUS: Native
CONSERVATION STATUS: A
FIRST YEAR: 1863 LATEST YEAR: 2010 NO OF RECORDS: 48
RECENT SQUARES: monads 17; tetrads 15; hectads 5
ALL SQUARES: monads 25; tetrads 22; hectads 8

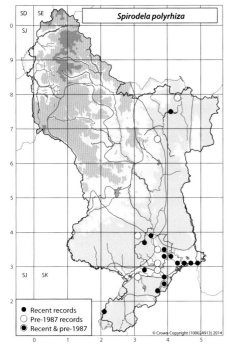

slow-moving waters. It is only recorded from the southern and eastern parts of the county (Melbourne Pool SK3924, River Derwent at Alvaston SK3834, Staveley Works SK4174 & Sawley Cut SK4730). It is a lowland species that rarely flowers in Britain (Preston *et al.* 2002).

Lemna gibba L.
Fat Duckweed

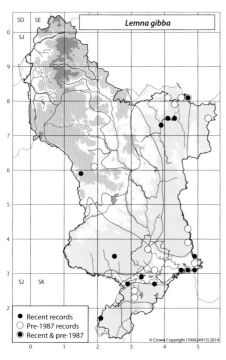

COUNTY STATUS: Native
CONSERVATION STATUS: A
FIRST YEAR: 1881 LATEST YEAR: 2011 NO OF RECORDS: 54
RECENT SQUARES: monads 17; tetrads 14; hectads 9
ALL SQUARES: monads 30; tetrads 26; hectads 15

Fat Duckweed is a very rare, native floating aquatic of still waters. It generally occurs in lowland parts of south and east Derbyshire (Trusley SK2535, Sawley SK4631 & Hollingwood SK4174). There is also an isolated record from the Peak District at Biggin Dale (SK1458). Previously it appears to have been more frequent over much the same parts. Nationally it is a southern species, towards the northern edge of its range here.

Lemna minor L.
Common Duckweed

COUNTY STATUS: Native
CONSERVATION STATUS: None
FIRST YEAR: 1829 LATEST YEAR: 2013 NO OF RECORDS: 1,160
RECENT SQUARES: monads 482; tetrads 342; hectads 40
ALL SQUARES: monads 553; tetrads 382; hectads 41

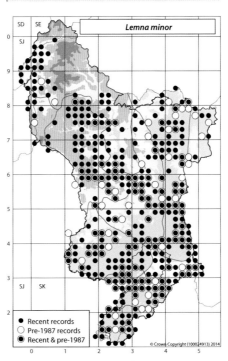

Common Duckweed is a floating native perennial of ponds, ditches and canals plus the slower reaches of rivers and streams. It is frequent throughout the county except for the more upland parts of the Peak District. It has the local name of Duck's Meat (Grigson 1975).

Lemna turionifera Landolt
Red Duckweed
Red Duckweed is a casual perennial of slowly moving waterbodies. It was discovered at its sole station of Walton-on-Trent (SK2017) in 2010 by N. Law. Probably

overlooked before, it grows naturally in North America and Asia.

Lemna minuta Kunth
Least Duckweed

COUNTY STATUS: Established (Neophyte)
CONSERVATION STATUS: None
FIRST YEAR: 1996 LATEST YEAR: 2013 NO OF RECORDS: 62
RECENT SQUARES: monads 50; tetrads 43; hectads 20
ALL SQUARES: monads 50; tetrads 43; hectads 20

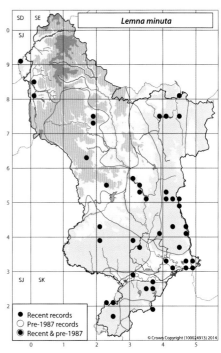

Least Duckweed is a rare established floating perennial of ponds, canals and the slower reaches of rivers. Native to the Americas, it has spread rapidly since first noted in 1996 at Longford Hall (SK2138). Now, apart from the more upland parts of the Peak District, it is found throughout Derbyshire (Burton upon Trent SK2421, Trent Lock SK43V, Ilkeston SK4642 & Etherow SJ9791). This is part of a wider national spread that began in the late 1980s (Preston *et al.* 2002).

Lemna trisulca L.
Ivy-leaved Duckweed

COUNTY STATUS: Native
CONSERVATION STATUS: None
FIRST YEAR: 1829 LATEST YEAR: 2013 NO OF RECORDS: 146
RECENT SQUARES: monads 48; tetrads 47; hectads 24
ALL SQUARES: monads 70; tetrads 66; hectads 29

Ivy-leaved Duckweed is a submerged native perennial of ponds and canals. It occurs rarely throughout the county from Glossop (SK0395) and the Chesterfield Canal (SK4681) in the north to Marston on Dove (SK2328) and Trent Lock (SK4831) in the south. It appears

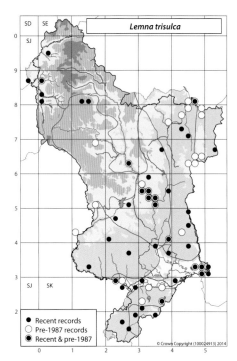

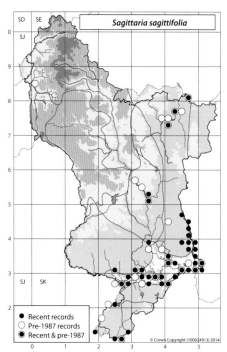

COUNTY STATUS: Native
CONSERVATION STATUS: None
FIRST YEAR: 1789 LATEST YEAR: 2013 NO OF RECORDS: 694
RECENT SQUARES: monads 258; tetrads 194; hectads 33
ALL SQUARES: monads 308; tetrads 218; hectads 35

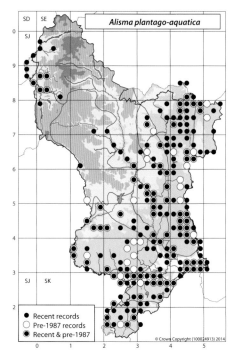

to have become less abundant since Clapham's 1969 Flora, which described it as frequent. This is probably due to increased nutrient enrichment, making waterbodies less clear.

TOFIELDIACEAE

Tofieldia pusilla (Michx.) Pers.
Scottish Asphodel

Scottish Asphodel is a very rare, planted perennial of damp calcareous grassland and is native to northern England. All records refer to just a single site, Hopton Quarry Reserve (SK2656), to where plants were transferred from Teesdale in 1971. They were transplanted because their habitat at Cow Green was to be destroyed by construction of a reservoir. They survived here until at least 1984.

ALISMATACEAE

Sagittaria sagittifolia L.
Arrowhead

COUNTY STATUS: Native
CONSERVATION STATUS: B
FIRST YEAR: 1829 LATEST YEAR: 2012 NO OF RECORDS: 200
RECENT SQUARES: monads 62; tetrads 44; hectads 13
ALL SQUARES: monads 81; tetrads 59; hectads 16

Arrowhead is an emergent native perennial found in or on the edges of canals, ponds and slow-flowing rivers. It is recorded occasionally through southern and eastern parts (River Mease SK2711, Sawley Cut SK4830, Cromford Canal SK3451 & Slittingmill Ponds SK4376). There is also a 1977 record in the north-west at New Mills (SK0084).

Baldellia ranunculoides (L.) Parl.
Lesser Water-plantain

COUNTY STATUS: Native
CONSERVATION STATUS: DRDB (Cat2), NT, B
FIRST YEAR: 1787 LATEST YEAR: 2004 NO OF RECORDS: 6
RECENT SQUARES: monads 1; tetrads 1; hectads 1
ALL SQUARES: monads 2; tetrads 2; hectads 3

Lesser Water-plantain is a very rare, native perennial of the sides of ponds and streams. There is one recent record from Poolsbrook (SK4473) in 2004, and it has previously been found only at three other sites. These are Repton (SK32) in 1866, between Derby and Burton in 1903, and Pebley Pond (SK4878) in 1787 and 1950. This mirrors a wider loss from many sites across central England due to the overgrowth of other plants (Preston *et al.* 2002).

Luronium natans (L.) Raf.
Floating Water-plantain

COUNTY STATUS: Native
CONSERVATION STATUS: DRDB (Cat1), HabsRegs, Bern, WCA8, NS, NERC, B, C
FIRST YEAR: 1973 LATEST YEAR: 1973 NO OF RECORDS: 1
RECENT SQUARES: monads 0; tetrads 0; hectads 0
ALL SQUARES: monads 1; tetrads 1; hectads 1

Floating Water-plantain is a very rare, native perennial. The sole record is from the side of Peak Forest Canal (SJ9984) in 1973. It is a Nationally Scarce species that is included in a number of local, national and international lists of conservation concern.

Alisma plantago-aquatica L.
Water-plantain

Water-plantain is an emergent native perennial that grows in or on the edges of

ponds, canals and streams. It is also found in swamps and open marshes. Frequent throughout southern and eastern parts, there are also a few records from the north-western region around New Mills and Glossop. It often turns up as one of the first colonists of new waterbodies and cleaned out ditches.

Alisma lanceolatum With.
Narrow-leaved Water-plantain

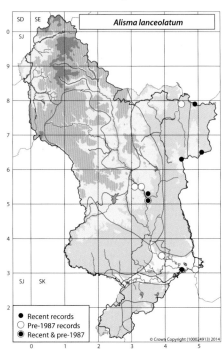

COUNTY STATUS: Native
CONSERVATION STATUS: DRDB (Cat5a), A, B
FIRST YEAR: 1903 LATEST YEAR: 2006 NO OF RECORDS: 29
RECENT SQUARES: monads 8; tetrads 6; hectads 5
ALL SQUARES: monads 13; tetrads 11; hectads 7

Narrow-leaved Water-plantain is a native emergent perennial which grows on the edges of canals, ponds and streams. It occurs very rarely throughout the eastern half of the county (Cromford Canal SK3551, Derwent Mouth SK4530, Great Pond Hardwick SK4563, Pebley Pond SK4879 & Pleasley Park SK5165). It was previously recorded at Dove Dale (SK15) in 1903. It is perhaps overlooked in some places for the larger and commoner Water-plantain (*A. plantago-aquatica*).

BUTOMACEAE

Butomus umbellatus L.
Flowering-rush

COUNTY STATUS: Native
CONSERVATION STATUS: B
FIRST YEAR: 1789 LATEST YEAR: 2011 NO OF RECORDS: 173
RECENT SQUARES: monads 60; tetrads 44; hectads 16
ALL SQUARES: monads 70; tetrads 52; hectads 18

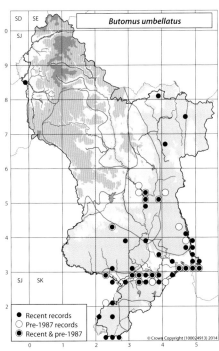

Flowering-rush is an emergent native perennial, found on the margins of ponds, canals and rivers. It occurs occasionally throughout southern and eastern Derbyshire: Melbourne (SK3327), Trent Lock (SK4830), Cromford Canal (SK3452) and Hoodcroft Ponds (SK4775). There is also an isolated record from the north-west at Hague Bar Pond (SJ9885). It is a shy flowerer, so is probably under-recorded.

HYDROCHARITACEAE

Stratiotes aloides L.
Water-soldier

Water-soldier is an established submerged perennial of ponds and lake margins. All records are from 1999 and 2010, coming from only six sites: New Mills (SJ9885/9985), Hilton Brook Pond (SK2628), Peasehill (SK4049), Forbes Hole (SK4932) and Pleasley (SK4964). It is sometimes grown in ornamental ponds from where it can escape into more natural-looking waterbodies. It is indigenous to eastern England.

Elodea canadensis Michx.
Canadian Waterweed

COUNTY STATUS: Established (Neophyte)
CONSERVATION STATUS: WCA9
FIRST YEAR: 1864 LATEST YEAR: 2013 NO OF RECORDS: 334
RECENT SQUARES: monads 116; tetrads 102; hectads 30
ALL SQUARES: monads 164; tetrads 138; hectads 35

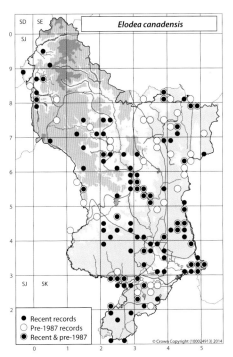

Canadian Waterweed is an established submerged perennial of ponds, canals and slow-flowing streams. It is found occasionally throughout the county except for the higher parts of the Peak District where it is virtually absent. It is often grown in garden ponds and aquaria from whence it is spread into more natural waterbodies. It is a native of North America.

Elodea nuttallii (Planch.) H. St. John
Nuttall's Waterweed

Nuttall's Waterweed is an established submerged perennial of ponds, canals and slow rivers. It occurs occasionally throughout the more lowland parts of Derbyshire: the River Mease (SK2812),

COUNTY STATUS: Established (Neophyte)
CONSERVATION STATUS: WCA9
FIRST YEAR: 1970 LATEST YEAR: 2013 NO OF RECORDS: 111
RECENT SQUARES: monads 68; tetrads 65; hectads 20
ALL SQUARES: monads 73; tetrads 70; hectads 22

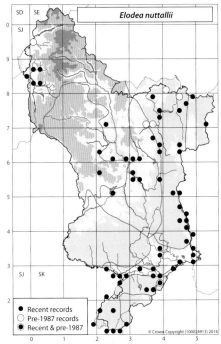

Melbourne Pool (SK3824), Oakerthorpe (SK3955), Pebley Reservoir (SK4878) and Birch Vale (SK0286). It is much grown by aquarists and pond keepers, and is indigenous to North America.

Lagarosiphon major (Ridl.) Moss ex V.A. Wager
Curly Waterweed

Curly Waterweed is a recently established, submerged perennial of ponds and canals.

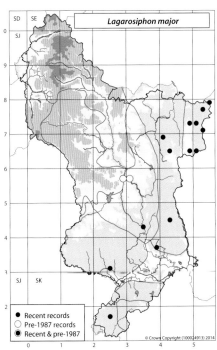

COUNTY STATUS: Established (Neophyte)
CONSERVATION STATUS: WCA9
FIRST YEAR: 1967 LATEST YEAR: 2011 NO OF RECORDS: 21
RECENT SQUARES: monads 14; tetrads 14; hectads 9
ALL SQUARES: monads 17; tetrads 17; hectads 12

It occurs rarely through southern and eastern parts: Hilton Gravel Pits (SK2431), Winsick (SK4068), Whitwell Wood (SK5277) and Steetley Quarry (SK5478). This South African native is commonly cultivated here and spreads rapidly from discarded material.

APONOGETONACEAE

Aponogeton distachyos L. f.
Cape-pondweed

Cape-pondweed is an established, emergent perennial of ponds and shallow water. Our only modern record is from Mag Clough (SK2377) in 2003. Older ones come from the same site in 1985, plus Frith Wood (SK3678) in 1978. Planted around ponds for ornament, it can become naturalised or survive as a relic of cultivation. It grows naturally in South Africa.

JUNCAGINACEAE

Triglochin palustris L.
Marsh Arrowgrass

COUNTY STATUS: Native
CONSERVATION STATUS: DRDB (Cat5b)
FIRST YEAR: 1829 LATEST YEAR: 2012 NO OF RECORDS: 181
RECENT SQUARES: monads 30; tetrads 31; hectads 16
ALL SQUARES: monads 71; tetrads 64; hectads 31

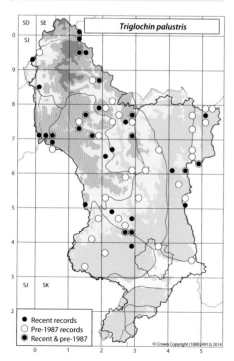

Marsh Arrowgrass is a rare native perennial of damp grasslands and marshes. It occurs sparsely throughout northern and central

regions of the county (Tom Wood SJ9993, Solomon's Temple SK0571, Long Side SK1399 & Pleasley SK4963). It was previously also recorded from a few more southerly sites (Stapenhill SK22 in 1903, Repton Rocks SK32 in 1903 & Risley Glebe SK4635 in 1975).

POTAMOGETONACEAE

Potamogeton natans L.
Broad-leaved Pondweed

COUNTY STATUS: Native
CONSERVATION STATUS: None
FIRST YEAR: 1789 LATEST YEAR: 2013 NO OF RECORDS: 504
RECENT SQUARES: monads 203; tetrads 170; hectads 35
ALL SQUARES: monads 240; tetrads 192; hectads 36

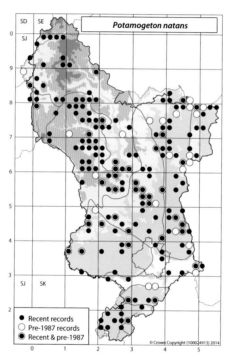

Broad-leaved Pondweed is a native aquatic perennial with floating leaves that occurs on a wide range of still and slowly-flowing waters including ponds, lakes and rivers. It is our commonest pondweed and is found occasionally throughout Derbyshire from Woodhead Reservoir (SK0899) and Upper Derwent (SK1889) in the north, through Minninglow Pit (SK2057) and Cromford Canal (SK3056), to Linton (SK2615) and Forbes Hole (SK4932) in the south.

Potamogeton polygonifolius Pourr.
Bog Pondweed

COUNTY STATUS: Native
CONSERVATION STATUS: None
FIRST YEAR: 1881 LATEST YEAR: 2013 NO OF RECORDS: 202
RECENT SQUARES: monads 93; tetrads 64; hectads 15
ALL SQUARES: monads 102; tetrads 69; hectads 20

Bog Pondweed is a native aquatic perennial with floating leaves of still and slowly-flowing acid waters that can also

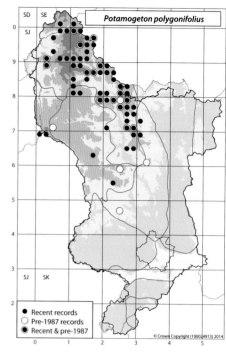

grow almost as a terrestrial plant on beds of Sphagnum moss. Recent records are virtually confined to the Dark and South West Peak where it is occasional: The Intakes (SK0389), Abney Moor (SK1879) and Jagger's Clough (SK1587). Elsewhere there are only isolated records (Middleton Common, SK16R). It previously grew further south with records at Hulland Moss (SK2546) up to 1980, Ilkeston (SK44) in the 1940s and Repton Rocks (SK32) in 1903.

Potamogeton lucens L.
Shining Pondweed

Shining Pondweed is a very rare, submerged native perennial of ponds and

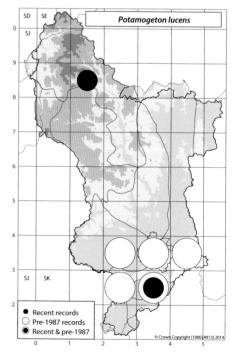

COUNTY STATUS: Native	
CONSERVATION STATUS: DRDB (Cat5a), A, B	
FIRST YEAR: 1829 **LATEST YEAR:** 2002 **NO OF RECORDS:** 14	
RECENT SQUARES: monads 2; tetrads 2; hectads 2	
ALL SQUARES: monads 4; tetrads 4; hectads 6	

slowly moving streams. There are only three sites where it has been seen recently: Blue Circle Pond (SK1782) in the north, plus Anchor Church (SK3327) and Stanton by Bridge (SK32) in south Derbyshire. Formerly it was more widespread in the south: Sutton Brook (SK2234) and New Stanton (SK4539) both pre-1968. Clapham's 1969 Flora noted it grew on base-rich inorganic substrates.

Potamogeton alpinus Balb.
Red Pondweed

COUNTY STATUS: Native	
CONSERVATION STATUS: DRDB (Cat5a), A, B	
FIRST YEAR: 1887 **LATEST YEAR:** 1995 **NO OF RECORDS:** 14	
RECENT SQUARES: monads 1; tetrads 1; hectads 1	
ALL SQUARES: monads 7; tetrads 5; hectads 4	

Red Pondweed is a very rare, native perennial of slow-moving to still waters. There is only one recent record, Birch Vale (SK0286). It formerly occurred scattered through the county in non-calcareous waters on organic substrates at sites such as Umberley Brook (SK2970 for 1969), Fritchley (SK35 for 1900) and near Ingleby Toft (SK3525 for 1960).

Potamogeton praelongus Wulfen
Long-stalked Pondweed

COUNTY STATUS: Native	
CONSERVATION STATUS: DRDB (Cat2), NT, A, B	
FIRST YEAR: 1863 **LATEST YEAR:** 1990 **NO OF RECORDS:** 9	
RECENT SQUARES: monads 2; tetrads 1; hectads 1	
ALL SQUARES: monads 3; tetrads 2; hectads 3	

Long-stalked Pondweed is a very rare, native submerged perennial of rivers and pools. It has been recorded recently only from the Trent Lock area, both in the River Trent (SK4830) and a nearby borrow pit (SK4931) in 1990. Formerly it was scattered over a wider area of southern Derbyshire (Willington SK2928 in 1968) where it also occurred in canals as in Derby (SK33 in 1863).

Potamogeton perfoliatus L.
Perfoliate Pondweed

COUNTY STATUS: Native	
CONSERVATION STATUS: DRDB (Cat5b), A	
FIRST YEAR: 1829 **LATEST YEAR:** 2009 **NO OF RECORDS:** 35	
RECENT SQUARES: monads 8; tetrads 7; hectads 4	
ALL SQUARES: monads 19; tetrads 17; hectads 13	

Perfoliate Pondweed is a very rare, native aquatic. It grows submerged in still and gently flowing waters over organically

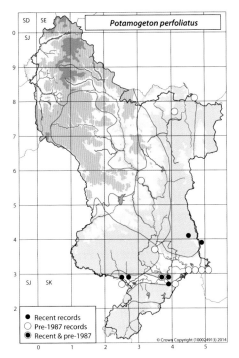

enriched substrates. Current records are only from the south-eastern corner of the county (Straws Bridge SK4541 & the Trent and Mersey Canal SK3828). Previously it was recorded throughout southern and eastern parts (Killamarsh SK4681 in the 1960s, Whatstandwell SK35 in 1903 & the River Dove SK2527 in 1979).

Potamogeton × cooperi (Fryer) Fryer
Cooper's Pondweed

Locally extinct, Cooper's Pondweed was a submerged native perennial of canals known from just three old sites, all from the south of the county. These are: Willington (SK2928) in 1969, near Chaddesden (SK33) in 1903, and between Borrowash and Chaddesden (SK43) in 1884. It is the hybrid of Perfoliate (*P. perfoliatus*) and Curled Pondweed (*P. crispus*).

Potamogeton friesii Rupr.
Flat-stalked Pondweed

COUNTY STATUS: Native	
CONSERVATION STATUS: DRDB (Cat2), NT, NS, A, B	
FIRST YEAR: 1829 **LATEST YEAR:** 1991 **NO OF RECORDS:** 27	
RECENT SQUARES: monads 1; tetrads 1; hectads 1	
ALL SQUARES: monads 8; tetrads 8; hectads 8	

Flat-stalked Pondweed is a very rare, native perennial of slowly moving waters. There is only one recent record, Norwood (SK4681) in 1991. Previously there were some 20 odd records throughout southern and eastern parts between 1829 and 1976. These included: Spondon (SK3935) and Weston-on-Trent (SK4127). Clapham (1969) noted that it grew especially over muddy bottoms.

Potamogeton × lintonii Fryer
Linton's Pondweed

COUNTY STATUS: Native	
CONSERVATION STATUS: None	
FIRST YEAR: 1895 **LATEST YEAR:** 1969 **NO OF RECORDS:** 7	
RECENT SQUARES: monads 0; tetrads 0; hectads 0	
ALL SQUARES: monads 1; tetrads 1; hectads 6	

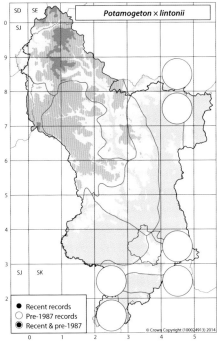

Locally extinct, Linton's Pondweed was a submerged native perennial of canals and rivers, with just a handful of old records from southern and eastern parts. The most recent are from Weston-on-Trent (SK4127) and Trent Lock (SK43), both for 1969; and from Renishaw Canal (SK47) in 1947. It was also recorded in the 1890s from the River Trent (SK21 & 22) and the Killamarsh Canal (SK48). It is the hybrid of Flat-stalked (*P. friesii*) and of Curled Pondweed (*P. crispus*), and commemorates our Flora writer, W.R. Linton (Preston 1988).

Potamogeton obtusifolius Mert. & W.D.J. Koch
Blunt-leaved Pondweed

COUNTY STATUS: Native	
CONSERVATION STATUS: DRDB (Cat5a), A, B	
FIRST YEAR: 1842 **LATEST YEAR:** 2010 **NO OF RECORDS:** 22	
RECENT SQUARES: monads 3; tetrads 3; hectads 3	
ALL SQUARES: monads 7; tetrads 6; hectads 7	

Blunt-leaved Pondweed is a very rare, native submerged perennial of slowly moving water. It has only been recorded from three sites in recent years: Cressbrook Mill (SK1772), Hulland Fish Ponds (SK2446) and Wingerworth Lido (SK3766). Previously it grew scattered throughout the county excluding the Dark Peak, for example in Killamarsh Canal (SK4681 in 1979),

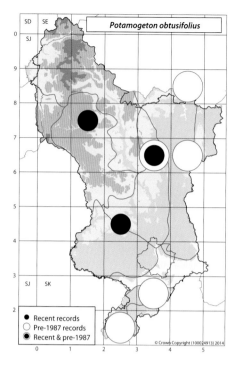

Recent records
Pre-1987 records
Recent & pre-1987

© Crown Copyright (100024913) 2014

Chellaston (SK3729 in 1968) and Netherseal (SK21 in 1842).

Potamogeton pusillus L.
Lesser Pondweed

COUNTY STATUS: Native
CONSERVATION STATUS: A, B
FIRST YEAR: 1863 LATEST YEAR: 2010 NO OF RECORDS: 66
RECENT SQUARES: monads 26; tetrads 23; hectads 14
ALL SQUARES: monads 42; tetrads 38; hectads 19

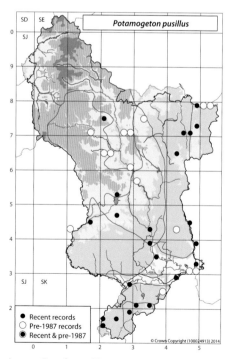

Recent records
Pre-1987 records
Recent & pre-1987

© Crown Copyright (100024913) 2014

Lesser Pondweed is a very rare, native submerged aquatic of still and slowly flowing waters. Except for the extreme north-western corner, it is currently recorded throughout the county (Stoney

Middleton SK2075, Bolsover Colliery SK4571 & Darley Abbey SK3539). Earlier records cover the same area (Norbury SK1142 & the Cranfleet Cut SK4931). The Stoney Middleton site is the highest known locality in Britain (Preston *et al.* 2002). It is considered to be spreading nationally, possibly due to increasing nutrient-enrichment (Preston *et al.* 2002), but there is no evidence for this locally.

Potamogeton berchtoldii Fieber
Small Pondweed

COUNTY STATUS: Native
CONSERVATION STATUS: A, B
FIRST YEAR: 1861 LATEST YEAR: 2011 NO OF RECORDS: 41
RECENT SQUARES: monads 13; tetrads 15; hectads 9
ALL SQUARES: monads 19; tetrads 18; hectads 10

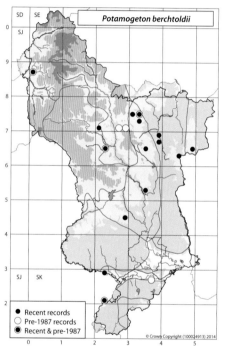

Recent records
Pre-1987 records
Recent & pre-1987

© Crown Copyright (100024913) 2014

Small Pondweed is a very rare, native submerged aquatic of still and slowly moving waters. It is currently recorded sporadically across Derbyshire (Highfield Lane SK2844 & Hardwick Hall SK4563), including both limestone (Hassop Park SK2171) and non-limestone areas (Drakelow Reserve SK2220 & Marston on Dove SK2328).

Potamogeton trichoides Cham. & Schltdl.
Hairlike Pondweed

Hairlike Pondweed is a very rare, casual submerged aquatic of standing waterbodies. Our only records come from newly-constructed fishing ponds near Derby (SK3539), found by T. Taylor in 2004 and 2005.

Potamogeton compressus L.
Grass-wrack Pondweed

Grass-wrack Pondweed is a very rare, native perennial which typically grows

COUNTY STATUS: Native
CONSERVATION STATUS: DRDB (Cat2), EN, NS, NERC, A, B, C
FIRST YEAR: 1835 LATEST YEAR: 2010 NO OF RECORDS: 142
RECENT SQUARES: monads 4; tetrads 3; hectads 3
ALL SQUARES: monads 36; tetrads 32; hectads 14

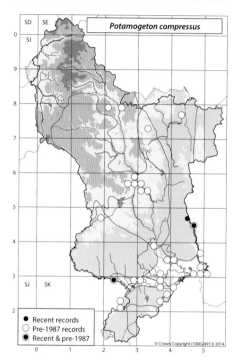

Recent records
Pre-1987 records
Recent & pre-1987

© Crown Copyright (100024913) 2014

submerged in slow-flowing rivers and canals. It is currently only known in three localities: the Old River Dove at Marston (SK2328), the Erewash Canal (SK4546, 4547 & 4645) and Bolsover Colliery (SK47). It was formerly more widespread, growing along stretches of the Cromford Canal (SK3056) and the River Trent (SK2522 & SK4831), as well as the Derby Canal at Breadsall (SK3539), Spondon (SK3934) and Borrowash (SK4134). It occurs occasionally in central England and eastern Wales, though its range has also contracted here (Lockton & Whild 1998). It is Nationally Scarce and a UK Priority Biodiversity Action Plan Species.

Potamogeton crispus L.
Curled Pondweed

COUNTY STATUS: Native
CONSERVATION STATUS: None
FIRST YEAR: 1829 LATEST YEAR: 2013 NO OF RECORDS: 207
RECENT SQUARES: monads 86; tetrads 79; hectads 25
ALL SQUARES: monads 123; tetrads 107; hectads 31

Curled Pondweed is a submerged native perennial of canals, ponds and streams. It occurs occasionally through the county from Buxworth (SK0182) in the north, through Bradford Dale (SK2164) and Cromford Canal (SK3851), to Trent Lock (SK4831) and Grangewood Farm (SK2614) in the south. It is one of the more distinctive pondweeds and is probably better recorded than some others in the genus.

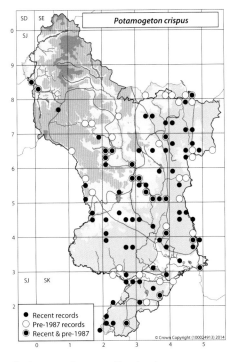

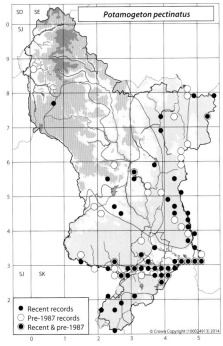

Potamogeton pectinatus L.
Fennel Pondweed

COUNTY STATUS: Native

CONSERVATION STATUS: None

FIRST YEAR: 1829 **LATEST YEAR:** 2010 **NO OF RECORDS:** 164

RECENT SQUARES: monads 77; tetrads 54; hectads 19

ALL SQUARES: monads 105; tetrads 78; hectads 25

Fennel Pondweed is a submerged native perennial of lakes, canals and rivers. It occurs occasionally in southern and eastern Derbyshire (Sudbury SK1531, Hilton Gravel Pits SK2431, Trent Lock SK4831, Loscoe SK4247 & Steetley Quarry SK5478). There is also an isolated record from Victory Quarry (SK0777) in the Peak District. It was previously

noted for more northern parts as at Watford Lodge (SK0086) in 1978. It can tolerate more nutrient-enrichment and disturbance than most Pondweeds, so is often the only pondweed left in many sites today.

Groenlandia densa (L.) Fourr.
Opposite-leaved Pondweed

COUNTY STATUS: Native

CONSERVATION STATUS: DRDB (Cat2), VU, B

FIRST YEAR: 1829 **LATEST YEAR:** 1979 **NO OF RECORDS:** 23

RECENT SQUARES: monads 0; tetrads 0; hectads 0

ALL SQUARES: monads 10; tetrads 8; hectads 10

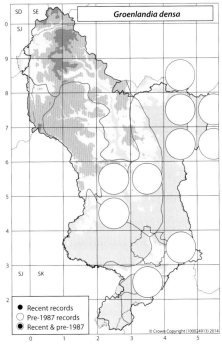

Opposite-leaved Pondweed is a submerged native perennial of streams, ponds and canals with no recent records. It previously occurred widely, but rarely throughout southern and eastern parts in clear, often fast-flowing waters. The latest records are from the Magnesian Limestone Area at Pleasley (SK5164) and Markland Grips (SK5074) in the 1970s. There are also earlier sightings from New Stanton (SK4639) in 1969, and from Cromford (SK25) and Calke Abbey (SK32) both for 1903. This local loss is matched by a national decline prior to 1930 due to nutrient enrichment of waters (Preston *et al.* 2002).

Zannichellia palustris L.
Horned Pondweed

COUNTY STATUS: Native

CONSERVATION STATUS: DRDB (Cat5b), A, B

FIRST YEAR: 1856 **LATEST YEAR:** 2012 **NO OF RECORDS:** 62

RECENT SQUARES: monads 15; tetrads 15; hectads 11

ALL SQUARES: monads 30; tetrads 31; hectads 24

Horned Pondweed is a very rare, native aquatic of still and slowly moving

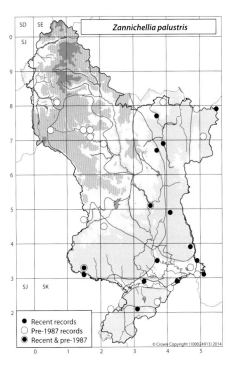

waterbodies, where it grows as a submerged perennial. Current records are from lowland southern and eastern Derbyshire (Sudbury Hall Lake SK1531, Cromford Canal SK3551 & Chesterfield Fishing Lake SK3868). Previous records cover the same area plus the Peak District (Miller's Dale SK1772 & Chapel-en-le-Frith SK0681). It has declined nationally, probably due to drainage and more intensive ditch maintenance (Preston *et al.* 2002).

NARTHECIACEAE

Narthecium ossifragum (L.) Huds.
Bog Asphodel

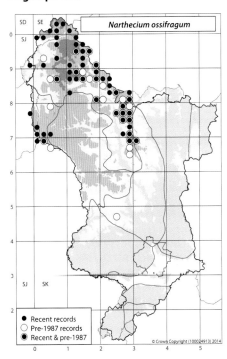

COUNTY STATUS: Native
CONSERVATION STATUS: None
FIRST YEAR: 1789 LATEST YEAR: 2013 NO OF RECORDS: 233
RECENT SQUARES: monads 88; tetrads 57; hectads 14
ALL SQUARES: monads 110; tetrads 70; hectads 17

Bog Asphodel is an attractive native perennial of bogs, moors and wet heaths. It occurs occasionally in the upland parts of the South West and Dark Peak Areas as at Cistern Clough (SK0369), Oaken Clough (SK0786), Lodge Cote (SK1987) and Harland Sick (SK2868). It was also known at Hulland Moss (SK2446) in 1976.

DIOSCOREACEAE

Tamus communis L.
Black Bryony

COUNTY STATUS: Native
CONSERVATION STATUS: None
FIRST YEAR: 1789 LATEST YEAR: 2013 NO OF RECORDS: 1,485
RECENT SQUARES: monads 721; tetrads 377; hectads 30
ALL SQUARES: monads 790; tetrads 393; hectads 31

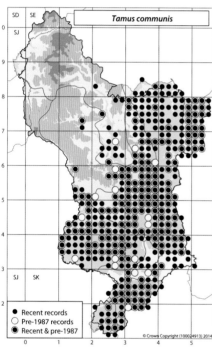

Black Bryony is a scrambling native perennial of hedges, scrub and wood margins on moist, but well-drained, fertile soils. It is common throughout the lowland south and east Derbyshire. In the more upland White, Dark and South West Peak Character Areas it is very rare: Biggin Dale (SK1458), Miller's Dale (SK1672) and Bamford (SK2083).

MELANTHIACEAE

Paris quadrifolia L.
Herb-Paris

Herb-Paris is a very rare, native perennial of moist woods. It occurs on the Magnesian

Herb-Paris (*Paris quadrifolia*) in Monk's Dale woodland (SK1374), July 2008 (Peter Smith)

COUNTY STATUS: Native
CONSERVATION STATUS: DRDB (Cat5b), A
FIRST YEAR: 1787 LATEST YEAR: 2012 NO OF RECORDS: 131
RECENT SQUARES: monads 7; tetrads 5; hectads 3
ALL SQUARES: monads 15; tetrads 9; hectads 14

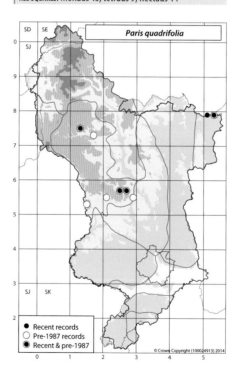

Limestone (Whitwell Wood SK5178/5278) and in the White Peak (Monk's Dale SK1374 & the Via Gellia SK2556/2656). It previously grew over a much larger region, including non-limestone areas, from near Mellor in the north (SJ98) to Newton Wood (SK45) and Repton Rocks in the south (SK32) all from 1903. Nationally it is

considered an indicator of ancient woodland and has shown some decline due to the destruction and coniferisation of woods (Preston *et al.* 2002).

ALSTROEMERIACEAE

Alstroemeria aurea Graham
Peruvian Lily

Peruvian Lily is a very rare, casual perennial of roadsides, and is indigenous to Chile. It is known from only two sites: Beeley Moor (SK2666) in 1994 and Freebirch (SK3073) in 1998. Often cultivated for ornament, these are probably both garden throwouts. Note: the Freebirch plant was originally recorded in error as **Orange Lily** (***Lilium* × *hollandicum*** Woodcock & Stearn) in Moyes & Willmot (2002).

COLCHICACEAE

Colchicum autumnale L.
Meadow Saffron

COUNTY STATUS: Native
CONSERVATION STATUS: DRDB (Cat6), NT, A, B
FIRST YEAR: 1787 LATEST YEAR: 1969 NO OF RECORDS: 14
RECENT SQUARES: monads 0; tetrads 0; hectads 0
ALL SQUARES: monads 3; tetrads 2; hectads 4

Locally extinct, Meadow Saffron was a very rare, native perennial of damp meadows and woods. There are no recent records, although one for SK45 was submitted in error and published in Preston *et al.* (2002). It was previously recorded between 1787 and 1969 in a number of southern sites including Cubley (SK1538), Allestree

(SK3540) and Anchor Church (SK32). Derbyshire is on the northern edge of its British range, possibly making it especially sensitive to agricultural improvement – the likely cause of its decline.

LILIACEAE

Gagea lutea (L.) Ker Gawl.
Yellow Star-of-Bethlehem

COUNTY STATUS: Native
CONSERVATION STATUS: DRDB (Cat5b), B
FIRST YEAR: 1787 LATEST YEAR: 2013 NO OF RECORDS: 160
RECENT SQUARES: monads 17; tetrads 14; hectads 4
ALL SQUARES: monads 28; tetrads 22; hectads 10

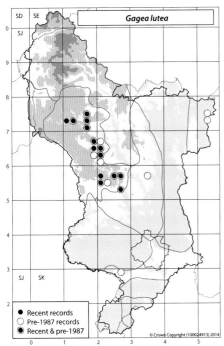

Gagea lutea

Recent records
Pre-1987 records
Recent & pre-1987

© Crown Copyright (100024913) 2014

Yellow Star-of-Bethlehem is a native perennial of damp base-rich woods, scrub and grassland. Recent records indicate that it is a rare plant of the White Peak (Cressbrook Dale SK1774, Greaves Hollow SK2065 & Pitty Wood SK2752). It was previously recorded for the Magnesian Limestone (Creswell Crags SK5374 in 1955), and was scattered elsewhere in the south (Derby SK33 in 1903). A record for Old Egginton Hall (SK2628) in 1982 is an introduction. It is a shy and early flowerer so is probably under-recorded.

Tulipa sylvestris L.
Wild Tulip

Wild Tulip is an established perennial of damp grasslands by streams and in parklands, with just one recent record: Sudbury Hall (SK1532). It was known there in 1903, as well as at Kedleston (SK34 in 1903), The Holmes, Derby (SK33 in 1829) and SK24 in 1903. Popularly planted in the 18th and 19th centuries, these records

probably derive from such cultivation or from garden throwouts. It is a native of southern Europe.

Fritillaria meleagris L.
Fritillary

COUNTY STATUS: Casual
CONSERVATION STATUS: None
FIRST YEAR: 1981 LATEST YEAR: 2013 NO OF RECORDS: 13
RECENT SQUARES: monads 7; tetrads 6; hectads 6
ALL SQUARES: monads 8; tetrads 7; hectads 7

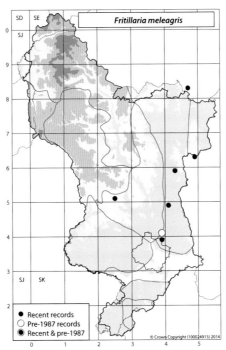

Fritillaria meleagris

Recent records
Pre-1987 records
Recent & pre-1987

© Crown Copyright (100024913) 2014

Fritillary is a very rare, casual perennial of waste ground and waysides. It also occurs planted in grasslands in natural-looking situations. All records are from lowland parts of the county outside The Peak District: Killamarsh (SK4682) and Carsington Water (SK2550). Planted records are from Peasehill (SK4049), Tibshelf (SK4359) and the Rowthorne Trail (SK4863). There is a previous record from Morley Churchyard (SK3940) in 1981. It is considered native to southern England and as such is a Nationally Scarce species.

Lilium martagon L.
Martagon Lily

Martagon Lily is a very rare, casual perennial of woods and parkland, and a native of continental Europe. There are four recent records between 1996 and 2012: Bamford (SK2182), Pleasley Park (SK5165), Bretby Hospital (SK2922) and Risley (SK4635). Previous records extend back to an unlocalised report from SK28 in 1950. Often grown for ornament, our plants probably represent relics of cultivation or garden throwouts.

Lilium pyrenaicum Gouan
Pyrenean Lily

Pyrenean Lily is a very rare, casual perennial of roadside verges. The only recent record is from Cop Low (SK1679) in 2009, and there is one other from Spitalhill (SK1846) in 1971. These plants are probably the result of discarded garden waste. It is indigenous to the Pyrenees.

ORCHIDACEAE

Cypripedium calceolus L.
Lady's-slipper

COUNTY STATUS: Native
CONSERVATION STATUS: DRDB (Cat6), HabsRegs, CitesB, Bern, WCA8, CR, NR, NERC
FIRST YEAR: 1800 LATEST YEAR: 1933 NO OF RECORDS: 2
RECENT SQUARES: monads 0; tetrads 0; hectads 0
ALL SQUARES: monads 1; tetrads 1; hectads 2

Locally extinct, Lady's-slipper was a native perennial of lightly shaded limestone scree slopes. It was last seen below cliffs at The Heights of Abraham (SK25) around the early 1800s. Writing about this sole location, Derby botanist J. Whittaker wrote: "long since extirpated from the county" (Crewe & Whittaker 1864). This suggests over-collecting was the cause of its demise, though no Derbyshire specimen has yet been found in any herbarium. In 1933 stock of continental origin was planted in woodland near its last seen location in SK25 (Garnett 1934), but did not survive. Recent re-introductions from micro-propagated specimens have been attempted, but locations remain confidential.

Cephalanthera damasonium (Mill.) Druce
White Helleborine

COUNTY STATUS: Native
CONSERVATION STATUS: DRDB (Cat6), VU, NERC
FIRST YEAR: 1789 LATEST YEAR: 1789 NO OF RECORDS: 1
RECENT SQUARES: monads 0; tetrads 0; hectads 0
ALL SQUARES: monads 0; tetrads 0; hectads 1

Locally extinct, White Helleborine was a native perennial of limestone woods. The only record is from Newton Wood, Alfreton (SK45) in 1789. Clapham's 1969 Flora mistakenly gave this record as Newton Wood (SK22). It is a southern species and this site was on the northern limit its British range.

Epipactis palustris (L.) Crantz
Marsh Helleborine

COUNTY STATUS: Native
CONSERVATION STATUS: DRDB (Cat4), CitesB, A, B
FIRST YEAR: 1789 LATEST YEAR: 1993 NO OF RECORDS: 20
RECENT SQUARES: monads 1; tetrads 1; hectads 1
ALL SQUARES: monads 2; tetrads 2; hectads 5

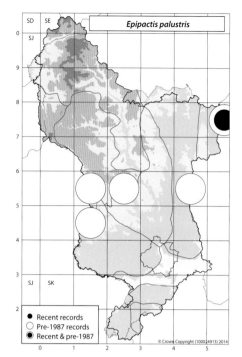

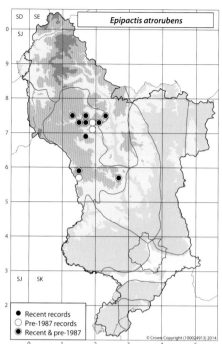

Epipactis helleborine (L.) Crantz
Broad-leaved Helleborine

COUNTY STATUS: Native	
CONSERVATION STATUS: None	
FIRST YEAR: 1787 **LATEST YEAR:** 2013 **NO OF RECORDS:** 296	
RECENT SQUARES: monads 77; tetrads 62; hectads 23	
ALL SQUARES: monads 112; tetrads 92; hectads 30	

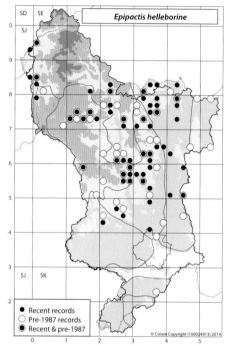

Marsh Helleborine is an attractive and very rare, native perennial of base-rich mires and fen woods in the north of the county. Long known at just one site (Whitwell Wood, SK5278), it was last reported flowering in 1990 but last seen in 1993. A search in 2002 found nothing. It was previously known in central Derbyshire, including Ashbourne (SK14, SK15) and Matlock (SK25), all in 1903. Note: a 1995 record for SK27 was published in error in the New Atlas (Preston *et al.* 2002).

Epipactis atrorubens (Hoffm.) Besser
Dark-red Helleborine

COUNTY STATUS: Native	
CONSERVATION STATUS: DRDB (Cat3), NS, A, B, C	
FIRST YEAR: 1813 **LATEST YEAR:** 2010 **NO OF RECORDS:** 145	
RECENT SQUARES: monads 11; tetrads 9; hectads 5	
ALL SQUARES: monads 17; tetrads 12; hectads 5	

Dark-red Helleborine is a very rare, native perennial of the White Peak where it grows in rocky grasslands and vegetated screes on limestone, often amongst woody plants on the edges of scrub or woodland. It occurs most frequently around Coombs Dale (SK27H), Cressbrook Dale (SK17S) and Priestcliffe Lees (SK17L), but has also been found in Biggin Dale (SK15P) and the Via Gellia (SK25T). One of the best sites on Longstone Edge was destroyed in the 1960s under an existing planning permission for mineral working, and translocations were unsuccessful. Coombs Dale also used to have one of the most extensive colonies. One area was fenced off to exclude sheep, but this did not help much. The fence is presently derelict, and there are now few orchids. There have also been thefts by

collectors from known sites. Categorised as Nationally Scarce, it occurs locally on limestone in upland Britain, with Derbyshire being its southern limit in northern England.

Dark-red Helleborine (*Epipactis atrorubens*), Coombs Dale (SK27), July 2011 (Peter Smith)

Broad-leaved Helleborine is a native perennial of woods, scrub and waysides. It is occasional in central Derbyshire (Blackwell Mill SK1172, Derwent Hotel SK3354, Milltown Quarry SK3562 & Black Rocks SK2955). It occurs rarely in the upland north-western corner, but grows there only in more lowland parts (Gamesley Wood SK0194). There are no recent records south of Derby, nor on the Magnesian Limestone, but there are older records for Spring Wood Reserve (SK3722) in 1977 and Whitwell Wood (SK5278) in 1969. In his 1903 Flora, Linton described a Derbyshire plant he called ***Epipactis atroviridis***. This is not recognised today, and was probably just a more robust form of this species.

Epipactis phyllanthes G.E. Sm.
Green-flowered Helleborine

COUNTY STATUS: Native	
CONSERVATION STATUS: DRDB (Cat3), CitesB, NS, A, B, C	
FIRST YEAR: 1969 **LATEST YEAR:** 1994 **NO OF RECORDS:** 9	
RECENT SQUARES: monads 1; tetrads 1; hectads 1	
ALL SQUARES: monads 1; tetrads 1; hectads 1	

Green-flowered Helleborine is a native perennial of wet woodland on the Magnesian Limestone. It has only ever been found at Whitwell Wood (SK57J). It was first recorded there in Clapham

(1969) and subsequently noted on several occasions up until 1994. Categorised as Nationally Scarce, it occurs scattered throughout mainland Britain, except for northern Scotland. Like many self-pollinating species, plants are very variable from area to area.

Neottia ovata (L.) Bluff & Fingerh.
Common Twayblade

COUNTY STATUS: Native
CONSERVATION STATUS: None
FIRST YEAR: 1789 LATEST YEAR: 2013 NO OF RECORDS: 537
RECENT SQUARES: monads 165; tetrads 108; hectads 26
ALL SQUARES: monads 190; tetrads 122; hectads 31

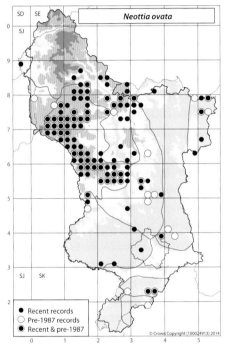

Common Twayblade is a native perennial of grasslands, woods, disused quarries, abandoned gravel pits and, rarely, moorlands. It is frequent throughout the White Peak, as at Dove Holes (SK0877), Parsley Hay Reserve (SK1463) and Middleton Moor (SK2655). Elsewhere it is only rare, though where it does occur it can grow in profusion, as at Hilton Gravel Pits (SK2431), Ticknall Quarries (SK3623) and Markland Grips (SK5075).

Neottia cordata (L.) Rich.
Lesser Twayblade

COUNTY STATUS: Native
CONSERVATION STATUS: DRDB (Cat4), B
FIRST YEAR: 1677 LATEST YEAR: 2012 NO OF RECORDS: 8
RECENT SQUARES: monads 1; tetrads 1; hectads 1
ALL SQUARES: monads 3; tetrads 3; hectads 4

Lesser Twayblade is a very rare, native perennial of moors and rock ledges in the Dark Peak. It was once regarded as locally extinct, having last been recorded

Bird's-nest Orchid (*Neottia nidus-avis*) at Great Shacklow Wood (SK1670), June 2008 (Peter Smith)

in the 1950s. However, in 2010 C. & M. Smith discovered seven flowering spikes near a stream in Hope Forest (SK19) which reappeared in 2011 and 2012. Previous records are from near Grindleford (SK2680) and Cupola (SK2582) in the 1940s and Kinder Scout (SK08) and Hassop (SK27) in 1903. It was probably lost by a combination of excessive grazing, burning of heather moors and over-enthusiastic collecting (Anderson & Shimwell 1981). For this reason only a 10km location is given here for the recent record.

Neottia nidus-avis (L.) Rich.
Bird's-nest Orchid

COUNTY STATUS: Native
CONSERVATION STATUS: DRDB (Cat2), CitesB, NT, A, B
FIRST YEAR: 1802 LATEST YEAR: 2012 NO OF RECORDS: 67
RECENT SQUARES: monads 11; tetrads 9; hectads 5
ALL SQUARES: monads 13; tetrads 10; hectads 10

Bird's-nest Orchid is a very rare, native perennial of shady woods on limestone. It is one of the few flowering plants that feed off decaying vegetation, so it only appears above ground to flower. This could mean its rarity is partly an illusion, caused by under-recording. There are modern records from both the Magnesian Limestone (Scarcliffe Park SK5171) and the Carboniferous Limestone of the White Peak (Shacklow Wood SK1670). Previously

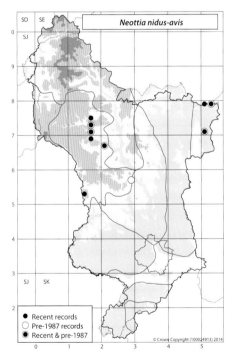

the species had a wider distribution with records off the limestone areas from Wyaston Brook (SK14) to Mottram (SK09) in the Dark Peak and Meersbrook (SK38) all for 1903. It occurs scattered throughout most of Britain but has declined lately, probably due to changes in woodland management, including coniferisation (Preston *et al.* 2002).

Orchidaceae

Spiranthes spiralis (L.) Chevall.
Autumn Lady's-tresses

COUNTY STATUS: Native
CONSERVATION STATUS: DRDB (Cat2), NT, A
FIRST YEAR: 1790   LATEST YEAR: 1969   NO OF RECORDS: 9
RECENT SQUARES: monads 0; tetrads 0; hectads 0
ALL SQUARES: monads 0; tetrads 0; hectads 7

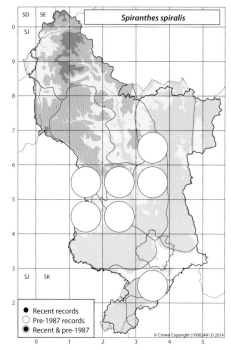

Locally extinct, Autumn Lady's-tresses was a very rare, native perennial of short grassland generally on calcareous soils. It was last reported at Bonsall (SK25) by Clapham (1969) though the record was probably much earlier. Before that, Linton's 1903 Flora gave records from Dove Dale (SK15), Repton (SK32), Osmaston Manor (SK24) and Matlock (SK35); he gave 1790-1795 as the earliest record. This local decline is mirrored by a national loss from many inland sites due to agricultural intensification or undergrazing.

Platanthera chlorantha (Custer) Rchb.
Greater Butterfly-orchid

COUNTY STATUS: Native
CONSERVATION STATUS: DRDB (Cat2), NT, A
FIRST YEAR: 1870   LATEST YEAR: 2012   NO OF RECORDS: 86
RECENT SQUARES: monads 8; tetrads 7; hectads 6
ALL SQUARES: monads 24; tetrads 17; hectads 20

Greater Butterfly-orchid is a very rare, native perennial of woods and unimproved grasslands on calcareous or neutral soils. Its current distribution is the South West Peak and Dark Peak (Edale Valley SK1385 & Abney Clough SK2079) plus the White Peak (Parsley Hay SK1463 & Priestcliffe Lees SK1572), and the Peak Fringe (Alderwasley SK3253). Linton (1903) shows it was previously scattered throughout

Greater Butterfly-orchid (*Platanthera chlorantha*) near Parsley Hay (SK1463), July 2008 (Peter Smith)

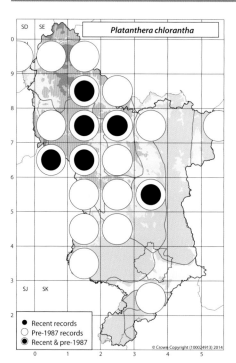

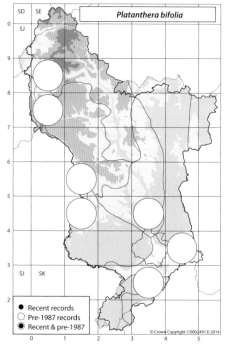

the county, from Charlesworth Coombs (SK09) in the north, to Snelston Park (SK14) and Calke (SK32) in the south. It has shown a similar decline nationally due to the coniferisation of woods and the improvement of grasslands.

Platanthera bifolia (L.) Rich.
Lesser Butterfly-orchid

COUNTY STATUS: Native
CONSERVATION STATUS: DRDB (Cat2), VU, NERC
FIRST YEAR: 1865   LATEST YEAR: 1969   NO OF RECORDS: 11
RECENT SQUARES: monads 0; tetrads 0; hectads 0
ALL SQUARES: monads 1; tetrads 1; hectads 7

Locally extinct, Lesser Butterfly-orchid was a very rare, native perennial of grasslands and open woods on at least moderately base-rich soils. The latest record came from The Goyt Valley (SK0178) in Clapham (1969), though was probably based on an earlier record. All others are from Painter's 1889 Flora or that of Linton in 1903, who considered them doubtful. They were scattered over the county from Newfield (SK08) in the north, to Milton (SK32) and near Dale (SK43) in the south. This loss mirrors a more general decline in the English Midlands due to agricultural intensification. A record for SK27 published in the *New Atlas of the British and Irish Flora* is a known error (Preston *et al.* 2002).

Pseudorchis albida (L.) A. & D. Loeve
Small-white Orchid

COUNTY STATUS: Native
CONSERVATION STATUS: DRDB (Cat6), CitesB, VU, NERC, B
FIRST YEAR: 1829 LATEST YEAR: 1938 NO OF RECORDS: 4
RECENT SQUARES: monads 0; tetrads 0; hectads 0
ALL SQUARES: monads 1; tetrads 1; hectads 2

Locally extinct, Small-white Orchid was a very rare, native perennial of short upland grassland. It was last seen "prior to 1939" in the Goyt Valley (SK0176), and was also recorded from the Glossop area (SK09) before 1903. A plant of upland Britain, these two sites are on the south-eastern margin of its main English distribution.

Gymnadenia R. Br.
Fragrant Orchids

COUNTY STATUS: Native
CONSERVATION STATUS: None
FIRST YEAR: 1789 LATEST YEAR: 2013 NO OF RECORDS: 335
RECENT SQUARES: monads 67; tetrads 49; hectads 13
ALL SQUARES: monads 87; tetrads 59; hectads 18

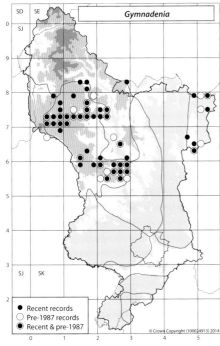

Fragrant Orchids are attractive native perennials of calcareous grasslands, old quarries and waysides. Three species occur here (see below) although until 2010 they were regarded merely as subspecies which few recorders differentiated. This map and account consider all plants together. They occur occasionally throughout the White Peak and Magnesian Limestone areas (Chee Dale SK1272, Hartington Quarry SK1561, Rose End Meadows SK2956 & Teversal Trail SK4963). They are very

rarely found outside these Character Areas (Northwood SK2664 & Houndkirk Moor SK2882). Older records are known from southern Derbyshire, as at Dale (SK43) and near Osmaston Church (SK24), both in 1903.

Gymnadenia conopsea (L.) R. Br.
Chalk Fragrant-orchid

Chalk Fragrant-orchid is an occasional native perennial of limestone grassland on both Carboniferous and Magnesian Limestone. Most Fragrant-orchid records must refer to this species, but there are only two actual records for it: grassland by Middleton Lagoon (SK2075) in 2000, and SK07 in 1950.

Gymnadenia densiflora (Wahlenb.) A. Dietr.
Marsh Fragrant-orchid

Marsh Fragrant-orchid is a very rare, native perennial of north-facing or damp grasslands and fens, frequently associated with lime slurry in quarries. It is only known from the White Peak (Priestcliffe Lees SK1472, Slaley area SK2657, Harpur Hill SK0570 & Peak Dale SK0976-SK0975) and the Magnesian Limestone (Teversal Trail SK4963). All sightings are recent and it is probably under-recorded.

Gymnadenia borealis (Druce) R.M. Bateman, Pridgeon & M.W. Chase
Heath Fragrant-orchid

Heath Fragrant-orchid is a very rare, native perennial of rough upland grasslands. The only localised record is a recent one from near Hartington Station Quarry (SK1661). It is probably under-recorded.

Chalk Fragrant-orchid (*Gymnadenia conopsea*), Chee Dale Quarry (SK1373), July 2008 (Peter Smith)

Coeloglossum viride (L.) Hartm.
Frog Orchid

COUNTY STATUS: Native
CONSERVATION STATUS: DRDB (Cat2), VU, NERC
FIRST YEAR: 1793 LATEST YEAR: 2013 NO OF RECORDS: 290
RECENT SQUARES: monads 48; tetrads 34; hectads 10
ALL SQUARES: monads 76; tetrads 55; hectads 21

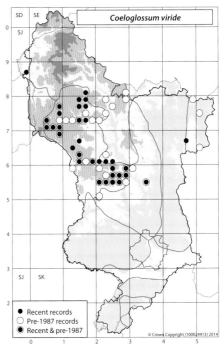

Frog Orchid is a rare native perennial of pastures and rough grassland, generally on limestone. The majority of records are from the White Peak (Grin Low SK0571, Priestcliffe Lees Reserve SK1472, Hartington Station Quarry SK1460, Middleton Moor SK2655 & Hopton Quarry Reserve SK2656). Elsewhere it is very rare in the northern half of the county (Mellor Moor SJ9887, Crich Tramway Museum SK3455 & Glapwell Reclamation Site SK4667). Linton's 1903 Flora shows it once occurred in southern Derbyshire (Calke SK32, Spondon Fields SK33/43 & Stanton-by-Dale SK43), a loss probably due to agricultural intensification.

✕ *Dactyloglossum mixtum* (Asch. & Graebn.) Rauschert
A hybrid orchid

This hybrid orchid is a very rare, native perennial of calcareous grassland. There are only two records: Tissington Trail (SK1461) in 2011 and Middleton-by-Wirksworth (SK2755) in 1971. It is the hybrid of Frog Orchid (*Coeloglossum viride*) and Common spotted-orchid (*Dactylorhiza fuchsii*).

Dactylorhiza fuchsii (Druce) Soo
Common Spotted-orchid

Common Spotted-orchid is an occasional native perennial of grasslands, waste places, marshy areas and woods on base-

COUNTY STATUS: Native

CONSERVATION STATUS: None

FIRST YEAR: 1789 **LATEST YEAR:** 2013 **NO OF RECORDS:** 1,258

RECENT SQUARES: monads 412; tetrads 270; hectads 37

ALL SQUARES: monads 459; tetrads 300; hectads 38

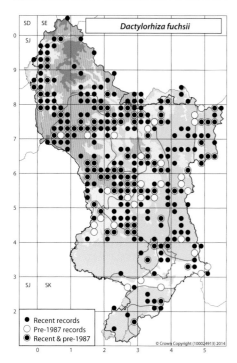

rich to neutral soils. It occurs throughout Derbyshire from Torside Reservoir (SK0698) and Moss Valley (SK3880) in the north, to Swainspark (SK2917) and Ticknall Quarries (SK3623) in the south. It has been lost from some sites due to agricultural improvement but these have been balanced by its ability to colonise new, often man-made, habitats. The striking variety *rhodochila* with uniformly magenta flowers has been recorded rarely, as at Slaley (SK2657) in 2002 and near Buxton (SK0975) in 1984 (Ettlinger 1991). The species has the local name of Nightcaps, though this is also applied to the Heath Spotted-orchid (*D. maculata*) Grigson (1975).

Dactylorhiza × *transiens* (Druce) Soo
A hybrid spotted-orchid

COUNTY STATUS: Native

CONSERVATION STATUS: None

FIRST YEAR: 1950 **LATEST YEAR:** 1995 **NO OF RECORDS:** 5

RECENT SQUARES: monads 4; tetrads 4; hectads 3

ALL SQUARES: monads 4; tetrads 4; hectads 4

This hybrid spotted-orchid is a very rare, native perennial of rough grassy areas where base-rich and base-poor soils co-exist. It has been recorded only in the northern half of the county at Chelmorton Rake (SK1170), Beeley (SK2766), Owler Bar (SK2876) and Calver (SK2375). In 1950 it was also found in SK28. It is the sterile hybrid

of Common (*D. fuchsii*) and Heath Spotted-orchid (*D. maculata*), so only occurs as isolated individuals.

Dactylorhiza × *kernerorum* (Soo) Soo
A hybrid orchid

This hybrid orchid is a very rare, native perennial that occurs in wet grasslands and calcareous marshes with its parents. It was discovered in 1991 by L. Storer on a roadside on the Hucklow/Bradwell Moors (SK1679). There have been two subsequent sightings: Monsal Trail (SK1172) and Ramsley Moor (SK2876). It is the sterile hybrid of Common Spotted-orchid (*D. fuchsii*) and Early Marsh-orchid (*D. incarnata*), so only occurs as isolated individuals.

Dactylorhiza × *grandis* (Druce) P.F. Hunt
A hybrid orchid

COUNTY STATUS: Native

CONSERVATION STATUS: None

FIRST YEAR: 1969 **LATEST YEAR:** 2013 **NO OF RECORDS:** 75

RECENT SQUARES: monads 26; tetrads 23; hectads 12

ALL SQUARES: monads 34; tetrads 29; hectads 13

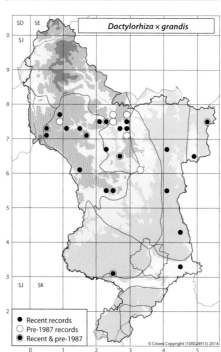

This hybrid orchid is a very rare, native perennial of rough and wet grassy areas in marshes, fens, old quarries and industrial wasteland. It occurs scattered over central parts (Grin Wood SK0472, Rowsley Sidings SK2664, Mortimer Wilson School grounds SK4155 & Hilton Gravel Pits SK2431). At 380m a site near Buxton holds the UK altitude record for the plant. Its parents are Common Spotted-orchid (*D. fuchsii*) and Southern Marsh-orchid (*D. praetermissa*), with which it generally occurs.

Dactylorhiza × *venusta* (T. & T.A. Stephenson) Soo
A hybrid orchid

COUNTY STATUS: Native

CONSERVATION STATUS: None

FIRST YEAR: 1973 **LATEST YEAR:** 2004 **NO OF RECORDS:** 13

RECENT SQUARES: monads 7; tetrads 6; hectads 2

ALL SQUARES: monads 8; tetrads 6; hectads 2

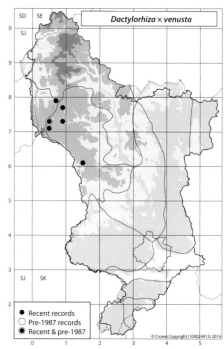

This hybrid orchid is a very rare, native perennial of damp and rough grassy areas in marshes, fens, old quarries and industrial wasteland. It was discovered in 1973 at Grin Wood (SK0472) by R. Carr and found in five other areas since, all recent: Cow Dale (SK0872), Peak Dale (SK0876), Longsidings Quarry (SK0976), Dove Holes (SK0778) and Hartington Station (SK1561). It is the partly fertile hybrid of Common Spotted-orchid (*D. fuchsii*) and Northern Marsh-orchid (*D. purpurella*), so can occur in back-cross with its parents. A plant of upland Britain, Derbyshire is on the south-eastern edge of its range.

Dactylorhiza maculata (L.) Soo
Heath Spotted-orchid

COUNTY STATUS: Native

CONSERVATION STATUS: None

FIRST YEAR: 1880 **LATEST YEAR:** 2013 **NO OF RECORDS:** 133

RECENT SQUARES: monads 45; tetrads 47; hectads 17

ALL SQUARES: monads 67; tetrads 64; hectads 20

Heath Spotted-orchid is a rare native perennial of damp peaty areas in grasslands, heaths, bogs and marshes. It occurs throughout northern Derbyshire (Upper Derwent SK1096, Goyt's Clough SK0172 v.c.58, Blacka Moor SK2880 & near Matlock SK36A). In the south there are isolated

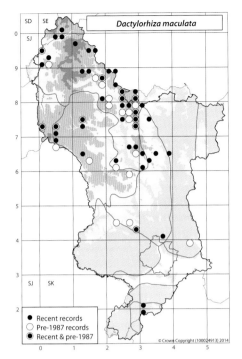

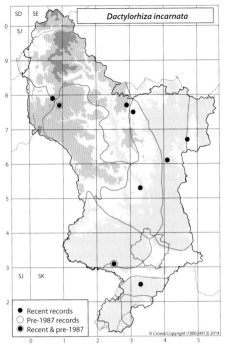

occurrences at Mugginton Bottoms (SK2843), Midway Clay Site (SK3019 & SK3020) and Breadsall (SK3741). It was previously known from Dale Abbey (SK4438) in 1945. Our plant is ssp. *ericetorum* (E.F. Linton) P.F. Hunt & Summerh. and has a local name of Nightcaps, though this appears to have applied to Common Spotted-orchid (*D. fuchsii*) as well (Grigson 1975).

Dactylorhiza × formosa (T. & T.A. Stephenson) Soo
A hybrid orchid
This hybrid orchid is a very rare, native perennial. It was discovered at Howe Green (SK0467) in 1975 by P. Torry. Surprisingly it has not been recorded since, as it is a fully fertile hybrid resulting from the spontaneous crossing of Heath Spotted-orchid (*D. maculata*) with Northern Marsh-orchid (*D. purpurella*).

Dactylorhiza incarnata (L.) Soo
Early Marsh-orchid

COUNTY STATUS: Native
CONSERVATION STATUS: DRDB (Cat5a), A, B
FIRST YEAR: 1969 LATEST YEAR: 2012 NO OF RECORDS: 21
RECENT SQUARES: monads 9; tetrads 9; hectads 7
ALL SQUARES: monads 10; tetrads 9; hectads 7

Early Marsh-orchid is a very rare, native perennial of wet meadows and marshes. It is scattered over central and southern regions (Longsidings Quarry SK0975/0976, Ramsley Moor SK2876, Hilton Gravel Pits SK2431, Glapwell Reclamation Site SK4669 & Alderwasley SK3253).Three subspecies have been recorded: **ssp. incarnata** is taken to be the "common" plant in Derbyshire (Clapham, 1969); **ssp. coccinea** (Pugsley) Soo and **ssp. pulchella** (Druce) Soo have both

been recorded, but only for Longsidings Quarry (SK0976). Plants were first found by P. Torry in 1996, and subsequently determined by separate experts as different subspecies! The former is a plant of base-rich sandy marshes near the sea, so its occurrence here is unexpected. The latter is found on acid to neutral mires (Stace 2010).

Dactylorhiza × wintoni (A. Camus) P.F. Hunt
A hybrid marsh-orchid
This hybrid Marsh-orchid is a very rare, native perennial discovered at Ramsley Moor (SK2876) in 1993 by L. Storer, but has

not been recorded since. It results from the crossing of Early (*D. incarnata*) with Southern Marsh-orchid (*D. praetermissa*).

Dactylorhiza praetermissa (Druce) Soo
Southern Marsh-orchid

COUNTY STATUS: Native
CONSERVATION STATUS: None
FIRST YEAR: 1903 LATEST YEAR: 2013 NO OF RECORDS: 356
RECENT SQUARES: monads 123; tetrads 98; hectads 28
ALL SQUARES: monads 144; tetrads 115; hectads 29

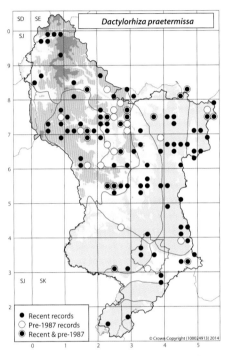

Southern Marsh-orchid is an occasional native perennial of marshes, damp

Southern Marsh-orchid (*Dactylorhiza praetermissa*) near Breaston (SK43), June 2008 (Peter Smith)

grasslands and fens, often in the context of disused gravel pits, quarries or industrial waste ground. It occurs throughout Derbyshire, though becomes rarer on high ground in the north and in intensively farmed areas of the south. Typical sites include Coombs Dale (SK2274), Harborough Works (SK2355), Hilton Gravel Pits (SK2431), Holbrook Meadows (SK4480) and Golden Brook Storage Lagoon (SK4633).

Dactylorhiza × *insignis* (T. & T.A. Stephenson) Soo
A hybrid marsh-orchid

This native hybrid marsh-orchid has only been recorded from the Buxton area. It was first found by L. Storer at Grin Low (SK0571) in 1988. It was subsequently found again at Grin Low and then at Harpur Hill (SK0670) both in 2010. It results from the crossing of Southern and Northern Marsh-orchids (*D. praetermissa*) and (*D. purpurella*).

Dactylorhiza purpurella (T. & T.A. Stephenson) Soo
Northern Marsh-orchid

COUNTY STATUS: Native	
CONSERVATION STATUS: B	
FIRST YEAR: 1969 **LATEST YEAR:** 2012 **NO OF RECORDS:** 54	
RECENT SQUARES: monads 21; tetrads 17; hectads 7	
ALL SQUARES: monads 24; tetrads 19; hectads 8	

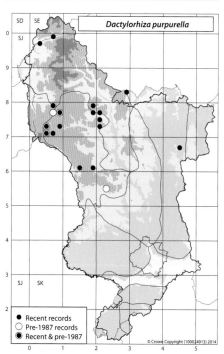

Northern Marsh-orchid is a very rare, native perennial of marshes, wet grasslands and fens, often in association with disused industrial sites such as abandoned quarries. It occurs in the northern half of the county (Longdendale SK0698, Doveholes Dale SK0877, Hartington Station Quarry SK1561, Houndkirk Moor SK2882 & M1 Junction

29 SK4566). A plant of upland Britain, our sites are on the south-eastern limit of its UK distribution (Preston *et al.* 2002).

Orchis mascula (L.) L.
Early-purple Orchid

COUNTY STATUS: Native	
CONSERVATION STATUS: None	
FIRST YEAR: 1789 **LATEST YEAR:** 2013 **NO OF RECORDS:** 675	
RECENT SQUARES: monads 178; tetrads 107; hectads 18	
ALL SQUARES: monads 204; tetrads 122; hectads 31	

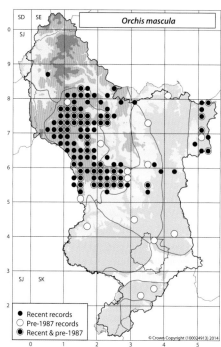

Early-purple Orchid is an attractive native perennial of grasslands and woods, generally on base-rich soils. It is frequent in the White Peak (Laughman Tor SK1077, Cressbrook Dale SK1774 & Middleton Moor SK2655) and on the Magnesian Limestone (Pleasley SK5165 & Whitwell Wood SK5278). In the White Peak grasslands it can be common enough to turn the dalesides purple in spring, but elsewhere in Derbyshire it is only found sporadically (Windmill Field SK3959). It did previously occur in southern Derbyshire (Hartshorne SK3222 in 1977 & Ticknall Quarry SK3624 in 1966), but this loss is sadly part of a more general decline in central England due to agricultural intensification (Preston *et al.* 2002).

Orchis anthropophora (L.) All.
Man Orchid

COUNTY STATUS: Established (Neophyte)	
CONSERVATION STATUS: B, C	
FIRST YEAR: 1959 **LATEST YEAR:** 1984 **NO OF RECORDS:** 6	
RECENT SQUARES: monads 0; tetrads 0; hectads 0	
ALL SQUARES: monads 1; tetrads 1; hectads 1	

Man Orchid is a perennial plant of open grassy woodland on limestone, discovered

at its only site in a quarry at Ashover (SK3562) in 1959 by R. Carr. It was last recorded there in 1984, and believed to have become extinct by 1994 at the latest. Its origins are uncertain, and there has long been speculation it was planted. Nationally it is a southern species, with Derbyshire outside its native range.

Neotinea ustulata (L.) R.M. Bateman, Pridgeon & M.W. Chase
Burnt Orchid

COUNTY STATUS: Native	
CONSERVATION STATUS: DRDB (Cat2), CitesB, EN, NS, NERC, A, B, C	
FIRST YEAR: 1789 **LATEST YEAR:** 2010 **NO OF RECORDS:** 132	
RECENT SQUARES: monads 6; tetrads 5; hectads 2	
ALL SQUARES: monads 13; tetrads 8; hectads 5	

Burnt Orchid is a very rare, native perennial of limestone grasslands. This beautiful and distinctive plant now grows in just five 1km squares in the White Peak (Brassington region, SK25). It has been suggested that one site, containing over 620 flowering spikes in May 2000, holds more plants than the whole of northern England put together. A further site containing just three orchids was discovered by R. Frost in 1986 on the Magnesian Limestone (Scarcliffe Park region, SK57), but has not been seen since 1994. It was formerly more widespread, though still very limited in range (Ashwood Dale SK07 in 1903, Winster

Burnt Orchid (*Neotinea ustulata*) in calcareous grassland, Brassington region (SK25), June 2013 (Peter Smith)

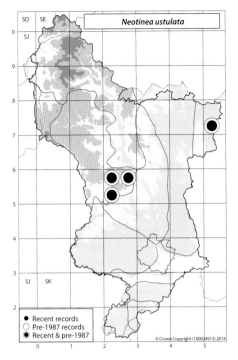

SK26 in 1970 & Alfreton SK45 in 1903). Elsewhere, it grows very rarely throughout England, and is thus a Nationally Scarce species. Because of recent orchid thefts, the map is only accurate to 5km. We ask anyone knowing their locations not to publish them.

Anacamptis pyramidalis (L.) Rich.
Pyramidal Orchid

COUNTY STATUS: Native
CONSERVATION STATUS: B
FIRST YEAR: 1789 LATEST YEAR: 2012 NO OF RECORDS: 154
RECENT SQUARES: monads 33; tetrads 25; hectads 15
ALL SQUARES: monads 42; tetrads 29; hectads 17

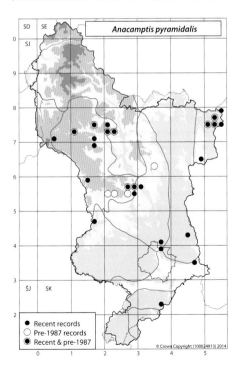

Pyramidal Orchid is a rare native perennial of well-drained grassland that can also colonise old quarries and wasteland. This beautiful plant is mainly seen in the White Peak and on the Magnesian Limestone (Topley Pike SK1072, Deep Rake SK2273, Rose End Meadows SK2856 & Bakestone Moor SK5276). Elsewhere it occurs only as isolated populations (Shipley Country Park SK4443 & south of Morley Lane SK3741).

Anacamptis morio (L.) R.M. Bateman, Pridgeon & M.W. Chase
Green-winged Orchid

COUNTY STATUS: Native
CONSERVATION STATUS: DRDB (Cat2), CitesB, NT, A, B
FIRST YEAR: 1789 LATEST YEAR: 2003 NO OF RECORDS: 52
RECENT SQUARES: monads 2; tetrads 2; hectads 1
ALL SQUARES: monads 13; tetrads 13; hectads 16

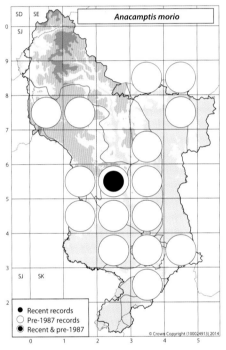

Green-winged Orchid is a very rare, native perennial of unimproved grassland in the White Peak. There are only two recent records: Carsington Water (SK2452) in 2003 and Rose End Meadows (SK2956) in 2000. It formerly grew throughout Derbyshire, except for the Dark Peak, with sites ranging from Ashwood Dale (SK07) and Troway (SK3980) in the north, to Repton (SK32) in the south. This contraction in range was due mostly to agricultural improvement. It disappeared, for example, from Weston Fields Farm Chellaston (SK3929) in 1975 due to being ploughed up. This was the last known site in the county until its recent rediscovery.

Ophrys insectifera L.
Fly Orchid

Fly Orchid is a very rare, native perennial of scrub and quarry spoil tips on limestone.

Fly Orchid (*Ophrys insectifera*) at Goodluck Mine (SK2656), May 2000 (Peter Smith)

COUNTY STATUS: Native
CONSERVATION STATUS: DRDB (Cat2), VU, NERC, A, B
FIRST YEAR: 1793 LATEST YEAR: 2012 NO OF RECORDS: 110
RECENT SQUARES: monads 13; tetrads 10; hectads 5
ALL SQUARES: monads 17; tetrads 13; hectads 10

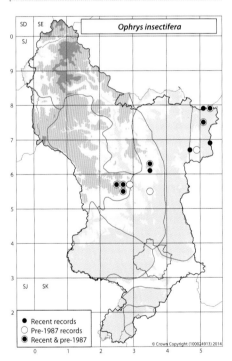

All records come from the White Peak (Hopton Quarry SK2656), the Peak Fringe (Fallgate Quarry SK3562) or the Magnesian Limestone (Markland Grips SK5074). Previously records came from the same Character Areas but were more widely spread over the White Peak, from as far north as Monsal Dale (SK17). It grows sporadically throughout England and Wales, and has shown a similar decline in national distribution due to scrub encroachment, wood clearance and drainage (Preston *et al.* 2002).

Ophrys apifera Huds.
Bee Orchid

COUNTY STATUS: Native	
CONSERVATION STATUS: CitesB	
FIRST YEAR: 1789 LATEST YEAR: 2012 NO OF RECORDS: 451	
RECENT SQUARES: monads 121; tetrads 83; hectads 26	
ALL SQUARES: monads 138; tetrads 93; hectads 26	

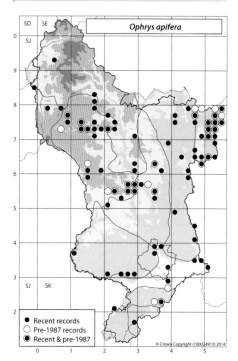

Bee Orchid is an attractive native perennial of grassland, scrub and quarry-waste, often colonising recently disturbed sites. Apart from the South West Peak and Dark Peak, where it is very rare, it occurs occasionally throughout the county (Millers Dale SK1373, Hopton Quarry SK2656, Derby SK3638, Pleasley SK4963 & Steetley Quarry SK5478). Variety *trollii* has been recorded in the past at Ticknall (SK3523). At 335m a site near Parsley Hay holds the national altitude record (Preston *et al.* 2002). The number of flower spikes varies greatly from year to year at any one site, and may depend on factors such as fluctuations in rabbit grazing or winter freezing. Climate change may explain the national doubling in frequency since 1987-1988 seen in the BSBI's Local Change Survey (Braithwaite *et al.* 2006).

IRIDACEAE

Sisyrinchium bermudiana L.
Blue-eyed-grass

COUNTY STATUS: Established (Neophyte)	
CONSERVATION STATUS: None	
FIRST YEAR: 1969 LATEST YEAR: 2012 NO OF RECORDS: 9	
RECENT SQUARES: monads 2; tetrads 1; hectads 1	
ALL SQUARES: monads 7; tetrads 7; hectads 7	

Blue-eyed-grass is an established perennial of waste ground and meadows. The only

two recent records come from the Pleasley area (SK4964 & 4965). There are a handful of earlier records, from near Bugsworth (SK0182) for 1969 in the north, to Derby City (SK33) for 1986 in the south. Much grown as a garden ornamental, it seeds or is discarded into more natural situations. It is native to North America and possibly the west of Ireland.

Sisyrinchium montanum Greene
American Blue-eyed-grass
American Blue-eyed-grass is a casual perennial of waste ground and waysides. It has only ever been recorded from near Bradwell (SK1680) in 2005. However, older records in Clapham (1969) for Blue-eyed-grass (*S. bermudiana*) may possibly be errors for this species. Often cultivated in gardens, it is a native of North America.

Sisyrinchium striatum Sm.
Pale Yellow-eyed-grass
Pale Yellow-eyed-grass is a casual evergreen perennial. The only record was made by A. Mylward on disturbed ground in Derby (SK3635) in 2004. Frequently grown in gardens, it is indigenous to South America.

Iris germanica L.
Bearded Iris

COUNTY STATUS: Established (Neophyte)	
CONSERVATION STATUS: None	
FIRST YEAR: 1973 LATEST YEAR: 2007 NO OF RECORDS: 8	
RECENT SQUARES: monads 4; tetrads 4; hectads 4	
ALL SQUARES: monads 5; tetrads 5; hectads 5	

Bearded Iris is an established perennial of waste ground, waysides and tips. It has only been recorded at four sites recently: Longstone Edge (SK2373), Raynesway (SK3834), Spital (SK3870) and Beighton Marsh (SK4384). Regularly grown in gardens for ornament, these probably represent relics of cultivation or garden throwouts.

Iris sibirica L.
Siberian Iris
Siberian Iris is an established perennial of waste ground, and a native of central Europe. Grown in gardens for ornament, our sole record from Sandhill Lane (SJ9890) in 1996 was probably a garden throwout.

Iris pseudacorus L.
Yellow Iris

COUNTY STATUS: Native	
CONSERVATION STATUS: None	
FIRST YEAR: 1789 LATEST YEAR: 2013 NO OF RECORDS: 1,022	
RECENT SQUARES: monads 488; tetrads 359; hectads 40	
ALL SQUARES: monads 516; tetrads 372; hectads 40	

Yellow Iris is a frequent native perennial. It grows on the margins of ponds, lakes and rivers, and also occurs in wet meadows, marshes and fens. Apart from the high moors of the South West and Dark Peak Character Areas, it has been noted throughout the county from near Chew (SJ9992) and Normanton Springs (SK4084) in the north, to Coton in the Elms (SK2415) and Trent Lock (SK4831) in the south. It is increasingly

Yellow Iris (*Iris pseudacorus*) at Calver Marshes (SK2475), June 2008 (Peter Smith)

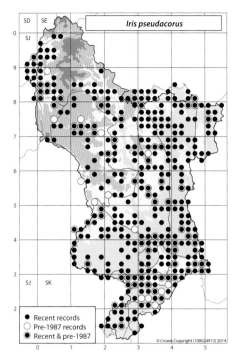

planted around ornamental waterbodies, so some records may represent introductions.

Iris foetidissima L.
Stinking Iris

COUNTY STATUS: Established (Neophyte)
CONSERVATION STATUS: None
FIRST YEAR: 1997 **LATEST YEAR:** 2013 **NO OF RECORDS:** 13
RECENT SQUARES: monads 7; tetrads 7; hectads 5
ALL SQUARES: monads 7; tetrads 7; hectads 5

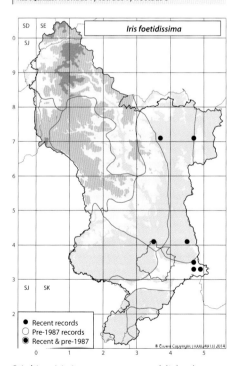

Stinking Iris is a very rare, established perennial of waysides and waste ground, but is a native of southern Britain. It is recorded sparingly for the eastern half of

the county between 1997 and 2013. There are records from Holme Brook (SK3771) in the north, to Risley Glebe (SK4635) in the south. The record in Clapham's 1969 Flora for "Nr. Willersley Park" in SK25 is based on Linton (1903), but is considered an error for Willersley Park in Leicestershire. Grown for ornament, local records are probably of garden throwouts.

Crocus vernus (L.) Hill
Spring Crocus

Spring Crocus is a casual perennial of waysides and amenity grasslands, and is a native of southern Europe. It is only recorded from six sites, all between 1998 and 2012: Taxal (SK0079), Flagg Moor (SK1368), Rose End Meadows (SK2956), Long Walk (SK3040), Holymoorside (SK3369) and Long Eaton (SK4934). It is the commonest Crocus grown in gardens, so these records probably represent throwouts or relics of cultivation.

Crocus tommasinianus Herb.
Early Crocus

Early Crocus is an established perennial of waysides. There are only three recent records: Ollersett (SK0285), Trent Lock (SK4831) and Long Eaton (SK4834) plus an earlier one from the Via Gellia (SK2556) in 1978. It is grown in gardens and probably establishes itself from discarded waste. It is indigenous to south-eastern Europe.

Crocus nudiflorus Sm.
Autumn Crocus

Autumn Crocus is an established perennial of waysides and amenity grasslands

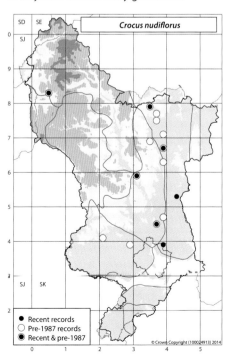

COUNTY STATUS: Established (Neophyte)
CONSERVATION STATUS: None
FIRST YEAR: 1787 **LATEST YEAR:** 2012 **NO OF RECORDS:** 71
RECENT SQUARES: monads 8; tetrads 7; hectads 7
ALL SQUARES: monads 20; tetrads 15; hectads 10

where it is often deliberately planted for naturalising. It is found very rarely throughout the county from Chinley (SK0483) and Gosforth Wood (SK3478) in the north, to Breadsall (SK3839) in the south. It was previously noted at Repton (SK32) in 1903. Often grown in gardens, these records are mainly relics of cultivation or throwouts. It was transplanted from the Setts to Wingerworth Churchyard (SK3867) around 1980 to commemorate R. Carr, a local naturalist. It is indigenous to south-western Europe.

Crocosmia × crocosmiiflora (Lemoine) N.E. Br.
Montbretia

COUNTY STATUS: Established (Neophyte)
CONSERVATION STATUS: WCA9
FIRST YEAR: 1968 **LATEST YEAR:** 2013 **NO OF RECORDS:** 140
RECENT SQUARES: monads 92; tetrads 95; hectads 28
ALL SQUARES: monads 98; tetrads 101; hectads 29

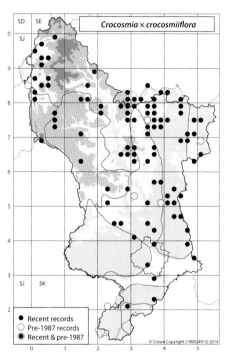

Montbretia is an established perennial of waysides and waste ground. It is occasional throughout the county, from near Gamesley (SK0194) and Totley Bents (SK3080) in the north, to Newhall (SK2920) and Sinfin (SK3532) in the south. Frequently grown in gardens, it often escapes as a throwout. It is of cultivated origin from the hybridisation of Pott's Montbretia (*C. pottsii* (Macnab ex Baker) N.E. Br.) with Golden Montbretia (*C. aurea* (Hook.) Planch.).

XANTHORRHOEACEAE

Phormium tenax J.R. & G. Forst.
New Zealand Flax

New Zealand Flax is a casual perennial of waysides. The only record is from Buxworth (SK0281) in 2003 where it was seeding itself from individuals planted in a roadside amenity scheme. It is a native of New Zealand.

ALLIACEAE

Allium schoenoprasum L.
Chives

Chives is an established perennial of waysides and tips. It is very rare, with only three recent records: Long Line (SK2982), Brockwell (SK3671) and Wragg's Quarry (SK2866). There is an earlier record from Winster (SK26) in 1889. Commonly grown as a herb, these are all probably relics of cultivation or garden throwouts. It is native elsewhere in Britain.

Allium cepa L.
Onion

Onion is a casual of waysides and tips. The sole record is from Fairfield (SK0674) in 1996. Of cultivated origin, it is commonly grown in gardens, and is probably ignored by most botanists.

Allium roseum L.
Rosy Garlic

Rosy Garlic is a casual perennial of waste ground. The sole record is from Long Eaton (SK4932) in 2008. A garden ornamental, it is native to the Mediterranean.

Allium moly L.
Yellow Garlic

Yellow Garlic is a casual perennial of waste ground. There are only two records: Derby (SK3635) and Brailsford (SK2541). A garden ornamental, it is native to Spain and France.

Allium triquetrum L.
Three-cornered Garlic

COUNTY STATUS: Established (Neophyte)	
CONSERVATION STATUS: WCA9	
FIRST YEAR: 2000 LATEST YEAR: 2011 NO OF RECORDS: 10	
RECENT SQUARES: monads 7; tetrads 7; hectads 6	
ALL SQUARES: monads 7; tetrads 7; hectads 6	

Three-cornered Garlic is an established perennial of waysides and rough ground, and is indigenous to the western Mediterranean. It grows very rarely throughout central parts of the county: Monk's Dale (SK1373/1374), Holloway (SK3256) and Hallam Fields (SK4739). Grown in gardens for ornament, it escapes by being thrown out or by seeds being

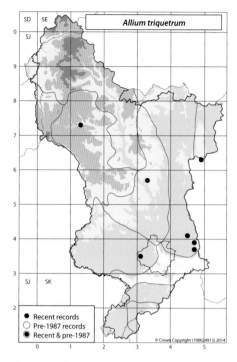

dispersed by ants. Its increase here is mirrored by a similar national trend since 1962 (Preston *et al.* 2002).

Allium paradoxum (M. Bieb.) G. Don
Few-flowered Garlic

COUNTY STATUS: Casual	
CONSERVATION STATUS: WCA9	
FIRST YEAR: 1977 LATEST YEAR: 2009 NO OF RECORDS: 6	
RECENT SQUARES: monads 4; tetrads 3; hectads 3	
ALL SQUARES: monads 5; tetrads 4; hectads 4	

Few-flowered Garlic is a very rare, casual perennial of waysides and rough ground. There are recent records from only three areas: Breadsall (SK3739), Derby Canal (SK4734 & 4735) and Norton (SK3682). There is also an old one from Beauchief (SK3381) in 1977. A garden ornamental, it is native to the Caucasus.

Allium ursinum L.
Ramsons

COUNTY STATUS: Native	
CONSERVATION STATUS: None	
FIRST YEAR: 1789 LATEST YEAR: 2013 NO OF RECORDS: 1,268	
RECENT SQUARES: monads 474; tetrads 306; hectads 38	
ALL SQUARES: monads 506; tetrads 323; hectads 38	

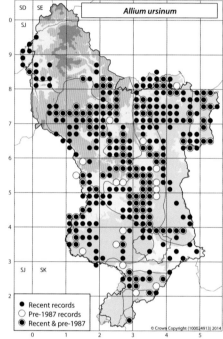

Ramsons is a native perennial of damp shaded habitats such as woodland floors and riverbanks. Except for the high moors

Ramsons (*Allium ursinum*) near Cromford Canal (SK3255), April 2008 (Peter Smith)

of the South West and Dark Peak Character Areas, it is frequent throughout the county: New Mills (SJ9885), Ginny Spring (SK5278), Netherseal (SK2912) and Melbourne (SK3824). It can form dense, aromatic stands over large areas as Farey (1815) noted "I saw a great deal of this weed in Matlock Bath Dale", where it still grows today.

Allium oleraceum L.
Field Garlic

COUNTY STATUS: Native
CONSERVATION STATUS: DRDB (Cat2), VU, B
FIRST YEAR: 1829 LATEST YEAR: 2012 NO OF RECORDS: 101
RECENT SQUARES: monads 23; tetrads 19; hectads 10
ALL SQUARES: monads 39; tetrads 30; hectads 14

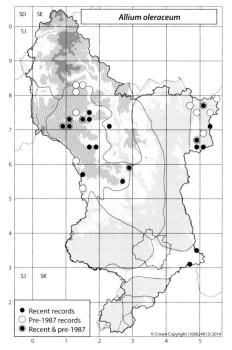

Field Garlic is a native perennial of rock ledges and dry grassland generally over limestone. It is found occasionally in both the White Peak (Miller's Dale SK1573, Deep Dale SK1071 & Pic Tor SK2959) and on the Magnesian Limestone (Stoney Houghton SK4866). Elsewhere it is known from Sawley Oxbow (SK4631) and the Erewash Canal (SK4834). It was also noted from near Thrumpton Ferry (SK53) in 1968 and Knowle Hills (SK32) in 1903.

Allium scorodoprasum L.
Sand Leek

COUNTY STATUS: Native
CONSERVATION STATUS: DRDB (Cat5a), A, B
FIRST YEAR: 1938 LATEST YEAR: 2003 NO OF RECORDS: 19
RECENT SQUARES: monads 5; tetrads 4; hectads 1
ALL SQUARES: monads 9; tetrads 5; hectads 2

Sand Leek is a very rare, native perennial of dry grassland and scrub. All recent records come from a small area around Rowsley

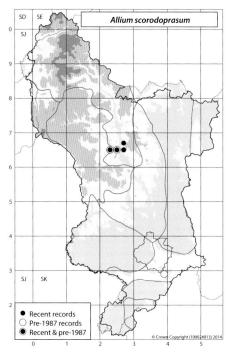

(SK2364 to 2766) and there is an old record from the canal side at Swarkestone (SK3829) for 1938. It is a northern species, with Derbyshire on the southern limit of its native range.

Allium vineale L.
Wild Onion

COUNTY STATUS: Native
CONSERVATION STATUS: None
FIRST YEAR: 1787 LATEST YEAR: 2013 NO OF RECORDS: 133
RECENT SQUARES: monads 29; tetrads 22; hectads 8
ALL SQUARES: monads 46; tetrads 35; hectads 21

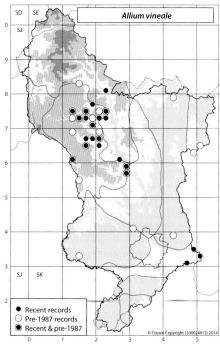

Wild Onion is a native perennial of cliff-ledges, walls, grassland and rough ground

generally on dry calcareous to neutral soils. It is occasional in the White Peak: Tansley Dale (SK1674), Monsal Dale (SK1871) and the Via Gellia (SK2857). Elsewhere it is very rare and confined to the area around Attenborough (SK5032). Previous records cover most of the county: Sudbury Hall grounds (SK1532) in 1977 and near Pleasley (SK4863) in 1979. Two varieties have been reported, *compactum* (Thuill.) Boreau and *vineale*, though there are no recent records of either.

Nectaroscordum siculum (Ucria) Lindl.
Honey Garlic

Honey Garlic is an established bulbous perennial. Its sole station is in Wye Dale (SK1072), where it was found by J. Hodgson in 2002 and refound in 2006. A garden plant from southern Europe, it is probably a garden throwout here.

Tristagma uniflorum (Lindl.) Traub
Spring Starflower

Spring Starflower is a casual bulbous perennial of waysides known only from Spondon (SK4036) where it was found by R. Martin in 2006. It is native to South America.

Leucojum aestivum L.
Summer Snowflake

Summer Snowflake is a casual bulbous perennial of waysides. Our one record was made at Williamthorpe (SK4266) by R. Frost in 2002. There are two subspecies in Britain: a native from southern England (ssp. *aestivum*) and a garden plant from the western Mediterranean (ssp. *pulchellum* (Salisb.) Briq.). Our record probably relates to the latter.

Galanthus nivalis L.
Snowdrop

COUNTY STATUS: Established (Neophyte)
CONSERVATION STATUS: None
FIRST YEAR: 1829 LATEST YEAR: 2013 NO OF RECORDS: 254
RECENT SQUARES: monads 126; tetrads 127; hectads 33
ALL SQUARES: monads 167; tetrads 154; hectads 34

Snowdrop is an established perennial of waysides, grasslands and open woods. It is also often planted in these situations as well as in churchyards and gardens. It is occasional throughout the county from Dinting Vale Wood (SK0194) and Beauchief (SK3281) in the north, through Hopton Hall (SK2553), to Netherseal (SK2812) and Shardlow (SK4330) in the south. The earliest record is 1829 but it is thought to have been established much earlier. At Middleton by Youlgrave Castle (SK1963) there is a legend that it was planted with its building, but this is certainly an

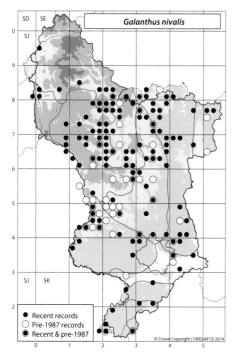

exaggeration. However, it has been known for long enough to be represented in traditional Ashford Black Marble inlay work. It is a native of southern Europe.

Narcissus L.
Daffodils

COUNTY STATUS: Native
CONSERVATION STATUS: None
FIRST YEAR: 1940 LATEST YEAR: 2013 NO OF RECORDS: 394
RECENT SQUARES: monads 273; tetrads 244; hectads 36
ALL SQUARES: monads 283; tetrads 250; hectads 36

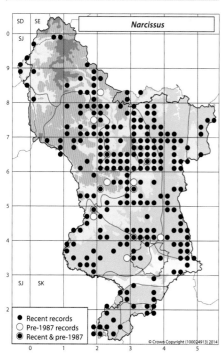

As well as the native Daffodil, numerous cultivated species, hybrids and cultivars are

established throughout Derbyshire. If identified to type, they are included below. Many others have not been, so are collectively mapped above. They include the Findern Daffodil that grows around the village (SK3030). It is reputed by local legend to have been brought back from the Holy Lands and cultivated by the Fyndyrne family.

Narcissus × *medioluteus* Mill.
Primrose-peerless

Locally extinct, Primrose-peerless was an established perennial of meadows. It was reported for Starkholmes (SK25), Matlock (SK35) and Heanor (SK44) in Linton (1903), but has not been reported since. They were probably relics of cultivation or garden throwouts. It is the horticultural hybrid of Bunch-flowered (*N. tazetta* L.) and Pheasant's-eye Daffodil (*N. poeticus*).

Narcissus poeticus L.
Pheasant's-eye Daffodil

COUNTY STATUS: Established (Neophyte)
CONSERVATION STATUS: None
FIRST YEAR: 1888 LATEST YEAR: 2009 NO OF RECORDS: 9
RECENT SQUARES: monads 6; tetrads 6; hectads 4
ALL SQUARES: monads 8; tetrads 8; hectads 6

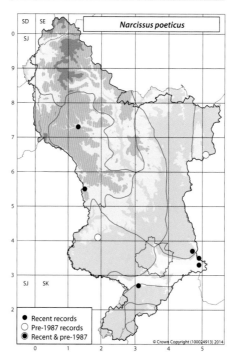

Pheasant's-eye Daffodil is a very rare, established perennial of waysides and rough grassland. Recent records are scattered throughout central and southern parts, from Miller's Dale (SK1373) to Askew Hill (SK3127). It is a native of southern Europe and much grown in gardens, so plants in natural settings are probably throwouts.

Narcissus × *incomparabilis* Mill.
Nonesuch Daffodil

Nonesuch Daffodil is a very rare, casual perennial. There are only four records, all recent: Ashbourne Cemetery (SK1746) where it was probably originally planted, Fox Covert (SK4833), Bostock's Lane (SK4734) and Roundring Plantation (SK3153). It is of garden origin from the crossing of Pheasant's-eye (*N. poeticus*) with Wild Daffodil (*N. pseudonarcissus*).

Narcissus pseudonarcissus L.
Wild Daffodil

COUNTY STATUS: Native
CONSERVATION STATUS: B
FIRST YEAR: 1789 LATEST YEAR: 2011 NO OF RECORDS: 166
RECENT SQUARES: monads 49; tetrads 43; hectads 20
ALL SQUARES: monads 67; tetrads 53; hectads 23

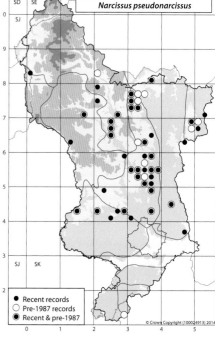

Wild Daffodil is an attractive native perennial of damp grasslands and woods, though some records are probably of escapes or introductions. It is occasional in the Peak Fringe Character Area: Derwentside Reserve (SK3255), Horsley Castle (SK3748), Hay Wood (SK3041) and Mercaston Hall fields (SK2842). Elsewhere it is very rare: Taddington Wood (SK1670) and Long Wood (SK3780), and often under suspicion of having been planted as at Snelston Churchyard (SK1543). It was previously more frequent, particularly in the south: Calke, Repton (SK32), Swarkestone (SK32) and Drakelow (SK21) all for 1903. These losses are no doubt due to the agricultural "improvement" of grasslands. It has a local name of Lent-lily (Grigson 1975). A double cultivar 'Telamonius Plenus' has been known

Wild Daffodil (*Narcissus pseudonarcissus*) by side of Cromford Canal (SK3155), April 2008 (Peter Smith)

from old pasture at Cutthorpe (SK3472) for over 300 years. It was reputedly used to treat a medical condition of Queen Anne (Stubbs 1984).

Narcissus hispanicus Gouan
Spanish Daffodil

Spanish Daffodil is an established perennial of rough grasslands and waysides and a native of the Iberian Peninsula. There are modern records from just four areas: Ashbourne Cemetery (SK1746), Great Longstone (SK2071), Eyam Moor (SK2278 & 2378) and Long Eaton (SK4934). Grown in gardens, our records probably represent throwouts or relics of cultivation.

ASPARAGACEAE

Convallaria majalis L.
Lily-of-the-valley

COUNTY STATUS: Native
CONSERVATION STATUS: B
FIRST YEAR: 1789 LATEST YEAR: 2012 NO OF RECORDS: 193
RECENT SQUARES: monads 30; tetrads 24; hectads 11
ALL SQUARES: monads 47; tetrads 35; hectads 21

Lily-of-the-valley is a rare native perennial of ancient woods on limestone and scree slopes in the White Peak: Water-cum-Jolly Dale (SK1672), Lathkill Dale (SK1865) and Hopton Wood (SK2650). Elsewhere it is very rare in woods and on waysides: Rose Wood (SK3175), Cromford Canal (SK3452) and the Moss Valley (SK3175). In such situations it is often under suspicion of being a garden

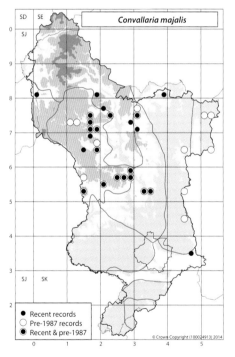

escape or throwout as it is commonly grown around houses. It was previously recorded from the Magnesian Limestone at Pleasley Vale (SK5265) in 1969, and Anchor Church (SK32) in 1903 where it may have been native. Having attractive flowers, it was often picked for household decoration and pictured in local craftwork. Children at Monsal Head used to collect it for their mothers in a sort of local pilgrimage, while at Cressbrook Dale it was gathered for sale in Manchester markets. It was

also frequently represented in traditional Ashford Black Marble inlay work.

Polygonatum multiflorum (L.) All.
Solomon's-seal

COUNTY STATUS: Native
CONSERVATION STATUS: B
FIRST YEAR: 1789 LATEST YEAR: 2012 NO OF RECORDS: 136
RECENT SQUARES: monads 40; tetrads 34; hectads 18
ALL SQUARES: monads 56; tetrads 45; hectads 22

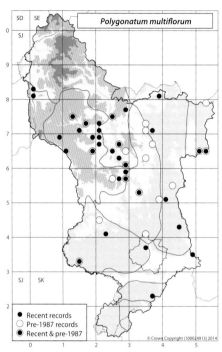

Solomon's-seal is a rare native perennial of ancient woods typically on limestone. It is also grown in gardens, so some records probably relate to throwouts or relics of cultivation. It is undoubtedly native in the White Peak: Cressbrook Dale (SK1772) and the Via Gellia (SK2957). Elsewhere its status is less certain: Shining Cliff Woods (SK3352), Ticknall Quarries (SK3623) and Pleasley Vale (SK5164), and particularly at Sudbury Hall (SK1532) and Birleyhay Mill Pond (SK3980). It has a local name of David's Harp (Grigson 1975).

Polygonatum × *hybridum* Bruegger
Garden Solomon's-seal

COUNTY STATUS: Established (Neophyte)
CONSERVATION STATUS: None
FIRST YEAR: 1970 LATEST YEAR: 2013 NO OF RECORDS: 40
RECENT SQUARES: monads 26; tetrads 26; hectads 18
ALL SQUARES: monads 32; tetrads 31; hectads 20

Garden Solomon's-seal is an established perennial of waysides, waste ground and woods. It occurs rarely throughout the county from Mill Brow (SJ9889) and the Longdendale Trail (SK0892) in the north, to Breadsall (SK3638) and the banks of the River Ecclesbourne (SK3046) in the

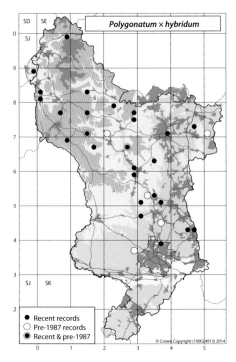

Polygonatum × hybridum

on shaded ledges of limestone often in very inaccessible places, where it is difficult to see, let alone record. It is currently known from only two localities in the White Peak (Deep Dale SK0971 & Wye Dale SK1673). It was previously also recorded further south in the White Peak (The Nabs SK1453 & Brassington Rocks SK2154 both in 1969) and the Peak Fringe (Shining Cliff Woods SK3352 in 1969). It occurs scattered throughout upland England and Wales in limestone woods and is Nationally Scarce.

Ornithogalum umbellatum L.
Star-of-Bethlehem

COUNTY STATUS: Established (Neophyte)	
CONSERVATION STATUS: B	
FIRST YEAR: 1829 **LATEST YEAR:** 2005 **NO OF RECORDS:** 44	
RECENT SQUARES: monads 12; tetrads 12; hectads 8	
ALL SQUARES: monads 22; tetrads 18; hectads 11	

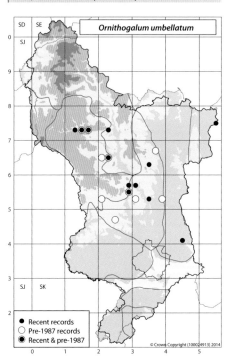

Ornithogalum umbellatum

Star-of-Bethlehem is an established perennial of grasslands, waysides and rough ground. It occurs rarely scattered throughout central parts of the county: Miller's Dale (SK1573), Gang Vein (SK2855), Fallgate (SK3562) and Belph (SK5475). Previously it was also recorded from southern Derbyshire: the Holmes, Derby (SK33) in 1829 and near Calke (SK32) in 1973. The local plant is ssp. *campestre* Rouy. Sometimes grown around houses, our records are probably garden escapes or throwouts. It is sometimes considered native in eastern England.

Ornithogalum nutans L.
Drooping Star-of-Bethlehem
Locally extinct, Drooping Star-of-Bethlehem was an established perennial

of meadows near Derby (SK33) in 1825, although Painter (1889) considered the report uncertain. There are no other records. A garden ornamental, it is native to central Europe.

Scilla forbesii (Baker) Speta
Glory-of-the-snow
Glory-of-the-snow is a very rare, casual perennial of waysides and waste ground which is indigenous to western Turkey. There are recent records for three sites in central Derbyshire: Stretton (SK3961) in 1998, Swanwick (SK4152) in 2011 and Stanedge Road (SK2168) in 2002 plus one from Priestcliffe Lees (SK1572) in 1985. Much grown in gardens, it can escape as seeds or throwouts.

Scilla luciliae (Boiss.) Speta
Boissier's Glory-of-the-snow
Boissier's Glory-of-the-snow is a very rare, casual perennial of grasslands. It is only known from two recent records: Churchdale Hall (SK2070) and Dore (SK3181). Grown as an ornamental in gardens, it is native to Turkey.

Hyacinthoides non-scripta (L.) Chouard ex Rothm.
Bluebell

COUNTY STATUS: Native	
CONSERVATION STATUS: WCA8, C	
FIRST YEAR: 1789 **LATEST YEAR:** 2013 **NO OF RECORDS:** 4,168	
RECENT SQUARES: monads 1,327; tetrads 587; hectads 41	
ALL SQUARES: monads 1,386; tetrads 599; hectads 41	

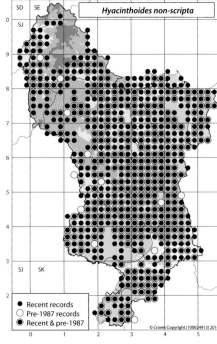

Hyacinthoides non-scripta

Bluebell is an attractive native perennial that forms carpets of blue in springtime woods. It also occurs in hedges, scrub and

south. It is the commonly grown garden plant, generally escaping as a throw-out. It is of cultivated origin from the crossing of Solomon's-seal (*P. multiflorum*) with Angular Solomon's-seal (*P. odoratum*).

Polygonatum odoratum (Mill.) Druce
Angular Solomon's-seal

COUNTY STATUS: Native	
CONSERVATION STATUS: DRDB (Cat3), NS, A, B	
FIRST YEAR: 1873 **LATEST YEAR:** 2007 **NO OF RECORDS:** 39	
RECENT SQUARES: monads 2; tetrads 2; hectads 2	
ALL SQUARES: monads 8; tetrads 7; hectads 5	

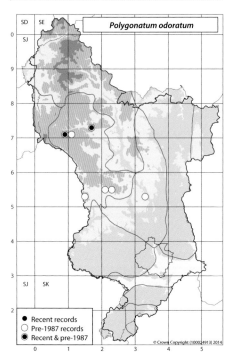

Polygonatum odoratum

Angular Solomon's-seal is a very rare, native and rhizomatous perennial. It grows

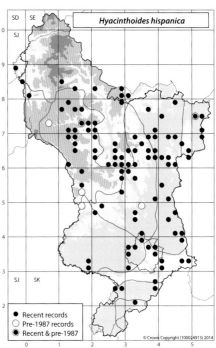

Bluebell (*Hyacinthoides non-scripta*) in woodland near Bretby (SK3023), May 2008 (Peter Smith)

grassland on all but the most acid soils. It is common throughout the county, only being absent from the high moors of the Dark Peak, the plateau grasslands of the White Peak, and some intensively farmed areas in the lowlands. It has a local name of Cuckoo's Stockings (Grigson 1975).

Hyacinthoides × *massartiana* Geerinck
Hybrid Bluebell

Hybrid Bluebell is an established perennial of copses, waysides, hedges,

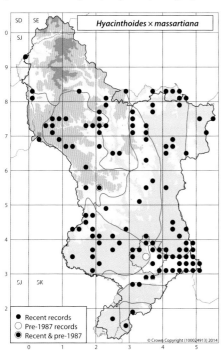

COUNTY STATUS: Established (Neophyte)
CONSERVATION STATUS: None
FIRST YEAR: 1978 LATEST YEAR: 2013 NO OF RECORDS: 189
RECENT SQUARES: monads 154; tetrads 121; hectads 35
ALL SQUARES: monads 155; tetrads 122; hectads 35

rough ground and waste places. It is occasional throughout Derbyshire from Far Woodseats (SJ9892) and Sothall (SK4482) in the north, to Rosliston (SK2416) and Long Eaton (SK5032) in the south. Being the most frequently planted bluebell in gardens, it can escape into the wild as seed or discarded bulbs. Although of cultivated origin, it can also form spontaneously when Spanish Bluebells (*H. hispanica*) escape from gardens and cross with our native Bluebell (*H. non-scripta*).

Hyacinthoides hispanica (Mill.) Rothm.
Spanish Bluebell

COUNTY STATUS: Established (Neophyte)
CONSERVATION STATUS: None
FIRST YEAR: 1949 LATEST YEAR: 2013 NO OF RECORDS: 137
RECENT SQUARES: monads 88; tetrads 104; hectads 27
ALL SQUARES: monads 92; tetrads 108; hectads 29

Spanish Bluebell is an established perennial of copses, waysides, hedges, rough ground and waste places. It occurs occasionally throughout the county from Marple Bridge (SJ9689) and Houndkirk Moor (SK2882) in the north, to Newton Solney (SK2725) and Melbourne Town (SK3825) in the south. Sometimes grown in gardens, it escapes as seed or bulbs into

more natural habitats. It is a native of the Iberian Peninsula.

Hyacinthus orientalis L.
Hyacinth

Hyacinth is a casual bulbous perennial of rough grassland and waste ground, and is native to South-western Asia. There are just two records both from 2006: Dockholme Lock (SK4835) and Trent Meadows Tip (SK5032). Grown as an ornamental, it generally escapes as a garden throwout.

Muscari neglectum Guss. ex Ten.
Grape-hyacinth

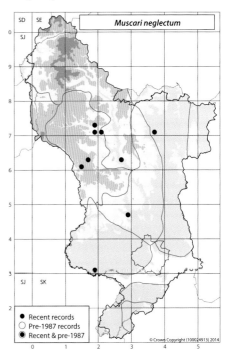

COUNTY STATUS:	Casual
CONSERVATION STATUS:	None
FIRST YEAR: 1987	LATEST YEAR: 2013 NO OF RECORDS: 11
RECENT SQUARES:	monads 9; tetrads 9; hectads 7
ALL SQUARES:	monads 9; tetrads 9; hectads 7

Grape-hyacinth is a very rare, casual perennial of waysides, rough ground and disturbed land. It occurs throughout the county from Longstone Edge (SK1972) and Ashgate (SK3671) in the north, to Scropton (SK1930) and Bull Hill (SK2847) in the south. Indigenous to East Anglia, it is sometimes grown in gardens and can escape into more natural habitats.

Muscari armeniacum Leichtlin ex Baker
Garden Grape-hyacinth

COUNTY STATUS:	Casual
CONSERVATION STATUS:	None
FIRST YEAR: 1991	LATEST YEAR: 2013 NO OF RECORDS: 27
RECENT SQUARES:	monads 25; tetrads 23; hectads 15
ALL SQUARES:	monads 25; tetrads 23; hectads 15

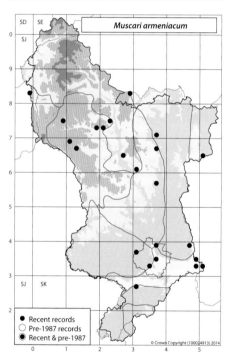

Garden Grape-hyacinth is a rare casual perennial of waysides and waste ground. It occurs scattered throughout the county: Hardybarn (SK0875), Lady Canning's Plantation (SK2883), Wessington Green (SK3657) and Sinfin Station (SK3532). Indigenous to eastern Europe, this is the common Grape-hyacinth that escapes from gardens as seeds or throwouts into more natural settings.

Asparagus officinalis L.
Garden Asparagus
Garden Asparagus is a rare casual perennial of waste ground, waysides and cultivated land. It occurs scattered throughout

COUNTY STATUS:	Casual
CONSERVATION STATUS:	None
FIRST YEAR: 1950	LATEST YEAR: 2013 NO OF RECORDS: 46
RECENT SQUARES:	monads 29; tetrads 25; hectads 10
ALL SQUARES:	monads 29; tetrads 25; hectads 10

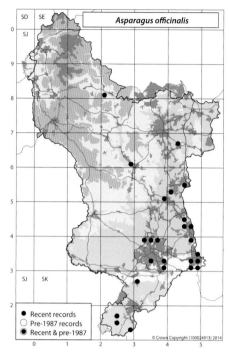

Derbyshire from Offerton (SK2181) in the north, to Coton in the Elms (SK2415) in the south. Grown in gardens as a vegetable, our records represent relics of this cultivation or bird dispersal. It is native to continental Europe.

Ruscus aculeatus L.
Butcher's-broom

COUNTY STATUS:	Casual
CONSERVATION STATUS:	None
FIRST YEAR: 1903	LATEST YEAR: 1978 NO OF RECORDS: 10
RECENT SQUARES:	monads 0; tetrads 0; hectads 0
ALL SQUARES:	monads 8; tetrads 8; hectads 5

Butcher's-broom is a casual evergreen undershrub of wasteland and shrubberies. Native only to southern Britain, there are no recent records but it was previously recorded rarely in south-western parts, as at Norbury (SK1242) and Ednaston (SK2342) both in the 1970s. It is grown as a garden ornamental and, since it is generally found near buildings, records probably represent relics of cultivation or garden throwouts.

PONTEDERIACEAE

Eichhornia crassipes (Mart.) Solms.
Water-hyacinth
Water-hyacinth is a casual floating aquatic. It was found in its sole local station of Old Hay Brook (SK3080) by K. Balkow in 2006. It can become a troublesome

weed of waterbodies but fortunately is frost sensitive so unlikely to establish here. Increasingly grown in ponds as an ornamental, it is native to South America.

TYPHACEAE

Sparganium erectum L.
Branched Bur-reed

COUNTY STATUS:	Native
CONSERVATION STATUS:	None
FIRST YEAR: 1829	LATEST YEAR: 2013 NO OF RECORDS: 827
RECENT SQUARES:	monads 306; tetrads 233; hectads 38
ALL SQUARES:	monads 365; tetrads 265; hectads 39

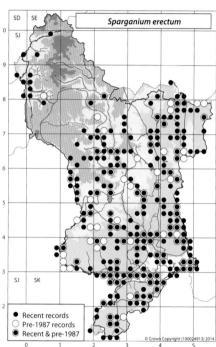

Branched Bur-reed is a native perennial that forms large stands in or by the edges of ponds, lakes, canals and slow rivers. It can also occur on bare mud and in marshy fields. It is occasional in the southern and eastern lowlands, but becomes rare in the more upland White, South West and Dark Peak Character Areas. Normally recorded to species level only, four subspecies have been noted. **Ssp. *erectum*** was previously found throughout the area, though has only one modern record (Locko Park SK4038). **Ssp. *microcarpum*** (Neuman) Domin. was previously recorded across Derbyshire, but has no recent records. It was found from Brough (SK18) and Ley's Fen (SK37) in the north, both for 1903, to Egginton (SK22) and Weston-on-Trent (SK42) in the south, both for 1956. **Ssp. *neglectum*** (Beeby) K. Richt. has one modern record from Morley Brickyards (SK3841), but was previously noted from near Hassop (SK2271) in the north, to Caldwell (SK2517) in the south, both for 1969. **Ssp. *oocarpum*** (Celak.) Domin. has only been recorded is the south, as at Egginton (SK22) and Borrowash (SK43), both for 1956.

Sparganium emersum Rehmann
Unbranched Bur-reed

COUNTY STATUS: Native
CONSERVATION STATUS: None
FIRST YEAR: 1829 LATEST YEAR: 2011 NO OF RECORDS: 131
RECENT SQUARES: monads 53; tetrads 40; hectads 19
ALL SQUARES: monads 80; tetrads 61; hectads 25

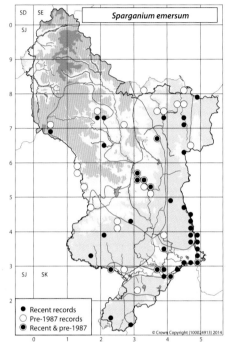

Unbranched Bur-reed is a native perennial of the margins of ponds and slow-moving streams that sometimes grows as a floating plant. It occurs rarely throughout the county except for the South West and Dark Peak Areas where it is virtually absent. Example localities include Booth Farm (SK0568) and Pebley (SK4878) in the north, Cromford Canal (SK3452), and Edingale (SK2111) and Netherseal (SK2812) in the south.

Sparganium angustifolium Michx.
Floating Bur-reed
Floating Bur-reed is a very rare, casual perennial of upland peaty ponds. A native of western Britain, it has only ever been recorded at Longshaw Pond (SK2679), where it was noted between 1964 and 1979.

Typha latifolia L.
Bulrush

COUNTY STATUS: Native
CONSERVATION STATUS: None
FIRST YEAR: 1829 LATEST YEAR: 2013 NO OF RECORDS: 1,584
RECENT SQUARES: monads 560; tetrads 383; hectads 41
ALL SQUARES: monads 609; tetrads 406; hectads 41

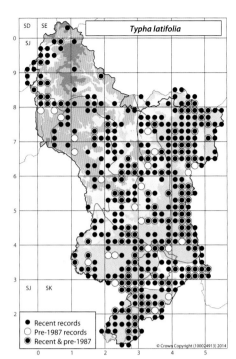

Bulrush is a native perennial that forms dense stands on the margins of ponds, shallow lakes, canals and slow-flowing rivers. It can also occur on bare mud, in swamps and in ditches. It favours nutrient-rich habitats. Frequent in the lowland southern and eastern parts, it is only occasional in the uplands of the South West, Dark and White Peak Character Areas. Braithwaite *et al.* (2006) found it had increased dramatically in upland areas due to nutrient enrichment of habitats.

Typha × *glauca* Godr.
Hybrid Bulrush
Hybrid Bulrush is an emergent native perennial. Its sole station is McGregor's Pond (SK3868) where it was discovered in 2007 by N. Law and reconfirmed there in 2010. Probably under-recorded, it is the hybrid of Bulrush (*T. latifolia*) and Lesser Bulrush (*T. angustifolia*).

Typha angustifolia L.
Lesser Bulrush

COUNTY STATUS: Native
CONSERVATION STATUS: B
FIRST YEAR: 1829 LATEST YEAR: 2013 NO OF RECORDS: 127
RECENT SQUARES: monads 30; tetrads 29; hectads 14
ALL SQUARES: monads 48; tetrads 42; hectads 21

Lesser Bulrush is a rare native perennial found on the margins of ponds, canals and slow-flowing streams. It generally grows at lower altitudes than its larger cousin, Bulrush, and ranges from Watford Lodge (SK0086) and Pebley Reservoir (SK4879) in the north, through Mapperley Reservoir (SK4443) to Sudbury

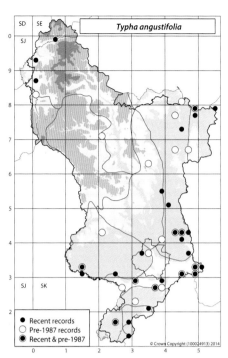

Hall (SK1532) and Netherseal (SK2813) in the south.

JUNCACEAE

Juncus subnodulosus Schrank
Blunt-flowered Rush

COUNTY STATUS: Native
CONSERVATION STATUS: DRDB (Cat5a), B
FIRST YEAR: 1863 LATEST YEAR: 2006 NO OF RECORDS: 17
RECENT SQUARES: monads 2; tetrads 2; hectads 1
ALL SQUARES: monads 7; tetrads 7; hectads 7

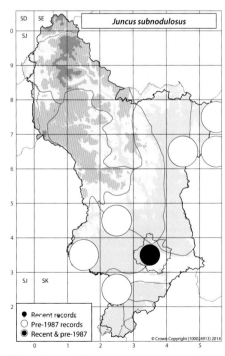

Blunt-flowered Rush is a very rare, native perennial of fens and marshes, in southern and eastern parts. There are only two

recent records: Sinfin (SK3531) in 2005 and Sinfin Moor (SK3630) in 2006. Previously there were records from eight sites, the most recent being: Bradley Brook (SK2343) in 1980, Pleasley (SK4863) in 1974 and The Walls Whitwell (SK5078) in 1969. The five earlier sites are from Linton (1903) and include: Scropton (SK13), Burton (SK22) and the first county record, an unlocalised one, from Mosley (1863). This decline mirrors a national one as it has disappeared from many sites in southern England due to drainage (Preston *et al.* 2002).

Juncus articulatus L.
Jointed Rush

COUNTY STATUS: Native

CONSERVATION STATUS: None

FIRST YEAR: 1789 **LATEST YEAR:** 2013 **NO OF RECORDS:** 1,643

RECENT SQUARES: monads 697; tetrads 474; hectads 42

ALL SQUARES: monads 803; tetrads 526; hectads 42

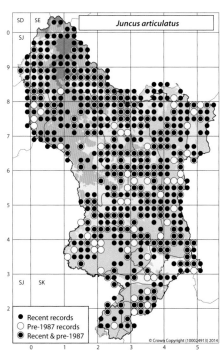

Jointed Rush is a frequent native perennial of wet grasslands, marshes and the margins of ponds. It occurs throughout the county, only being absent from the drier parts of the White Peak and some of the intensively farmed lowlands.

Juncus × *surrejanus* Druce ex Stace & Lambinon
A hybrid rush

Locally extinct, this hybrid rush was a very rare, native perennial of marshy areas. The sole record is from north Derbyshire (SK28) around 1950. It is the hybrid of Jointed (*J. articulatus*) and Sharp-flowered Rush (*J. acutiflorus*). Nationally it is common where its parents occur together (Stace 2010), as they often do locally, so it is probably under-recorded.

Juncus acutiflorus Ehrh. ex Hoffm.
Sharp-flowered Rush

COUNTY STATUS: Native

CONSERVATION STATUS: None

FIRST YEAR: 1789 **LATEST YEAR:** 2013 **NO OF RECORDS:** 557

RECENT SQUARES: monads 248; tetrads 205; hectads 37

ALL SQUARES: monads 299; tetrads 234; hectads 38

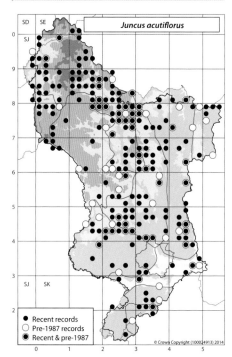

Sharp-flowered Rush is a native perennial of wet grasslands, marshes, swamps and moorland flushes usually on acid soils. It is frequent throughout the South West Peak, Dark Peak and Peak Fringe Character Areas: Long Clough (SK0392), Westend Valley (SK1493) and Flash Dam (SK36C). Elsewhere it is rare, for example at Bonsall Brook (SK2759) in the White Peak, and Golden Brook (SK4633) in the Trent Valley.

Juncus bulbosus L.
Bulbous Rush

COUNTY STATUS: Native

CONSERVATION STATUS: None

FIRST YEAR: 1789 **LATEST YEAR:** 2013 **NO OF RECORDS:** 384

RECENT SQUARES: monads 193; tetrads 137; hectads 24

ALL SQUARES: monads 223; tetrads 153; hectads 27

Bulbous Rush is a frequent native perennial of a range of damp habitats in the South West and Dark Peak including marshes, moors, bogs and streamsides. Typical localities include Long Clough (SK0392), Axe Edge Moor (SK07F) and Upper Burbage Brook (SK2583). It is very rare elsewhere, occurring in isolated areas of acid soils as at Mugginton Bottoms (SK2843) and Carver's Rocks (SK3222). Plants previously recorded as *Juncus kochii* F.W. Schultz are no longer considered as a separate species and are included here.

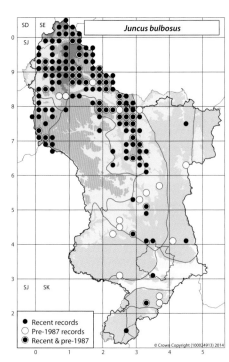

Juncus squarrosus L.
Heath Rush

COUNTY STATUS: Native

CONSERVATION STATUS: None

FIRST YEAR: 1829 **LATEST YEAR:** 2013 **NO OF RECORDS:** 1,021

RECENT SQUARES: monads 448; tetrads 190; hectads 22

ALL SQUARES: monads 271; tetrads 208; hectads 28

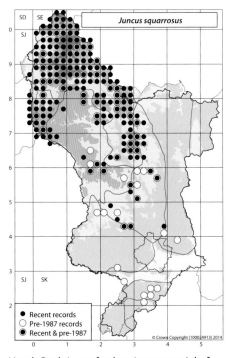

Heath Rush is a tufted native perennial of moors, heaths and flushes on acid soils. It is common and locally abundant throughout the Dark and the South West Peak Areas: Lady Booth Clough (SK1486) and Upper Padley (SK2479). Elsewhere it is very scattered and rare: Biggin Moor (SK1758), Wessington Green (SK3757) and Mugginton

Bottoms (SK2843). It previously also occurred further south in the county: Hilton Gravel Pits (SK2431) in 1973 and Ticknall (SK3523) in 1969. This local loss is part of a national decline, having disappeared from many lowland sites since 1962 due to agricultural improvement (Preston *et al.* 2002).

Juncus tenuis Willd.
Slender Rush

COUNTY STATUS: Established (Neophyte)	
CONSERVATION STATUS: None	
FIRST YEAR: 1903 LATEST YEAR: 2012 NO OF RECORDS: 68	
RECENT SQUARES: monads 27; tetrads 23; hectads 9	
ALL SQUARES: monads 38; tetrads 34; hectads 15	

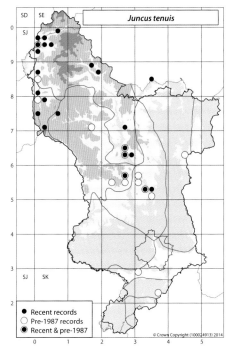

Slender Rush is an established tufted perennial of damp bare ground by waysides, and is a native of the Americas. It is rare throughout the north of the county: Dinting Wood (SK0194), Crook Hill (SK1886), Northwood (SK2664) and Cromford Canal (SK3452). Previously it also occurred in the south, as at Ticknall Quarries (SK3623) in 1971.

Juncus compressus Jacq.
Round-fruited Rush

COUNTY STATUS: Native	
CONSERVATION STATUS: DRDB (Cat2), NT, A, B	
FIRST YEAR: 1789 LATEST YEAR: 2012 NO OF RECORDS: 30	
RECENT SQUARES: monads 6; tetrads 6; hectads 3	
ALL SQUARES: monads 13; tetrads 13; hectads 8	

Round-fruited Rush is a very rare, native perennial of marshes and wet grasslands. All recent records are from eastern Derbyshire: Darley Tip (SK3538), Courtaulds (SK3934 & 4034), Erewash Canal (SK4836 & 4736) and Steetley Quarry (SK5478). Previous records are from the same area

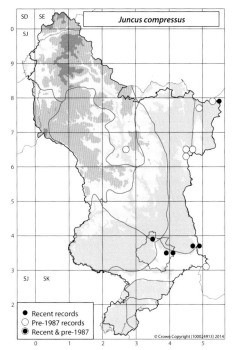

and further west at Rowsley Sidings (SK2665) in 1984. This suggests a local decline matching a national loss due to drainage and general improvement of grasslands (Preston *et al.* 2002).

Juncus gerardii Loisel.
Saltmarsh Rush
Saltmarsh Rush is a very rare, established perennial, known only from waste ground at Ilkeston (SK4642) where it was discovered in 2003 by B. Gough and was still present in 2008. It grows naturally in coastal salt marshes and is occasionally found as an introduction in saline areas inland. With no obvious signs of salinity, the reason for its occurrence at Ilkeston is a mystery.

Juncus foliosus Desf.
Leafy Rush

COUNTY STATUS: Native	
CONSERVATION STATUS: DRDB (Cat4)	
FIRST YEAR: 1996 LATEST YEAR: 1996 NO OF RECORDS: 1	
RECENT SQUARES: monads 1; tetrads 1; hectads 1	
ALL SQUARES: monads 1; tetrads 1; hectads 1	

Leafy Rush is a very rare, native annual. Our only record is from Chatsworth Park (SK2568) where it was discovered in 1996 by D. Dupree. It is a native of southern and western Britain so is on the north-eastern edge of its range here. Its occurrence so far from other native sites is a puzzle; it may have been introduced with cattle from Wales that were sometimes grazed in the area.

Juncus bufonius L.
Toad Rush
Toad Rush is a frequent native annual of open damp areas in arable fields, on

COUNTY STATUS: Native	
CONSERVATION STATUS: None	
FIRST YEAR: 1829 LATEST YEAR: 2013 NO OF RECORDS: 1,124	
RECENT SQUARES: monads 631; tetrads 448; hectads 42	
ALL SQUARES: monads 708; tetrads 487; hectads 42	

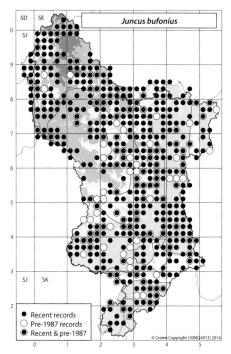

waysides and around the margins of ponds, streams and marshes. It is found throughout the county except for some of the higher parts of the Dark and White Peak Character Areas.

Juncus inflexus L.
Hard Rush
Hard Rush is a tufted native perennial of wet grasslands, marshes and the margins

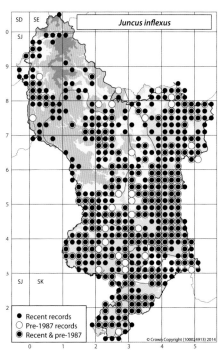

COUNTY STATUS: Native
CONSERVATION STATUS: None
FIRST YEAR: 1829 LATEST YEAR: 2013 NO OF RECORDS: 1,932
RECENT SQUARES: monads 741; tetrads 463; hectads 41
ALL SQUARES: monads 817; tetrads 490; hectads 41

of lakes and rivers, typically on heavy base-rich soils. It is common throughout Derbyshire's lowlands but only rare in the White, Dark and South West Peak Areas.

Juncus × diffusus Hoppe
A hybrid rush

This hybrid rush is a tufted native perennial of wet grasslands and marshes. There are only two recent records: Williamthorpe Ponds (SK4366) and a fish pond at Bradley (SK2443). Previously it was more widely recorded in southern and central parts: Shirley (SK24), Calke Park SK32, Cromford Canal (SK35) and Ockbrook (SK43) all for 1903. It is the hybrid of Hard (*J. inflexus*) and Soft Rush (*J. effusus*).

Juncus effusus L.
Soft Rush

COUNTY STATUS: Native
CONSERVATION STATUS: None
FIRST YEAR: 1789 LATEST YEAR: 2013 NO OF RECORDS: 5,310
RECENT SQUARES: monads 1,754; tetrads 693; hectads 45
ALL SQUARES: monads 1,834; tetrads 699; hectads 45

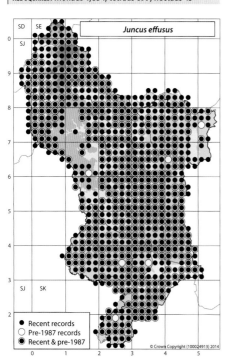

Soft Rush is a very common, native perennial of wet grasslands, marshes, ditches, streamsides and flushes, usually on acid soils. It is widespread and abundant everywhere except for the limestone areas. Variety *subglomeratus* DC. has been recorded recently but, as few note its occurrence, the records tell us more about the botanists than the plant!

Juncus conglomeratus L.
Compact Rush

COUNTY STATUS: Native
CONSERVATION STATUS: None
FIRST YEAR: 1789 LATEST YEAR: 2013 NO OF RECORDS: 1,099
RECENT SQUARES: monads 536; tetrads 389; hectads 41
ALL SQUARES: monads 598; tetrads 423; hectads 41

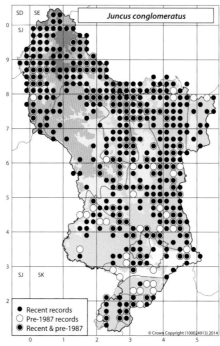

Compact Rush is a tufted native perennial of grasslands, marshes, ditches and streamsides. Although frequent throughout the county, it tends to avoid the limestone areas and the more intensively farmed parts of the lowlands. Previously it was more widespread in southern Derbyshire. This loss is no doubt due to agricultural intensification. There is a single record of variety *subuliflorus*

(Drejer) Asch. & Graebn. from Midway Clay Site (SK3019) in 2008.

Luzula pilosa (L.) Willd.
Hairy Wood-rush

COUNTY STATUS: Native
CONSERVATION STATUS: None
FIRST YEAR: 1829 LATEST YEAR: 2013 NO OF RECORDS: 373
RECENT SQUARES: monads 114; tetrads 92; hectads 29
ALL SQUARES: monads 149; tetrads 114; hectads 35

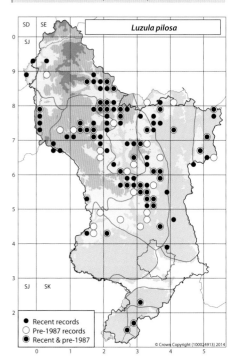

Hairy Wood-rush is an occasional native perennial of old woods and hedges, usually amongst acid leaf litter and moss as it cannot stand competition from larger plants. It is recorded intermittently throughout northern parts (Long Clough SK0392, Priddock Wood SK2086, Clough

Hairy Wood-rush (*Luzula pilosa*) in woodland near Totley (SK3179), April 2013 (Ken Balkow)

Wood SK2561 & Scarcliffe Park SK5170). In the south it is rarer (Grange Wood SK2714, Swainspark SK2916 & Repton Shrubs SK3123), but was previously more widespread there (Bretby Wood SK22 & Shirley Wood SK24 both for 1903). This local decrease is part of a more general decline in central and eastern England since 1950 (Preston *et al.* 2002).

Luzula sylvatica (Huds.) Gaudin
Great Wood-rush

COUNTY STATUS: Native
CONSERVATION STATUS: None
FIRST YEAR: 1829 LATEST YEAR: 2013 NO OF RECORDS: 584
RECENT SQUARES: monads 208; tetrads 156; hectads 26
ALL SQUARES: monads 249; tetrads 176; hectads 31

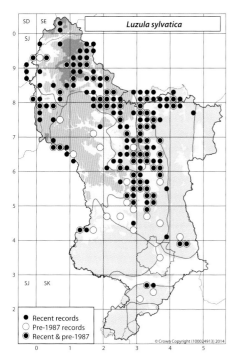

Great Wood-rush is a tufted native perennial of damp woods, moors and pastures. In more open areas it is often confined to rocky or wet ground due to its intolerance of grazing. It is frequent and locally abundant in the South West Peak, Dark Peak and Peak Fringe Character Areas: Long Clough (SK0392), Priddock Wood (SK2086), Handley Wood (SK3248) and Hardwick Wood (SK3765). Outside these Areas it is only occasional in occurrence, for example at Anchor Church (SK3327) and Hermit's Wood (SK4338).

Luzula campestris (L.) DC.
Field Wood-rush

COUNTY STATUS: Native
CONSERVATION STATUS: None
FIRST YEAR: 1789 LATEST YEAR: 2013 NO OF RECORDS: 2,378
RECENT SQUARES: monads 994; tetrads 563; hectads 42
ALL SQUARES: monads 1,097; tetrads 597; hectads 42

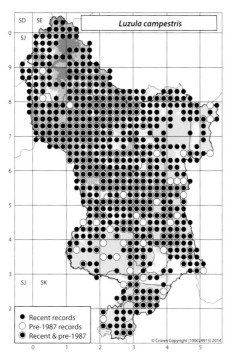

Field Wood-rush is a common native perennial of a wide range of infertile grasslands throughout the county. There is some evidence for a recent reduction of frequency in southern parts, probably due to agricultural intensification.

Luzula multiflora (Ehrh.) Lej.
Heath Wood-rush

COUNTY STATUS: Native
CONSERVATION STATUS: None
FIRST YEAR: 1883 LATEST YEAR: 2013 NO OF RECORDS: 550
RECENT SQUARES: monads 255; tetrads 163; hectads 28
ALL SQUARES: monads 309; tetrads 199; hectads 33

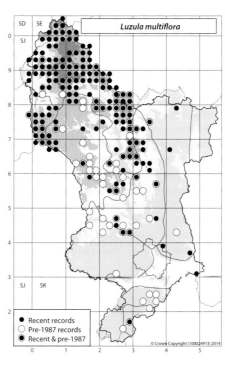

Heath Wood-rush is a tufted native perennial of damp moorlands and open woodlands generally on acid peaty soils. It is frequent throughout the South West and Dark Peak Areas: Pym Chair (SJ9976), Woodhead Reservoir (SK0899), Burbage Moor (SK2682) and Sydnope (SK2964). Elsewhere it only occurs in isolated sites, for example at Swainspark (SK2916) and Stoney Clouds (SK4737). It was formerly more widespread in southern Derbyshire, a decline probably due to agricultural "improvement". **Ssp. *congesta*** (Thuill.) Arcang. and ***multiflora*** have both been recorded recently for the South West and Dark Peak Areas. However, there are insufficient records to give a proper idea of their occurrence.

CYPERACEAE

Eriophorum angustifolium Honck.
Common Cottongrass

COUNTY STATUS: Native
CONSERVATION STATUS: ERL
FIRST YEAR: 1789 LATEST YEAR: 2013 NO OF RECORDS: 1,099
RECENT SQUARES: monads 374; tetrads 162; hectads 21
ALL SQUARES: monads 403; tetrads 183; hectads 29

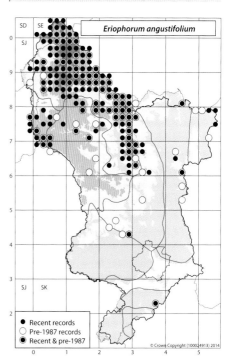

Common Cottongrass is a native perennial of bogs, flushes, fens and wet heaths. It is frequent and often locally abundant in the upland South West and Dark Peak Areas (Locker Brook SK1689, Ringinglow Bog SK2783 & Farley Moor SK3063). Elsewhere it is very rare and only occurs at widely separated locations (Mugginton Bottoms SK2843, Ticknall Quarries SK3623 & Steetley Quarry SK5478). Previously it was more frequently recorded outside the upland

Common Cottongrass (*Eriophorum angustifolium*) in expanse of blanket bog at Rakes Moss (SE0500), July 2003 (Barry Parker)

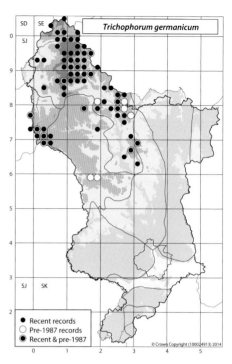

Trichophorum germanicum

areas (Bradley Brook Marsh SK2244 in 1969 & Blackwell Marsh SK4457 in 1983). These losses are part of a more general decline in the British lowlands due to agricultural improvement (Preston *et al.* 2002).

Eriophorum latifolium Hoppe
Broad-leaved Cottongrass

COUNTY STATUS: Native
CONSERVATION STATUS: DRDB (Cat4), A, B
FIRST YEAR: 1864 LATEST YEAR: 2004 NO OF RECORDS: 11
RECENT SQUARES: monads 3; tetrads 2; hectads 2
ALL SQUARES: monads 3; tetrads 2; hectads 3

Broad-leaved Cottongrass is a very rare, native perennial of marshy woodlands on limestone. There are recent records from a long-known site at Whitwell Wood (SK5278 & 5279) on the Magnesian Limestone, and from Wye Dale (SK1770) on the Carboniferous Limestone in the 1990s. There are earlier records from Scarcliffe Park Wood (SK57) in 1903 and Morley Moor (SK34) in 1864. The latter one was probably Common Cottongrass (*E. angustifolium*) as they were considered the same species at that time.

Eriophorum vaginatum L.
Hare's-tail Cottongrass

COUNTY STATUS: Native
CONSERVATION STATUS: None
FIRST YEAR: 1794 LATEST YEAR: 2013 NO OF RECORDS: 792
RECENT SQUARES: monads 319; tetrads 139; hectads 16
ALL SQUARES: monads 335; tetrads 150; hectads 23

Hare's-tail Cottongrass is a tufted native perennial of moorlands and the drier areas of bogs. It is frequent and locally abundant over large parts of the upland South West and Dark Peak Character Areas, for example at Axe Edge (SK0270),

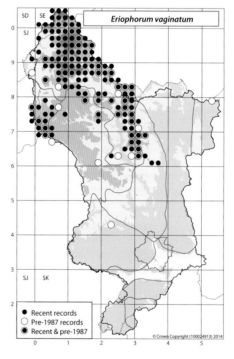

Eriophorum vaginatum

Chunal (SK0390), Upper Deep Grain (SK1296) and Matlock Moor (SK3063). Recent records in the lowlands are rare. However, there are a few earlier ones, as at Bradley Brook Marsh (SK2343) in 1970, and Ockbrook (SK43) and Pleasley (SK56) both for 1903. Their loss is part of a wider national decline in lowland sites since 1930 (Preston *et al.* 2002).

Trichophorum germanicum Palla
Deergrass

COUNTY STATUS: Native
CONSERVATION STATUS: None
FIRST YEAR: 1829 LATEST YEAR: 2013 NO OF RECORDS: 212
RECENT SQUARES: monads 107; tetrads 68; hectads 14
ALL SQUARES: monads 118; tetrads 74; hectads 16

Deergrass is a tufted native perennial of the drier areas of moorlands that is resistant to grazing and burning. It is occasional in the South West and Dark Peak Areas (Berry Clough SK0272, Torside Reservoir SK0796, Upper Derwent SK1694 & Beeley Moor SK2967). There are only a handful of records outside these Areas (Berrystall Lodge SK1479 & Longstone Edge SK1973). Earlier records cover the same area with a few more outlying ones at Gotham (SK1958) in 1979 and Allestree Park (SK34) in 1903. These losses are part of a general decline in southern and eastern England since before 1962 (Preston *et al.* 2002). Examination of local plants may also demonstrate the presence of the newly differentiated **Northern Deergrass** (*Trichophorum cespitosum* (L.) Hartm.).

Scirpus sylvaticus L.
Wood Club-rush

COUNTY STATUS: Native
CONSERVATION STATUS: DRDB (Cat5b)
FIRST YEAR: 1829 LATEST YEAR: 2010 NO OF RECORDS: 130
RECENT SQUARES: monads 27; tetrads 23; hectads 12
ALL SQUARES: monads 53; tetrads 44; hectads 23

Wood Club-rush is a rare native perennial of wet woods, relic oxbows and the sides of ponds and streams. It occurs scattered throughout the county from Watford Lodge (SK0086) and Moss Valley (SK4180) in the north, through Winster (SK2460) and Hardwick Great Pond (SK4563), to Newton Solney (SK2825) and Trent Meadows (SK5031) in the south. Previously it also occurred in a number of other sites, mostly in the south. These include Mapperley Ponds (SK4243) in 1972, Drakelow (SK21) in

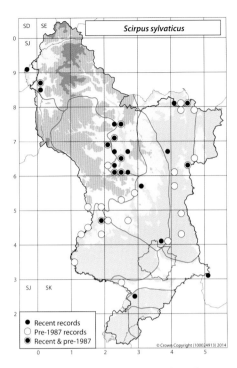

1903 and Calke (SK32) in 1903. These losses mirror a general national decline in south-eastern England since 1962.

Schoenoplectus lacustris (L.) Palla
Common Club-rush

COUNTY STATUS: Native

CONSERVATION STATUS: None

FIRST YEAR: 1829 LATEST YEAR: 2012 NO OF RECORDS: 236

RECENT SQUARES: monads 83; tetrads 63; hectads 23

ALL SQUARES: monads 93; tetrads 71; hectads 24

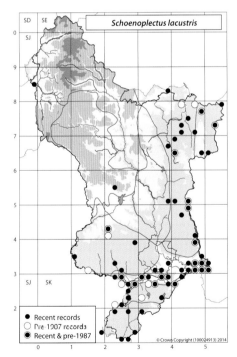

Common Club-rush is an emergent native perennial that grows on the margins of lakes, ponds, canals and slowly flowing rivers. It is occasional throughout the

lowland south and east (Croxall SK1913, Trent Lock SK4830, Brinsley Meadows SK4450 & Harlesthorpe Dam SK4976). It is very rare elsewhere (New Pond SJ9985 & Manor Farm SK2355).

Schoenoplectus tabernaemontani
(C.C. Gmel.) Palla
Grey Club-rush

COUNTY STATUS: Native

CONSERVATION STATUS: A, B

FIRST YEAR: 1903 LATEST YEAR: 2012 NO OF RECORDS: 65

RECENT SQUARES: monads 26; tetrads 21; hectads 11

ALL SQUARES: monads 30; tetrads 23; hectads 11

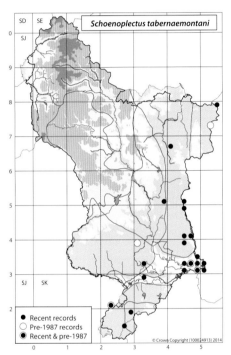

Grey Club-rush is a rare native perennial. It grows as an emergent in the sides of ponds and slow-moving rivers. Recent records are from southern and eastern parts (Swadlincote SK2819, Trent Lock SK4831, Erewash Meadows SK4450, Grassmoor SK4166 & Steetley Quarry SK5478). There are relatively few earlier records, suggesting the species has been expanding its distribution recently.

Eleocharis palustris (L.) Roem. & Schult.
Common Spike-rush

COUNTY STATUS: Native

CONSERVATION STATUS: None

FIRST YEAR: 1789 LATEST YEAR: 2013 NO OF RECORDS: 533

RECENT SQUARES: monads 200; tetrads 182; hectads 38

ALL SQUARES: monads 242; tetrads 210; hectads 38

Common Spike-rush is a tufted native perennial of damp grasslands, marshes and the margins of ponds and streams. It is occasional throughout the county from Tom Wood Meadow (SJ9993) and Dovestone Clough (SK1989) in the north,

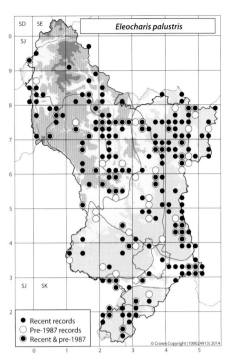

through Bees Nest Pit (SK2454) and Wessington Green (SK3757), to Swadlincote (SK2819) and Trent Junction (SK4931) in the south. Plants are probably all ssp. *vulgaris* Walters, which has been recorded recently for SK28. The drawing of this plant in Keble Martin's 1965 Flora came from a specimen collected at Dove Dale (Keble Martin 1968).

Eleocharis multicaulis (Sm.) Desv.
Many-stalked Spike-rush

COUNTY STATUS: Native

CONSERVATION STATUS: DRDB (Cat6), B

FIRST YEAR: 1871 LATEST YEAR: 1903 NO OF RECORDS: 5

RECENT SQUARES: monads 0; tetrads 0; hectads 0

ALL SQUARES: monads 0; tetrads 0; hectads 3

Locally extinct, Many-stalked Spike-rush was a very rare, native perennial of marshy places by pools. The latest record is from Ringinglow Bog (SK28) in 1903, with earlier records from Repton (SK32) in 1881 and Ockbrook (SK43) in 1871. This local extinction is part of a general loss from many sites in eastern England due to drainage and land-use changes (Preston *et al.* 2002).

Eleocharis quinqueflora (Hartmann) O. Schwarz
Few-flowered Spike-rush

COUNTY STATUS: Native

CONSERVATION STATUS: DRDB (Cat4), B

FIRST YEAR: 1894 LATEST YEAR: 2004 NO OF RECORDS: 13

RECENT SQUARES: monads 2; tetrads 2; hectads 2

ALL SQUARES: monads 4; tetrads 4; hectads 4

Few-flowered Spike-rush is a very rare, native perennial of damp peaty areas with moderately base-rich soils. There are recent records only from Ginny Spring SSSI/Whitwell Wood (SK5278) in 2004 and Brampton Moor (SK2970) in 2004. There are earlier records from the same sites plus a specimen in Derby Museum from Repton Rocks (SK23) in 1894, and in Linton (1903) for Umberley Brook (SK27). This local decline is part of a national loss from many lowland sites due to drainage and lack of grazing (Preston *et al.* 2002).

Eleocharis acicularis (L.) Roem. & Schult.
Needle Spike-rush

COUNTY STATUS: Native	
CONSERVATION STATUS: DRDB (Cat5a), A, B	
FIRST YEAR: 1877 LATEST YEAR: 2004 NO OF RECORDS: 26	
RECENT SQUARES: monads 4; tetrads 2; hectads 2	
ALL SQUARES: monads 6; tetrads 4; hectads 6	

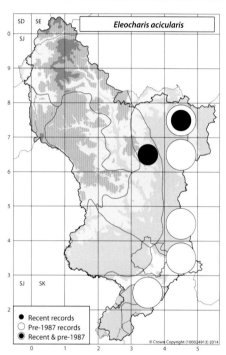

Needle Spike-rush is a very rare, native perennial which forms low, sparse tufts in marshes and the margins of ponds. Modern records are only from the Great Pond of Stubbing (SK3667) and the area of Pebley Pond (SK4878, 4879 & 4978). It previously occurred scattered throughout eastern areas, from Pebley Pond (SK4879) in the north, through Hardwick (SK4564) and Ockbrook (SK43) to Repton (SK32) in the south.

Isolepis setacea (L.) R. Br.
Bristle Club-rush

COUNTY STATUS: Native	
CONSERVATION STATUS: None	
FIRST YEAR: 1829 LATEST YEAR: 2012 NO OF RECORDS: 179	
RECENT SQUARES: monads 69; tetrads 65; hectads 25	
ALL SQUARES: monads 106; tetrads 93; hectads 29	

Bristle Club-rush is a tufted native annual of damp open areas in marshes,

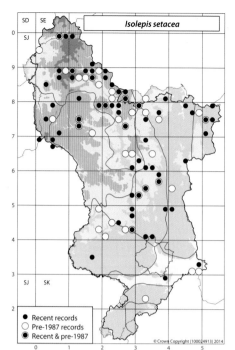

moors and grasslands, generally on acidic or at least infertile soils. It is occasional throughout the county from Longdendale (SK0799 v.c.58) and Holmesfield (SK3178) in the north, to Woodlands Field (SK3440) and Chellaston (SK3829) in the south.

Cyperus longus L.
Galingale

COUNTY STATUS: Established (Neophyte)	
CONSERVATION STATUS: None	
FIRST YEAR: 1997 LATEST YEAR: 2010 NO OF RECORDS: 18	
RECENT SQUARES: monads 12; tetrads 12; hectads 9	
ALL SQUARES: monads 12; tetrads 12; hectads 9	

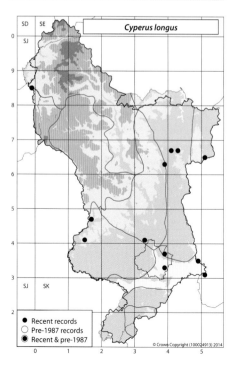

Galingale is an established perennial of the sides of ponds and streams. It occurs very rarely throughout lowland parts: New Pond (SJ9985), Callow Top (SK1747), Clay Cross (SK3862), Grassmoor (SK4167) and Erewash Canal (SK4835). Probably introduced here as a pondside ornamental, it occurs naturally near the coast in south-western Britain.

Cyperus eragrostis Lam.
Pale Galingale

Pale Galingale is a very rare, casual perennial. The only two records are from waste ground at Kirk Hallam (SK4639) in 1998, and a dried-up pond at Barlow Grange (SK3173) in 2008. A native of tropical America, it is sometimes grown for ornament but also gets introduced as a wool or grass-seed alien.

Blysmus compressus (L.) Panz. ex Link
Flat-sedge

COUNTY STATUS: Native	
CONSERVATION STATUS: DRDB (Cat2), VU, NERC, A, B	
FIRST YEAR: 1801 LATEST YEAR: 2007 NO OF RECORDS: 56	
RECENT SQUARES: monads 5; tetrads 4; hectads 1	
ALL SQUARES: monads 9; tetrads 6; hectads 3	

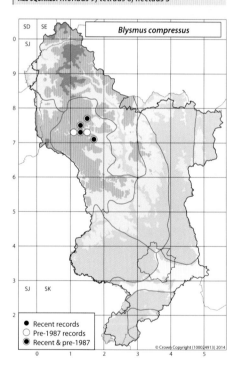

Flat-sedge is a very rare, native and rhizomatous perennial of marshy areas in limestone dales. It now only occurs in the "Wye Dale area" of the White Peak (Chee Dale SK1373, Monk's Dale SK1374, Brook Bottom SK1477 & Monsal Dale SK1770). Previously it ranged over a slightly wider area from near Buxton (SK07) in the west, to Bakewell (SK26) in the east. Over recent years its national distribution has been much reduced by agricultural "improvement" (Preston *et al.* 2002), though locally it does not seem to have suffered as much.

Schoenus nigricans L.
Black Bog-rush

COUNTY STATUS: Native	
CONSERVATION STATUS: DRDB (Cat6)	
FIRST YEAR: 1829 **LATEST YEAR:** 1829 **NO OF RECORDS:** 1	
RECENT SQUARES: monads 0; tetrads 0; hectads 0	
ALL SQUARES: monads 0; tetrads 0; hectads 0	

Locally extinct, Black Bog-rush was a tufted native perennial of moorland bogs, known only from an unlocalised listing in Glover (1829).

Carex paniculata L.
Greater Tussock-sedge

COUNTY STATUS: Native	
CONSERVATION STATUS: None	
FIRST YEAR: 1789 **LATEST YEAR:** 2012 **NO OF RECORDS:** 343	
RECENT SQUARES: monads 82; tetrads 67; hectads 26	
ALL SQUARES: monads 111; tetrads 90; hectads 32	

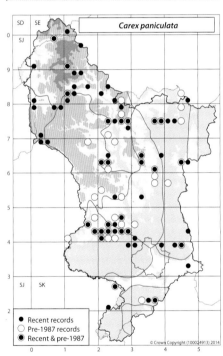

Greater Tussock-sedge is an occasional native perennial of fens, swamps and carrs. It only occurs occasionally throughout the county, but can form considerable stands of large tussocks (Torside Reservoir SK0799, Snake Plantation SK1091, Woolley Moor SK36Q, Bradley Brook Marsh SK2343 & Mere Pond SK3622). It normally grows on peaty soils flushed with somewhat base-enriched water, though it generally avoids limestone areas.

Carex × boenninghausiana Weihe
A hybrid sedge
This hybrid sedge is a very rare, native perennial of wet grassland, only known

from Shirley Brook (SK2141) where it was recorded by K.M. Hollick in 1977. It is the spontaneous hybrid of Greater Tussock-sedge (*C. paniculata*) and Remote Sedge (*C. remota*).

Carex diandra Schrank
Lesser Tussock-sedge

COUNTY STATUS: Native	
CONSERVATION STATUS: DRDB (Cat6), NT, A	
FIRST YEAR: 1854 **LATEST YEAR:** 1889 **NO OF RECORDS:** 2	
RECENT SQUARES: monads 0; tetrads 0; hectads 0	
ALL SQUARES: monads 0; tetrads 0; hectads 1	

Locally extinct, Lesser Tussock-sedge was a very rare, native perennial. The only localised record was from the mid-19th century between Shirley Wood and Rodsley (SK24) and there was an unlocalised one in Painter (1889). This local extinction mirrors a more general loss from lowland sites in England over the last two centuries.

Carex otrubae Podp.
False Fox-sedge

COUNTY STATUS: Native	
CONSERVATION STATUS: None	
FIRST YEAR: 1950 **LATEST YEAR:** 2013 **NO OF RECORDS:** 458	
RECENT SQUARES: monads 162; tetrads 120; hectads 25	
ALL SQUARES: monads 187; tetrads 143; hectads 28	

False Fox-sedge is a tufted native perennial of wet grasslands on the sides of ditches, streams, canals and ponds. Usually growing on heavy non-peaty soils, it occurs occasionally throughout lowland parts of the county, for example Drakelow Power Station (SK2219), Cromford Canal (SK3452) and Brearley Park (SK3974). It is

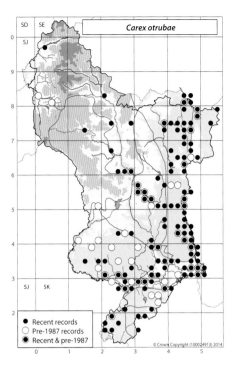

much rarer in the White Peak (Miller's Dale SK1573) and Dark Peak Character Areas (Padfield SK0396).

Carex × pseudoaxillaris K. Richt.
A hybrid sedge
This hybrid sedge is a very rare, native perennial of damp grasslands with its parents. It has only been recorded from three tetrads, all from the eastern side of the county: Fox Covert SK4833 in 2005 and 2013, Chesterfield Canal SK4174 in 2009 and Pebley Reservoir SK4878 in 1998. It is the natural cross of False Fox-sedge (*C. otrubae*) and Remote Sedge (*C. remota*).

Greater Tussock-sedge (*Carex paniculata*) at Sheepbridge (SK3775), May 2013 (Ken Balkow)

Carex spicata Huds.
Spiked Sedge

COUNTY STATUS: Native
CONSERVATION STATUS: None
FIRST YEAR: 1969 LATEST YEAR: 2013 NO OF RECORDS: 214
RECENT SQUARES: monads 108; tetrads 96; hectads 27
ALL SQUARES: monads 137; tetrads 119; hectads 28

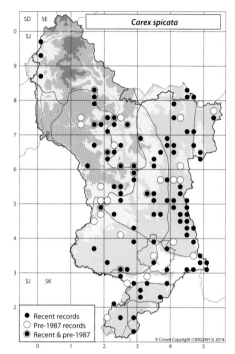

Spiked Sedge is a tufted native perennial of rough grassland often in damp areas by ditches, streams, canals and ponds. It occurs occasionally throughout the county from Gamesley (SK0093) and Beardhough Farm (SK0086) in the north, through Shining Cliff (SK2959), to Overseal (SK2916) and Calke Park (SK3622) in the south.

Carex muricata L.
Prickly Sedge

COUNTY STATUS: Native
CONSERVATION STATUS: DRDB (Cat5b), A, B
FIRST YEAR: 1854 LATEST YEAR: 2007 NO OF RECORDS: 45
RECENT SQUARES: monads 2; tetrads 2; hectads 2
ALL SQUARES: monads 14; tetrads 14; hectads 22

Prickly Sedge is a very rare, native perennial. It grows as dense tufts in open grassy places, usually on dry acid soils. The only current records come from Swarkestone Bridge (SK3628) and Park Brook (SK4679). It was previously known across the county from Alport Dale (SK19) and Bolsover (SK47) in the north, to Trent Lock (SK43), Willington and Egginton Common (SK22) in the south. This decrease is probably due partly to agricultural intensification. Our plant is **ssp. pairae** (F.W. Schultz) Celak. Note that Clapham (1969) erroneously gave records

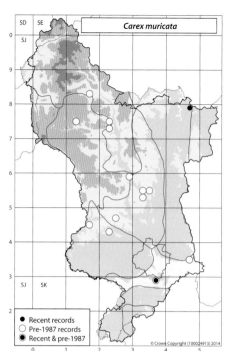

for this plant under **ssp. muricata**, which has never been recorded here.

Carex divulsa Stokes
Grey Sedge

COUNTY STATUS: Native
CONSERVATION STATUS: DRDB (Cat5a), A, B
FIRST YEAR: 1837 LATEST YEAR: 2012 NO OF RECORDS: 62
RECENT SQUARES: monads 12; tetrads 10; hectads 7
ALL SQUARES: monads 21; tetrads 16; hectads 10

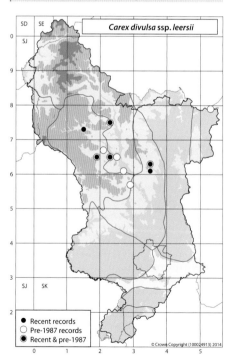

Two subspecies of Grey Sedge have been recorded locally. **Ssp. divulsa** is a very rare, native perennial of rough grassy areas, often associated with shrubs. The only recent records are Coombs Dale (SK2274)

in 2010 and Longstone Edge (SK2373) in 2007. There is one other from Rodsley (SK24) in 1890. **Ssp. leersii** (F.W. Schultz) W. Koch is a very rare, native perennial. It grows as dense tufts in hedges, wood edges and rough grassy areas on calcareous soils. There are a handful of recent records from the Peak Fringe (Milltown SK3561) and the White Peak (Coombs Dale SK2274), plus a form with unusually long bracts confirmed by C. Jermy from Lathkill Dale (SK1965). It previously occurred in the same areas, but was also found in the Magnesian Limestone (Whitwell Wood SK5278 in 1951). Note: statistics refer to the species while the map refers to ssp. *leersii* only.

Carex arenaria L.
Sand Sedge

Sand Sedge is an established rhizomatous perennial of bare or grassy areas. It has only ever been recorded at Rowsley Sidings (SK2565 & 2664), where it was known between 1970 and 1996. It typically grows on sand near the sea, so its occurrence here in the absence of other maritime species is remarkable.

Carex disticha Huds.
Brown Sedge

COUNTY STATUS: Native
CONSERVATION STATUS: DRDB (Cat5b), A, B
FIRST YEAR: 1835 LATEST YEAR: 2013 NO OF RECORDS: 95
RECENT SQUARES: monads 22; tetrads 22; hectads 10
ALL SQUARES: monads 40; tetrads 36; hectads 19

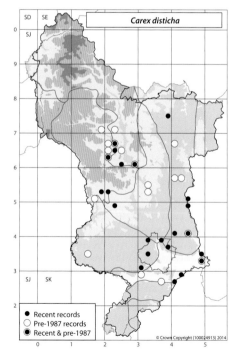

Brown Sedge is a rare native perennial of marshes and wet meadows. Recent records are mostly from central and southern Derbyshire (Youlgrave SK2163, Atlow Moat

Farm SK2248, Brearley SK3974, Erewash Meadows SK4450 & Fox Covert SK4833). Other records are from much the same area but indicate it was formerly more frequent. This is part of a more general national decline due to drainage (Preston *et al.* 2002).

Carex remota L.
Remote Sedge

COUNTY STATUS: Native
CONSERVATION STATUS: None
FIRST YEAR: 1789 LATEST YEAR: 2013 NO OF RECORDS: 835
RECENT SQUARES: monads 334; tetrads 237; hectads 36
ALL SQUARES: monads 389; tetrads 273; hectads 38

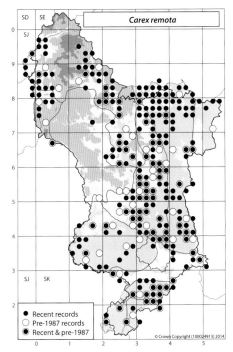

Remote Sedge is a tufted native perennial of damp shaded habitats, typically streamsides in woods. It occurs frequently throughout the county except for the White Peak and the higher moors of the Dark Peak where it is generally absent. Sample locations are: Watford Lodge (SK0086), Jagger's Clough (SK1587), Higham (SK3858), Ticknall Quarries (SK3623) and Linton (SK2715).

Carex leporina L.
Oval Sedge

COUNTY STATUS: Native
CONSERVATION STATUS: None
FIRST YEAR: 1829 LATEST YEAR: 2013 NO OF RECORDS: 621
RECENT SQUARES: monads 325; tetrads 240; hectads 37
ALL SQUARES: monads 362; tetrads 261; hectads 37

Oval Sedge is a tufted native perennial of rough grassy areas usually on damp acid soils. It is frequent throughout the South West Peak, Dark Peak and Peak Fringe Areas as at Combs Reservoir (SK0379), Abney Clough (SK2079) and Wessington

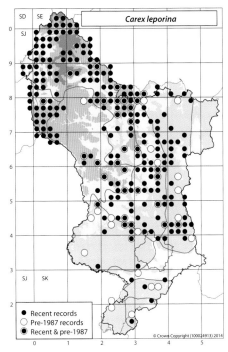

Green (SK3757). It is rare elsewhere: Blake Moor (SK1662) in the White Peak and Overseal (SK2915) in the Coal Measures area. It was previously more frequent in lowland parts, but was probably lost due to agricultural improvement of grazing land. This mirrors the many losses in southern and eastern England during the last century (Preston *et al.* 2002).

Carex echinata Murray
Star Sedge
Star Sedge is a tufted native perennial of unshaded wet acid habitats. It is frequent on moors, in flushes and bogs of the South West Peak and Dark Peak Areas, as at Chunal

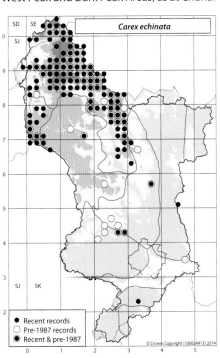

COUNTY STATUS: Native
CONSERVATION STATUS: None
FIRST YEAR: 1800 LATEST YEAR: 2013 NO OF RECORDS: 500
RECENT SQUARES: monads 219; tetrads 123; hectads 18
ALL SQUARES: monads 238; tetrads 135; hectads 26

(SK0390), Lady Booth Clough (SK1486) and Ramsley Moor (SK2975). Elsewhere it occurs rarely in marshy areas and grasslands as at Monsal Dale (SK1770), Wessington Green (SK3757) and Carver's Rocks (SK3222). It was previously more widespread in lowland Derbyshire, but has been lost from many such sites probably due to agricultural improvement, just as elsewhere in lowland England (Preston *et al.* 2002).

Carex dioica L.
Dioecious Sedge

COUNTY STATUS: Native
CONSERVATION STATUS: DRDB (Cat5a), A, B
FIRST YEAR: 1829 LATEST YEAR: 2004 NO OF RECORDS: 23
RECENT SQUARES: monads 2; tetrads 2; hectads 2
ALL SQUARES: monads 6; tetrads 4; hectads 4

Dioecious Sedge is a very rare, native perennial of base-rich mires and flushes where it grows in loose tufts. The only recent records are from Whitwell Wood (SK5278) in 2004 and Brampton Moor (SK2970) in 2004, but it was previously known from Hulland Moss (SK2546) in 1949 and Grindsbrook (SK18) in 1829.

Carex canescens L.
White Sedge
White Sedge is an occasional native perennial of acid mires, flushes and moors in the South West and Dark Peak Areas (Axe Edge SK0270, Cowper Stone SK2583

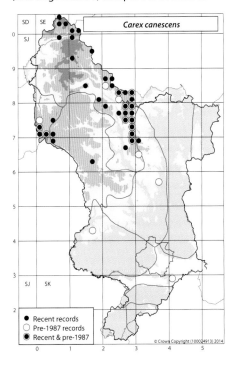

COUNTY STATUS: Native
CONSERVATION STATUS: B
FIRST YEAR: 1789 LATEST YEAR: 2013 NO OF RECORDS: 167
RECENT SQUARES: monads 53; tetrads 38; hectads 12
ALL SQUARES: monads 62; tetrads 45; hectads 20

& Beeley Moor SK2868). Elsewhere it is currently very rare (Middleton Common SK1662) but previously occurred at a few other localities in the south (Snelston SK1642 & Weston-on-Trent SK4028, both in 1969).

Carex hirta L.
Hairy Sedge

COUNTY STATUS: Native
CONSERVATION STATUS: None
FIRST YEAR: 1829 LATEST YEAR: 2013 NO OF RECORDS: 898
RECENT SQUARES: monads 401; tetrads 293; hectads 38
ALL SQUARES: monads 463; tetrads 332; hectads 39

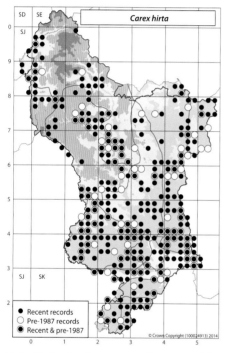

Hairy Sedge is a frequent native perennial of damp grasslands, marshes and waysides in Derbyshire's lowlands. It is much less frequent in upland parts of the Dark and White Peak Character Areas.

Carex acutiformis Ehrh.
Lesser Pond-sedge

COUNTY STATUS: Native
CONSERVATION STATUS: None
FIRST YEAR: 1829 LATEST YEAR: 2013 NO OF RECORDS: 437
RECENT SQUARES: monads 137; tetrads 113; hectads 32
ALL SQUARES: monads 160; tetrads 128; hectads 34

Lesser Pond-sedge is a rhizomatous native perennial that forms dense stands on the margins of ponds, canals and streams, and in areas of marsh, wet grassland and fen-wood. It occurs occasionally throughout the county from Mill Fields (SK0084) and

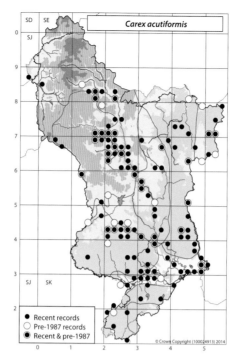

Scarcliffe Park (SK5170) in the north, to Coton in the Elms (SK2314) and Weston-on-Trent (SK4027) in the south.

Carex riparia Curtis
Greater Pond-sedge

COUNTY STATUS: Native
CONSERVATION STATUS: None
FIRST YEAR: 1789 LATEST YEAR: 2013 NO OF RECORDS: 241
RECENT SQUARES: monads 114; tetrads 90; hectads 27
ALL SQUARES: monads 124; tetrads 98; hectads 30

Greater Pond-sedge is a rhizomatous native perennial that forms stands on the margins of ponds, canals and streams, and occasionally grows in wet woods. It is virtually absent from the South West and Dark Peak but occurs occasionally elsewhere from Thornbridge Meadows

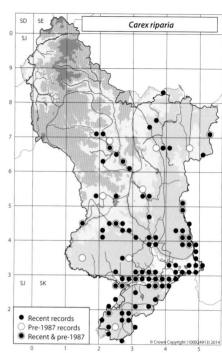

(SK1970) and Frecheville (SK38W) in the north, to Drakelow Power Station (SK2219) and the River Mease (SK2711) in the south. It is particularly frequent in the Trent Valley.

Carex pseudocyperus L.
Cyperus Sedge

COUNTY STATUS: Native
CONSERVATION STATUS: A, B
FIRST YEAR: 1837 LATEST YEAR: 2011 NO OF RECORDS: 51
RECENT SQUARES: monads 15; tetrads 13; hectads 10
ALL SQUARES: monads 21; tetrads 18; hectads 11

Cyperus Sedge is a very rare, native perennial of marshy areas in southern and eastern Derbyshire. It occurs from Foxstone Dam (SK4277) in the north, through Hulland (SK2446) and Hilton Gravel Pits (SK2531) to Forbes Hole (SK4932)

Cyperus Sedge (*Carex pseudocyperus*) at Holmebrook Valley (SK3572), August 2013 (Ken Balkow)

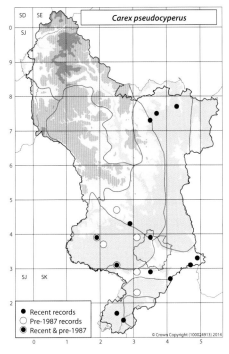

Bottle Sedge is a rhizomatous native perennial of wet peaty areas, and the margins of ponds and streams. It is occasional in the South West and Dark Peak Areas, as at Bleaklow (SK1399) and the Longshaw Estate (SK2679). It is very rare elsewhere: Row Ponds (SK4563) and Bradley Brook Marsh (SK2343). It was previously found at Drakelow Wildfowl Reserve (SK2220) in 1981 and Sharp's Bottom (SK3320) in 1977. This loss from the south of the county is part of a more widespread loss from southern and eastern England in the 20th century (Preston *et al.* 2002).

Carex vesicaria L.
Bladder-sedge

COUNTY STATUS: Native	
CONSERVATION STATUS: DRDB (Cat5b), B	
FIRST YEAR: 1829 LATEST YEAR: 2010 NO OF RECORDS: 90	
RECENT SQUARES: monads 22; tetrads 24; hectads 14	
ALL SQUARES: monads 34; tetrads 34; hectads 20	

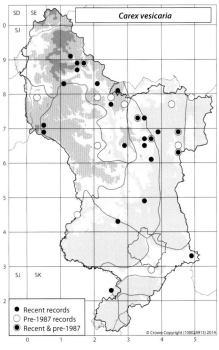

Bladder-sedge is a rare native perennial of marshes, and of the margins of ponds and streams, usually where the water is at least slightly basic. It occurs sporadically throughout the county from Fairholmes (SK1789) and Linacre Reservoir (SK3272) in the north, to Mercaston Marsh (SK2643) and Trent Bridge (SK2522) in the south.

Carex pendula Huds.
Pendulous Sedge

COUNTY STATUS: Native	
CONSERVATION STATUS: B	
FIRST YEAR: 1829 LATEST YEAR: 2013 NO OF RECORDS: 257	
RECENT SQUARES: monads 116; tetrads 102; hectads 30	
ALL SQUARES: monads 124; tetrads 106; hectads 30	

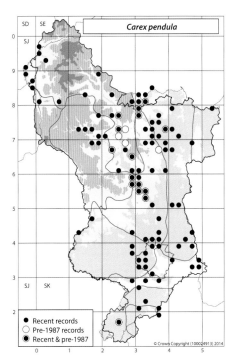

Pendulous Sedge is a tufted native perennial of damp shaded habitats, particularly on heavier soils in woods and on the sides of streams. It is also widely grown in gardens for ornament from where it frequently escapes to become naturalised, sometimes even as a street weed. It is recorded occasionally throughout the county from Simmondley (SK0293) and Totley (SK3281) in the north, through Lovers' Walk (SK2958) and Alderwasley (SK3253), to South Wood (SK3620) and Caldwell Covert (SK2517) in the south.

Carex sylvatica Huds.
Wood-sedge

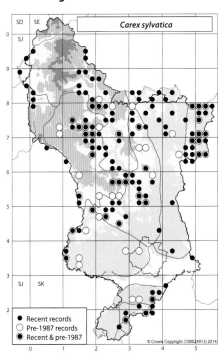

and Botany Bay (SK2615) in the south. Nationally it is a southern species that has declined in much of its range, though it can colonise new areas of wet open habitats and has been planted in some areas (Preston *et al.* 2002). Locally it has shown little contraction in range.

Carex rostrata Stokes
Bottle Sedge

COUNTY STATUS: Native	
CONSERVATION STATUS: B	
FIRST YEAR: 1833 LATEST YEAR: 2013 NO OF RECORDS: 156	
RECENT SQUARES: monads 43; tetrads 37; hectads 15	
ALL SQUARES: monads 55; tetrads 47; hectads 22	

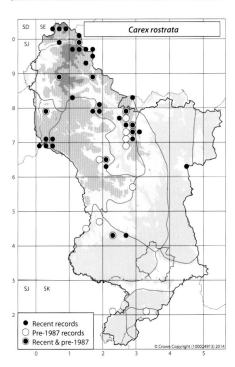

COUNTY STATUS: Native
CONSERVATION STATUS: None
FIRST YEAR: 1789 LATEST YEAR: 2013 NO OF RECORDS: 464
RECENT SQUARES: monads 174; tetrads 130; hectads 35
ALL SQUARES: monads 207; tetrads 153; hectads 36

Wood-sedge is a tufted native perennial of damp heavy soils in woods and scrub. It is found occasionally throughout the county from Linch Clough (SK1694) and Ginny Spring (SK5278) in the north, through the Via Gellia (SK2857), to Sidford Wood (SK1035) and Swainspark (SK2916) in the south.

Carex strigosa Huds.
Thin-spiked Wood-sedge

COUNTY STATUS: Native
CONSERVATION STATUS: DRDB (Cat5a), A, B
FIRST YEAR: 1858 LATEST YEAR: 2012 NO OF RECORDS: 33
RECENT SQUARES: monads 10; tetrads 10; hectads 8
ALL SQUARES: monads 13; tetrads 13; hectads 11

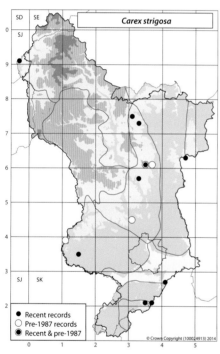

Thin-spiked Wood-sedge is a very rare, native perennial of damp woods. Modern records are scattered throughout lowland Derbyshire from Etherow (SJ9791) in the north, through Linacre (SK3372) and Ogston Woodlands (SK3560), to South Wood (SK3620) in the south.

Carex flacca Schreb.
Glaucous Sedge

Glaucous Sedge is a rhizomatous native perennial of unimproved grasslands and open ground on neutral to calcareous soils, and of moorland flushes. It is very common in the White Peak, where it can be the dominant plant on thin limestone soils. It is occasional elsewhere, and

COUNTY STATUS: Native
CONSERVATION STATUS: None
FIRST YEAR: 1829 LATEST YEAR: 2013 NO OF RECORDS: 2,052
RECENT SQUARES: monads 707; tetrads 420; hectads 40
ALL SQUARES: monads 765; tetrads 440; hectads 40

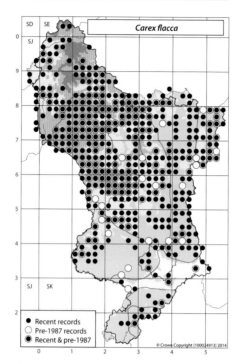

absent from large parts of the Dark Peak, the Claylands and the Trent Valley Character Areas.

Carex panicea L.
Carnation Sedge

Carnation Sedge is a native perennial of damp unimproved grasslands, heaths, fens and upland flushes. It is frequent in the South West, Dark and White Peak,

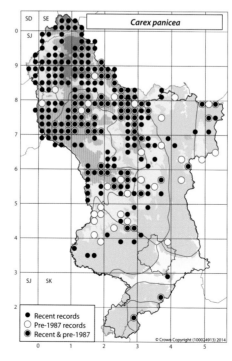

as at Abney Moor (SK1980), Hay Dale (SK1177) and Long Dale (SK1959). It is rare elsewhere, occurring only sporadically as at Swainspark (SK2916) and Ticknall Quarries (SK3623).

Carex laevigata Sm.
Smooth-stalked Sedge

COUNTY STATUS: Native
CONSERVATION STATUS: None
FIRST YEAR: 1866 LATEST YEAR: 2013 NO OF RECORDS: 186
RECENT SQUARES: monads 86; tetrads 56; hectads 12
ALL SQUARES: monads 103; tetrads 69; hectads 20

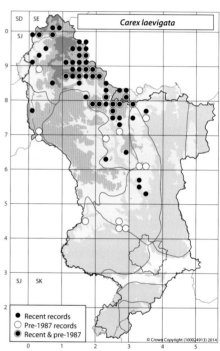

Smooth-stalked Sedge is a tufted native perennial of damp woods, marshes and moors. It occurs occasionally in the Dark Peak Area as at Longdendale (SK0798), Lady Booth Brook (SK1486), Blacka Moor (SK2880) and Cratcliffe (SK2362). Elsewhere it is very rare, as at Fernilee Reservoir (SK0176 v.c.58) and Crich Chase (SK3453). It was previously more frequent in southern parts as at Ashbourne (SK1745) and Hulland Carr (SK2645) both in 1969.

Carex binervis Sm.
Green-ribbed Sedge

COUNTY STATUS: Native
CONSERVATION STATUS: None
FIRST YEAR: 1837 LATEST YEAR: 2013 NO OF RECORDS: 302
RECENT SQUARES: monads 162; tetrads 100; hectads 21
ALL SQUARES: monads 175; tetrads 112; hectads 26

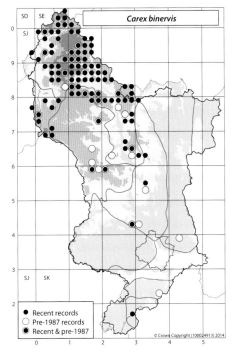

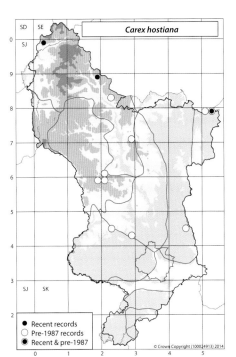

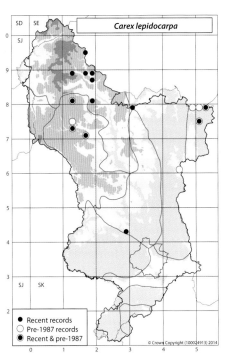

Green-ribbed Sedge is a tufted native perennial of moorlands, rough grasslands and open woodlands. It is frequent in the South West and Dark Peak Areas as at Overhill Farm (SK0278), Arnfield Brook (SK0298 v.c.58), Cowms Rocks (SK1290) and Whitesprings Plantations (SK2865). Elsewhere it is rare: Newhaven (SK1758), Mugginton Bottoms (SK2843) and Swainspark (SK2917).

Carex distans L.
Distant Sedge

COUNTY STATUS:	Native
CONSERVATION STATUS:	DRDB (Cat4)
FIRST YEAR: 1970	LATEST YEAR: 1996 NO OF RECORDS: 5
RECENT SQUARES:	monads 2; tetrads 2; hectads 1
ALL SQUARES:	monads 3; tetrads 3; hectads 2

Distant Sedge is a very rare, tufted native perennial of marshes. The only recently recorded site is St Chads Water (SK4331 & 4432) in 1996 but it was previously known at Pleasley (SK4963) where it was discovered by J. Hodgson in 1975.

Carex hostiana DC.
Tawny Sedge

COUNTY STATUS:	Native
CONSERVATION STATUS:	DRDB (Cat5b), A, B
FIRST YEAR: 1875	LATEST YEAR: 2003 NO OF RECORDS: 33
RECENT SQUARES:	monads 3; tetrads 3; hectads 3
ALL SQUARES:	monads 12; tetrads 12; hectads 10

Tawny Sedge is a very rare, native perennial of fens and flushes. Recent records come only from the north: Tintwistle Low Moor (SK0298 v.c.58), Grainfoot (SK1988) and Whitwell Wood

(SK5278). It was formerly scattered through central Derbyshire as far south as Bradley Brook (SK2244) in 1952.

Carex × fulva Gooden.
A hybrid sedge
This hybrid sedge is a very rare, native perennial known from just three early records. These are Bradley Brook (SK2244) in 1969, Whitwell Wood (SK5278) in 1969 and Abney Moor (SK1879) in the 1970s. It is the spontaneous cross of Tawny (*C. hostiana*) with Long-stalked Yellow Sedge (*C. lepidocarpa*).

Carex flava group
Yellow-sedges
Recorded between 1789 and 2013, this group contains four native species, of which three occur in Derbyshire. Individual accounts are given below.

Carex lepidocarpa Tausch
Long-stalked Yellow-sedge

COUNTY STATUS:	Native
CONSERVATION STATUS:	B
FIRST YEAR: 1941	LATEST YEAR: 2007 NO OF RECORDS: 74
RECENT SQUARES:	monads 17; tetrads 13; hectads 6
ALL SQUARES:	monads 24; tetrads 17; hectads 10

Long-stalked Yellow-sedge is a very rare, native perennial of marshes, fens and flushes that are at least moderately base-rich. It is recorded from both of the limestone Character Areas (Chee Dale SK1273, Lees Bottom SK1770 & Markland Grips SK5074), and elsewhere too (Hagg Side SK1688 & Mugginton Bottoms SK2843).

Carex demissa Hornem.
Common Yellow-sedge

COUNTY STATUS:	Native
CONSERVATION STATUS:	None
FIRST YEAR: 1969	LATEST YEAR: 2013 NO OF RECORDS: 457
RECENT SQUARES:	monads 230; tetrads 147; hectads 30
ALL SQUARES:	monads 259; tetrads 167; hectads 34

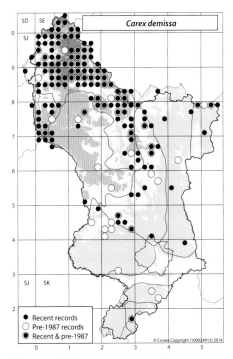

Common Yellow-sedge is a native perennial of flushes, marshes and streamsides. It is frequent in the South West and Dark Peak Areas (Axe Edge Moor SK07F, Whiteley Nab SK0292, Cowms Rocks SK1290 & Abney Moor SK1980). Elsewhere, including the limestone areas, it is rare (Hulland Moss SK2446 & Swainspark Wood

SK2917). It was previously more frequent in lowland parts, and this decrease is part of a more general decline in central and southern England due to drainage and habitat loss (Preston *et al.* 2002).

Carex oederi Retz.
Small-fruited Yellow-sedge

COUNTY STATUS:	Native
CONSERVATION STATUS:	B
FIRST YEAR: 1969	LATEST YEAR: 1984 NO OF RECORDS: 3
RECENT SQUARES:	monads 0; tetrads 0; hectads 0
ALL SQUARES:	monads 1; tetrads 1; hectads 1

Small-fruited Yellow-sedge is a very rare, native perennial of damp base-rich areas. The only records are from Whitwell Wood (SK5278), between 1969 and 1984.

Carex pallescens L.
Pale Sedge

COUNTY STATUS:	Native
CONSERVATION STATUS:	DRDB (Cat5b), B
FIRST YEAR: 1829	LATEST YEAR: 2012 NO OF RECORDS: 108
RECENT SQUARES:	monads 32; tetrads 26; hectads 14
ALL SQUARES:	monads 52; tetrads 42; hectads 25

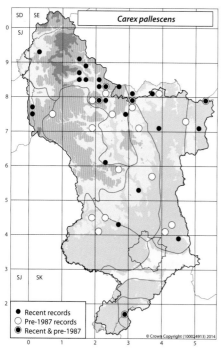

Pale Sedge is a tufted native perennial of damp grasslands and open woods on mildly acid to neutral soils. It occurs rarely throughout the county from Hood Brook (SK2382), Holmesfield (SK3178) and Whitwell Wood (SK5278) in the north, to Mercaston Marsh (SK2643) and Swainspark (SK2917) in the south. It was formerly more frequent in the south, being known from Shirley Brook (SK2141) in 1969 and Shipley Country Park (SK4343) in 1977. This decrease is part of a wider decline throughout Britain since 1950 (Preston *et al.* 2002).

Carex digitata L.
Fingered Sedge

COUNTY STATUS:	Native
CONSERVATION STATUS:	DRDB (Cat3), NS, A, B
FIRST YEAR: 1829	LATEST YEAR: 2006 NO OF RECORDS: 60
RECENT SQUARES:	monads 9; tetrads 7; hectads 3
ALL SQUARES:	monads 11; tetrads 7; hectads 3

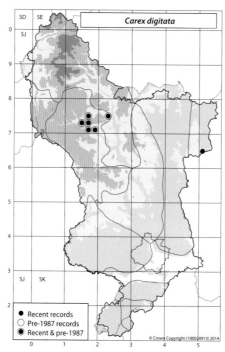

Fingered Sedge is a very rare, native perennial. It grows in open limestone grassland and on rocky ledges, sometimes under a light shade of trees. It is mostly recorded from a small part of the White Peak (Priestcliffe Lees SK1572, Cressbrook Dale SK1773 & Coombs Dale SK2274); but there is one record from the Magnesian Limestone (Pleasley Vale SK5165). This is a Nationally Scarce species.

Carex ornithopoda Willd.
Bird's-foot Sedge

COUNTY STATUS:	Native
CONSERVATION STATUS:	DRDB (Cat3), NR, A, B, C
FIRST YEAR: 1874	LATEST YEAR: 2011 NO OF RECORDS: 132
RECENT SQUARES:	monads 8; tetrads 5; hectads 2
ALL SQUARES:	monads 10; tetrads 6; hectads 2

Bird's-foot Sedge is a very rare, native, perennial that grows locally in short limestone grassland, generally on the shallower soils of dalesides. It is currently only known from the Chee Dale (SK1172)/ Miller's Dale (SK1572)/ Monsal Dale (SK1672)/Cressbrook Dale (SK1774) area of the White Peak, plus one isolated part of the Magnesian Limestone (Pleasley Park SK5165). It was in the Miller's Dale area that this sedge was found new to Britain in 1874 (Trimen 1874). Occurring only sporadically in the Midlands and

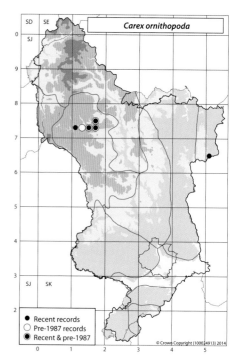

northern England, it is categorised as Nationally Rare.

Carex caryophyllea Latourr.
Spring-sedge

COUNTY STATUS:	Native
CONSERVATION STATUS:	None
FIRST YEAR: 1940	LATEST YEAR: 2013 NO OF RECORDS: 749
RECENT SQUARES:	monads 271; tetrads 157; hectads 23
ALL SQUARES:	monads 310; tetrads 180; hectads 29

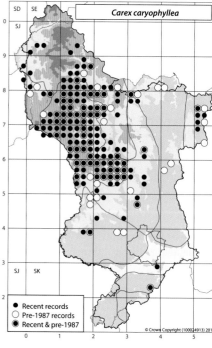

Spring-sedge is a native perennial of short dry grassland and heathy areas. It is very common in the White Peak (Laughman Tor SK1077, Ludwell Farm SK1262 & Harborough Rocks SK2455); occasional on the

Magnesian Limestone (Markland Grips SK5074), and rare in other areas (Alkmonton SK1939, Lumb Brook SK3347 & Calke Park SK3622). It has declined in the English Midlands since 1950 (Preston *et al.* 2002) though there is only a little evidence for this locally. It has been one of the plants studied recently by the Buxton Climate Change Impacts Lab. Group (Fridley *et al.* 2007).

Carex ericetorum Pollich
Rare Spring-sedge

COUNTY STATUS:	Native
CONSERVATION STATUS:	DRDB (Cat2), VU, NS, NERC, A, B, C
FIRST YEAR: 1945	LATEST YEAR: 2009 NO OF RECORDS: 22
RECENT SQUARES:	monads 1; tetrads 1; hectads 1
ALL SQUARES:	monads 3; tetrads 1; hectads 1

Rare Spring-sedge is a native perennial of dry short calcareous grassland over Magnesian Limestone. It is only known from Markland Grips (SK5074, SK5075), where it was discovered in 1945 (Brown 1945). Subsequently it has been recorded several times up until 2009. It grows in scattered localities in eastern and northern England, and is a Nationally Scarce species.

Carex montana L.
Soft-leaved Sedge

COUNTY STATUS:	Native
CONSERVATION STATUS:	DRDB (Cat3), NS, A, B, C
FIRST YEAR: 1885	LATEST YEAR: 2009 NO OF RECORDS: 40
RECENT SQUARES:	monads 3; tetrads 1; hectads 1
ALL SQUARES:	monads 3; tetrads 1; hectads 1

Soft-leaved Sedge is a very rare, native perennial of rough grassland and open woods on the Magnesian Limestone. First identified in Britain in 1843, it was thought to be confined to southern Britain. Its discovery in Hollinhill and Markland Grips in the 1880s by C. Waterfall was therefore significant and unexpected (Waterfall 1891). Subsequently it has been recorded in at least 19 separate years up to 2009, but is still only known from this one site albeit from three monads (SK5074, 5075 & 5175). Nationally it grows in a wider range of habitats, though is still very local in southern Britain, north to Derbyshire. It is a Nationally Scarce species.

Carex pilulifera L.
Pill Sedge

COUNTY STATUS:	Native
CONSERVATION STATUS:	None
FIRST YEAR: 1863	LATEST YEAR: 2013 NO OF RECORDS: 225
RECENT SQUARES:	monads 134; tetrads 101; hectads 23
ALL SQUARES:	monads 153; tetrads 119; hectads 28

Pill Sedge is a tufted native perennial of heaths, moors, rough grassland and open

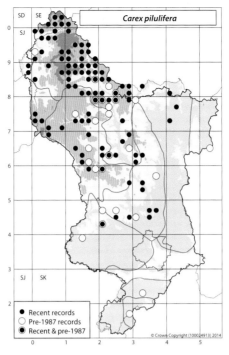

woods usually on base-poor or peaty soils. It is occasional in the South West and Dark Peak, as at Upper Longdendale (SK1199), Win Hill (SK1885) and Beeley (SK2767). Elsewhere it is very rare as at Shirley Park (SK2042), and in grassland on limestone dalesides, as at Cressbrook Dale (SK1774) and Gratton Dale (SK2059).

Carex acuta L.
Slender Tufted-sedge
Slender Tufted-sedge is a very rare, native perennial of marshy areas by streams and rivers. It grows scattered throughout the county from Longsidings Quarry Buxton (SK0976) in the north, to

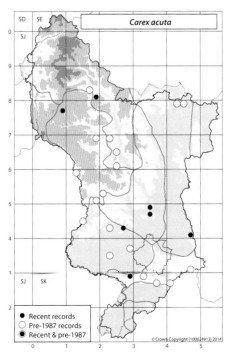

COUNTY STATUS:	Native
CONSERVATION STATUS:	DRDB (Cat5b), A
FIRST YEAR: 1854	LATEST YEAR: 2007 NO OF RECORDS: 42
RECENT SQUARES:	monads 7; tetrads 7; hectads 6
ALL SQUARES:	monads 25; tetrads 25; hectads 19

Mercaston Marsh (SK2643) and Milford (SK3446) in the south, amongst other recent sites. It was formerly more frequent, though still only rare, having probably been lost from many sites by land drainage and agricultural improvement.

Carex nigra (L.) Reichard
Common Sedge

COUNTY STATUS:	Native
CONSERVATION STATUS:	None
FIRST YEAR: 1829	LATEST YEAR: 2013 NO OF RECORDS: 829
RECENT SQUARES:	monads 381; tetrads 240; hectads 37
ALL SQUARES:	monads 427; tetrads 266; hectads 39

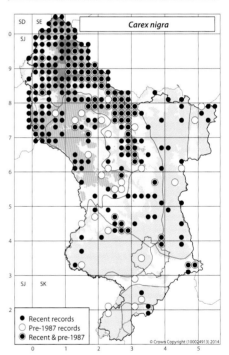

Common Sedge is a native perennial of a wide range of wet habitats, including marshes, flushes, moors and grasslands, usually on acid soils. Its growth form is very variable, from dense tussocks and extensive stands to single stems intermingled with other plants. It is common and locally abundant in the South West and Dark Peak (Goyt's Clough SK0172, Laneside Farm SK0283, Whitely Nab SK0292 & Big Bumper Piece SK2866). Elsewhere it is only rare to occasional (Mercaston Marsh SK2643 & Long Eaton SK4833). Previously it was more frequently encountered in the south where it was found at Drakelow Wildfowl Reserve (SK2219) in 1974 and Swadlincote (SK32A) in 1978. This decline mirrors a more general one in south-eastern Britain due to drainage (Preston *et al.* 2002).

Carex elata All.
Tufted-sedge

COUNTY STATUS: Native
CONSERVATION STATUS: DRDB (Cat4), B
FIRST YEAR: 1969 LATEST YEAR: 1989 NO OF RECORDS: 2
RECENT SQUARES: monads 1; tetrads 1; hectads 1
ALL SQUARES: monads 2; tetrads 2; hectads 2

Tufted-sedge is a tufted native perennial of fens, streamsides and ditches, with a single record from Marple Bridge (SJ9689) in the late 1980s. The only other is from New Stanton (SK4639), based on an undated record by A. Proctor in Clapham (1969).

Carex pulicaris L.
Flea Sedge

COUNTY STATUS: Native
CONSERVATION STATUS: ERL
FIRST YEAR: 1829 LATEST YEAR: 2013 NO OF RECORDS: 174
RECENT SQUARES: monads 60; tetrads 49; hectads 15
ALL SQUARES: monads 83; tetrads 63; hectads 20

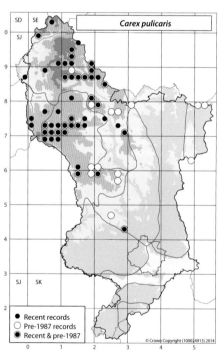

Flea Sedge is a tufted native perennial of flushes, fens, damp grasslands and wet heaths. It is occasional in both the Dark Peak (Nab Brow SK0588 & Lodge Cote SK1987) and the White Peak (Back Dale SK0970 & Biggin Dale SK1458). In the latter it is a feature of grasslands on the upper parts of north-facing slopes. Elsewhere it is very rare, the only recent record being from Mugginton Bottoms (SK2843), though it was formerly recorded at Hulland Moss (SK2546) in 1969, Whitwell Wood (SK5278) in 1969 and Foremark Park (SK32) in 1903.

POACEAE

Nardus stricta L.
Mat-grass

COUNTY STATUS: Native
CONSERVATION STATUS: ERL
FIRST YEAR: 1789 LATEST YEAR: 2013 NO OF RECORDS: 1,616
RECENT SQUARES: monads 583; tetrads 232; hectads 28
ALL SQUARES: monads 631; tetrads 262; hectads 34

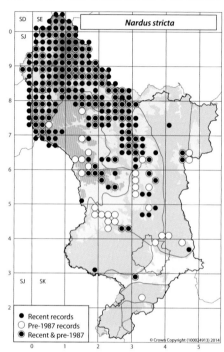

Mat-grass is a tufted native perennial of moors, heaths and grasslands on acid soils. It is very common and locally abundant in the Character Areas of the South West and Dark Peak (Axe Edge SK0270, Ashop Clough SK0990 & Priddock Wood SK2086). It is particularly abundant in areas of heavy sheep grazing. It is rare in the White Peak (Bigginmoor SK1758 & Carsington Pasture SK2454), where it grows in patches of acid or leached soil over the limestone. Elsewhere in Derbyshire it is very rare (Willington Junction SK3029, Wessington Green SK3757 & Hardwick Hall SK4563). It was previously more widespread, having been lost from many lowland sites as part of a widespread decline in Britain due to habitat destruction (Braithwaite *et al.* 2006).

Milium effusum L.
Wood Millet

COUNTY STATUS: Native
CONSERVATION STATUS: None
FIRST YEAR: 1829 LATEST YEAR: 2013 NO OF RECORDS: 568
RECENT SQUARES: monads 232; tetrads 161; hectads 32
ALL SQUARES: monads 273; tetrads 188; hectads 34

Wood Millet is a tufted native perennial of deciduous woods on all but the most acid of soils. It is rare in the South West Peak

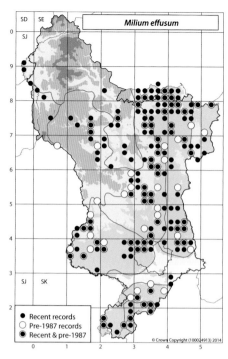

(Hilltop SK0280), Dark Peak (Compstall SJ9791) and White Peak (Kenslow Wood SK1962). Elsewhere it is occasional (Walton Wood SK2116, Sharp's Bottom SK3420, Ogston Woods SK3659 & Ford SK4080). It is regarded as an indicator of ancient woodlands in eastern England but can colonise new woods in upland areas.

Schedonorus pratensis (Huds.) P. Beauv.
Meadow Fescue

Meadow Fescue is a tufted native perennial of grass fields, grassy waysides and waste ground usually on moist nutrient-rich soils. It was so often sown for fodder that it is now impossible to distinguish native

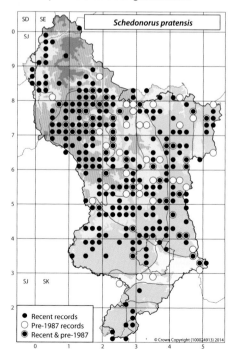

COUNTY STATUS: Native
CONSERVATION STATUS: None
FIRST YEAR: 1903 LATEST YEAR: 2012 NO OF RECORDS: 570
RECENT SQUARES: monads 313; tetrads 250; hectads 35
ALL SQUARES: monads 374; tetrads 285; hectads 37

plants from introduced ones. It is recorded occasionally throughout the county from Deep Clough (SK0497) and Salter's Brook (SE1300 v.c.58) in the north, to Swadlincote (SK2819) and Forbes Hole (SK4932) in the south.

Schedonorus arundinaceus (Schreb.) Dumort.
Tall Fescue

COUNTY STATUS: Native
CONSERVATION STATUS: None
FIRST YEAR: 1863 LATEST YEAR: 2013 NO OF RECORDS: 486
RECENT SQUARES: monads 280; tetrads 232; hectads 38
ALL SQUARES: monads 317; tetrads 250; hectads 39

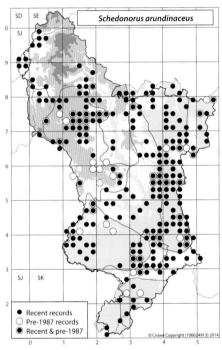

Tall Fescue is a robust native perennial of damp grasslands, rough ground and waste land on a range of soil types. It is also often sown for hay or planted in restoration schemes, so its native distribution is impossible to distinguish now. It occurs occasionally from Glossop (SK0294) and Westfield Plantation (SK4282) in the north, to Linton (SK2614) and Trent Meadows (SK5032) in the south.

Schedonorus giganteus (L.) Holub
Giant Fescue

COUNTY STATUS: Native
CONSERVATION STATUS: None
FIRST YEAR: 1789 LATEST YEAR: 2013 NO OF RECORDS: 1,350
RECENT SQUARES: monads 573; tetrads 387; hectads 40
ALL SQUARES: monads 664; tetrads 420; hectads 41

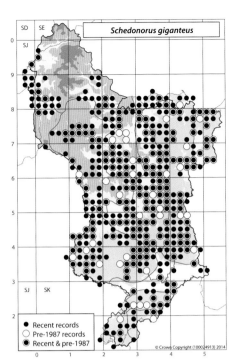

Giant Fescue is a tufted native perennial of damp woods, stream banks and hedgerows. It is frequent throughout the county except for the more upland areas of the Peak District where it is virtually absent.

✕ *Schedolium loliaceum* (Huds.) Holub
Hybrid Fescue

COUNTY STATUS: Native
CONSERVATION STATUS: None
FIRST YEAR: 1898 LATEST YEAR: 2012 NO OF RECORDS: 58
RECENT SQUARES: monads 17; tetrads 17; hectads 11
ALL SQUARES: monads 40; tetrads 39; hectads 23

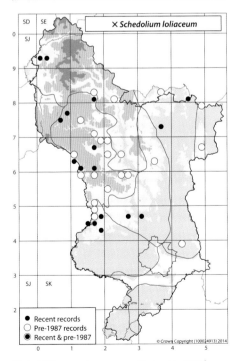

Hybrid Fescue is a rare native perennial of grasslands, particularly on damp rich

soils near rivers. It is recorded sporadically from Glossop (SK0393) and the River Rother (SK4481) in the north, to Osmaston (SK1843) and Derby (SK33) in the south, but is probably under-recorded. It is the spontaneous hybrid of Meadow Fescue (*Schedonorus pratensis*) and Perennial Rye-grass (*Lolium perenne*).

Lolium perenne L.
Perennial Rye-grass

COUNTY STATUS: Native
CONSERVATION STATUS: None
FIRST YEAR: 1789 LATEST YEAR: 2013 NO OF RECORDS: 4,989
RECENT SQUARES: monads 1,956; tetrads 723; hectads 44
ALL SQUARES: monads 2,055; tetrads 725; hectads 44

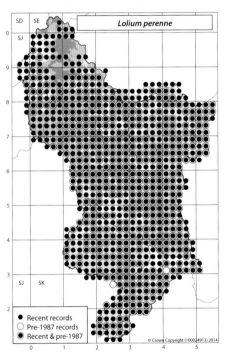

Perennial Rye-grass is a very common, native perennial of waysides, cultivated land, waste places and rough ground. It is also widely sown as a constituent of grass-seed mixes for agricultural, amenity and recreational grasslands. Apart from the high moors of the Dark Peak, it is recorded throughout the county but is more frequent and abundant on the better soils of the lowlands than the poorer uplands.

Lolium ✕ *boucheanum* Kunth
Hybrid Rye-grass

COUNTY STATUS: Native
CONSERVATION STATUS: None
FIRST YEAR: 1974 LATEST YEAR: 2000 NO OF RECORDS: 2
RECENT SQUARES: monads 1; tetrads 1; hectads 1
ALL SQUARES: monads 2; tetrads 2; hectads 2

Hybrid Rye-grass is a very rare, native annual or short-lived perennial of grass fields and waste places. It is also planted as a constituent of grass-seed mixes for agricultural use. The only recent record is from Sandiacre (SK4736) with another from Derby City (SK3536) in 1974. Probably under-recorded, it is the spontaneous hybrid of Perennial (*L. perenne*) and Italian Rye-grass (*L. multiflorum*).

Lolium multiflorum Lam.
Italian Rye-grass

COUNTY STATUS:	Established (Neophyte)
CONSERVATION STATUS:	None
FIRST YEAR: 1903 LATEST YEAR: 2012 NO OF RECORDS: 475	
RECENT SQUARES:	monads 257; tetrads 222; hectads 38
ALL SQUARES:	monads 346; tetrads 280; hectads 38

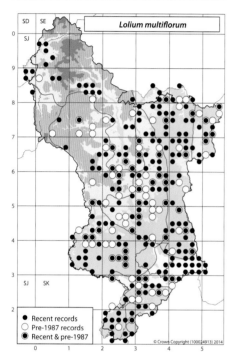

Italian Rye-grass is an established annual or short-lived perennial of grass fields, waysides and waste places. It is widely planted on improved neutral soils for hay and silage, and is native to the Mediterranean area.

Lolium temulentum L.
Darnel

Darnel is a very rare, casual annual of arable fields and waste ground that is introduced as a contaminant of grains. It is indigenous to the Mediterranean region. Latest records are from a roadside at Bamford (SK2082) in 1974 and from Dimple Dump (SK2960) in the 1960s. Linton (1903) records it from Miller's Dale Station (SK17), Rodsley (SK24) and Parson's Hill (SK32), and gives the first record as Glover (1829).

Festuca altissima All.
Wood Fescue

Wood Fescue is a very rare, native perennial of moist rocky slopes in woods. Recent records are from two distinct parts of the county: around Matlock (Hagg Wood

COUNTY STATUS:	Native
CONSERVATION STATUS:	DRDB (Cat5a), A, B
FIRST YEAR: 1789 LATEST YEAR: 2008 NO OF RECORDS: 31	
RECENT SQUARES:	monads 6; tetrads 6; hectads 3
ALL SQUARES:	monads 6; tetrads 6; hectads 5

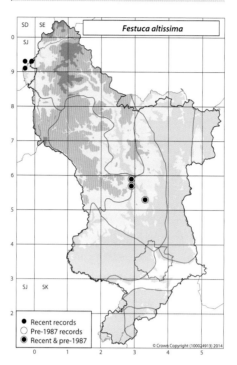

SK2957 & Shiningcliff Wood SK3352) and the Glossop area (Etherow Reserve SJ9791 & Stirrup Wood SJ9892). Earlier records are from the same areas, plus Ashwood Dale (SK07) in 1903.

Festuca rubra L.
Red Fescue

Red Fescue is a very common, native perennial that grows in a wide range

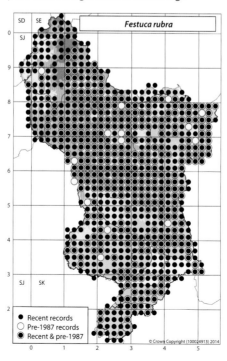

COUNTY STATUS:	Native
CONSERVATION STATUS:	None
FIRST YEAR: 1829 LATEST YEAR: 2013 NO OF RECORDS: 4,524	
RECENT SQUARES:	monads 1,538; tetrads 699; hectads 44
ALL SQUARES:	monads 1,691; tetrads 714; hectads 44

of grasslands, waysides and heaths. It is also a frequent constituent of grass-seed mixes sown for lawns and amenity plantings. Occurring throughout the county, it is often abundant over large areas of unimproved grassland. Three subspecies have been recorded. **Ssp. *rubra*** is a common native throughout the county. **Ssp. *commutata*** Gaudin (**Chewing's Fescue**) is a native often used in grass seed mixes but has only been recorded twice (Swanwick SK4053 & Erewash Canal SK43Y). **Ssp. *megastachys*** Gaudin is a casual from Europe that has been planted on roadsides, but is only recorded from Alport Height (SK3051).

Festuca ovina L.
Sheep's-fescue

COUNTY STATUS:	Native
CONSERVATION STATUS:	None
FIRST YEAR: 1789 LATEST YEAR: 2013 NO OF RECORDS: 2,444	
RECENT SQUARES:	monads 878; tetrads 426; hectads 38
ALL SQUARES:	monads 957; tetrads 457; hectads 40

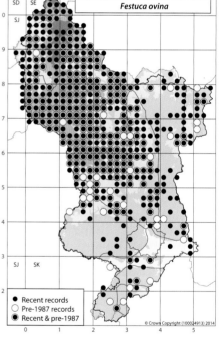

Sheep's-fescue is a tufted native perennial of dry unproductive grasslands on both acid and calcareous soils. It is very common throughout the South West Peak, the Dark Peak, the White Peak and parts of the Peak Fringe. Here it is locally dominant over large areas of limestone dalesides and the lower slopes of rough hill grazings. Elsewhere throughout the county it is only occasional. Three subspecies, all native, have been recorded. **Ssp. *ovina*** is the common Derbyshire plant. **Ssp. *hirtula*** (Hack. ex Travis) M.J. Wilk. is known from Snake Plantation (SK1091) and Cramside Wood (SK1673). **Ssp. *ophioliticola*** (Kerguelen) M.J. Wilk. is listed for the county by Wilkinson & Stace (1991), but prior to 1970.

Festuca filiformis Pourr.
Fine-leaved Sheep's-fescue

COUNTY STATUS: Native	
CONSERVATION STATUS: DRDB (Cat5a)	
FIRST YEAR: 1903 LATEST YEAR: 2003 NO OF RECORDS: 9	
RECENT SQUARES: monads 1; tetrads 1; hectads 1	
ALL SQUARES: monads 4; tetrads 4; hectads 8	

Fine-leaved Sheep's-fescue is a tufted native perennial of grasslands, heaths and open woods on acid soils. The only recent record is for Wet Withens (SK2279). It was previously found sporadically, from Fair Brook near Snake Inn (SK19) for 1903 in the north, to Woodeaves (SK1850) for 1977 and Willington (SK3029) for 1977 in the south. It is probably under-recorded.

Festuca lemanii Bastard
Confused Fescue

Confused Fescue is a very rare, tufted native perennial. Our only localised record is for Monk's Dale (SK17) in 1987, though it is also listed for the county in Wilkinson & Stace (1989). Despite the paucity of records, Preston *et al.* (2002) describes it as characteristic of limestone cliff rock crevices in Derbyshire, so is probably under-recorded.

Festuca brevipila R. Tracey
Hard Fescue

Hard Fescue is a very rare, casual perennial of roadsides where it is introduced in grass-seed mixes. There is a single recent record from Poulter Country Park (SK5270) in 1999, and three earlier ones from Taddington By-pass (SK1371), Pleasley (SK5064) and Alport (SK2164), all in the 1970s. These latter three records were originally recorded as **Blue Fescue (*F. longifolia* Thuill.).** A native of Europe, Preston *et al.* (2002) observe that Taddington holds the altitudinal record for British plants at 365 metres.

Vulpia bromoides (L.) Gray
Squirreltail Fescue

COUNTY STATUS: Native	
CONSERVATION STATUS: B	
FIRST YEAR: 1829 LATEST YEAR: 2012 NO OF RECORDS: 200	
RECENT SQUARES: monads 92; tetrads 77; hectads 26	
ALL SQUARES: monads 116; tetrads 95; hectads 30	

Squirreltail Fescue is an occasional native annual of dry open areas on waste ground, on waysides, in grassy places and on walls. It is often present in small amounts but

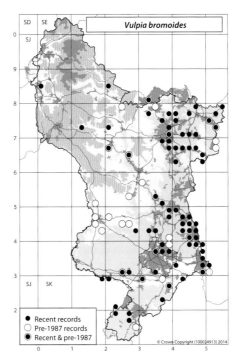

can form extensive patches on recently disturbed ground. It occurs scattered throughout the county from Goytside Meadows (SK0084 v.c.58) and Steetley Quarry (SK5478) in the north, to Drakelow (SK2219) and Lock Lane Ash Tip (SK4831) in the south.

Vulpia myuros (L.) C.C. Gmel.
Rat's-tail Fescue

COUNTY STATUS: Established (Archaeophyte)	
CONSERVATION STATUS: B	
FIRST YEAR: 1949 LATEST YEAR: 2013 NO OF RECORDS: 191	
RECENT SQUARES: monads 101; tetrads 84; hectads 27	
ALL SQUARES: monads 119; tetrads 94; hectads 29	

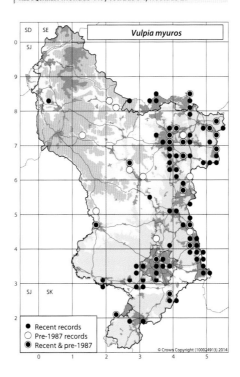

Rat's-tail Fescue is a long-established annual of dry open habitats on rough ground, waste places, waysides and walls. A native of southern Europe, it is probably introduced as a contaminant of seed or grain. It is occasional in the lowland south and east (Drakelow Power Station SK2220, King's Newton SK3926, Alfreton Station SK4256 & Arkwright Town SK47F). However, it is very rare in upland north and west Derbyshire (Brierley Green SK0282 & Rowsley Sidings SK2664). It has spread rapidly since first being found here in 1949, mirroring a national increase since 1962 (Preston *et al.* 2002).

Vulpia ciliata Dumort.
Bearded Fescue

Bearded Fescue is a very rare, casual annual of waste ground, and is native to coastal areas of southern Britain. All records were made by J. Hodgson at Shirebrook North Station (SK5268) in 1977. They refer to ssp. *ambigua* (Le Gall) Stace & Auquier, which is probably a contaminant of grain.

Vulpia unilateralis (L.) Stace
Mat-grass Fescue

Mat-grass Fescue is a very rare, casual annual of open ground. The only known site is Clifton Goods Yard (SK1644) where it was first noted in 1941, then again in 1969, but was extinct by 1976. It is native to southern and central England.

Cynosurus cristatus L.
Crested Dog's-tail

Crested Dog's-tail is a very common, native perennial of unimproved grasslands on all but the most acid of soils. It is also

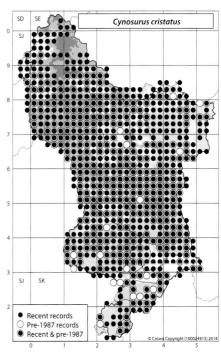

COUNTY STATUS: Native
CONSERVATION STATUS: None
FIRST YEAR: 1789 LATEST YEAR: 2013 NO OF RECORDS: 3,781
RECENT SQUARES: monads 1,472; tetrads 655; hectads 43
ALL SQUARES: monads 1,560; tetrads 672; hectads 43

increasingly being sown in amenity plantings. It occurs throughout Derbyshire, only being absent from upland moors and some intensively farmed lowland parts.

Cynosurus echinatus L.
Rough Dog's-tail

Locally extinct, Rough Dog's-tail was a very rare, casual annual of waste ground. The only record is from Sturston Tip (SK1946) in 1932. A native of Europe, it was probably introduced as a contaminant of seed or grain.

Puccinellia distans (Jacq.) Parl.
Reflexed Saltmarsh-grass

COUNTY STATUS: Established (Neophyte)
CONSERVATION STATUS: B
FIRST YEAR: 1969 LATEST YEAR: 2012 NO OF RECORDS: 158
RECENT SQUARES: monads 102; tetrads 93; hectads 29
ALL SQUARES: monads 110; tetrads 99; hectads 29

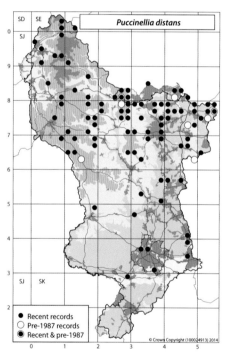

Reflexed Saltmarsh-grass is an established tufted perennial of bare compacted soil by the side of salt-treated roads. First recorded near Steetley Quarry (SK57) in 1969, it has since spread along major roads to occur occasionally throughout the county (Heyden Bridge SE0900 v.c.58, Rowfield SK1949, Stony Ridge SK2780, Ilkeston SK4641 & Hodthorpe SK5476). This is part of a general increase along roadsides in central and eastern England since 1970 (Preston *et al.* 2002) due to increased use of road salt. It is native to coastal salt-marshes in England.

Briza media L.
Quaking-grass

COUNTY STATUS: Native
CONSERVATION STATUS: ERL
FIRST YEAR: 1789 LATEST YEAR: 2013 NO OF RECORDS: 1,840
RECENT SQUARES: monads 551; tetrads 302; hectads 35
ALL SQUARES: monads 620; tetrads 338; hectads 37

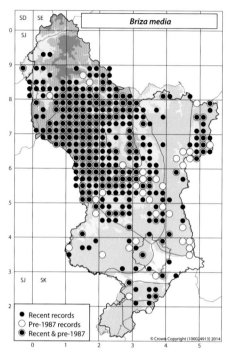

Quaking-grass is a native perennial of unimproved grasslands on a wide range of soil types. It is very common and locally abundant on the dry calcareous soils of the White Peak: Batham Gate (SK1078), Lathkill Dale (SK1665) and Hopton Quarry (SK2656). Elsewhere it is much more sporadic in occurrence: Long Clough (SK0392) in the Dark Peak, Markland Grips (SK5074) on the Magnesian Limestone and Chellaston Field (SK3829) in the Trent Valley. It was previously more frequent in lowland parts, and this loss is part of a national decline since 1962 due to agricultural improvement (Preston *et al.* 2002). It has a local name of Doddering Dillies.

Briza maxima L.
Greater Quaking-grass

COUNTY STATUS: Casual
CONSERVATION STATUS: None
FIRST YEAR: 1976 LATEST YEAR: 2010 NO OF RECORDS: 9
RECENT SQUARES: monads 7; tetrads 7; hectads 5
ALL SQUARES: monads 8; tetrads 8; hectads 6

Greater Quaking-grass is a very rare, casual annual of cultivated ground, waysides and waste places. Records are scattered over northern and eastern Derbyshire (Jodrell Road SK0181 v.c.58, Bradway SK3280, Eckington SK4379 & Leabrooks SK4253). In 1976 it was also found in Derby (SK3338).

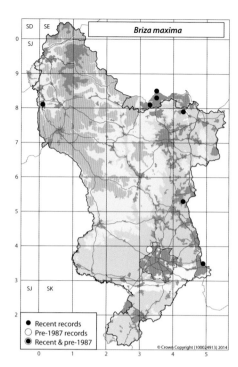

Indigenous to the Mediterranean region, it is grown for ornament and is usually just a garden escape.

Poa annua L.
Annual Meadow-grass

COUNTY STATUS: Native
CONSERVATION STATUS: None
FIRST YEAR: 1789 LATEST YEAR: 2013 NO OF RECORDS: 4,808
RECENT SQUARES: monads 2,029; tetrads 746; hectads 45
ALL SQUARES: monads 2,119; tetrads 750; hectads 45

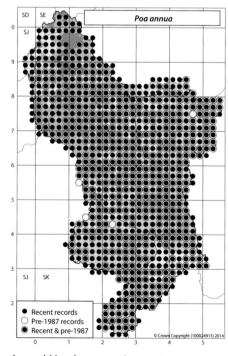

Annual Meadow-grass is a very common, native annual or short-lived perennial of a range of habitats. It occurs in grass fields, lawns and cultivated land plus on disturbed ground and along paths. It grows throughout the county except for the highest moors of the Dark Peak.

Poa trivialis L.
Rough Meadow-grass

COUNTY STATUS: Native
CONSERVATION STATUS: None
FIRST YEAR: 1829 LATEST YEAR: 2013 NO OF RECORDS: 3,960
RECENT SQUARES: monads 1,434; tetrads 676; hectads 44
ALL SQUARES: monads 1,624; tetrads 696; hectads 44

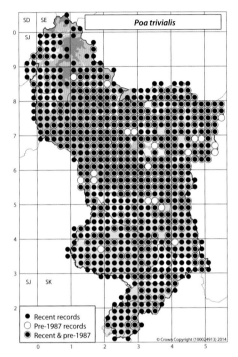

Rough Meadow-grass is a very common, native perennial of grasslands, waysides, marshy areas and waste places throughout the county. It was also often sown in agricultural grass-seed mixes, and is now used in amenity and wild-flower grassland plantings.

Poa humilis Ehrh. ex Hoffm.
Spreading Meadow-grass

COUNTY STATUS: Native
CONSERVATION STATUS: B
FIRST YEAR: 1903 LATEST YEAR: 2012 NO OF RECORDS: 44
RECENT SQUARES: monads 17; tetrads 26; hectads 14
ALL SQUARES: monads 20; tetrads 29; hectads 19

Spreading Meadow-grass is a rare native perennial of damp grasslands and marshy areas. Recent records are from northern and central parts extending from Lady Clough Moor (SK1092) and Apperknowle (SK37Z) in the north, to Butterley (SK3951) and Swanwick Churchyard (SK4053) in the south. Previous records have a more southerly distribution, for example Marston Montgomery (SK13) and Hilton Common (SK23). It is probably under-recorded.

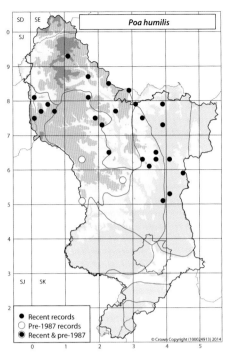

Poa pratensis L.
Smooth Meadow-grass

COUNTY STATUS: Native
CONSERVATION STATUS: None
FIRST YEAR: 1829 LATEST YEAR: 2013 NO OF RECORDS: 2,143
RECENT SQUARES: monads 855; tetrads 533; hectads 44
ALL SQUARES: monads 1,093; tetrads 594; hectads 44

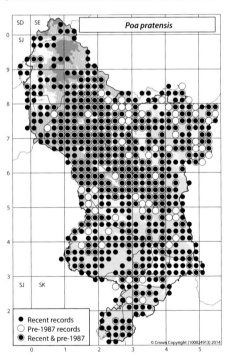

Smooth Meadow-grass is a common native perennial found throughout the county in grasslands, on waysides and rough ground, on all but the most acid or wet soils. It was commonly included in agricultural grass-seed mixes, and is used for amenity and wildflower plantings. Though probably under-recorded, our maps may well

include some data for the closely-related Spreading (*P. humilis*) and Narrow-leaved Meadow-Grass (*P. angustifolia*).

Poa angustifolia L.
Narrow-leaved Meadow-grass

COUNTY STATUS: Native
CONSERVATION STATUS: DRDB (Cat5a), A
FIRST YEAR: 1969 LATEST YEAR: 2009 NO OF RECORDS: 17
RECENT SQUARES: monads 7; tetrads 7; hectads 6
ALL SQUARES: monads 12; tetrads 12; hectads 11

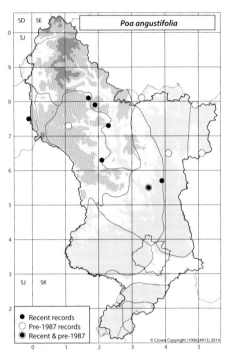

Narrow-leaved Meadow-grass is a very rare, native perennial of rough grassland. It currently grows sporadically throughout the northern (Within Leach Moor SJ9975 & Abney SK1979) and central parts of Derbyshire (Cliffside Wood SK3455). It previously also grew in the south of the county (Derby SK33). It is probably under-recorded due to confusion with Smooth Meadow-grass (*P. pratensis*).

Poa chaixii Vill.
Broad-leaved Meadow-grass

Broad-leaved Meadow-grass is a tufted casual perennial of grasslands and waste ground. The sole recent record is from Derby City (SK33) in 1988, but there are earlier ones from Losehill Hall (SK1583) in 1981 and SK25 in 1960. A native of central and southern Europe, it is grown in gardens for ornament and is probably under-recorded.

Poa compressa L.
Flattened Meadow-grass

Flattened Meadow-grass is an occasional native perennial of dry open grasslands, walls and disturbed ground. It generally

COUNTY STATUS: Native
CONSERVATION STATUS: None
FIRST YEAR: 1829 **LATEST YEAR:** 2013 **NO OF RECORDS:** 161
RECENT SQUARES: monads 71; tetrads 67; hectads 28
ALL SQUARES: monads 106; tetrads 98; hectads 31

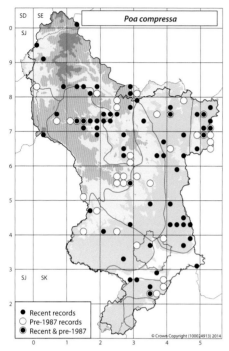

occurs in small amounts but can form extensive patches on waste ground. It grows scattered throughout the county from Salter's Brook (SE1300 v.c.58) and Houndkirk Moor (SK2882) in the north, to Ticknall (SK3523) and Lock Lane Ash Tip (SK4831) in the south.

Poa palustris L.
Swamp Meadow-grass

Locally extinct, Swamp Meadow-grass was a casual tufted perennial of damp grasslands and cultivated ground. The only records are from a market garden at Ashbourne (SK1746) in 1956, and Bretby Pond (SK32) in 1954. Indigenous to central Europe, it was sown as a fodder grass and has sometimes been introduced in imported grain.

Poa nemoralis L.
Wood Meadow-grass

COUNTY STATUS: Native
CONSERVATION STATUS: None
FIRST YEAR: 1829 **LATEST YEAR:** 2013 **NO OF RECORDS:** 278
RECENT SQUARES: monads 143; tetrads 124; hectads 32
ALL SQUARES: monads 162; tetrads 137; hectads 34

Wood Meadow-grass is a tufted native perennial of woods and shaded hedge banks that is sometimes also sown in woods and parks for ornament. Occurring occasionally throughout the county, there are records from Etherow Reserve

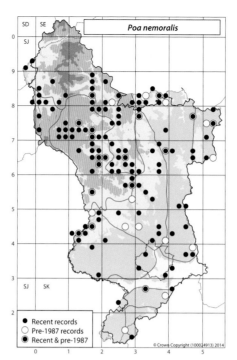

(SJ9791) and Creswell Crags (SK5374) in the north, through Lathkill Dale (SK1865) and Alsop en le Dale (SK1655), to Netherseal (SK2813) and The Wiggs (SK4026) in the south.

Dactylis glomerata L.
Cock's-foot

COUNTY STATUS: Native
CONSERVATION STATUS: None
FIRST YEAR: 1789 **LATEST YEAR:** 2013 **NO OF RECORDS:** 7,393
RECENT SQUARES: monads 2,151; tetrads 723; hectads 45
ALL SQUARES: monads 2,231; tetrads 725; hectads 45

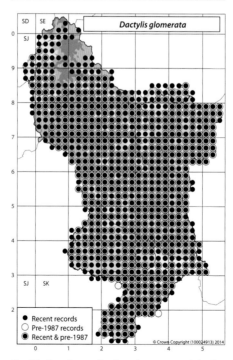

Cock's-foot is a tufted native perennial of grasslands, waysides, cultivated ground,

waste places and open woods, usually on fertile neutral to basic soils. It was also much grown for hay and pasture so the larger varieties from artificial habitats are probably the remnants of planting. It is very common everywhere, avoiding only the high moorlands of the Dark Peak.

Catabrosa aquatica (L.) P. Beauv.
Whorl-grass

COUNTY STATUS: Native
CONSERVATION STATUS: DRDB (Cat5a), A, B
FIRST YEAR: 1854 **LATEST YEAR:** 1997 **NO OF RECORDS:** 28
RECENT SQUARES: monads 3; tetrads 2; hectads 2
ALL SQUARES: monads 10; tetrads 7; hectads 8

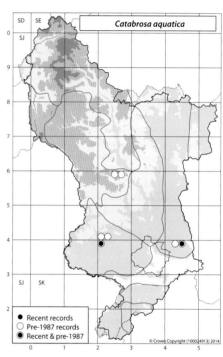

Whorl-grass is a stoloniferous native perennial of ditches and marshes. There are only two recent records: Longford Hall (SK2138) and Furnace Pond at Dale Moor (SK4438). It was formerly scattered throughout central Derbyshire as far north as Buxton (SK07) and Whitwell (SK57), and as far south as Swarkestone (SK32).

Catapodium rigidum (L.) C.E. Hubb.
Fern-grass

COUNTY STATUS: Native
CONSERVATION STATUS: None
FIRST YEAR: 1800 **LATEST YEAR:** 2012 **NO OF RECORDS:** 174
RECENT SQUARES: monads 85; tetrads 63; hectads 26
ALL SQUARES: monads 105; tetrads 77; hectads 28

Fern-grass is an occasional native annual of dry bare areas on banks, walls and rock outcrops. It also grows in short open grassland, waste ground and pavement cracks. It occurs in the limestone areas (Dove Dale SK1452 & Creswell Crags

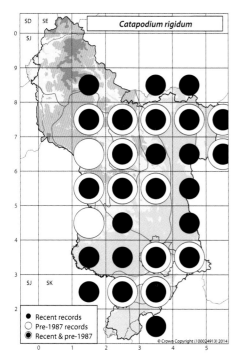

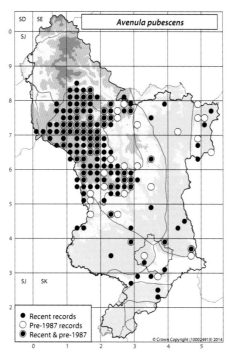

SK1263 & Carsington Pasture SK2354), but is very rare elsewhere (Cromford Canal SK4451 & Batley Lane SK4963). It was previously also found in unimproved grasslands in the south (Burton SK22 & Repton SK32 in 1903). This loss is part of a more widespread decline due to agricultural "improvement" of grasslands (Preston *et al.* 2002).

Arrhenatherum elatius (L.) P. Beauv. ex J. & C. Presl
False Oat-grass

COUNTY STATUS: Native	
CONSERVATION STATUS: None	
FIRST YEAR: 1789 LATEST YEAR: 2013 NO OF RECORDS: 5,450	
RECENT SQUARES: monads 1,845; tetrads 696; hectads 43	
ALL SQUARES: monads 1,982; tetrads 700; hectads 43	

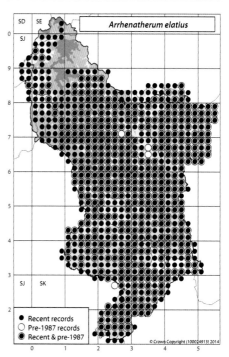

False Oat-grass is a native perennial of tall coarse grasslands, waysides, waste ground and limestone screes. It is very common and locally abundant throughout the county except for the high moors of the Dark Peak. It is particularly characteristic of roadside verges that are only mown once a year.

Avena strigosa Schreb.
Bristle Oat

Bristle Oat is a very rare, casual annual of arable fields and waysides. The sole recent record is from Turnditch (SK2946) in 2010. It had previously only been known at Brassington Rocks (SK25) in 1903. It is probably of cultivated origin.

Avena fatua L.
Wild-oat

Wild-oat is a casual annual of arable land and waste ground. Occurring occasionally

SK5374), and is increasingly being recorded in southern and eastern parts (Swadlincote SK3019, King's Newton SK3827, A61 Derby SK3637 & Millhouses SK3383).

Sesleria caerulea (L.) Ard.
Blue Moor-grass

COUNTY STATUS: Native	
CONSERVATION STATUS: DRDB (Cat3), NS, A, B	
FIRST YEAR: 1985 LATEST YEAR: 2007 NO OF RECORDS: 12	
RECENT SQUARES: monads 1; tetrads 1; hectads 1	
ALL SQUARES: monads 1; tetrads 1; hectads 1	

Blue Moor-grass is a very rare, native perennial, known only from Monks Dale (SK1373 & 1374). Discovered in the mid-1980s, it grows as tussocks in calcareous grassland amongst limestone outcrops. It has subsequently been recorded on a number of occasions up to 2007. Nationally Scarce, it occurs in rocky limestone grassland in northern England, with Derbyshire at its southern limit.

Avenula pubescens (Huds.) Dumort.
Downy Oat-grass

COUNTY STATUS: Native	
CONSERVATION STATUS: None	
FIRST YEAR: 1789 LATEST YEAR: 2013 NO OF RECORDS: 541	
RECENT SQUARES: monads 207; tetrads 140; hectads 24	
ALL SQUARES: monads 256; tetrads 164; hectads 27	

Downy Oat-grass is a native perennial of unimproved grasslands and waysides, usually on calcareous soils. It is very common in the White Peak (Wheston village SK1376, Bole Hill SK1867 & Bonsall Leys SK2657) but rare elsewhere (Meynell

Langley SK2939, Cloud House SK4737 & Whitwell village SK5276).

Avenula pratensis (L.) Dumort.
Meadow Oat-grass

COUNTY STATUS: Native	
CONSERVATION STATUS: None	
FIRST YEAR: 1789 LATEST YEAR: 2013 NO OF RECORDS: 541	
RECENT SQUARES: monads 158; tetrads 90; hectads 14	
ALL SQUARES: monads 179; tetrads 101; hectads 20	

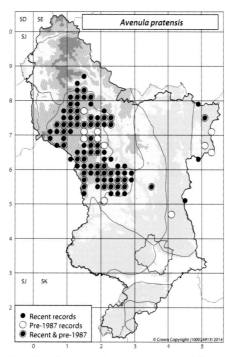

Meadow Oat-grass is a native perennial of unimproved grasslands and rocky outcrops, generally on base-rich soils. It is common and locally abundant in the White Peak (Wheston SK1277, Pilsbury Lodge

COUNTY STATUS: Casual
CONSERVATION STATUS: None
FIRST YEAR: 1829 LATEST YEAR: 2012 NO OF RECORDS: 201
RECENT SQUARES: monads 119; tetrads 112; hectads 32
ALL SQUARES: monads 140; tetrads 128; hectads 33

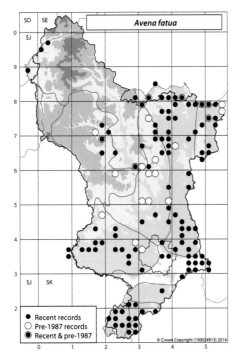

throughout the county, except for the Dark Peak, it rarely persists for long in any one site. It appears to be more frequent now than in 1969. This rise is part of a more general increase in England since 1945 (Preston *et al.* 2002). It is a native of the eastern Mediterranean.

Avena sativa L.
Oat

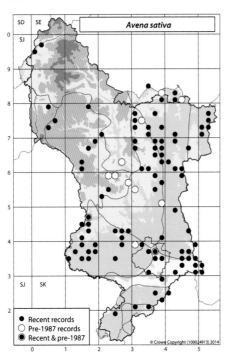

COUNTY STATUS: Casual
CONSERVATION STATUS: None
FIRST YEAR: 1969 LATEST YEAR: 2012 NO OF RECORDS: 143
RECENT SQUARES: monads 87; tetrads 97; hectads 27
ALL SQUARES: monads 96; tetrads 107; hectads 28

Oat is a casual annual of waste ground and arable land as a relic of cultivation, though it seldom persists at any one site for long. It is also grown as a field crop though less now than previously. Occasional throughout the county except for the White and Dark Peak Areas, it is probably of cultivated origin from Wild Oat (*A. fatua*).

Trisetum flavescens (L.) P. Beauv.
Yellow Oat-grass

COUNTY STATUS: Native
CONSERVATION STATUS: None
FIRST YEAR: 1829 LATEST YEAR: 2013 NO OF RECORDS: 1,610
RECENT SQUARES: monads 666; tetrads 413; hectads 39
ALL SQUARES: monads 758; tetrads 460; hectads 40

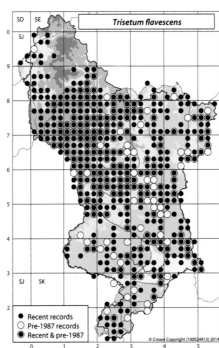

Yellow Oat-grass is a frequent native perennial of unimproved grasslands and waysides on well-drained neutral to calcareous soils. It occurs throughout the county, except for the high moors of the Dark Peak, and is particularly frequent in the limestone areas. It is increasingly being used in restoration and amenity plantings.

Koeleria macrantha (Ledeb.) Schult.
Crested Hair-grass
Crested Hair-grass is an occasional native perennial of short infertile grasslands, rock outcrops and old lead workings in the White Peak (Priestcliffe Lees SK1473, Dove Dale

COUNTY STATUS: Native
CONSERVATION STATUS: None
FIRST YEAR: 1799 LATEST YEAR: 2013 NO OF RECORDS: 724
RECENT SQUARES: monads 208; tetrads 106; hectads 15
ALL SQUARES: monads 246; tetrads 121; hectads 19

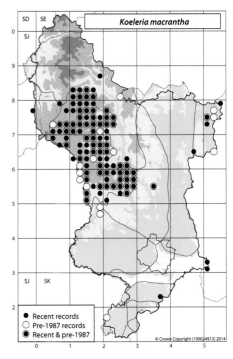

SK1451 & Gang Mine SK2855). Elsewhere it is a very rare native in unimproved grasslands (Calke Park SK3622, Trent Meadows SK53B & Elmton Green SK5073). It has been one of the plants recently studied by the Buxton Climate Change Impacts Lab. group (Fridley *et al.* 2007).

Deschampsia cespitosa (L.) P. Beauv.
Tufted Hair-grass

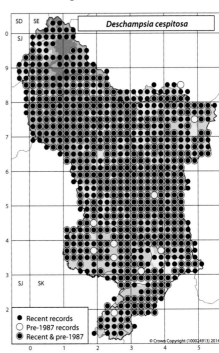

COUNTY STATUS: Native
CONSERVATION STATUS: None
FIRST YEAR: 1829 LATEST YEAR: 2013 NO OF RECORDS: 5,124
RECENT SQUARES: monads 1,670; tetrads 687; hectads 43
ALL SQUARES: monads 1,769; tetrads 697; hectads 43

Tufted Hair-grass is a very common perennial that grows throughout the county in grassland, marshes, scrub and wood. Two subspecies occur here. **Ssp. *cespitosa*** is an occasional native of wet unimproved grasslands, marshes and waysides on damp heavy soils, found throughout Derbyshire. **Ssp. *parviflora*** (Thuill.) Dumort. is a rare but probably under-recorded native of damp woods, also throughout the county.

Deschampsia flexuosa (L.) Trin.
Wavy Hair-grass

COUNTY STATUS: Native
CONSERVATION STATUS: None
FIRST YEAR: 1789 LATEST YEAR: 2013 NO OF RECORDS: 2,389
RECENT SQUARES: monads 855; tetrads 395; hectads 39
ALL SQUARES: monads 938; tetrads 428; hectads 40

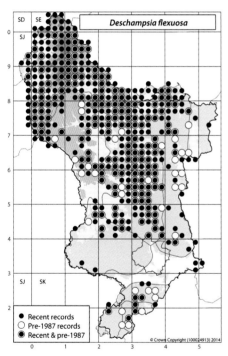

Wavy Hair-grass is a tufted native perennial of moors, heaths, open woods and rock outcrops with dry acid soils. It is very common and locally abundant throughout the South West Peak, Dark Peak and Peak Fringe. Elsewhere it is only occasional though was previously more frequent in these parts. This mirrors a national decline in lowland areas (Preston *et al.* 2002), mainly due to agricultural "improvement" of grasslands. It has a local name of Silver Spoons.

Deschampsia danthonioides (Trin.) Munro ex Benth.
A hair-grass

This alien hair-grass is a casual annual, known from only one record at Ashbourne (SK1746) in 1977. A native of western North America, it is usually imported into Britain as a contaminant of grass seed. A voucher specimen is at Derby Museum.

Holcus lanatus L.
Yorkshire-fog

COUNTY STATUS: Native
CONSERVATION STATUS: None
FIRST YEAR: 1829 LATEST YEAR: 2013 NO OF RECORDS: 6,371
RECENT SQUARES: monads 1,997; tetrads 728; hectads 44
ALL SQUARES: monads 2,123; tetrads 733; hectads 44

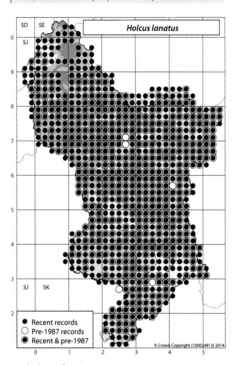

Yorkshire-fog is a very common, native perennial of rough grasslands, waysides, waste ground, flushes, open woods and arable fields. It is recorded across the county except for the high moors of the Dark Peak.

Holcus mollis L.
Creeping Soft-grass

COUNTY STATUS: Native
CONSERVATION STATUS: None
FIRST YEAR: 1829 LATEST YEAR: 2013 NO OF RECORDS: 2,309
RECENT SQUARES: monads 948; tetrads 538; hectads 42
ALL SQUARES: monads 1,119; tetrads 586; hectads 42

Creeping Soft-grass is a sprawling native perennial of grassy places, heaths, scrub, open woods and arable fields, generally on acidic soils. It is common throughout the county except for limestone areas and some intensively farmed parts of the lowlands.

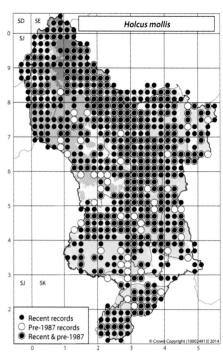

Aira caryophyllea L.
Silver Hair-grass

COUNTY STATUS: Native
CONSERVATION STATUS: None
FIRST YEAR: 1829 LATEST YEAR: 2012 NO OF RECORDS: 161
RECENT SQUARES: monads 69; tetrads 56; hectads 24
ALL SQUARES: monads 97; tetrads 76; hectads 30

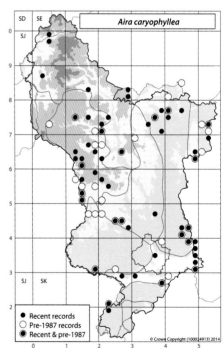

Silver Hair-grass is an occasional native annual of open habitats with thin dry soils, such as around rocky outcrops, on waste ground, in heathlands and on walls. There are records from Deep Clough (SK0497) and Houndkirk Moor (SK2882) in the north, to Drakelow (SK2219) and Lock Lane Ash Tip (SK4831) in the south.

Aira praecox L.
Early Hair-grass

COUNTY STATUS: Native

CONSERVATION STATUS: None

FIRST YEAR: 1789 LATEST YEAR: 2013 NO OF RECORDS: 256

RECENT SQUARES: monads 135; tetrads 114; hectads 28

ALL SQUARES: monads 160; tetrads 130; hectads 31

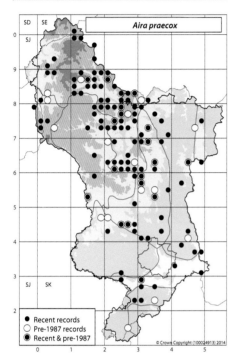

Early Hair-grass is an occasional native annual of dry open situations on light shallow soils. It occurs near rock outcrops, in acid grasslands and on heathy areas. It is

recorded from Moorfield (SK0492) and Withens Brook (SE1000 v.c.58) in the north, through Mansell Sand Pit (SK2544) and Crich Chase (SK3452), to Bretby Park (SK2922) and Lock Lane Ash Tip (SK4831) in the south.

Anthoxanthum odoratum L.
Sweet Vernal-grass

COUNTY STATUS: Native

CONSERVATION STATUS: None

FIRST YEAR: 1789 LATEST YEAR: 2013 NO OF RECORDS: 3,705

RECENT SQUARES: monads 1,379; tetrads 648; hectads 43

ALL SQUARES: monads 1,488; tetrads 667; hectads 43

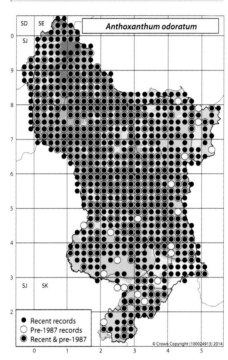

Sweet Vernal-grass is a tufted native perennial of a wide range of grasslands, heaths and moors. It is very common throughout the county except for some areas of intensive farming where it is rare. Until the 1920s it was sown as part of grass-seed mixes for agricultural grasslands, but has since been lost from many farmed grasslands due to more intensive cultivation.

Phalaris arundinacea L.
Reed Canary-grass

COUNTY STATUS: Native

CONSERVATION STATUS: None

FIRST YEAR: 1789 LATEST YEAR: 2013 NO OF RECORDS: 1,710

RECENT SQUARES: monads 677; tetrads 430; hectads 41

ALL SQUARES: monads 741; tetrads 453; hectads 41

Reed Canary-grass is a frequent native perennial in and by the edges of ponds and streams where it can form large stands. It also grows in ditches, marshes, carr woods and wet meadows, and even occasionally on rough and waste ground. Occurring throughout the county, it avoids only the high moors of the Dark Peak.

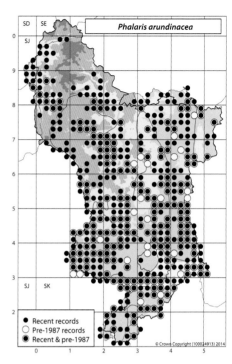

Phalaris canariensis L.
Canary-grass

COUNTY STATUS: Casual

CONSERVATION STATUS: None

FIRST YEAR: 1864 LATEST YEAR: 2012 NO OF RECORDS: 78

RECENT SQUARES: monads 35; tetrads 36; hectads 23

ALL SQUARES: monads 53; tetrads 53; hectads 28

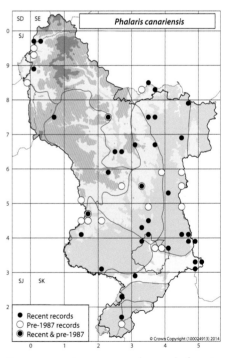

Canary-grass is a rare casual annual of waste ground and tips. It is recorded sporadically throughout the county from Hadfield (SK0296) and Spinkhill (SK4678) in the north, to Linton (SK2716) and Moor Lane (SK4137) in the south. Probably introduced as a contaminant of bird-seed or grain, it is a native of North Africa and the Canaries.

Sweet Vernal-grass (*Anthoxanthum odoratum*) Stonegravels Churchyard (SK3872) May 2013 (Ken Balkow)

Phalaris paradoxa L.
Awned Canary-grass

Awned Canary-grass is a casual annual of open or disturbed ground. Our sole record is from West Park Cemetery (SK4833), found by R. Martin in 2005. Probably a contaminant of bird-seed, it is native to southern Europe.

Agrostis capillaris L.
Common Bent

COUNTY STATUS: Native	
CONSERVATION STATUS: None	
FIRST YEAR: 1789 **LATEST YEAR:** 2013 **NO OF RECORDS:** 3,556	
RECENT SQUARES: monads 1,500; tetrads 673; hectads 42	
ALL SQUARES: monads 1,656; tetrads 702; hectads 42	

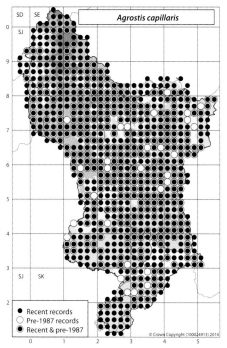

Common Bent is a very common, native perennial of grasslands, moors, heaths, scrub and rough ground, particularly on acid soils. It is also extensively used as a constituent of lawn seed mixtures. Growing throughout the county, it forms an important component of pastures in upland areas, even on the less-improved plateau grasslands of the White Peak.

Agrostis gigantea Roth
Black Bent

COUNTY STATUS: Established (Archaeophyte)	
CONSERVATION STATUS: None	
FIRST YEAR: 1903 **LATEST YEAR:** 2012 **NO OF RECORDS:** 305	
RECENT SQUARES: monads 157; tetrads 150; hectads 37	
ALL SQUARES: monads 220; tetrads 199; hectads 38	

Black Bent is an occasional, long-established perennial of cultivated and waste ground. It occurs throughout the county from Hadfield (SK0296) and Normanton Springs (SK4084) in the north,

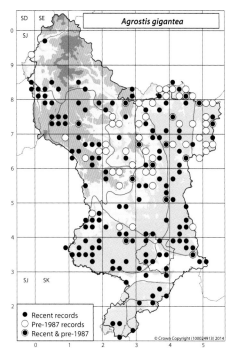

to Haunton (SK2411) and Long Eaton (SK53B) in the south. It is probably under-recorded.

Agrostis stolonifera L.
Creeping Bent

COUNTY STATUS: Native	
CONSERVATION STATUS: None	
FIRST YEAR: 1789 **LATEST YEAR:** 2013 **NO OF RECORDS:** 3,084	
RECENT SQUARES: monads 1,362; tetrads 659; hectads 45	
ALL SQUARES: monads 1,532; tetrads 692; hectads 45	

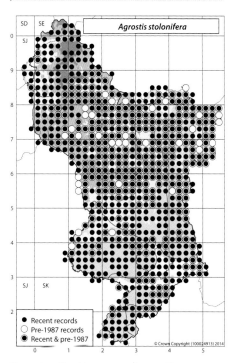

Creeping Bent is a sprawling native perennial of damp grasslands, marshes, disturbed ground and cultivated land. It is very common everywhere.

Agrostis canina L.
Velvet Bent

COUNTY STATUS: Native	
CONSERVATION STATUS: None	
FIRST YEAR: 1789 **LATEST YEAR:** 2011 **NO OF RECORDS:** 322	
RECENT SQUARES: monads 166; tetrads 170; hectads 34	
ALL SQUARES: monads 197; tetrads 198; hectads 35	

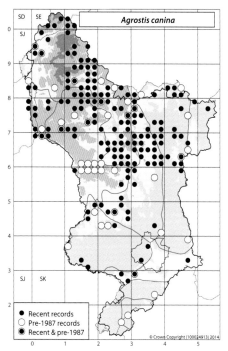

Velvet Bent is a creeping native perennial of damp grasslands, moors and marshes, generally on infertile acidic soils. It is occasional in northern Derbyshire (Upper Heyden SE0903 v.c.58, Abney Clough SK2079 & Horsleygate SK37D). Elsewhere it is rare (Hallfields Scrub SK2247 & Willington Grasslands SK3029). However, its exact distribution is uncertain due to confusion in the past with Brown Bent (*A. vinealis*), which may have led to some records for the latter being included here.

Agrostis vinealis Schreb.
Brown Bent

COUNTY STATUS: Native	
CONSERVATION STATUS: None	
FIRST YEAR: 1970 **LATEST YEAR:** 2012 **NO OF RECORDS:** 236	
RECENT SQUARES: monads 45; tetrads 35; hectads 14	
ALL SQUARES: monads 130; tetrads 95; hectads 19	

Brown Bent is a rare native perennial of grassy heaths and moors on dry acid soils in northern parts. It has been recorded recently from Tintwistle Low Moor (SK0298 v.c.58), Combs (SK0478), Clough Farm (SK1486), Flash Dam (SK36C) and Holmewood (SK46I). It appears to have been more frequent and widespread in the past. This is possibly due to agricultural improvement

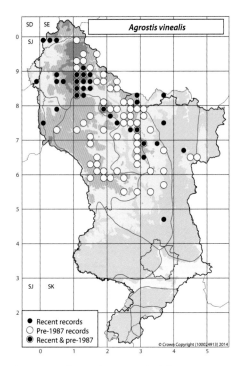

but it may be under-recorded due to confusion with other bent grasses (*Agrostis* spp.).

Calamagrostis epigejos (L.) Roth
Wood Small-reed

COUNTY STATUS: Native	
CONSERVATION STATUS: B	
FIRST YEAR: 1829 LATEST YEAR: 2012 NO OF RECORDS: 98	
RECENT SQUARES: monads 26; tetrads 24; hectads 15	
ALL SQUARES: monads 32; tetrads 28; hectads 17	

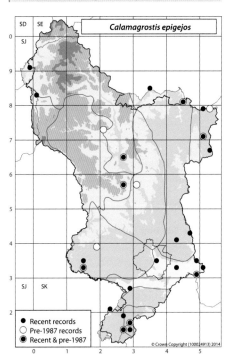

Wood Small-reed is a rare native perennial of damp woods, grassland, scrub and ditches. Recent records are spread across the county from Chisworth

(SJ9991) and Holbrook Ponds (SK4481) in the north, to Grange Wood (SK2714) in the south. It appears able to colonise grassland and scrub associated with waste ground and abandoned industrial sites such as old railways (Rowsley Sidings SK2665 & Long Eaton SK4831). This may explain why it seems to have become more frequent since Clapham's 1969 Flora.

Calamagrostis canescens (F.H. Wigg.) Roth
Purple Small-reed

COUNTY STATUS: Native	
CONSERVATION STATUS: DRDB (Cat4), B	
FIRST YEAR: 1901 LATEST YEAR: 1980 NO OF RECORDS: 7	
RECENT SQUARES: monads 0; tetrads 0; hectads 0	
ALL SQUARES: monads 5; tetrads 4; hectads 2	

Purple Small-reed is a very rare, native perennial of damp open woods and marshes. The latest records are from Whitwell Wood (SK5278 in 1980 & SK5178 in 1976). There are older records from Grange Wood (SK2714) and Gresley (SK2718) both for 1901. Nationally it has been lost from many sites since 1962, possibly due to a general lowering of water levels (Preston *et al.* 2002).

Ammophila arenaria (L.) Link
Marram

Marram is a very rare, casual perennial. The only record is from colliery shales at Cowley Bottom (SK3477) where it was known in the 1970s. A native of coastal sand dunes in Britain, its presence on colliery waste in central England may have been associated with the presence of salts in the Coal Measure deposits.

Apera spica-venti (L.) P. Beauv.
Loose Silky-bent

Loose Silky-bent is a very rare, casual annual of waste ground and arable fields on light dry soils. There are two recent records from Creswell (SK5273) in 2000 and Cromford Canal (SK3056) in 2012. However, there are older records from Ashbourne (SK1746), Hopton Top (SK2554), Sheepbridge (SK3774) and Whitwell Wood (SK5278) all for the 1970s. Linton (1903) gives records for Osmaston Park (SK14) and near Kedleston (SK34). It has probably been imported as a contaminant of grain and is considered by some as native in eastern England.

Apera interrupta (L.) P. Beauv.
Dense Silky-bent

Dense Silky-bent is a very rare, casual annual of rough ground and arable land. The only recent record is from Chesterfield coke works (SK3967), but there are earlier

COUNTY STATUS: Casual	
CONSERVATION STATUS: None	
FIRST YEAR: 1970 LATEST YEAR: 1997 NO OF RECORDS: 17	
RECENT SQUARES: monads 1; tetrads 1; hectads 1	
ALL SQUARES: monads 7; tetrads 7; hectads 5	

ones from Sheepbridge (SK3774), Brimington (SK4074) and Shirebrook (SK5265) all for the 1970s. It is indigenous to southern Europe.

Polypogon monspeliensis (L.) Desf.
Annual Beard-grass

Annual Beard-grass is a very rare, casual annual of disturbed ground. There are only two records, both recent: a supermarket flowerbed in Derby (SK3533) found by N. Moyes in 1998 and on open ground at Millennium Meadows (SK3443) in 2006. It is native to coastal areas of south-eastern England.

Polypogon maritimus Willd.
Southern Beard-grass

Southern Beard-grass is a very rare casual of disturbed ground, known only from old railway sidings at Chaddesden (SK3636 & 3635). It was discovered by A. Willmot in 2012 and confirmed by T. Ryves. It is native to southern and western Europe.

Alopecurus pratensis L.
Meadow Foxtail

COUNTY STATUS: Native	
CONSERVATION STATUS: None	
FIRST YEAR: 1789 LATEST YEAR: 2013 NO OF RECORDS: 2,995	
RECENT SQUARES: monads 1,400; tetrads 641; hectads 42	
ALL SQUARES: monads 1,479; tetrads 652; hectads 42	

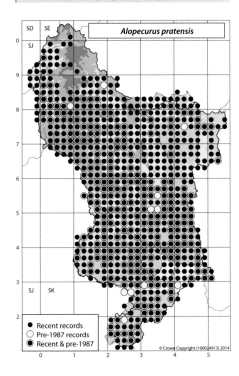

Meadow Foxtail is a very common, native perennial of grasslands, waysides and wood margins, generally on damp rich soils. Up until the 1950s it was also sown in seed mixes for pastures. It occurs throughout the county except for the high moorlands of the Dark Peak.

Alopecurus geniculatus L.
Marsh Foxtail

COUNTY STATUS: Native

CONSERVATION STATUS: None

FIRST YEAR: 1789 **LATEST YEAR:** 2013 **NO OF RECORDS:** 1,134

RECENT SQUARES: monads 620; tetrads 440; hectads 43

ALL SQUARES: monads 694; tetrads 472; hectads 43

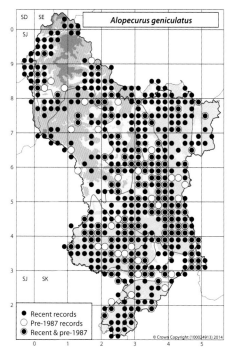

Marsh Foxtail is a creeping native perennial of wet grasslands, marshes and the sides of waterbodies, usually on fertile soils. It occurs frequently throughout Derbyshire, but is absent across large parts of the Dark and White Peak Character Areas.

Alopecurus aequalis Sobol.
Orange Foxtail

COUNTY STATUS: Native

CONSERVATION STATUS: DRDB (Cat5b), A, B

FIRST YEAR: 1900 **LATEST YEAR:** 2011 **NO OF RECORDS:** 65

RECENT SQUARES: monads 12; tetrads 11; hectads 10

ALL SQUARES: monads 22; tetrads 18; hectads 11

Orange Foxtail is a very rare, native annual or short-lived perennial of marshy pond margins. It occurs sporadically throughout the county from Ladybower (SK1687) and Pebley Reservoir (SK4879) In the north, to Ash Farm (SK2533) and Chaddesden Park (SK3836) in the south. It is probably under-recorded for Marsh Foxtail (*A. geniculatus*).

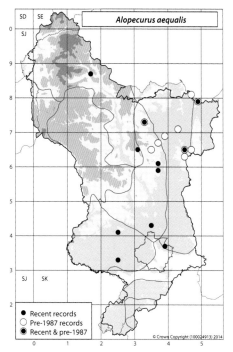

Alopecurus myosuroides Huds.
Black-grass

COUNTY STATUS: Established (Archaeophyte)

CONSERVATION STATUS: None

FIRST YEAR: 1789 **LATEST YEAR:** 2013 **NO OF RECORDS:** 82

RECENT SQUARES: monads 39; tetrads 40; hectads 19

ALL SQUARES: monads 56; tetrads 57; hectads 25

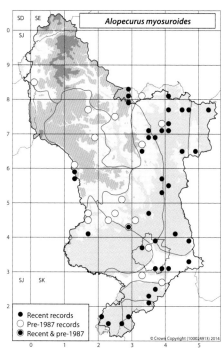

Black-grass is a rare long-established annual of cultivated and waste ground. It occurs from east of Ringinglow (SK2983) in the north, through Beresford Dale (SK15J), to Catton (SK2214) and near Pistern Hill (SK3421) in the south. Nationally it is decreasing in frequency (Stace 2010), but there is no evidence of this happening locally.

Phleum pratense L.
Timothy

COUNTY STATUS: Native

CONSERVATION STATUS: None

FIRST YEAR: 1940 **LATEST YEAR:** 2013 **NO OF RECORDS:** 1,530

RECENT SQUARES: monads 932; tetrads 533; hectads 41

ALL SQUARES: monads 988; tetrads 553; hectads 41

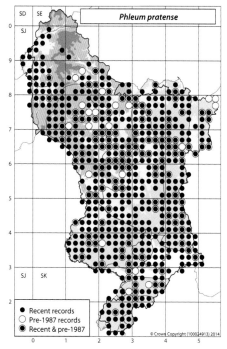

Timothy is a common native perennial of grasslands and waste places, generally on damp heavy soils. It is also commonly planted in agricultural grasslands, and

Timothy (*Phleum pratense*) at Goytside Meadows (SK0084), August 2012 (David Blowers)

occurs throughout the county except for the high moors of the Dark and South West Peak.

Phleum bertolonii DC.
Smaller Cat's-tail

COUNTY STATUS: Native	
CONSERVATION STATUS: None	
FIRST YEAR: 1871 LATEST YEAR: 2013 NO OF RECORDS: 544	
RECENT SQUARES: monads 305; tetrads 232; hectads 34	
ALL SQUARES: monads 361; tetrads 259; hectads 36	

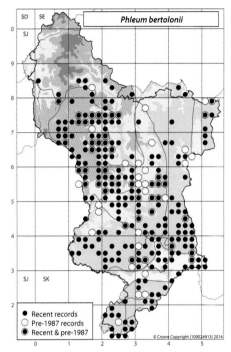

Smaller Cat's-tail is a native perennial of grasslands and rough ground, generally on lighter drier soils. It is occasional throughout the limestone and lowland areas, as at Priestcliffe Lees (SK1572), Ashleyhay (SK3151), Shipley Country Park (SK4444) and Breaston (SK4633). It is very rare elsewhere.

Glyceria maxima (Hartm.) Holmb.
Reed Sweet-grass

COUNTY STATUS: Native	
CONSERVATION STATUS: None	
FIRST YEAR: 1829 LATEST YEAR: 2013 NO OF RECORDS: 784	
RECENT SQUARES: monads 262; tetrads 175; hectads 39	
ALL SQUARES: monads 289; tetrads 189; hectads 40	

Reed Sweet-grass is an occasional native perennial that forms extensive stands in and by slow-flowing rivers, canals, ponds and lakes. It also grows in seasonally flooded grasslands. It is found frequently throughout the lowlands of the county, for example at Padfield (SK0396) and Brierley Green (SK0282) in the north-west, Centenary Ponds (SK4184) in the north-east, and Croxall (SK1913) and Calke Park (SK3623) in the south. Elsewhere it

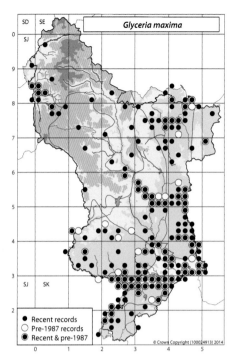

is rare or absent. It is increasingly being planted around ornamental ponds, which is beginning to obscure its natural distribution.

Glyceria fluitans (L.) R. Br.
Floating Sweet-grass

COUNTY STATUS: Native	
CONSERVATION STATUS: None	
FIRST YEAR: 1789 LATEST YEAR: 2013 NO OF RECORDS: 779	
RECENT SQUARES: monads 395; tetrads 330; hectads 38	
ALL SQUARES: monads 464; tetrads 371; hectads 41	

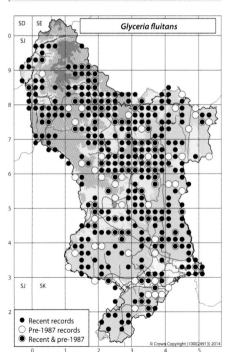

Floating Sweet-grass is an occasional native perennial of marshes, wet grasslands and the margins of slow-flowing

streams, canals and ponds. It is recorded sporadically from Simmondley (SK0293) and Upper Derwent (SK1497) in the north, to Catton (SK2214) and Fox Covert (SK4833) in the south.

Glyceria × *pedicellata* F. Towns.
Hybrid Sweet-grass

COUNTY STATUS: Native	
CONSERVATION STATUS: None	
FIRST YEAR: 1855 LATEST YEAR: 2009 NO OF RECORDS: 56	
RECENT SQUARES: monads 17; tetrads 16; hectads 13	
ALL SQUARES: monads 33; tetrads 29; hectads 24	

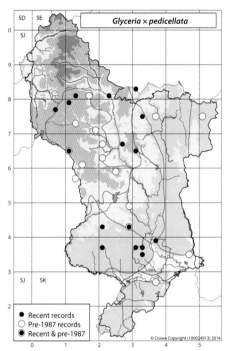

Hybrid Sweet-grass is a rare native perennial found on the margins of slow-flowing streams, ditches and ponds. It is scattered throughout the county from Oxlow Dam (SK1280) and Whirlow (SK3082) in the north, to Alder Carr (SK2037) and Mickleover (SK3235) in the south. It is the spontaneous hybrid of Floating (*G. fluitans*) and Plicate Sweet-grass (*G. notata*) though may occur in the absence of either parent.

Glyceria declinata Breb.
Small Sweet-grass

COUNTY STATUS: Native	
CONSERVATION STATUS: None	
FIRST YEAR: 1959 LATEST YEAR: 2013 NO OF RECORDS: 312	
RECENT SQUARES: monads 180; tetrads 171; hectads 35	
ALL SQUARES: monads 217; tetrads 194; hectads 35	

Small Sweet-grass is an occasional native perennial that grows in or by the margins of slow-flowing streams, canals and ponds. It is recorded sporadically throughout the county, from Arnfield (SK0098 v.c.58) and Woodhead Reservoir (SK0899) in the

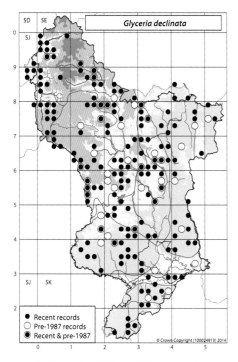

north, through Mill Dale (SK1454) and Stonebroom (SK4059), to Westbrook Farm (SK2312) and Aston-on-Trent (SK4229) in the south.

Glyceria notata Chevall.
Plicate Sweet-grass

COUNTY STATUS: Native	
CONSERVATION STATUS: None	
FIRST YEAR: 1884 LATEST YEAR: 2012 NO OF RECORDS: 180	
RECENT SQUARES: monads 67; tetrads 60; hectads 27	
ALL SQUARES: monads 116; tetrads 101; hectads 31	

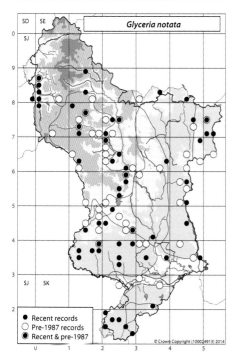

Plicate Sweet-grass is an occasional native perennial found in or by the margins of slow-flowing streams, canals and ponds. It

occurs sporadically throughout the county from New Mills (SK0086) and the Gleadless Valley (SK3783) in the north, to Netherseal (SK2912) and Dockholme Lock (SK4835) in the south.

Melica nutans L.
Mountain Melick

COUNTY STATUS: Native	
CONSERVATION STATUS: B	
FIRST YEAR: 1800 LATEST YEAR: 2013 NO OF RECORDS: 155	
RECENT SQUARES: monads 21; tetrads 14; hectads 6	
ALL SQUARES: monads 35; tetrads 23; hectads 11	

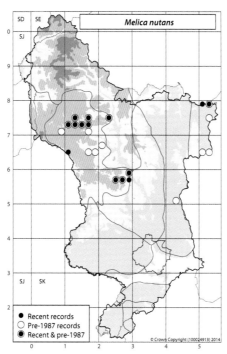

Mountain Melick is a very rare, native perennial of shady rock outcrops, woods and scrub on limestone. It is an upland plant with Derbyshire close to the south-eastern edge of its British range. In the White Peak it is recorded for Wye Dale (SK1072), Miller's Dale (SK1673) and the Via Gellia (SK2656), while on the Magnesian Limestone it is noted for Ginny Springs (SK5278). Previously it was known for the same areas, as well as near Codnor (SK4250) in 1969 and Norton (SK38) in 1903.

Melica uniflora Retz.
Wood Melick

COUNTY STATUS: Native	
CONSERVATION STATUS: None	
FIRST YEAR: 1829 LATEST YEAR: 2013 NO OF RECORDS: 851	
RECENT SQUARES: monads 274; tetrads 185; hectads 32	
ALL SQUARES: monads 310; tetrads 207; hectads 32	

Wood Melick is an attractive native perennial of woods and shaded rock outcrops. It occurs frequently in the north-eastern part of the county, for

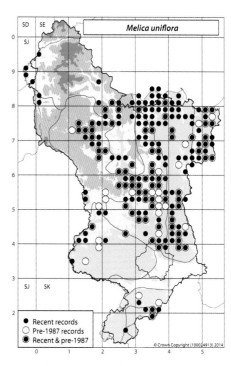

example at Upper Padley (SK2479), Langwith Wood (SK5068) and Booth's Wood (SK3645). Elsewhere it is absent or rare: Bruns Wood (SK2456), Dinting Reserve (SK0194), Rosliston (SK2614) and Smisby (SK3419).

Bromus commutatus Schrad.
Meadow Brome

Meadow Brome is a very rare, casual annual of agricultural grasslands, introduced as a contaminant of seed mixes. The three recent records are: Stancliffe Hall (SK2663) in 1994, Darley Bridge (SK2762) in 1994 and Ash (SK2533) in 2005. Previously it was recorded from waste ground and damp meadows in the south of Derbyshire where it may have been native (Clifton Goods-yard SK1644 & Osmaston SK24 both for 1969, and Hilton SK23 & Ticknall SK32 both for 1903). It is considered native in central and southern England.

Bromus racemosus L.
Smooth Brome

COUNTY STATUS: Native	
CONSERVATION STATUS: B	
FIRST YEAR: 1829 LATEST YEAR: 2011 NO OF RECORDS: 38	
RECENT SQUARES: monads 15; tetrads 13; hectads 4	
ALL SQUARES: monads 23; tetrads 21; hectads 12	

Smooth Brome is a very rare, native annual of grasslands and arable land, but is probably under-recorded. It occurs scattered from Besthill (SJ9993) and Bradwell (SK1780) in the north, through Darley Bridge (SK2762), to Littleover Sewage Works (SK3133) in the south.

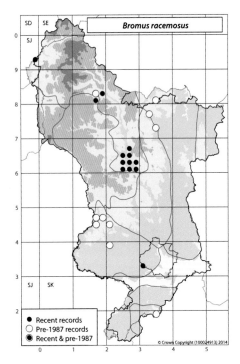

Previously it appears to have occurred more frequently, albeit over the same area.

Bromus hordeaceus L.
Soft-brome

COUNTY STATUS: Native
CONSERVATION STATUS: None
FIRST YEAR: 1829 LATEST YEAR: 2013 NO OF RECORDS: 1,641
RECENT SQUARES: monads 993; tetrads 576; hectads 43
ALL SQUARES: monads 1,067; tetrads 594; hectads 43

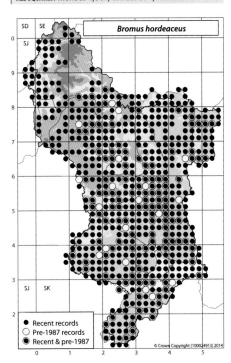

Soft-brome is a common native annual that occurs throughout the county except for the high moors of the Dark and South West Peak. Three subspecies are known here, but all are probably

under-recorded. **Ssp. *hordeaceus*** is a rare native annual of grasslands, waysides and rough ground mostly on fertile neutral soils. It is also introduced into sown fields as a contaminant of grass-seed mixes. It occurs throughout the county except the high moors of the Dark and South West Peak. **Ssp. *thominei*** (Hardouin) Braun-Blanq. is a very rare, casual annual of waste land and cultivated areas, known from just three records (Ashbourne SK1746 in 1967, Hognaston Winn SK2251 in 1949 & Mackworth Vicarage SK3137 in 1978). It is native to sand dunes around British coasts. **Ssp. *longipedicellatus*** Spalton is a very rare, native annual of field margins. It was only discovered by L. Spalton at Swadlincote near the A444 (SK2816) in 2002 but will probably turn up elsewhere once recorders learn to recognise it.

Bromus × pseudothominei P.M. Sm.
Lesser Soft-brome

COUNTY STATUS: Native
CONSERVATION STATUS: None
FIRST YEAR: 1970 LATEST YEAR: 2006 NO OF RECORDS: 12
RECENT SQUARES: monads 1; tetrads 2; hectads 2
ALL SQUARES: monads 9; tetrads 10; hectads 8

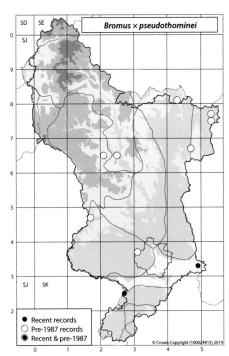

Lesser Soft-brome is a very rare, annual of grasslands and weedy places. It is considered here as native, but other authorities (Stace *et al.* 2003) have treated it as "newly established". The only recent records are from Trent Lane (SK4932) and Bladon (SK22S). Previously there were several other records all from the 1970s (Ashbourne SK1746, Raper Lodge SK2165, Wye Farm SK2565, Mackworth SK3137 & Whitwell SK5376). It is the hybrid of Soft-

brome (*B. hordeaceus*) and Slender Soft-brome (*B. lepidus*).

Bromus lepidus Holmb.
Slender Soft-brome

COUNTY STATUS: Casual
CONSERVATION STATUS: None
FIRST YEAR: 1949 LATEST YEAR: 1975 NO OF RECORDS: 15
RECENT SQUARES: monads 0; tetrads 0; hectads 0
ALL SQUARES: monads 10; tetrads 9; hectads 11

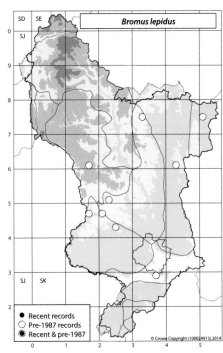

Slender Soft-brome is a very rare, casual annual of waste ground, waysides and grasslands. There are no recent records and only a scatter of older ones from the third quarter of the last century (Friden SK1760, Ednaston SK2442, Johnnygate SK3275, Swarkestone Bridge SK3628 & Markland Grips SK5074). This decline is part of a national decrease since 1962 (Preston *et al.* 2002). It was probably introduced as a contaminant of grass-seed mixes for agricultural grasslands, but from where is uncertain.

Bromus secalinus L.
Rye Brome

Rye Brome is a rare casual annual of arable fields and waste places, first recorded by Glover (1829). It was then only noted four times until 1986 (Spath Farm SK2235 & Cropper Top SK2336) and on a further three occasions up to 2010 (Unthank SK3075, Lidgate SK3077 & Barrow Hill SK4175). However, there have been 12 more records up until 2013, mostly as a contaminant of cereal crops. Nationally, it has declined since early last century (Preston *et al.* 2002) but has recently been increasing as a grass-seed contaminant (Stace 2010). It is of uncertain origin.

Bromus pseudosecalinus P.M. Sm.
Smith's Brome

COUNTY STATUS: Casual
CONSERVATION STATUS: None
FIRST YEAR: 1888 **LATEST YEAR:** 2002 **NO OF RECORDS:** 23
RECENT SQUARES: monads 4; tetrads 4; hectads 2
ALL SQUARES: monads 8; tetrads 8; hectads 6

Smith's Brome is a very rare, casual annual of unimproved hay meadows and waysides. All recent records are from floodplain hay meadows in the Hope/Hathersage area (Lower Hollins SK1385, Hope SK1683, Bradwell SK1781 & Hathersage SK2181). Previously it was recorded sporadically throughout the county as far south as Ashbourne (SK14) in 1888, Spath Farm (SK2235) in 1975, and Derby (SK33) in 1968. It was probably introduced as a contaminant of grass-seed mixes, though its origins are uncertain.

Anisantha diandra (Roth) Tutin ex Tzvelev
Great Brome

COUNTY STATUS: Casual
CONSERVATION STATUS: None
FIRST YEAR: 1998 **LATEST YEAR:** 2012 **NO OF RECORDS:** 17
RECENT SQUARES: monads 15; tetrads 15; hectads 10
ALL SQUARES: monads 15; tetrads 15; hectads 10

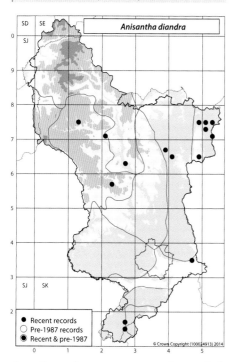

Great Brome is a very rare, casual annual of rough ground, waysides and arable fields with records scattered over central and southern parts (Longcliffe SK2256, Coton Park SK2617, Sandboro' Fields SK4635 & Pleasley SK4964). It is a bird-seed and grain alien, native to the Mediterranean.

Anisantha sterilis (L.) Nevski
Barren Brome

COUNTY STATUS: Established (Archaeophyte)
CONSERVATION STATUS: None
FIRST YEAR: 1789 **LATEST YEAR:** 2013 **NO OF RECORDS:** 1,684
RECENT SQUARES: monads 941; tetrads 506; hectads 40
ALL SQUARES: monads 999; tetrads 516; hectads 40

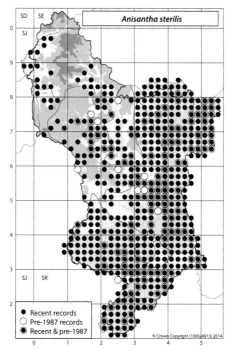

Barren Brome is an anciently established annual of waysides, hedges, rough ground and cultivated land. It is very common in southern and eastern parts of the county. Elsewhere, in the more upland White, Dark and South West Peak Areas, it is only occasional-to-rare, although Derbyshire holds the altitudinal record for this species in Britain at 365 metres.

Anisantha tectorum (L.) Nevski
Drooping Brome

Drooping Brome is a very rare, casual annual of waste ground. The only record is from Ashbourne (SK1746) in 1977. It is a contaminant of grass-seed and grain that is native to continental Europe.

Bromopsis ramosa (Huds.) Holub
Hairy-brome

COUNTY STATUS: Native
CONSERVATION STATUS: None
FIRST YEAR: 1789 **LATEST YEAR:** 2013 **NO OF RECORDS:** 1,446
RECENT SQUARES: monads 637; tetrads 390; hectads 38
ALL SQUARES: monads 710; tetrads 421; hectads 39

Hairy-brome is a tufted native perennial of damp shaded habitats, such as woods and hedges, usually on moderately base-rich soils. It occurs frequently throughout the county except for the high ground of the Peak District where it is virtually absent.

Hairy-brome (Bromopsis ramosa) on side of Monsal Trail in Chee Dale (SK1172), August 1993 (Ken Balkow)

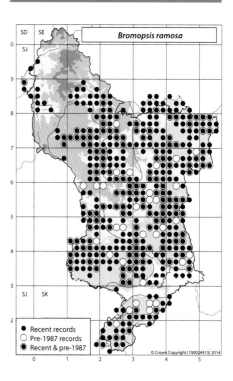

Bromopsis benekenii (Lange) Holub
Lesser Hairy-brome

COUNTY STATUS: Native
CONSERVATION STATUS: DRDB (Cat3), NS, A
FIRST YEAR: 1998 LATEST YEAR: 2012 NO OF RECORDS: 2
RECENT SQUARES: monads 2; tetrads 2; hectads 2
ALL SQUARES: monads 2; tetrads 2; hectads 2

Lesser Hairy-brome is a native perennial of woodland and is Nationally Scarce. A strong colony was discovered in 1998 by D. Dupree at Grange Wood, Moorhall (SK3174), where it was still present in 2011. A second site was found in 2012 at Hopton Wood (SK2556) by D. & M. Woods. It grows scattered throughout mainland Britain, usually occurring on basic soils in the presence of Hairy-brome (*B. ramosa*) (Preston *et al.* 2002). The Grange Wood location has two curious features: it is clearly not on limestone, probably having a neutral to slightly acid soil, plus it shows no sign of Hairy-brome (*B. ramosa*).

Bromopsis erecta (Huds.) Fourr.
Upright Brome

COUNTY STATUS: Native
CONSERVATION STATUS: DRDB (Cat5b)
FIRST YEAR: 1789 LATEST YEAR: 2010 NO OF RECORDS: 128
RECENT SQUARES: monads 26; tetrads 17; hectads 12
ALL SQUARES: monads 47; tetrads 34; hectads 22

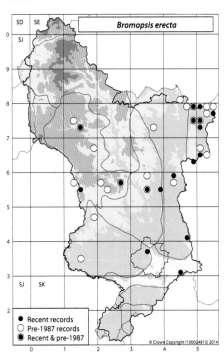

Upright Brome is a tufted native perennial of calcareous grasslands on dry infertile soils. Most recent records come from the Magnesian Limestone as at Batley Lane (SK4963), Pebley Sand Quarry (SK4878) and Markland Grips (SK5074). There are also a few records from the Carboniferous Limestone of the White Peak: Dove Dale

(SK1455), Miller's Dale Quarry (SK1473) and Hopton Quarry (SK2656). Elsewhere it is very rare with scattered records as at Crich Stand Quarry (SK3455) and Darley Park (SK3437).

Bromopsis inermis (Leyss.) Holub
Hungarian Brome

COUNTY STATUS: Established (Neophyte)
CONSERVATION STATUS: None
FIRST YEAR: 1970 LATEST YEAR: 2010 NO OF RECORDS: 29
RECENT SQUARES: monads 10; tetrads 10; hectads 11
ALL SQUARES: monads 13; tetrads 13; hectads 13

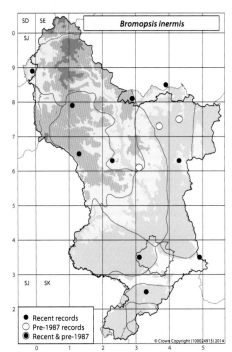

Hungarian Brome is an established perennial of waysides and rough grasslands. It occurs very rarely scattered throughout the county from Mellor (SJ9988) and Birley Vale (SK3984) in the north to Foremark Reservoir (SK3324) and Long Eaton (SK4934) in the south. It was formerly sown as a fodder crop but is now mostly introduced as a seed contaminant. Our plant is ssp. *inermis*, a native of continental Europe.

Brachypodium rupestre (Host) Roem. & Schult.
Tor-grass

COUNTY STATUS: Native
CONSERVATION STATUS: None
FIRST YEAR: 1837 LATEST YEAR: 2012 NO OF RECORDS: 321
RECENT SQUARES: monads 92; tetrads 57; hectads 15
ALL SQUARES: monads 120; tetrads 74; hectads 21

Tor-grass is a native perennial of grasslands, waysides, scrub and quarries, generally on calcareous soils. It is very common on the Magnesian Limestone (Pleasley Vale SK5064, Scarcliffe Park SK5070 & Ginny Spring SK5278) where it is locally dominant in calcareous grasslands. It is rare and generally less abundant

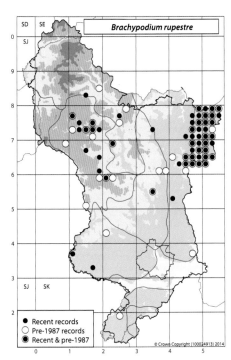

in the White Peak (Miller's Dale Station SK1373, Cressbrook Dale SK1774 & Gratton Dale SK2059), and very rare elsewhere (Crich SK3455 & Sudbury Park SK1633). It has spread locally, and nationally, since 1950 due to a decrease in grazing. It can swamp the growth of other plants and thus threaten other native species. A 1971 record near Chelmorton (SK0969) holds the national altitudinal record for this grass at 305m (Preston *et al.* 2002).

Brachypodium sylvaticum (Huds.) P. Beauv.
False Brome

False Brome is a tufted native perennial of woods, scrub and hedges on fertile neutral

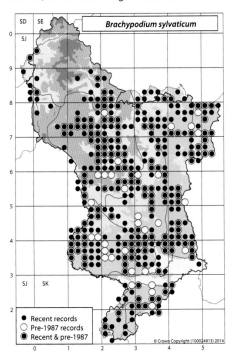

COUNTY STATUS: Native
CONSERVATION STATUS: None
FIRST YEAR: 1863 **LATEST YEAR:** 2013 **NO OF RECORDS:** 1,416
RECENT SQUARES: monads 488; tetrads 328; hectads 37
ALL SQUARES: monads 561; tetrads 359; hectads 37

soils, and a colonist of open grasslands, waste land and arable fields on calcareous soils over limestone. Apart from the Dark and South West Peak, where it is rare, it is occasional throughout the county from Dinting Reserve (SK0194) and Crook Hill (SK1886) in the north, to Haunton (SK2311) and Bryan's Coppice (SK3619) in the south.

Elymus caninus (L.) L.
Bearded Couch

COUNTY STATUS: Native
CONSERVATION STATUS: None
FIRST YEAR: 1829 **LATEST YEAR:** 2013 **NO OF RECORDS:** 704
RECENT SQUARES: monads 374; tetrads 273; hectads 38
ALL SQUARES: monads 442; tetrads 315; hectads 38

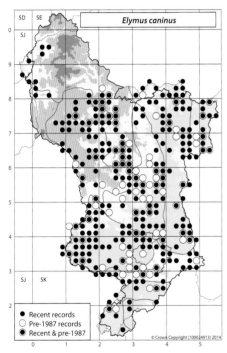

Bearded Couch is a native perennial grass of damp shaded habitats including woods, hedges, river banks and rock ledges, particularly on free-draining base-rich soils. It occurs occasionally throughout Derbyshire except for the high moors of the South West and Dark Peak Character Areas. Sites where it has been noted include Glossop (SK0395) and Beighton (SK4484) in the north, and Netherseal (SK2712) and Ticknall (SK3624) in the south.

Elytrigla repens (L.) Desv. ex Nevski
Common Couch

Common Couch is a native perennial of disturbed ground, rough grassland, waste ground and waysides, particularly on

COUNTY STATUS: Native
CONSERVATION STATUS: None
FIRST YEAR: 1789 **LATEST YEAR:** 2013 **NO OF RECORDS:** 2,650
RECENT SQUARES: monads 1,290; tetrads 638; hectads 43
ALL SQUARES: monads 1,476; tetrads 663; hectads 43

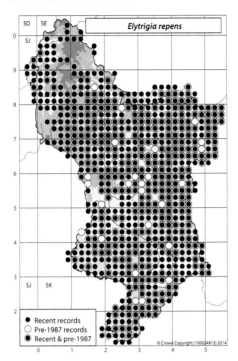

fertile soils. It is also a troublesome weed of cultivated ground in both fields and gardens. It is very common throughout the county except for the high moors of the South West and Dark Peak Areas. Our plant is ssp. *repens*, of which the form *aristata* (Schum.) Beetle has been noted.

Leymus arenarius (L.) Hochst.
Lyme-grass

Lyme-grass is a very rare, casual perennial of waste and cultivated ground with no recent records. Only four sites are known: Stonegravels Tips (SK3872) in 1974, Cowley Bottom (SK3477) in the 1970s, Froggatt (SK2476) in 1969 and Hulland Gravel Pit (SK2645) in 1958 and 1969. Sometimes grown as a garden ornamental, it is native to sand dunes on the British coast. The Cowley Bottom record is particularly interesting as it was found on bare colliery shale waste with Marram Grass (*Ammophila arenaria*), another species native to coastal dunes.

Hordelymus europaeus (L.) Jess. ex Harz.
Wood Barley

COUNTY STATUS: Native
CONSERVATION STATUS: DRDB (Cat3), NS, A, B, C
FIRST YEAR: 1787 **LATEST YEAR:** 2011 **NO OF RECORDS:** 153
RECENT SQUARES: monads 24; tetrads 22; hectads 11
ALL SQUARES: monads 43; tetrads 35; hectads 17

Wood Barley is a rare native perennial of woods and shady places, and occurs in a

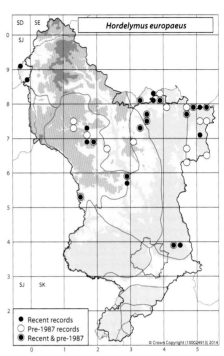

range of Character Areas. These include the White Peak (Lovers' Walk, Matlock SK2958), the Coal Measures (Dale Hermitage SK4338 & Birley Wood SK3272) and the Magnesian Limestone (Whaley SK5171). It is local in England and Wales, and a Nationally Scarce species.

Hordeum vulgare L.
Six-rowed Barley

COUNTY STATUS: Casual
CONSERVATION STATUS: None
FIRST YEAR: 1970 **LATEST YEAR:** 2012 **NO OF RECORDS:** 45
RECENT SQUARES: monads 15; tetrads 14; hectads 11
ALL SQUARES: monads 32; tetrads 30; hectads 17

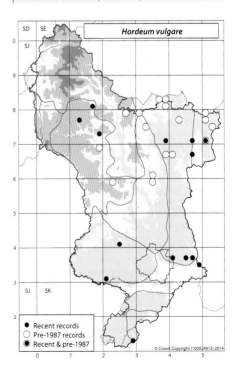

Six-rowed Barley is a very rare, casual annual of waste places, waysides and tips. Scattered throughout the county, it is probably under-recorded as few botanists bother to note its presence. Once widely cultivated in Britain, it is rarely grown now, so current records no doubt relate to bird-seed or grain contaminants. It is probably of cultivated origin.

Hordeum distichon L.
Two-rowed Barley

COUNTY STATUS:	Casual
CONSERVATION STATUS:	None
FIRST YEAR: 1987 LATEST YEAR: 2012 NO OF RECORDS: 51	
RECENT SQUARES: monads 47; tetrads 45; hectads 25	
ALL SQUARES: monads 47; tetrads 45; hectads 25	

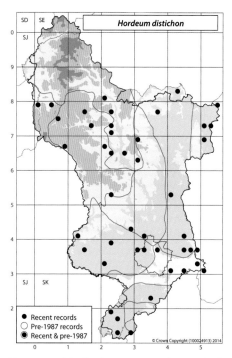

Two-rowed Barley is a rare casual annual of field margins, waysides and tips. It is now the commonly cultivated barley in Britain and as such current records probably relate to spilt grain or relics of cultivation. It is also introduced in bird-seed. Scattered throughout the county except for the high moors of the Dark Peak, it is probably of cultivated origin.

Hordeum murinum L.
Wall Barley

COUNTY STATUS:	Established (Archaeophyte)
CONSERVATION STATUS:	None
FIRST YEAR: 1789 LATEST YEAR: 2013 NO OF RECORDS: 907	
RECENT SQUARES: monads 471; tetrads 285; hectads 35	
ALL SQUARES: monads 499; tetrads 297; hectads 36	

Wall Barley is an anciently established annual of rough grassland, waysides and waste land. It is frequent in the eastern half of the county, as at Linton Heath (SK2816),

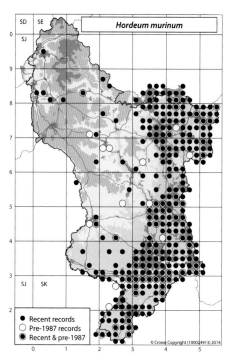

Pye Bridge (SK4252) and Eckington (SK4379). Elsewhere it is rare (Manor Park SK0394 & Thorntree SK1863). Our plant is ssp. *murinum*.

Hordeum jubatum L.
Foxtail Barley

COUNTY STATUS:	Established (Neophyte)
CONSERVATION STATUS:	None
FIRST YEAR: 1970 LATEST YEAR: 2003 NO OF RECORDS: 27	
RECENT SQUARES: monads 6; tetrads 5; hectads 6	
ALL SQUARES: monads 21; tetrads 19; hectads 13	

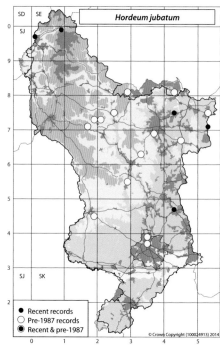

Foxtail Barley is an established perennial of waste places, resown grasslands and roadsides. It is very rare and scattered throughout the county from the flood

plain of the River Etherow (SK0196) and the Woodhead Reservoir (SK0899) in the north, through Staveley (SK4375) to Loscoe Dam (SK4247) in the south. It previously occurred over a wider geographic range, turning up further south in 1974 on a Derby roadside (SK3538). Probably introduced as a grain or bird-seed alien or even a garden throwout, it is a native of North America.

Hordeum secalinum Schreb.
Meadow Barley

COUNTY STATUS:	Native
CONSERVATION STATUS:	B
FIRST YEAR: 1789 LATEST YEAR: 2012 NO OF RECORDS: 106	
RECENT SQUARES: monads 33; tetrads 31; hectads 10	
ALL SQUARES: monads 50; tetrads 45; hectads 18	

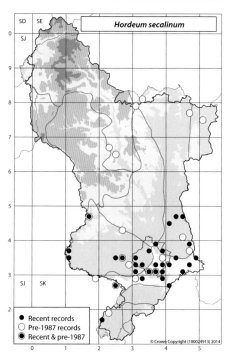

Meadow Barley is a rare native perennial of unimproved neutral grasslands and is increasingly being used in grassland restoration schemes. All recent records come from the south of the county, for example Sidford Wood (SK1035), Sinfin Moor Lane Meadows (SK3431) and Loscoe (SK4347). It was previously recorded from further north too: near Haddon Hall (SK2267) in 1975, Abbeydale Sports Club (SK3281) in 1973, and Markland Grips (SK5074) in 1969. Occurring as a native in central, southern and eastern England, our records are towards the north-western edge of its range.

Secale cereale L.
Rye

Rye is a very rare, casual annual of field margins, tips and waste places. It occurs mainly in the west of the county though this may be an artefact of recording. As it is rarely cultivated now, it is probably

COUNTY STATUS: Casual
CONSERVATION STATUS: None
FIRST YEAR: 1997 LATEST YEAR: 1998 NO OF RECORDS: 9
RECENT SQUARES: monads 8; tetrads 7; hectads 4
ALL SQUARES: monads 8; tetrads 7; hectads 4

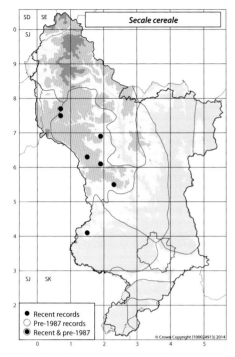

introduced as a contaminant of grass-seed or in bird-seed. It is only known as a cultivated plant.

Triticum aestivum L.
Bread Wheat
Bread Wheat, the common cultivated wheat, is an occasional casual annual of field margins, waysides and waste ground. It occurs throughout the county due to

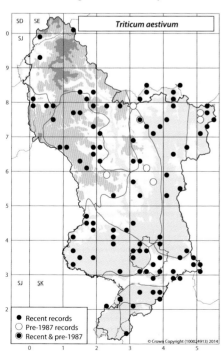

COUNTY STATUS: Casual
CONSERVATION STATUS: None
FIRST YEAR: 1970 LATEST YEAR: 2013 NO OF RECORDS: 142
RECENT SQUARES: monads 115; tetrads 99; hectads 32
ALL SQUARES: monads 121; tetrads 105; hectads 32

spilt grain or as a relic of cultivation, or as a bird-seed alien. It probably originated in cultivation.

Danthonia decumbens (L.) DC.
Heath-grass

COUNTY STATUS: Native
CONSERVATION STATUS: None
FIRST YEAR: 1858 LATEST YEAR: 2013 NO OF RECORDS: 516
RECENT SQUARES: monads 217; tetrads 153; hectads 33
ALL SQUARES: monads 270; tetrads 192; hectads 37

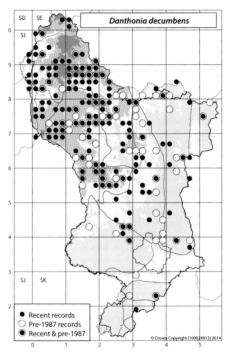

Heath-grass is a tufted native perennial of infertile grasslands generally on acid soils, though sometimes occurs on soils over limestone. It is occasional to frequent in the Peak District (Coldwell Clough SK0585, Ashopton SK1986, Wormhill SK1273 & Biggin Dale SK1458). Elsewhere it is only rare (Dale Hills SK4338 & South Street Grassland SK3118).

Cortaderia selloana (Schult. & Schult f.) Asch. & Graebn.
Pampas-grass
Pampas-grass is a tussock forming, casual perennial of waysides and waste ground. It is only known from the Derby area (Borrowash By-pass SK3835 & Little Chester SK3537). Large tussocks have been known on the former site since at least 1987 and appear to be slowly spreading today. Used as a garden ornamental and architectural plant, it is native to South America.

Molinia caerulea (L.) Moench
Purple Moor-grass

COUNTY STATUS: Native
CONSERVATION STATUS: None
FIRST YEAR: 1829 LATEST YEAR: 2013 NO OF RECORDS: 715
RECENT SQUARES: monads 289; tetrads 158; hectads 23
ALL SQUARES: monads 311; tetrads 175; hectads 26

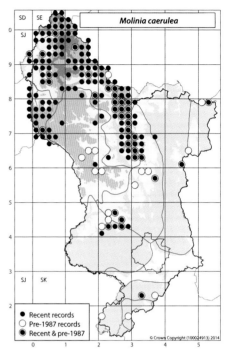

Purple Moor-grass is a tufted native perennial of moors, marshes and mires, on wet acid soils where there is some water movement. It is common and locally abundant throughout upland areas of the South West Peak and Dark Peak (Axe Edge SK0270, Torside Reservoir SK0698, Hathersage SK28G & Farley Moor SK3063). Elsewhere on the limestone and in the lowlands, it is very rare and localised (Black Brook Sand Pit SK2744 & Carver's Rocks SK3222). It was formerly more frequent in these areas. For example it was recorded at both Swainspark (SK2016) and Carr Ponds (SK4764) in the 1970s. The majority of plants are presumably **ssp. caerulea**, but there is one 2003 record for **ssp. arundinacea** (Schrank) K. Richt. from Leash Fen (SK2873).

Phragmites australis (Cav.) Trin. ex Steud.
Common Reed

COUNTY STATUS: Native
CONSERVATION STATUS: None
FIRST YEAR: 1829 LATEST YEAR: 2013 NO OF RECORDS: 417
RECENT SQUARES: monads 170; tetrads 135; hectads 33
ALL SQUARES: monads 187; tetrads 146; hectads 34

Common Reed is a clump-forming native perennial that grows in or by the edges of rivers, canals, ponds and lakes, as well as in fens and swamps. It is increasingly being planted beside waterbodies for ornament

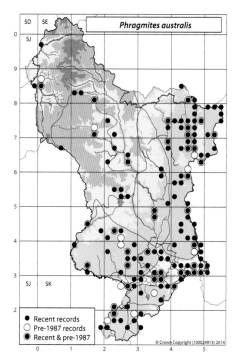

or as important habitat for birds and insects, and in sewage plants for final treatment of purified water. It is occasional in the lowlands of the south and east, but is rare in the uplands of the Peak District.

Panicum capillare L.
Witch-grass
Witch-grass is a very rare, casual annual of waste ground, known only from disturbed land at Heeley (SK3484) in 2003. It is a bird-seed casual from North America.

Panicum miliaceum L.
Common Millet

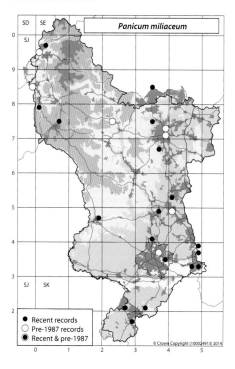

COUNTY STATUS: Casual	
CONSERVATION STATUS: None	
FIRST YEAR: 1960 **LATEST YEAR:** 2008 **NO OF RECORDS:** 29	
RECENT SQUARES: monads 20; tetrads 18; hectads 13	
ALL SQUARES: monads 27; tetrads 25; hectads 16	

Common Millet is a rare casual annual of tips, waste ground, arable land and waysides. It occurs scattered throughout the county from Hadfield (SK0296) in the north, to Breaston (SK4733) and Overseal (SK2916) in the south. A native of Asia, it is a constituent of bird-seed, a contaminant of imported grain and sometimes planted as a food source for game.

Echinochloa crus-galli (L.) P. Beauv.
Cockspur

COUNTY STATUS: Casual	
CONSERVATION STATUS: None	
FIRST YEAR: 1969 **LATEST YEAR:** 2012 **NO OF RECORDS:** 19	
RECENT SQUARES: monads 13; tetrads 10; hectads 8	
ALL SQUARES: monads 17; tetrads 14; hectads 10	

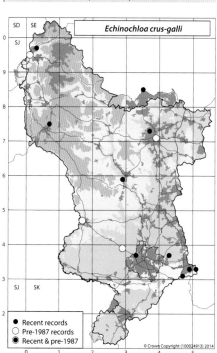

Cockspur is a very rare, casual annual of tips, waste land and cultivated ground. Recent records are scattered over the county from Hadfield (SK0296) and Heeley (SK3484) in the north, to Markeaton Park (SK3337) and Lock Lane (SK4731) in the south. Indigenous to the tropics, it is probably introduced from bird-seed mixes, but is sometimes sown as a source of food for game.

Echinochloa esculenta (A. Braun.) H. Scholz
Japanese Millet
Japanese Millet is a very rare, casual annual of tips and waste ground. The only recent records are from Hadfield (SK0296) in

1989 and Barlow (SK3475) in 2003. There are earlier ones from Melandra (SK0095) in 1976 and Hady Tip (SK3970) in 1969. Probably introduced in bird-seed mixes or sown as a source of food for game, it is of cultivated origin from Japan.

Echinochloa frumentacea Link
White Millet
White Millet is a very rare, casual annual, known only from a 1969 record at Hady Tip (SK3970). Probably introduced in bird-feed or as a contaminant of imported seeds, it is of cultivated origin from India.

Setaria pumila (Poir.) Roem. & Schult.
Yellow Bristle-grass

COUNTY STATUS: Casual	
CONSERVATION STATUS: None	
FIRST YEAR: 1975 **LATEST YEAR:** 2008 **NO OF RECORDS:** 18	
RECENT SQUARES: monads 12; tetrads 12; hectads 7	
ALL SQUARES: monads 14; tetrads 14; hectads 8	

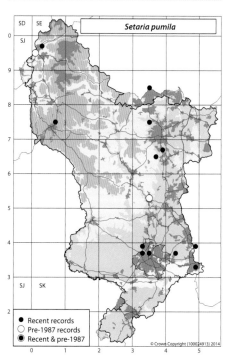

Yellow Bristle-grass is a very rare, casual annual of tips and waysides, with records scattered throughout the county from Hadfield Tip (SK0296) and Fairfield Tip (SK0674) in the north, to Cheapside (SK3536) and Stanton Gate (SK4838) in the south. Probably introduced as a constituent of bird-seed or a contaminant of imported seeds, it is native to the Mediterranean.

Setaria viridis (L.) P. Beauv.
Green Bristle-grass
Green Bristle-grass is a very rare, casual annual of tips, arable fields and waysides. It occurs sporadically through Derbyshire from Hadfield (SK0296) and Heeley

COUNTY STATUS: Casual
CONSERVATION STATUS: None
FIRST YEAR: 1899 LATEST YEAR: 2008 NO OF RECORDS: 23
RECENT SQUARES: monads 15; tetrads 14; hectads 11
ALL SQUARES: monads 19; tetrads 18; hectads 12

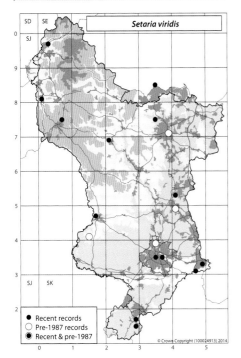

Setaria viridis

Recent records
Pre-1987 records
Recent & pre-1987

© Crown Copyright (100024913) 2014

(SK3484) in the north, to Old Sawley (SK4731) and Overseal (SK2815) in the south. Native to southern Europe, it is probably a constituent of bird-seed or a contaminant of imported seed.

Setaria italica (L.) P. Beauv.
Foxtail Bristle-grass

Foxtail Bristle-grass is a very rare, casual annual of waste tips. The only records are from Melandra Tip (SK0095) in 1977 and Hady Tip (SK3970) in 1969. Probably a bird-seed or grain alien, it is of cultivated origin from China.

Digitaria sanguinalis (L.) Scop.
Hairy Finger-grass

Hairy Finger-grass is a very rare, casual annual of waste tips and flower beds. The only records are from four sites, all during the 1970s and 1980s: Melandra Tip (SK0095), Ashbourne (SK1746), Alvaston (SK3832) and Mortimer Wilson School (SK4156). Probably imported as a part of bird-seed mixes, it is indigenous to southern Europe.

Sorghum halepense (L.) Pers.
Johnson-grass

Johnson-grass is a very rare, casual perennial, known only from Hady Tip (SK3970) in 1975. Probably introduced in bird-seed or as a contaminant of food grain, it is a native of the Mediterranean.

Sorghum bicolor (L.) Moench
Great Millet

Great Millet is a very rare, casual annual. The only records are from a roadside at Johnson's Mill (SK2862) in 1994, and a tip in Derby (SK3736) in 1969. A constituent or contaminant of bird-seed and food grains, it originates from sub-Saharan Africa.

Zea mays L.
Maize

Maize is a very rare, casual annual of waste ground, but is also planted as a field crop for animal fodder. Probably under-recorded, the only records come from Fairfield Tip (SK0674) in 1996 and disturbed ground at Heeley (SK3484) in 2003. Introduced into the wild via bird-seed or as a relic of cultivation, it originates from Central America.

CHAPTER 3

A history of Derbyshire field botany

Alan Willmot and Nick Moyes

This chapter provides a brief chronological account of the evolution of field botany in Derbyshire, with a more detailed look at the major figures involved. It does not offer an encyclopaedic biography of all the county's botanical recorders, but seeks to explain how our current state of knowledge on the flora of Derbyshire has come about.

Pre-17th century (pre-1600)

Prior to the 1600s people's interest in botany was almost entirely utilitarian. Plants were seen as a source of food, fuel and medicines, or as a raw material for building, implements and decoration; they were little seen as objects of interest in their own right. Only towards the end of the period did attitudes begin to change. Individuals such as **William Turner** (1508–1568) in England started to take an interest in plants and their distributions for their own sake. The botanical books that existed were still basically herbals; they listed plants useful as medicines or treatments, and were often based on species that grew in foreign parts. A few sources such as the Domesday Book, medieval charters and place-name studies do give some idea of what was present in the county. They are generally very vague by modern standards, but nevertheless provide a sense of what was growing here, and are valuable because of their rarity.

Plants are still used for decoration in Derbyshire well dressings, as here at Foolow in August 2005, though nowadays rarely use wild species

The **Domesday Book** in various modern translations (Morgan 1978) contains a great deal of information about our county's vegetation: what there was, how much of it there was, and where it occurred. It tells us about meadow, pasture, woodland pasture, underwood and even lead mines, from which we might be able to infer the presence of lead mine spoil heaps and their associated flora. It tells us that a quarter of the county was wooded, the majority being woodland pasture (Darby & Maxwell 1962). This provided wood for fuel and grazing for pigs. It does not tell us which species of grass grew in the meadows, nor which trees were present in the woods, but we might infer they contained a large number of Oaks, as their fruits are the most valuable for fattening pigs in autumn.

Medieval charters (and Anglo-Saxon charters elsewhere in the country) can be an important early source of plant records. Charters in general, and in Derbyshire in particular, are often concerned with parcels of land (Jeayes 1906). In the absence of maps, these were often identified by boundary markers. These were often trees and are frequently identified to species elsewhere, with Oak, Ash and Thorn being the commonest (Biggam 2003). Whilst investigation of Derbyshire charters could reveal some early plant records, care is needed as medieval monks were not above forging earlier Anglo-Saxon charters to prove the title of abbeys and monasteries to lands they held.

Place-name studies provide more specific early records, but are difficult to date as many were not written down until long after being first coined (Biggam 2003). They tell us where plants occurred, but not when. Most habitation names appear to be early medieval or Anglo-Saxon in origin, that is, dated between the departure of the Romans in the fifth century A.D. and the arrival of the Normans in 1066. Cameron (1959) in his scholarly account of the origin of county place-names, and Poulton-Smith (2005) in his more popular account, both demonstrate that flora and fauna are amongst the commonest descriptors. Local examples are: Alder in Alderwasley, Bracken in Brackenfield, Heather in Over Haddon and Maple in Mapleton. The names of "Hundreds", the old subdivisions of counties, are a particular case in point, often reflecting where the hundred assemblies met. Thus, Matlock in Wirksworth hundred refers to the Oak tree where meetings were held, and the meaning of Appletree Hundred is clear.

More specific studies into species of economic value allow us to be even more certain about their presence in past times. Holly might not immediately spring to mind as a fodder plant, but present-day cattle will happily browse it from field hedges. In the past, however, when winter feed was a much rarer and valuable commodity, Holly was specifically cultivated and managed in stands called "hollins" in northern Derbyshire (Spray 1981). There is even a reference to the use of Holly as fodder for sheep, dated to 1391 (Spray & Smith 1977).

Towards the end of the 16th century we begin to see a few mentions of plants for their own sake, not just as economic assets, including what might be considered as the first plant record for the county. This was for **Bird's-eye Primrose** (*Primula farinosa*), a specimen of which R. Garth gave **De L'Ecluse** from "the county of Derby" around 1581 (Raven 1947).

The 17th century (1600–1700)

Interest in the world around us increased during the 17th century. Coupled with greater availability of printing, it saw the first published references to Derbyshire plants for their own sake. No longer were they regarded simply as "useful"; plants now began to be seen as objects worthy of study in their own right. And this study had two aspects to it. One was an interest in which species occurred naturally in a given habitat; and the second was more geographic, concerned with where individual plants occurred in the wild. So began what we might today call "field botany", which later developed into the modern science of Botany, encompassing progressively anatomy, physiology, biochemistry and genetic modification.

The first localised reference to a wild plant growing in the county was made by **John Parkinson (1567–1650)** (Raven 1947) in his *Theatrum Botanicum*. Published in 1640, he recorded a species of Scurvygrass of which he noted *"I hear also that it groweth high unto a castle in the Peak of Darbishire"* (Parkinson 1640). This undoubtedly refers to **Pyrenean Scurvygrass** (*Cochlearia pyrenaica*) which still grows in the Peak District today. Although Parkinson gives some of what we now recognise as the first plant records for Great Britain, he was not a field botanist, but an apothecary (Mathew & Harrison 2004). His *Theatrum Botanicum* was a tool for apothecaries and a font of knowledge on the use of plants around the home.

The next work to record wild plants in Derbyshire was by a doctor, **William How** (Raven 1947). Published in 1650, his *Phytologia Britannica* was a different type of book. It was effectively a Checklist – a list of the plants that grew wild in England, with localities given for some of them. Linton (1903) credits How with the first records of **Mountain Pansy** (*Viola lutea*) and **Common Restharrow** (*Ononis repens*). After How there came a change from the medical background of botanical authors with the work of John Ray.

John Ray (1627–1705) was born in Essex. He was a naturalist and a natural theologian, and is often referred to as the "Father of English Natural History" (Raven 1950). A fellow of Trinity College Cambridge, he took holy orders in 1660 (Mathew & Harrison 2004). Although he primarily studied plants for their intrinsic interest, his work had a residual utilitarian aspect. He believed God created plants for a purpose, and gave occasional medical and pharmacological notes in his writings. In 1660 he published in Latin his *Catalogus plantarum circa Cantabrigiam nascentium (A catalogue of plants growing around Cambridge)*. This list of plants contained details of their habitats and locations, and is therefore considered the first English county *Flora*. He later travelled through Great Britain, making many botanical records which he published in his *Catalogus plantarum Angliae* (1670). This, and his second edition published in 1677, contains a number of records from Derbyshire. These include: **Giant Bellflower** (*Campanula latifolia*) *"in the mountainous parts of Darbyshire"*, **Stag's-horn Clubmoss** (*Lycopodium clavatum*) *"on the high hills of Darby-shire"* and **Golden Dock** (*Rumex maritimus*) *"ad Trentam fluvium prope Swarston pontem in Derbia"*. The latter still grows by the River Trent close to Swarkestone Bridge today. Ray published various other botanical works containing references to species in Derbyshire, and also contributed lists of plants from our county to the works of others, such as Gibson (1695).

The 18th century (1700–1800)

The 18th century saw a continuation of the trend previously set by Ray, with the publication of numerous works on the wild plants of various parts of the British Isles. Some included the first extensive species lists for Derbyshire. As in Ray and the other earlier works, these concentrate on the habitats of individual species and where they occur, but with less emphasis on their uses. For the first time these include scholarly papers published in journals and transactions of scientific societies. Apart from a few university professors of botany, their authors were mainly individual amateurs. Sometimes they were really only editors, amassing accounts of various aspects of a given geographic area into one work, and often with only a very short section on plants. Linton's 1903 *Flora* provides a detailed list of these publications, highlighting those in which individual Derbyshire species are first recorded. Notable amongst these are Martyn (1729), Withering (1787) and Pilkington (1789).

John Martyn (1699–1768) was a self-taught botanist who was born in London. From early life he was schooled by his father to become a merchant (Gorham 1830). However, he became interested in botany in his spare time and went on "herbarizing" excursions around London with various apothecaries and doctors. He gradually expanded his interest in the subject and his range of botanical acquaintances until, by 1725, he was giving lectures on the subject in London, and counted Sir Hans Sloane amongst his botanical circle. In 1727 he was appointed Professor of Botany at Cambridge University and admitted as a Fellow of the Royal Society. Two years later he presented his first paper to them which described some of the rare plants found in the Peak of Derbyshire (Martyn 1729). These included **Lesser Meadow-rue** (*Thalictrum minus*) and **Alpine Clubmoss** (*Diphasiastrum alpinum*). In 1762 he was succeeded as Professor of Botany at Cambridge by his son **Thomas Martyn (1735–1825)** who held the chair for 63 years (Gorham 1830). In 1763 Thomas published his *Plantae Cantabrigienses* which, whilst mainly an account of the plants around Cambridge, contained an appendix of rare plants occurring in other English counties. His list for Derbyshire is basically a compendium of what had already been published, apart from **Marsh Cinquefoil** (*Comarum palustre*) which he noted as growing at Pool's-hole near the ebbing and flowing well (Linton 1903).

Dr William Withering (1741–1799) was an eminent physician who worked in both Stafford and Birmingham (Peck & Wilkinson 1950), and was also a notable amateur botanist and geologist (Mathew & Harrison 2004). As a physician he is recognised for discovering the active constituent of Foxglove extract which he demonstrated was beneficial in cases of congestive heart failure. As a botanist he is renowned for his book entitled *A Botanical Arrangement of all the Vegetables Naturally Growing in Great Britain*. First published in 1776, it referred to a number of localities where plants grew in the wild. This was the first British *Flora* written entirely in English to use the then new Linnaean taxonomy. Later editions were published under slightly different titles. The second edition, published in 1787, was written in collaboration with **Jonathan Stokes**. Entitled *"A botanical arrangement of British Plants"*, it contained even more British plant localities. Details from Derbyshire were mainly provided by four gentlemen, none of whom actually lived in the county, although one came from nearby; the **Reverend S. Dickenson** was rector of Blymhill in Staffordshire. Between them they provided many first county records, including some of our most iconic species. **Jacob's-ladder** (*Polemonium caeruleum*) was recorded for Lovers Leap, Buxton and near Bakewell. **Mossy Saxifrage** (*Saxifraga hypnoides*) was noted in Dove Dale and Middleton Dale, while **Maiden Pink** (*Dianthus deltoides*) was given for *"hills between Bakewell and Chatsworth"*.

The Reverend James Pilkington (c.1751–1804) from Ipswich was minister of the Unitarian Chapel in Friar Gate, Derby when he published his work, *A view of the present state of Derbyshire,* in 1789 (Lysons & Lysons 1817). This was not a botanical textbook, but more a synopsis of the natural resources of the county, including a section on its plants. Pilkington's book saw the first attempt to draw up a complete list of Derbyshire's plants. It included just over 500 species, of which some 450 were first county records, according to Linton (1903). It appears to have been based on the work of both past and new recorders, including Pilkington himself. Previous workers referred to include Dr Withering and John Ray. New recorders who appear to have been consulted include: **Mr Whately** who was of assistance to Dr Withering with his Derbyshire records; the Rev. Dewes Coke of Brookhill Hall, Pinxton, and a **Dr Johnson**. As well as providing a systematic list of species, Pilkington also names many county locations. These include **Bog-myrtle** (*Myrica gale*) "*common about Wingerworth*"; **Wall-rue** (*Asplenium ruta-muraria*) at St Peter's Church Derby, and further records for **Jacob's-ladder** (*Polemonium caeruleum*) at Alfreton Brook and Bakewell meadows. As well as being interested in all aspects of the natural environment, Pilkington appears to have been something of a radical thinker. In 1795, just after the French Revolution, he published a book entitled "*The Doctrine of Equality*". It gave such offence that he felt obliged to offer his resignation as minister of the Chapel. However, a special meeting of the congregation refused to accept it, saying, in essence, that he was entitled to free expression of his ideas (Chapple 1997). Nevertheless he appears to have resigned soon after, in 1797.

Prior to the 19th century, botanical study in Derbyshire was the rare preserve of the amateur working alone and generally by those from outside the county. In the next period we see a marked increase in the number of publications written by people actually based here.

The 19th century (1800–1900)

This period saw the formation of a number of local natural history societies, and possibly even the beginnings of professional botany with the opening of Derby Museum in 1879. For the most part, botanical study was still concerned with which species occurred here and where they grew, although it did see the beginning of an interest in the relationship between plants and their environment, including features such as geology and altitude.

The 19th century saw the start of works on particular aspects of Derbyshire botany. There were publications on specific areas of the county, such as **Garneys'** 1881 *Contributions to the Flora and Fauna of Repton*, and on individual groups of plants, such as **Smith's** 1869 work *The Ferns of Derbyshire*. Accounts of Derbyshire plants began to appear in a greater range of publications. There were descriptions of the resources of the county by **Farey** in 1813; accounts of the history of the county by **Glover** in 1829, and tourist guides such as **Adams'** 1840 work on Matlock Bath. There were learned articles in the transactions of the new natural history societies, and finally there was the first full-scale *Flora* of Derbyshire at the end of the century, published by the **Reverend Painter** in 1889. With such a wealth of local botanical material, it is only possible here to touch on some of the more important local botanists and their works. These are described below in approximate chronological order.

John Farey (1766–1826) was a professional surveyor and geologist who was based in London around the turn of the 18th century. His most important work was a three volume description of the natural resources of Derbyshire entitled "*A General View of the Agriculture and Minerals of Derbyshire*", published between 1811 and 1817 (Mathew & Harrison 2004). This was similar in aim to Pilkington's slightly earlier work, but that did not include wild plants as part of the county's resources. However, in Farey's second volume published in 1813, which covers agriculture and forestry, he provides a description of the vegetation of early 19th century

Limestone Fern (*Gymnocarpium robertianum*) from Smith's "*Ferns of Derbyshire*" published 1869

Derbyshire, and mentions many plant species. These tend to be either useful ones such as trees, or those plants he considers a hindrance to economic development. One of the latter is **Heather** (*Calluna vulgaris*). On describing the improvement of the limestone uplands between Ashbourne and Buxton, which were at that time covered in heathland, he says of it: "*this noxious and useless plant will, I hope, disappear altogether from this district*".

Stephen Glover (d.1869) was a Derbyshire publisher who produced his *History of the County of Derby* in 1829 (Mathew & Harrison 2004). Published in Derby, it contained a long list of the wild plants found growing in the county, for which he credits two local ladies: a **Mrs Lucy Hardcastle** of Derby and **Mrs Margaret Stovin (1756–1846)** of Newbold. The former, who published a textbook on botany and ran a girls' school in the town, is suspected of being an illegitimate daughter of Erasmus Darwin, the grandfather of Charles Darwin (Smith & Arnott 2005). Margaret Stovin was born near Doncaster, but by the 1820s was living near Chesterfield and had built up a wide circle of correspondents, including some of the foremost botanists of the day. She collected throughout Derbyshire and established a garden at Newbold. In her seventies she befriended a young Florence Nightingale, and in 1833 presented 13 year old Florence with an album of plants they had collected together at Lea Hurst. In 1840 Stovin was one of the first women to be elected to the Botanical Society in London

(Mendelsohn 2008). Although Linton (1903) considered the list compiled by Glover's to be unreliable, he still credited him with some 200 new county records. Unfortunately only a selection of plants are given localities, such as **Mountain Currant** (*Ribes alpinum*) recorded in a hedge near Ilam, and **Lily-of-the-valley** (*Convallaria majalis*) in Dove Dale and the Via Gellia in abundance.

Glover the publisher, and Farey the geologist both enhanced understanding of Derbyshire's flora, but neither were botanists. It was only by the middle of the century that people who can be considered local experts became active in searching for and publishing county records. Most noticeable amongst these were: Joseph Whittaker; the Rev. Henry Harpur Crewe; the Rev. William Henry Purchas; the Rev. Andrew Bloxam and Thomas Gibbs, although many others contributed to the gradual accumulation of botanical knowledge. As this sample suggests, many were clergymen. Did they seek evidence for the hand of God by studying His creation? Or did they simply have more time and opportunity to travel around the countryside? The Rev. William Hunt Painter and the Rev. William Richardson Linton were also prominent here but both went further and wrote *Floras* of their own, which are discussed in their own sections later.

Joseph Whittaker (1813–1894) was a local lad, born and raised in Quarndon. His father was a labourer but somehow he managed to secure employment as a gardener to Lt. Col. George Gawler, who had family connections with Derby, and who was to become the second Governor of South Australia. Thus in 1838 Whittaker sailed with his employer for Adelaide. It is unlikely he did much real gardening whilst in Australia, but he certainly travelled around South Australia collecting and preserving plants.

Joseph Whittaker's gravestone St Matthew's churchyard Morley, May 2014 (Alan Willmot)

Some 300 specimens were subsequently placed in the herbarium at Kew Gardens, including a new species of sundew (*Drosera whittakeri*) that now bears his name. He returned to England in 1840 and by 1846 was living at Breadsall near Derby where he was a schoolmaster at the local boys' school. Whilst at Breadsall he collected herbarium specimens which he distributed via the Botanical Exchange Club, and published an article on plants in the surrounding area (Whittaker 1847). This contained a number of first county records, including **Square-stalked Willowherb** (*Epilobium tetragonum*) and **Heath Cudweed** (*Gnaphalium sylvaticum*). Later he began a partnership with the Rev. Henry Harpur Crewe who was the son of the rector of his local church. In 1864 they jointly produced a manuscript list of the plants of Derbyshire containing further first county records, including **Great Horsetail** (*Equisetum telmateia*) and **Lesser Marshwort** (*Apium inundatum*). Later in life he returned to his horticultural roots by becoming a seedsman and nurseryman. He also helped the authors of the first two Derbyshire *Floras*, Painter and Linton, with specimens and records. Apart from his Australian plants at Kew, Whittaker's botanical legacy consists of many hundreds of herbarium specimens at Derby Museum, plus others in museums throughout England due to his involvement with the Botanical Exchange Club (Kraehenbuehl & Moyes 1999).

The Reverend Henry Harpur Crewe (1828–1883) was the first of the many 19th century vicars who lived or botanised in Derbyshire. He was born here at Stanton by Bridge and studied at Trinity College, Cambridge from 1847 where he was awarded an MA in 1855. He was ordained a priest two years later whilst curate at Drinkstone and Creeting St Peter in Suffolk. In 1860 he became rector of Drayton Beauchamp in Buckinghamshire, a post he retained until his death there in 1883 (Crockford's 1874). It was during the late 1840s and 1850s that he appears to have botanised around Breadsall with Joseph Whittaker. During this period he was either living at home or visiting his father who was rector there from 1830 until his death in 1865. Although he produced his manuscript list of plants of Derbyshire with Whittaker in 1864, he appears to have stopped actively botanising in the county after becoming rector of Drayton. Apart from the manuscript list, his main legacy to Derbyshire botany is his collection of herbarium specimens, now at Derby Museum, which forms part of the Joseph Whittaker collection.

The Reverend William Henry Purchas (1823–1903) was born in Ross, Herefordshire. The son of a wine merchant, he worked for several years in his father's business. However the priesthood was his vocation and he only participated in the family business because of his father's poor health and until his younger brothers could take over. He then trained at Durham University College, becoming an ordained priest in 1858 whilst curate at Ticknall in Derbyshire. During his time there he was also chaplain at Calke Abbey and tutor to the young Vauncey Crewe. Afterwards he became curate in two Gloucestershire parishes, before finally becoming vicar at Alstonefield, Staffordshire in 1870 – a post he held until his death in 1903 (Crockford's 1874). It is interesting to note that his "patron in the living" at Alstonefield was Sir John H. Crewe Bart., a relative of the Reverend Crewe mentioned above. Purchas's botanical interests were wide and he produced catalogues of both the mosses and the flowering plants of southern Derbyshire. He studied the critical genera of *Rubus*, *Rosa* and *Hieracium*, and had a bramble named after him (*Rubus purchasianus*) by Rogers, though this is not a Derbyshire species. He published many botanical papers and co-authored *A Flora of Herefordshire* with A. Ley in 1889 (Desmond 1994). He is mentioned particularly in Linton's 1903 *Flora* for his catalogues of Derbyshire plants.

The Reverend Andrew Bloxam (1801–1878) was born in Rugby, the son of the Rev. R.R. Bloxam, a schoolmaster at Rugby School. He was educated at Worcester College, Oxford, but in 1824, at the age of 23, he sailed as the naturalist on HMS Blonde on its journey around South America and the Pacific. The main purpose of the voyage was to return the bodies of King Kamehameha II and his queen back to Hawaii, or the Sandwich Islands as they were then known; they had both died of measles during a visit to England. On the voyage Bloxam's natural history interests were directed mainly towards birds, and his specimens, many of now extinct species, are in the collections of the Natural History Museum, London. On his return in 1826 he seems to have redirected his career and interests. He was then ordained a priest in the Church of England in 1827 (Crockford's 1874) and took up an interest in botany, particularly in fungi and brambles. In 1833 he produced a manuscript list of plants found around Calke. He was appointed curate at Twycross in Leicestershire in the late 1830s, and subsequently became rector at Harborough Magna in Warwickshire in 1871, where he remained until his death in 1878. Ultimately Bloxam's contribution to Derbyshire field botany was relatively limited; he produced the manuscript list referred to by Linton in his 1903 *Flora*, and several of his records are mentioned in Painter's 1889 *Flora*. However, his contribution to botany in general was far greater (Desmond 1994). He was a major contributor to Kirby's (1850) *Flora of Leicestershire*, and Moseley's (1863) *Natural History of Tutbury*. He described at least eleven new species of fungi and six species of *Rubus*. In addition he is remembered in the name of at least one species of fungus (*Entoloma bloxamii*) and one bramble (*Rubus bloxamianus*). The latter was named from a specimen collected by Purchas at Calke.

Thomas Gibbs (1865–1919) was a solicitor living in Wirksworth who also had a particular interest in brambles (*Rubus* spp.) and fungi (Anonymous 1919, Desmond 1994). There are some 300 of his botanical specimens in Derby Museum and paintings of fungi in the Tolson Memorial Museum in Huddersfield. Gibbs was in contact with the Rev. W.R. Linton who named a new species of bramble based on specimens he collected. Unfortunately Linton failed to do a proper job on this, and it still awaits a correctly published name, though is known locally as *Rubus gibbsii*.

Painter and his 1889 Flora

Towards the end of the 19th century sufficient records had been collected by the botanists mentioned above, amongst others, that two enthusiastic clergymen were now separately working towards publishing their own *Floras* of the county. The Reverend W. H. Painter, then a curate in Staffordshire, was the first to complete this task in 1889. Meanwhile the Reverend W.R. Linton, who was actually based in the county at Shirley, did not finish his own *Flora* until just after the turn of the 20th century, in 1903.

The Reverend William Hunt Painter (1835–1910) was born in Aston, Warwickshire (Crockford's 1908). His father was a haberdasher and, originally, William seems to have been aiming for a career in banking since he was described in the 1851 census as a banker's clerk. But later in the decade he took up training with the Church Mission Society at Islington Missionary College (Cannon 2009). For some reason he abandoned the calling to be a foreign missionary as, by 1862, he was working simply as an ordained priest – the curate of Barbon, in what is now the South Lakeland District of Cumbria. It is here that he seems to have developed an interest in botany through the Rev. R. Wood who he met there. Between 1865 and 1866 he was briefly curate at High Wycombe in Buckinghamshire, where he befriended James Britten, the famous botanist. Their contact here is curious as Britten was a fervent Catholic, and he a devout protestant. After High Wycombe, Painter became curate at Edgbaston until 1871.

Painter moved to Derby later that year, becoming curate at Holy Trinity, a post he retained until 1879. Here he botanised energetically around the town, gathering records he would later publish in a short paper in 1893 entitled *"Botanical walks round Derby"*. In this he claimed *"Morley and Breadsall Moor will delight the botanist"*, noting that **Water-violet** (*Hottonia palustris*) grew in the clay pits, (which it still does). He noted **Nodding Bur-marigold** (*Bidens cernua*) at Locko Park, and even looked for **Golden Dock** (*Rumex maritimus*) at Swarkestone Bridge, but failed to re-find it. He terminated his article with a hope that the mention of these plants would stimulate others to study the flowers of the field which *"manifest the wisdom, and love and care of Him who has created them for the well-being and happiness of man..."*

In 1879 Painter transferred to Bristol to become curate at St Luke's in Bedminster, where he remained until 1884. In 1881 he began to publish a series of papers that were to become the basis of his subsequent *Flora* of Derbyshire (see below). He also continued with his botanical excursions, and in 1881 was investigating the flora around Bangor in north Wales. There he gave a talk to the Menai Society of Natural Science and Literature entitled the *Objects of a natural history society* (North Wales Chronicle 1881). In this he is reported as having said that *"The Bible is infallible and if science appeared to contradict it our ignorance and not our knowledge was to blame"*. He continued to move around the country, becoming curate at Knypersley, Staffordshire in 1885. It was whilst living there that his *Flora of Derbyshire* was published in 1889. Painter's final move came in 1894 when he was appointed rector of Stirchley in Shropshire. He appears to have continued with his excursions despite his increasing years, visiting Falmouth in 1898. There he became interested in mosses, which henceforth formed the focus of his botanical studies. In the early 1900s he published several papers on bryophytes, including a supplement in 1902 to his *Flora of Derbyshire*. He presented his herbarium to the University College, Aberystwyth in the mid-1910s, although he had already donated some material to Derby Museum in the 1880s. Failing health forced Painter to move to Shrewsbury in 1909 where he died a year later and was buried back in his old parish of Stirchley. He was obviously a very devout person as in the preface to his 1889 *Flora* he hoped that those who studied the distribution of plants *"may be led by that study into a deeper reverence for the wisdom of Him who has appointed the variation of climate..."* He is remembered by a hybrid fumitory (*Fumaria* × *painteri*) that he discovered in Shropshire, named after him by H.W. Pugsley (Murphy 2009), and in his obituary (Britten 1911).

Painter's *Flora of Derbyshire* is a rather slim volume by today's standards, running to about 150 pages. Published in 1889, it

Front page of Painter's 1889 *"Flora of Derbyshire"*

A CONTRIBUTION TO
THE FLORA OF DERBYSHIRE.

BEING AN ACCOUNT OF THE
FLOWERING PLANTS, FERNS, AND CHARACEÆ
FOUND IN THE COUNTY.

BY
THE REV. W. H. PAINTER,
CORRESPONDING MEMBER OF THE BIRMINGHAM NATURAL HISTORY AND
MICROSCOPICAL SOCIETY.

LONDON:
GEORGE BELL & SONS, YORK STREET,
COVENT GARDEN.
DERBY:
E. OLULOW, JUN.
1889.

includes 970 species and hybrids of vascular plants, although some he considers to be errors, bringing the county total down to some 950 taxa. For each taxon he attempts to note its county status, its British distribution, its altitudinal range and its occurrence within three topographical divisions of Derbyshire. He gives county status as a class of citizenship, using four major categories: Native, Denizen, Colonist and Alien. He uses the term Native just as we do today; Denizen and Colonist equate to what we now refer to as Established, whilst Alien roughly equates to Casual. It is thus possible to make a rough assessment of Painter's picture of the county flora in modern terms. Of the 950 plants recorded, 700 (74%) were Native, 93 (10%) Established, and 69 (7%) Casual. This leaves around 88 plants (9%) not assigned a class. He records British distributions using Watson's eight categories which are defined in the introduction. He records altitudinal range in three zones: Zone 1 or range 1 is up to an altitude of 450 feet; Zone 2 from 450 to 1050 feet and Zone 3 above 1,050 feet. His three topographic divisions are:

I   the Peak District (i.e. the modern White and Dark Peak areas),
II   the Central District (including the Coal Measures and Magnesian Limestone area)
III the Southern District (roughly the county south of Duffield and Ashbourne).

Where Painter knows a plant occurs within any of his topographical divisions, he gives one or more locations, supported by a reference as to where the information comes from. What he does omit from his *Flora* is any type of habitat description for each species.

Painter accepted his *Flora* was not a complete record of the plants of the county. The preface describes it as *"a pioneer of future efforts"*, and indeed it was actually entitled *"A Contribution to the Flora of Derbyshire"*. His achievement was to bring together into one simple book a summary of what was known of the county's vascular plant flora at the time. It does not appear to have been universally well-received, however. For example, it was rather critically reviewed by Bagnall (1889) who acknowledged Painter's efforts in bringing together the researches of others, but found little evidence of the compiler's own knowledge of either Derbyshire or its flora. It is interesting to speculate whether or not Painter knew that the Rev. William Richardson Linton was working on what was to be a rather more substantial Derbyshire *Flora*. Did Painter hasten to get a rather incomplete *Flora* published before Linton could claim priority? We may never know.

In 1902 Painter published a second volume: *A Supplement to a Contribution to the Flora of Derbyshire* which was simply a reprint of three of his papers that had appeared in The Naturalist between 1899 and 1902. They added a few new species to the county, and corrected a number of errors in the first publication. Most significantly it provided a list of Derbyshire mosses. The preface acknowledged his sources and the botanists who had provided material included in the supplement. One such was the Rev. Linton, who was soon to publish the next *Flora*. Painter particularly mentioned several local botanists who had recently died, including Joseph Whittaker of Morley, after which he adds *"happy are those who exchange earthly for heavenly service in the presence of God*!" He ends by noting that specimens of nearly all plants mentioned in his two publications have been placed in Derby Museum. He also stated that his own collection would be presented to the British Museum though, as already noted, it was eventually given to University College, Aberystwyth.

The 20th century (1900–2000)

The next *Flora of Derbyshire* – often called "Linton's *Flora*" – neatly bridges the gap in style between the 19th and 20th century publications. Appearing in 1903, it was clearly researched in the former period, and stylistically belongs to the era of the botanical clergymen. But it was based on records collected by systematic coverage of all parts of the county – something all future *Floras* would follow.

The **Reverend William Richardson Linton (1850–1908)** was born in Diddington, Huntingdonshire, where his father was a Church of England clergyman. He had three elder sisters and a brother with whom he was to work closely as a fellow botanist in years to come. He attended Repton School in Derbyshire and, in 1869, went up to Oxford where he matriculated at Corpus Christi College and was awarded his B.A. in 1873 (Foster 1968). Next he studied for the priesthood, being ordained a deacon in 1874 and a priest in 1875. Initially he worked as a curate at St Paul's in Upper Holloway until 1876, and then became a tutor at the Church Mission Society College in Islington. This was the same institution at which the Rev. Painter had studied some 20 years earlier. Linton moved to Derbyshire in 1886 to become vicar of Shirley (Crockford's 1898). A year later he married Alice Shirley in Oxford. She was the elder sister of the 11th Earl Ferrers, and came from a wealthy family that held the living of Shirley, so his appointment as vicar there was undoubtedly no coincidence. They had only one child, Viola Marion Linton, born in 1892. Linton remained vicar at Shirley until his death in 1908 (Linton, E. 1908), and is buried in a rather plain grave, near the church on its northern side.

The Rev. W.R. Linton from an obituary by his brother (Linton, E. 1908)

We do not know how Linton's botanical interests arose; they appear to have developed from a love of walking and mountaineering. By 1881 they seem to have been sufficiently well-developed for him to undertake a walking tour of the Holy Land. On this trip he collected so many botanical specimens that the local Arabs christened him the *"Father of Cabbages"* (Linton, E. 1908). Soon after his return to England he made regular visits to the Scottish Highlands with his elder brother, the **Rev. Edward F. Linton** (Crockford's 1908). So began his studies of British plants and in particular of brambles (*Rubus* spp.), hawkweeds (*Hieracium* spp.) and willows (*Salix* spp.). In 1890 he published a short article in the *Journal of Botany* describing a new species of hawkweed (*Hieracium holophyllum*). He discovered this in Dove Dale in 1887 with the **Rev.'s W.H. Purchas** and **A. Ley**. He went on to publish further papers on this genus, either on his own or with his brother, and in 1905 brought out his major work on the genus, *An Account of the British Hieracia*. It covered 124 species and 135 varieties and forms, and was the most useful work on the Hawkweeds for almost 50 years (Sell 1987). He also published sets of hawkweed and willow specimens with his brother, and sets of brambles with others. Later in life he became fascinated by mosses, and was a founder member of the Moss Exchange Club in 1896.

By about 1893 Linton seems to have formulated the idea of compiling a *Flora* for Derbyshire. This was formally announced in the *Journal of Botany* by Britten in 1896 and, until it was published in 1903, he personally covered the county visiting every parish. "*His method was to take farmhouse lodgings in some remote district, and explore systematically its neighbourhood...*" (Linton E. 1908). He also extensively worked through earlier references to the plants of the county, identifying first records and correcting the many errors he found, especially in the work of the Rev. Painter.

Linton and his 1903 Flora

Published in 1903, **Linton's *Flora of Derbyshire*** contained some 1,030 species of flowering plant and fern. He considered around 910 (88%) of these to be native, 70 (7%) aliens and 50 (5%) casuals. He also included mosses and liverworts, but these are not considered further here. For each species his accounts generally give county status, the date of the first Derbyshire record, and the habitats in which it occurs. These are followed by example records for each of the eight areas into which he subdivided the county, and which are loosely based on the underlying geology. He finally notes any local subspecies or varieties. Two maps of the county were included, as were illustrations of two plants he considered special to the area. *Rubus durescens*, a species of bramble described by him earlier and unique to Derbyshire, is illustrated in gold leaf on the *Flora's* cover. Inside he included a black and white line drawing of *Epipactis atroviridis*, which he regarded as a species new to science that grew locally. His bramble is still recognised as a true local species, but the orchid is no longer accepted as valid, being at most a form of the **Broad-leaved Helleborine** (*Epipactis helleborine*).

Linton considered his work to be not much more than a stage towards a complete account of the botany of the county, mainly because of the omission of fungi, lichens and algae. The *Flora's* introduction mentions 17 species of flowering plant which he felt had been overlooked. He believed they might yet be found,

Linton's 1903 *Flora of Derbyshire* showing *Rubus durescens* on the cover

because all occurred in adjacent counties. In fact seven, including **Chickweed-wintergreen** (*Trientalis europaea*) and **Annual Mercury** (*Mercurialis annua*), have subsequently been discovered in Derbyshire. Linton only included about 80 more species than Painter's 1889 *Flora*, and many of these were critical ones such as brambles or hawkweeds. So it was not in sheer numbers that Linton improved on Painter's work; rather, it was in his in-depth local knowledge of plants in the field. Linton included details of the habitats of each species, and more details of where each occurred in various parts of the

county. This was commented on at the time in Britten's (1903) review of the *Flora*. Britten was not wholly positive about Linton's work, in which he found "*a certain dryness*" of style and use of abbreviations extremely difficult to follow. On balance, however, he was complimentary of Linton's effort, especially since he had produced the whole work in just ten years. This superior appreciation of Linton's work continues to the present day; his *Flora* is still far better known and used than is Painter's.

Linton to Clapham's Flora 1903–1969

After Linton's *Flora* of 1903 there was no similar publication for another sixty six years until that edited by Professor Clapham appeared in 1969. There are many reasons for this hiatus, but there was certainly no lack of interest during this period. Botany was flourishing locally, whole new branches of the science were developing nationally, and there was a large increase in the number of professional botanists in museums and universities. These people were no longer just interested in the rather static aspect of which species grew where. Instead they were concerned with the more dynamic aspects of how plants interacted with one another and how they came to be where they are today. The first of these new dynamic branches was "**vegetation ecology**" – the study of which groups of plants occur together and why. The first major worker in this field locally was **Charles Edward Moss (1870–1930)**, curator of the Herbarium at the University of Cambridge and member of the British Vegetation Committee (Tansley 1931). He produced his work the *Vegetation of the Peak District* in 1913. This described the plant communities of both the White and Dark Peaks and contained the first vegetation maps of our area which showed the distribution of the various plant communities he recognised. He was also a significant contributor to Professor Tansley's *Types of British Vegetation,* published in 1911.

In 1938 **W.H. Pearsall (1891–1964)** became Professor of Botany at the University of Sheffield (Clapham 1971). He took over from **Professor Bentley**, under whose leadership there had been some ecological research. However Pearsall was himself an ecologist and this gave the subject a major boost. He initiated a series of studies in a number of ecological areas that have continued right into the 21st century. One such was the history of different vegetation types, or "**Quaternary ecology**". It had long been known that under many of the peats on the Derbyshire moors lay the remains of large trees, some with their roots still *in situ* within the underlying mineral soil. It was obvious that woodland had once occurred where moorland now lies. However, it had to await the development of **palynology** (pollen analysis) in Scandinavia earlier in the century for a method to permit the detailed study of vegetation history from peat deposits. Peat accumulates where waterlogged conditions prevent the decay of plant material and, as it accumulates, pollen that falls out of the air is trapped within it. It became possible to extract this pollen from the various layers of peat and to build up a picture of how pollen, and hence the vegetation that produced it, had changed over time.

Dr Vera Conway was the first to apply this technique in Derbyshire. She initially worked on Ringinglow Bog near Sheffield, and then on Kinder Scout and Bleaklow. Her results were published in a series of papers in the *Journal of Ecology* between 1947 and 1954. Later on **Dr John Tallis** (1964) of Manchester University studied various other local sites, including Featherbed Moss. Their work, and that of others, demonstrated how vegetation has altered since the last Ice Age (around 6000 BC), changing from wooded uplands to today's peat-covered moorlands (see **Chapter 1**).

In this early part of the 20th century, amateur field botany carried on alongside the professionals who were studying vegetation and peat deposits. Foremost in this, after Linton, was **Dr Eric Drabble (1877–1933)**. He was born in Chesterfield and studied botany at London University, obtaining a First Class Honours degree. He went on to teach botany in various colleges, becoming Head of the Botany Department in 1908 at the Northern Polytechnic in London. He contributed many plant records to Linton for his 1903 *Flora*, and continued to supply him with additional records after its publication. After Linton's death in 1908, Drabble published his new records in a series of papers from 1909 to 1916 in the *Journal of Botany*. These were written very much as "additions" to Linton's *Flora*, and added a number of new species to the county list, as well as extra records for species found in new geological districts. Later he changed his allegiance, publishing his discoveries in the *Journal of the Derbyshire Archaeological and Natural History Society* in 1917 and 1929. In between he produced a paper on Derbyshire pansies (*Viola* spp.), a group on which he was an expert. Drabble died in 1933, after which his work was taken up by the **Halls**, both father and son from Buxton, and by **Miss K.M. Hollick (1913–1993)** from Ashbourne. She was the first County Plant Recorder to be appointed by the Botanical Society of the British Isles (BSBI) – a post she fulfilled from 1949 until 1985 (McClintock & Burns 1995). Kathleen Hollick was also an accomplished ornithologist and artist, as well as a historian. She wrote a book about her local church (Hollick 1964), and is credited with only the second ever record for Griffon Vulture in Britain, seeing two birds at Ashbourne in 1927 (Frost 1978).

Miss K.M. Hollick, long-time county plant recorder, in her garden at Ashbourne in the mid 1970s (Stephen Jackson)

The Hollick family provides an interesting link across the 20th century, and between local and national botany. In 1906 the **Reverend W. Keble Martin (1877–1969)** was appointed curate at the parish church in Ashbourne (Mathew & Harrison 2004). Much later he published his accomplished set of paintings in *The Concise British Flora in Colour* (Martin 1965). He then published his autobiography in which he described drawing **Strawberry Clover** (*Trifolium fragiferum*) and **Knotted Pearlwort** (*Sagina nodosa*) from Ashbourne Green for that work while based here in Derbyshire (Martin 1968). He recounted how Dr Hollick, the local practitioner, took him for occasional rides in his dog-cart to any village he was visiting. This Dr Hollick was Miss Hollick's father who subsequently took her around on his own visits, too, so giving her the opportunity to botanise in different areas. Miss Hollick later became a botanical illustrator in her own right, although her published works were black and white line drawings rather than the coloured illustrations of Keble Martin. She provided illustrations for Butcher's 1961 *A New Illustrated British Flora,* and in the early 1960s began work on illustrations of alien plants for a projected volume by David McClintock. Unfortunately he died before it was completed, but her illustrations were later used in Clement *et al.'s* (2005) volume on alien species. She published regular botanical records for Derbyshire during the 1940s and was later to produce supplements to Clapham's 1969 *Flora*. She continued to live on in her father's Ashbourne home after his death. It was the magnificent red brick house adjacent to the church where she kept a noted flower garden and raised vegetables for the local school. Her garden was surrounded by a high brick wall, but was not as tall as she would have liked; she was regularly invaded by local youths during the annual Shrovetide football match.

Miss Hollick botanised mainly around Ashbourne where her father practiced, whereas the Halls who lived in Buxton predominantly searched out plants in the north of the county. **F.T. Hall (1881–1960)** and **R.H. Hall (1909–1998)** were also illustrators of plants, but by photography rather than drawings. It was the son, Bert Hall, who took the front cover photo of Jacob's-ladder for Clapham's *Flora of Derbyshire* and others that were used inside. He also wrote parts of **K.C. Edwards** 1962 Collins New Naturalist *The Peak District*. They published their observations on the flora of Buxton in the reports of the Botanical Exchange Club

Herbarium specimen of Chalk Fragrant-orchid (*Gymnadenia conopsea*) in Derby Museum collected by R.H. Hall & K.M. Hollick at Grin Wood Buxton in 1946

in the early 1940s. They both contributed to Clapham's *Flora* as members of the organising committee, but F.T. Hall died before the work was completed. **A.R.S. Proctor** was active in the Derby area where he was a botanical chemist who gave illustrated lectures on local plants. In 1927 he was involved in an "ecological survey of Derbyshire" for the **LMS (Derby) Natural History Society**, but it is not known what if anything became of this project.

In the first half of the 20th century, major changes were taking place nationally that would eventually have a significant impact on field botany in Derbyshire, just as they would everywhere else. Some were initiated by central government in the area of countryside protection and nature conservation, whilst amateur botanists initiated other changes in the field of plant recording. All were being led by the general public who were becoming increasingly interested in the outdoor environment, as evidenced by the famous mass trespass on Kinder Scout in 1932. Interest in the outdoors led to a greater concern for wildlife, including plants and their conservation. But all this was interrupted by the Second World War.

After World War II amateur naturalists, together with professional botanists in universities and museums, encouraged central government to start taking steps to protect nature. It responded with action as part of the reconstruction of the country. In 1949 an Act of Parliament was passed with all-party support, called the *National Parks and Access to the Countryside Act*. This set up the **Nature Conservancy** to run **National Nature Reserves** and also allowed the creation of National Parks, the first of which was established in the Peak District in 1951. Since both organisations needed data about where wild plants grew in order to protect them, this led to increased employment of professional botanists and naturalists. Subsequent to this, a number of non-governmental organisations (NGOs) were set up by interested amateurs to further protect the countryside and its wildlife. Foremost amongst these were the county Wildlife Trusts. Our own local Trust was established in 1962. Originally called the Derbyshire Naturalists' Trust, it is now known as the **Derbyshire Wildlife Trust**.

Shortly after government passed the National Parks Act, amateur and professional botanists from the BSBI and various universities held a conference in 1950. Entitled *Aims and Methods in the Study of the Distribution of British Plants*, one of its major themes was that Britain was languishing behind its continental compatriots in the study of plant distributions. Addressing the meeting, **Professor Arthur Roy Clapham (1904–1990)** of Sheffield University suggested the Society remedy this by publishing a set of national distribution maps based on the relatively new 10-kilometre grid squares system of the Ordnance Survey. His suggestion was taken up enthusiastically by the BSBI who set up a "Maps Committee", with Clapham as its secretary and a Maps Office with paid staff within the Botany School at Cambridge. Thus began the task of collecting records from the three thousand five hundred separate 10-kilometre squares (hectads) around the country. This herculean project was completed in just five years, using volunteers in every British county who together collected over one and a half million records. Data from Derbyshire were provided by our own "Flora Committee" and various individuals, including Miss K.M. Hollick, and were refereed by Professor Clapham and Dr C.D. Pigott. The results were published in 1962 as the *Atlas of the British Flora,* followed by the *Critical Supplement to the Atlas of the British Flora* in 1968 (Perring & Walters 1962, Perring 1968). In the latter work special mention was made of the studies of E.F. and W.R. Linton on critical species such as hawkweeds. All this recording effort gave a boost to field botany in general and to Derbyshire in particular, where work was already well underway for a new county *Flora*.

Clapham and his 1969 Flora

Unlike the earlier works of Painter (1889) and Linton (1903), the next *Flora of Derbyshire* was not the product of a single person, but of a group known as the "*Flora* Committee". It first met in Derby Museum in 1949 and continued to meet there until publication in 1969. It contained both local amateur field botanists and professionals, at least one of whom was of national standing: Professor Arthur Roy Clapham Ph.D. F.R.S. F.L.S. There were inevitably some tensions with this mixture of people. Professor Clapham wanted to include a series of vegetation studies in the *Flora* – as was eventually done – but others did not see this as relevant. The eventual publication of the

Clapham's 1969 *Flora of Derbyshire* with cover photo by R.H. Hall of Jacob's Ladder *Polemonium caeruleum*

1969 *Flora* of Derbyshire credited only Professor Clapham as the editor, something that upset a number of "*Flora* Committee" members who felt others had at least as much right as Clapham to be named as co-editors.

Arthur Roy Clapham (1904–1990), known generally by his second name, was born in Norwich, and was the eldest child of George Clapham, a schoolmaster. Roy was educated in Norwich and then at Downing College, Cambridge, where he developed his interest in both field and laboratory botany. After obtaining a doctorate at Cambridge in 1929, he worked at Rothamsted Research Station, and then taught at Oxford University Department of Botany. Whilst there he carried out and published a great deal of research, as well as being an outstanding lecturer and tutor. In 1944 he moved to take up the chair of botany at Sheffield University where he soon became an expert on the vegetation of Derbyshire. In Sheffield he developed the department built up by his predecessor W.H. Pearsall, author of Mountains and Moorland (1950), in both the teaching and research of plant ecology. Although he also encouraged research in plant ecology and field botany, he directed his own energies to completing with T.G. Tutin and E.F. Warburg their monumental identification work, *Flora of the British Isles*. First published in 1952, it had a second edition in 1962 and a third in 1987 with T.G. Tutin and D.M. Moore. Between 1959 and 1981 there were also cut-down versions for use in the field, known as an *Excursion Flora of the British Isles*. Affectionately known as "CTW" in its various guises, this book became the standard British *Flora* from 1952 until the publication of Clive Stace's *New Flora of the British Isles* in 1991. As mentioned above, from 1950 onwards Clapham played a major role in the production of the first *Atlas of the British Flora*. Outside the University he served on the committees of various national bodies and learned societies, such as the Nature Conservancy and the Peak District National Park. He was elected a Fellow of the Royal Society in 1959 and was appointed CBE in 1969. The achievements of Professor Clapham in building up the botany department in Sheffield meant that, by the time he retired in 1969, it had acquired both a national and international reputation for its work on plant ecology. After retirement he moved to Lancaster, where he died in 1990 (Pigott 1991).

The majority of the remaining members of the original "*Flora* Committee" were local amateur botanists. There was the father and son team, F.T. and R.H. Hall, plus Miss K.M. Hollick from Ashbourne and **Charles B. Waite (1904–1978)**, an industrial chemist who worked in the Sheffield steel industry. There was also **Mr A.L. Thorpe**, curator of Derby Museum at the time and secretary to the committee, plus seven other members. One such was **Frank W. Adams** from Sheffield who botanised with C.B. Waite and was responsible for extracting and converting many of Linton's published localities into 10km records, and for collating numerous others onto recording sheets. At the time of writing, Frank was the sole surviving member of the original "*Flora* Committee" that formed in 1949. Various others joined during the life of the Committee, including a number of Sheffield University botanists such as **Dr C.D. Pigott** and **Dr T.T. Elkington**. The latter joined in 1964, and became its executive editor. He was responsible for the large section on vegetation studies that caused such disquiet amongst the more traditional local botanists on the committee.

Published in 1969, this next incarnation of the *Flora of Derbyshire* contained accounts of 1,248 species of flowering plant and fern, broken down into 943 (76%) Native, 194 (16%) Established and 68 (5%) Casual, with the remainder unassigned (see **Chapter 6, Table 6.2**). The individual accounts were very much like those in Linton's *Flora*, except for the county being divided into thirty-three 10-kilometre grid squares (hectads), rather than his geologically based sub-divisions. Clapham's 33 grid squares were further organised into three groups. His "West" area roughly equated to the Peak District, his "East" to the Coal Measures and Magnesian Limestone, and his "South" to the rest of the county below Ashbourne and Derby. In the accounts a locality was given for each 10km grid square in which a plant occurred, apart from common species. Here the *Flora* would simply state "*Recorded for all squares except:*" Most localities were given as four-figure grid references (monads). It is not clear, however, exactly when these records date from; even the raw data sheets held at Derby Museum only sometimes showed a year. By implication the majority come from the twenty year period of the Committee i.e. 1949 to 1969. Where Linton (1903) had recorded a plant in an area from where there was no other modern record, he mentioned the fact. Clapham's *Flora* is silent on whether any records made between 1903 and 1949 were included. However, Hollick & Patrick (1980) state that 1930 was used as the earliest date for inclusion. No particular effort was given to referring to older records, other than those from Linton, or to give "first year recorded" dates. Considering Clapham's close involvement with the first national atlas of plant distributions, it is surprising no serious attempt was made to include distribution maps. In fact, only seventeen local maps were included, along with eleven from the national Atlas for comparison. It is worth noting that Miss Hollick once commented that, when they began work on the *Flora*, grid references were not used. The metric Ordnance Survey grid system we all know and love today was only introduced to British maps after the Second World War, the first appearing in Derbyshire in 1947. The raw data sheets collated for the *Flora* are held to this day with the herbarium and other biological records in Derby Museum's Natural Science office. However this team of two, and then one person, was finally dismantled altogether during stringent council budget cuts in 2011, so the future use of the collections and data is no longer as sure as it once was. Derby Museum published Clapham's *Flora* in 1969, and many of the copper printing blocks and Committee correspondence are included in its archive.

Clapham's *Flora* dealt entirely with vascular plants, or "higher plants" as they are often called *i.e.* flowering plants, conifers, ferns and fern allies. He included nothing about the lower plants (mosses, lichens, algae). Linton (1903) and Painter (1902) both covered the mosses and liverworts, but no one had attempted a lichen *Flora* until **David Hawksworth** published a major paper in The Lichenologist in 1969.

Clapham to the current Flora

All *Floras* stimulate recording after their publication as people realise, all too late, that certain plants or their favourite localities have been omitted. This was certainly the case in Derbyshire after Clapham's *Flora*. And so in 1974 **Mrs Susan J. Patrick** (nee Herriott) and Miss Kathleen Hollick collaborated to produce a first *Supplement to Clapham's Flora* (Patrick & Hollick 1974). Sue had joined Derby Museum in 1968 as Keeper of Natural History and had helped with the final preparation of Clapham's *Flora*. Miss Hollick, as BSBI county plant recorder, had taken on the role of keeping records up-to-date following its publication. She did this by maintaining a set of cards in Derby Museum, one for each species of vascular plant in the

county, to which were added new 10km records from any of the county's grid squares as she received them. By this time records were increasingly being made on "tick cards" produced by the BSBI on which all species seen in a given site or grid square could be quickly marked off. As data continued to come in, they produced a second supplement covering new records between 1974 and 1979 (Hollick & Patrick 1980). Mrs Patrick also published a short note on the botanical collections at Derby Museum in 1979.

The second Supplement contained the first significant set of county Dandelion records, produced by **Roy Smith**, who had begun studying the critical genera of *Taraxacum, Hieracium* and *Rubus* in Derbyshire. No doubt this series of supplements would have continued had not Mrs Patrick left Derby and emigrated to Australia in 1982, where she carried on her career as a botanist and botanical artist in Perth. Meanwhile Miss Hollick continued maintaining the cards at Derby Museum as county recorder well into the mid-1980s, but eventually had to give up due to ill-health. She was replaced briefly by **Mrs Ailsa Lee** (nee Burns) and she, in turn, by Roy Smith in 1991 who continued in post until 1996. Clapham's 1969 *Flora* was reprinted as a facsimile copy in 1992.

In addition to the work of Miss Hollick and Mrs Patrick, which was centred on Derby Museum, there was a considerable volume of activity elsewhere in the county at that time. Professional botany was more prevalent now that there were biologists employed by a number of county organisations as well as those at local universities. These included the Peak District National Park, Derbyshire County Council, the Derbyshire Naturalists' Trust and the Nature Conservancy Council. Amateur botany was still being pursued, and a number of local naturalist organisations, including the **Sorby Society** in Sheffield, and the **Natural History Societies** in **Derby**, **Long Eaton** and **New Mills** all catered for this interest. Some of the more important pieces of work carried out by these organisations and people are detailed below.

Professional botany was led by the school of plant ecology developed by Professor Clapham at Sheffield University, which continued after he left in 1969 under **Professor A.J. Willis** (Davy 2006). Amongst those who worked here at this time were **P.S. Lloyd**, **J.P. Grime** and **I.H. Rorison** who published on grasslands in the Sheffield area in 1971. Elsewhere, C.D. Pigott (1969) from the University of Lancaster demonstrated that both species of Lime (*Tilia cordata* and *T. platyphyllos*) were native to our local woodlands; while D.W. Shimwell (1974) was studying the effect of sheep grazing on blanket peat erosion in Edale.

In 1974 David Hawksworth published a first supplement to his *Lichen Flora of Derbyshire,* to which **Oliver Gilbert** added a second supplement in 1983. In 1981 **Penny Anderson** and **D.W. Shimwell** published their *Wild Flowers and other Plants of the Peak District*. She was, and is, a leading local ecological consultant. Despite the title, which suggests it is a *Flora* for the Peak District, their book is really about the vegetation of the region and its development since the last ice age. It is still the best introduction to the subject. Another, albeit more populist book which described the county's vegetation, was *The Nature of Derbyshire*. This was edited by **Dr Trevor Elkington** of Sheffield University for the Derbyshire Naturalists' Trust in 1986 and contained chapters by various local experts.

In the late 1980s two *Floras* were published that covered discrete parts of Derbyshire. In 1988 **Margaret Shaw** edited *A Flora of the Sheffield Area* for the Sorby Society which covered a large area in north-east Derbyshire down to Chesterfield and Chatsworth. It gave distribution maps of some 400 species, based on monads (1 × 1km squares), along with current and some older records going back 200 years. In 1989 **Keith Futter** and **Peter Raynes** privately published *The Flora of Derby* which was part of the result of a two year study on the wildlife of the City of Derby. This was a Community

Programme Scheme under the auspices of the Derbyshire Wildlife Trust. Although species entries are very brief, and generally reduced to a pair of symbols for habitat and abundance, the work gives a fascinating snapshot of the flora of the City at this point in time. A number of garden plants are included, but some doubt has been cast on a few of the more unusual records.

As previously mentioned, the advent of multiple distribution maps in the first national Atlas of plant distribution (Perring & Walters 1962) had very little effect on Clapham's *Flora of Derbyshire*, but it did herald a change in other county *Floras*. John Dony's 1967 *Flora of Hertfordshire* was the first to make extensive use of distribution dot maps based on tetrads (units of 2 × 2km). However, these were all plotted by hand and were completely separated from the species accounts at the end of the book. It was only with the advent of computers that distribution maps became fundamental and integral parts of county *Floras*. The 1971 *Flora of Warwickshire* by Cadbury *et al.* was the first to do this. Unfortunately its authors were rather too ambitious in using many different map symbols to show both habitats and distribution, which tended to obscure far more than they revealed. Later *Floras* used simpler dot maps, while cheaper and better printing methods allowed *Floras* to develop the more modern layout of species accounts adjacent to the relevant maps. Many, like ours, are indebted to **Dr Alan Morton** for his superb plotting program called DMAP. Many of its mapping features were modified in response to specific suggestions coming from our project, especially the ability to overlay symbols from two different time periods.

The 1970s and 1980s probably represented the zenith of field botany in Derbyshire. There was an increasing interest during those 20 years amongst the general population, as evidenced by the growth of concern for nature conservation, and a vigorous programme of academic research based at local universities. Biological Records Centres (BRCs) had their beginnings in local museums at this time, too. The availability of inexpensive desktop computers and the introduction in 1993 of RECORDER software at Derby Museum gave a powerful kick to the rapid processing and mapping of botanical records, which again lent support to a desire to produce a revised *Flora of Derbyshire*. However, by the latter half of the 1980s field botany was becoming less important at universities. Nowhere was this more marked than at the University of Sheffield where, in 1988, the Department of Botany disappeared to become part of a new Department of Animal and Plant Sciences. Closer to home, the small plant collection at the University of Derby was transferred to Derby Museum's herbarium in the 1990s, although in 2011 the Museum itself axed most of its expert curatorial staff following the UK economic downturn, including one of the authors.

The 21st century (2000+)

The 2015 *Flora of Derbyshire*
The idea for this *Flora* arose in the mid-1990s when the Botanical Society of the British Isles (now Botanical Society of Britain and Ireland) sought help to collect data for a second national atlas of British plants – a project they called "**Atlas 2000**". As usual, they turned to their network of county recorders. In Derbyshire this was **Roy Smith**. He, with others in the county, namely **Nick Moyes**, Keeper of Natural Sciences at Derby Museum, and **Dr Alan Willmot**, a lecturer in Biology at Derby University, saw this as an opportunity to do more. They decided to make the work of collecting data for the national atlas the start of a much larger project to produce a new *Flora* for Derbyshire. However, despite already having carried out a lot of the preparatory recording work, Roy felt unable to devote the time or resources to collect and prepare data for both the new national atlas and a new local *Flora*. He therefore stood

down as county recorder and suggested that Dr Willmot should take on the role, which he duly did in 1996.

Despite the intense recording activity that then continued for many years behind the scenes, as far as new publications were concerned, this was a relatively quiet time. *Endangered Wildlife in Derbyshire* edited by Dr Trevor Elkington and Dr Alan Willmot was published by the Derbyshire Wildlife Trust in 1996. This was essentially the first **Local Red Data Book** for a wide range of organisms. The section on vascular plants was written by **Mrs Pat Brassley**, the long-time conservation officer of the Derbyshire Wildlife Trust. In 2001 **Leonora Dobson's** *Common Trees in the Peak District* was published by the Sorby Natural History Society of Sheffield. This was a brief identification guide to some 40 of the common trees and shrubs of the area. It followed the appearance in 2000 of **Harding & Oxley**'s *Wild Flowers of the Peak District*, a selection of sixty characteristic species with hand-drawn illustrations by a range of Sheffield-based botanical artists.

Work to prepare for the current *Flora of Derbyshire* led first to the publication of *A Checklist of the Plants of Derbyshire* (Moyes & Willmot 2002), followed by an Update in 2007. In the same year they published an interim online *Flora* of draft maps and accounts, which was made available on Derby City Council's website. This was followed two years later in 2009 by a major piece of work by the present authors to publish online a new and more critically assessed *Red Data List of Derbyshire's Vascular Plants*. Records held for all the species identified in the *Red Data List* were supplied electronically to Derbyshire Wildlife Trust, The Peak District National Park, Derbyshire County Council and Natural England. By the time the present *Flora* was ready for publication, some 880,000 records had been computerised, spanning over 400 years.

This current *Flora* contains some 1,919 separate accounts which cover 1044 Native plants, 425 Established or introduced plants and 433 Casuals plus a few unassigned plants. When comparing these numbers with those included in previous *Floras*, three important changes in recording should be remembered. Firstly, many more so-called "**microspecies**" of critical genera such as Dandelions (*Taraxacum*) have been recorded, partly because there are now far better identification works available. Secondly, many species once regarded as native are now thought of as "ancient introductions". And finally, there has been an increase over the years in people's willingness to record non-native and planted species. Further details of the development of the current work are given in **Chapter 6**, with acknowledgements to all those involved at the back of this book.

Plant recording does not stop with the publication of this *Flora*. With national recording schemes still running, surveying in Derbyshire continues to this day with data being fed into the national BSBI on-line mapping system. With the redundancy after 25 years of Derby Museum's Senior Keeper of Natural Sciences, Nick Moyes, and thus the sudden demise of the Derbyshire Biological Records Centre, responsibility for collation of vascular plant records has been taken over by the county plant recorder, Alan Willmot. This involved a change of software from RECORDER to MAPMATE, but now means records can be uploaded electronically to a central data store and viewed on-line within just a few weeks of having been made in the field.

Looking back across the centuries we have seen considerable changes in the way plant information has been collected and made available, and in the reasons for recording it in the first place. With GPS-enabled smart phones now being used by some national plant recording schemes which can put mapped data online within minutes of being collected, we cannot help but wonder what techniques those who follow us might utilise to produce and present the next reworking of *The Flora of Derbyshire*.

Appendix: Derbyshire plants in British Herbaria

Graeme L.D. Coles

The former practice of plant collectors exchanging specimens with each other means that Derbyshire specimens, particularly of the more attractive and rare species such as Jacob's-ladder (*Polemonium caeruleum*) and Nottingham Catchfly (*Silene nutans*), can be expected to crop up in any major collection of herbarium specimens. All the large national collections therefore have examples of the county's plants*.

The following is a list of the more important collections, which either concentrate on the County's plants or have interesting specimens.

Birmingham University has a large collection (>1000) of William Hunt Painter's (1835–1910) Derbyshire plants.

Bolton Museum purchased the Philip Brookes Mason (1842–1903) herbarium in 1907 which included Derbyshire plants collected by himself and John T. Harris, Arthur Henfrey and William Garneys.

Derby Museum has important and substantial numbers of local herbarium specimens from John Wesley Carr (1862–1939), Thomas Gibbs (1865–1919), Kathleen Margaret Hollick (1913–1993), William Hunt Painter, William Henry Purchas (1823–1903) and Joseph Whittaker (1813–1894). Also incorporated are specimens from the University of Derby given to it in 1993, and many sheets of ferns from Dr A. Willmot, donated in 1996.

Liverpool Museum has the William Harrison (1873–1960) herbarium including Derbyshire plants and the collection of Hawkweed (*Hieracium*) species collected by William Richardson Linton. Some 200 of his Derbyshire specimens, determined by P.D. Sell or J.N. Mills, have been imported into the database used to prepare this *Flora*.

Dorman Museum, Middlesbrough has the herbarium of Margaret Stovin (1756–1846) with many important early Derbyshire specimens, collected mainly in the 1820s and 1830s. These include scarce natives, such as Upright Chickweed (*Moenchia erecta*)

collected near her home at Newbold in 1828 and Small-flowered Sweet-briar (*Rosa micrantha*) from Leahurst collected 1833 as well as critical genera such as hawkweeds (*Hieracium*) and brambles (*Rubus*), and some aliens that were not included by Linton in his *Flora*, such as Creeping Bellflower (*Campanula rapunculoides*).

Manchester Museum acquired the collection of **Repton School** in unusual circumstances. This had suddenly been disposed of to a car boot sale in 2001 and what survived was offered to Derby Museum. However some 800 sheets from 1910–1950 found their way to Manchester Museum instead, where they now reside. Some 20% are from Derbyshire.

Nottingham Natural History Museum has John Hagger's (1824–1895) herbarium of Derbyshire plants.

Oxford University has G.C. Druce's herbarium which includes John Ansell's collection of Derbyshire plants dating from 1820–1840.

Sheffield Museum has some of the oldest surviving Derbyshire specimens, namely those collected by Jonathan Salt (1759–1815) dating from the late 18th and early 19th century, and listed, although none too accurately, in the catalogue titled *List of plants collected in the neighbourhood of Sheffield chiefly by Jonathan Salt* (1889). The museum also has two other herbaria containing Derbyshire plants, those of Charles Byron Waite (1904–1978) collected mainly in the 1950s and 1960s, and Albert William Bartlett (1875–1943), whose specimens date largely from the period 1910 to 1914.

Sheffield University has three herbaria containing Derbyshire specimens, those of Trevor Thomas Elkington, John O. Comber (1869–1930) and Charles Waterfall (1851–1938).

University College of Wales, Aberystwyth, has some of William Hunt Painter's Derbyshire plants.

---

* Authors' footnote: During the course of computerising past records for this current Flora, the authors were not able to extract historical data from all the herbaria listed above. Further study may well push back some of the earliest dates of plants being recorded in Derbyshire. Surprisingly we have yet to locate a single Derbyshire specimen of Lady's Slipper (*Cypripedium calceolus*) in any UK herbarium, and would welcome records should they ever be unearthed.

CHAPTER 4

Conserving Derbyshire's flora

Kieron Huston [1]

Introduction

The richness and abundance of our county's plants has been much reduced since Clapham published his *Flora of Derbyshire* in 1969, and even more so since Linton's in 1903. In the intervening century Derbyshire's population has doubled to just over one million, and there has been an agricultural revolution. Villages, towns and cities have grown, and there have been new roads, quarries, mines, ironworks, railways and business parks, as well as increases in many forms of outdoor recreation. The pressure on wildlife has been relentless.

The habitats we think of as *semi-natural,* or even on rare occasions *natural,* have been replaced, modified and reduced in size till in many places they have all but vanished. They have retreated to the margins of our landscapes, such as the steep slopes, crags and rock outcrops, the inhospitable marshes and the upland moors and bogs. Hardest hit have been Derbyshire's lowlands, especially in the east and south where intensive farming combined with industry and denser human population has squeezed and corralled the natural environment into ever smaller spaces. Many waterbodies, watercourses and wetlands have suffered from nutrient enrichment and half Derbyshire's ancient woodlands have been replanted.

The first step in conserving biodiversity is to know what species we have, and what we have lost. Understanding which plants are the most threatened and which are showing the greatest local decline is central to taking the right action. Helping us with this task is the *Red Data List of Derbyshire's Vascular Plants* (Moyes & Willmot 2009). This is a valuable document, naming all the native plant species with a national conservation status, as well as allocating local conservation statuses to those others that are scarce or locally declining within Derbyshire. Reproduced with revisions in **chapter 9**, it lists 47 species as "Locally Extinct", including Lesser Butterfly-orchid (*Platanthera bifolia*), Lady's-slipper (*Cypripedium calceolus*), Mountain Avens (*Dryas octopetala*), Mousetail (*Myosurus minimus*), Bog-myrtle (*Myrica gale*) and Greater Water-parsnip (*Sium latifolium*). Another 198 species are on the *Red List* because they fall into various categories of rarity and/or recent decline, usually as a direct consequence of human activities. (*N.B.* A further 59 species were added to this list in late 2014 following the publication of the first England Red Data List (Stroh *et al.* 2014). Today, as many as one in six of Derbyshire's native plants have a national or local conservation status. We also know that semi-natural habitat continues to be agriculturally "improved", built upon, unsympathetically managed or just simply abandoned.

Despite this, Derbyshire has still managed to retain some wonderful habitats and wildlife sites, and even a few small areas of intact semi-natural landscape such as the now largely protected limestone dales. In recent decades the winding down of Britain's industrial heartland has allowed nature to reassert itself amid the ashes of collieries, the dust of worked out and moth-balled limestone and sand quarries, and the watery gravel pits of the Trent Valley. New nature reserves and Country Parks have emerged in

their place. Financial incentives for land owners have also played a positive role through both **agri-environment** and **woodland grant schemes**. Since 1990 thousands of hectares of land have been managed as part of these agreements. The importance of managing land for wildlife has also been accepted as a key objective for the way publicly-owned land is now looked after.

This chapter examines in more detail the recent changes in semi-natural habitats. It also considers the past and present conservation efforts to protect, restore and enhance those habitats across Derbyshire. We also look at the challenges ahead, and discuss the opportunities and thinking that may determine what Derbyshire's flora looks like in the future.

Derbyshire's conservation roots

The seeds of nature conservation were sown back in the 1800s, brought about in part by changing values and ideals, and a growing interest in the natural world. Many societies were formed during the late 1800s and early 1900s such as the *Derbyshire Archaeological and Natural History Society*, founded in 1878. Derbyshire's first *Flora* by W.H. Painter was published in 1889 (see **Chapter 3**). The growing threats to the plants and vegetation communities of the British Isles were recognised during this period, often relating to over-collection, but also to new pressures on habitats from development and industry. In the 1930s and 40s nature preservation and the protection of visual amenity as well as access to the countryside had become significant issues. In 1925 the *Council for the Preservation of Rural England* (CPRE) was founded and one of its first acts in 1931 was to purchase 1,087 acres of the Longshaw Estate, now owned and managed by the *National Trust*. Around this time the rambling movement was fighting for better access to the countryside and in particular to the moors around Sheffield and Manchester. Conflicts with private landowners led to the historic Kinder Scout Trespass in 1932, an event still commemorated today. CPRE and others continued to promote the idea of National Parks and in 1944 published an influential report, *The Peak District: A National Park* (CPRE 1944). Other reports were prepared by John Dower, though not published in full till later (Dower 1945, 1958, Hobhouse 1947). These culminated in the *National Parks and Access to the Countryside Act* 1949, paving the way for the appointment of a *National Parks Commission* and the establishment of the *Nature Conservancy*. In 1951 the **Peak District** became Britain's first National Park, extending over 80,000ha of upland limestone and gritstone, of which 60% lies within Derbyshire. Concurrent with efforts to promote and establish policy for National Parks were a series of reports on nature conservation produced during and after the war. The *Nature Conservancy* (it has since been renamed several times and is today known as *Natural England*), were ultimately charged with identifying and selecting the best examples of semi-natural and natural vegetation communities across the UK. Much of this work was undertaken in the 1950s and 1960s, and by the early 1970s most of the key sites we know today had been selected for statutory designation as **Sites of Special Scientific Interest (SSSIs)** and, in

1 Kieron Huston is Senior Local Wildlife Sites Officer for Derbyshire Wildlife Trust. The maps and data presented in this chapter relate to the Trust's area of responsibility – namely modern geographic Derbyshire. The botanical vice-county 57 is not included in the statistics presented here.

the case of many in the Dales, as part of the country's network of **National Nature Reserves (NNRs)**.

Local Non-governmental Conservation Organisations (NGOs)

Whilst the above legislative changes brought about significant progress, many important sites continued to be lost or remained threatened. In 1960 a threat to a botanically-rich site in south Derbyshire, known as Ticknall Limeyards, resulted in a group of concerned individuals coming together to oppose a plan to use the site to tip fly ash. The proposal was ultimately rejected at public enquiry. Those who fought it went on to found the **Derbyshire Naturalists' Trust** in 1962, and the Limeyards became the Trust's first reserve (Elkington 1986, Brown 2012). Known today as **Derbyshire Wildlife Trust**, it now manages 42 nature reserves covering 680ha. These include many SSSIs such as Chee Dale, Priestcliffe Lees, Rose-end Meadows, Hilton Gravel Pits and Carver's Rocks, as well as other floristically diverse sites such as Long Clough, Lea Woods, Avenue Washlands, Erewash Meadows and Golden Brook. Other non-governmental organisations also play a significant role in land management, not least the **National Trust** which owns iconic sites such as Dove Dale, Biggin Dale, Calke Park, Hardwick Hall Estate, Longshaw Estate and, together with the **RSPB**, manages the Eastern Moors, including the botanically-rich Leash Fen. The organisation **Plantlife** owns and manages Deepdale near Sheldon – another classic limestone dale. **The Woodland Trust** was formed in 1972 and now owns and manages nine woodlands from Glossop to Swadlincote, including several important ancient woodlands: Burr Wood, Bow Wood, Birch Wood, Halldale Wood and Tom Wood.

Smaller groups and societies such as the **Derbyshire Flora Group**, **Sorby Natural History Society**, **Matlock Field Club**, **Ashbourne Field Club** and the **Derby** and the **Long Eaton Natural History Societies** have also played an important role in expanding and improving our understanding of the county's plants. Much of our knowledge about where species occur is dependent upon the observations of these volunteers. Their data also provides an invaluable early warning system for identifying threats and declines. In some cases key individuals have helped to improve our understanding of habitat management. One such was Eileen Thorpe who promoted better management of ash woodlands at High Tor and along the Via Gellia.

Between 1980 and 2000 there was an increased focus on plant recording, and particular efforts were made to locate and record rare or uncommon taxa. In some cases a species was subject to in-depth study or monitoring, such as Dark-red Helleborine (*Epipactis atrorubens*) and Globeflower (*Trollius europaeus*) at Priestcliffe Lees. The records collected during this time were used in landmark publications such as the *Scarce Plants in Britain* (Stewart *et al.* 1994) and *Endangered Wildlife in Derbyshire* (Elkington & Willmot 1996). This last publication was Derbyshire's first Red Data Book and is still a vital reference today, despite the vascular plant lists being twice revised since. More recently the records collected were used in the *New Atlas of the British and Irish Flora* (Preston *et al.* 2002) and now for this new *Flora of Derbyshire*.

Nature conservation designations

Within the Derbyshire Peak District, **Sites of Special Scientific Interest** (SSSIs) now cover 32% of the land. These consist mainly of moorland and blanket bog habitats in the uplands, typically above 300m, but also include nationally significant habitats such as calcareous grassland and ancient woodlands, as well as many upland ash woods, hay meadows, fens and parklands (see **Figure 4.1**).

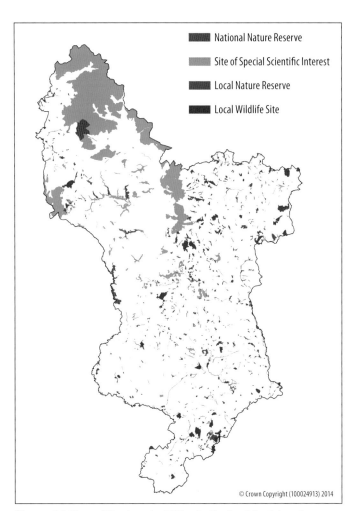

National Nature Reserve

Site of Special Scientific Interest

Local Nature Reserve

Local Wildlife Site

© Crown Copyright (100024913) 2014

Figure 4.1 Map of Designated Sites in Derbyshire (showing SSSIs, NNRs, LNRs and Local Wildlife Sites).

By complete contrast, in that part of Derbyshire outside of the Peak District, the SSSI land cover is only 0.77%. Sites include a reservoir, old parkland, ancient woodland and a few small areas of neutral and limestone grasslands and lowland fen. This disparity is not entirely due to the lack of qualifying habitats in the lowlands, but it does reflect a strong historic focus on the Peak District. Encouragingly, since 2000, a further twelve new SSSIs covering 209ha have been designated of which 130ha are in the lowlands. These include Wall Lands Meadows SSSI and Crich Chase SSSI. Their ecological interest is primarily lowland meadow and ancient woodland habitat.

Crich Chase Meadows, part of a new 118ha SSSI in Lowland Derbyshire
(Kieron Huston)

There are also four **National Nature Reserves (NNR)** in Derbyshire covering 1,810.5ha. One lies in the south of the county at Calke Park, while the other three are all within the Peak District National Park. These are Dove Dale NNR, Kinder Scout NNR and Derbyshire Dales NNR (itself comprising five quite separate dales).

More recently, habitat protection has been increased through the designation of **Special Areas of Conservation (SAC)** under The Habitats Directive (Council Directive 92/43/EEC of May 1992). This required EU Member States to create a network of protected wildlife areas, known as Natura 2000, across the *European Union*. Across geographic Derbyshire, SACs cover 26,960ha (27,878ha within "Greater Derbyshire") and generally encompass the existing SSSI network within the Peak District. Collectively the National Park, SSSI, NNR and SAC designations all confer significant protection and responsibility for good management to these sites.

As early as the 1980s it was clear that there was an urgent need for a non-statutory designation to complement the statutory sites. Understandably this was felt most acutely in areas outside the Peak District National Park where at that time very few sites had any nature conservation recognition at all. After a comprehensive habitat survey in 1983 and 1984, Derbyshire's **Local Wildlife Site** system was born. Today there are 1,175 sites extending to over 10,000ha across much of Derbyshire (**Figure 4.1**) including parts of the broader Peak District, but not within the Peak District National Park itself, which operates a separate but similar system of habitat inventories (DWT 2014).

The Local Wildlife Site designation is a "non-statutory" one. It affords a degree of protection from activities that require planning permission, but does not confer any protection from normal land management activities, and there are no specific incentives for management, other than through agri-environment schemes and woodland grant schemes. Whilst many of the best examples of remaining semi-natural habitat have now been found and designated, there are still sites, especially small grasslands, awaiting further survey work. Equally, there are many new areas of interest on brownfield sites to be found. The system also enables a dialogue with landowners and more effective targeting of resources as well as the opportunity to respond to planning applications and other proposals.

Lastly it is worth highlighting the presence of 49 **Local Nature Reserves (LNR)** in geographic Derbyshire (or 55 LNRs across "Greater Derbyshire" as used in this *Flora*.) Many of these LNRs are located in the east and south of the County especially Erewash Valley, Amber Valley and Derby City. The designation, which is a statutory one, has been helpful in raising awareness about wildlife and attracting project funding. In terms of planning, the level of protection in practice seems to be a little above that of a Local Wildlife Site, but below that of a SSSI.

The changing fortunes of the county's vegetation and flora

The one factor driving the need for site designations since the 1960s has been the frightening decline of many semi-natural habitats of conservation significance. These declines are rooted in a combination of technological advances in agricultural methods and changes to policies that started during the Second World War when the country needed to be more self-sufficient in food production. In the decades that followed, farming changed forever and became increasingly intensive. Meadows were improved, wetlands drained, herbicide and fertiliser use increased, and fields became bigger at the expense of hedgerows and field margins. During the same period upland moors and bogs were afforested and ancient woodlands were converted to plantations. At the same time many traditional woodland management practices ceased. Habitats have been, and continue to be, adversely affected by residential, business and industrial development, resulting in loss and damage to sites in and around urban areas, as well as across the wider countryside due to new infrastructure needs. Mineral extraction, in particular, has impacted on many parts of the County. Land abandonment has also become a problem, effecting marginal farmland and land on the urban fringes as well as bits of land cut off from mainstream agriculture.

The Derbyshire Red Data List

The impact of these changes on semi-natural habitats and the plants that they support has resulted in significant declines in many species. The 2009 *Red Data List of Derbyshire's Vascular Plants* identifies 245 native species in six categories of conservation significance; see **Table 4.1** and **Chapter 9** for further details (Moyes & Willmot 2009). The most worrying aspect of this list is the local extinction of so many species over the last 46 years. The current rate of extinction of vascular plants in Derbyshire is thought to be 0.31 species per year (Plantlife 2012). Whilst this is lower than the average for counties in England, it is still a cause for concern, especially when so many species are still declining. However, at least one species thought to have been locally extinct in Derbyshire, Lesser Twayblade (*Neottia cordata*), was recently rediscovered, and others may yet be found.

Table 4.1 **Categories of *Derbyshire Red Data List* plants showing number of species in each category (from Moyes & Willmot 2009).** See species lists in **Chapter 9**.

The *Red Data List* is divided into six categories as follows:	
Category 1 Internationally Rare (IUCN Red Lists, EU Habitats Directive or Bern Convention)	2 taxa
Category 2 Nationally Threatened (all IUCN categories CR = Critically Rare; EN = Endangered; VU = Vulnerable and NT = Near Threatened)	59 taxa
Category 3 Nationally Rare or Scarce (NR = in 15 or less GB hectads; NS = in 16 to 100 GB hectads)	24 taxa
Category 4 Locally Rare (known in 3 or fewer 1km squares/monads from 1969 onwards, and not in any of the above categories)	24 taxa
Category 5 Locally Scarce or Locally Declining (a: known in 4 to 10 1km squares from 1969 onwards and not in a category above or b: shown to be exhibiting serious recent local decline)	89 taxa
Category 6 Locally Extinct (any native taxon recorded in Derbyshire, but not found since 1968)	47 taxa
TOTAL	**245 taxa**

The distribution of extant *Red Data List* plants across the county is illustrated by **Figure 4.2**. Major hotspots occur within the limestone dales and ancient woodlands of the White Peak and parts of the Magnesian Limestone, the Peak Fringe and the eastern end of the Trent Valley. More limited and scattered hotspots also occur in the Dark Peak and Coal Measures, but the northern Dark Peak, most of the Claylands, extensive areas of the Coal Measures and much of the rest of the Trent valley support few notable concentrations of *Red Data List* plants.

Analysis carried out by Moyes and Willmot whilst preparing the *Red Data List* revealed that 57% of Red List plants have decreased nationally and/or within Derbyshire since 1969. These declines are noticeable within many different habitats, as **Figure 4.3** highlights. It shows the most notable plant losses are associated with grasslands, fens and swamps, disturbed ground and open water. (*N.B.* A further 59 species were added in late 2014 following the publication of the first *England Red Data List* (Stroh *et al.* 2014), and these include a significant number of heathland and moorland species.

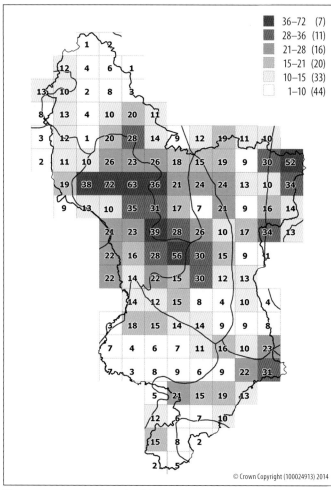

Figure 4.2 Count of *Derbyshire Red Data List* species recorded within each 5km × 5km square in the county. (Bracketed figures indicate how many squares fall into each category. Newly identified English Red List species are not included on this map).

Figure 4.3 The status of *Derbyshire Red Data List* plants within broad habitat types, determined by both national trends (Preston *et al.* 2002) and apparent local change (Moyes & Willmot 2009).

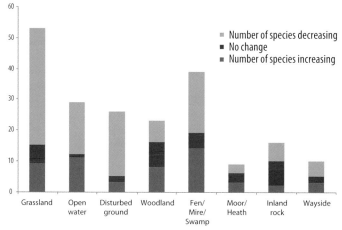

Distribution and state of plant habitats

Instead of mapping and identifying "hotspots" for Red List species, an alternative approach is to map plants which are simply "typical" of a particular habitat – so-called "**Habitat Indicator Species**". **Figures 4.4** to **4.10** highlight hotspots in species richness for plant assemblages indicative of broad habitat types.

These cover:

- Semi-natural grassland (**Figure 4.4**)
- Ancient woodland (**Figure 4.5**)
- Lowland fen & swamp (**Figure 4.6**)
- Open & running water (**Figure 4.7**)
- Arable (**Figure 4.8**)
- Open mosaic habitats (**Figure 4.9**)
- Moorland and heathland (**Figure 4.10**)

Each map shows the number of Habitat Indicator Species recorded within each tetrad (2km x 2km squares) between 1987 and 2011 (The numbers in brackets simply show how many tetrads fall into each category). The species used as indicators for each habitat are drawn from those used in the selection of Local Wildlife Sites in Derbyshire. A full list is provided in **Chapter 10**.

Grasslands

The extent of semi-natural grasslands within the modern geographic county of Derbyshire, including Derby is estimated to be about 13,500 hectares, of which 11,000ha falls inside the National Park and 2,500ha outside it. This includes both species-rich unimproved and semi-improved calcareous grassland, neutral grassland, plus around 9,000ha of acid grassland found predominantly in the uplands.

Grasslands are one of the most important habitats in Derbyshire, supporting over 300 native vascular plants. Fifty-four of these species are on the *Derbyshire Red List* and 38 of them (70%) are in decline either nationally, locally or both. It is likely that some twenty more threatened grassland species will also be added once the implications of the brand new *Vascular Plant Red List for England* are fully taken into consideration (Stroh *et al.* 2014). Historically, flower-rich semi-natural grasslands would once have been widespread, but by 1987 it was estimated that across England 95% had already gone (Fuller 1987). In Derbyshire a Phase I survey of grasslands was undertaken between 1997 and 1999 that covered the County south and east of the National Park. It highlighted an 80–91% decline in the extent of species-rich grassland in comparison to the early 1980s (Huston 2001). In the Peak District National Park another study revealed a 50% loss of flower-rich hay meadows between the mid 1980s and 1995–97 (Buckingham *et al.* 1997). These declines have continued into the 2000s despite additional resources targeted at the owners of key sites. In recent years a number of species-rich grasslands have been lost to agricultural intensification, whilst several other sites, both in the uplands and the lowlands, have been destroyed by ploughing (pers. com. R. Newman, PDNP). Other grasslands have been lost or have declined in biodiversity simply due to cessation of good management.

The impact of such extensive loss of semi-natural grassland across the County is clear, both from the number of *Red List* grassland plants, but also in the decline of more common and widespread species. This was highlighted by the PDNP 1997 Hay Meadow Study which revealed losses of between 54% and 95% amongst species like Lady's Bedstraw (*Galium verum*), Field Scabious (*Knautia arvensis*), Great Burnet (*Sanguisorba officinalis*), Rough Hawkbit (*Leontodon hispidus*) and even Common Knapweed (*Centaurea nigra*). Declines of common species such as Devil's-bit Scabious (*Succisa pratensis*), Meadow Saxifrage (*Saxifraga granulata*), Sneezewort (*Achillea ptarmica*) and Cowslip (*Primula veris*) have also been noted in the lowlands, and in south Derbyshire many of these are now either very rare or even absent.

Today, the most important areas for our remaining semi-natural grasslands are the White Peak and parts of the Peak Fringe and Magnesian Limestone. As **Figure 4.4** shows, these areas have recorded very high numbers of grassland indicator species

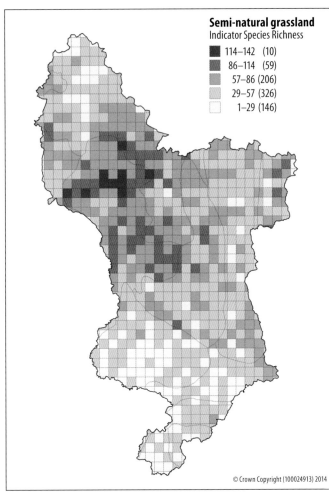

Semi-natural grassland
Indicator Species Richness

■ 114–142 (10)
▨ 86–114 (59)
▨ 57–86 (206)
▨ 29–57 (326)
□ 1–29 (146)

© Crown Copyright (100024913) 2014

Figure 4.4 Species richness of plants typically associated with semi-natural unimproved grasslands, showing the number of Habitat Indicator Species recorded in tetrads between 1987 and 2011. (Bracketed figures give a count of the tetrads falling into each category).

The Magnesian Limestone remains an important area for grassland despite having been intensively managed for many decades. The most notable site is Hollinhill and Markland Grips SSSI, but small species-rich remnants also occur along abandoned railway lines, on road verges and quarry edges. Thankfully, there have also been some gains through enlightened restoration and management of former collieries and limestone quarries. The Magnesian Limestone is important for several nationally threatened and scarce species found nowhere else in Derbyshire, most notably Soft-leaved Sedge (*Carex montana*) and Rare Spring-sedge (*Carex ericetorum*), both of which occur at Hollinhill and Markland Grips SSSI. The area is also home to important populations of Clustered Bellflower (*Campanula glomeratum*) and Saw-wort (*Serratula tinctoria*) both of which are in decline. Amongst the more characteristic and widespread plants associated with the Magnesian Limestone grasslands are Yellow-wort (*Blackstonia perfoliata*), which occurs here in relative abundance (but is a rarity on the Carboniferous Limestone further west), plus Bee Orchid (*Ophrys apifera*) which reaches its greatest abundance in the county at several locations in this Landscape Character Area. Many of the surviving sites are owned and managed by Derbyshire County Council.

Flower-rich grasslands are less common in the Coal Measures, but 21 *Red List* grassland species occur here, including Early-purple Orchid (*Orchis mascula*) and Pepper-saxifrage (*Silaum silaus*). There are also a number of diverse sites in the Dark Peak such as Goytside Meadows Local Nature Reserve in New Mills. The Erewash Valley remains an area of interest, though it is under growing pressure. To the south, in the Trent Valley and Claylands, flower-rich grassland has virtually disappeared, and even species like Devil's-bit Scabious (*Succisa pratensis*) and Great Burnet (*Sanguisorba officinalis*) have become rare.

Calaminarian grasslands associated with former lead mines are also worth a mention here as they support significant populations of two nationally scarce plants. These are Alpine Penny-cress (*Noccaea caerulescens*) and Spring Sandwort (*Minuartia verna*). These mineral-rich grasslands are very fragmented, and most examples are small, but they often occur in association with limestone grasslands and are to be found almost exclusively within the White Peak.

Ancient woodlands

Ancient woodlands cover 5,000ha in Derbyshire and support over 200 plant species, including 23 that are on the county *Red Data List*. As **Figure 4.5** shows, concentrations of ancient woodland indicator plants occur in the White Peak, Magnesian Limestone and the northern Peak Fringe, as well as in several larger woodlands in the south around Calke and Linton. The Derwent and Wye Valleys between Ambergate, Hathersage and Buxton are especially important areas. Elsewhere a combination of more isolated ancient woodlands and secondary woodlands support localised concentrations of typical woodland species such as in Derby, Erewash, the Claylands and in the south-west, close to the River Dove.

One of the main impacts upon ancient woodlands in the past 50 years has been their conversion to plantations. This has affected an estimated 2,000ha (40%) of this habitat in Derbyshire. Dense conifer plantations clearly have a detrimental impact upon most plants of the woodland field layer as well as on broad-leaved trees and shrubs. The impact on the field layer is somewhat reduced in Beech (*Fagus sylvatica*) and Sycamore (*Acer pseudoplatanus*) plantations, or where conifers stands were thinned early on, but they can still be significant. Invasive species such as Rhododendron (*Rhododendron ponticum*), Snowberry (*Symphoricarpos albus*) and

over the past 25 years. In the White Peak 38 *Red List* grassland plant species occur and many of the most important grassland assemblages are to be found here. Notable species include Frog Orchid (*Coeloglossum viride*), Burnt Orchid (*Neotinea ustulata*), Dark-red Helleborine (*Epipactis atrorubens*), Spring Cinquefoil (*Potentilla tabernaemontani*), Clustered Bellflower (*Campanula glomerata*), Pale St John's-wort (*Hypericum montanum*), Nottingham Catchfly (*Silene nutans*) and Globeflower (*Trollius europaeus*), to name but a few. The fact that more species-rich grasslands have survived in the White Peak is probably due to a mix of statutory protection (most of the limestone dales are designated as SSSI), geology (resulting in more difficult terrain) and the cooler, wetter climate. In some areas of the White Peak a combination of lead mining, small field sizes and thin soils has helped to reduce (though not eliminate) the vulnerability of grasslands to agricultural pressure. Despite this, much of the limestone plateau has been "improved" for agriculture, and is now species-poor.

The Peak Fringe is a predominantly gritstone area with many river and stream valleys, and a fairly cool and wet climate. It is characterised by numerous small meadows and pastures which often occupy marshy areas next to streams, or are to be found on thinner soils over steeper ground. Much of the Peak Fringe is relatively high, too, at between 150–300m. Over 200 grassland plants have been recorded, including 20 *Derbyshire Red List* species such as Greater Butterfly-orchid (*Platanthera chlorantha*), Marsh Arrowgrass (*Triglochin palustris*) and Pale Sedge (*Carex pallescens*).

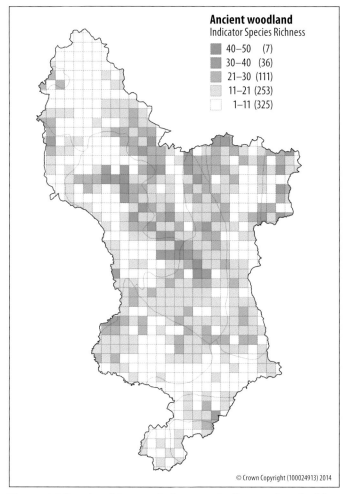

Ancient woodland
Indicator Species Richness

■	40–50	(7)
■	30–40	(36)
■	21–30	(111)
■	11–21	(253)
□	1–11	(325)

© Crown Copyright (100024913) 2014

Figure 4.5 Species richness of plants typically associated with ancient woodland, showing the number of Habitat Indicator Species recorded in tetrads between 1987 and 2011. (Bracketed figures give a count of the tetrads falling into each category).

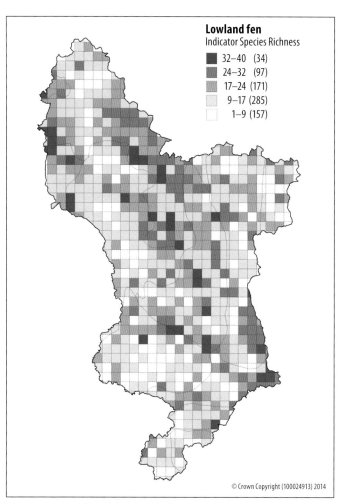

Lowland fen
Indicator Species Richness

■	32–40	(34)
■	24–32	(97)
■	17–24	(171)
■	9–17	(285)
□	1–9	(157)

© Crown Copyright (100024913) 2014

Figure 4.6 Species richness of plants typically associated with fens, swamps and mires showing the number of Indicator Species recorded in tetrads between 1987 and 2011. (Bracketed figures give a count of the tetrads falling into each category).

Himalayan Balsam (*Impatiens glandulifera*) are a serious problem in some woods. Amongst the *Red List* species in decline are Herb-Paris (*Paris quadrifolia*), Common Gromwell (*Lithospermum officinale*) and Fly Orchid (*Ophrys insectifera*). Mezereon (*Daphne mezereum*) is also thought to have declined in woods on the Magnesian Limestone. Sadly, many other more common plants have also declined in our ancient woodlands.

Marshes – fens, swamps and mires

There are marshes present in most of Derbyshire's river catchments. They tend be small and fragmented, although rush-pasture mires sometimes occur within larger mosaics of unimproved grassland vegetation and around gravel pits. The latter can be relatively large, though not always biodiverse. The extent of lowland fen is difficult to calculate because some vegetation communities overlap with grasslands, mires, blanket bog and upland flushes. In lowland Derbyshire 140 hectares of fen, swamp and mire have has been identified, with another 32ha of reed bed recorded. In the Peak District only 25ha of fen is recognised, but there are 655ha of upland flush and large areas of mire habitat.

As many as 120 plant species depend to some extent on these wetland habitats, and analysis using 76 of them as Habitat Indicators highlights hotspots of diversity (**Figure 4.6**) These include the eastern end of the Trent Valley and much of the Erewash Valley (associated in part with the Erewash Canal, but also the river and small marshes surviving along tributaries). The

Derwent Valley is also important, although only around 10 to 15 sites with significant areas of "marsh" now remain between Derby and Ladybower Reservoir. Sedge swamps and mires are now rare, but can be very diverse locally along the Shirley, Spinneyford and Mercaston Brooks. They reach their most impressive at Mercaston Marsh and Mugginton Bottoms SSSI. Within the Peak District, swamps and mires are more widespread, especially across the Eastern Moors where well-known sites such as Leash Fen, Stoke Flat and marshes near Curbar are to be found. In the south and east of the County swamps are more typically characterised by Bulrush (*Typha latifolia*), Reed Sweet–grass (*Glyceria maxima*) and Branched Bur-reed (*Sparganium erectum*). In the Trent valley and parts of the National Forest small sedge swamps dominated by Greater Pond-sedge (*Carex riparia*) occur. Tall herb fen, characterised by plants like Meadowsweet (*Filipendula ulmaria*), Hemp-agrimony (*Eupatorium cannabinum*) and Wild Angelica (*Angelica sylvestris*), is also highly localised with very few good examples of this habitat type now remaining in lowland Derbyshire. Elsewhere hotspots occur in the Wye Valley, parts of High Peak (Whaley Bridge to New Mills) and a few sites in the Coal Measures.

There are 39 marsh plants on the *Derbyshire Red Data List*, and 51% of these are in decline. Three species have not been recorded since 1986: Marsh Lousewort (*Pedicularis palustris*), Marsh St John's-wort (*Hypericum elodes*) and Purple Small-reed (*Calamagrostis canescens*) Their habitats have been lost or adversely affected by drainage and other agricultural improvements, although some losses were due to urbanisation, especially around Derby. The establishment of trees such as willow (*Salix* spp.) and Alder (*Alnus glutinosa*) or even Bulrush (*Typha latifolia*) and Reed Sweet-grass (*Glyceria maxima*) is a threat to some sites. Whatever the cause, it is very difficult to produce definitive figures on the amounts actually lost.

Running and standing water

Rivers, canals, lakes and ponds are home to over 100 native aquatic and semi-aquatic plants. Of these, 29 are included on the *Derbyshire Red Data List*. Several have always been rare and appear to show little overall change, but over half (59%) are declining. Examples of the latter include Water-violet (*Hottonia palustris*), Horned Pondweed (*Zannichellia palustris*), Perfoliate Pondweed (*Potamogeton perfoliatus*), Whorled Water-milfoil (*Myriophyllum verticillatum)* and Lesser Marshwort (*Apium inundatum*). Many ponds have been lost in recent decades, and many others are much altered due to successional changes such as siltation and the development of willow and alder carr woodland. In a study of 800ha of land in South Derbyshire the number of ponds had fallen from 99 to 22 between 1882 and 2003, a decline of 78% (Precey 2003). A survey of Derby City reported a loss of 88% in the number of ponds between 1890 and 2005 (Taylor 2005). According to the **Environment Agency** many of Derbyshire's rivers suffer from poor water quality as a result of increased silt and eutrophication from farm run-off and inputs from sewage treatment works

(Environment Agency 2009). As a result, very few are classed as being of good ecological quality. There are now a number of catchment-based projects aimed at improving this situation, driven mainly by the EU Water Framework Directive.

Recent pond surveys undertaken by DWT have shown that only 17% of ponds (out of 76 surveyed) were of good quality, based on both plant and aquatic invertebrate diversity (DWT Conservation Team, unpublished survey data). Losses of important aquatic species are known to have occurred, such as Grass-wrack Pondweed (*Potamogeton compressus*) which is no longer found in the Cromford Canal. However, plants can and do re-appear after management. For example in 2013 Water-violet (*Hottonia palustris*) was recorded for the first time in 14 years at Forbes Hole Local Nature Reserve.

The most important areas for aquatic and semi-aquatic plants (**Figure 4.7**) are to be found in south and south-east Derbyshire, associated with the Trent and Erewash River valleys at sites such as Fox Covert, Golden Brook Lagoon and Forbes Hole. Other notable hotspots include the Cromford Canal, Chesterfield Canal, Great Pond of Stubbing, Pebley Reservoir and the ponds at Hardwick Estate, as well as more localised areas further north, especially in the White Peak, centred on the River Lathkill and the lower reaches of the Wye.

Arable

Opportunities for arable plants to flourish in the countryside have declined steadily for many decades now. Whilst Derbyshire may not be renowned for its arable flora, a number of plants are still

Figure 4.7 Species richness of plants typically associated with open and running water, showing the number of Habitat Indicator Species recorded in tetrads between 1987 and 2011. (Bracketed figures give a count of the tetrads falling into each category).

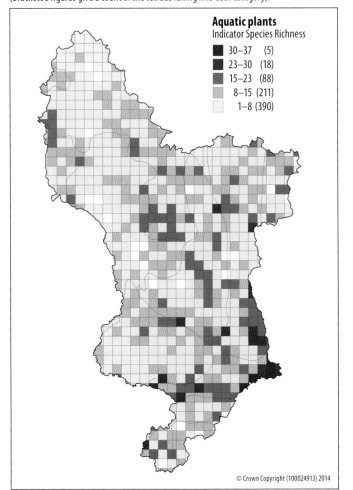

Aquatic plants
Indicator Species Richness

30–37	(5)
23–30	(18)
15–23	(88)
8–15	(211)
1–8	(390)

© Crown Copyright (100024913) 2014

Figure 4.8 Species richness of plants typically associated with arable land, showing the number of Habitat Indicator Species recorded in tetrads between 1987 and 2011. (Bracketed figures give a count of the tetrads falling into each category).

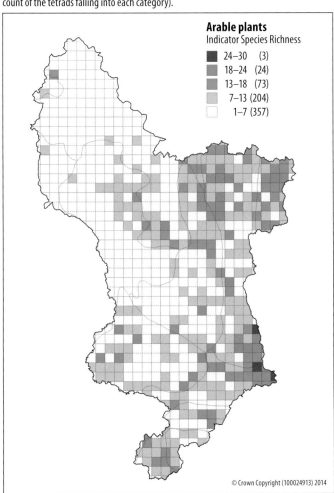

Arable plants
Indicator Species Richness

24–30	(3)
18–24	(24)
13–18	(73)
7–13	(204)
1–7	(357)

© Crown Copyright (100024913) 2014

largely confined to this habitat. Some, such as Common Ramping-fumitory (*Fumaria muralis*) and Hairy Buttercup (*Ranunculus sardous*), have actually increased, although often only by one or two new sites. At least 9 other species have declined, including Corn Buttercup (*Ranunculus arvensis*), Venus's-looking-glass (*Legousia hybrida*), Prickly Poppy (*Papaver argemone*), Shepherd's-needle (*Scandix pecten-veneris*), Dwarf Spurge (*Euphorbia exigua*) and Sharp-leaved Fluellen (*Kickxia elatine*). There are a further five species, amongst them Stinking Chamomile (*Anthemis cotula*) once recorded from 10 monads, that have not been seen since 1987. In total there are at least 17 "arable" plant species on the *Derbyshire Red Data List*. Of these, all but three are declining, with 13 experiencing more than a 50% decline since the 1965–1987 period. Conservation efforts targeted at these species have been all but non-existent and we are not aware of any positive measures in place on any farms in Derbyshire specifically for them. Today, arable plants are largely restricted to the east, with possible hotspots remaining in the Erewash Valley down to the confluence with the River Trent and locally in the Coal Measures and Magnesian Limestone (see **Figure 4.8**).

Open mosaic habitats

Brownfield sites often come to support a mosaic of habitats that can include grasslands, tall herb, marshes, ponds, disturbed ground and bare ground. The vegetation communities that develop can be very biodiverse, but also quite different in character. At the

Figure 4.9 **Species richness of plants typically associated with open mosaic habitats on previously developed land, showing the number of Habitat Indicator Species recorded in tetrads between 1987 and 2011.** (Bracketed figures give a count of the tetrads falling into each category).

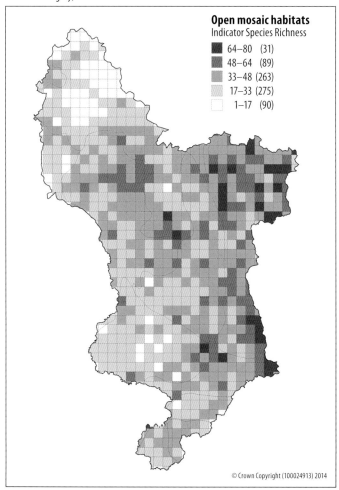

Open mosaic habitats
Indicator Species Richness
- 64–80 (31)
- 48–64 (89)
- 33–48 (263)
- 17–33 (275)
- 1–17 (90)

© Crown Copyright (100024913) 2014

Cinderhill Tip, near Kilburn – a brownfield site threatened by remediation works and home to Common Cudweed, Meadow Saxifrage and many other species (DWT)

best sites over 150 higher plant species may be found. In the past 30 years many such sites have appeared in Derbyshire – a legacy of mining, quarrying, railways and ironworks, as well as smaller derelict building sites. Today an estimated 700–800ha of such open mosaic habitats occur across the county. **Figure 4.9** shows the biodiversity hotspots for indicators of open mosaic habitats as listed by Maddock (2011). These are present mainly in the north-east around Chesterfield and across Bolsover, and in the south-east through the Erewash Valley. There are also diverse sites within Derby City and scattered through the Trent Valley. Further north the picture is more blurred as open mosaic species occur both in unimproved grasslands and have colonised many former limestone quarries, but diverse sites also occur north and north-east of Buxton and around Longstone Edge and Middleton.

Examples of *Derbyshire Red List* plants found in these habitats include: Small Cudweed (*Filago minima*), Common Cudweed (*F. vulgaris*), Early Marsh-orchid (*Dactylorhiza incarnata*), Round-fruited Rush (*Juncus compressus*), Narrow-leaved Everlasting-pea (*Lathyrus sylvestris*) and Yellow Bird's-nest (*Hypopitys monotropa*).

Moorland and heathland

Moorland (including upland heathland and blanket bog) covers an estimated 35,000 hectares in Derbyshire, predominantly within the Peak District National Park. Lowland heathland is much rarer, and really only occurs as a few very small scattered fragments.

These habitats have suffered losses as a result of intensive agricultural use, afforestation and development over the past 100 years or more. For example Matlock Moor (a 50ha site) is all that is left of a once great expanse of moorland, mires and bogs covering over 500ha bordering the northern edge of Matlock. The area is now a mix of coniferous woodland, improved fields and a golf course. Elsewhere overgrazing by sheep, land drainage and use of fire in heather management for grouse shooting have all impacted heavily upon the plant diversity of these habitats. There are 9 species on the *Red List* for this habitat. These include three that are in steep decline: Stag's-horn Clubmoss (*Lycopodium clavatum*) affected by scrub invasion and poor management, Bog Pimpernel (*Anagallis tenella*) and Heath Cudweed (*Gnaphalium sylvaticum*). The latter has declined from being found in 9 tetrads between 1965 and 1987 to just two tetrads between 1987 and 2008. Another species Bearberry (*Arctostaphylos uva-ursi*) is thought to be declining due to moorland burning by the grouse-shooting industry. Areas with a high number of typical moorland/heathland indicators (see **Figure 4.10**) are to be found across much of the

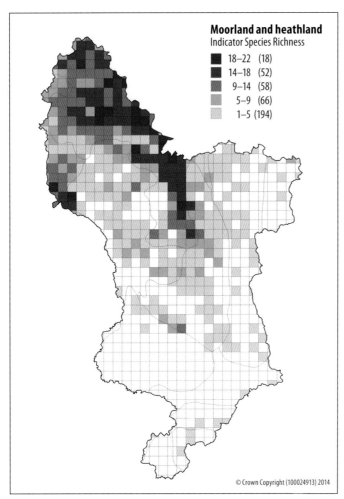

Moorland and heathland
Indicator Species Richness

■ 18–22 (18)
■ 14–18 (52)
▨ 9–14 (58)
▨ 5–9 (66)
▨ 1–5 (194)

© Crown Copyright (100024913) 2014

Figure 4.10 Species richness of plants typically associated with moorland and heathland, showing the number of Habitat Indicator Species recorded in tetrads between 1987 and 2011. (Bracketed figures give a count of the tetrads falling into each category).

Dark Peak and the South West Peak Landscape Character Areas. Elsewhere there are scattered locations where small numbers of indicator species may be found in the White Peak and Peak Fringe and, to a much lesser degree, the Coal Measures and Southern Coal Measures. Despite the losses and damage to these habitats they remain extensive in northern Derbyshire and in many areas efforts are underway to try and restore them. Nonetheless notable challenges remain.

Other notable habitats
Limestone and gritstone outcrops, together with limestone screes, provide habitats for a number of interesting plant species, including 18 that are on the *Derbyshire Red Data List*. Many of these are stable or even increasing, but a few have declined. Angular Solomon's-seal (*Polygonatum odoratum*) has declined from 8 monads to just two, and Red Hemp-nettle (*Galeopsis angustifolia*) has been lost from 8 of the 14 tetrads in which it has been recorded. Most of these latter losses were probably on arable land, whereas the scree populations are more stable. Encroachment from shrubs and rough grassland may be an issue for some of these plants in the limestone dales, however.

Around 12 *Derbyshire Red List* species are associated with "wayside" habitats such as hedgerows and other linear boundary features, and 6 of these show decreases. Cat-mint (*Nepeta cataria*), for example, has been recorded in only 6 tetrads, of which 4 have been on the Magnesian Limestone.

Recent conservation of plants and habitats

The last 20 years has seen considerable progress in understanding the distribution, extent and condition of many of the most important semi-natural habitats found in Derbyshire. It has also seen the preparation and implementation of Biodiversity Action Plans (BAPs) in both the Peak District (PDNP 2001, 2011) and Lowland Derbyshire (LDBP 1997, 2001, 2011). The BAP process provides a useful framework within which objectives can be defined and set, and progress monitored. In relation to plants, this BAP process has been very habitat focused and few if any plants are lucky enough to have their own action plan in the County.

The more extensive and detailed collection of survey data especially since 1997 has helped in the mapping of Priority BAP habitats, as defined by the UK Biodiversity Action Plan (Maddock 2011). In the case of grasslands many of the best sites have been identified since this time and 119 of them have now been designated as Local Wildlife Sites and several as SSSIs. **Grasslands** are now the primary habitat within almost half of all Local Wildlife Sites in Derbyshire. The conservation of **grasslands, mires, fens and upland habitats** over the past 30 years has primarily focused on encouraging and facilitating the uptake of agri-environment schemes. In lowland Derbyshire this has been partially successful with, for example, around 90 key grassland sites currently in Higher Level Stewardship which gives landowners payments for undertaking specific management actions which benefit biodiversity. In the Peak District the Hay Time Project successfully promoted sympathetic management of hay meadows, and many such meadows as well as limestone dales are now managed under these agreements. In addition some sites not in Stewardship have been included within management programmes funded by various projects over the years, whilst in other cases management has been taken forward by enthusiastic owners or local volunteers.

However, an estimated 300–500 hectares of Priority UK grassland habitat lying outside of the Peak District National Park remain without any kind of nature conservation designation, and most of these are not signed up to any agri-environment scheme agreement. Many important grassland sites remain very vulnerable to further deterioration and loss from either intensive agricultural use, horse-grazing or under-management. Only a few sites have been directly affected by development-related pressures in recent years, but where these situations do arise, the end result often sees the total loss of habitat.

The **conservation of woodlands** has been encouraged by grants administered by the Forestry Commission which in the last 20 years have had a strong emphasis on the protection and restoration of biodiversity. Uptake has been strong amongst landowners with the resources to deliver the required management. Around 800ha of ancient semi-natural woodland and 850–1,000ha of plantation on ancient woodland sites (as well as some older secondary woodland sites) are now managed under Stewardship agreement. Other initiatives have included the Ravine Woodlife Project that restored upland ash woods across the White Peak, and more recently the Clough Woodland Project that aims to regenerate woodland around the moorland fringes. In the lowlands the DerwentWISE project aims to manage 200ha of ancient and secondary broad-leaved woodlands, tackling invasive species like rhododendron and enhancing the structure of woodlands. Many woods remain unmanaged, however, and uptake amongst owners of smaller woodland has been lower. The main ecological challenges in woodlands today are the prevalence of non-native species; the loss of structural diversity; cessation of traditional management (for some sites) and tree diseases. All of these potentially result in changes in plant composition and diversity.

The loss of **hedgerows** has been widely publicised over the last few decades. By the time the Hedgerow Regulations Act came into force in 1997, thousands of kilometres of hedges had been lost across the country. In Derbyshire these losses have been most significant in the south and east where opportunities for increasing field sizes to improve yields and simplify management are greatest. Surveys undertaken by DWT in respect of hedgerow removal notices have revealed that only around 20–25% of hedgerows qualified as 'important' under the 1997 Act. In many cases where hedges have been retained they are in poor condition, as seen across parts of the Magnesian Limestone plateau, and in the Claylands where over-management has taken its toll. Hedgerows can support a rich flora, including shrubs, trees and field layer plants. However, only a few *Red List* plants are actually closely associated with hedgerows.

The **conservation of wetlands** has met with a mixture of both success and failure. On the one hand, many new wetland sites have been established such as Willington Gravel Pits, Drakelow, Pleasley Pit and Carr Vale, but more specialist wetland habitats such as sedge swamps and tall herb fens have declined, with many disappearing altogether. Lack of management threatens several of the best sites, including Milford Riverside Meadows on the Derwent, Shirley Brook Swamp and various sites along the Mercaston and Brailsford Brooks. Many farmers no longer have cattle breeds that are sufficiently hardy to cope with the tougher vegetation found in these wetter habitats, not to mention the worry of expensive beasts getting stuck in the mud. Where once there would have been intermittent grazing or cutting, today willows (*Salix* spp.) and Alder (*Alnus glutinosa*) threaten to overwhelm many excellent sites. Positive actions have included the reintroduction of late summer/autumn grazing by hardy cattle breeds, such as Highlands, to places like Spinneyford Brook swamp, and the clearance of some willow and Alder saplings from several sites in recent years. A few key sites are now managed under payments from agri-environment agreements usually within the Higher Level Stewardship. **Ponds** have been the focus of successful restoration projects, for example in Derby City where 25 ponds were restored and/or managed (Golson 2012), and in the Peak District where many dew ponds have been restored. A number of new ponds have been created in the past 15 years on former colliery sites or as balancing ponds for factories or new residential areas.

Brownfield sites are under enormous pressure from redevelopment and to a degree from poor restoration. For many sites, development plans for industry, recreation and housing are already on the table or underway. Other threats include further extraction of limestones, gravels and pulverised fuel ash. Permitted activities like infilling and in some cases re-working or extending quarrying to new faces also affects several sites. Planning guidance from the Government on brownfield sites requires local authorities to try and re-use the land. Often there is considerable support for the re-use of brownfield sites over greenfield ones. The Wildlife Trusts, Buglife and others have fought hard to try and raise awareness of the value of these sites for plants and other wildlife, and are promoting the protection of the best ones as Local Wildlife Sites and as part of the county's Ecological Network. Inevitably many will be lost, and it remains to be seen whether agreed mitigation and compensation schemes will ever be successful at preventing an overall loss in the biodiversity of these important wildlife refuges.

Assessing site condition

The condition of statutory and non-statutory sites in Derbyshire is very different. Only 17.33% of **SSSIs** are in a "favourable" condition, but 81.03% are classed as "unfavourable-recovering" and just 1.64% of sites are either "unfavourable" with no sign of change, or are in

decline (Natural England 2014). How long it will take for restoration of all SSSIs to be achieved is unclear, but one assumes that if these sites are recovering then sympathetic management is in place.

Assessing the condition of the much more numerous **Local Wildlife Sites (LWS)** is fraught with difficulties, not least because many are only visited once every ten years, or even longer. It is estimated from records held at DWT that 130 LWSs were destroyed between 1984 and 2008 and a further 62 damaged (Huston 2009). Where known, the main causes were agriculture (70 sites) and development (41 sites). For example, 50% of Steetley Quarry LWS, where over 200 plant species were recorded, has now been built on. Lack of sympathetic management, and to a lesser extent development pressures, are thought to be having a significant adverse impact on a further 200 Local Wildlife Sites, and many are likely to be lost in the near future if no action is taken. The Wildlife Trust also estimate that of the 1,175 Local Wildlife Sites in existence, as many as 70 sites are threatened by future development proposals for housing, industry, business, road and rail improvements and for mineral extraction.

Our best estimate is that, at the end of 2013, only 36% of LWSs were considered to have been positively managed in the preceding five years (Derbyshire Wildlife Trust 2014). These sites cover an estimated 5,500ha or 55% of the area covered by Local Wildlife Sites in total (including several large waterbodies). Around 3,500ha of land in positive management is in public or charitable ownership. Most of the land within Local Wildlife Sites not considered to be positively managed is in private ownership.

Engaging with the planning process has become increasingly important and during the last few years between 800 and 1000 applications were checked annually by staff at DWT, DCC and the PDNP. Local planning policies (past and present) remain relatively strong for statutory sites, but, as we have seen, less so for non-statutory ones.

Aiding us in our conservation efforts across the County has been the improvements in the accuracy and presentation of biological data. In the last decade we have increased our knowledge of the distribution and abundance of habitats and species, and this data has been digitised. It has been widely circulated within a variety of datasets for use in Geographical Information Systems (*i.e.* computerised mapping). Every record for every *Derbyshire Red List* plant is now mapped and available to conservation staff at DWT, DCC, NE and PDNP. This Derbyshire Biodiversity Alert Map has become an increasingly powerful tool for use in a wide range of conservation initiatives and activities. The data is also on the National Biodiversity Network's online "Gateway".

Conserving our flora – is there a brighter future?

Given the scale and unrelenting nature of habitat losses during the past few centuries (especially since the 1950s) and the limited resources in terms of policy, legislation and funding available during most if not all of this time, it is not surprising that the Government target for halting Biodiversity loss by 2010 was not achieved (Wildlife and Countryside Link 2011). Whether or not this came as a shock to the Government of the day is unclear, but at some point the then Labour Government was prompted to commission a report into the existing network of wildlife sites across England. That report, entitled **Making Space for Nature,** concluded that the current national system of nature conservation was insufficient to provide a coherent and robust ecological network which could maintain biodiversity and meet the challenges of future impacts such as climate change (Lawton *et al.*

2010). The report called for a "step change" in nature conservation thinking towards landscape-scale planning, and it made a series of recommendations to try and achieve this.

The Coalition Government's response to the Lawton report is set out within two documents, firstly the Natural Choice – the first **Environmental White Paper** in 20 years (Defra 2011a) which outlines the Government's vision for the natural environment, shifting the emphasis from *"piecemeal conservation action towards a more integrated landscape scale approach"*. The second document is the Government's **Biodiversity 2020 Strategy** (Defra 2011b) which develops these ideas and themes within a series of statements and policy ideas that sound quite encouraging and could be quite far reaching, but in reality are underpinned by very little in the way of funds, regulations or incentives. Nonetheless the White Paper committed to establishing 12 pilot **Nature Improvement Areas** (NIAs) in England and one of these pilot areas is located in the Dark Peak. It has so far generated £3,300,000 in grants and additional resources and work has started on the restoration and management of semi-improved grasslands, blanket bog, heathland and woodland. The overall success of this approach is still being evaluated, but early signs are encouraging. More NIAs may follow, but at present there is no commitment from Government to fund these. The recent formation of 48 **Local Nature Partnerships (LNPs)** across England may well result in further NIAs being determined locally. LNPs are intended to be high-powered, strategic organisations whose aim is to embed environmental thinking into local decision-making, and to promote the greening of economic growth.

A further key document is the **National Planning Policy Framework (NPPF)** which sets out the Government's planning policies for England (DCLG 2012). In relation to the natural environment, the NPPF states that the planning system should contribute to and enhance the natural and local environment by:

- protecting and enhancing valued landscapes, geological conservation interests and soils;
- recognising the wider benefits of ecosystem services;
- minimising impacts on biodiversity and providing net gains in biodiversity where possible, contributing to the Government's commitment to halt the overall decline in biodiversity, including by establishing coherent ecological networks that are more resilient to current and future pressures;

Implicit in the NPPF is the idea that impacts on the environment can be satisfactorily addressed by avoiding, minimising, mitigating and in the last resort compensating for those impacts. Whilst achieving a net gain for biodiversity is a laudable aim, it is largely unproven and often unrealistic especially when habitats of high value are threatened. Any gains are likely to come through habitats of lower value being replaced with higher value ones, or where significant financial contributions are made for the management of high value sites. But losses of long-established grasslands and wetlands, of ancient woodlands and even very diverse brownfield sites cannot be replaced through compensatory habitats. Successful refusal of applications that have a high impact on wildlife will be a clear test of this policy, but will also have to be hard won.

Interestingly the NPPF also requires Local Authorities to map an **ecological network** consisting of core sites, corridors and stepping stone sites. The guidance on this is rather hazy, but Derbyshire Wildlife Trust has now provided most of the County's Local Authorities with a network map for inclusion in their final strategies. We shall have to wait to discover exactly what it means in practice.

Within other organisations including Local Authorities and NGOs there has also been a shift towards valuing the contribution

Moorland restoration: Gully blocking using stone dams to raise water tables, Woodhead Moor, August 2013 (P. Anderson)

that the environment makes through **ecosystem services** and landscape-scale processes. Most organisations including Natural England and the Environment Agency, National Park Authorities, Wildlife Trusts, RSPB and the National Trust have all developed new strategies that reflect this shift.

In Derbyshire the most obvious example of a long-running scheme addressing a landscape-scale problem is the **Moors for the Future** project. Moorland and blanket bogs play an important role in storing carbon and retaining water as well as supporting a distinctive flora and fauna. The erosion of peat and soils from these uplands caused by pollution, overgrazing and intensive management for grouse shooting has resulted in increased run-off, siltation of watercourses, loss of habitat and the release of stored carbon. The project has started to try and address this through a wide-scale restoration programme.

Taking a slightly different approach, the **Limestone Journeys** project on the Magnesian Limestone, which ended in 2015, and the **DerwentWISE** project in the Derwent Valley between Derby and Matlock are attempting to manage and restore ancient woodlands and grasslands, and enhance and create new flower-rich grasslands. These efforts can make existing habitats better or create additional opportunities for plants and animals to colonise

Coles Hill Quarry near Wirksworth. Grasslands at the National Stone Centre are exceptionally diverse and will be restored and managed as part of DWT's DerwentWISE project (Kieron Huston)

and establish new populations. The Wildlife Trust and others are developing further projects aimed at restoring and enhancing clusters of Local Wildlife Sites through better management, improved connectivity and creation of new habitat.

However, does any of this truly represent a *"step change"*, as called for by Lawton (2010), or is it just a change of language and emphasis? It is relatively easy to badge projects as "landscape-scale", but can they really achieve anything different to similar projects ten years ago? In many cases we can still only secure the management of land for a limited period of time and, where landowners do not have the funds or skills to maintain management, it is easy for sites to slip back into an unfavourable condition. We only rarely have the funds to buy up large areas of land and create the scale of management needed to give us a coherent and robust ecological network of interconnected sites.

Reducing environmental pressures such as agriculture, forestry, water management and development has recently been picked up by the Government in its current strategies. But action to address these problems has been slow to materialise, and there are currently rather low expectations for the latest Countryside Stewardship Scheme (originally known as NELMS),due mainly to reduced budgets and tighter targeting than in previous agri-environment schemes. The scheme should target priority habitats including grasslands and wetlands. The focus for woodlands appears to be on creation, but arguably it is the restoration of ancient woodlands where significant gains for woodland flora (and other wildlife) could be achieved. Woodland creation may be beneficial in the longer term, but few woodland plants of note have colonised new plantations during the last 15 years of planting.

Future land use, whether for food, other agricultural products, recreation, horse grazing or new development and infrastructure, all threaten further losses of semi-natural habitats and make it difficult to find cheap opportunities for land enhancement and restoration. In lowland Derbyshire the predicted footprint of development will bring many floristically rich sites closer to centres of human population and increase their vulnerability to being damaged.

Also posing an ongoing threat to some vegetation communities are **Invasive non-native species (INNS)**. Their spread can impact heavily on native plants, especially in lowland fens, ponds, watercourses and woodland habitats. Controlling some of them is costly, and has to be co-ordinated at large scales *i.e.* whole river catchments.

Looming over all of these issues is the spectre of **climate change**. A rise in global temperatures of between 1.7°–2°C or more is now predicted by the end of the 21st century (IPCC 2013) and is likely to lead to irreversible changes in our habitats, our landscapes, and the distribution of species. There will be more extreme weather events and changes in terms of seasonal rainfall and temperature patterns, with more frequent hot and fewer cold temperature extremes over most land areas. In Derbyshire we have three climatic zones. Two of these are in cooler, wetter climates associated with the Peak District. Both are at risk of shrinking or disappearing altogether if rainfall and temperature patterns do change. Many plants at the southern extent of their range in England, such as Alpine Cinquefoil (*Potentilla crantzii*), Globeflower (*Trollius europaeus*), Bearberry (*Arctostaphylos uva-ursi*), Mountain Pansy (*Viola lutea*), Limestone Bedstraw (*Galium sterneri*), Alpine Clubmoss (*Diphasiastrum alpinum*) and Green Spleenwort (*Asplenium viride*) are dependent upon these cooler damper habitats found mainly in dales and moorland of the Peak District. These will be put at risk of decline or even extinction. In the lowlands a combination of a changing climate,

coupled with the resultant alterations in how humans manage the land seems likely to impact greatly upon a wide range of habitats and species.

If we are to build a robust network we need to halt the ongoing declines in our best sites, many of them already designated Sites of Special Scientific Interest or Local Wildlife Sites and at the same time look to the creation of new places for wildlife. To achieve this we must do as much of the following as possible:

a) Designate some of the best remaining sites as new SSSIs. We might strive for another 200–300ha to be declared over the next 10 years to 2025.

b) Increase the number of sites managed in funded land-management schemes. For Local Wildlife Sites we should aim to get another 50 sites in management agreements by 2020. Given what we have seen during the consultation stage of the new Countryside Stewardship Scheme, this could be a challenge.

c) Assist landowners to manage their sites by establishing a wider countryside management team.

d) Buy land whenever possible and try to link up sites and expand existing sites to buffer them and improve the ecological network.

e) Build a more joined up nature conservation movement in which voluntary organisations work together with individuals and other sectors in Society.

f) Green our parks, towns and cities.

g) Make people who plan to damage or impact upon biodiversity accountable to the principles of mitigation – avoid, minimise, mitigate, compensate.

h) We will need to simultaneously inspire new generations about wildlife, continue to make a compelling case for nature conservation and maintain pressure on future Governments and Government bodies. The protection of biodiversity is still not integrated through Government policy, and bodies such as Natural England, the Environment Agency and Forestry Commission are often uncoordinated, poorly funded and have been weakened in recent years by political decisions.

i) For plants specifically we should seek to understand the threats faced by individual species or key sites and address those threats. We must maintain and update both our own county *Red List* and, now, also our new country *Red List* of threatened plants, and work co-operatively to target action.

j) We must build a network of volunteer champions for our flora.

k) We must keep recording our plants.

Ragged-Robin (*Silene flos-cuculi*) found on a Local Wildlife Site in Derbyshire, and now categorised as Near Threatened in England (Kieron Huston)

The funds available for nature conservation in the immediate future will come from the usual medley of grants, membership fees of organisations, donations and legacies, coupled with whatever the new land management scheme has to offer and possibly some increase in developer contributions. Funds from local Government also continue to play an important role in Derbyshire, enabling the employment of staff in the National Park, the Derbyshire Countryside Service and for some staff at Derbyshire Wildlife Trust to provide Local Authorities with the expert ecological advice they are obliged to obtain and use, but for which some do not have the internal expertise. Central Government funding is much scarcer and likely to be linked to NIAs for the moment. There is scope for exploring the idea of localised taxes or levies to assist in specific management of high profile sites, but this is politically some way off.

The important role of **volunteers** in helping to record and conserve our flora will remain vital. This encompasses everything from ensuring we know exactly where a plant is located, to what threats it faces and how it needs to be managed. In some cases volunteers will be needed to help manage important sites, to collect and propagate seeds or to study certain species to help us understand more about their life-cycles and ecological interactions. The value of this contribution is immense and cannot be replaced.

In conclusion, Derbyshire's floristic diversity is not distributed evenly; the plants that occur here have different habitat preferences and life strategies. Some species and habitats are of greater value than others and many are difficult or impossible to replace. Whilst many plants may find a home in the newly forged or restored habitats in the lowlands, much of our flora is dependent upon our long-established in some cases ancient semi-natural habitats, whether in the limestone and gritstone uplands or elsewhere. These places are the beating heart of Derbyshire's flora. We must tackle the management problems that already exist, and seek to expand and buffer these habitats at every available opportunity whilst remaining vigilant to the threats and challenges that face them.

Addendum

England Red List (ERL)

The publication in September 2014 of the first ever **Vascular Plant Red List for England** was a significant step forward in identifying species under threat in our country (Stroh *et al.* 2014). Unfortunately it came just as this *Flora* was being finalised for printing and too late to incorporate new English threat statuses into the main species accounts, apart from ensuring the Conservation Code field in the Statistics Boxes included "ERL" as appropriate. However, the most significant changes and additions can be found in **Chapter 9**, **Table 9.9**. On top of the existing 245 *Derbyshire Red List* species, there will now be a further 59 completely new species to incorporate, plus an upgrading of 25 Locally Significant plants to ones of National significance. A further 15 species of GB Red List significance, and thus already on our Derbyshire Red Data List, now have an increased threat status here in England, too.

Of the 59 new species identified in Table 9.9, some 20 are species found on grassland habitats, and around a dozen or so are plants of heaths and moors, including the three heather species which are especially vulnerable in lowland parts. It is a sad reflection of the degraded state of our environment in England that numerous once-common species have now come to be formally assessed as Near Threatened. These include Harebell (*Campanula rotundifolia*), Crosswort (*Cruciata laevipes*), Wild Strawberry (*Fragaria vesca*), Hoary Plantain (*Plantago media*), Mat-grass (*Nardus stricta*), Wood-sorrel (*Oxalis acetosella*), Tormentil (*Potentilla erecta*) and Ragged-Robin (*Silene flos-cuculi*). Now regarded as "Vulnerable" in England under IUCN threat criteria are Moonwort (*Botrychium lunaria*), Lousewort (*Pedicularis sylvatica*) and Grass-of-Parnassus (*Parnassia palustris*). Clearly a further revision of the *Derbyshire Red List* will be needed following the publication of this *Flora*. An up-to-date county Red Data Book provides a valuable and robust tool in the arsenal of local conservationists and ecologists who need to identify key wildlife sites, or advise planners and developers on the potential impact of their actions and ensure that suitable mitigation plans are put in place to offset any likely damage.

Pleasley Pit Country Park occupies 70 hectares of former colliery on the Magnesian Limestone. It has combined old habitats with new to establish an area of great floristic richness and attractiveness. Across much of lowland Derbyshire it is places like this that need to be nurtured, protected and managed in order to ensure they continue to play a crucial role in the conservation of Derbyshire's flora (DWT)

CHAPTER 5

Where to see plants in Derbyshire

Mary Smith, Claire Smith and Alan Willmot

Introduction

Think of Derbyshire, and for many botanists the limestone dales immediately come to mind with their rich flora which includes many rarities. But beyond the dales lie some very different habitats, from the heather-covered high moorlands in the north, to the low-lying farmlands of the Trent Valley in the south, each with their own distinctive vegetation.

The aim of this section is to provide visitors and local enthusiasts with details of sites they can visit to begin exploring this rich mix of habitats and species for themselves. Sites are arranged by **Derbyshire Landscape Character Areas** which are used throughout this work, and described in **Chapter 1**. All are publicly accessible and many are "open access". Examples are given of characteristic, interesting or notable plant species and directions on reaching each site. As some are farmed, visitors are asked to keep to the footpaths. Note that all visits are made at the participants' own risk and care should be taken, especially in inclement weather on the high moors.

1 SITES IN THE WHITE PEAK

The White Peak is an upland plateau of Carboniferous Limestone, dissected by various narrow, steep-sided valleys known locally as "dales". Most are dry but some contain streams, especially in winter. Undoubtedly the best place to start a visit to this Character Area for its wild flowers is in that part of the **Wye Valley** centred on the old railway station of Miller's Dale, just 8km east of Buxton. From here five of the premier nature reserves of the White Peak are easily accessible. These are of such importance that parts have been designated as a **National Nature Reserve** (NNR) and many of the individual reserves are **Sites of Special Scientific Interest** (SSSI), of which the Wye Valley SSSI is the most extensive. The flora of the dales is at its most abundant in mid to late summer but other seasons have their own attractions, including **Moschatel** (*Adoxa moschatellina*), **Spring Cinquefoil** (*Potentilla tabernaemontani*) and **Mezereon** (*Daphne mezereum*) during the early months of the year. Many parts of the White Peak were quarried extensively over a number of years and the

Figure 5.1 Main sites to visit in each Derbyshire Landscape Character Area. See key for location names.

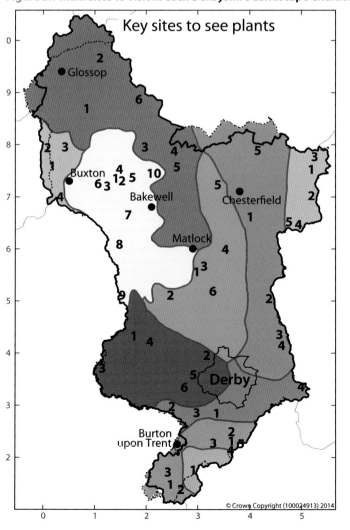

Key sites to see plants

© Crown Copyright (100024913) 2014

KEY

1 THE WHITE PEAK
1 Miller's Dale Quarry (SSSI)
2 Priestcliffe Lees (SSSI)
3 Chee Dale (SSSI)
4 Monk's Dale (SSSI/NNR)
5 Cressbrook Dale (SSSI)
6 Topley Pike and Deep Dale (SSSI)
7 Lathkill Dale (SSSI/NNR)
8 Hartington Meadows
9 Dove Dale (SSSI)
10 Coombs Dale (SSSI)

2 THE DARK PEAK
1 Kinder Scout (SSSI/NNR)
2 Bleaklow (SSSI)
3 Abney and Bretton Cloughs (SSSI)
4 Padley Wood and Gorge (SSSI)
5 Froggatt and Curbar Edges (SSSI)
6 Ladybower Reservoir

3 THE SOUTH WEST PEAK
1 Southern Goyt Valley (SSSI)
2 Hillbridge and Shallcross Woods
3 Combs Reservoir (SSSI)
4 Axe Edge and Moor (SSSI)

4 THE MAGNESIAN LIMESTONE
1 Hollinhill and Markland Grips (SSSI)
2 Scarcliffe Park
3 Whitwell Wood
4 Pleasley Pit Country Park
5 Hardwick Hall Country Park

5 THE PEAK FRINGE
1 Black Rocks
2 Carsington Water
3 Cromford Canal (SSSI)
4 Highoredish
5 Linacre Woods
6 Shining Cliff Woods (SSSI)

6 THE COAL MEASURES
1 The Avenue Washlands
2 Erewash Meadows
3 Woodside
4 Straw's Bridge
5 Moss Valley (SSSI)

7 THE CLAYLANDS
1 Holly Wood
2 Kedleston Park (SSSI)
3 Sedsall Rough Area
4 Shirley Park
5 Radbourne Hall
6 Great Northern Greenway

8 THE TRENT VALLEY
1 Anchor Church
2 Hilton Gravel Pits (SSSI)
3 Trent and Mersey Canal, Willington
4 Trent Lock

9 THE PARKLANDS
1 Calke Park (SSSI/NNR)
2 Ticknall Limeyards (SSSI)
3 Carver's Rocks (SSSI)
4 South Wood and Bryan's Coppice
5 Dimminsdale (SSSI)

10 THE SOUTHERN COAL MEASURES
1 Gresley Woods, Swainspark

11 THE MEASE LOWLANDS
1 Coton in the Elms
2 Grange Wood and Potter's Wood
3 Rosliston Forestry Centre

older abandoned workings are becoming important refuges for wildlife. Amongst the notable plant species to be found in the old quarries are **Bee Orchid** (*Ophrys apifera*) and, in the Castleton area, **Pyrenean Scurvygrass** (*Cochlearia pyrenaica*).

1.1 Miller's Dale Quarry (SK140731)

This Derbyshire Wildlife Trust reserve is the nearest to Miller's Dale Station, and forms part of the larger Wye Valley SSSI. **Yellow Bird's-nest** (*Hypopitys monotropa*) is often seen in the broad-leaved woodland around the steps leading up into the reserve, while the calcareous grassland of the quarry floor supports a rich flora including **orchid species, Cowslips** (*Primula veris*), **Carline Thistle** (*Carlina vulgaris*) and **Limestone Bedstraw** (*Galium sterneri*).

- **Location and directions**: 8km east of Buxton and 9km north-west of Bakewell. From A6 at top of Taddington bypass, take B6049, signposted to Tideswell and Miller's Dale. At bottom of dale turn left immediately after crossing River Wye, signposted to Wormhill. Pass under two railway bridges in quick succession. Car park is on the left (pay-and-display/toilets/refreshments).
- **Parking**: Miller's Dale Station (SK137732).
- **Access**: From car park walk through station, turning left onto Monsal Trail (signposted). Immediately after crossing viaduct take steps on right, climbing past old lime kilns to reach quarry.

1.2 Priestcliffe Lees (SK151729)

This reserve is an SSSI managed by Derbyshire Wildlife Trust in conjunction with nearby Miller's Dale Quarry. The two reserves demonstrate the succession of vegetation in this landscape from bare rock, through grassland and limestone scrub, to ash woodland. The first footpath into the reserve climbs through damp calcareous grassland with **Common Valerian** (*Valeriana officinalis*), **Meadowsweet** (*Filipendula ulmaria*) and **Grass-of-Parnassus** (*Parnassia palustris*), continuing through Hazel scrub to reach the improved farmland at the top of the Dale. An energetic climb up the second path leads through similar grassland, but towards the top it passes through spoil heaps with lead-tolerant plants such as **Spring Sandwort** (*Minuartia verna*), **Wild Thyme** (*Thymus polytrichus*) and both the yellow and purple forms of **Mountain Pansy** (*Viola lutea*) in evidence.

- **Location and directions**: As for Miller's Dale Quarry (see 1.1 above).
- **Parking**: Miller's Dale Station (SK137732).
- **Access**: From station car park walk through station, turning left onto Monsal Trail (signposted). After crossing viaduct, walk about 1km to reach the first of two public footpaths on the right. Continue on Trail for second footpath.

1.3 Chee Dale (SK112726 to SK137732)

This is the third Derbyshire Wildlife Trust reserve and part of the extensive Wye Valley SSSI, accessed from Miller's Dale Station. Chee Dale stretches some five kilometres westward along the River Wye. It consists of a mixture of Ash woodland, a diverse shrub layer including **Buckthorn** (*Rhamnus cathartica*), limestone crags supporting **Yew** (*Taxus baccata*), and grassland with **Common Rock-rose** (*Helianthemum nummularium*) and **Jacob's-ladder** (*Polemonium caeruleum*). **Common Wintergreen** (*Pyrola minor*) and **Greater Burnet-saxifrage** (*Pimpinella major*) can be seen on the higher path along the Monsal Trail with **Butterbur** (*Petasites hybridus*), **Water Avens** (*Geum rivale*) and **Dame's-violet** (*Hesperis matronalis*) along the riverside path.

- **Location and directions**: As for Miller's Dale Quarry (see 1.1 above).
- **Parking**: Miller's Dale Station (SK137732).

The River Wye at the bottom of the ravine in Chee Dale, June 2011 (DWT)

- **Access**: From station car park walk through station to turn right along Monsal Trail (signposted). A number of footpaths lead into the reserve, the most popular being on the right, about 1km along the trail, beyond lime kilns and immediately before viaduct. (Note: Two sets of stepping stones must be negotiated along the riverside path, which can be difficult when in spate. Avoid them by returning to Monsal Trail and walk through lit tunnels to travel further along the reserve, before exploring another cross path.) Part accessible to those with limited mobility.

1.4 Monk's Dale SSSI (SK141735 to SK131754)

This reserve forms part of the Derbyshire Dales National Nature Reserve (NNR). It is most easily reached from Miller's Dale Station. As the path descends into the Dale there are many bushes of the nationally rare **Mountain Currant** (*Ribes alpinum*) amongst the scrub on each side. The initial grassland area supports **Pale St John's-wort** (*Hypericum montanum*), but of particular interest are the marshy areas higher up the dale by the stream. These contain **Common Butterwort** (*Pinguicula vulgaris*) and **Flat-sedge** (*Blysmus compressus*). Beyond the marshy areas, the second half of the Dale is mainly wooded and quite hard walking but can be extremely rewarding. **Herb-Paris** (*Paris quadrifolia*), **Narrow-leaved Bitter-cress** (*Cardamine impatiens*) and **Nettle-leaved Bellflower** (*Campanula trachelium*) are all found here.

- **Location and directions**: As for Miller's Dale Quarry (see 1.1 above).
- **Parking**: Miller's Dale Station (SK137732).
- **Access**: Walk out of car park via vehicle entrance. Turn left onto Wormhill road for 500m and, where road makes a sharp left turn by Glebe Farm, take footpath on the right. Follow path crossing a field, bearing left into Monk's Dale upon reaching a drystone wall.

1.5 Cressbrook Dale SSSI (SK172734 to SK180755)

This SSSI is part of the Derbyshire Dales National Nature Reserve. Initially passing through broad-leaved woodland and scrub, the final section is an extremely steep slope of calcareous grassland. The whole length of the dale contains many plants of major importance such as **Bird's-foot Sedge** (*Carex ornithopoda*), **Lily-of-the-valley** (*Convallaria majalis*), **Globeflower** (*Trollius europaeus*), **Yellow Star-of-Bethlehem** (*Gagea lutea*) and **Stone Bramble** (*Rubus saxatilis*).

- **Location and directions**: The dale runs about 2–3km north from the village of Cressbrook, and can be reached from Miller's Dale station to the west (see 1.1 above). For a more convenient approach from the east, take A6 to Ashford in the Water, then turn onto A6020 (B6465) as far as Monsal Head. Immediately after large public house take minor road on the left, dropping steeply into the valley of the Wye. Follow road for 1km, past Upperdale Farm to small car park on left.
- **Parking**: Small car park near Upperdale Farm (SK177722).
- **Access**: From car park continue ahead on foot to Cressbrook Mill and, shortly after, take right fork. Continue on this, before taking very narrow road to the right past Ravensdale Cottages to enter Cressbrook Dale.

1.6 Topley Pike and Deep Dale SSSI (SK103724 to SK096710)

This is a Derbyshire Wildlife Reserve and an SSSI. There is relatively easy walking at the beginning of this dale, but it soon becomes much rockier as the path winds through deciduous woodland, scrub and calcareous grassland with its spectacular display of **Bloody Crane's-bill** (*Geranium sanguineum*). There are extensive limestone crags with **Rock Whitebeam** (*Sorbus rupicola*) and a good variety of ferns including **Green Spleenwort** (*Asplenium viride*). Other notable plants are **Nottingham Catchfly** (*Silene nutans*), **Wall Whitlowgrass** (*Draba muralis*), **Hoary Whitlowgrass** (*Draba incana*) and **Angular Solomon's-seal** (*Polygonatum odoratum*).

- **Location and directions**: The reserve is 4.5km east of Buxton on the A6, adjacent to Topley Pike Quarry. This is a working quarry, immediately recognisable by processing buildings situated at the foot of a long, steep hill.
- **Parking**: Pay & display car park opposite Topley Pike Quarry (SK104725).
- **Access**: From car park cross A6 and take footpath beside road at quarry entrance. This is clearly fenced and easily followed to a small gate on the right which leads into Deep Dale.

1.7 Lathkill Dale SSSI (SK166660 to SK211656)

The dale is situated 3km south-west of Bakewell and can be accessed from various points along its 6km length. It is of sufficient importance to have been designated as part of the Derbyshire Dales National Nature Reserve and an SSSI. During June and July the visiting botanist is likely to gravitate to the far western end, with its rocky heaps of spoil dumped from nearby Ricklow Quarry. For it is here that **Jacob's-ladder** (*Polemonium caeruleum*) is plentiful at the path side. Continuing eastwards towards Conksbury Bridge, the path passes through species-rich calcareous grassland, scrub and ash woodland. **Early-purple Orchid** (*Orchis mascula*), **Fragrant Agrimony** (*Agrimonia procera*) and **Goldilocks Buttercup** (*Ranunculus auricomus*) are all present at the appropriate time of the year.

- **Location and directions**: 1km east of Monyash on B5005 from Bakewell.
- **Parking**: Small car park (SK157664), plus adjacent verges.
- **Access**: Footpath into dale commences from Monyash car park. (Note: There is also a pay-and-display car park at Over Haddon (SK203664) at opposite end of the dale where the walking is easier, but starts with a steep descent.)

1.8 Hartington Meadows (SK150611)

Located halfway between Ashbourne and Buxton, this Derbyshire Wildlife Trust reserve differs from others in the White Peak in being part of the limestone plateau, rather than along a dale. It consists mainly of hay meadow and rough calcareous grassland with a disused quarry and ponds. The grasslands are floristically rich with **orchid species**, **Clustered Bellflower** (*Campanula glomerata*) and **Dropwort** (*Filipendula vulgaris*).

- **Location and directions**: Leave A515 just north of Newhaven Corner (at SK158612), taking B5054 signposted to Hartington. After 1km, and just before a high bridge over road (SK149612), turn left into Hartington Station car park on the Tissington Trail.
- **Parking**: Hartington Station pay-and-display car park with toilets (SK149611).
- **Access**: From car park walk south along Trail to steps and stile on the left which lead into the reserve along a public footpath.

Flower-rich grassland at Hartington Reserve, June 2009 (DWT)

1.9 Dove Dale SSSI (SK147510 to 142534)

This is another part of the Derbyshire Dales National Nature Reserve and an SSSI. It is *the* iconic Derbyshire dale and hence regularly visited by large numbers of tourists, especially at weekends. However, it is botanically still well worth a visit. The River Dove forms the county boundary between Derbyshire and Staffordshire, with the western bank belonging to the latter. Entering the dale from the south on the Staffordshire side necessitates crossing the famous Stepping Stones which are not quite as daunting as they once were, having been raised in height recently. However, due to the popularity of this dale, be prepared to queue in high season. The alternative eastern bank has large areas of reactivated fossilised scree and these are home to **Hutchinsia** (*Hornungia petraea*). Beyond the stepping stones interesting plants that may be seen include **Long-stalked Crane's-bill** (*Geranium columbinum*) and **Basil Thyme** (*Clinopodium acinos*) in the grassland and at scrub edges. From here the dale is mainly wooded with patches of **Orpine** (*Sedum telephium*) and a good variety of ferns before returning to grassland just before Milldale.

- **Location and directions**: Dove Dale is signposted from the A515 north of Ashbourne. Follow signs through Thorpe village and continue on, eventually descending steep hill to cross the River Dove. Take right turn into Dove Dale to reach car park.
- **Parking**: Dove Dale Car Park (SK146509) (fee/toilets/refreshments).
- **Access**: Walk on from car park north along road, passing through gates to arrive at footbridge. Here, either stay on road on the Staffordshire side until Stepping Stones are reached, or avoid them by crossing the river here to enter Dover Dale on a rather rougher footpath on the Derbyshire side. (Alternative car park at Milldale, SK136547)

1.10 Coombs Dale SSSI (SK224745)

Despite having been worked for fluorspar until very recent times, this dale is an SSSI and a botanist's delight. Situated off the A623 between Stoney Middleton and Calver, the track from the main road passes through light woodland and then steep-sided pasture with an attractive display of grasses including **Quaking-grass** (*Briza media*) and **Yellow Oat-grass** (*Trisetum flavescens*). Continue along this track to reach the heart of the dale where the path is lined with an abundance of calcicole species including **Kidney Vetch** (*Anthyllis vulneraria*), **Wild Basil** (*Clinopodium vulgare*) and **Ploughman's-spikenard** (*Inula conyzae*). Much in evidence at any time of the year is **Woolly Thistle** (*Cirsium eriophorum).* Look for the basal rosettes or its tall, stately stems. The side paths in the dale also have much to offer. In places small pockets of the original heath still exist and **Heather** (*Calluna vulgaris*), **Bilberry** (*Vaccinium myrtillus*) and **Tormentil** (*Potentilla erecta*) may be seen alongside large scree beds containing **Limestone Fern** (*Gymnocarpium robertianum*).

- **Location and directions**: Situated off the A623 between Stoney Middleton and Calver. The nearest parking is at SK238749 close to the Calver Crossroads where the Bakewell to Grindleford road crosses the A623 at the traffic lights. It is possible to park here in the short road next to a playing field which is north-west of the lights.
- **Parking**: On road beside playing field (SK238749) Just north-west of Calver Crossroads.
- **Access**: To reach Coombs Dale return to A623 and walk in the direction of Stoney Middleton for 300m. Just before another playing field on the left-hand side of the road a footpath sign at SK235750 points the way south-westwards up track into the Dale.

Further sites of interest in the White Peak

- **Cave Dale** (SK150826) – an SSSI near Castleton on the northernmost limit of the Carboniferous Limestone in the Peak District. In addition to species-rich limestone grassland there are rock-ledge communities not found elsewhere.
- **Bradford Dale** (SK199633 to SK220645) near Youlgreave is an attractive river valley with ash woodland. Notable plants are **Narrow-fruited Water-cress** (*Nasturtium microphyllum*) in the clear river, **Mossy Saxifrage** (*Saxifraga hypnoides*) in clearings in the woodland and **Maiden Pink** (*Dianthus deltoides*) in the grassland.
- **Grin Low** (SK050724) just south of Buxton is a reclaimed limestone quarry with extensive woodland, botanically rich spoil areas and acid grassland. It is a country park and an SSSI.
- **Rose End Meadows** (SK291566) at Cromford consists of semi-improved traditional small hay meadows with lead spoil. **Leadwort (Alpine Penny-cress)** (*Noccaea caerulescens*) is a feature of the site. This is a Derbyshire Wildlife Trust reserve and an SSSI.
- **Great Shacklow Wood** (SK176696) by the A6 between Bakewell and Buxton is a large mixed woodland with **Toothwort** (*Lathraea squamaria*) and **Bird's-nest Orchid** (*Neottia nidus-avis*) being notable species within it.
- **High Peak Trail** (SK313560 to SK110673) The whole length of this abandoned railway line between Cromford and Buxton is interesting with typical limestone plants and, additionally, remnants of plantings made when the railway was operational. It is now a long distance footpath and cycle route, connecting at Parsley Hay with the botanically even more interesting Tissington Trail, going southwards to Ashbourne.
- **Longstone Moor** (SK195735) is an SSSI just north of Great Longstone, it is the only sizeable area of heath remaining over limestone. Heathland plants can be seen intermixed with limestone and lead-tolerant species.

2 SITES IN THE DARK PEAK

This Landscape Character Area is one of a rugged high sandstone plateau covered in moorland which is cut by various river valleys, both small and large. The sandstone is generally coarse and known locally as Gritstone. The smaller valleys are known as Cloughs; the sides of the larger valleys are crenellated with gritstone outcrops known as Edges. Two large areas are now designated as Sites of Special Scientific Interest: The Dark Peak SSSI and the Eastern Peak District Moors SSSI. Whilst not having the variety of species of the White Peak, there are some interesting hot-spots of higher diversity, especially where there are wet seepages in the moorland areas forming flushes. These flushes and some of the cloughs are not without their rarities which include **Ivy-leaved Bellflower** (*Wahlenbergia hederacea*), **Bog Pimpernel** (*Anagallis tenella*), **Cranberry** (*Vaccinium oxycoccos*) and **Bearberry** (*Arctostaphylos uva-ursi*). There are few actual nature reserves in the area but there are extensive stretches of Open Access land, much of it owned by the National Trust, so that access is generally easy. The weather is very changeable at these higher altitudes and the botanist should go prepared for this, and take map and compass.

2.1 Kinder Scout (SK087874)

At 636 metres above sea level, the broad plateau of Kinder Scout is the highest point in both Derbyshire and the Peak District. It may be reached from the A57 which passes west from Sheffield over the Dark Peak, attaining over 500m at Snake Pass, before plunging steeply down to Glossop. Kinder is the region's newest National Nature Reserve (NNR) and is part of the much larger Dark Peak SSSI, consisting mainly of eroded blanket bog with small patches of sub-alpine dwarf shrub heath. Blanket bog has a very limited world distribution and a key objective of Kinder Scout's designation is the restoration of this internationally important habitat. The dominant plants are **Cottongrasses** (*Eriophorum* spp.), often to the exclusion of almost all others. This paucity of species is peculiar to the blanket bogs of the South Pennine region. Another significant feature of the Kinder plateau is the depth of the peat which is considerably greater than that of blanket bogs in other parts of Britain.

- **Location and directions**: From the north, park on A57 Snake Pass (SK088929) and take Pennine Way, at first south-west for 3.7km, then sourh-east for 3km to Kinder.
- **Alternative routes**: From the south: Approach by parking at Barber Booth (SK107847), then walk 1km north-west along minor road to Upper Booth where road joins the Pennine Way. This leads to Jacob's Ladder, a well-made but steep path to the gritstone plateau.

  From the north-east: Use lay-by on A57 (SK109914) to the north of Snake Inn. From here go south to cross bridge over River Ashop (SK114901), then follow Fair Brook up to Fairbrook Naze on northern side of the plateau.

2.2 Bleaklow (SK100965)

This part of the Dark Peak SSSI is the easiest to reach of the high moorland areas. The moor is mainly blanket bog with species of **Cottongrass** (*Eriophorum* spp.) but where the peat is somewhat drier **Cloudberry** (*Rubus chamaemorus*) can be quite abundant, lending colour to an otherwise monotone landscape. With the recent rediscovery here of **Fir Clubmoss** (*Huperzia selago*) and **Royal Fern** (*Osmunda regalis*), it is possible that other under-recorded species may be found on the plateau by the diligent botanist.

Flora Group members stopping for Labrador-tea near Bleaklow, September 2009 (Nick Moyes)

Padley Wood and Gorge in winter, November 2013 (DWT)

- **Location and directions**: Bleaklow lies immediately north of the A57 at Snake Pass where the Pennine Way crosses the main road. Park here to pick up the Pennine Way heading north-north-east to Bleaklow. The moors may also be accessed from Doctor's Gate Culvert where the old Roman road leaves the A57 at SK096928.
- **Parking**: A57 at Snake Pass (SK088929).

2.3 Abney and Bretton Cloughs SSSI (SK198798 to SK224798)

This interesting complex of cloughs is centred on and around Stoke Ford. There is mainly woodland with interesting flushes and rock outcrops near the brook. However the main interest is later in the year when small patches of both **Oak Fern** (*Gymnocarpium dryopteris*) and **Beech Fern** (*Phegopteris connectilis*) can be found. Further south in Bretton Clough, and to the west in Abney Clough, there are areas of unimproved acid grassland with a wide range of species, including **Greater Butterfly-orchid** (*Platanthera chlorantha*) in the latter.

- **Location and directions**: 1.5km south-west of Hathersage take minor road that leaves the B6001 Hathersage to Grindleford road at Leadmill opposite a public house (SK233804). After 2.5km the road runs high up along north side of Abney Clough.
- **Parking**: A few spaces along wooded road north of Abney Clough. (SK210797)
- **Access**: Take one of two public footpaths that run down southwards into clough.

2.4 Padley Wood and Gorge (SK251788 to SK261807)

This rocky wooded gorge is more correctly known as Yarncliff Wood SSSI, and is much beloved of photographers. It runs up Burbage Brook from Grindleford Station near Nether Padley to the edge of the moors at Toad's Mouth on the A6187. Starting from the station, the gorge is occupied by an upland oak wood, predominately of **Sessile Oak** (*Quercus petraea*) with a heathy understorey of **Bilberry** (*Vaccinium myrtillus*) and **Heather** (*Calluna vulgaris*). For many years the wood was sheep-grazed, so failed to regenerate and was slowly dying. Pioneering ecological work by Sheffield University provided proof of sheep depredation, and as a result the whole wood was fenced off and is once more flourishing. There are many ferns, with **Scaly Male-fern** (*Dryopteris affinis* agg.) being particularly abundant, and patches of **Common Cow-wheat** (*Melampyrum pratense*) and **Climbing Corydalis** (*Ceratocapnos claviculata*). Higher up, the woodland gives way to acid grassland

with flushes east of the path containing **Round-leaved Sundew** (*Drosera rotundifolia*), while patches of drier heathland near the main roads exhibit **Heath Milkwort** (*Polygala serpyllifolia*).

- **Location and directions**: Beside Burbage Brook, near Nether Padley.
- **Parking**: On side of lane leading to Grindleford Station (SK251787). This is off the B6521, opposite Maynard Arms, about 800m north of bridge over the River Derwent at Grindleford.
- **Access**: Continue down lane towards Grindleford Station, past café and over railway bridge. A public footpath on the right leads into the wood.
    Alternative car parks at the upper end of the gorge:
    a) Public one at SK251800 just over 2km south-east of Hathersage on A6187. b) National Trust car park near Fox House Inn at SK266800.

2.5 Froggatt and Curbar Edges (SK252773 to SK262747)

These form one of the more impressive gritstone edge complexes in the county and are just a small part of the **Eastern Peak District Moors SSSI**. They extend from just below Nether Padley in the north, along the western edge of Big Moor, to Curbar and Calver in the south. The path from the north initially passes through birch woodland with a heathland understorey containing **Bell Heather** (*Erica cinerea*) and **Crowberry** (*Empetrum nigrum*), but further south the landscape becomes more open. Stretching away to the east, in front of and beyond White Edge, are the rolling heathlands and bogs of Big Moor, while the boulder-strewn slopes of the edges to the west provide fine views over the Derwent Valley. The edges and their backing moors are not species-rich but are typical of the Dark Peak. A careful search will usually find something of interest such as **Bog Asphodel** (*Narthecium ossifragum*), **White Sedge** (*Carex canescens*) or **Early Hair-grass** (*Aira praecox*).

- **Location and directions**: 16km south-west of Sheffield on the east side of the A625 just past The Grouse Inn.
- **Parking**: National Trust car park off A625 at SK255777, or lay-by on A625 at SK255775, both near northern end.
- **Access**: From car park walk south down to stream and take steps on the far side to the road. Turn right and cross road. After 50m a public footpath leads through gate onto Froggatt Edge. From the lay-by the footpath is about 100m down the road to the west. (Alternative car park at southern end, at Curbar Gap, SK262747).

2.6 Ladybower Reservoir (SK185883)
The Derwent Dams reservoir complex and their surrounding conifer plantations are a prominent feature of the Dark Peak landscape. The eastern bank of Ladybower Reservoir has some interesting plants both in the drawdown zone, **Shoreweed** (*Littorella uniflora*) and **Water-purslane** (*Lythrum portula*), and in the drier areas above, **Sand Spurrey** (*Spergularia rubra*), **Red Goosefoot** (*Chenopodium rubrum*) and **Trailing St John's-wort** (*Hypericum humifusum*). There is also upland oak wood on this bank, but heavy grazing has prevented the development of an understorey. The western bank is more heavily shaded with conifers, but marshy areas provide interest with **Smooth-stalked Sedge** (*Carex laevigata*), **Pale Sedge** (*Carex pallescens*) and **Tufted Forget-me-not** (*Myosotis laxa*). Inlet streams on both sides of the reservoir are productive, typically with **Large Bitter-cress** (*Cardamine amara*), **Water Mint** (*Mentha aquatica*) and **Round-leaved Crowfoot** (*Ranunculus omiophyllus*).

- **Location and directions**: 16km west of Sheffield and 3km north of Bamford, on the A57 Sheffield to Glossop road.
- **Parking**: For eastern bank, park at long lay-by on main A57 road (SK196864) just east of Ashopton Viaduct.
- **Access**: From lay-by walk towards Viaduct. Footpath is signposted on the right, up a track then ahead through gate. To explore opposite bank, take minor road immediately west of Viaduct, towards Fairholmes. There are three car parks (some free) along this road which at weekends culminates at Fairholmes, a pay-and-display car park with visitor facilities. Various footpaths start here, including access onto moorland. On weekdays vehicle access is permitted further north to park at end of reservoir complex (SK167938). Bus available at weekend peak periods only.

Further sites of interest in the Dark Peak
- **Jaggers Clough** (SK155873) At south-eastern end of clough there is mixed woodland with flushes and a large area of interesting marsh beyond the trees. The rock ledges by stream support **Oak Fern** (*Gymnocarpium dryopteris*). This is an SSSI.
- **Eastern Peak District Moors SSSI** (Centred on SK283757) These consist of Ramsley Moor, Big Moor and Leash Fen in Derbyshire and also Houndkirk Moor within the vice-county, but outside modern Derbyshire. Between them they display virtually the full range of upland vegetation characteristic of the southern Pennines as well as populations of regionally scarce plants, including **Chickweed-wintergreen** (*Trientalis europaea*) at Houndkirk Moor.
- **Long Clough** (SK031925) A Derbyshire Wildlife Trust reserve with mixed deciduous woodland, unimproved acid grassland, bracken beds and streams.
- **Chatsworth Estate** (SK262702) The Park is best known for its veteran trees, a scarce resource in this Landscape Character Area. The margins of the Emperor Lake also reward examination, though it is necessary to pay to enter the gardens to view them.

3 SITES IN THE SOUTH WEST PEAK

This upland area of moorland is very similar in many ways to the Dark Peak and, as with that Landscape Character Area, the flushes in the valleys have much to interest the botanist, including **Flea Sedge** (*Carex pulicaris*), **Star Sedge** (*Carex echinata*), **Southern Marsh-orchid** (*Dactylorhiza praetermissa*) and **Ragged-Robin** (*Silene flos-cuculi*).

3.1 The Southern Goyt Valley SSSI (SK015758 to SK017715)
Lying some 5km to the west of Buxton, this part of the valley extends from the northern end of Errwood Reservoir to Derbyshire Bridge in the south, much of which is an SSSI. At The Street car park (SK013756) next to Errwood Reservoir, the valley is dominated by the reservoir and woodlands, both broadleaved and coniferous, with areas of acid grassland. The grassland typically displays **Wavy Hair-grass** (*Deschampsia flexuosa*) and **Purple Moor-grass** (*Molinia caerulea*) with **Pignut** (*Conopodium majus*) also present. Moving on south to Errwood Hall car park (SK012748), a walk to the derelict hall can be recommended. Although there has been much invasion by planted **Rhododendron** (*Rhododendron ponticum*), the woodland remains interesting with **Hairy Wood-rush** (*Luzula pilosa*) and **Hornbeam** (*Carpinus betulus*). The ruins of the hall have provided a new habitat for plants such as **Slender Rush** (*Juncus tenuis*) and **New Zealand Willowherb** (*Epilobium brunnescens*). There is a return to the natural terrain at Goytsclough Quarry car park (SK011734) with a variety of ferns and typical plants of the dwarf shrub heath in the quarry itself. A walk south along the road leads to a series of flushes with **Heath Spotted-orchid** (*Dactylorhiza maculata*), **Marsh Hawk's-beard** (*Crepis paludosa*) and the three heathers native to the county, **Heather** (*Calluna vulgaris*), **Bell Heather** (*Erica cinerea*), and **Cross-leaved Heath** (*Erica tetralix*). Across the old packhorse bridge a larger marshy area is worth studying. From Goytsclough Quarry the road south slowly climbs, leaving the woodland behind and crossing open moorland with large areas of bog, until almost the southern end of the Goyt Valley is reached at Derbyshire Bridge car park (SK018715). South-east between the car park and the A54 there are large numbers of mires and flushes with good populations of species typical of this habitat including **Bog Asphodel** (*Narthecium ossifragum*), **Carnation Sedge** (*Carex panicea*) and **Bog Pondweed** (*Potamogeton polygonifolius*).

- **Location, directions and parking**: The road through the valley is one-way. The first three car parks can only be accessed from the north via the A5004 Buxton to Whaley Bridge road. Starting at Buxton, leave the A5004 at a right hand bend, taking a minor road on the left, signposted Goyt Valley (SK032752). Follow this until it crosses reservoir to reach The Street car park. Take note of traffic regulations here as they vary with the day of the week and time of day. At peak times the road is closed to traffic, but is always open to pedestrians.

  Alternatively, use car park at Derbyshire Bridge (SK018716) and *walk* north. This is 4.5km south-west of Buxton, just off the A537. Take either of two minor roads leaving the A537 north, one close to the A54 junction (SK019710), the other near the Cat and Fiddle Inn (SK003717).

Goyt Valley moorland in the South West Peak, May 2013 (Penny Anderson)

3.2 Hillbridge and Shallcross Woods (SK007795)

These woodlands lie on either side of the River Goyt and are the largest upland oak woods in the area. They have a range of canopy tree species and an extremely varied ground flora. **Ferns**, **wood-rushes** (*Luzula* spp.), and **horsetails** (*Equisetum* spp.) are particularly well represented. Shallcross Wood has a number of wet slopes that further increase the plant variety. South of the woods there are attractive meadows with a number of grasses as well as **Common Spotted-orchid** (*Dactylorhiza fuchsii*) and **Yellow-rattle** (*Rhinanthus minor*). The banks of the river are home to **Lemon-scented Fern** (*Oreopteris limbosperma*) and **Bay Willow** (*Salix pentandra*).

- **Location and directions**: 2km south of Whaley Bridge.
- **Parking**: Large lay-by on A5004 (SK008798).
- **Access**: From lay-by follow footpath down towards river, but do not cross it. Turn left to remain in Shallcross Wood.

    To reach Hillbridge Wood: either a) continue southwards down footpath to bridge over River Goyt (SK011786) or b) park at Taxal Church (SK006798) and go south on foot along private road for 300m to take footpath on left across fields to the Wood.

Hillbridge Wood in the South West Peak (DWT)

3.3 Combs Reservoir SSSI (SK037797)

The shores of this reservoir, and the watercourses which enter it, support a large number of aquatic and marsh plants, but the overriding interest of this site is the plants of the draw-down zone. **Shoreweed** (*Littorella uniflora*), **Mudwort** (*Limosella aquatica*), **Water-purslane** (*Lythrum portula*) and **Lesser Marshwort** (*Apium inundatum*) are all regularly seen here.

- **Location and Directions**: Take B5470 Chapel-en-le-Frith to Whaley Bridge road. The reservoir is equidistant between the two towns.

- **Parking**: Car park (SK033797) is down a small road on western side of reservoir, and south of the B5470.
- **Access**: Cross road from car park and take public footpath between reservoir and brook.

3.4 Axe Edge and Moor (SK030700)

This exposed complex of acid grassland, peat bog and upland heath is part of Leek Moors SSSI and, whilst it may present a bleak aspect, it encapsulates perfectly this Derbyshire Landscape Character Area. Many plants such as **Knotted Pearlwort** (*Sagina nodosa*) and **Deergrass** (*Trichophorum germanicum*) can be found quite close to the road and some, such as **Marsh Arrowgrass** (*Triglochin palustris*), can be abundant on the road edge.

- **Location**: 4.5km south-west of Buxton, on A53 Buxton-to-Leek road.
- **Parking:** Lay-by at SK034698 on A53. Alternatively, just north of lay-by use unfenced minor road that crosses moor to A54 via Dane Head. This has a number of places to park and footpaths for access.

4 SITES IN THE MAGNESIAN LIMESTONE

The main botanical interest in this Landscape Character Area lies in the grips, which are narrow rocky valleys incised into a plateau of limestone. The archetypal grip is Creswell Crags, famous for its caves which have yielded some of the earliest evidence of prehistoric man in Great Britain. There is also a wide range of woodland plants on the Crags, supporting the idea that they are a refugia for the native woodland flora that occupied the British countryside before the advent of farming. However, new areas of botanical interest are opening up in the Area with modern man's inheritance of disused collieries and industrial sites. These are being colonised by a wide variety of opportunistic plants, including garden escapes and other unexpected species. Following reclamation, some of the sites have been designated as Country Parks and are thus easily accessible to the botanist.

4.1 Hollinhill and Markland Grips SSSI (SK513752)

This is a large complex of narrow rocky valleys, or grips, but access is somewhat limited. Upon entering Hollinhill Grips from the A616 there is semi-natural woodland with **Yew** (*Taxus baccata*) and **Lime** (*Tilia* spp.) to be seen on the crags and areas of calcareous grassland with the rare sedges, **Soft-leaved Sedge** (*Carex montana*) and **Rare Spring-sedge** (*Carex ericetorum*) under the power lines at SK510753. Access to Markland Grips to the south is more restricted, but there is a similar mix of crag woodland and calcareous

Large-leaved Lime (*Tilia platyphyllos*) growing on the side of the grip at Markland, June 2004 (P. & G. Dishart)

grassland here with wetter areas at the bottom of the valley. The northern part can be reached by walking to the eastern end of Hollinhill Grips (SK515751) and taking the other footpath south-west into the Grips. **Dropwort** (*Filipendula vulgaris*) and **Bugle** (*Ajuga reptans*) are present in the grassland.

- **Location and directions**: South of the A616 between Clowne and Creswell.
- **Parking**: Lay-by on north side of A616, about 2km east of Clowne (SK512754).
- **Access**: Cross A616 and walk east to a track. This leads to a bridge over disused railway (SK512753). Cross bridge and turn right for Hollinhill Grips or turn left and follow track to Upper Mill Farm, there taking the narrow footpath on the right that leads to Markland Grips.

4.2 Scarcliffe Park (SK513706)

Situated on the Magnesian Limestone plateau, this large wood has been turned over mainly to forestry woodland. Although access is confined to a single bridleway, this site has an extremely rich woodland edge flora. **Common Gromwell** (*Lithospermum officinale*), which is generally scarce in the county, is quite abundant here.

- **Location and directions**: 4km east of Bolsover, just north of A632.
- **Parking**: Most convenient car parking is at Poulter Country Park (SK519712).
- **Access**: From Poulter Country Park walk north along lane for some 500m, forking left to then pick up bridleway in Whaley to head back southwards into Scarcliffe Park. Alternatively, from A632 between Bolsover and Nether Langwith, walk north from Old Hall at SK521697 on the Archaeological Trail into the Park.

4.3 Whitwell Wood (SK523783)

This woodland site is owned by the Forestry Commission, but is open access. Despite being managed as a plantation for many years there is still a good flora in the rides and on the woodland edges, including **Wild Service-tree** (*Sorbus torminalis*) and **Bird's-nest Orchid** (*Neottia nidus-avis*). There are also seepages and springs in the wood that generate marshy conditions with **Broad-leaved Cottongrass** (*Eriophorum latifolium*) and **Few-flowered Spike-rush** (*Eleocharis quinqueflora*). The lay-by is also of interest as **Wild Liquorice** (*Astragalus glycyphyllos*) grows here.

- **Location**: On A619 near Whitwell, midway between Barlborough and Worksop.
- **Parking**: Large lay-by on north side of A619 (SK525772).
- **Access**: Take path north from lay-by to go directly into wood.

4.4 Pleasley Pit Country Park (SK495642)

The carefully restored headstocks and buildings of the former colliery provide a dramatic backdrop to this botanically interesting site. Amongst the familiar species of rough ground, such as **Common Centaury** (*Centaurium erythraea*) and **Wild Parsnip** (*Pastinaca sativa*), there are other less common finds. **Yellow-wort** (*Blackstonia perfoliata*) is a characteristic species of the Magnesian Limestone, found only infrequently outside this Landscape Character Area. **Intermediate Evening-primrose** (*Oenothera* × *fallax*), **Argentinian Vervain** (*Verbena bonariensis*) and **Blue-eyed-grass** (*Sisyrinchium bermudiana*) all occur here.

- **Location and directions**: Situated 5km south-east of Junction 29 of M1. Take A617 to roundabout at Pleasley (SK502646). Here take minor road (4th exit) south towards Teversal, then immediately first right into Pit Lane. Continue ahead to car park.
- **Parking**: Pleasley Pit Country Park car park (SK499643).

4.5 Hardwick Hall Country Park (SK459639)

This National Trust property offers a variety of interesting habitats. The ponds and their surrounding grassland are probably the best starting point for the botanist. **Heath-grass** (*Danthonia decumbens*) and **Tor-grass** (*Brachypodium rupestre*) are found here, the latter being a dominant species of this Character Area but rare elsewhere in the county. The series of small ponds hold aquatic species such as **Rigid Hornwort** (*Ceratophyllum demersum*) and **Spiked Water-milfoil** (*Myriophyllum spicatum*) with the two large ponds displaying taller marginal plants. The locally rare **Wood Club-rush** (*Scirpus sylvaticus*) is abundant around the Great Pond. Further afield on the estate the mature woodlands have excellent displays of spring flowers, while the farmlands are less intensively cultivated than some areas of the plateau and so retain historic landscape features.

- **Location and directions**: Situated 3km south of Junction 29 of the M1. Exit J29 to head west onto A6175 signposted Holmewood. In 500m take minor road running south, parallel to motorway, signposted to Hardwick Hall. Continue ahead for 2.5km, ignoring turnings. After swinging left under motorway at SK452638, turn immediately left into car park.
- **Parking**: National Trust car park at Hardwick Ponds (SK453639).
- **Access**: Direct from car park to reach all parts of the estate.

Further sites of interest on the Magnesian Limestone

- **Pleasley Park** (SK519655) is a further example of a grip with woodland and a pond. Notable plants include **Solomon's-seal** (*Polygonatum multiflorum*), **Spurge-laurel** (*Daphne laureola*), and **Fingered Sedge** (*Carex digitata*).
- **Poulter Country Park** (SK526708) is comprised of newly restored industrial land with interesting communities of open calcareous grassland and wetlands. **Wild Basil** (*Clinopodium vulgare*) is present, one of the characteristic plants of the Magnesian Limestone.
- **Rowthorne Trail** (SK476647 to SK492637) This is a long-disused railway with varied woodland and an extensive area of floristically rich grassy embankment. It is also a Local Nature Reserve.

5 SITES IN THE PEAK FRINGE

The transitional nature of the Peak Fringe is reinforced by the presence here of plants that are more readily associated with neighbouring areas. For example, **Sweet Cicely** (*Myrrhis odorata*) and **Meadow Crane's-bill** (*Geranium pratense*) are perceived to be plants of the more calcareous soils of the White Peak, while the small patches of dry heath with **Bilberry** (*Vaccinium myrtillus*) and **Wavy Hair-grass** (*Deschampsia flexuosa*) are more usually linked to the Dark Peak. The hilly nature of the Peak Fringe has allowed some small but interesting pockets of vegetation to remain. Steep-sided pastures may harbour **Lousewort** (*Pedicularis sylvatica*), with the fields falling away to small, shaded streams supporting **Large Bitter-cress** (*Cardamine amara*). Many of the small woodlands have superb displays of **Wood Anemone** (*Anemone nemorosa*).

5.1 Black Rocks (SK292558)

Black Rocks sits on the edge of the Millstone Grit where it overlies the Carboniferous Limestone. In the past mines were dug through the gritstone to reach lead deposits in the limestone below. This has resulted in a very varied area with a wide range of habitats and plants. There are patches of heathland and acid woodland with **Bilberry** (*Vaccinium myrtillus*), **Cowberry** (*Vaccinium vitis-idaea*), **Heather** (*Calluna vulgaris*) and **Great Wood-rush** (*Luzula sylvatica*) alongside Millstone Grit outcrops and lead mine spoil waste heaps with **Spring Sandwort** (*Minuartia verna*) and **Moonwort** (*Botrychium lunaria*). The High Peak Trail passes through the site and **Broad-leaved Helleborine** (*Epipactis helleborine*) is often found along its edges.

- **Location and directions**: 5km south of Matlock, above the valley of the River Derwent, between Cromford and Wirksworth.
- **Parking**: Black Rocks picnic site (SK290557)
- **Access**: Turn off A6 at Cromford traffic lights (SK296569), taking A5012 (B5036) signposted Wirksworth and Ashbourne. Almost immediately the A5012 turns right, but ignore this. Continue straight ahead on B5036 signposted Wirksworth up the steep Cromford Hill. At the top, turn left into Black Rocks picnic site, with car parks on two levels. From far end of upper car park cross over cycle trail to see lead-mining scars and the gritstone outcrops immediately ahead.

5.2 Carsington Water (SK250520)

This is a relatively new pump storage reservoir situated in the countryside 8km south-west of Matlock. There are a number of car parks but probably the best for plant life and for bird-watching is at Sheepwash, at the northern end of the reservoir near Carsington village. From the car park follow the path north towards the bird hide to see unimproved fields with orchids around the reservoir margins. This path is of fairly recent origin but already has a good variety of species to either side. It is possible to continue this walk down the eastern flank of the reservoir through Hall Wood. This has a good woodland flora and some interesting wet seepages with **Great Horsetail** (*Equisetum telmateia*). The full circuit is a 13km walk or cycle.

- **Location and directions**: 8km north-east of Ashbourne, on B5035 Ashbourne to Cromford road. Look for left turn to Carsington village, but take right turn immediately opposite it (SK249530) into Sheepwash car park. (If approaching from Cromford, ignore the right turn to Hopton and Carsington, but continue a further 1.5km alongside the reservoir before turning left at SK249530 to Sheepwash).
- **Parking**: Sheepwash car park (SK248528).
- **Access**: Follow path north from car park towards the bird hide. To continue the walk to the eastern flank of the reservoir, follow cycle path alongside the B5035 for 1.5km before turning sharp right down the reservoir-side path.

Evening light at Carsington Water in the Peak Fringe, May 2011 (DWT)

5.3 Cromford Canal SSSI (SK300570 to SK347519)

This disused canal extends south for 6km, from Cromford Wharf down the valley of the River Derwent to Ambergate and beyond. The whole length remains interesting for waterside plants, although the variety of submerged pondweeds has declined in recent years. **Skullcap** (*Scutellaria galericulata*) and **Hemp-agrimony** (*Eupatorium cannabinum*) are usually quite abundant at the canal margins while bridges and retaining walls are also worth examining for small ferns, and the banks even support large species such as **Small Teasel** (*Dipsacus pilosus*). Walking south reaches the Derbyshire Wildlife Trust reserve at Derwentside with fine springtime shows of **Wild Daffodils** (*Narcissus pseudonarcissus*).

- **Location and directions**: There are various car parks down the Derwent valley, but High Peak Junction (SK314560) gives access to the most interesting part of the canal (from SK313559 to SK348519). Note: this car park is on opposite side of river and canal from the A6. So, at Cromford traffic lights (SK296569) follow signs to Lea/Holloway/High Peak Junction and drive down road for 2.7km until car park is reached on the right.
- **Parking**: High Peak Junction (SK314560).
- **Access**: At rear of car park take footpath to cross bridges over both river and railway to reach Cromford Canal. Follow towpath in either direction. To view Derwentside Reserve turn left along towpath for about 500m. The Reserve occupies the land on the south bank of the canal down to the River Derwent. There is no public access, although the Daffodils can be easily seen from the towpath. Partly accessible to those with limited mobility.

Cromford Canal in the Peak Fringe, late summer 2003 (DWT)

5.4 Highoredish (SK351592)

This is a small area of varied habitat, including original heathland, situated 5km east of Matlock towards Ogston Reservoir. From the car park there are good views of the surrounding countryside which show the typical farmed landscape of this Character Area. A bridleway leads across semi-improved grassland with **Yellow-rattle** (*Rhinanthus minor*) before reaching the heath with **Mat-grass** (*Nardus stricta*), **Sheep's Sorrel** (*Rumex acetosella*) and **Western Gorse** (*Ulex gallii*). A small pond has **Broad-leaved Pondweed** (*Potamogeton natans*), **Water-starwort** (*Callitriche* spp.) and **Common Marsh-bedstraw** (*Galium palustre*).

- **Location and directions**: From Matlock take A615 east towards Alfreton. Fork left at Tansley (SK330595) onto B6014, then take third right after 1.5km down Coldharbour Lane. Car park is on the left after 700m.
- **Parking**: Highoredish Picnic Site (SK351596).
- **Access**: Cross road from car park and follow bridleway at SK350597, south through conifer plantation.

5.5 Linacre Woods (SK331726)

This is a large complex of woods and reservoirs with a good woodland flora including **Wood Barley** (*Hordelymus europaeus*) and **Soft Shield-fern** (*Polystichum setiferum*), and with **Wild Daffodil** (*Narcissus pseudonarcissus*) early in the year. The reservoirs also support a variety of aquatic species.

- **Location and directions**: 5km west of Chesterfield near Cutthorpe. From B6050, take a minor road 1km west of Cutthorpe, signposted south to Linacre Reservoirs. After 600m the first of a series of car parks is reached.
- **Parking**: Severn Trent car parks (SK334729).
- **Access**: From any of the car parks proceed down track on foot into the wood. There are numerous woodland paths to explore.

5.6 Shining Cliff Woods SSSI (SK335520)

This is a large area of damp mixed deciduous woodland with streams and flushes set on the steep slopes of a rocky valley. The top of the wood along the Peatpits Brook at SK323522 is floristically the richest area, with a typical damp woodland flora including **Small Balsam** (*Impatiens parviflora*) and the only patch of **Beech Fern** (*Phegopteris connectilis*) outside the Peak District. Other notable plants in the woods are **Narrow-leaved Bitter-cress** (*Cardamine impatiens*) and **Rue-leaved Saxifrage** (*Saxifraga tridactylites*). There are also considerable quantities of **Hemp-agrimony** (*Eupatorium cannabinum*) and **Sweet Cicely** (*Myrrhis odorata*) to be seen close to the river, the fragrance of the latter unmistakable on a warm day.

- **Location and directions**: Situated in the valley of the River Derwent, 9km south of Matlock, the wood is best approached at its southern end from the minor road that leaves the A6 westwards at Ambergate (SK348514). This is Holly Lane, just 175m south of the A610 T-junction and the Hurt Arms. (Look for small church on one corner and large cricket pitch on the other). Follow road across narrow bridge over River Derwent to where a wide track leads rightwards into woodland. It is possible to park on Holly Lane here (SK346514).
- **Parking**: Bottom of Holly Lane (SK346514).
- **Access**: Walk north along track off Holly Lane into woodland. Where it divides take left fork into Beggarswell Wood and the upper reaches of Peatpits Brook.

Further sites of interest in the Peak Fringe

- **Cocking Tor and Gregory Mine** (SK345616) An area of spoil heaps with lead-tolerant plants set amidst woodland and heath, just south of Ashover.
- **Allestree Park** (SK345405) A public park just north of Derby off the A6. Easily accessible with a variety of habitats including parkland, woodland, open water and a small sandstone quarry. This is a Local Nature Reserve.

6 SITES IN THE COAL MEASURES

Botanically this Landscape Character Area has benefited from the cessation of coal-mining activities and associated heavy industries. This has allowed derelict land to be turned over to country parks and natures reserves with the old railways becoming new walking and cycling trails.

6.1 The Avenue Washlands (SK398666)

This Derbyshire Wildlife Trust reserve is mainly on the site of a demolished coking works and occupies land on both sides of a railway line. On the western side, nearest the A61, the reserve is mainly marsh and open water, while on the east it is mainly scrub and grassland. This grassland is botanically the most interesting habitat with a number of species characteristic of damp, unimproved meadows including **Dyer's Greenweed** (*Genista tinctoria*) and **Southern Marsh-orchid** (*Dactylorhiza praetermissa*). Note that the grassland is grazed, and can only be viewed from the edges. There are also species characteristic of abandoned industrial sites such as **Viper's-bugloss** (*Echium vulgare*) and **Blue Fleabane** (*Erigeron acris*).

- **Location and directions**: Situated 4km south of Chesterfield. At southern edge of Wingerworth leave A61 and take a minor road east called Mill Lane (SK390672). After 300m park on roadside just beyond houses.
- **Parking**: Mill Lane roadside (SK393671).
- **Access**: Having parked, continue down the now narrow lane for 400m towards railway bridges. Enter the reserve on right either before or after them (SK396670). Part accessible to those with limited mobility.

The Avenue Washlands Reserve, a restored coking works near Chesterfield, September 2006 (DWT)

6.2 Erewash Meadows (SK445503)

This Wildlife Trust reserve is situated on the Derbyshire/ Nottinghamshire border and is co-owned by the two county Trusts. It is part of a large area of floodplain grassland and wetland, some of it shaped by mining subsidence, the local "flashes". It is a haven for birds, both breeding and visitors, and botanists are asked to keep to the paths to avoid disturbance to them. Typical wetland plants are **Reed Sweet-grass** (*Glyceria maxima*), **Greater Bird's-foot-trefoil** (*Lotus pedunculatus*), **Marsh Ragwort** (*Senecio aquaticus*) and **Lesser Water-parsnip** (*Berula erecta*). **Marsh Cudweed** (*Gnaphalium uliginosum*) and **Sneezewort** (*Achillea ptarmica*) also occur, with **Red Bartsia** (*Odontites vernus*) in drier areas.

- **Location and directions:** 5km east of Ripley. There are various access points. The best approach is from the A610 at Codnor (SK420496). At the A610/A6007 traffic lights, look for a minor road (Alfreton Road) to the north of the lights which goes to Golden Valley and Riddings. Continue on this for 2km, then turn right into Coach Road just before a bridge over the canal. The car park is on the left in a little over a kilometre by a reservoir.
- **Parking:** Codnor Park Reservoir car park (SK433515).
- **Access:** From Reservoir car park follow towpath eastwards along the far side of the canal. After passing under two roads and a railway line the path reaches open countryside. Continue along the overgrown canal as far as a disused railway embankment. From here the canal has been filled in and the reserve proper starts. Part accessible to those with limited mobility.

Erewash Meadows on the border with Nottinghamshire in the Coal Measures, June 2013 (DWT)

6.3 Woodside (SK448436)

This relatively new Derbyshire Wildlife Trust reserve contains a large expanse of semi-improved grassland, with patches of scrub and secondary woodland, which extends almost to the A6007. Neglected hay meadows with orchid species, vetches and other typical plants such as **Great Burnet** (*Sanguisorba officinalis*) are being managed by the Trust with the introduction of suitable grazing animals. The wet meadows are being similarly upgraded. Where the reserve adjoins Shipley Lake, on the site of a now defunct theme park, there are large, open areas of broken tarmac which support the likes of **Wild Carrot** (*Daucus carota*) and **Flattened Meadow-grass** (*Poa compressa*).

- **Location and directions:** Between Ilkeston and Heanor, just west of the A6007. The reserve is best accessed from car parks in Shipley Country Park, the nearest being at Mapperley Reservoir. Take A609 between Ilkeston and Stanley Common. On eastern edge of West Hallam turn off north at crossroads signposted Mapperley (SK435421). Drive straight through village and across the dam wall of the reservoir. The car park is immediately on the left.
- **Parking:** Mapperley Reservoir car park (SK434436).
- **Access:** Across the road from car park is Mapperley Wood Nature Reserve. A path skirts round the woodland, leading to Woodside Reserve. Part accessible to those with limited mobility.

6.4 Straw's Bridge (SK452413)

Located near Ilkeston, this former opencast mine is now given over to recreational use. This area is also known as Pewit Carr and is a Local Nature Reserve (LNR). The habitats are very varied. The wet alder woodland known as "carr" has formed in the "flashes", which

are areas of mining subsidence. There are also a number of open ponds, a species-rich hay meadow, a dismantled railway and large brownfield sites. Close to the car park are two notable records: **Smith's Pepperwort** (*Lepidium heterophyllum*) and **Buttonweed** (*Cotula coronopifolia*). The ponds beyond the car park have good marginal flora and within them are species such as **Fan-leaved Water-crowfoot** (*Ranunculus circinatus*) and **Mare's-tail** (*Hippuris vulgaris*). At the north-west of the site much of the land is returning to scrub and heath but the open areas support **Squirreltail Fescue** (*Vulpia bromoides*), **Rat's-tail Fescue** (*Vulpia myuros*) and **Wild Mignonette** (*Reseda lutea*).

- **Location and directions:** 1km west of Ilkeston. The large car park is obvious and signposted on the north of the A609 beside a lake.
- **Parking:** Straw's Bridge car park (SK452413).
- **Access:** Access to the LNR is beyond and to the north of the car park lake.

6.5 Moss Valley SSSI (SK415802)

The existence of these attractive woodlands and meadows between Sheffield and Eckington, in a part of the county perceived to be heavily industrialised, will come as a surprise to many. The site demonstrates many of the features of the Character Area that existed before man exploited its resources and which led to its subsequent urbanisation. The mixed broad-leaved woodland is probably of ancient origin with the presence of **Yellow Archangel** (*Lamiastrum galeobdolon*) tending to support this. The Moss brook flows through the site creating pools, open marshy grassland and shady wet woodland. Wet grassland plants found here include **Common Bistort** (*Persicaria bistorta*) and **Common Spike-rush** (*Eleocharis palustris*) while the drier neutral grassland has **Devil's-bit Scabious** (*Succisa pratensis*) and **Betony** (*Betonica officinalis*). The valley and the surrounding hedgerows provide a rare chance to see trees at all stages of growth with the dead and rotting wood providing ideal conditions to support other species and maintain biodiversity.

- **Location and directions:** 1km north of Eckington. On the B6056 Eckington to Dronfield road, 2km west of Eckington at Marsh Lane (SK406791), take the minor road north to Ford. Follow this through a sharp right hand bend into village, then at next sharp left hand bend the car park is on the right.
- **Parking:** Car park at SK401804.
- **Access:** From car park follow footpath eastwards round the pond and along The Moss.

Further sites of interest on the Coal Measures
- **Chesterfield Canal** (SK392737 to SK415746) Waterside plants can be seen both on the canal and on the banks of the nearby River Rother. There is still much derelict land that may be accessed from the canal. Part of this area is also known as Bluebank Pools Local Nature Reserve.
- **Poolsbrook Country Park** (SK438737) is on the site of a former colliery near Staveley, with a mix of woodland, grassland and open water. The older grassland exhibits interesting species such as **Pepper-saxifrage** (*Silaum silaus*).

7 SITES IN THE CLAYLANDS

Being a rural area dominated by improved grassland and with few settlements does not mean the loss of all botanical interest here. There are reminders of a busier past in the form of deserted villages, such as Hungry Bentley (SK178386). Here the fields and nearby brooks display a varied flora with plants such as **Pink Water-speedwell** (*Veronica catenata*) and

Spring-sedge (*Carex caryophyllea*); the hummocks of the ruins and the medieval ridge and furrow fields having deterred wholesale agricultural improvement. The boundary hedges compensate for the lack of woodland by sheltering **Dog's Mercury** (*Mercurialis perennis*), **Common Dog-violet** (*Viola riviniana*) and **Yellow Archangel** (*Lamiastrum galeobdolon*). **Primroses** (*Primula vulgaris*) are abundant in the hedgerows around Great Cubley (SK165381) and even along the A515 to Ashbourne. By taking a little care the botanist may find that walking the quiet lanes of this Landscape Character Area can sometimes be quite productive.

7.1 Holly Wood (SK173428)

This small woodland near Ashbourne is a Derbyshire Wildlife Trust reserve. There is a mixed deciduous woodland canopy with marshy areas and pond. The wet areas typically display **Marsh-marigold** (*Caltha palustris*), **Remote Sedge (***Carex remota***)** and **Opposite-leaved Golden-saxifrage** (*Chrysosplenium oppositifolium*). There is a good show of **Bluebells** (*Hyacinthoides non-scripta*) and **daffodils** (*Narcissus* spp.) in spring, although many of the latter are clearly planted. A more notable plant here is **Upland Enchanter's-nightshade** (*Circaea × intermedia*).

- **Location and directions**: 4km south of Ashbourne. Head south on A515, passing through Clifton, then take second minor road on the left (at SK171433) signposted to Edlaston. The wood is about 500m down the lane on the right hand side, in the bottom of a small valley.
- **Parking**: Very limited roadside parking at SK174431.
- **Access**: Wood is adjacent to south side of Edlaston Lane.

Holly Wood on the edge of the Claylands near Ashbourne, May 2014 (DWT)

7.2 Kedleston Park SSSI (SK309409)

Kedleston Hall near Derby is a National Trust property, much of which is a Site of Special Scientific Interest. It lies on the north-western outskirts of Derby between the villages of Quarndon and Kirk Langley. The majority of the estate is classic parkland with scattered trees, many of them veterans, over grassland. There is also old woodland and open water with fringing marshy vegetation including **Greater Tussock-sedge** (*Carex paniculata*). The Long Walk has been landscaped along a narrow strip of woodland around a large paddock which gives good shows of **Bluebells** (*Hyacinthoides non-scripta*) and **Pink Purslane** (*Claytonia sibirica*) in spring.

A veteran pollarded tree in Kedleston Park, June 2007 (DWT)

- **Location and directions**: 6km north-west of Derby. From the city ring road take A52 signposted Ashbourne for 5km to Kirk Langley village. At crossroads (SK288388) turn right onto minor road, northwards towards Kedleston. Take the next right, proceed for 2.5km keeping right at a T-junction, and the hall and park entrance is on the right hand side. An alternative access route is *via* Kedleston Road near Quarndon.
- **Parking**: Car park within Kedleston Park (SK309403) free for National Trust members.
- **Access**: From NT car park turn right into park and follow the ha-ha wall round to the right. This leads to the start of the "Long Walk". Another interesting route is the "Wilderness Walk". To access this, walk over bridge crossing the lake on the main drive, then turn north along the shore of the lake into Hay Wood.

7.3 Sedsall Rough Area (SK113381)

This is an area of ancient woodland on a steep slope overlooking the valley of the River Dove on the extreme western edge of the county. There is only limited access to the Rough by footpath but the route to it travels through semi-improved grasslands with marshy patches along the bank of the river. **Giant Hogweed** (*Heracleum mantegazzianum*) may be seen on the river banks. The path is part of the Staffordshire Way and can be followed for some considerable distance south through riverside grasslands. Ultimately this brings you to Sidford Wood at SK105354 which is only 2km or so north-east of Uttoxeter.

- **Location and directions**: Between Ashbourne and Uttoxeter, about 1.5km south-east of the small Staffordshire town of Rocester. The area is reached from a minor road that runs east through Rocester from the B5030, eventually meeting the A515 at Great Cubley. If approaching from Rocester, cross bridge over River Dove and after 400m look for lay-by on left side of the road. From the opposite direction this is just after the entrance to Abbotsholme School.
- **Parking**: Lay-by at SK119391.
- **Access**: Two public footpaths run south from here down the Dove valley. One follows the private road to Abbotsholme School; the other leaves the road by the bridge over the Dove and runs alongside the river. Both arrive at Sedsall Rough, beyond the school, at the point where the river and wood almost meet at SK113382.

7.4 Shirley Park (SK210420)

This is part of the Osmaston Estate near Ashbourne. At first sight the Park may not seem very productive; there are only two footpaths and both pass through conifer plantations. But by Shirley Brook to the south of the Park a boardwalk leads across an interesting area of swamp vegetation with **Greater Tussock-sedge** (*Carex paniculata*) and **Bristle Club-rush** (*Isolepis setacea*). The plantation rides are very wet and support a number of species that may be expected in that habitat, including **Water-pepper** (*Persicaria hydropiper*). In drier areas **Climbing Corydalis** (*Ceratocapnos claviculata)* may be found. There is also an ornamental lake with its associated marginal flora.

- **Location and directions**: The Park is 5km south-east of Ashbourne, and best accessed from Shirley village. If approaching from Derby on A52, turn left about 1.5km beyond Brailsford (SK237419), signposted Shirley. Upon reaching Shirley turn right at T-junction and drive on past the church (where W.R. Linton the 1903 *Flora* writer is buried). Where the road forks there is room to park on the left.
- **Parking**: Limited roadside parking on Church Lane at SK217417.
- **Access**: Go up steps from road to follow a public footpath west across fields to Shirley Brook. This crosses the brook at SK210416 by the swamp, then turns right into Shirley Park.

7.5 Radbourne Hall (SK286356)

Although privately owned and modest in comparison to Kedleston, the parkland at Radbourne displays characteristic species. The footpath across the Park passes through mixed woodland, and the lanes surrounding the estate provide views into various copses and coverts. Typical woodland grasses are well represented by **Wood Millet** (*Milium effusum*), **Giant Fescue** (*Schedonorus giganteus*), **Hairy-brome** (*Bromopsis ramosa*) and **Bearded Couch** (*Elymus caninus*). There are also woodland flowers such as **Wood Speedwell** (*Veronica montana*) and **Three-nerved Sandwort** (*Moehringia trinervia*). The old pasture on the estate contains **Adder's-tongue** (*Ophioglossum vulgatum*).

- **Location and directions**: The Hall is 7km west of Derby, and easy walking distance from Mickleover. By car it is best reached from Radbourne Lane, or the B5020 that runs between Mickleover and Kirk Langley (itself accessible from the A52). At SK307364 the B5020 makes a sharp turn northwards. Take the minor road here, westwards towards Trusley. In a little under 2km, where the footpath through the Park crosses the road, there is a wide verge suitable for cars.
- **Parking**: Radbourne Lane, roadside verge (SK291355)
- **Access**: Direct public footpath access northward through gate from road. Note there is no public access to the Park in general.

7.6 Great Northern Greenway (SK308359 to SK261298)

This former railway line runs south-westward from Mickleover on the west side of Derby, towards the village of Hilton. It is now part of Route 54 of the National Cycle Network. As well as embankments affording views over this Character Area, there are flatter sections flanked by streams and marshy areas with **Lesser Pond-sedge** (*Carex acutiformis*), **Reed Sweet-grass (***Glyceria maxima*) and **Common Reed** (*Phragmites australis*). The shadier streams are of interest in the spring with **Moschatel** (*Adoxa moschatellina*) and **Ramsons** (*Allium ursinum*). The wider verges support **Hairy Violet** (*Viola hirta*), **Small Toadflax** (*Chaenorhinum minus*) and **Welted Thistle** (*Carduus crispus*).

- **Location and directions**: From Derby, take A516 towards Etwall, leaving at roundabout (SK275326) to enter the village. From this direction take first turning on the right (Sutton Lane). Travel to end of lane to park.

- **Parking**: Small parking area at end of Sutton Lane, Etwall (SK267322).
- **Access**: A gate bars entry to vehicles but proceed down here on foot to access steps onto the Greenway.
    Alternative start: Car park off Station Road, Mickleover (SK308358). Descend down metalled track to gain access to the Greenway, just past former station buildings. This entry point allows connection to Radbourne Hall (see above).

Further sites of interest on the Claylands

- **Mercaston Marsh SSSI** (SK272430) Tall fen and marshy grassland with a wide range of marshland herbs. An outstanding lowland valley mire and an exceptional habitat for the county.
- **Mugginton Bottoms SSSI** (SK269435) Similar to Mercaston Marsh but more acidic. Together they make up a single SSSI – the largest and most species-rich area of marsh in Derbyshire.

8 SITES IN THE TRENT VALLEY

The corridor of the River Trent with its marshes and waterbodies provides the main stronghold in Derbyshire for a number of wetland plants including **Hemlock Water-dropwort** (*Oenanthe crocata*), **Common Club-rush** (*Schoenoplectus lacustris*) and **Purple-loosestrife** (*Lythrum salicaria*).

8.1 Anchor Church (SK339272)

This is not a church at all but a hermit's cave cut into a natural outcrop of sandstone overlooking the River Trent, near Ingleby. The path to the hermitage enables a number of habitats to be explored including acid grassland and semi-natural woodland. The bank of the fast-flowing River Trent displays a different flora to that of the quieter backwater and marshy area by the Church. Notable plants include **Common Meadow-rue** (*Thalictrum flavum*), **Shining Pondweed** (*Potamogeton lucens*) and **Navelwort** (*Umbilicus rupestris*) on the outcrop itself.

- **Location and directions**: 9km south of Derby off minor road between Swarkestone and Repton. From A50 follow A514 over River Trent (in direction of Swarkestone Bridge), but turn immediately right after crossing river. Continue for 3km on minor road to hamlet of Ingleby. As road makes a sweep to the left at end of hamlet it is possible to park on the roadside.
- **Parking**: Roadside verge (SK346269).
- **Access**: Cross road and go back a short distance to a farm gate and signposted footpath. The route westwards is clearly marked, initially down to the River then along its bank to the "Church".

8.2 Hilton Gravel Pits SSSI (SK250314)

Now a Derbyshire Wildlife Trust reserve, this was one of the earlier sites for gravel extraction in the county. It was simply abandoned when it was worked out, rather than restored. This has left open areas of deep water but the shallower areas were soon colonised with dense willow scrub and woodland. The Wildlife Trust now works to maintain glades in the woodland for fine stands of **orchids** (*Dactylorhiza* spp. and *Neottia ovata*). **Purple Toothwort (***Lathraea clandestina*) can be found here amongst **willows** (*Salix* spp.). The reserve is important for its population of **Native Black-poplars** (*Populus nigra* ssp. *betulifolia*) found in relic hedges on the site. The marshes and swamps surrounding the pools contain **Cyperus Sedge** (*Carex pseudocyperus*).

- **Location and Directions**: 11km south-west of Derby by village of Hilton. The best approach is from Derby on the A516. At junction with A50 (SK255312) take third exit at the first roundabout onto a minor road (Willowpit Lane). After 150m turn off left into small parking area.

Hilton Gravel Pits, a restored industrial site now an SSSI (DWT)

- **Parking and access**: Park off Willowpit Lane (SK253313) with direct reserve access. Disabled/wheelchair access to 50% of reserve.

8.3 Trent and Mersey Canal, Willington (SK294286)

Willington is a village close by the River Trent. It is immediately recognisable by the vast cooling towers of the former power station which still stand at the eastern end of the village. There is easy, pleasant walking along the towpath in either direction with **Orange Balsam** (*Impatiens capensis*) and **Marsh Woundwort** (*Stachys palustris*) being examples of a number of marsh and waterside plants that will be encountered. If turning right at the canal to walk north-east back towards Derby, the towpath passes old flooded borrow pits at SK302291. These support further aquatic vegetation including both species of **Bulrush** (*Typha* spp.) and **Ivy-leaved Duckweed** (*Lemna trisulca*). Returning by the alternative footpath at SK304293 that passes between the railway and the former power station gives an entirely different flora as the soil is thin and dry. Here may be found **Small Cudweed** (*Filago minima*), **Squirreltail Fescue** (*Vulpia bromoides*) and possibly **Bird's-foot** (*Ornithopus perpusillus*).
- **Location and directions**: 9.5km south-west of Derby, near A38/A50 junction. From A38/A50 roundabout, take exit onto B5008 (signposted Willington and Repton). In 1.3km at Willington village, turn left onto A5132 (signposted Swarkestone). In 100m turn left into car park just before railway bridge.
- **Parking and access**: Willington Picnic Site and car park, The Green. (SK295286). Direct access onto towpath.

8.4 Trent Lock (SK490311)

This site is situated at the meeting point of the Rivers Trent and Soar with the Erewash and the Cranfleet Canals. A number of interesting walks are possible from Trent Lock car park. To the east, following the Cranfleet Canal, there are grassland plants such as **Spiny Restharrow** (*Ononis spinosa*) and **Field Mouse-ear** (*Cerastium arvense*); to the north there is the Erewash Canal with **Flowering-rush** (*Butomus umbellatus*) and **Yellow Water-lily** (*Nuphar lutea*); to the west along the banks of the Trent are various **Willows** (*Salix* spp.) and a **hybrid thistle** (*Carduus* × *stangii*). Although it is often very crowded in good weather the pub garden and the steps down to the river are worth examining. **Fat Duckweed** (*Lemna gibba*), **Wood Small-reed** (*Calamagrostis*

epigejos) and **Nodding Bur-marigold** (*Bidens cernua*) have all been recorded here.
- **Location and directions**: 15km south-east of Derby, and due south of Long Eaton, Trent Lock is best approached from the A52 Derby–Nottingham road where it meets the M1 at Junction 25. At junction roundabout, take minor road that runs south (signposted Long Eaton). After 1km go right at roundabout onto B6002 (SK473347). Follow this to Long Eaton over two roundabouts for 2.5km to reach fourth roundabout in centre of Long Eaton by railway station. Take third exit here onto B6540 signposted Castle Donington, going under a railway bridge. After 800m, turn left down Lock Lane at SK476316, clearly signed to Trent Lock, to reach car park at end.
- **Parking**: Large public car park at far end of Lock Lane by river (SK489312).
- **Access**: Direct access from car park to walks described above.

9 SITES IN THE PARKLANDS

The essence of this Character Area is the beautiful landscaped parks with their veteran trees. As much of it is now within the National Forest, the planting of new woodland will lend continuity to the area.

9.1 Calke Park SSSI (SK364226)

Calke Abbey is a large National Trust property with associated parkland close to the estate village of Ticknall. In the Park there are extensive areas of semi-improved neutral and acidic grasslands with veteran trees, several ponds with surrounding marshes, and large expanses of plantation woodlands. There are good stands of **Sweet Chestnut** (*Castanea sativa*) in the north-east of the park with specimen trees, such as **London Plane** (*Platanus* × *hispanica*) to the south, and numerous large veteran **Oaks** (*Quercus robur*). In the grasslands nearer the house may be found **Hound's-tongue** (*Cynoglossum officinale*) and **Toothwort** (*Lathraea squamaria*), with **Fern-grass** (*Catapodium rigidum*) growing amongst the cobbles surrounding the main outbuildings, and **Musk** (*Mimulus moschatus*) at the base of the Hall itself. Much of the estate north of the Hall is also a National Nature Reserve.
- **Location and directions**: 13km south of Derby at Ticknall village. From A50 south of Derby, follow A514 (signposted to Swadlincote) for 7km to reach Ticknall. A one-way system operates in the park so it must be entered from the Ticknall side. The entrance is clearly signed, and is next to stone bridge over the road at SK356240. A long, tree-lined avenue leads to the National Trust property and adjacent car park.
- **Parking and access**: On-site car park (free to members), or use village car park (SK352240) and walk into Park on public footpaths.

9.2 Ticknall Limeyards SSSI (SK362238)

This site consists of flooded limestone quarries which lie on either side of a track at the eastern end of Ticknall village. It is actually part of the NT Calke Park Estate and is more correctly known as Ticknall Quarries SSSI. The surrounding calcareous grassland supports a typical limestone flora with **Bee Orchid** (*Ophrys apifera*) and **Autumn Gentian** (*Gentianella amarella*) while the scrub areas, unusually for Derbyshire, are festooned with the trailing stems of **Traveller's-joy** (*Clematis vitalba*). Although this site has developed only through quarrying activities, it has become botanically rich with very varied habitats.
- **Location and Directions**: At Ticknall village, 13km south of Derby. Reach Ticknall via the A514 (see 9.1 above) and park in the village car park, 500m beyond bridge.

Carboniferous Limestone outcrops at Ticknall Limeyards, August 2004 (P. & G. Dishart)

- **Parking**: Ticknall car park (SK352240).
- **Access**: Return to main road and turn left to walk to a signposted track at SK360240 which leads into the Limeyards.

9.3 Carver's Rocks SSSI (SK330227)

This is a Derbyshire Wildlife Trust reserve, situated at the southern end of Foremark Reservoir on a small outlier of Upper Carboniferous sandstone. Here can be found one of the last remaining areas of lowland heathland in Derbyshire. Initially the access path passes through modern plantation woodland, but this soon changes to semi-natural wet woodland with **Alder Buckthorn** (*Frangula alnus*) and **Great Horsetail** (*Equisetum telmateia*). On top of the sandstone outcrop on the left is an area with **Heather** (*Calluna vulgaris*) and **Wavy Hair-grass** (*Deschampsia*

The remnant area of Heather (*Calluna vulgaris*) at Carver's Rocks, September 2010 (DWT)

flexuosa) which is part of the important lowland heath on the reserve. The bottom of the valley, at the head of the reservoir, has a small area of marsh/fen with **Purple Moor-grass** (*Molinia caerulea*), **Narrow Buckler-fern** (*Dryopteris carthusiana*) and *Sphagnum* moss.

- **Location and directions**: The reserve is adjacent to the A514, 2.5km south of Ticknall, and 14km south of Derby. Visitors must park on the roadside as access into the reserve has been closed to vehicles, and is for pedestrian use only. The entrance is on the western side of the road just below the crest of a hill.
- **Parking**: Roadside parking only, on A514, at SK334222.
- **Access**: Follow the former access road north-west for about 400m to a small gate and footpath sign on the left. This is the entrance to the reserve.

9.4 South Wood and Bryan's Coppice (SK362207)

This is a National Trust woodland, consisting mainly of mixed wet semi-natural woodland with a canopy of mature **Pedunculate Oak** (*Quercus robur*) and **Ash** (*Fraxinus excelsior*) with an understorey of **Hazel** (*Corylus avellana*).

- **Location and directions**: On the county boundary near Calke Abbey, 16km south of Derby. From the A514 at Ticknall (see 9.1 above), take B5006 towards Ashby-de-la-Zouch. After 1.5km, turn left onto Staunton Lane (SK347226). After 2km, at T-junction with Heath Lane, park carefully on roadside verge.
- **Parking**: Roadside verge near T-junction (SK363212).
- **Access**: Take footpath south-east across field to enter the wood.

9.5 Dimminsdale SSSI (SK375218)

This is one of two adjacent Wildlife Trust reserves that straddle the boundary between Leicestershire and Derbyshire. It is a series of flooded limestone quarries surrounded by semi-natural woodland, famous for its magnificent show of **Snowdrops** (*Galanthus nivalis*) in early spring. The other reserve, Spring Wood, has access restricted to Trust members only.

- **Location and directions**: Approximately 4km south of Melbourne, near Staunton Harold Reservoir. From Melbourne take B587 south for some 2.5km to reach a minor road on the right signposted Calke at SK384220. Follow this and, after the road takes a sharp turn to the left, a large car park will come into view on the left
- **Parking**: Severn Trent's Staunton Harold car park (SK378220).
- **Access**: From car park carry on walking down road, cross over the end of the reservoir and as the road climbs again the reserve is signposted to the left.

10 SITES IN THE SOUTHERN COAL MEASURES

With the demise of the extractive industries, and the rise of the National Forest initiative, this Character Area is becoming more accessible, which will be advantageous to botanists in future years.

10.1 Gresley Woods, Swainspark (SK295175)

A restored area of old coal and clay workings which has returned to woodland, scrub and acid grassland. There are also streams and wet areas where plants of interest include **Pale Sedge** (*Carex pallescens*), and **Wood Small-reed** (*Calamagrostis epigejos*). There is still some rough ground – a remnant of opencast mining, but this is gradually maturing. The area holds the distinction of having one of the very few records in southern Derbyshire for the rare native perennial **Trailing Tormentil** (*Potentilla anglica*).

- **Location and directions:** Situated about 8km south-east of Burton upon Trent. Take A444 from Burton towards Castle Gresley. At roundabout continue on towards Overseal. In 1km turn left at small roundabout (SK289167) onto minor road (Park Road) towards Albert Village. About 800m along, and just past the railway, it is possible to park on the roadside.
- **Parking and access:** On Occupation Road (SK296170). Alternatively use large car park further along road on right (at SK298173) from which there are footpaths accessing the area across the road.

11 SITES IN THE MEASE LOWLANDS

This is very much a developing area botanically, with the new woodlands of the National Forest enriching the landscape here for the future and mitigating the effects of the intensive farming practiced in some other parts of this Landscape Character Area. The River Mease is the only Special Area of Conservation (SAC) in Lowland Derbyshire, but was designated for its animal life, not its botanical interest.

11.1 Coton in the Elms (SK245153)

Coton village acts as a convenient central point from which to explore the various habitats of the area. Until recently it was surrounded by a modern farmed landscape, but there have been both public and private initiatives to restore woodland, wildflower meadows and ponds here which are increasing its botanical interest. Both **Soft Hornwort** (*Ceratophyllum submersum*) and **Greater Spearwort** (*Ranunculus lingua*) have been found in new ponds recently. A car park gives immediate access to Coton Wood, which is one of the new National Forest plantings, with an even larger area of new woodland just past the southern end of Coton. Walking north to Rosliston or east to Botany Bay takes in both the farmland and a few semi-wild areas on field margins that have escaped cultivation.

- **Location and directions**: Coton is situated 8km south of Burton upon Trent in the far south of the county, between the villages of Rosliston and Lullington. From Derby or Burton, take the A38 south to exit at the Barton Turn (SK203183). Follow road east towards Walton-on-Trent. Cross over the river by a narrow bridge with traffic lights to reach a staggered junction. Go left, then immediately right, to continue straight on. Follow minor road through to Coton. Bear right to follow road towards Lullington. Car park is just south of the village on the left, past the last house.
- **Parking**: Coton village car park (SK245148).
- **Access**: Footpaths run south from here into the area, or in other directions from within the village.

11.2 Grange Wood and Potter's Wood (SK275145)

These adjacent sites form one of the largest, best developed areas of semi-natural woodland within south Derbyshire. Much of it is ancient oak woodland, but there has been extensive new planting further west. **Small-leaved Lime** (*Tilia cordata*) is also present and there is a developed understorey with **Bluebells** (*Hyacinthoides non-scripta*), **Woodruff** (*Galium odoratum*) and **Wood Horsetail** (*Equisetum sylvaticum*). There is no public access to these woods but from the car park a network of footpaths trace the periphery. The new woodland contains some mature trees, and there are wet scrapes to encourage aquatic life.

- **Location and directions**: 2km south-west of Overseal and 6km south-west of Swadlincote. From Derby or Burton, take A38 south to exit at Barton Turn (SK203183), following signs eastwards through Walton-on-Trent. Then follow directions

to Coton (see 11.1 above). At Coton, turn left onto Elms Road after church, then right at T-junction (SK246154) bearing left on Chapel Street, following sign to Overseal. In just over 2km there is a small car park at Sisters Wood on the left hand side.
- **Parking**: Sisters Wood car park (SK265143).
- **Access**: Use local footpath network or road-walking to reach Grange Wood in 500m.

11.3 Rosliston Forestry Centre (SK242175)

This is the visitor centre for the new National Forest. Obviously its core purpose is to inform the public on the plans for, and progress of the Forest. But amongst the newly planted woodland there are some interesting areas of wet grassland and marsh that should not be ignored by the botanist. As with Coton in the Elms, a walk in the surrounding area will reveal other habitats, too. An example is the footpath from the main street of Rosliston to Caldwell (SK246166) which crosses arable fields with a variety of weed species, giving way to wet areas flanked by older woodland with **Clustered Dock** (*Rumex conglomeratus*). It finally reaches a fishermen's pond surrounded by trees and an eclectic mix of plants that probably had their origin as part of the grounds of Caldwell Hall.

- **Location and Directions**: 5km south of Burton and 1km north of Rosliston village. From Derby or Burton take A38 south to exit at Barton Turn (SK203183). Follow signs eastwards through Walton-on-Trent, reaching a staggered junction. Go left, then immediately right onto Coton Road. Continue on, bearing leftwards to follow road towards Rosliston for approximately 2.5km. Turn left at T-junction (SK242170), and Forestry Centre is 800m down road on the right.
- **Parking and Access**: Rosliston Forestry Centre, visitors pay-and-display car park (SK242176) from which paths lead round the site.

Derbyshire Wildlife Trust (DWT) reserves

Derbyshire
Wildlife Trust

Listed below are the names and map references of all 42 reserves owned or managed by DWT. Visit their website for more details on access, parking and biodiversity interests.

* Those marked with an asterisk are by permit for Trust members only.

1	Barton Pool	SK504331*
2	Broadhurst Edge Wood	SJ999875
3	Brockholes Wood SSSI	SK072996
4	Carr Vale	SK459701
5	Carver's Rocks SSSI	SK330227
6	Chee Dale SSSI	SK120727
7	Cromford Canal LNR/SSSI	SK384519, SK332543
8	Derwentside	SK316556, SK326554
9	Duckmanton Railway Cutting SSSI	SK423703*
10	Erewash Meadows	SK441517, SK446496, SK447487
11	Golden Brook Storage Lagoon	SK470332*
12	Hartington Meadows	SK150611
13	Hillbridge and Park Woods	SK010787
14	Hilton Gravel Pits SSSI	SK249315
15	Hollinhill and Markland Grips	SK509752, SK507748
16	Holly Wood	SK173430
17	Hopton Quarry SSSI	SK262562*
18	Ladybower Wood SSSI	SK205867
19	Lock Lane Ash Tip	SK485318*
20	Long Clough	SK031925
21	Mapperley Wood	SK439433

22	Miller's Dale Quarry SSSI	SK140731
23	Morley Brickyards SSSI	SK388418
24	North Wingfield	SK404643
25	Oakerthorpe LNR	SK390553
26	Overdale	SK185805
27	Priestcliffe Lees SSSI	SK147730, SK155728
28	Risley Glebe	SK461359
29	Rose End Meadows	SK293567
30	Rowsley Sidings	SK260650
31	Spring Wood SSSI	SK379225*
32	Watford Lodge LNR	SK007805
33	Wyver Lane	SK345493*
34	Gang Mine	SK284558
35	Willington Gravel Pits	SK285274
36	Hadfields Quarry	SK162822*
37	Deep Dale and Topley Pike SSSI	SK099717
38	Cramside Wood SSSI	SK166730
39	The Avenue Washlands	SK398668
40	Drakelow	SK223204*
41	Woodside	SK448436
42	Lea Wood	SK318558

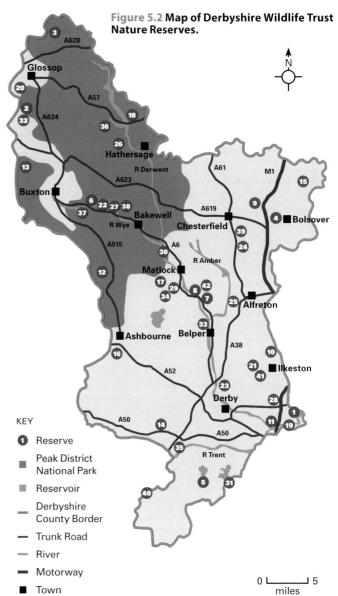

Figure 5.2 Map of Derbyshire Wildlife Trust Nature Reserves.

KEY

- ● Reserve
- ■ Peak District National Park
- ▦ Reservoir
- -- Derbyshire County Border
- — Trunk Road
- — River
- ▬ Motorway
- ■ Town

0 ⌞————⌟ 5
miles

CHAPTER 6

The Derbyshire Flora Project

Alan Willmot and Nick Moyes

Introduction

The **Derbyshire Flora Project** began life back in 1994 when UK botanists responded to a proposal from the Botanical Society of the British Isles (BSBI) to produce a new National Atlas of vascular plants. Their project was called **Atlas 2000**, and covered all of Britain and Ireland. Derbyshire's botanists joined forces to help them, and soon began recording the distribution of our county's wild plants in a scheme we named **"Derbyshire Flora 2000"**. That task ended in December 2000 with the submission of our county's survey results and the appearance two years later of the *New Atlas of the British and Irish Flora* (Preston *et al.* 2002).

A second aim of the Derbyshire Flora Project was to collect enough new data to enable us to publish a completely updated book on our wild plants, offering distribution maps and accounts of every known species. It would take the name of the previous work – ***The Flora of Derbyshire*** – which had appeared thirty years previously (Clapham 1969).

Clapham's 1969 *Flora* had been followed by two later **Supplements**, the second of which listed new records up to 1979 (Hollick & Patrick 1980). But since that time there have been significant and often devastating losses in habitat and species diversity across many parts of Derby and Derbyshire, mostly through intensification of farming practices and urban development (see **Chapter 4**). Some gains to our flora also appear to have occurred because many introduced species are now routinely recorded by botanists, whereas in the past they were ignored. It was felt that a new county flora was needed to record all these changes. It would be of interest to botanists, students, general naturalists, professional ecologists and conservation workers.

Since 1997 the project has been led by two people. Dr Alan Willmot is Derbyshire's County Plant Recorder for the BSBI, and a retired lecturer in biology at The University of Derby. Computerisation and preparation of data has been overseen since the project's inception by Nick Moyes, Keeper of Natural Sciences at Derby Museum & Art Gallery for 25 years. Both undertook much of this work in their own time, and also worked closely over the years with around 100 volunteer recorders and data inputters. Many of the botanical recorders worked on their own, whilst others helped on field meetings specifically arranged to collect data for the *Flora*. Regular members of these recording sessions became known as the Derbyshire Flora Group some of whom are shown here (see also Acknowledgements).

Survey method

The national Atlas 2000 survey required data to be collected only to hectad accuracy (10km × 10km squares). This was far too coarse for a new county *Flora*, so we decided to map plants at tetrads accuracy (2km × 2km squares), whilst always encouraging data to be collected at monad level (1km × 1km squares), or even better for interesting or rare species. This would match the accuracy of records given in Clapham's (1969) *Flora*. Data was to be gathered by volunteers and entered by more helpers onto a RECORDER 3 database at the Derbyshire Biological Records Centre, housed at Derby Museum. This would then pass on data to the BSBI for the national atlas and, using DMAP software, produce maps for the new *Flora of Derbyshire*. It all sounded so easy!

Appeals went out to all known botanists and naturalists in the county for help to gather records. Many people sent in short lists or individual records, but a number of the more able volunteers were allocated to take charge of collecting records for particular hectads. Where people could not be found, meetings of local botanists were organised to cover these. At first the standard BSBI plant recording card for the Midlands was used (known by its reference number as an "RP28 card"). Printed with abbreviated Latin names, they were found to be rather off-putting for some users. So local recording cards were produced using English names, showing just 340 of the most frequently recorded or characteristic Derbyshire plants. These so-called "TC2" plant recording cards proved popular and were used by numerous recorders at all but the expert level (see **Figure 6.1**). A second plant-recording card was then designed for use by hill-walkers and naturalists in the high moorland areas. Here the quantity of species encountered is incredibly low, but the number of map squares covered in a day can be high. Five or six monads could be surveyed and recorded on a single card.

All records and cards were first sent to the county recorder for checking and to manually tally up the number of species being recorded per hectad. This was done to ensure reasonably uniform coverage across Derbyshire. They then reached Derby Museum where a team of volunteers over a number of years entered them all onto a RECORDER 3 database. In 1999 we generated a species list with latest years from this database for every hectad in the county. Matched for data inputting errors against the list compiled by the county recorder, each was then forwarded electronically to the BSBI as Derbyshire's contribution to the *New Atlas of the British and Irish Flora* (Preston *et al.* 2002).

The publication of the national Atlas meant that attention could finally be turned towards our own *Derbyshire Flora*. The first step was to produce a basic **Checklist** of all the vascular plants known in the county as a guide to what needed to be included within it,

Flora group members Staveley August 2013 – Seated left to right Rodney Hyde, Brian Gough with Jason, Mary Smith, Claire Smith and Alan Willmot; standing left to right Graeme Coles and Ken Balkow (Ken Balkow)

Figure 6.1 Front page of Common Plant Recording Card (TC2), devised at Derby Museum for the Flora project.

and to indicate the county status of each. This task was helped by a national exercise known as the "Vice-county Census Catalogue" (VCCC) that had been on-going for some years, too. This was a BSBI scheme intended to produce a definitive list of all vascular plants growing in each individual British vice-county. Roy Smith, as the then county recorder for Derbyshire (v.c.57), had been responsible for collating our county's contribution back in the early nineties. In the event, our Derbyshire list appeared just ahead of the national one. *A Checklist of the Plants of Derbyshire* (Moyes & Willmot 2002) was published by Derby Museum with financial aid from **The Friends of Derby Museum**. The national list, the *Vice-county Census Catalogue of the Vascular Plants of Great Britain* by C.A. Stace *et al.* was published by the BSBI in 2003.

Flora website

With the Derbyshire plant checklist now published, but with the production of the new *Flora of Derbyshire* still some way off, it was realised in 2006 that a great deal of provisional species accounts and biological data was locked away in the database at Derby Museum where it was not easily accessible, except to direct enquirers. To remedy this it was decided to make an internet version freely available within the website of Derby City Council – a sort of "in progress" version of the *Flora*. This would demonstrate to all those volunteers who had collected or collated data that their efforts were being used and were worthwhile, and it would put useful information into the hands of ecologists, consultants and naturalists. This online version of the *Flora* contained distribution maps with records up to 2007 produced by N. Moyes, but with

accounts prepared by A. Willmot based on earlier maps in 2002. At the time of going to press, this was still available at www.derby.gov. uk/flora. The website also contained a downloadable copy of the 2002 Plant Checklist referred to above.

Derbyshire Red Data List

One final use of the Derby Museum database was made before work began on the printed *Flora* you are now reading, and that was the preparation and online publication of the *Red Data List of Derbyshire's Vascular Plants* (Moyes & Willmot 2009). It listed 244 of the county's native plants under six categories of local and national conservation concern. The most innovative development for any Derbyshire red data list up to that point was a category for "**locally declining**" plants. This was an attempt to analyse over 40 years' worth of collected data, and to identify and list all recently declining species against a general background of an increasing quantity of plant records being submitted. This was done by comparing the change in number of records of a given species against the overall increase in all plant data being sent in from across the county. A species was labelled as "locally declining" if the number of records for it had markedly failed to increase when compared to all other plants. The presence of *Derbyshire Red Data List* species is now one very important criterion in the formal selection process use for designating Local Wildlife Sites (see **Chapter 4**), and the 2009 *Red List* itself is repeated with minor revisions in **Chapter 9**, and also includes additional *England Red Data List* species identified by Stroh *et al. (2014)*.

At the start of 2011 the database of records was essentially "frozen", and from this new maps, accounts and statistics were produced for the *Flora* you are now reading. Final editing in 2013 allowed all the accounts and statistics to be brought up to date with latest year of recording, and for a few accounts and maps to be modified in the light of recent significant finds – such as the rediscovery of Royal Fern (*Osmunda regalis*) as a native county plant.

This *Flora* therefore gives a picture of all the plants of Derbyshire as at the start of 2014.

Coverage

Species covered
This *Flora* has surveyed and recorded all species and hybrids of vascular plants ever found growing in a wild situation in Derby and Derbyshire. It covers flowering plants, including trees and grasses, as well as conifers, ferns, horsetails and clubmosses. Both native and introduced species are included, and all receive individual systematic accounts, although one or two members of critical groups such as Hawkweeds (*Hieracium* species) have been included in accounts of closely related species.

Garden plants, street trees and agricultural species are excluded unless they have escaped and are spreading in the wider environment, or thought liable to do so in the near future. Deliberately planted specimens are excluded unless they, too, are in a wild setting or have a particular local interest. Non-vascular plant groups such as liverworts, mosses, lichens and algae are not covered here.

Area covered
The county of Derbyshire forms the basis of the area surveyed. However, as well as the modern geographic county we also include the older "botanical vice-county" (v.c.57). Both are shown in the maps accompanying the species accounts in this book. A solid line represents the current Derbyshire county boundary, with the botanical vice-county shown as a broken one. In many places they

Figure 6.2 Map of "Greater Derbyshire" showing the modern geographic county, plus botanical vice-county (red).

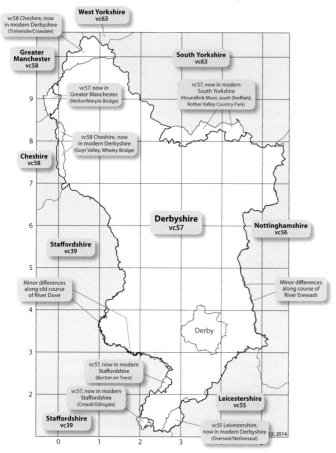

which were entered onto the database at Derby Museum by a team of volunteers. This dataset includes 575,000 new field records which were specifically collected for the project. A concerted effort was made whilst collecting new data to visit previously under-recorded parts such as towns and agricultural areas, as well as the botanically more interesting and well-known regions. In the course of this resurvey every tetrad, or 2km by 2km square, was visited at least once (see **Figure 6.3**). The maps associated with the species accounts for **Common Nettle** (*Urtica dioica*) and **Hawthorn** (*Crataegus monogyna*) reflect the two most frequently recorded Derbyshire plants, being based upon 8,627 and 8,398 records respectively. Information going back over 400 years has been extracted from earlier works, particularly Linton's 1903 *Flora* and Clapham's 1969 *Flora* with its two later supplements. Many tens of thousands of earlier plant records made on RP3 recording cards in the 1970s and 1980s were also computerised. Records from the BSBI's 1987 "rare plants survey" have been added, whilst datasets have also been imported electronically from a number of individual botanists, as well as Monks Wood BRC, Peak National Park and Derbyshire Wildlife Trust, to name but a few. It proved too difficult or time consuming to extract records in paper form from some organisations such as English Nature (now Natural England), and, until recently, even from Derby Museum's own herbarium!

Figure 6.3 Species Density Map showing number of taxa (species and hybrids) recorded in each tetrad in "Greater Derbyshire".

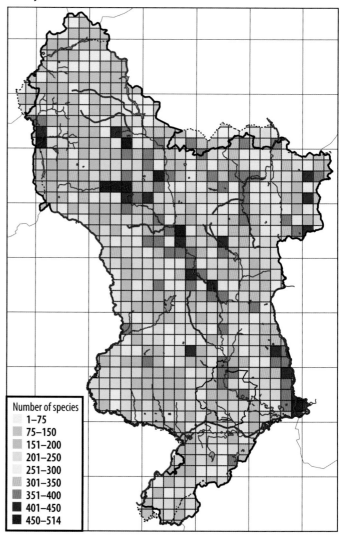

Number of species
1–75
75–150
151–200
201–250
251–300
301–350
351–400
401–450
450–514

still coincide. The City of Derby is also included, and is shown with a solid line in the 10km grid square, SK33 (see **Figure 6.2**).

Unless explicitly stated in the accounts, all species should be assumed to occur within the botanical vice-county of Derbyshire, v.c.57. In fact only one plant, **Tasteless Stonecrop** (*Sedum sexangulare*), occurs within modern Derbyshire, but not in v.c.57.

Time coverage

The *Flora* project has computerised records from the sixteenth century right up to the start of 2011, and the majority have been used to create the distribution maps. Later records have been and still are being collected and computerised, but are not generally shown here except that all species accounts have been updated to show Latest Year up to 2013. There may also be the occasional mention of new locations in the systematic accounts for rarer, particularly native, species. See **Chapter 7** for a list of newly discovered species from Derbyshire which were found too late to be included in these accounts.

First and latest year of recording are included in the statistics box, or within the accounts themselves. Records are mapped to two date groups: Modern or "**recent records**" are those made from the start of 1987 to the present day. Older, earlier or "**previous records**" were made any time prior to 1987. Where a plant has not been recorded since Clapham's *Flora* of 1969, it is regarded as "**locally extinct**". Note that many of the records in Clapham (1969) are believed to have already been up to 20 years old when the work was published.

Extent of coverage

This book is based on a database of 850,000 records amassed by the *Flora of Derbyshire* project since work began in 1994, all of

Results

Status categories

The total number of plants recorded for Derbyshire in this *Flora* is 1,919. This includes species, microspecies and hybrids, but excludes subspecies and varieties. These can be divided into status categories as shown in **Table 6.1.**

Table 6.1 Count of plants in major status categories in this *Flora*.

Status category	Number of plants		Number of plants
Native	1,044	Native species	937
		Native hybrids	107
Established	425	Anciently established	89
		Recently established	336
Casual	433	Casual	433
Unassigned	17	Planted	15
		Unconfirmed	2
Total	1,919		1,919

It has never been easy for botanists to determine the status of a plant in a given area. Workers have differed in how they define and apply their categories (introduced, alien, established, denizen *etc.*) Early on in the Derbyshire Flora Project we used a fairly simplistic classification of **Native** or **Alien** (introduced), with alien divided into **Established**, **Casual** or **Planted** (Moyes & Willmot 2002). To a large extent these categories mirror those used in Clapham, Tutin & Warburg (1952) and Stace (1991). See **Glossary** for explanation of status categories as used here.

Recently, however, there has been a major change in the way species are considered to be native or not in the United Kingdom with the adoption of the concepts of **Archaeophytes** and **Neophytes** (Preston *et al.* 2004). These categories both refer to plants that arrived here with the help of people, but separate those that arrived before 1500 AD (**archaeophyte = anciently established**) from those that reached these shores later (**neophyte= recently established**). This effectively separates plants that arrived with the onset of agriculture in Neolithic and later times from those brought here after the expansion of world-wide trade in the seventeenth century. Most of the plants we now term "Established (Archaeophyte)" were previously regarded as Natives. They comprise about 10% of the total British flora, *i.e.* 150 Archaeophytes compared to 1,407 Native species (Preston *et al.* 2004). Here in Derbyshire we have 89 Anciently Established (Archaeophytes) and 336 Recently Established plants (Neophytes).

In the accounts within this book, Archaeophytes are simply referred to as "Anciently Established" whilst Neophytes just as "Established". If in doubt, refer to the statistics box in each account for clarification.

Comparison with previous *Floras*

If we want to compare this current *Flora of Derbyshire* with the three previous *Floras* we need to temporarily remove the new concepts of Archaeophyte and Neophyte, and re-apply the simpler categories of Native, Established, Casual and Planted to them all.

Table 6.2 Count of plants in major status categories of the four Derbyshire *Floras*. (Note that for this reanalysis the 89 archaeophytes listed in the current *Flora* were removed from the Established category and placed back with the Natives.)

Flora	Number of native plants	Number of established plants	Number of casual plants	Number of unassigned plants	Total number of plants
Painter (1889)	700	93	69	88	950
Linton (1903)	910	70	50	0	1,030
Clapham (1969)	943	194	68	43	1,248
Willmot & Moyes (2015)	1,133	336	433	17	1,919

Table 6.2 shows how our ideas of what constitutes our county flora have changed over time.

The results clearly show that the total number of plants (species *and* hybrids) recognised in Derbyshire has increased over time. Whilst the number of Native taxa has risen, it is in the categories of Casual and Established plants where there has been the greatest increase. This does not mean our Derbyshire countryside has suddenly been overrun by aliens since the 1970s; it mostly demonstrates the greater willingness of modern plant hunters to record them.

Types of change in a Flora

The presence of a series of *Flora of Derbyshire* books allows the possibility of examining changes over time. Unfortunately, whilst the differences between them may be real, they might equally be artefacts cause by differences in recording methods. We therefore need to try and distinguish between real and apparent change when comparing *Floras*. **Apparent Change** is what we *see* when two *Floras* are compared, whilst **Real Change** is what has *actually happened*. Apparent Change is thus made up of "Real Change" plus "artefacts" due to differences in the methods of collecting data, such as recording effort, taxonomic change, or skill levels of surveyors.

Recording effort is a particularly useful example to consider. If a botanist today puts more work into searching for a plant than their predecessors, then any increase in the number of records they generate could either be a reflection of that extra effort, or actually the fact that there are now more plants around to be recorded. The former is clearly only an apparent change, while the latter is a real one. In the case of changes involving the genuine loss or addition of species to an area (so-called **absolute** or **qualitative changes**) it is relatively easy to disentangle real from apparent change. But it is considerably more difficult to do so when considering changes involving the abundance of species, so-called **quantitative** or **abundance differences**.

General reasons for change

Real change in the presence and distribution of plants in a given area may be brought about by changes in the plants themselves (evolution) or by changes in their environment. Over the tiny timescales involved here (1889 to the present day) evolution can be mostly ruled out. So alterations in the environment must be the major reason for changes in the plants present in an area, and these can be brought about by either natural or human causes.

As with evolution, the effects of natural change over 120 years are likely to be miniscule, especially compared to the changes wrought by people. The main effect of humans on the environment can be summed up as being due to an increase in economic activity, not only because there are more and more of us, but also because each of us is demanding a better lifestyle. This impacts on how we utilise the available land.

This increase in economic activity impinges both directly and indirectly on plants. Indirect ways are mainly to do with pollution, and direct ways with disturbance. Aerial pollution in the form of greenhouse gases in the atmosphere appears to be causing climate change. Terrestrial and aquatic pollution in the form of phosphates and nitrates from agriculture and sewage is allowing weedy species that can utilise the extra nutrients to thrive. These in turn are out-competing many native species, so reducing floral diversity (Hodgson 1986). Disturbance which directly kills or damages plants comes from all sorts of economic activity. It comes from the building of houses, factories and roads, from increasingly mechanised and intensive farming, from mineral extraction and from the feet of tourists and the wheels of mountain bikes. Disturbance may also come from people directly collecting plants but, apart from a few notable showy species, collecting of wild plants has been insignificant since the 1890s. A more significant cause of disturbance has been the introduction of alien species, either deliberately or accidentally.

Local change 1: Absolute gains

The number of plants considered to be Native in Derbyshire has increased from around 700 in Painter's 1889 *Flora* to over 1,100 in the current one **(see Table 6.2)**. For the most part this is only an "apparent increase", in that the majority of these extra native species have always grown here, but were simply not recorded for one reason or another. There are five reasons for this:

1. This current *Flora* contains many more so-called "critical species" belonging to the difficult groups of the **dandelions** (*Taraxacum*), the **hawkweeds** (*Hieracium*) and **brambles** (*Rubus fruticosus* agg.). Painter (1889) included only one species of dandelion with four varieties, whereas this *Flora* names 92 separate native species.

2. Botanists have shown an increasing willingness and ability over the years to record hybrids, such that in this current *Flora* there are over 100 examples listed.

3. There has been some increase in Native plant numbers simply due to the splitting of certain ones into two or more species. For example, **whitlowgrasses** (*Erophila*) were regarded as a single species in Clapham (1969) but are now seen as three species here – an apparent increase of two.

4. The area of this *Flora* is slightly greater than that of previous ones (by 92 km$^{2)}$. The current *Flora* covers not only the historic county (or vice-county) of Derbyshire, but also parts of surrounding regions now included within the modern geographic county of Derbyshire. The most significant of these is the area which was once Cheshire that lies north of the Longdendale Valley (see **Figure 6.2** or **Figure 2.1**).

5. Increased communication techniques and computerisation of data means the network of active recorders is much larger than before, and that data can now be readily exchanged between experts and organisations.

If all these changes are taken into account, there are only 14 species which appear to be proper, newly discovered species in Derbyshire since Clapham's (1969) *Flora* (see **Table 6.3**). But it is by no means certain all these plants are genuinely new native species to the area. **Rough Horsetail** (*Equisetum hyemale*), for example, has been recorded earlier, but the records were discounted by, or unknown to, the earlier flora writers. And **Leafy Rush** (*Juncus foliosus*) may well have been imported on the feet of cattle from Wales. However, they are all treated here as new natives until shown to be otherwise.

Table 6.3 Native species discovered new to Derbyshire since Clapham's (1969) *Flora*, shown with first year recorded.

NEW NATIVE SPECIES		
Scientific name	**Common name**	**First year**
Bromopsis benekenii	Lesser Hairy-brome	1998
Callitriche hermaphroditica	Autumnal Water-starwort	2002
Callitriche truncata	Short-leaved Water-starwort	1978
Carex distans	Distant Sedge	1970
Equisetum hyemale	Rough Horsetail	1975
Juncus foliosus	Leafy Rush	1996
Luronium natans	Floating Water-plantain	1973
Populus nigra	Black-poplar	1973
Pyrola rotundifolia	Round-leaved Wintergreen	2005
Sesleria caerulea	Blue Moor-grass	1980
Thelypteris palustris	Marsh Fern	1991
Trichomanes speciosum	Killarney Fern	1990
Ulmus minor	An elm	1998
Vaccinium uliginosum	Bog Bilberry	2004

Local change 2: Absolute losses

The total loss, or "**local extinction**", of a species in an area can involve any type of plant, but is generally considered much more significant when it involves native ones. Only these will be considered here. Clearly it is not possible to know every corner of a county intimately, so one can never say with absolute certainty that a plant has been lost. So botanists take a span of time, (usually 50 years), after which if a plant is not recorded in a given area it is considered to be "Locally Extinct". Here in Derbyshire we have used the period since the last *Flora* to decide on local extinction (44 years). So, if a plant has not been found in the county since Clapham's (1969) *Flora*, it is classed as locally extinct. Using this criterion some 34 Native species are known to have become extinct locally since recording began here in the 17th century (see **Table 6.4**). N.B. this table does not include microspecies of the critical groups, such as the hawkweeds and brambles, as they are under-recorded in comparison with most other species, and these add another 13 names to the list if incorporated, as shown in **Chapter 9**, **Table 9.7**. Hybrids are also excluded for similar reasons.

Table 6.4 List of Locally Extinct native species (excluding hybrids and microspecies) with first and last year recorded. (34 taxa)

LOCAL EXTINCTIONS			
Scientific name	**Common name**	**First year**	**Last year**
Anagallis arvensis ssp. *foemina*	Blue Pimpernel	1968	1968
Asperula cynanchica	Squinancywort	1789	1903
Campanula patula	Spreading Bellflower	1903	1903
Carex diandra	Lesser Tussock-sedge	1854	1889
Centunculus minimus	Chaffweed	1969	1969
Cephalanthera damasonium	White Helleborine	1789	1789
Colchicum autumnale	Meadow Saffron	1787	1969
Cryptogramma crispa	Parsley Fern	1805	1805
Cypripedium calceolus*	Lady's-slipper	1800	1933
Drosera anglica	Great Sundew	1851	1864
Dryas octopetala	Mountain Avens	1811	1811
Dryopteris oreades	Mountain Male-fern	1855	1855
Eleocharis multicaulis	Many-stalked Spike-rush	1871	1903
Gentiana pneumonanthe	Marsh Gentian	1789	1789
Gentianella uliginosa	Dune Gentian	1898	1898
Hypericum elodes	Marsh St John's-wort	1829	1969
Juniperus communis*	Common Juniper	1884	1884
Lycopodiella inundata	Marsh Clubmoss	1805	1864
Moenchia erecta	Upright Chickweed	1828	1828
Myosurus minimus	Mousetail	1787	1903
Myrica gale	Bog-myrtle	1789	1789
Orobanche purpurea	Yarrow Broomrape	1969	1969
Orobanche rapum-genistae	Greater Broomrape	1789	1903
Pilosella peleteriana ssp. *tenuiscapa*	Shaggy Mouse-ear-hawkweed	1968	1968
Platanthera bifolia	Lesser Butterfly-orchid	1865	1969
Pseudorchis albida	Small-white Orchid	1829	1938
Ranunculus parviflorus	Small-flowered Buttercup	1829	1950
Schoenus nigricans	Black Bog-rush	1829	1829
Selaginella selaginoides	Lesser Clubmoss	1805	1805
Sium latifolium	Greater Water-parsnip	1923	1923
Spiranthes spiralis	Autumn Lady's-tresses	1790	1969
Ulmus plotii	Plot's Elm	1969	1969
Utricularia vulgaris	Greater Bladderwort	1829	1889
Valerianella rimosa	Broad-fruited Cornsalad	1864	1903
* More recent records occur, but these are considered as introductions			

We know nothing for certain about the actual reason for the extinction of any of the plants in **Table 6.4**. However, the fact they were mostly plants of what was once marginal agricultural land such as heaths, marshes and bogs suggests that agricultural intensification has caused most of them to disappear from Derbyshire. In some cases, such as **Many-stalked Spike-rush** (*Eleocharis multicaulis*) and **Marsh St John's-wort** (*Hypericum elodes*), increased drainage has been the major factor. In others, such as **Greater Bladderwort** (*Utricularia vulgaris*), it was probably the increased use of fertilisers. Contributing to this local extinction was the fact that most were always rare here, and often on the edges of their British distributions. For example, **Bog-myrtle** (*Myrica gale*) and **Small-white Orchid** (*Pseudorchis albida*) are both plants of north-western England which were on the south-eastern limits of their range here. There may also have been specific causes of extinction contributing to the loss of particular species. In the case of attractive species such as **Lady's-slipper** (*Cypripedium calceolus*) and **Marsh Gentian** (*Gentiana pneumonanthe*), collection may well have played a part in their demise. In the case of **Plot's Elm** (*Ulmus plotii*), disease may have been involved.

Recording changes in abundance

It is relatively easy to record absolute changes in the occurrence of plants *i.e. Is it new here? Has it gone extinct?* But it is much more difficult to determine the changes in abundance of species between two time periods. If identical recording methods are used across both periods, then it may be possible to measure changes in abundance. However, this rarely happens, so it becomes very difficult to disentangle real from apparent change.

One way round this problem is to look at "**Relative Change**", that is, how one plant seems to have changed when compared to all plants in general. This was the approach taken in the 2009 *Derbyshire Red Data List* which tried to judge which species were locally increasing and which were locally declining in abundance (see **Chapter 9**).

The first step in that analysis was to work out for each species how many Derbyshire monads it was recorded in during two equal time periods of 21 years. These were:

- 1965–1986 inclusive
- 1987–2008 inclusive

These two figures were then used to calculate the **Apparent Change** for each species by dividing the latter by the former and multiplying by 100 to give a percentage change. Thus, if a plant was recorded in 100 monads in the more recent time period and in 25 in the earlier one, it generated an apparent change of 400%. In other words, the plant *appeared* to be four times more frequent now than previously. However, there has been considerably more plant recording happening in the recent time period than in the earlier one, so this Apparent Change might simply reflect greater recording effort. To solve this problem, the average Apparent Change for all species was calculated. This came out at around 550%. This means on average each species was recorded in five and a half times more monads in the later time period than in the earlier one. Finally, the **Relative Apparent Change** was calculated for each individual plant by dividing its own Apparent Change by the average Apparent Change of all species. Thus, a plant with an Apparent Change of 1100% had a Relative Apparent Change of 2, as its number of monads on our database increased by twice the average increase over the time studied.

We accept that the above calculation of Relative Apparent Change is a very rough and ready one, and it is not possible to apply confidence levels in any proper statistical sense to the values obtained. However, it does allow us to see which species have been increasing or decreasing most, when compared to the average change for all the plants studied. Note that these changes are to do with the frequency of occurrence of monads containing individual species or hybrids. Thus a plant with a Relative Apparent Change of 3 was recorded in three times more monads between 1965–1986 and 1987–2008 than the average plant was. (Once again, it is important to stress that this method cannot reflect abundance changes of a species within individual monads.)

Local change 3: Gains in abundance

There are 37 species and hybrids that have exhibited a Relative Apparent Change of greater than 2.4 (see **Table 6.5**). Although the choice of 2.4 is arbitrary, it does select the plants that increased most in frequency over the time studied. The great majority of these (28 species and one hybrid) are alien plants, and of these most are recent introductions or neophytes (16 species and one hybrid). Only 8 native plants have shown a major increase, of which three are hybrids.

Table 6.5 Derbyshire plants exhibiting an increase in abundance between 1965–1986 and 1987–2008 with a relative apparent change greater than 2.4. Grouped by status category. (37 taxa)

LOCAL INCREASE			
Scientific name	Common name	Status	Relative apparent change
Silene × *hampeana*	Hybrid Campion	Native	5.8
Quercus × *rosacea*	Hybrid Oak	Native	4.4
Montia fontana	Blinks	Native	3.9
Sagina procumbens	Procumbent Pearlwort	Native	3.0
Cerastium glomeratum	Sticky Mouse-ear	Native	2.9
Salix × *multinervis*	A hybrid willow	Native	2.8
Oenanthe crocata	Hemlock Water-dropwort	Native	2.7
Epilobium montanum	Broad-leaved Willowherb	Native	2.5
Lactuca serriola	Prickly Lettuce	Archaeophyte	10.7
Tripleurospermum inodorum	Scentless Mayweed	Archaeophyte	8.6
Euphorbia peplus	Petty Spurge	Archaeophyte	4.0
Matricaria chamomilla	Scented Mayweed	Archaeophyte	2.6
Papaver rhoeas	Common Poppy	Archaeophyte	2.5
Cochlearia danica	Danish Scurvygrass	Neophyte	28.8
Hyacinthoides × *massartiana*	Hybrid Bluebell	Neophyte	22.9
Picea sitchensis	Sitka Spruce	Neophyte	6.6
Brassica napus	Rape	Neophyte	4.9
Sedum rupestre	Reflexed Stonecrop	Neophyte	4.0
Buddleja davidii	Butterfly-bush	Neophyte	3.8
Ribes sanguineum	Flowering Currant	Neophyte	3.6
Campanula persicifolia	Peach-leaved Bellflower	Neophyte	3.3
Puccinellia distans	Reflexed Saltmarsh-grass	Neophyte	3.1
Oxalis corniculata	Procumbent Yellow-sorrel	Neophyte	2.9
Meconopsis cambrica	Welsh Poppy	Neophyte	2.9
Lactuca virosa	Great Lettuce	Neophyte	2.9
Epilobium ciliatum	American Willowherb	Neophyte	2.9
Hyacinthoides hispanica	Spanish Bluebell	Neophyte	2.7
Fallopia baldschuanica	Russian-vine	Neophyte	2.5
Crassula helmsii	New Zealand Pigmyweed	Neophyte	2.5
Crepis vesicaria	Beaked Hawk's-beard	Neophyte	2.5
Triticum aestivum	Bread Wheat	Casual	18.6
Alnus incana	Grey Alder	Casual	8.8
Solanum lycopersicum	Tomato	Casual	4.2
Alnus cordata	Italian Alder	Casual	3.3
Solanum tuberosum	Potato	Casual	3.3
Ligustrum ovalifolium	Garden Privet	Casual	2.6
Avena sativa	Oat	Casual	2.6

The reason for the increase in all the hybrids is almost certainly because recorders over the years have become more ready and able to recognise and record them. Thus their increases are likely to be more apparent than real. However, three of the remaining 5 native species are plants of open, often disturbed, habitats: **Procumbent Pearlwort** (*Sagina procumbens*), **Sticky Mouse-ear** (*Cerastium glomeratum*) and **Broad-leaved Willowherb** (*Epilobium montanum*). Their increases are likely to be more real than apparent, due to the increase in availability of such habitats locally (Hodgson 1986).

The two remaining native species are plants of wetlands: **Blinks** (*Montia fontana*) is a plant of upland moorland flushes and **Hemlock Water-dropwort** (*Oenanthe crocata*) is a plant of the sides of lowland waterbodies. The increase in the former species is again likely to be more apparent than real. It is a very small, insignificant plant which is easily overlooked, and our survey specifically encouraged more extensive upland recording. The latter is a much larger plant which grows mostly in southern Derbyshire which have been less visited by botanists in the past than the more botanically attractive north. Some of its increase may thus be only apparent, but other factors may be operating as well, causing a real increase. In a national study of species change, out of the 8 native Derbyshire plants showing an increase here, only Sticky Mouse-ear showed a significant national increase (Braithwaite *et al.* 2006). This was partly associated with a general increase of nitrogen levels in the countryside, no doubt mainly from fertilisers. The seven other species were either not examined in the national study or, in the case of four species, showed no significant national change. These were: **Blinks** (*Montia fontana*), **Procumbent Pearlwort** (*Sagina procumbens*), **Hemlock Water-dropwort** (*Oenanthe crocata*) and **Broad-leaved Willowherb** (*Epilobium montanum*).

There are five anciently introduced species (Archaeophytes) in Derbyshire that have shown a major apparent increase here, and all are plants of open disturbed areas (see **Table 6.5**). Four are weeds of cultivated and disturbed ground in general whilst the fifth, **Prickly Lettuce** (*Lactuca serriola*), is a plant of disturbed ground on development and demolition sites. The increase in all five plants is thus likely to be a real rise in number of sites occupied, rather than an artefact of recording, as there has been a general increase in disturbed habitats across the county (Hodgson 1986). Other factors may also be operating here in particular cases. For example, it has been suggested that Prickly Lettuce may be increasing nationally due to climate change (Braithwaite *et al.* 2006). **Common Poppy** (*Papaver rhoeas*) also requires special mention as its case is rather different from the others, since it appears to have been both increasing and decreasing at the same time! Increasing in the number of sites occupied as discussed here, but decreasing in the number of fields turned bright red by its growth. This apparent contradiction may be explained by there being an increase in the number of monads across Derbyshire in which a few plants occur, but a decrease in the number of sites where there are large enough numbers of individuals massed together to cause whole fields to turn red. In Braithwaite *et al.'s* (2006) national study, three of the five archaeophyte species here showed a significant increase in occurrence: **Prickly Lettuce**, **Petty Spurge** (*Euphorbia peplus*) and **Scented Mayweed** (*Matricaria chamomilla*). In the case of Scented Mayweed the increase was thought due in part at least to the inclusion of this plant in mixtures sown along the verges of major new roads. The other two species showed no significant change in occurrence: **Common Poppy** and **Scentless Mayweed** (*Tripleurospermum inodorum*).

Ten of the seventeen recently established plants, or Neophytes, listed in **Table 6.5** are garden species which have escaped into the wild relatively recently. They include **Hybrid Bluebell** (*Hyacinthoides × massartiana*) and **New Zealand Pigmyweed** (*Crassula helmsii*). The increase of these ten is likely to have been both real and apparent. Increasingly they are being planted in gardens from where they escape or are thrown out and, as has been mentioned previously, over the years more recorders have been inclined to note the presence of aliens. Two other species in **Table 6.5** are crop plants: **Sitka Spruce** (*Picea sitchensis*) and **Rape** (*Brassica napus*). The reason for their apparent increase is almost certainly the same as for the garden plants, except that they are grown for commercial rather than decorative purposes. The five remaining species fall into two groups. There are two species with connections to the seaside: **Danish Scurvygrass** (*Cochlearia danica*) and **Reflexed Saltmarsh-grass** (*Puccinellia distans*). Their increase is clearly part of the nationwide spread of maritime species along inland roads that are nowadays "gritted" with salt in winter to prevent ice forming.

The remaining three species are plants of open disturbed ground: **Great Lettuce** (*Lactuca virosa*), **American Willowherb** (*Epilobium ciliatum*) and **Beaked Hawk's-beard** (*Crepis vesicaria*). Their increase is also likely to be more real than apparent, but due in this instance to an increase in areas of disturbed ground associated with industrial sites. There are probably extra reasons for the spread of some species. Great Lettuce, for example, is thought to have been spreading nationally due to higher summer temperatures (Braithwaite *et al.* 2006). In his survey of national change all of these neophytes showed a significant positive increase in distribution, apart from three. Two of these were not included in the study at all: **Sitka Spruce** (*Picea sitchensis*) and **Russian-vine** (*Fallopia baldschuanica*). Only **Beaked Hawk's-beard** (*Crepis vesicaria*) showed no significant national change, but has increased here in Derbyshire.

The seven Casual species in **Table 6.5** that show a significant apparent increase include four crop plants: **Bread Wheat** (*Triticum aestivum*), **Tomato** (*Solanum lycopersicum*), **Potato** (*Solanum tuberosum*) and **Oat** (*Avena sativa*). The others are all woody plants, much used in landscape gardening. **Garden Privet** (*Ligustrum ovalifolium*) is often planted around domestic properties. **Grey** (*Alnus incana*) and **Italian Alder** (*A. cordata*) on the other hand are increasingly used in large scale restoration schemes such as on former opencast coal sites. The apparent rise in all seven species is likely to be a mixture of a real increase due to their greater use in the countryside, plus an additional apparent increase due to the willingness of modern botanists to record aliens of planted origin. All four of the crop plants here showed a significant national increase in occurrence in Braithwaite *et al.'s* (2006) national study of change, while the three woody species were not included in that research.

Recently there has been much national debate about alien plants increasing in abundance or spreading, and which are damaging habitats by swamping out native species. These problem plants have been christened **Invasive Non-Native Species (INNS)**, and the most troublesome are listed in Schedule 9 of the Wildlife and Countryside Act 1981. The sale of some of these plants was

Table 6.6 Invasive non-native species found in Derbyshire (*i.e.* plants on Schedule 9 of the Wildlife and Countryside Act 1981).

INVASIVE NON-NATIVE SPECIES		
Scientific names	Common names	First year
Allium paradoxum	Few-flowered Garlic	1977
Allium triquetrum	Three-cornered Garlic	2000
*Azolla filiculoides**	Water Fern	1965
Cotoneaster bullatus	Hollyberry Cotoneaster	1987
Cotoneaster horizontalis	Wall Cotoneaster	1968
Cotoneaster integrifolius	Entire-leaved Cotoneaster	1965
Cotoneaster simonsii	Himalayan Cotoneaster	1970
*Crassula helmsii**	New Zealand Pigmyweed	1984
Crocosmia × crocosmiiflora	Montbretia	1968
Eichhornia crassipes	Water-hyacinth	2006
Elodea spp.	Waterweeds	1864
Fallopia japonica	Japanese Knotweed	1949
Fallopia sachalinensis	Giant Knotweed	1950
Gunnera tinctoria	Giant-rhubarb	1995
Heracleum mantegazzianum	Giant Hogweed	1969
*Hydrocotyle ranunculoides**	Floating Pennywort	2002
Impatiens glandulifera	Indian Balsam	1948
Lagarosiphon major	Curly Waterweed	1967
Lamiastrum galeobdolon ssp. *argentatum*	Garden Yellow Archangel	1987
*Myriophyllum aquaticum**	Parrot's-feather	1997
Parthenocissus quinquefolia	Virginia-creeper	1971
Pistia stratiotes	Water-lettuce	2006
Rhododendron luteum	Yellow Azalea	1998
Rhododendron ponticum	Rhododendron	1968
Rosa rugosa	Japanese Rose	1988
* Species whose sale was banned from 2014		

prohibited by further legislation in 2013. They are a major concern for conservationists who have to spend considerable time and effort in controlling them. Those Schedule 9 species which occur in Derbyshire are listed in **Table 6.6.**

Luckily only one of them, **New Zealand Pigmyweed** (*Crassula helmsii*), is currently showing any appreciable increase in abundance in Derbyshire. However, three other plants listed in **Table 6.6** are already being controlled in the county, despite not appearing in the list of plants increasing in abundance (see **Table 6.5**). These are **Rhododendron** (*Rhododendron ponticum*), **Indian Balsam** (*Impatiens glandulifera*) and **Japanese Knotweed** (*Fallopia japonica*). The former had probably already expanded its Derbyshire range before the time period of this study. But quite why the other two are not shown as having expanded is unclear. They both have Relative Apparent Change values of around 1.00, and thus on paper the number of records for them appears to have increased by no more than the average for all other Derbyshire plants. However, where they do occur they can soon utterly dominate and swamp out all other native vegetation.

Local change 4: Losses of abundance

Just as a Relative Apparent Change value of more than 1 indicates that a plant has increased in Derbyshire more than the average, so a Relative Apparent Change value of less than 1 indicates a plant which has increased less than the average over the two 21-year time periods. Where the value is 0.20 or less, this is taken to indicate a plant which has *actually* decreased in its frequency of occurrence. As before, the choice of a value of 0.20 as a cut-off is arbitrary, but it does capture all those plants which have increased the least (in relative terms). Notice also that attention is only given here to native plants; aliens are not discussed in this section. Some 54 native taxa are considered as having shown a real decrease in Derbyshire between the two time periods of the survey, and are categorised in the *Derbyshire Red Data List* as "Locally Declining" (see **Chapter 9**). These species are also listed in **Table 6.7**, where they are grouped by the major habitats they occur in. The largest group are those plants associated with wet grassland, marsh or fen. No doubt these have decreased due to agricultural improvement of marginal land, whether by drainage, ploughing-up, reseeding or application of fertilisers coupled with subsequent increased grazing or mowing. A further group of 11 species including **Saw-wort** (*Serratula tinctoria*) and **Pepper-saxifrage** (*Silaum silaus*) are associated with **unimproved grasslands**. These have no doubt decreased for similar reasons to the wet grassland group, though with the lack of need for extensive land drainage.

Seven plants are associated with **aquatic habitats**; these have probably decreased due to a loss of ponds and an increased input of nutrients into the remaining waterbodies. This can lead to excessive growth of water plants which, when they die, use up oxygen and cause stagnation.

Another group of 11 plants are associated with **woodlands**. These species have probably decreased either through a lack of traditional woodland management such as coppicing, or because woods have been converted to conifers or clear-felled for agriculture. The remaining species are either upland plants or ones of open, disturbed ground. Upland species, such as **Mountain Everlasting** (*Antennaria dioica*), have probably declined due to increased grazing, or the spread of conifer plantations. The decrease of any plants of open disturbed ground is unexpected when one considers there has been such a general increase in disturbance due to new building and other developments (Hodgson 1986). It may be related to an increased level of plant nutrients in the soil which often accompanies ground disturbance.

Table 6.7 List of native Derbyshire plants exhibiting a decrease in abundance between 1965–1986 and 1987–2008 with a relative apparent change of less than 0.2 (54 taxa, arranged by habitat type).

LOCALLY DECLINING		
Habitat type	**Scientific names**	**Common names**
Aquatic	*Callitriche brutia* ssp. *hamulata*	Intermediate Water-starwort
	Callitriche platycarpa	Various-leaved Water-starwort
	Hottonia palustris	Water-violet
	Nasturtium microphyllum	Narrow-fruited Water-cress
	Potamogeton perfoliatus	Perfoliate Pondweed
	Ranunculus circinatus	Fan-leaved Water-crowfoot
	Zannichellia palustris	Horned Pondweed
Grassland	*Agrimonia procera*	Fragrant Agrimony
	Bromopsis erecta	Upright Brome
	Campanula glomerata	Clustered Bellflower
	Carex muricata ssp. *pairae*	Prickly Sedge
	Clinopodium ascendens	Common Calamint
	Genista tinctoria	Dyer's Greenweed
	Jasione montana	Sheep's-bit
	Leontodon saxatilis	Lesser Hawkbit
	Ononis spinosa	Spiny Restharrow
	Serratula tinctoria	Saw-wort
	Silaum silaus	Pepper-saxifrage
Wet grassland/marsh/fen	*Alopecurus aequalis*	Orange Foxtail
	Anagallis tenella	Bog Pimpernel
	Apium inundatum	Lesser Marshwort
	Carex acuta	Slender Tufted-sedge
	Carex disticha	Brown Sedge
	Carex hostiana	Tawny Sedge
	Carex pallescens	Pale Sedge
	Carex vesicaria	Bladder-sedge
	Comarum palustre	Marsh Cinquefoil
	Galium uliginosum	Fen Bedstraw
	Menyanthes trifoliata	Bogbean
	Pinguicula vulgaris	Common Butterwort
	Thalictrum flavum	Common Meadow-rue
	Triglochin palustris	Marsh Arrowgrass
	Valeriana dioica	Marsh Valerian
	Veronica scutellata	Marsh Speedwell
Open/disturbed ground	*Lepidium heterophyllum*	Smith's Pepperwort
	Ornithopus perpusillus	Bird's-foot
	Spergularia rubra	Sand Spurrey
	Verbascum nigrum	Dark Mullein
Upland	*Antennaria dioica*	Mountain Everlasting
	Asplenium viride	Green Spleenwort
	Diphasiastrum alpinum	Alpine Clubmoss
	Lycopodium clavatum	Stag's-horn Clubmoss
	Trollius europaeus	Globeflower
Woodland	*Circaea* × *intermedia*	Upland Enchanter's-nightshade
	Dipsacus pilosus	Small Teasel
	Dryopteris carthusiana	Narrow Buckler-fern
	Epilobium roseum	Pale Willowherb
	Gagea lutea	Yellow Star-of-Bethlehem
	Helleborus viridis	Green Hellebore
	Lithospermum officinale	Common Gromwell
	Paris quadrifolia	Herb-Paris
	Rubus saxatilis	Stone Bramble
	Salix purpurea	Purple Willow
	Scirpus sylvaticus	Wood Club-rush

Geographic analysis of native species

Sitting as it does in the centre of England at the southern end of the Pennines, it has long been appreciated that Derbyshire has a very geographically diverse flora. The production of this book has allowed this to be re-examined. The classic biogeographical analysis of the flora of the British Isles was conducted by Matthews (1955). He classified native British flowering plants into 16 types of geographical distribution, based on the pattern of occurrence of the species in Europe. He referred to these types of geographical distribution as "Elements". Note that he did not classify ferns, hybrids or microspecies of genera such as *Taraxacum*, *Hieracium* or *Rubus*. These sixteen Elements can be grouped into six major patterns of European distribution:

- Widespread
- Southern
- Continental
- Northern
- Alpine
- Endemic

Three Elements referred to by Matthews respectively as: Wide, Eurasian and European can be grouped together as plants with a **widespread distribution** in Europe and often further afield into Asia and even North America. These constitute something over 50% of the entire British flora and include locally common plants such as: **Annual Meadow-grass** (*Poa annua*), **Wild Carrot** (*Daucus carota*) and **Bulbous Buttercup** (*Ranunculus bulbosus*).

Four of the 16 Elements contain plants that have a predominantly **southern distribution** in Europe. One of these is Matthew's (1955) "Mediterranean Element" which contains 38 species whose chief centre of distribution is, unsurprisingly, the Mediterranean. None of these occur naturally in Derbyshire, and only one plant, **Spotted Medick** (*Medicago arabica*), occurs as a casual species here. The other three Southern elements all contain a number of species which occur naturally in Derbyshire (**Table 6.8**).

Table 6.8 Examples of native Derbyshire species with different European geographic distribution patterns, after Matthews (1955). (21 taxa)

European distribution	Scientific name	Common name
Northern	*Antennaria dioica*	Mountain Everlasting
	Arctostaphylos uva-ursi	Bearberry
	Minuartia verna	Spring Sandwort (Leadwort)
	Narthecium ossifragum	Bog Asphodel
	Parnassia palustris	Grass-of-Parnassus
	Polemonium caeruleum	Jacob's-ladder
	Rubus chamaemorus	Cloudberry
Continental	*Cynoglossum officinale*	Hound's-tongue
	Dianthus deltoides	Maiden Pink
	Epipactis palustris	Marsh Helleborine
	Hypericum montanum	Pale St John's-wort
	Ophrys insectifera	Fly Orchid
	Quercus robur	Pedunculate Oak
	Sorbus torminalis	Wild Service-tree
Southern	*Anagallis tenella*	Bog Pimpernel
	Clematis vitalba	Traveller's-joy
	Daphne laureola	Spurge-laurel
	Erica tetralix	Cross-leaved Heath
	Hyacinthoides non-scripta	Bluebell
	Ilex aquifolium	Holly
	Wahlenbergia hederacea	Ivy-leaved Bellflower

Matthews has a single Element with a **continental distribution** in Europe, that is, native British plants with a European distribution, which are centred on the middle of the continent with neither a southern nor a northern bias. Again, this Element is well represented in the native plants of Derbyshire in **Table 6.8**.

He has six Elements with a **northern distribution** in Europe, all of which have representatives (**Table 6.8**) in the local flora except one. This is his North American Element which consists of species whose main centre of distribution is outside Europe and in North America. None of the six species in this Element are native here, but two occur as introduced plants. These are **Slender Rush** (*Juncus tenuis*) and **Blue-eyed-grass** (*Sisyrinchium bermudiana*).

Closely related to those Elements with a northern distribution is his Element with an **alpine distribution** in Europe. These occur in the mountains of central Europe but not in the northern arctic areas. Only one Derbyshire plant has this distribution, and this is Alpine Penny-cress, more commonly known here as **Leadwort** (*Noccaea caerulescens*).

Matthews' final Element includes species **endemic** to the British Isles. These are plants whose total world distribution is in Britain and whose European distribution is hence clearly British. None of his species in this Element occur in Derbyshire, though there are two microspecies which only occur in the county and are hence endemic to Britain as well. These are **a bramble** (*Rubus durescens*) and **Derby Hawkweed** (*Hieracium naviense*).

Overall the flora of Derbyshire contains species with all types of European distribution patterns. Particularly well-represented are plants with northern, central and southern European patterns. Poorly represented are those with alpine, Mediterranean and North American affinities.

Conclusions

Analysis of the current results demonstrates how our knowledge and understanding of Derbyshire's flora has altered over the years. There have been changes caused by processes operating in the real world such as habitat loss, or introductions of novel crops and garden plants, as well as changes due to botanists' readiness to record aliens and critical groups. There is no sign that these changes have stopped, as evidenced by the list of additions to our *Flora* in **Chapter 7**, made since the majority of systematic accounts were written for this work. It will be interesting to see in the future if the roadside salt-tolerant plants continue to spread and whether or not conservationists manage to stem the increase of the invasive aliens.

Although not so obvious in the discussions here, there have also been changes in the methods of publication. With their numerous illustrations and computer-generated distribution maps in full colour, modern day Floras would be almost unrecognisable to Linton or Painter. With modern forms of communication, it is quite possible that this, the fourth printed *Flora of Derbyshire*, will be the last produced on paper. One can imagine in the near future that botanists will be able to call up information on pocket communication devices to identify new plants in the field and then to add them immediately to a virtual Flora in "the cloud". But there is still something to be said for a book you can pick up anytime from a shelf, and which does not run out of batteries!

CHAPTER 7

New species records

Alan Willmot

This chapter lists all those plants which have been discovered new to the vice-county of Derbyshire (v.c.57) since the bulk of the systematic accounts were prepared.

As well as most being recent arrivals, many are still of uncertain status here. This is either because we know insufficient about how they got to be where they were found, or simply because they have not been seen growing here long enough to be adjudged either "Casual" or "Established", which requires a minimum of five years.

One plant, Upright Chickweed (*Moenchia erecta*) has very recently been added back to our county list, despite first being recorded in 1828, and having for many years been thought to be an error. There is also one other species, Great Fen-sedge (*Cladium mariscus*) which, although having been recorded some years ago, has only just come to the attention of Derbyshire botanists as it was previously considered as growing just within the vice-county of South West Yorkshire (v.c.63).

Maidenhair Fern (*Adiantum capillus-veneris* L.) was observed growing down a pavement light-well in Normanton Road, Derby (SK3535) by A. Wilmot in 2012. Probably only casual, it may become established in time.

A hybrid bent (*Agrostis gigantea* × *stolonifera*) was collected from the edge of a cereal field in SK4361 by C. Smith in 2013 and determined by G. Coles. Although a sterile hybrid, as a perennial it may eventually become established.

Japanese Anemone (*Anemone* × *hybrida* Paxton) was found growing in a disused quarry on Moss Rake (SK1480) by G. Wheeldon in 2011. Judging by how long it can take to establish in gardens, it was probably established as a neophyte on the site.

Austrian Chamomile (*Anthemis austriaca* Jacq.) A single plant was found on disturbed soil near Batley Lane (SK4963) by the Flora Group in 2012. It was probably a casual.

Buck's-beard (*Aruncus dioicus* (Walter) Fernald) was found beside Lea Brook, Dronfield (SK3578) by K. Balkow in 2012, probably established as a neophyte.

Mrs Wilson's Barberry (*Berberis wilsoniae* Hemsl.) A single well-grown bush was found growing by a footpath at Nether Padley (SK2578) by the Flora Group in 2013. It was probably established as a neophyte.

Heath False-brome (*Brachypodium pinnatum* (L.) P. Beauv.) Tor-grass has long been known from areas of limestone grassland in the county and nationwide under the Latin name of *Brachypodium pinnatum*. However, it has recently been shown that this was in fact two species and that the common local plant should now be known as Tor-grass (*Brachypodium rupestre*). In 2013 C. Smith found the other species, Heath False-brome, the new *Brachypodium pinnatum* at Tibshelf (SK4460) where it is possibly native.

Great Fen-sedge (*Cladium mariscus* (L.) Pohl) The excellent *Plant Atlas of South Yorkshire* by Wilmore *et al.* (2011) records this

species for Cadman Wood (SK4180) in 1986 which, although it is administratively in South Yorkshire, also lies within v.c.57 Derbyshire.

Spreading Cotoneaster (*Cotoneaster divaricatus* Rehder & E.H. Wilson) was reported from Cunning Dale (SK0872 & 0772) by D. & M. Woods in 2012. It was probably established.

Small-leaved Cotoneaster (*Cotoneaster microphyllus* Wall. ex Lindl.) was discovered in Longcliffe Cutting (SK2355) by C. & M. Smith in 2012. It was probably established.

Leptinella (*Cotula squalida* (Hook f.) Hook f.) was reported growing close to Corsican Toadflax at Whirlow Brook Park (SK3082) by A. Baker in 2013 with the appearance of an established neophyte.

Lucifer (*Crocosmia* × *curtonus*) is an attractive garden plant with bright crimson flowers, found growing on the canal bank at Staveley (SK4274) by K. Balkow in 2013. It was probably a garden throwout which may become an established neophyte in time.

Corsican Toadflax (*Cymbalaria hepaticifolia* (Poir.) Wettst.) was reported growing vigorously in a wall at Whirlow Brook Park (SK3082) by A. Baker in 2013, with the appearance of being an established neophyte.

Chinese Hound's-tongue (*Cynoglossum amabile* Stapf & J.R. Drumm.) was found by K. Balkow in 2012, growing on ground disturbed by the building of the new canal basin at Staveley (SK4374). It was the form with blue flowers. Undoubtedly a casual as it did not reappear the next year.

Cut-leaved Teasel (*Dipsacus laciniatus* L.) was recorded at the Woodside Reserve (SK4443) Bioblitz in 2012 by A. Willmot. Having been seen there in previous years, it was probably an established neophyte.

Slender Spike-rush (*Eleocharis uniglumis* (Link) Schult.) was discovered at Steetley Quarry (SK 545784) in 2010 by P. Hoy. Because of development threats, specimens were translocated to SK544786 and remained until at least 2013. It was probably native. Material grown in cultivation was subsequently determined by S. Wilde. Voucher in Herb. N.J. Law.

A hybrid willowherb (*Epilobium* × *brevipilum* Hausskn.) This hybrid of Great and Square-stalked Willowherb was reported at Dalton Quarry (SK2175) by G. Kitchener in 2011. It was probably native.

A hybrid willowherb (*Epilobium* × *nutantiflorum* Smejkal) This hybrid of Pale and American Willowherb was reported from Haddon Hall (SK2366) by G. Kitchener in 2011. It was probably native.

A hybrid willowherb (*Epilobium* × *vicinum* Smejkal) This hybrid of Short-fruited and American Willowherb was reported from between Froggatt and Curbar (SK2475) by G. Kitchener in 2011. It was probably native.

Mexican Fleabane (*Erigeron karvinskianus* DC.) was first recorded in 2010 at Swanwick (SK4053) by R. Smith. Having been seen elsewhere before and afterwards, it is no doubt an established neophyte locally.

Winter Jasmine (*Jasminum nudiflorum* Lindl.) was discovered growing in Hopton Quarries (SK2655) by C. & M. Smith in 2012, where it was probably an established neophyte.

Crimson Flax (*Linum grandiflorum* Desf.) was found as variety *rubrum* by K. Balkow on disturbed ground next to the new canal basin at Staveley (SK4374) in 2012. Undoubtedly a casual as it did not reappear the next year.

Royal Mallow (*Malva trimestris* (L.) Salisb.) This attractive plant was found by K. Balkow growing in ground disturbed by the extension to the canal at Staveley (SK4375) in 2012, along with a wide range of other exotic species. It did not reappear the next year and so can only be regarded as a casual.

Upright Chickweed (*Moenchia erecta* P. Gaertn., B. Mey. & Scherb.) A voucher specimen found in the Dorman Museum, Middlesbrough, proves this plant was recorded at Newbold by Margaret Stovin in 1828. Despite positive records given in Clapham (1969) and Linton (1903), it has long been considered an erroneously recorded species and was flagged as such in Moyes &

Part of herbarium voucher sheet of Upright Chickweed (*Moenchia erecta*)
(Courtesy of Dorman Museum, Middlesbrough Council)

Willmot (2002). Its status as a native, albeit a Locally Extinct one, can now be restored.

Baby-blue-eyes (*Nemophila menziesii* Hook. & Arn.) was another of the colourful exotics found on ground disturbed by the building of the new canal basin at Staveley (SK4374) in 2012. This plant was found by G. Coles. No doubt a casual as it did not reappear the next year.

Water Bent (*Polypogon viridis* (Gouan) Breistr.) was found growing in pavement cracks on Church Road, New Mills (SK0085) by J. Hawksford in 2012. It is spreading as an established neophyte in southern England and can be expected to do the same here soon.

Short-styled Field-rose (*Rosa stylosa* Desv.) was reported for Cow Dale (SK0872) in 2010 by P. Harvey but requires confirmation as it is generally a southern species not otherwise found locally.

A hybrid dock (*Rumex × dufftii* Hausskn.) was reported growing south-east of Bakewell (SK2267) in 2011 by G. Kitchener. It is the native hybrid of Wood and Broad-leaved Dock.

A hybrid dock (*Rumex × sagorskii* Hausskn.) was recorded for Cressbrook Dale (SK1774) by G. Kitchener in 2011. It is the native hybrid of Curled and Wood Dock.

Clary (*Salvia sclarea* L.) was another of the exotic plants noted as a casual following work on the canal at Staveley (SK4375) in 2012 by G. Coles.

Roseroot (*Sedum rosea* (L.) Scop.) was discovered on a disused railway track at Swanwick (SK4153) by R. Smith in 2012. Native in northern Britain, it was at most a plant established from garden waste here.

Rough Bristle-grass (*Setaria verticillata* (L.) Beauv.) was found growing as a casual in a field of Maize at Little Cubley (SK1637) by A. Willmot in 2012.

Rose-of-heaven (*Silene coeli-rosa* (L.) Godr.) was another of the attractive casual species that turned up on ground disturbed by the extension to the canal at Staveley (SK4374 & 4375) in 2012, and which was found by K. Balkow

Lange's Spiraea (*Spiraea × brachybotrys* Lange) was discovered in the High House Farm area (SK4367) by the Flora Group in 2011. Growing on restored land, it may have been planted or introduced with garden waste.

A dandelion (*Taraxacum cherwellense* A.J. Richards) A record for this plant was made in 2009 for Derbyshire as *Taraxacum stenoglossum* but as the record cannot currently be traced, it needs further confirmation.

Western Red-cedar (*Thuja plicata* Donn ex D. Don) was reported for Northwood Carr (SK2664) by D. & M. Woods in 2012. It is not known if it was planted there or self-sown.

Dwarf Gorse (*Ulex minor* Roth) A rather unusual-looking gorse that was reported by K. Balkow for the Williamthorpe Ponds area (SK4266) is probably this species. As the area is a restored coal mining area, it may have been planted or introduced with soil-making material.

CHAPTER 8

Errors and unconfirmed species

Nick Moyes

Over the last 200 years or so of botanical publishing, numerous species have been listed as occurring in Derbyshire which we now regard as being errors, or at least in need of confirmation. These are shown below. The majority were formally published, although a few have appeared in nationally held datasets. In their respective *Floras*, both Painter and Linton listed many species they themselves clearly regarded as incorrect or dubious. We have not felt it necessary to repeat these here.

Causes of errors

i) Taxonomic reassessment of a species can cause once-valid names to no longer be appropriate for use today, such as *Galium pumilum* and *Carex vulpina*.

ii) Modern-day experts may recommend rejecting all records of a species on the grounds they would not be likely to occur here: (*e.g. Rubus dumnoniensis*)

iii) Some taxa are simply not regarded as valid at all (*e.g. Quercus cerris × robur*).

iv) Sometimes a recorder realises they have incorrectly determined a species whose record had already been accepted and published (*e.g. Lilium × hollandicum*)

v) Some reports seem so unlikely that even where there is a confirmed record from a recognised authority, other experts still feel some mistake must have led to it. (*e.g. Rubia peregrina*).

vi) "It's on computer, so it must be correct"

But we can still be proved wrong. Such is the case with *Moenchia erecta*, where the discovery of a valid voucher specimen from 1828 just before publication of this work saw its swift removal from the list of erroneous records and its insertion into the list of New Species Records to the county (see **Chapter 7**).

Table 8.1 lists all species believed to have been published in error. Where known, the date of the actual record is given. Years in brackets refer to the date of publication containing that record. See **References** for full bibliography. This list below now replaces that published in Moyes and Willmot (2002).

Atlas 2000 errors

Despite rigorous error-checking protocols for collecting and computerising data at Derby Museum, the Derbyshire Flora Project was itself responsible for three errors ending up in print in the *New Atlas of the British & Irish Flora* (Preston *et al.* 2002). We did spot them all, but not in time to prevent publication. **Table 8.2** lists three Derbyshire records plotted in the 2002 Atlas which should be ignored.

Table 8.2 Erroneous records published in the *New Atlas of the British and Irish Flora* (Preston *et al.* 2002).

Species name	Hectad
Colchicum autumnale	SK45
Epipactis palustris	SK27
Platanthera bifolia	SK27

Table 8.1 List of plants published in error for Derbyshire (v.c.57). * valid records of *Thymus pulegioides* were made of this taxon in 2001 and 2010 as introductions.

ERRONEOUS SPECIES					
Scientific name	Record date (Publication date)	Publication	Scientific name	Record date (Publication date)	Publication
Ajuga alpina	(1805, 1889)	Turner & Dilwyn; Painter	*Prunus dulcis*	(1989, 2002, 2003)	Futter & Raynes; Moyes & Willmot; Stace *et al.*
Asplenium obovatum	(1969)	Clapham			
Bromus arvensis	(1829, 1889)	Glover; Painter	*Quercus cerris × robur*	1980 (2002)	Moyes & Willmot
Carex appropinquata (=C. paradoxa)	1854–1870 (1889)	Painter	*Ranunculus baudotii*	(1889, 1903)	Painter; Linton
Carex muricata ssp. *muricata*	(1969)	Clapham	*Rorippa islandica*	(1969, 1974, 1980)	Clapham; Patrick & Hollick; Hollick & Patrick
Carex vulpina	(1789, 1903)	Pilkington; Linton			
Caucalis daucoides	(1866, 1903)	Wyatt & Thornton; Linton	*Rubia peregrina*	(1903, 1950)	Linton; Lousley
Caucalis platycarpos	(1866, 1903, 1969, 1989)	Wyatt & Thornton; Linton; Clapham; Futter & Raynes	*Rubus adspersus*	(1889, 1903, 1969)	Painter; Linton; Clapham
			Rubus dentatifolius	(1969, 1980)	Clapham; Hollick & Patrick
Circaea alpina	(1805, 1889, 1903)	Turner & Dillwyn; Painter; Linton	*Rubus dumnoniensis*	(1903, 1969)	Linton; Clapham
			Rubus trichodes	(1903, 1969)	Linton; Clapham
Clinopodium calamintha	(1789, 1903)	Pilkington; Linton	*Saxifraga geum*	(1903)	Linton
Dryopteris × uliginosa (Lastraea uliginosa)	(1873, 1889)	Watson HC; Painter	*Solanum sarachoides*	1971 (1974)	Patrick & Hollick
Empetrum nigrum ssp. *hermaphroditum*	(1969)	Clapham	*Taraxacum hamatulum*	(1980)	Hollick & Patrick
Epilobium hirsutum × obscurum	(1969, 2002)	Clapham; Moyes & Willmot	*Taraxacum inopinatum*	(2002)	Moyes & Willmot
Epipactis atroviridis nov.sp. Linton	(1903)	Linton	*Taraxacum laetiforme*	(1980)	Hollick & Patrick
Euphorbia esula	1942 (1969, 2002)	Clapham; Moyes & Willmot	*Taraxacum laetum*	(1980)	Hollick & Patrick
Galium pumilum (=G. silvestre)	(1889, 1903)	Painter; Linton	*Taraxacum procerisquameum*	(1980)	Hollick & Patrick
Gentianella germanica	(1911, 2003)	Drabble; Stace *et al.*	*Taraxacum procerum*	(1980)	Hollick & Patrick
Hieracium subplanifolium	(1969)	Clapham	*Taraxacum pseudolacistophyllum*	(1980)	Hollick & Patrick
Hieracium calcaricola	1896 (2002)	Moyes & Willmot	*Taraxacum rhamphodes*	(1980)	Hollick & Patrick
Hieracium caledonicum	(1969, 2003)	Clapham; Stace *et al.*	*Taraxacum scotiniforme*	(1980)	Hollick & Patrick
Hieracium submutabile	1978 (1980)	Hollick & Patrick	*Taraxacum septentrionale*	(1980)	Hollick & Patrick
Hymenophyllum wilsonii	(1969)	Clapham	*Taraxacum sinuatum*	(1980)	Hollick & Patrick
Lilium × hollandicum	1988 (2002)	Moyes & Willmot	*Thymus pulegioides**	(1969)	Clapham
Malva (= Lavatera) thuringiaca	2000 (2002)	Moyes & Willmot	*Verbascum nigrum × V. virgatum*	(1974, 1980)	Patrick & Hollick; Hollick & Patrick
Mentha longifolia	(1903)	Linton			
Orobanche ramosa	(1829, 1903)	Glover; Linton	*Viola lutea × tricolor*	1990 (2002)	Moyes & Willmot
Persicaria mitis	(1969)	Clapham	*× Gymnaglossum jacksonii*	1969 (1974)	Patrick & Hollick

CHAPTER 9

Derbyshire Red Data List

Nick Moyes

Published online in 2009, the *Derbyshire Red Data List* tabulated all vascular plant species in our county which have either a local or a national Conservation Status (Moyes & Willmot 2009). It superseded two previous *Red Lists* and has proved useful in setting selection criteria for Local Wildlife Sites, as well as highlighting the rarest or most threatened species in the county. For earlier RDB plant lists for Derbyshire, see Moyes & Willmot (2002) or Elkington & Willmot (1996)

Because the original document was generally only available online (at www.derby.gov.uk/flora), we decided to reproduce the main species lists here. It has been revised only to reflect recent name changes and a few minor updates made to status category, or to remove one neophyte and an invalid taxon. Four notable changes are a) the transfer of **Lesser Twayblade** (*Neottia cordata*) from Locally Extinct to Locally Rare following its rediscovery, b) the reinstatement of **Upright Chickweed** (*Moenchia erecta*) to the county list, albeit as Locally Extinct, c) the addition of a small number of previously overlooked critical taxa to the Locally Extinct category, and d) the addition of threat. Please refer to individual species accounts to see the full range of national and local conservation statuses which each plant holds.

Note: English Red Data List

Just as this Flora was going to press, the first ever *Vascular Plant Red List for England* was published (Stroh *et al* 2014). It was impossible to incorporate the 100 or so status changes into every species account as these had already been sent for typesetting. However, all the new England Red List threat categories have been added to their stats boxes and to the tables below. **Table 9.9** lists these additional species, all of which ought now to be regarded as "*Derbyshire Red Data Book (Red List) species*". So, on top of the existing 245 Derbyshire Red List plants, there will now be a further 59 completely new species to incorporate, plus an upgrading of 25 Locally Significant plants to ones that are now seen as nationally threatened in England under IUCN Criteria. A further 15 species already of International or GB Red List significance now also have an increased threat status here in England, too. See **Chapter 4** for further consideration of the significance of the *Red Data List of Derbyshire's Vascular Plants* to the future conservation of our county's flora.

All 245 original *Derbyshire Red Data List* species are grouped in one of seven conservation categories as set out below, together with the latest known date for each.

Red Data Book Category — **Significance**
Derbyshire RDB Category 1 — Internationally Rare (**Table 9.1**) 2 taxa
- *has International status: IUCN Red Lists, EU Habitats Directive or Bern Convention*
Derbyshire RDB Category 2 — Nationally Threatened (**Table 9.2**) 59 taxa
- *includes all IUCN threat categories CR, EN, VU, NT (see glossary)*
Derbyshire RDB Category 3 — Nationally Rare or Scarce (**Table 9.3**) 24 taxa
- *Nationally Rare (in 15 or less GB hectads) or Nationally Scarce (in 16 to 100 GB hectads)*
Derbyshire RDB Category 4 — Locally Rare (**Table 9.4**) 24 taxa
- *known in 3 or less Derbyshire monads since 1969; no national status*
Derbyshire RDB Category 5a — Locally Scarce (**Table 9.5**) 35 taxa
- *known in 4 to 10 Derbyshire monads since 1969; no national status*
Derbyshire RDB Category 5b — Locally Declining (**Table 9.6**) 54 taxa
- *exhibiting serious recent decline in Derbyshire over the last 20 years*
Derbyshire RDB Category 6 — Locally Extinct (**Table 9.7**) 47 taxa
- *not found since previous 1969 Flora of Derbyshire*

plus:
Locally Extinct hybrids (not regarded as Derbyshire RDB species) (**Table 9.8**) 27 taxa
Additional *England Red List* (ERL) species (from 2014) (**Table 9.9**) 60 taxa

Conservation Codes used: CR = Critically Endangered; EN = Endangered; VU = Vulnerable; NT = Near Threatened; NR = Nationally Rare; NS = Nationally Scarce; LC = Least Concern; WL = Waiting List; DD=Data Deficient; RE = Regionally Extinct (i.e. in England)

Table 9.1 Internationally Rare species (= Derbyshire RDB List, Category 1). (2 taxa)

INTERNATIONALLY RARE				
Scientific name	Common name	Latest year	GB status	England status
Luronium natans	Floating Water-plantain	1973	LC	NT
Trichomanes speciosum	Killarney Fern	2011	LC+NR	LC

Table 9.2 Nationally Threatened species, based on IUCN criteria (= Derbyshire RDB List, Category 2. CR, EN, VU, NT). (59 taxa)

NATIONALLY THREATENED				
Scientific name	Common name	Latest year	GB status	England status
Allium oleraceum	Field Garlic	2012	VU	VU
Anacamptis morio	Green-winged Orchid	2003	NT	VU
Anthemis cotula	Stinking Chamomile	1979	VU	VU
Asplenium trichomanes ssp. *pachyrachis*	A maidenhair spleenwort	2004	NT	NT
Baldellia ranunculoides	Lesser Water-plantain	2004	NT	VU
Blysmus compressus	Flat-sedge	2007	VU	VU
Cardamine impatiens	Narrow-leaved Bitter-cress	2013	NT	LC
Carex ericetorum	Rare Spring-sedge	2009	VU	VU
Chamaemelum nobile	Chamomile	1977	VU	VU
Clinopodium acinos	Basil Thyme	2006	VU	VU
Coeloglossum viride	Frog Orchid	2013	VU	VU
Cynoglossum officinale	Hound's-tongue	2013	NT	NT
Daphne mezereum	Mezereon	2009	VU	VU
Dianthus deltoides	Maiden Pink	2012	NT	VU
Euphorbia exigua	Dwarf Spurge	2012	NT	VU
Euphrasia officinalis	An eyebright	1995	VU	VU
Filago vulgaris	Common Cudweed	2012	NT	NT
Galeopsis angustifolia	Red Hemp-nettle	2007	CR	CR
Galeopsis speciosa	Large-flowered Hemp-nettle	2011	VU	VU
Genista anglica	Petty Whin	2009	NT	VU
Gentianella campestris	Field Gentian	2012	VU	EN
Gnaphalium sylvaticum	Heath Cudweed	1994	EN	EN
Groenlandia densa	Opposite-leaved Pondweed	1979	VU	VU
Hieracium naviense	Derby Hawkweed	2013	CR	CR
Hyoscyamus niger	Henbane	2006	VU	VU
Hypericum montanum	Pale St John's-wort	2012	NT	LC
Hypopitys monotropa	Yellow Bird's-nest	2013	EN	EN
Juncus compressus	Round-fruited Rush	2012	NT	VU
Lithospermum arvense	Field Gromwell	2001	EN	EN
Mentha pulegium	Pennyroyal	1997	EN	CR
Minuartia hybrida	Fine-leaved Sandwort	1997	EN	EN
Minuartia verna	Spring Sandwort	2013	NT	LC
Myriophyllum verticillatum	Whorled Water-milfoil	2005	VU	NT
Neotinea ustulata	Burnt Orchid	2010	EN	EN
Neottia nidus-avis	Bird's-nest Orchid	2012	NT	VU
Nepeta cataria	Cat-mint	2003	VU	VU
Oenanthe fistulosa	Tubular Water-dropwort	2009	VU	VU
Ophrys insectifera	Fly Orchid	2012	VU	VU
Papaver argemone	Prickly Poppy	2008	VU	EN
Persicaria minor	Small Water-pepper	2012	VU	LC
Platanthera chlorantha	Greater Butterfly-orchid	2012	NT	LC
Potamogeton compressus	Grass-wrack Pondweed	2010	EN	EN

Table 9.2 Nationally Threatened species (… continued)

Scientific name	Common name	Latest year	GB status	England status
Potamogeton friesii	Flat-stalked Pondweed	1991	NT	VU
Potamogeton praelongus	Long-stalked Pondweed	1990	NT	EN
Potentilla argentea	Hoary Cinquefoil	2012	NT	NT
Pyrola rotundifolia	Round-leaved Wintergreen	2011	NT	VU
Ranunculus arvensis	Corn Buttercup	1997	CR	EN
Saxifraga hypnoides	Mossy Saxifrage	2013	VU	LC
Scandix pecten-veneris	Shepherd's-needle	1996	CR	EN
Scleranthus annuus	Annual Knawel	2004	EN	EN
Silene nutans	Nottingham Catchfly	2013	NT	NT
Stachys arvensis	Field Woundwort	2010	NT	NT
Stellaria palustris	Marsh Stitchwort	1998	VU	VU
Teesdalia nudicaulis	Shepherd's Cress	2009	NT	NT
Turritis glabra	Tower Mustard	1985	EN	EN
Valerianella dentata	Narrow-fruited Cornsalad	1979	EN	EN
Viola canina	Heath Dog-violet	2010	NT	VU
Viola tricolor	Wild Pansy	2012	NT	NT
Wahlenbergia hederacea	Ivy-leaved Bellflower	2012	NT	NT

Table 9.3 Nationally Rare (NR) or Nationally Scarce (NS) species
(= Derbyshire RDB List, Category 3. (24 taxa)

NATIONALLY RARE (NR) or NATIONALLY SCARCE (NS)				
Scientific name	Common name	Latest year	GB status	England status
Bromopsis benekenii	Lesser Hairy-brome	2012	LC+NS	LC
Callitriche truncata	Short-leaved Water-starwort	2002	LC+NS	LC
Carex digitata	Fingered Sedge	2006	LC+NS	LC
Carex montana	Soft-leaved Sedge	2009	LC+NS	LC
Carex ornithopoda	Bird's-foot Sedge	2011	LC+NR	LC
Draba muralis	Wall Whitlowgrass	2013	LC+NS	LC
Epipactis atrorubens	Dark-red Helleborine	2010	LC+NS	LC
Epipactis phyllanthes	Green-flowered Helleborine	1994	LC+NS	LC
Gymnocarpium robertianum	Limestone Fern	2013	LC+NS	LC
Helleborus foetidus	Stinking Hellebore	2012	LC+NS	LC
Hordelymus europaeus	Wood Barley	2011	LC+NS	LC
Hornungia petraea	Hutchinsia	2012	LC+NS	LC
Limosella aquatica	Mudwort	2011	LC+NS	LC
Noccaea caerulescens	Leadwort (Alpine Penny-cress)	2012	LC+NS	LC
Polemonium caeruleum	Jacob's-ladder	2013	LC+NR	LC
Polygonatum odoratum	Angular Solomon's-seal	2007	LC+NS	LC
Potentilla crantzii	Alpine Cinquefoil	2004	LC+NS	LC
Potentilla tabernaemontani	Spring Cinquefoil	2013	LC+NS	LC
Ribes alpinum	Mountain Currant	2013	LC+NS	LC
Rubus durescens	A bramble	2013	NR	LC
Sesleria caerulea	Blue Moor-grass	2007	LC+NS	LC
Sorbus rupicola	Rock Whitebeam	2013	LC+NS	LC
Thelypteris palustris	Marsh Fern	2012	LC+NS	LC
Tilia platyphyllos	Large-leaved Lime	2012	LC+NS	LC

Table 9.4 Locally Rare species (= Derbyshire RDB List, Category 4). (24 taxa)

LOCALLY RARE				
Scientific name	Common name	Latest year	GB status	England status
Calamagrostis canescens	Purple Small-reed	1980	LC	LC
Callitriche hermaphroditica	Autumnal Water-starwort	2002	LC	LC
Carex distans	Distant Sedge	1996	LC	LC
Carex elata	Tufted-sedge	1990	LC	NT
Ceratophyllum submersum	Soft Hornwort	2003	LC	LC
Eleocharis quinqueflora	Few-flowered Spike-rush	2004	LC	LC
Epipactis palustris	Marsh Helleborine	1993	LC	NT
Equisetum hyemale	Rough Horsetail	2010	LC	LC
Eriophorum latifolium	Broad-leaved Cottongrass	2004	LC	LC
Euphorbia amygdaloides	Wood Spurge	2011	LC	LC
Fumaria capreolata	White Ramping-fumitory	2012	LC	LC
Geranium sylvaticum	Wood Crane's-bill	1982	LC	NT
Juncus foliosus	Leafy Rush	1996	LC	LC
Lathyrus nissolia	Grass Vetchling	2012	LC	LC
Neottia cordata	Lesser Twayblade	2012	LC	LC
Oenanthe fluviatilis	River Water-dropwort	2006	LC	LC
Osmunda regalis	Royal Fern	2012	LC	LC
Pedicularis palustris	Marsh Lousewort	1986	LC	VU

Table 9.4 Locally Rare species (… continued)

Scientific name	Common name	Latest year	GB status	England status
Polypodium cambricum	Southern Polypody	2009	LC	LC
Ranunculus sardous	Hairy Buttercup	2004	LC	LC
Samolus valerandi	Brookweed	2005	LC	LC
Trientalis europaea	Chickweed-wintergreen	2009	LC	LC
Trifolium fragiferum	Strawberry Clover	1979	LC	VU
Vaccinium uliginosum	Bog Bilberry	2008	LC	LC

Table 9.5 Locally Scarce species (= Derbyshire RDB List, Category 5a). (35 taxa)

LOCALLY SCARCE				
Scientific name	Common name	Latest year	GB status	England status
Alisma lanceolatum	Narrow-leaved Water-plantain	2006	LC	LC
Allium scorodoprasum	Sand Leek	2003	LC	LC
Anthriscus caucalis	Bur Chervil	1995	LC	LC
Arctostaphylos uva-ursi	Bearberry	2012	LC	NT
Callitriche obtusangula	Blunt-fruited Water-starwort	2010	LC	LC
Carex dioica	Dioecious Sedge	2004	LC	LC
Carex divulsa	Grey Sedge	2012	LC	LC
Carex strigosa	Thin-spiked Wood-sedge	2012	LC	LC
Catabrosa aquatica	Whorl-grass	1997	LC	VU
Cirsium dissectum	Meadow Thistle	2006	LC	LC
Dactylorhiza incarnata	Early Marsh-orchid	2012	WL	WL+NT
Eleocharis acicularis	Needle Spike-rush	2004	LC	NT
Festuca altissima	Wood Fescue	2008	LC	LC
Festuca filiformis	Fine-leaved Sheep's-fescue	2003	LC	LC
Filago minima	Small Cudweed	2009	LC	NT
Fumaria muralis	Common Ramping-fumitory	2010	LC	LC
Hippocrepis comosa	Horseshoe Vetch	2013	LC	LC
Juncus subnodulosus	Blunt-flowered Rush	2006	LC	LC
Kickxia elatine	Sharp-leaved Fluellen	2010	LC	LC
Lathyrus sylvestris	Narrow-leaved Everlasting-pea	2012	LC	LC
Legousia hybrida	Venus's-looking-glass	1998	LC	LC
Lotus tenuis	Narrow-leaved Bird's-foot-trefoil	2010	LC	LC
Myriophyllum alterniflorum	Alternate Water-milfoil	2009	LC	LC
Oenanthe aquatica	Fine-leaved Water-dropwort	2011	LC	LC
Orobanche minor	Common Broomrape	2013	LC	LC
Poa angustifolia	Narrow-leaved Meadow-grass	2009	LC	LC
Potamogeton alpinus	Red Pondweed	1995	LC	VU
Potamogeton lucens	Shining Pondweed	2002	LC	LC
Potamogeton obtusifolius	Blunt-leaved Pondweed	2010	LC	LC
Scrophularia umbrosa	Green Figwort	1998	LC	LC
Sison amomum	Stone Parsley	2003	LC	LC
Stellaria pallida	Lesser Chickweed	2011	LC	LC
Trifolium subterraneum	Subterranean Clover	2007	LC	LC
Verbena officinalis	Vervain	2012	LC	NT
Vicia sylvatica	Wood Vetch	2011	LC	LC

Table 9.6 Locally Declining species (= Derbyshire RDB List, Category 5b). The method used to determine Local Decline is outlined in **Chapter 6**. (54 taxa)

LOCALLY DECLINING				
Scientific name	Common name	Latest year	GB status	England status
Agrimonia procera	Fragrant Agrimony	2013	LC	LC
Alopecurus aequalis	Orange Foxtail	2011	LC	LC
Anagallis tenella	Bog Pimpernel	2011	LC	LC
Antennaria dioica	Mountain Everlasting	2013	LC	VU
Apium inundatum	Lesser Marshwort	2011	LC	VU
Asplenium viride	Green Spleenwort	2013	LC	LC
Bromopsis erecta	Upright Brome	2010	LC	LC
Callitriche brutia ssp. hamulata	Intermediate Water-starwort	2003	LC	LC
Callitriche platycarpa	Various-leaved Water-starwort	2011	LC	LC
Campanula glomerata	Clustered Bellflower	2011	LC	LC
Carex acuta	Slender Tufted-sedge	2007	LC	LC
Carex disticha	Brown Sedge	2013	LC	LC
Carex hostiana	Tawny Sedge	2003	LC	LC
Carex muricata	Prickly Sedge	2007	LC	LC
Carex pallescens	Pale Sedge	2012	LC	LC
Carex vesicaria	Bladder-sedge	2010	LC	VU
Circaea × intermedia	Upland Enchanter's-nightshade	2009	–	–

Table 9.6 Locally Declining species (... continued)

Scientific name	Common name	Latest year	GB status	England status
Clinopodium ascendens	Common Calamint	2010	LC	LC
Comarum palustre	Marsh Cinquefoil	2012	LC	NT
Diphasiastrum alpinum	Alpine Clubmoss	2012	LC	LC
Dipsacus pilosus	Small Teasel	2012	LC	LC
Dryopteris carthusiana	Narrow Buckler-fern	2013	LC	LC
Epilobium roseum	Pale Willowherb	2012	LC+NS	LC
Gagea lutea	Yellow Star-of-Bethlehem	2013	LC	LC
Galium uliginosum	Fen Bedstraw	2013	LC	LC
Genista tinctoria	Dyer's Greenweed	2013	LC	VU
Helleborus viridis	Green Hellebore	2012	LC	LC
Hottonia palustris	Water-violet	2013	LC	VU
Jasione montana	Sheep's-bit	2008	LC	VU
Leontodon saxatilis	Lesser Hawkbit	2011	LC	LC
Lepidium heterophyllum	Smith's Pepperwort	2010	LC	LC
Lithospermum officinale	Common Gromwell	2012	LC	LC
Lycopodium clavatum	Stag's-horn Clubmoss	2011	LC	VU
Menyanthes trifoliata	Bogbean	2013	LC	LC
Nasturtium microphyllum	Narrow-fruited Water-cress	2009	LC	LC
Ononis spinosa	Spiny Restharrow	2011	LC	NT
Ornithopus perpusillus	Bird's-foot	2013	LC	LC
Paris quadrifolia	Herb-Paris	2012	LC	LC
Pinguicula vulgaris	Common Butterwort	2012	LC	VU
Potamogeton perfoliatus	Perfoliate Pondweed	2009	LC	LC
Ranunculus circinatus	Fan-leaved Water-crowfoot	2011	LC	LC
Rubus saxatilis	Stone Bramble	2012	LC	LC
Salix purpurea	Purple Willow	2012	LC	LC
Scirpus sylvaticus	Wood Club-rush	2010	LC	LC
Serratula tinctoria	Saw-wort	2012	LC	LC
Silaum silaus	Pepper-saxifrage	2012	LC	LC
Spergularia rubra	Sand Spurrey	2013	LC	LC
Thalictrum flavum	Common Meadow-rue	2012	LC	LC
Triglochin palustris	Marsh Arrowgrass	2012	LC	NT
Trollius europaeus	Globeflower	2013	LC	LC
Valeriana dioica	Marsh Valerian	2013	LC	NT
Verbascum nigrum	Dark Mullein	2008	LC	LC
Veronica scutellata	Marsh Speedwell	2010	LC	NT
Zannichellia palustris	Horned Pondweed	2012	LC	LC

Note: *Veronica polita* was formerly on this list but is now regarded as a Neophyte, so has been deleted.

Table 9.7 Locally Extinct species (Derbyshire RDB List, Category 6). (47 taxa)

LOCALLY EXTINCT				
Scientific name	Common name	Latest year	GB status	England status
Anagallis arvensis ssp. foemina	Blue Pimpernel	1968	NS	DD
Asperula cynanchica	Squinancywort	1903	LC	LC
Campanula patula	Spreading Bellflower	1930	EN	CR
Carex diandra	Lesser Tussock-sedge	1889	NT	VU
Centunculus minimus	Chaffweed	1969	NT	EN
Cephalanthera damasonium	White Helleborine	1789	VU	VU
Colchicum autumnale	Meadow Saffron	1969	NT	LC
Cryptogramma crispa	Parsley Fern	1805	LC	VU
Cypripedium calceolus*	Lady's-slipper	1933	CR	CR
Drosera anglica	Great Sundew	1864	NT	EN
Dryas octopetala	Mountain Avens	1811	LC+NS	VU
Dryopteris oreades	Mountain Male-fern	1855	LC	LC
Eleocharis multicaulis	Many-stalked Spike-rush	1903	LC	LC
Gentiana pneumonanthe	Marsh Gentian	1789	LC	NT
Gentianella uliginosa	Dune Gentian	1898	WL	WL
Hieracium eboracense	Northern Hawkweed	1969	LC	LC
Hieracium mirandum	Remote Hawkweed	1946	CR	CR
Hieracium placerophylloides	Purplish-leaved Hawkweed	1903	LC	LC
Hieracium scabrisetum	Scabrous Hawkweed	1898	LC	RE
Hieracium subcrocatum	Dark-styled Hawkweed	1969	LC	LC
Hieracium subprasinifolium	Leek-coloured Hawkweed	1954	VU	EN
Hypericum elodes	Marsh St John's-wort	1969	LC	NT
Juniperus communis **	Common Juniper	2013	LC	NT
Lycopodiella inundata	Marsh Clubmoss	1864	EN	EN
Moenchia erecta	Upright Chickweed	1828	LC	VU
Myosurus minimus	Mousetail	1903	VU	VU
Myrica gale	Bog-myrtle	1789	LC	NT
Orobanche purpurea	Yarrow Broomrape	1969	VU	VU

Table 9.7 Locally Extinct species (...continued)

Scientific name	Common name	Latest year	GB status	England status
Orobanche rapum-genistae	Greater Broomrape	1903	NT	NT
Pilosella peleteriana ssp. tenuiscapa	Shaggy Mouse-ear-hawkweed	1968	NT	LC
Platanthera bifolia	Lesser Butterfly-orchid	1969	VU	EN
Pseudorchis albida	Small-white Orchid	1938	VU	VU
Ranunculus parviflorus	Small-flowered Buttercup	1950	LC	LC
Rubus arrheniiformis	A bramble	1891	–	–
Rubus fissus	A bramble	1896	–	–
Rubus gratus	A bramble	1887	–	–
Rubus pistoris	A bramble	1894	–	–
Rubus plicatus	A bramble	1889	–	–
Rubus rubristylus	A bramble	1965	–	–
Schoenus nigricans	Black Bog-rush	1829	LC	LC
Selaginella selaginoides	Lesser Clubmoss	1805	LC	LC
Sium latifolium	Greater Water-parsnip	1923	EN	EN
Spiranthes spiralis	Autumn Lady's-tresses	1969	NT	NT
Taraxacum gelertii	A dandelion	1918	LC	LC
Ulmus plotii	Plot's Elm	1969	–	–
Utricularia vulgaris sens.lat.	Greater Bladderwort	1889	LC	LC
Valerianella rimosa	Broad-fruited Cornsalad	1903	EN	EN

* Extinct as a native, but recently reintroduced as part of a recovery plan.
** Extinct as a native, yet grows as an Established plant.

In addition to the above Locally Extinct species, a number of native hybrids have not been seen in Derbyshire since 1969. These are listed in **Table 9.8**, but are provided for information only, and should not be regarded as *Derbyshire Red List* entries.

Table 9.8 Locally Extinct hybrid taxa (not regarded as valid for Derbyshire Red List). (27 taxa)

LOCALLY EXTINCT HYBRIDS		
Scientific name	Latest year	Conservation status
Apium × moorei	1911	None
Epilobium × dacicum	1903	None
Epilobium × goerzii	1911	None
Epilobium × rivulare	1969	None
Epilobium × schmidtianum	1903	None
Euphrasia officinalis × E. confusa	1956	None
Galium × pomeranicum	1969	None
Juncus × surrejanus	1950	None
Potamogeton × cooperi	1969	None
Potamogeton × lintonii	1969	None
Ranunculus × kelchoensis	1888	None
Rosa arvensis × R. caesia ssp. vosagiaca	1890	None
Rosa caesia × R. obtusifolia	1889	None
Rosa caesia × R. rubiginosa	1889	None
Rosa caesia × R. sherardii	1890	None
Rosa × andegavensis	1913	None
Rosa × andrzejowskii	1884	None
Rosa × biturigensis	1898	None
Rosa × dumetorum	1918	None
Rosa × gallicoides	1889	None
Rosa × molletorum	1913	None
Rosa × scabriuscula	1913	None
Salix × alopecuroides	1969	None
Salix × forbyana	1969	None
Ulmus × elegantissima	1969	None
Viola × bavarica	1949	None
Viola × contempta	1969	None

Table 9.9 Additional England Red List species to add to Derbyshire Red List (from Stroh *et al.* (2014). (60 taxa)

ENGLAND RED LIST SPECIES (from 2014)				
Scientific name	Common name	Latest year	GB status	England status
Andromeda polifolia	Bog-rosemary	2007	LC	NT
Arabis hirsuta	Hairy Rock-cress	2013	LC	NT
Botrychium lunaria	Moonwort	2012	LC	VU
Briza media	Quaking-grass	2013	LC	NT

Table 9.9 Additional England Red List species (...continued)

Scientific name	Common name	Latest year	GB status	England status	Scientific name	Common name	Latest year	GB status	England status
Calluna vulgaris	Heather	2013	LC	NT	*Hieracium prenanthoides*	Rough-leaved Hawkweed	2000	LC	EN
Campanula rotundifolia	Harebell	2013	LC	NT	*Hieracium stenopholidium*	Western Hawkweed	1981	LC	NT
Carex echinata	Star Sedge	2013	LC	NT	*Hydrocotyle vulgaris*	Marsh Pennywort	2013	LC	NT
Carex pulicaris	Flea Sedge	2013	LC	NT	*Inula helenium*	Elecampane	2012	LC	NT
Carlina vulgaris	Carline Thistle	2013	LC	NT	*Knautia arvensis*	Field Scabious	2013	LC	NT
Cerastium arvense	Field Mouse-ear	2011	LC	NT	*Lathyrus linifolius*	Bitter-vetch	2013	LC	NT
Chenopodium bonus-henricus	Good-King-Henry	2012	VU	VU	*Lepidium campestre*	Field Pepperwort	2012	LC	NT
Cirsium heterophyllum	Melancholy Thistle	2012	LC	NT	*Melampyrum pratense*	Common Cow-wheat	2011	LC	NT
Cruciata laevipes	Crosswort	2013	LC	NT	*Mentha arvensis*	Corn Mint	2012	LC	NT
Drosera rotundifolia	Round-leaved Sundew	2013	LC	NT	*Nardus stricta*	Mat-grass	2013	LC	NT
Erica cinerea	Bell Heather	2013	LC	NT	*Oxalis acetosella*	Wood-sorrel	2013	LC	NT
Erica tetralix	Cross-leaved Heath	2013	LC	NT	*Parnassia palustris*	Grass-of-Parnassus	2013	LC	VU
Eriophorum angustifolium	Common Cottongrass	2013	LC	VU	*Pedicularis sylvatica*	Lousewort	2013	LC	VU
Euphrasia arctica	Arctic Eyebright	1998	DD	VU	*Plantago media*	Hoary Plantain	2013	LC	NT
Euphrasia confusa	Confused Eyebright	2011	DD	VU	*Polygala serpyllifolia*	Heath Milkwort	2013	LC	NT
Euphrasia nemorosa	Common Eyebright	2013	LC	NT	*Potentilla erecta*	Tormentil	2013	LC	NT
Euphrasia officinalis ssp. *anglica*	English Eyebright	1996	EN	EN	*Pyrola minor*	Common Wintergreen	2013	LC	NT
Euphrasia officinalis ssp. *pratensis*	Rostkov's Eyebright	1995	VU	VU	*Ranunculus flammula*	Lesser Spearwort	2013	LC	VU
Fragaria vesca	Wild Strawberry	2013	LC	NT	*Sagina nodosa*	Knotted Pearlwort	2012	LC	VU
Gentianella amarella	Autumn Gentian	2012	LC	NT	*Salix repens*	Creeping Willow	2013	LC	NT
Geranium sanguineum	Bloody Crane's-bill	2013	LC	NT	*Sanicula europaea*	Sanicle	2013	LC	NT
Glebionis segetum	Corn Marigold	2011	VU	VU	*Senecio aquaticus*	Marsh Ragwort	2012	LC	NT
Gymnocarpium dryopteris	Oak Fern	2011	LC	NT	*Silene flos-cuculi*	Ragged-Robin	2013	LC	NT
Helianthemum nummularium	Common Rock-rose	2013	LC	NT	*Solidago virgaurea*	Goldenrod	2013	LC	NT
Hieracium angustisquamum	Red-tinted Hawkweed	2010	LC	EN	*Spergula arvensis*	Corn Spurrey	2013	VU	VU
Hieracium britannicum	British Hawkweed	1994	VU	DD	*Succisa pratensis*	Devil's-bit Scabious	2013	LC	NT
Hieracium holophyllum	Undivided-leaved Hawkweed	2006	NT	LC	*Valeriana officinalis*	Common Valerian	2013	LC	NT
					Veronica officinalis	Heath Speedwell	2013	LC	NT
					Viola lutea	Mountain Pansy	2013	LC	NT

Harebell (*Campanula rotundifolia*) on steep slopes in Lathkill Dale. It was added to the first *Vascular Plant Red List for England*, published in 2014, and is now regarded as **Near Threatened** (Nick Moyes)

CHAPTER 10

Habitat indicator species

The formal selection and designation of Local Wildlife Sites (LWS) in Derbyshire is based on a number of criteria. These vary depending upon the feature or habitat being assessed, but whenever sites are surveyed the presence of Red Data List species is looked for, as is the presence of "typical" plants associated with individual habitats. These plants are referred to as "**Habitat indicator species**".

The maps presented in **Chapter 4** (Figures 4.4 to 4.10) illustrate the number of Habitat Indicator Species present within each tetrad (2km × 2km square) across modern, geographic Derbyshire. Each major habitat is mapped separately in that chapter, but the Indicator Species used in those analyses are listed below.

For the purposes of this *Flora*, the list of species used for LWS selection have been modified to exclude plants that have a broader association with similar habitats *e.g.* the woodland list used here

is more tightly focused on ancient woodlands, whilst the LWS list takes in a wider range of woodland types, and the open mosaic list is taken directly from the UK BAP habitat definition.

The following tables list the Indicator Species for each major habitat used in the analysis in **Chapter 4**. These are taken from *Local Wildlife Sites Handbook, Vol. 2. (Derbyshire Wildlife Trust 2011).*

Grassland indicators (224 taxa)	**Table 10.1** (see also Figure 4.4)
Woodland indicators (72 taxa)	**Table 10.2** (see also Figure 4.5)
Fen, mire and swamp indicators (82 taxa)	**Table 10.3** (see also Figure 4.6)
Freshwater indicators (84 taxa)	**Table 10.4** (see also Figure 4.7)
Arable indicators (59 taxa)	**Table 10.5** (see also Figure 4.8)
Open mosaic indicators (128 taxa)	**Table 10.6** (see also Figure 4.9)
Moorland and heathland indicators (36 taxa)	**Table 10.7** (see also Figure 4.10)

Table 10.1 List of indicator plants for grassland habitats in Derbyshire.

GRASSLAND HABITAT INDICATORS			
Scientific name	**Common name**	**Scientific name**	**Common name**
Achillea ptarmica	Sneezewort	*Carex ericetorum*	Rare Spring-sedge
Agrimonia eupatoria	Agrimony	*Carex flacca*	Glaucous Sedge
Agrimonia procera	Fragrant Agrimony	*Carex laevigata*	Smooth-stalked Sedge
Agrostis canina	Velvet Bent	*Carex leporina*	Oval Sedge
Agrostis vinealis	Brown Bent	*Carex montana*	Soft-leaved Sedge
Aira praecox	Early Hair-grass	*Carex muricata*	Prickly Sedge
Ajuga reptans	Bugle	*Carex nigra*	Common Sedge
Alchemilla filicaulis ssp. *vestita*	Hairy Lady's-mantle	*Carex panicea*	Carnation Sedge
Alchemilla glabra	Smooth Lady's-mantle	*Carex pilulifera*	Pill Sedge
Alchemilla xanthochlora	Pale Lady's-mantle	*Carex pulicaris*	Flea Sedge
Allium oleraceum	Field Garlic	*Carlina vulgaris*	Carline Thistle
Allium scorodoprasum	Sand Leek	*Catapodium rigidum*	Fern-grass
Alopecurus aequalis	Orange Foxtail	*Centaurea nigra*	Common Knapweed
Anacamptis morio	Green-winged Orchid	*Centaurea scabiosa*	Greater Knapweed
Anacamptis pyramidalis	Pyramidal Orchid	*Centaurium erythraea*	Common Centaury
Anemone nemorosa	Wood Anemone	*Cerastium arvense*	Field Mouse-ear
Angelica sylvestris	Wild Angelica	*Cirsium acaule*	Dwarf Thistle
Antennaria dioica	Mountain Everlasting	*Cirsium dissectum*	Meadow Thistle
Anthyllis vulneraria	Kidney Vetch	*Cirsium eriophorum*	Woolly Thistle
Aphanes australis	Slender Parsley-piert	*Cirsium heterophyllum*	Melancholy Thistle
Aquilegia vulgaris	Columbine	*Clinopodium acinos*	Basil Thyme
Arabis hirsuta	Hairy Rock-cress	*Coeloglossum viride*	Frog Orchid
Arenaria serpyllifolia	Thyme-leaved Sandwort	*Conopodium majus*	Pignut
Astragalus glycyphyllos	Wild Liquorice	*Crepis capillaris*	Smooth Hawk's-beard
Avenula pratense	Meadow Oat-grass	*Crepis paludosa*	Marsh Hawk's-beard
Avenula pubescens	Downy Oat-grass	*Cruciata laevipes*	Crosswort
Betonica officinalis	Betony	*Dactylorhiza fuchsii*	Common Spotted-orchid
Blackstonia perfoliata	Yellow-wort	*Dactylorhiza incarnata*	Early Marsh-orchid
Blysmus compressus	Flat-sedge	*Dactylorhiza maculata*	Heath Spotted-orchid
Botrychium lunaria	Moonwort	*Dactylorhiza praetermissa*	Southern Marsh-orchid
Briza media	Quaking-grass	*Dactylorhiza purpurella*	Northern Marsh-orchid
Bromopsis erecta	Upright Brome	*Danthonia decumbens*	Heath-grass
Bromus racemosus	Smooth Brome	*Daucus carota*	Wild Carrot
Caltha palustris	Marsh-marigold	*Deschampsia flexuosa*	Wavy Hair-grass
Campanula glomerata	Clustered Bellflower	*Dianthus deltoides*	Maiden Pink
Campanula rotundifolia	Harebell	*Digitalis purpurea*	Foxglove
Cardamine pratensis	Cuckooflower	*Epilobium palustre*	Marsh Willowherb
Carduus nutans	Musk Thistle	*Epilobium parviflorum*	Hoary Willowherb
Carex caryophyllea	Spring-sedge	*Epipactis atrorubens*	Dark-red Helleborine
Carex demissa	Common Yellow-sedge	*Equisetum sylvaticum*	Wood Horsetail
Carex disticha	Brown Sedge	*Erigeron acris*	Blue Fleabane
Carex echinata	Star Sedge	*Erodium cicutarium*	Common Stork's-bill

Table 10.1 List of indicator plants for grassland habitats in Derbyshire (... continued)

Scientific name	Common name	Scientific name	Common name
Euphrasia confusa	Confused Eyebright	*Ophrys insectifera*	Fly Orchid
Euphrasia nemorosa	Common Eyebright	*Orchis mascula*	Early Purple-orchid
Euphrasia officinalis	An eyebright	*Origanum vulgare*	Wild Marjoram
Festuca ovina agg.	Sheep's Fescue	*Ornithopus perpusillus*	Bird's-foot
Filago vulgaris	Common Cudweed	*Parnassia palustris*	Grass-of-Parnassus
Filipendula ulmaria	Meadowsweet	*Pedicularis sylvatica*	Lousewort
Filipendula vulgaris	Dropwort	*Persicaria bistorta*	Common Bistort
Fragaria vesca	Wild Strawberry	*Phleum bertolonii*	Smaller Cat's-tail
Galeopsis angustifolia	Red Hemp-nettle	*Picris hieracioides*	Hawkweed Oxtongue
Galium palustre	Common Marsh-bedstraw	*Pilosella officinarum*	Mouse-ear-hawkweed
Galium saxatile	Heath Bedstraw	*Pimpinella major*	Greater Burnet-saxifrage
Galium sterneri	Limestone Bedstraw	*Pimpinella saxifraga*	Burnet-saxifrage
Galium uliginosum	Fen Bedstraw	*Plantago media*	Hoary Plantain
Galium verum	Lady's Bedstraw	*Platanthera chlorantha*	Greater Butterfly-orchid
Genista anglica	Petty Whin	*Poa compressa*	Flattened Meadow-grass
Genista tinctoria	Dyer's Greenweed	*Poa humilis*	Spreading Meadow-grass
Gentianella amarella	Autumn Gentian	*Polemonium caeruleum*	Jacob's-ladder
Gentianella campestris	Field Gentian	*Polygala serpyllifolia*	Heath Milkwort
Geranium columbinum	Long-stalked Crane's-bill	*Polygala vulgaris*	Common Milkwort
Geranium pratense	Meadow Crane's-bill	*Potentilla anglica*	Trailing Tormentil
Geranium pusillum	Small-flowered Crane's-bill	*Potentilla argentea*	Hoary Cinquefoil
Geranium sanguineum	Bloody Crane's-bill	*Potentilla crantzii*	Alpine Cinquefoil
Geum rivale	Water Avens	*Potentilla erecta*	Tormentil
Gnaphalium sylvaticum	Heath Cudweed	*Potentilla reptans*	Creeping Cinquefoil
Gymnadenia conopsea	Chalk Fragrant-orchid	*Potentilla sterilis*	Barren Strawberry
Helianthemum nummularium	Common Rock-rose	*Poterium sanguisorba*	Salad Burnet
Hieracium sp.	A hawkweed species	*Primula veris*	Cowslip
Hippocrepis comosa	Horseshoe Vetch	*Prunella vulgaris*	Selfheal
Hordeum secalinum	Meadow Barley	*Pulicaria dysenterica*	Common Fleabane
Hypericum hirsutum	Hairy St John's-wort	*Ranunculus flammula*	Lesser Spearwort
Hypericum humifusum	Trailing St John's-wort	*Rhinanthus minor*	Yellow-rattle
Hypericum maculatum	Imperforate St John's-wort	*Rumex acetosella*	Sheep's Sorrel
Hypericum montanum	Pale St John's-wort	*Sagina nodosa*	Knotted Pearlwort
Hypericum perforatum	Perforate St John's-wort	*Sanguisorba officinalis*	Great Burnet
Hypericum pulchrum	Slender St John's-wort	*Saxifraga granulata*	Meadow Saxifrage
Hypericum tetrapterum	Square-stalked St John's-wort	*Scabiosa columbaria*	Small Scabious
Hypochaeris radicata	Cat's-ear	*Scorzoneroides autumnalis*	Autumnal Hawkbit
Inula conyzae	Ploughman's-spikenard	*Sedum acre*	Biting Stonecrop
Isolepis setacea	Bristle Club-rush	*Sedum anglicum*	English Stonecrop
Jasione montana	Sheep's-bit	*Senecio aquaticus*	Marsh Ragwort
Juncus acutiflorus	Sharp-flowered Rush	*Senecio erucifolius*	Hoary Ragwort
Juncus squarrosus	Heath Rush	*Serratula tinctoria*	Saw-wort
Knautia arvensis	Field Scabious	*Silaum silaus*	Pepper-saxifrage
Koeleria macrantha	Crested Hair-grass	*Silene flos-cuculi*	Ragged-Robin
Lathyrus linifolius	Bitter-vetch	*Stellaria alsine*	Bog Stitchwort
Lathyrus pratensis	Meadow Vetchling	*Stellaria graminea*	Lesser Stitchwort
Leontodon hispidus	Rough Hawkbit	*Stellaria palustris*	Marsh Stitchwort
Leontodon saxatilis	Lesser Hawkbit	*Succisa pratensis*	Devil's-bit Scabious
Leucanthemum vulgare	Oxeye Daisy	*Teucrium scorodonia*	Wood Sage
Linum catharticum	Fairy Flax	*Thalictrum flavum*	Common Meadow-rue
Lotus corniculatus	Common Bird's-foot-trefoil	*Thalictrum minus*	Lesser Meadow-rue
Lotus pedunculatus	Greater Bird's-foot-trefoil	*Thymus polytrichus*	Wild Thyme
Lotus tenuis	Narrow-leaved Bird's-foot-trefoil	*Tragopogon pratensis*	Goat's-beard
Luzula campestris	Field Wood-rush	*Trifolium arvense*	Hare's-foot Clover
Luzula multiflora	Heath Wood-rush	*Trifolium campestre*	Hop Trefoil
Lysimachia nummularia	Creeping-Jenny	*Trifolium medium*	Zigzag Clover
Malva moschata	Musk-mallow	*Trifolium micranthum*	Slender Trefoil
Medicago lupulina	Black Medick	*Trifolium striatum*	Knotted Clover
Mentha aquatica	Water Mint	*Triglochin palustre*	Marsh Arrowgrass
Molinia caerulea	Purple Moor-grass	*Trisetum flavescens*	Yellow Oat-grass
Myosotis discolor	Changing Forget-me-not	*Trollius europaeus*	Globeflower
Myosotis ramosissima	Early Forget-me-not	*Valeriana officinalis*	Common Valerian
Myosotis scorpioides	Water Forget-me-not	*Veronica scutellata*	Marsh Speedwell
Myosotis secunda	Creeping Forget-me-not	*Vicia cracca*	Tufted Vetch
Narcissus pseudonarcissus	Daffodil	*Vicia sativa* ssp. *sativa*	Common Vetch
Neotinea ustulata	Burnt Orchid	*Viola canina*	Heath Dog Violet
Ononis repens	Common Restharrow	*Viola hirta*	Hairy Violet
Ononis spinosa	Spiny Restharrow	*Viola lutea*	Mountain Pansy
Ophioglossum vulgatum	Adder's-tongue	*Viola reichenbachiana*	Early Dog-violet
Ophrys apifera	Bee Orchid	*Viola riviniana*	Common Dog-violet

Table 10.2 List of indicator plants for ancient woodland habitats in Derbyshire.

WOODLAND HABITAT INDICATORS			
Scientific name	Common name	Scientific name	Common name
Adoxa moschatellina	Moschatel	*Luzula pilosa*	Hairy Wood-rush
Allium ursinum	Ramsons	*Luzula sylvatica*	Great Wood-rush
Anemone nemorosa	Wood Anemone	*Lysimachia nemorum*	Yellow Pimpernel
Aquilegia vulgaris	Columbine	*Melampyrum pratense*	Common Cow-wheat
Arctium nemorosum	Wood Burdock	*Melica uniflora*	Wood Melick
Bromopsis ramosa	Hairy-brome	*Milium effusum*	Wood Millet
Calamagrostis epigejos	Wood Small-reed	*Moehringia trinervia*	Three-nerved Sandwort
Campanula trachelium	Nettle-leaved Bellflower	*Myosotis sylvatica*	Wood Forget-me-not
Cardamine amara	Large Bitter-cress	*Narcissus pseudonarcissus*	Daffodil
Cardamine impatiens	Narrow-leaved Bitter-cress	*Neottia nidus-avis*	Bird's-nest Orchid
Carex laevigata	Smooth-stalked Sedge	*Orchis mascula*	Early-purple Orchid
Carex pallescens	Pale Sedge	*Oxalis acetosella*	Wood-sorrel
Carex pendula	Pendulous Sedge	*Paris quadrifolia*	Herb-Paris
Carex remota	Remote Sedge	*Poa nemoralis*	Wood Meadow-grass
Carex strigosa	Thin-spiked Wood-sedge	*Polygonatum multiflorum*	Solomon's-seal
Carex sylvatica	Wood-sedge	*Polystichum aculeatum*	Hard Shield-fern
Chrysosplenium alternifolium	Alternate-leaved Golden-saxifrage	*Polystichum setiferum*	Soft Shield-fern
Chrysosplenium oppositifolium	Opposite-leaved Golden-saxifrage	*Primula vulgaris*	Primrose
Convallaria majalis	Lily-of-the-Valley	*Pyrola minor*	Common Wintergreen
Crataegus laevigata	Midland Hawthorn	*Ranunculus auricomus*	Goldilocks Buttercup
Daphne laureola	Spurge-laurel	*Ribes alpinum*	Mountain Currant
Daphne mezereum	Mezereon	*Ribes nigrum*	Black Currant
Dryopteris carthusiana	Narrow Buckler-fern	*Ribes rubrum*	Red Currant
Elymus caninus	Bearded Couch	*Sanicula europaea*	Sanicle
Equisetum sylvaticum	Wood Horsetail	*Schedonorus giganteus*	Giant Fescue
Euphorbia amygdaloides	Wood Spurge	*Scirpus sylvaticus*	Wood Club-rush
Festuca altissima	Wood Fescue	*Sorbus rupicola*	Rock Whitebeam
Frangula alnus	Alder Buckthorn	*Sorbus torminalis*	Wild Service-tree
Gagea lutea	Yellow Star-of-Bethlehem	*Tamus communis*	Black Bryony
Galium odoratum	Woodruff	*Tilia cordata*	Small-leaved Lime
Holcus mollis	Creeping Soft-grass	*Tilia platyphyllos*	Large-leaved Lime
Hordelymus europaeus	Wood Barley	*Veronica montana*	Wood Speedwell
Hyacinthoides non-scripta	Bluebell	*Vicia sylvatica*	Wood Vetch
Lamiastrum galeobdolon ssp. *montanum*	Yellow Archangel	*Viola reichenbachiana*	Early Dog-violet
Lathraea squamaria	Toothwort	*Viola riviniana*	Common Dog-violet
Lathyrus sylvestris	Narrow-leaved Everlasting-pea		

Table 10.3 List of indicator plants for fen, mire and swamp habitats in Derbyshire.

FEN, MIRE AND SWAMP HABITAT INDICATORS			
Scientific name	Common name	Scientific name	Common name
Achillea ptarmica	Sneezewort	*Epipactis palustris*	Marsh Helleborine
Ajuga reptans	Bugle	*Equisetum fluviatile*	Water Horsetail
Anagallis tenella	Bog Pimpernel	*Equisetum palustre*	Marsh Horsetail
Angelica sylvestris	Wild Angelica	*Eriophorum latifolium*	Broad-leaved Cottongrass
Berula erecta	Lesser Water-parsnip	*Eupatorium cannabinum*	Hemp-agrimony
Caltha palustris	Marsh-marigold	*Filipendula ulmaria*	Meadowsweet
Cardamine pratensis	Cuckooflower	*Galium palustre*	Common Marsh-bedstraw
Carex acuta	Slender Tufted-sedge	*Galium uliginosum*	Fen Bedstraw
Carex acutiformis	Lesser Pond-sedge	*Geranium pratense*	Meadow Crane's-bill
Carex canescens	White Sedge	*Geum rivale*	Water Avens
Carex demissa	Common Yellow-sedge	*Hydrocotyle vulgaris*	Marsh Pennywort
Carex dioica	Dioecious Sedge	*Hypericum tetrapterum*	Square-stalked St John's-wort
Carex disticha	Brown Sedge	*Iris pseudacorus*	Yellow Iris
Carex echinata	Star Sedge	*Isolepis setacea*	Bristle Club-rush
Carex elata	Tufted-sedge	*Juncus compressus*	Round-fruited Rush
Carex hostiana	Tawny Sedge	*Juncus subnodulosus*	Blunt-flowered Rush
Carex lepidocarpa	Long-stalked Yellow-sedge	*Lotus pedunculatus*	Greater Bird's-foot-trefoil
Carex nigra	Common Sedge	*Lycopus europaeus*	Gypsywort
Carex panicea	Carnation Sedge	*Lysimachia nummularia*	Creeping-Jenny
Carex pseudocyperus	Cyperus Sedge	*Lysimachia vulgaris*	Yellow Loosestrife
Carex riparia	Great Pond-sedge	*Lythrum portula*	Water-purslane
Carex rostrata	Bottle Sedge	*Lythrum salicaria*	Purple-loosestrife
Carex vesicaria	Bladder-sedge	*Mentha aquatica*	Water Mint
Cirsium dissectum	Meadow Thistle	*Molinia caerulea*	Purple Moor-grass
Comarum palustre	Marsh Cinquefoil	*Montia fontana*	Blinks
Dactylorhiza incarnata	Early Marsh-orchid	*Myosotis laxa*	Tufted Forget-me-not
Dactylorhiza praetermissa	Southern Marsh-orchid	*Myosotis scorpioides*	Water Forget-me-not
Eleocharis palustris	Common Spike-rush	*Myosotis secunda*	Creeping Forget-me-not
Eleocharis quinqueflora	Few-flowered Spike-rush	*Nasturtium officinale*	Water-cress
Epilobium palustre	Marsh Willowherb	*Persicaria amphibia*	Amphibious Bistort

Table 10.3 List of indicator plants for fen, mire and swamp habitats in Derbyshire (... continued)

Scientific name	Common name	Scientific name	Common name
Persicaria hydropiper	Water-pepper	*Scutellaria minor*	Lesser Skullcap
Phragmites australis	Common Reed	*Silene flos-cuculi*	Ragged-Robin
Pinguicula vulgaris	Common Butterwort	*Sparganium emersum*	Unbranched Bur-reed
Potentilla anserina	Silverweed	*Sparganium erectum*	Branched Bur-reed
Pulicaria dysenterica	Common Fleabane	*Stellaria palustris*	Marsh Stitchwort
Ranunculus flammula	Lesser Spearwort	*Thalictrum flavum*	Common Meadow-rue
Rorippa amphibia	Great Yellow-cress	*Triglochin palustre*	Marsh Arrowgrass
Rorippa palustris	Marsh Yellow-cress	*Valeriana dioica*	Marsh Valerian
Rorippa sylvestris	Creeping Yellow-cress	*Valeriana officinalis*	Common Valerian
Scirpus sylvaticus	Wood Club-rush	*Veronica beccabunga*	Brooklime
Scutellaria galericulata	Skullcap	*Veronica scutellata*	Marsh Speedwell

Table 10.4 List of indicator plants for freshwater habitats in Derbyshire.

FRESHWATER HABITAT INDICATORS			
Scientific name	Common name	Scientific name	Common name
Alisma lanceolatum	Narrow-leaved Water-plantain	*Nymphaea alba*	White Water-lily
Alisma plantago-aquatica	Water-plantain	*Oenanthe aquatica*	Fine-leaved Water-dropwort
Apium inundatum	Lesser Marshwort	*Oenanthe crocata*	Hemlock Water-dropwort
Apium nodiflorum	Fool's-water-cress	*Oenanthe fistulosa*	Tubular Water-dropwort
Berula erecta	Lesser Water-parsnip	*Oenanthe silaifolia*	Narrow-leaved Water-dropwort
Butomus umbellatus	Flowering-rush	*Persicaria amphibia*	Amphibious Bistort
Callitriche brutia	A water-starwort	*Potamogeton alpinus*	Red Pondweed
Callitriche hermaphroditica	Autumnal Water-starwort	*Potamogeton berchtoldii*	Small Pondweed
Callitriche obtusangula	Blunt-fruited Water-starwort	*Potamogeton compressus*	Grass-wrack Pondweed
Callitriche platycarpa	Various-leaved Water-starwort	*Potamogeton crispus*	Curled Pondweed
Callitriche truncata	Short-leaved Water-starwort	*Potamogeton friesii*	Flat-stalked Pondweed
Carex acuta	Slender Tufted-sedge	*Potamogeton lucens*	Shining Pondweed
Carex acutiformis	Lesser Pond-sedge	*Potamogeton natans*	Broad-leaved Pondweed
Carex disticha	Brown Sedge	*Potamogeton obtusifolius*	Blunt-leaved Pondweed
Carex pseudocyperus	Cyperus Sedge	*Potamogeton pectinatus*	Fennel Pondweed
Carex riparia	Great Pond-sedge	*Potamogeton perfoliatus*	Perfoliate Pondweed
Carex rostrata	Bottle Sedge	*Potamogeton polygonifolius*	Bog Pondweed
Catabrosa aquatica	Whorl-grass	*Potamogeton praelongus*	Long-stalked Pondweed
Ceratophyllum demersum	Rigid Hornwort	*Potamogeton pusillus*	Lesser Pondweed
Comarum palustre	Marsh Cinquefoil	*Ranunculus aquatilis*	Common Water-crowfoot
Eleocharis palustris	Common Spike-rush	*Ranunculus circinatus*	Fan-leaved Water-crowfoot
Equisetum fluviatile	Water Horsetail	*Ranunculus flammula*	Lesser Spearwort
Eupatorium cannabinum	Hemp-agrimony	*Ranunculus fluitans*	River Water-crowfoot
Glyceria declinata	Small Sweet-grass	*Ranunculus hederaceus*	Ivy-leaved Crowfoot
Glyceria fluitans	Floating Sweet-grass	*Ranunculus omiophyllus*	Round-leaved Crowfoot
Glyceria notata	Plicate Sweet-grass	*Ranunculus peltatus*	Pond Water-crowfoot
Hippuris vulgaris	Mare's-tail	*Ranunculus penicillatus*	Stream Water-crowfoot
Hottonia palustris	Water-violet	*Ranunculus trichophyllus*	Thread-leaved Water-crowfoot
Hydrocotyle vulgaris	Marsh Pennywort	*Rumex hydrolapathum*	Water Dock
Iris pseudacorus	Yellow Iris	*Rumex maritimus*	Golden Dock
Lemna gibba	Fat Duckweed	*Sagittaria sagittifolia*	Arrowhead
Lemna trisulca	Ivy-leaved Duckweed	*Schoenoplectus lacustris*	Common Club-rush
Littorella uniflora	Shoreweed	*Schoenoplectus tabernaemontani*	Grey Club-rush
Mentha aquatica	Water Mint	*Scirpus sylvaticus*	Wood Club-rush
Menyanthes trifoliata	Bogbean	*Sparganium emersum*	Unbranched Bur-reed
Myosotis laxa	Tufted Forget-me-not	*Sparganium erectum*	Branched Bur-reed
Myosotis scorpioides	Water Forget-me-not	*Spirodela polyrhiza*	Greater Duckweed
Myosotis secunda	Creeping Forget-me-not	*Veronica anagallis-aquatica*	Blue Water-speedwell
Myriophyllum alterniflorum	Alternate Water-milfoil	*Veronica beccabunga*	Brooklime
Myriophyllum spicatum	Spiked Water-milfoil	*Veronica catenata*	Pink Water-speedwell
Nasturtium officinale	Water-cress	*Veronica scutellata*	Marsh Speedwell
Nuphar lutea	Yellow Water-lily	*Zannichellia palustris*	Horned Pondweed

Table 10.5 List of indicator plants for arable habitats in Derbyshire.

ARABLE HABITAT INDICATORS			
Scientific name	Common name	Scientific name	Common name
Aethusa cynapium	Fool's Parsley	*Avena fatua*	Wild-oat
Agrostemma githago	Corncockle	*Avena sativa*	Oat
Agrostis gigantea	Black Bent	*Centaurea cyanus*	Cornflower
Aira praecox	Early Hair-grass	*Cerastium arvense*	Field Mouse-ear
Anagallis arvensis	Scarlet Pimpernel	*Cerastium semidecandrum*	Little Mouse-ear
Anchusa arvensis	Bugloss	*Chaenorhinum minus*	Small Toadflax
Apera interrupta	Dense Silky-bent	*Chenopodium album*	Fat-hen
Apera spica-venti	Loose Silky-bent	*Chenopodium polyspermum*	Many-seeded Goosefoot
Aphanes arvensis	Parsley-piert	*Chenopodium rubrum*	Red Goosefoot

Table 10.5 List of indicator plants for arable habitats in Derbyshire (... continued)

Scientific name	Common name	Scientific name	Common name
Glebionis segetum	Corn Marigold	*Papaver rhoeas*	Common Poppy
Lepidium coronopus	Swine-cress	*Persicaria lapathifolia*	Pale Persicaria
Erodium cicutarium	Common Stork's-bill	*Ranunculus arvensis*	Corn Buttercup
Euphorbia exigua	Dwarf Spurge	*Ranunculus sardous*	Hairy Buttercup
Euphorbia helioscopia	Sun Spurge	*Scandix pecten-veneris*	Shepherd's-needle
Filago vulgaris	Common Cudweed	*Sherardia arvensis*	Field Madder
Fumaria muralis	Common Ramping-fumitory	*Silene latifolia*	White Campion
Fumaria officinalis	Common Fumitory	*Silene noctiflora*	Night-flowering Catchfly
Galeopsis bifida	Bifid Hemp-nettle	*Sinapis arvensis*	Charlock
Galeopsis speciosa	Large-flowered Hemp-nettle	*Solanum nigrum*	Black Nightshade
Geranium pusillum	Small-flowered Crane's-bill	*Spergula arvensis*	Corn Spurrey
Kickxia elatine	Sharp-leaved Fluellen	*Stachys arvensis*	Field Woundwort
Lamium amplexicaule	Henbit Dead-nettle	*Thlaspi arvense*	Field Penny-cress
Legousia hybrida	Venus's-looking-glass	*Trifolium arvense*	Hare's-foot Clover
Lepidium campestre	Field Pepperwort	*Urtica urens*	Small Nettle
Lepidium heterophyllum	Smith's Pepperwort	*Valerianella carinata*	Keeled-fruited Cornsalad
Lepidium ruderale	Narrow-leaved Pepperwort	*Valerianella locusta*	Common Cornsalad
Lithospermum arvense	Field Gromwell	*Veronica agrestis*	Green Field-speedwell
Mentha arvensis	Corn Mint	*Veronica polita*	Grey Field-speedwell
Ornithopus perpusillus	Bird's-foot	*Viola arvensis*	Field Pansy
Papaver argemone	Prickly Poppy		

Table 10.6 List of indicator plants for open mosaic habitats in Derbyshire.

OPEN MOSAIC HABITAT INDICATORS			
Scientific name	**Common name**	**Scientific name**	**Common name**
Achillea millefolium	Yarrow	*Galeopsis bifida*	Bifid Hemp-nettle
Aira praecox	Early Hair-grass	*Galeopsis speciosa*	Large-flowered Hemp-nettle
Anthemis arvensis	Corn Chamomile	*Galeopsis tetrahit*	Common Hemp-nettle
Anthyllis vulneraria	Kidney Vetch	*Geranium molle*	Dove's-foot Crane's-bill
Artemisia absinthium	Wormwood	*Glebionis segetum*	Corn Marigold
Artemisia vulgaris	Mugwort	*Gnaphalium uliginosum*	Marsh Cudweed
Aster novi-belgii	Confused Michaelmas-daisy	*Helminthotheca echioides*	Bristly Oxtongue
Atriplex patula	Common Orache	*Hieracium sabaudum*	Autumn Hawkweed
Atriplex prostrata	Spear-leaved Orache	*Hypericum perforatum*	Perforate St John's-wort
Ballota nigra	Black Horehound	*Hypochaeris radicata*	Cat's-ear
Blackstonia perfoliata	Yellow-wort	*Juncus inflexus*	Hard Rush
Campanula rotundifolia	Harebell	*Lactuca serriola*	Prickly Lettuce
Carduus crispus	Welted Thistle	*Lactuca virosa*	Great Lettuce
Carduus nutans	Musk Thistle	*Lamium amplexicaule*	Henbit Dead-nettle
Carduus tenuiflorus	Slender Thistle	*Lamium hybridum*	Cut-leaved Dead-nettle
Carex arenaria	Sand Sedge	*Lathyrus linifolius*	Bitter-vetch
Carex otrubae	False Fox-sedge	*Leontodon hispidus*	Rough Hawkbit
Catapodium rigidum	Fern-grass	*Lepidium ruderale*	Narrow-leaved Pepperwort
Centaurea cyanus	Cornflower	*Leucanthemum vulgare*	Oxeye Daisy
Centaurea nigra	Common Knapweed	*Linaria purpurea*	Purple Toadflax
Centaurium erythraea	Common Centaury	*Linaria repens*	Pale Toadflax
Centranthus ruber	Red Valerian	*Linaria vulgaris*	Common Toadflax
Cerastium fontanum	Common Mouse-ear	*Linum catharticum*	Fairy Flax
Chaenorhinum minus	Small Toadflax	*Lotus corniculatus*	Common Bird's-foot-trefoil
Chenopodium album	Fat-hen	*Lotus tenuis*	Narrow-leaved Bird's-foot-trefoil
Chenopodium bonus-henricus	Good-King-Henry	*Marrubium vulgare*	White Horehound
Chenopodium ficifolium	Fig-leaved Goosefoot	*Matricaria chamomilla*	Scented Mayweed
Chenopodium polyspermum	Many-seeded Goosefoot	*Matricaria discoidea*	Pineappleweed
Chenopodium rubrum	Red Goosefoot	*Medicago lupulina*	Black Medick
Cichorium intybus	Chicory	*Medicago sativa* ssp. *sativa*	Lucerne
Clinopodium acinos	Basil Thyme	*Melilotus albus*	White Melilot
Clinopodium vulgare	Wild Basil	*Melilotus altissimus*	Tall Melilot
Conium maculatum	Hemlock	*Melilotus officinalis*	Ribbed Melilot
Conyza canadensis	Canadian Fleabane	*Mentha arvensis*	Corn Mint
Crepis biennis	Rough Hawk's-beard	*Odontites vernus*	Red Bartsia
Crepis capillaris	Smooth Hawk's-beard	*Oenothera biennis*	Common Evening-primrose
Dactylorhiza praetermissa	Southern Marsh-orchid	*Ononis spinosa*	Spiny Restharrow
Deschampsia flexuosa	Wavy Hair-grass	*Onopordum acanthium*	Cotton Thistle
Dipsacus fullonum	Wild Teasel	*Ophrys apifera*	Bee Orchid
Echium vulgare	Viper's-bugloss	*Origanum vulgare*	Wild Marjoram
Equisetum arvense	Field Horsetail	*Orobanche minor*	Common Broomrape
Erigeron acris	Blue Fleabane	*Parentucellia viscosa*	Yellow Bartsia
Erodium cicutarium	Common Stork's-bill	*Picris hieracioides*	Hawkweed Oxtongue
Euphrasia sp.	An eyebright	*Pilosella aurantiaca*	Fox-and-cubs
Filago minima	Small Cudweed	*Pilosella officinarum*	Mouse-ear-hawkweed
Filago vulgaris	Common Cudweed	*Plantago media*	Hoary Plantain
Galega officinalis	Goat's-rue	*Poa compressa*	Flattened Meadow-grass

Table 10.6 List of indicator plants for open mosaic habitats in Derbyshire (... continued)

Scientific name	Common name	Scientific name	Common name
Reseda lutea	Wild Mignonette	*Trifolium medium*	Zigzag Clover
Reseda luteola	Weld	*Trifolium micranthum*	Slender Trefoil
Saponaria officinalis	Soapwort	*Trifolium pratense*	Red Clover
Scabiosa columbaria	Small Scabious	*Trifolium scabrum*	Rough Clover
Scorzoneroides autumnalis	Autumn Hawkbit	*Trifolium striatum*	Knotted Clover
Scrophularia nodosa	Common Figwort	*Trisetum flavescens*	Yellow Oat-grass
Senecio squalidus	Oxford Ragwort	*Tussilago farfara*	Colt's-foot
Silene vulgaris	Bladder Campion	*Valerianella carinata*	Keeled-fruited Cornsalad
Spergularia rubra	Sand Spurrey	*Valerianella locusta*	Common Cornsalad
Tanacetum vulgare	Tansy	*Verbascum nigrum*	Dark Mullein
Teucrium scorodonia	Wood Sage	*Verbascum thapsus*	Great Mullein
Thymus polytrichus	Wild Thyme	*Veronica agrestis*	Green Field-speedwell
Tragopogon pratensis	Goat's-beard	*Vicia cracca*	Tufted Vetch
Trifolium arvense	Hare's-foot Clover	*Vicia hirsuta*	Hairy Tare
Trifolium campestre	Hop Trefoil	*Vicia tetrasperma*	Smooth Tare
Trifolium dubium	Lesser Trefoil	*Vulpia bromoides*	Squirreltail Fescue
Trifolium hybridum	Alsike Clover	*Vulpia myuros*	Rat's-tail Fescue

Table 10.7 List of indicator plants for moorlands and heathlands in Derbyshire.

MOORLAND AND HEATHLAND HABITAT INDICATORS			
Scientific name	Common name	Scientific name	Common name
Anagallis tenella	Bog Pimpernel	*Eriophorum angustifolium*	Common Cottongrass
Andromeda polifolia	Bog-rosemary	*Eriophorum latifolium*	Broad-leaved Cottongrass
Arctostaphylos uva-ursi	Bearberry	*Eriophorum vaginatum*	Hare's-tail Cottongrass
Calluna vulgaris	Heather	*Genista anglica*	Petty Whin
Carex binervis	Green-ribbed Sedge	*Huperzia selago*	Fir Clubmoss
Carex canescens	White Sedge	*Juncus squarrosus*	Heath Rush
Carex demissa	Common Yellow-sedge	*Luzula multiflora*	Heath Wood-rush
Carex dioica	Dioecious Sedge	*Lycopodium clavatum*	Stag's-horn Clubmoss
Carex echinata	Star Sedge	*Narthecium ossifragum*	Bog Asphodel
Carex hostiana	Tawny Sedge	*Pinguicula vulgaris*	Common Butterwort
Carex pilulifera	Pill Sedge	*Scleranthus annuus*	Annual Knawel
Dactylorhiza maculata	Heath Spotted-orchid	*Scutellaria minor*	Lesser Skullcap
Diphasiastrum alpinum	Alpine Clubmoss	*Sesleria caerulea*	Blue Moor-grass
Drosera rotundifolia	Round-leaved Sundew	*Trichophorum germanicum*	Deergrass
Empetrum nigrum	Crowberry	*Vaccinium myrtillus*	Bilberry
Epipactis helleborine	Broad-leaved Helleborine	*Vaccinium oxycoccos*	Cranberry
Erica cinerea	Bell Heather	*Vaccinium vitis-idaea*	Cowberry
Erica tetralix	Cross-leaved Heath	*Veronica scutellata*	Marsh Speedwell

Common Centaury (*Centaurium erythraea*) flowering on open mosaic grassland habitat at The Sanctuary Local Nature Reserve, Pride Park, Derby (Nick Moyes)

Acknowledgements

This book would not have been possible without the knowledge, skills and freely-given time of numerous people, amounting to well over 15,000 hours of unpaid labour over the last 20 years.

Recorders

In particular we would like to acknowledge help from the following botanists, all of whom have made a significant contribution to the recording of Derbyshire's plant life. Each submitted at least 500 records apiece, with those in **bold** supplying over 10,000 and sometimes considerably more.

Mrs S. Amer; P. Ardron; M. Bailey; **K. Balkow**; Mrs K. Barnacle; A. Bousie; P. Bowdler; M.J. Boyd; **R.D. Branson**; Mrs P. Brassley; D. Broughton; M. Brown; Mrs P. Brown; D.M. Bryce; Miss A. Burns; G. Coles; Ms D. Court; L. Craig; N. Croll; B. Cuttell; V. Dale; **Derby Nat. Hist. Soc.**; **Derbyshire Wildlife Trust**; T. Dines; **T.W.J.D. Dupree**; D.P. Earl; EMEC; Mrs J.E. Emerson; English Nature; K. Fidler; Mrs B.M. Flint; J. Frith; R.A. Frost; Dr O. Gilbert; Mrs J. Glasscock; B. Gough; R.H. Hall; **J.E. Hawksford**; Miss M.C. Hewitt; **C. Higginbottom**; Dr J.A. Higgins; S.Hind; G. Hirons; **J.G. Hodgson**; Miss K.M. Hollick; I.J. Hopkins; Mrs R. Hunter; **K. Huston**; R. Hyde; Mrs F. Jackson; J & Mrs P. Joyce; G.M. Kay; E. Kearns; P. Kirby; H. Lake; **N.J. Law**; P. Longbottom; A.B. Loy; Mrs H. Luft; Lyme Nat. Hist. Soc.; D. Mallon; **R.D. Martin**; R. Merritt; Mrs H. Metcalfe; J. Middleton; A. Miller; Monks Wood BRC; Ms A. Morgan; Moss Valley Wildlife Group; **N.J. Moyes**; Miss B.A. Noaks; J. Ogden; B. Parker; Mrs S.J. Patrick; Peak District National Park Authority; Mrs H. Perkins; P. Precey; M. Rand; Mrs B. Rhodes; D. Roberts; Mrs L.A. Roberts; **D.J. Scott**; R. Shaw; Ms M.R. Shaw; Ms L. Slack; R. Slaney; Mrs M. Smith (nee Bryce); **Miss C.N. Smith**; **R. Smith**; **Mrs M. Smith**; Dr W.J. Smyllie; Sorby Nat. His. Soc.; Dr L.A. Storer; **T. Taylor**; J.A. Thickitt; **R. Thomas**; W. Thompson; Mrs E.M. Thorpe; Mrs P.M. Torry; S. Trotter; Mrs E.R. Tryner; J. Turner; Upper Derwent Survey Team; C.B. Waite; D. Walstow; **G.S. Wheeldon**; **Mrs G.W. Wheeldon**; **Dr A. Willmot**; A. Withington; D.C. Wood and M. Woods.

George and Grace Wheeldon – two of our stalwart band of plant recorders – looking at Common Butterwort on volcanic outcrop in Monk's Dale (Nick Moyes)

Over 650 people directly or indirectly supplied plant records used in this *Flora*, and we are only sorry we could not acknowledge them all. Some datasets were imported electronically, and for this we thank the Botanical Society for Britain & Ireland; CEH Monks Wood; Derbyshire Wildlife Trust; J.G. Hodgson; K. Huston; E. Kearns; N.J. Law; Liverpool Museum; Lyme Natural History Society; D.J. Scott and R. Thomas.

Data inputters

A stalwart band of volunteers has worked away behind the scenes, mostly at Derby Museum, helping to put the last 300 years of the county's plant records onto a Recorder 3 database. This flora could not have been achieved in the same timescale had their help not been available. The following have computerised over 1,000 records, with those in bold inputting at least 10,000 apiece.

DRA; RJB; **A. & R.D. Branson**; **A. Brown**; DJC; C. Cauldwell; JCD; R. Davison-Fenn; Derbyshire Wildlife Trust staff; A. Dodd; **S. Eastwood**; **Mrs J.E. Emerson**; L. Gilfedder; **A. Hall**; L. Hayward; J. Higgins; **K. Huston**; S. Laver; N.J. Law; **R. Lynam**; **R.D. Martin**; **W. & H. Metcalfe**; P. Morton; **N.J. Moyes**; **Mrs K. Patrick**; **J. Poll**; J. Rana; **L. Roberts**; JS; L. Sharratt; **A. Shaw**; T. Wabeke; A. Wheeler and **Dr A. Willmot**. Special thanks must go to Ruth Lynam and Kath Patrick who computerised over 85,000 and 135,000 records, respectively.

IT credits

Dr Alan Morton has given considerable help over the years, making special modifications to his DMAP mapping programme to allow us to include overlain symbols in all the distribution maps shown here. Thanks to C. Roper for advice with inserting map images into Access reports, and especially to Kevin Brewer and the Derby City Council's Webteam for building the online Flora website.

The records supplied by all the recorders were entered on a Recorder 3 database, maintained by the Natural History staff of Derby Museum & Art Gallery which housed the Derbyshire Biological Records Centre for 40 years. With local government cutbacks and the loss of the last remaining Natural Sciences post in 2011, the database was transferred to Derbyshire Wildlife Trust. All supporting paper records and herbarium voucher specimens remained at Derby Museum. The county plant recorder, Dr A. Willmot, now stores all new plant records on a MapMate database.

Volume preparation

The majority of this book was written by the authors. However, a number of other local botanists and naturalists helped in various ways with the preparation of the text, all of whose assistance is gratefully acknowledged. K. Huston of the Derbyshire Wildlife Trust prepared Chapter 4 on the history of wildlife conservation in the county. He was assisted in this task by R. Thomas, Ecologist at the Peak District National Park Authority, who helped with analysis of plant declines within different habitats and provided comments and advice at various stages of its development. T. Taylor at DWT and the authors of this *Flora* also provided advice and comments on early drafts.

Mrs M. Smith and Ms C.N. Smith of the Wild Flower Society co-authored Chapter 5 "Where to See Plants in Derbyshire". K. Balkow,

G. Coles, G. Ellis, R.D. Martin, K. Patrick, R. Smith, Ms C.N. Smith and Mrs M. Smith all commented on various drafts of the systematic entries and/or introductory sections. Our thanks, too, go to G. Coles for providing information on Derbyshire specimens in British herbaria, and to Professor Clive Stace for kindly agreeing to write the Foreword to this book. The knowledge and advice of all these friends significantly improved the usefulness and accuracy of the final volume but, as ever, all the errors are ours.

Photographs

A number of local botanists and photographers have made available pictures of plants and scenery from Derbyshire from which the included illustrations have been selected. Our thanks is due to all of them, including: P. Anderson; K. Balkow; D. Blowers; R.D. Branson; R. Butterfield; P. & G. Dishart; DWT; W. Grange; K. Huston; S. Jackson; N. Moyes; M. Neal; B. Parker; P. Precey; P. Smith; R. & R. Smith; S. Trotter and Dr A. Willmot. Thanks, too, to the Landscape Team at Derbyshire County Council for use of some of their images.

Financial assistance

Although we have never specifically solicited financial help from individuals for the publication of this *Flora*, a few have made generous donations to assist the project, and we should like to thank N. Brown; J. & P. Joyce and K. White in this respect. S. Jones and J. Bland have together written and organised quizzes which have raised considerable funds for us. Together, these efforts have significantly helped reduce the cover price of this book. The following organisations have also generously supported its production:

The Botanical Society of Britain & Ireland is the leading charitable society promoting the study and enjoyment of British and Irish wild plants with a membership of about 3,000 amateur and professional botanists. It maintains: a network of 152 Vice-county recorders, a central database of threatened plants, a panel of referees for difficult plants and a comprehensive scientific database that enables the list of British and Irish plants to be kept up to date. It carries out national surveys and publishes the results of these as well as authoritative identification handbooks on difficult plants such as sedges and roses. Its journals enable members to share their observations and the results of their studies. It promotes the publication of local Floras such as this and county rare plant registers. It holds field meetings and conferences to bring botanists together, whether amateur or professional, and encourages the training of botanists of all ages. More information will be found on the BSBI website at www.bsbi.org.uk. Membership and other enquiries may be sent to BSBI Honorary General Secretary, c/o Department of Botany, The Natural History Museum, Cromwell Road, London, SW7 5BD.

The Derbyshire Wildlife Trust is the leading local wildlife organisation which promotes the conservation of all wildlife throughout the county. It manages and maintains a network of over 40 nature reserves, many of which are mentioned in **Chapter 5** "Where to see Plants in Derbyshire". It encourages conservation across the countryside by its Living Landscape projects, by commenting on planning applications and its Local Wildlife Sites System run in conjunction with Local Authorities. It also operates the local biological records centre.

The Wildflower Society is a national charitable organisation founded in 1886 which aims to promote a greater knowledge of field botany among the general public and particularly young people. It also aims to advance education in matters relating to the conservation of wild flowers, the British flora and the countryside in general. It produces a magazine for all members three times a year.

Other credits

The Flora of Derbyshire project would not have begun at all had not R. Smith, the county plant recorder for Derbyshire until 1996, taken up the challenge of starting to organise the systematic botanical recording of our region. R.D. Branson gave help in extracting local plant names from Grigson (1975), whilst he and his wife worked tirelessly for two years to extract herbarium data from the Derby Museum collections. Mrs J.E. Emerson, Dr J.A. Higgins and Mrs F. Jackson kindly extracted records from various past Floras for us. Our long-suffering families must be thanked for their never-ending patience as we worked on this scheme, and we wish to record thanks to our employers, past and present, for the encouragement and support they have at various times given to this important project. These are: Derby City Council, Derbyshire County Council and the University of Derby. The work of the Landscape Team at Derbyshire County Council proved invaluable in preparation of the introductory Chapter 1. Their report on Derbyshire landscapes is available on the County Council website. Vice-county boundary data was digitised by the National Biodiversity Network (NBN) Gateway and 1:625k geology data was made available by the British Geological Survey. Map data is Crown Copyright, with all rights reserved, and provided by Ordnance Survey under licence no: 100024913.

To those whose data we might have missed or mangled along the way, or whose help we may have omitted to acknowledge here, we offer our apologies. We did our best with the resources available to capture as much data as possible, and as accurately as possible.

Glossary

Agri-environment schemes – Funding schemes by which central government pays farmers and/or owners of land for managing it in a more environmentally friendly manner, and according to a schedule of approved enhancements and reimbursements. These include: **Entry Level Stewardship** (ELS); **Higher Level Stewardship** (HLS); and, more recently, the **New Environmental Land Management Scheme** (NELMS), renamed **Countryside Stewardship Scheme**.

Alien – A plant considered to have been introduced to Derbyshire by human activity, either accidentally or intentionally. Aliens may be: Anciently Established (**Archaeophytes**); Recently Established (**Neophytes**); **Casual** or **Planted**.

Anciently Established – See Archaeophyte.

Archaeophyte (Anciently Established) – An alien species that arrived in the county *prior* to 1500 A.D. and which maintains itself in the wild either by sexual or asexual reproduction. Many arrived here around 5,000 years ago as weeds of cultivated land created by the earliest farmers.

Bern – A conservation status code used in this book to indicate strictly protected flora species listed in Appendix 1 of the **Bern Convention**, an international treaty which came into force in 1982. Also known as the **Bern Convention on the Conservation of European Wildlife and Natural Habitats.** The EU meets its obligations under this Convention by means of the Habitats Directive, adopted in 1992 (*q.v.*).

BAP – See Biodiversity Action Plan.

Biodiversity Action Plan (BAP) – A formal plan drawn up by governments and non-governmental conservation bodies to identify, maintain and enhance the key wildlife features of a specified area. Usually relating to countries or large regions such as counties and National Parks, they can be produced for individual sites. They work by partnership agreement, setting targets for priority species or habitats over a defined time period.

BRCs (Biological Records Centres) – Centres for the collection, interpretation and dissemination of wildlife records. Also called Local Records Centres (LRCs), they originated in the museums sector in the 1970s, but most are now operated by Wildlife Trusts or local authority planning departments. **DBRC** refers to **Derbyshire Biological Records Centre**, based at Derby Museum's Natural History Department from the 1980s to 2011, but now managed by Derbyshire Wildlife Trust at their offices.

BSBI (Botanical Society of Britain and Ireland formerly **Botanical Society of the British Isles)** – The foremost organisation in the country concerned with the study and understanding of the vascular plants found growing wild here.

Calaminarian grassland – Vegetation that has developed on soils rich in poisonous metals such as lead and copper. It is usually thin open grassland dominated by plants tolerant of heavy metals (**metallophytes**). Locally it develops on waste deposited after the mining of lead-rich ores in the White Peak.

Carboniferous Period – A unit of geological time, usually split into two periods: Upper Carboniferous (*c*.290mya–320mya) – typical rocks: sandstone, gritstone, shale, coal; and Lower Carboniferous (*c*.320mya–360mya) – typical rocks: Carboniferous limestone.

Casual – An Alien plant that grows in the wild, but which does not maintain its presence by reproduction. Casual plants do not therefore persist in any given location beyond the life span of the original colonists. They rely on repeated introduction of seeds or plants to maintain a presence here.

CITES (Convention on International Trade in Endangered Species) – An international treaty designed to control and regulate trading of endangered species. Drawn up in 1973, virtually all countries are now signed up to it. It is implemented in Europe as the **EU Wildlife Trade Regulations**, listing species in four "Annexes", one of which includes orchids.

Clough – A narrow steep-sided and often rocky valley in the uplands of the Dark Peak. These watercourses are generally clothed in open moorland vegetation but may contain patches of woodland.

Conservation Status – A categorisation of the threat to survival faced by a plant or animal in an area. This book lists all current national and local statuses, including any affected by legislation on sale or release into the wild. Main IUCN threat codes used here are: CR, EN, VU, NT. Main rarity codes are NR and NS (*q.v.*). See also **Chapter 2 (Explanation of Species Accounts)** and **Chapter 9 (Derbyshire Red Data List).**

CPRE (Campaign to Protect Rural England) – (formerly known as the Council for the Preservation of Rural England and also the Council for the Protection of Rural England).

CR (Critically Endangered) – A conservation status code used in this book to indicate the most serious conservation threat category, indicating a species evaluated using IUCN criteria and found to be facing an *extremely high risk* **of extinction** in the wild unless conditions change. (See also EN, VU, NT, LC).

Dale – A shallow steep-sided valley cut into the Carboniferous Limestone plateau of the White Peak. They generally have rocky outcrops along their sides, often accompanied by scree slopes. Many are dry but some such as Dove Dale and Lathkill Dale have permanent streams flowing in them. They are botanically the richest areas in Derbyshire.

DCC – Derbyshire County Council. (in some contexts may also refer to Derby City Council)

DRDB (Derbyshire Red Data Book) – See Red Data List.

DWT (Derbyshire Wildlife Trust) – The leading local wildlife organisation which promotes the conservation of all wildlife throughout Derbyshire. See Acknowledgements.

Edges – Outcrops of coarse sandstone known as Millstone Grit that line the upper slopes of valleys in the Dark Peak. At around 20 metres high, they are important scenic aspects of their area but are botanically generally rather disappointing.

EN (Endangered) – A conservation status code used in this book to indicate the second severest conservation threat category, next to Critically Endangered, which indicates a species evaluated using IUCN criteria and found to be facing a *very high risk* of extinction in the wild unless conditions change. (See also CR, VU, NT, LC).

Ephemeral – An herbaceous plant which completes its life cycle from seed to seed within a few weeks and which may do so many times in one year *e.g.* **Thale Cress** (*Arabidopsis thaliana*). They generally occur in short-lived habitats such as regularly weeded flowerbeds.

ERL (England Red List) – see Red Data List.

Established – see Archaeophyte and Neophyte.

Flash – An area of wet low-lying countryside caused by the subsidence of ground due to coalmining, generally occupied by marshy areas with patches of damp scrub and open water.

Frequency – A term used here to reflect presence or absence in tetrads (2km by 2km squares). It does not refer to abundance, but describes the total number of tetrads a species has been found in.
- **Very common** – A plant occurs in around 80–100% of all tetrads in the county.
- **Common** – A plant occurs in about two-thirds (*i.e.* 60–79%) of tetrads in the county.
- **Frequent** – A plant occurs in about half (*i.e.* 40–59%) of tetrads in the county.
- **Occasional** – A plant occurs in up to one third (*i.e.* 6–39%) of the tetrads in the county.
- **Rare** – A plant occurs in only 2–5% of the tetrads in the county.
- **Very rare** – A plant occurs in 1% or less of all tetrads in the county.
For example, two tree species might both occur in one third of all the mapped tetrads in Derbyshire. For one species there may be only a single tree per tetrad, for the other there may be 100 trees per tetrad. Clearly the latter is much more abundant than the former, yet both would be described as "occasional" based on the criteria shown above. These relative terms may also be applied to smaller subdivisions of the county, such as Landscape Character Areas.

"Greater Derbyshire" – The basic recording area used in this *Flora*. It includes both the modern geographic county of Derbyshire (including Derby) *and* the Watsonian vice-county of Derbyshire (v.c.57). This slightly larger, combined area should be assumed whenever "the county" or "Derbyshire" is referred to in this book with the exception of **Chapter 4**, the data in which relates specifically to the modern county only. See Table 1.1 for Derbyshire statistics and Figure 2.1 for a detailed map of both boundaries.

Grips – Narrow steep sided valleys cut into the Magnesian Limestone, often with rocky outcrops along them. Although not quite as botanically rich or famous as the Dales of the White Peak, they do have considerable floristic interest. Note that access to them is often very limited.

Growth form – The overall appearance or form of a plant. Unless otherwise described, the **species accounts in** this book assume all plants to be deciduous, self-supporting, non-spiny, and self-feeding by means of photosynthesis. They are considered to be either herbaceous or woody (trees, shrubs or undershrubs). **Trees** have a single main woody stem that arises from ground level. "Large trees" generally grow to 40m or more when mature, whilst "trees" only reach between 20 to 39m and "small trees" are generally less than 20m tall. **Shrubs** have a number of roughly equal sized woody stems that arise together from ground level. **Undershrubs** are shrubs that generally only reach half a metre in height. Aquatic species, whether submerged, floating or emergent, are all considered herbaceous. Terrestrial herbaceous plants may be either: **Perennial, Biennial, Annual** or **Ephemeral**. Growth form may be qualified by terms such as: climbing, scrambling, spiny or evergreen.

Habitat Indicator Species – Species which are taken to be particularly characteristic of a specific type of vegetation or plant community. Thus, locally, **Moschatel** (*Adoxa moschatellina*) is taken to be indicative of ancient woodland. Together with Derbyshire Red Data Book (DRDB) species, their presence on a site helps inform decisions regarding the designation of Local Wildlife Site status. See **Chapter 10** for lists of species indicators, arranged by habitat.

Habitats Directive – EU legislation in response to the Bern Convention, requiring member states to take measures to maintain or restore natural habitats and wild species listed in the Annexes to the Directive at a favourable conservation status, and to introduce robust protection for habitats and species of European importance, such as the designation of Special Areas of Conservation (SACs).

HabsRegs (Habitat Regulations) – A conservation status code used in this book to indicate plants listed in Schedule 5 of the **Conservation of Habitats and Species Regulations 2010.** This Act consolidated amendments made to similar Regulations in 1994, which was our government's enactment of the EC Habitats Directive – the cornerstone of Europe's nature conservation policy. Often abbreviated to "Habitats Regulations" or "HabsRegs", they provide for the designation and protection of "European sites" and "European protected species"'. Plant species are derived from Annexe IVb of the EC Habitats Directive.

Hectad – A recording unit of 10km by 10km, marked on 1:50,000 scale OS maps by a slightly thicker easting and northing. They are uniquely identified by a pair of letters, followed by two digits relating to the easting and northings that intersect at the bottom left corner of that grid square. For example, SK33 is the hectad containing the majority of the City of Derby. All hectads in Derbyshire start with SK, except for a few in the extreme north-west and north, which are SJ and SE respectively. A Hectad contains one hundred 1km squares (or monads *q.v.*). Note that a grid reference given as SK3030, whilst being within the hectad SK33 would specifically refer to a single monad.

Hectare (ha) – A metric unit of land area 100m by 100m or 10,000 m². (Usually abbreviated to "ha", 1ha – 2.47 acres. 100ha = 1 km²).

Hybrid – A plant produced when two different species interbreed. Hybrids are frequently intermediate in appearance to their parents and often infertile. However they are sometimes fertile and can backcross with one or both of their original parents, producing what are termed **hybrid swarms**. Hybrids frequently occur where established habitats have been disturbed, but are not as common as might be supposed from superficial examination of unusual individuals.

INNS (Invasive Non-native Species) – A plant or animal which is not native to an area, and is causing a serious conservation problem such as excluding native species from that area e.g. **Indian Balsam** (*Impatiens glandulifera*).

IUCN – The *International Union for Conservation of Nature* is the world's main authority on the conservation status of species. Publishes the IUCN Red List of Threatened Species, which assesses the conservation status of plants and animals using defined criteria reflecting threat to survival.

Landscape Character Area – A natural subdivision of the countryside with a relatively uniform appearance, based upon a shared combination of landscape features, biodiversity, land-use and soil type. Eleven Character Areas are described in this book for "Greater Derbyshire" (see **Chapter 1**) and closely follow the National Character Area designations of Natural England.

LC (Least Concern) – A conservation status code indicating a species has been assessed using IUCN criteria and found not to be facing any threat to its survival at the present time. It is the default status allocated to native species not deemed to be Near Threatened (NT) or Threatened (CR, EN, VU). Note: a species can be both Nationally Rare (NR) and of Least Concern if its populations are small but not currently threatened (*e.g. Rubus durescens*, endemic to south Derbyshire). Species of Least Concern will have a Conservation Status given as "None" in this work.

LNPs (Local Nature Partnerships) – High-level partnerships of local organisations, businesses and individuals intended to bring about positive change by influencing key strategic decision-making across all sectors. There are 48 LNPs in England, with the Lowland Derbyshire and Nottinghamshire LNP, plus the Peak District LNP, covering all of Derbyshire. Equivalent in status to Local Enterprise Partnerships they resulted from the government's 2011 Natural Environment White Paper.

Local Nature Reserve (LNR) – A statutory designation, optionally applied to land in the ownership of a Local Authority which, working closely with Natural England, declares it as being dedicated for the benefit of wildlife and for people. There 56 LNRs within "Greater Derbyshire".

Local Wildlife Site (LWS) – An area of land designated by local government or wildlife organisation as being of local importance for its biodiversity. Recognised within the planning system, their selection in Derbyshire is made by a panel of experts, based on set guidelines and criteria, such as the presence of certain numbers of Red Data List or Habitat Indicator Species (*q.v.*). Such designation gives no protection from land management changes, nor any right of access. Their geological equivalents are Regionally Important Geological Sites (RIGS).

Locally Declining – A conservation status category used in the *Red Data List of Derbyshire's Vascular Plants* (Moyes & Willmot 2009) to indicate a species with no national status, but exhibiting serious recent decline in Derbyshire over the last 20 years, based on analysis of "Relative Apparent Change" described in **Chapter 6**. Allocated the code "**DRDB Cat5b**" in this book. See also **Chapter 9**.

Locally Extinct – A conservation status category used in the *Red Data List of Derbyshire's Vascular Plants* (Moyes & Willmot 2009) to indicate a species not found here since the previous 1969 Flora of Derbyshire – a period of 44 years. Allocated the code "**DRDB Cat6**" in this book. See also **Chapter 9**.

Locally Rare – A conservation status category used in the *Red Data List of Derbyshire's Vascular Plants* (Moyes & Willmot 2009) to indicate a species known in 3 or less Derbyshire monads, and with no national status. Allocated the code "**DRDB Cat4**" in this book. See also **Chapter 9**.

Locally Scarce – A conservation status category used in the *Red Data List of Derbyshire's Vascular Plants* (Moyes & Willmot 2009) to indicate a species known in 4 to 10 Derbyshire monads, and with no national status. Allocated the code "**DRDB Cat5a**" in this book. See also **Chapter 9.**

Lowland Derbyshire – Those parts of Derbyshire falling outside the Peak District's area of coverage for its Biodiversity Action Plan. Essentially, this is all of the county except for the Dark Peak, South West Peak and White Peak Landscape Character Areas. (Note: the Peak District National Park Authority's boundary does not follow Landscape Character Areas, although its BAP does).

LWS – See Local Wildlife Site.

Metallophytes – Plants associated with soils contaminated with heavy metals such as lead. They are simply more tolerant of this pollution than most plants, so flourish where others cannot. Our best known examples are **Spring Sandwort** (*Minuartia verna*), **Alpine Penny-cress** (*Noccaea caerulescens*) and **Mountain Pansy** (*Viola lutea*). Their habitats are sometimes described as **Calaminarian grasslands** (*q.v.*).

Monad – A recording unit of 1km by 1km, marked on Ordnance Survey maps by intersecting eastings and northings. Monads are the main unit of recording for many biological surveys. They are identified by a pair of letters, followed by four digits referring to those easting and northings that intersect at the bottom left corner of the given grid square. These are sometimes termed "4-figure grid references" (*e.g.* Monsal Head, SK1871). There are 100 monads in a hectad, and 2,960 whole and partial monads within "Greater Derbyshire" (*q.v.*).

Native – A plant believed to be present in Derbyshire due entirely to natural processes, and generally thought to have arrived here before the advent of agriculture *i.e. prior* to 5,000 years ago at the latest. The alternative term is "**Alien**" (*q.v.*).

National Nature Reserve (NNR) – An area formally designated by Natural England on behalf of government as being amongst the finest wildlife or geological sites in the country which are managed to maintain that interest and to which the public generally have access. These 143 statutory sites are a selection of the very best parts of England's SSSIs (*q.v.*), of which four are in "Greater Derbyshire".

NELMS (New Environmental Land Management Scheme) – an environmental stewardship, or "agri-environment scheme" (*q.v.*), renamed **Countryside Stewardship Schemes** in 2015, and likely to inject less funding into environmental benefits than previous Stewardship schemes as a result of EU CAP reforms.

Neophyte (Recently Established) – An alien species that arrived in the county *after* 1500 A.D. and which maintains itself in the wild either by sexual or asexual reproduction. Many were originally imported from overseas as garden plants. It must maintain itself in the wild for at least 5 years before it can be classed as established.

NERC– A conservation status code used in this book to indicate **Species of Principal Importance** for the conservation of biodiversity in England. They are listed in Section 41 of the **Natural Environment and Rural Communities Act 2006** (NERC Act) which contains the same 943 species that required action under the UK's BAP. These species continue to be regarded as conservation priorities under the UK Post-2010 Biodiversity Framework, so are still referred to as **UK BAP Priority Species**. Section 40 of the NERC Act obliges all public bodies to have regard to biodiversity conservation when carrying out their functions. (Note that NERC is also an acronym used for the Natural Environment Research Council).

NGO (Non-Governmental Organisation) – Any non-profit, voluntary citizens' group that is organised on a local, national or international level. Task-orientated and driven by people with a common interest, NGOs perform a variety of functions and may complement, replace or even challenge the actions of government-funded bodies.

NIAs (Nature Improvement Areas) – Twelve landscape-scale areas designated by central government which aim to revitalise urban and rural areas by creating bigger inter-connected networks of wildlife sites and other habitats to help achieve nature's recovery. They should improve the health of the natural environment to support food production, reduce flood risk and increase access to nature. "Locally-determined NIAs" may be designated by local planning authorities.

NNR – See National Nature Reserve.

NPPF (National Planning Policy Framework) – A document setting out government planning policies for England and acting as key guidance for local authorities and decision-takers, both in drawing up local plans and in considering planning applications.

NR (Nationally Rare) – A conservation status term applied to an organism occurring in 15 or fewer hectads in Great Britain. This is not an IUCN measurement of threat or population decline, but a useful indicator of a species with a very restricted distribution.

NS (Nationally Scarce) – A conservation status term applied to an organism occurring in between only 16 and 100 hectads in Great Britain. It is not an IUCN measurement of threat or decline, but provides a useful indicator of a species with a limited distribution.

NT (Near Threatened) – A conservation status given to a species which has been evaluated under IUCN threat criteria as neither Critically Endangered, Endangered nor Vulnerable, but is close to qualifying as such or is likely to qualify as such in the near future.

PDNP (Peak District National Park) – One of 15 areas of protected countryside designated by national government under the National Parks and Access to the Countryside Act 1949. Each is characterised by its beautiful countryside, wildlife and cultural heritage, with planning and conservation matters administered by a **National Park Authority** (NPA). Unlike national parks abroad, the land is not all owned by government nor is all the land open access for the general public. The Peak District National Park was the first to be designated in this country in 1951.

Peak District – The upland area of over 1,430 square kilometres in midland England, at the southern end of the Pennine Chain. It covers large parts of north-western Derbyshire, plus lesser areas of South and West Yorkshire, Cheshire and Staffordshire. Despite the name, it does not contain any significant peaks, rather the area is one of elevated tracts of incised limestone plateau, or high moorland with rounded contours. Its highest point is on Kinder Scout at 636m. Conservation, planning and management actions are administered by the Peak District National Park Authority (PDNPA).

Planted – A status description used for species believed to have been deliberately placed in a natural setting. Recorders generally exclude such plants in their surveys, particularly crop and forestry species.

Rake – A local miners' term for the main type of mineral deposit found in the White Peak Landscape Character Area. They are found at geological faults in the limestone that have been filled with mineral deposits, such as lead and barium ore. They are linear exposures, sometimes several metres wide, and can run for a kilometre or more across the landscape. Extensively mined for over 2,000 years, many are still rich in heavy metals, and can support interesting communities of metal-tolerant plants (metallophytes) where not shaded by trees.

Recently Established – See Neophyte.

Red Data List (= Red Data Book) – A publication naming the most threatened, rarest or declining species in an area, usually allocating one of a series of threat levels to each. Red Lists may be local, national or international in coverage. The most recent Red Data Book for Derbyshire vascular plants was produced by Moyes & Willmot in 2009 and listed species in one of six categories, ranging from Internationally Rare to Locally Extinct (coded here as **DRDB Cat1 to Cat6**). This *Red List* is repeated with minor revisions in **Chapter 9**. The first *England Red List (ERL)* for vascular plants was published by Stroh *et al.* in 2014, using IUCN threat criteria. A list of additional species and threat classifications resulting from it is also given in chapter 9.

RSPB (Royal Society for the Protection of Birds) – The largest nature conservation charity in the UK with more than a million members. Primarily concerned with the protection of birds and their habitats, this NGO works nationally and internationally to promote nature conservation issues.

SACs (Special Areas of Conservation) – strictly protected sites designated under the EC Habitats Directive (*q.v.*) and forming part of a European network of important high-quality conservation sites that will make a significant contribution to conserving the 189 habitat types and 788 species identified in Annexes I and II of the Directive. Four SACs occur within "Greater Derbyshire".

Sough – A man-made tunnel cut into the Carboniferous Limestone to drain water from deep lead mines. They often run from the sides of dales well into the heart of the limestone plateau. Some are now dry but many still carry streams of drainage water out of the limestone massif.

Species – The basic unit of plant classification. All individuals of one species should look alike and be able to reproduce with each other, but not with members of other species. In practice, two species can sometimes interbreed producing **hybrid** individuals. These are often incapable of producing offspring themselves but when they do it can cause considerable problems of identification. The term is abbreviated as "sp." while the plural form is "spp.". See also "subspecies".

SSSI (Site of Special Scientific Interest) – A statutory conservation designation denoting a highly protected area formally declared by Natural England as being of national importance for wildlife or geology. Such designation should give sites protection from development and inappropriate land management, but no public right of access. There are over 4,100 SSSIs in England, covering 7% of the land area, of which 106 fall within "Greater Derbyshire".

Status – A descriptive category used to indicate whether a species is **Native** or **Alien**, based on our current understanding of its presence and origin in Derbyshire. Where a native plant, such as **Jacob's-ladder** (*Polemonium caeruleum*), is imported into gardens and subsequently escapes into the wild it could theoretically have two statuses. In such cases priority is given to the native status. The same logic is applied to species which can be both established and casual (*cf.* **Conservation Status**).

Derbyshire's county flower, Jacob's-ladder (*Polemonium caeruleum*), grows as a native in Lathkill Dale, but the species is also cultivated in gardens and may sometimes escape (Nick Moyes)

Subspecies – Individuals of some species may sometimes fall into two or more recognisable types which are called subspecies. These can interbreed but are usually prevented from doing so because they occur in different geographical areas or habitats. The term is abbreviated as "ssp." plural "sspp.".

Tetrad – A recording and mapping unit 2km by 2km square. Commonly used by botanists, they are not specifically marked on Ordnance Survey maps. There are 25 tetrads within one hectad (10km by 10km grid square). A unique tetrad reference is given as a combination of the 10km grid square number, with the relevant letter appended *e.g.* Thulston SK43A. Tetrads never overlap one another, and are allocated a letter as shown below in an arrangement referred to as "DINTY" – from the only line that makes a pronounceable word.

E	J	P	U	Z
D	I	N	T	Y
C	H	M	S	X
B	G	L	R	W
A	F	K	Q	V

Alphabetic codes allocated to Tetrads within a Hectad.

Vascular plants – A grouping of all the flowering plants, conifers, ferns and fern allies. They are so-called because all contain specialised conducting cells known as "vascular tissue" which transport water and sugars around the plant. Simpler plants such as mosses, algae and lichens do not contain such specialised tissues.

Vice-county (v.c.) – A geographical division of the British Isles used for the purposes of biological recording and other scientific data-gathering. Sometimes called Watsonian vice-counties, they were introduced by H.C. Watson in 1852 based on the British counties at that time. They provide a stable basis for county-based recording and mapping as they remain unchanged by constant local government reorganisations, allowing historical and modern data to be more accurately compared. There are 112 vice counties in England, Wales and Scotland, with Derbyshire numbered as "v.c.57". It is shown together with the modern geographic county of Derbyshire on all the distribution maps in this book. Adjacent vice-counties are Staffordshire (v.c.39) to the west; Leicestershire (v.c.55) to the south-east; Nottinghamshire (v.c.56) to the east; Cheshire (v.c.58) to the north-west; and South West Yorkshire (v.c.63) to the north. See Figure 2.1.

Voucher Specimen – A preserved specimen in a museum or private collection which is retained as proof of a plant's identity, and hence of a record.

VU (Vulnerable) – A conservation status code used in this book to indicate a species evaluated using IUCN criteria and found to be facing a ***high risk*** of extinction in an area unless conditions change. It is the least severe of the extinction threat categories. (See also CR, EN, NT, LC).

WCA8 – A conservation status code used in this book to indicate protected plant species listed on Schedule 8 of the **Wildlife and Countryside Act 1981** (as amended), making it an offence to pick, uproot, destroy, sell or offer for sale part of any so-listed wild plant, including its seeds.

WCA9 – A conservation status code used in this book to indicate invasive non-native species listed in Schedule 9 Part II of the **Wildlife and Countryside Act 1981** (as amended), making it an offence to cause that plant to grow in the wild. See Table 6.6 for a list of those occurring in Derbyshire.

References

Adams, W. (1840) *The Gem of the Peak or Matlock Bath and its Vicinity.* London.

Akeroyd, J.R., Gornall, R.J., Preston. C.D., Robson, N.K.B. & Rushton, B.S. (1986) Plant records. *Watsonia* 16: 183–198.

Amer, S.R. & Dalton, R.T. (1983) Hedgerow evolution in the parish of Burnaston, near Derby. *East Midlands Geographer* 8: 89–97.

Anderson, D.J. (1965) Studies on structure in plant communities, I. An analysis of limestone grassland in Monk's Dale, Derbyshire. *Journal of Ecology* 53: 9–107.

Anderson, P. (1988) *A Review of the Role, Status, Control and After-treatment of Bracken on Moorland.* Peak District National Park, Bakewell.

Anderson, P. & Shimwell, D. (1981) *Wild Flowers and Other Plants of the Peak District.* Moorland, Ashbourne.

Anderson, P. & Yalden, D.W. (1981) Increased sheep numbers and the loss of heather moorland in the Peak District, England. *Biological Conservation* 20: 195–213.

Anonymous (1919) In Memoriam: Thomas Gibbs 1865–1919. *The Naturalist* 44: 177–180.

Bagnall, J.E. (1889) A review of: A contribution to the flora of Derbyshire. *Journal of Botany* 27: 318–320.

Balme, O.E. (1953) Edaphic and vegetation zoning on the Carboniferous Limestone of the Derbyshire Dales. *Journal of Ecology* 41: 331–343.

Band, S.R. (1972a) Some botanical aspects of Ashover, Derbyshire. *Sorby Record* 3: 27–28.

Band, S.R. (1972b) *Alchemilla alpina* L. – In Derbyshire. *Watsonia* 9: 139–140.

Band, S.R. (1975) *Alchemilla alpina* L. – In Derbyshire. *Watsonia* 10: 411.

Beresford, J.E. & Wade, P.M. (1979) The flora of ponds in the Long Eaton and Sawley district of Derbyshire. *Watsonia* 12: 391.

Beswick, P. & Rotherham, I.D. (1993). *Ancient Woodlands: Their Archaeology and Ecology, a Coincidence of Interest.* Landscape Conservation Forum, Sheffield.

Bevan, J. (1990) *Hieracium britannicum* F.J.Hanb in Wales. *Watsonia* 18: 199–200.

Biggam, C.P. Ed. (2003) *From Earth to Art – The Many Aspects of the Plant-world in Anglo-saxon England.* Editions Rodopi, Amsterdam.

Boulter, M.C. (1971) A palynological study of two of the Neogene plant beds in Derbyshire. *Bulletin of the British Museum (Natural History) Geology* 19: 361–410.

Boulter, M.C., Ford, T.D., Ijtaba, M. & Walsh, P.T. (1971) Brassington formation: a newly recognised Tertiary formation in the southern Pennines. *Nature* 231: 134–136.

Boulter, M.C.& Chaloner, W.G. (1970) Neogene fossil plants from Derbyshire England. *Review of Palaeobotany and Palynology* 10: 61–78.

Braithwaite, M.E., Ellis, R.W. & Preston, C.D. (2006) *Change in the British Flora 1987–2004.* Botanical Society of the British Isles, London.

Bridges, E.M. (1966) *The Soils and Land Use of the District North of Derby.* Soil Survey, Harpenden.

Britten, J. (1896) Book-notes, News, etc. *Journal of Botany* 34: 46–48.

Britten, J. (1903) A review of: Flora of Derbyshire. *Journal of Botany* 41: 409–411.

Britten, J. (1911) William Hunt Painter (1835–1910). *Journal of Botany* 49: 125–126.

Britten, J. & Boulger, G.S. (1931) *A Biographical Index of Deceased British and Irish Botanists.* Taylor & Francis, London.

Brookes, N. & Bradley, R. (2003) *The Black Poplar in Derbyshire.* Derbyshire Wildlife Trust, Belper.

Brown, J. (1945) *Carex ericetorum* Poll. in south-west Yorkshire and Derbyshire. *The Naturalist* 111.

Brown, N. (2012) Derbyshire, in Sands, T., Ed. Wildlife in Trust, a Hundred Years of Nature Conservation. The Wildlife Trusts, Newark.

Buckingham, H., Chapman, J. & Newman, R. (1997) *Meadows Beyond the Millennium – the Future for Hay Meadows in the Peak District.* Peak District National Park, Bakewell.

Buckland, S.M., Grime, J.P., Hodgson, J.G. & Thompson, K. (1997) A comparison of plant responses to the extreme drought of 1995 in northern England. *Journal of Ecology* 85: 875– 882.

Burek, C. (1977) An unusual occurrence of sands and gravels in Derbyshire. *Mercian Geologist* 6: 123–130.

Butcher, R.W. (1961) *A New Illustrated British Flora.* Leonard Hill, London.

Cadbury, D.A., Hawkes, J.G. & Readett, R.C. (1971) *A Computer-mapped Flora: a Study of the County of Warwickshire.* Academic Press, London.

Cameron, K. (1959) *The Place-names of Derbyshire.* Cambridge University Press, Cambridge.

Cannon, J. (2009) *A Dictionary of British History.* Oxford University Press, Oxford.

Capper, M. (2001) Labrador Tea *Ledum groenlandicum* in the Upper Derwent Valley: a brief update. *Sorby Record* 37: 34–36.

Caulton, E. (1961) *Calla palustris* L. from Allestree Park lake, 1960. *Transactions of the Derby Natural History Society* 2: 16–17.

Cavalot, K.V. (2005) Survey of *Vaccinium × intermedium* (Hybrid Bilberry) in Great Britain. *BSBI News* 98: 17–21.

Chapple, J. (1997) *Elizabeth Gaskell: The Early Years.* Manchester University Press, Manchester.

Charter, J.R. (1997) The spread of Japanese Knotweed and Himalayan Balsam, invasive alien weeds, in Chesterfield, Derbyshire. *BSBI News* 75: 51–54.

Charter, J.R. (1999) Observations on the spread of Japanese Knotweed and Himalayan Balsam, invasive alien weeds, in Chesterfield, Derbyshire. *Journal of Practical Ecology and Conservation* 3: 41–47.

Charter, J.R. (2002) The Grey Squirrel and Sycamore bark-stripping in north-east Derbyshire. *BSBI News* 90:15–17.

Charter, J.R. (2003) Giant Hogweed – an "invisible" alien weed in Chesterfield and north-east Derbyshire. *BSBI News* 93: 60–63.

Cheffings, C.M. & Farrell, L., Eds (2006) *The Vascular Plant Red List for Great Britain.* Joint Nature Conservation Committee, Peterborough.

Cheffings, C.M. & Farrell, L., Eds (2007) *The Vascular Plant Red List for Great Britain.* Joint Nature Conservation Committee, Peterborough.

Christian, R. (1978) *Derbyshire.* Batsford, London.

Clapham, A.R. (1971) William Harold Pearsall 1891-1964. *Biographical Memoirs of Fellows of the Royal Society* 17: 511–540.

Clapham, A.R., Ed. (1969) *Flora of Derbyshire.* County Borough of Derby, Derby.

Clapham, A.R., Tutin, T.G. & Moore, D.M. (1987) *Flora of the British Isles 3rd Ed.* Cambridge University Press, Cambridge.

Clapham, A.R., Tutin, T.G. & Warburg, E.F. (1952) *Flora of the British Isles*. Cambridge University Press, Cambridge.

Clapham, A.R., Tutin, T.G. & Warburg, E.F. (1962) *Flora of the British Isles 2nd Ed.* Cambridge University Press, Cambridge.

Clarke, W.A (1900) *First records of British Flowering Plants*. West, Newman & Co., London.

Clarkson, K. & Garland, S. (1988) Colonisation of Sheffield's urban wastelands – vascular plants. *Sorby Record* 25: 5–21.

Clement, E.J. (2001) *Bidens ferulifolia* in town. *BSBI News* 86: 48–49.

Clement, E.J., & Foster, M.C. (1994) *Alien Plants of the British Isles*. Botanical Society of the British Isles, London.

Clement, E.J., Smith, D.P.J. & Thirlwell, I.R. (2005) *Illustrations of Alien Plants of the British Isles*. Botanical Society of the British Isles, London.

Conway, V.M. (1947) Ringinglow Bog near Sheffield, part 1 Historical. *Journal of Ecology* 34: 149–181.

Conway, V.M. (1949) Ringinglow Bog near Sheffield, part 2 The present surface. *Journal of Ecology* 37: 148–170.

Conway, V.M. (1954) Stratigraphy and pollen analysis of southern Pennine blanket bogs. *Journal of Ecology* 42: 117–147.

CPRE (1944) *The Peak District: A National Park*. Council for the Protection of Rural England, Sheffield.

Crockford's (1874) *Crockford's Clerical Directory for 1874*. Horace Cox, London.

Crockford's (1898) *Crockford's Clerical Directory for 1898*. Horace Cox, London.

Crockford's (1908) *Crockford's Clerical Directory for 1908*. Horace Cox, London.

Crowther, K.A. & Aitchison, J.W. (1993) *Derbyshire: A Survey of the Biological Characteristics and Management of Common Land*. Defra, London.

Cullen, W.R., Wheater, C.P. & Dunleavy, P.J. (1997) Establishment of species-rich vegetation on reclaimed limestone quarry faces in Derbyshire UK. *Biological Conservation* 84: 25–33.

Dalton, R., Fox, H. & Jones P. (1999) *The Classic Landforms of the Dark Peak*. Geographical Association, Sheffield.

Dalton, R., Fox, H. & Jones P. (1999) *The Classic Landforms of the White Peak*. Geographical Association, Sheffield.

Darby, H.C. & Maxwell, I.S., Eds (1962) *The Doomsday Geography of Northern England*. Cambridge University Press, Cambridge.

David, R.W. (1980) The distribution of *Carex ornithopoda* Willd. in Britain. *Watsonia* 13: 53–54.

Davies, D.P. (1811) *A New Historical and Descriptive View of Derbyshire*. S. Mason, Belper.

Davis, B.N.K. (1977) The *Hieracium* flora of chalk and limestone quarries in England. *Watsonia* 11: 345–351.

Davy, A.J. (2006) Professor Arthur J. Willis (1922–2006). *Journal of Ecology* 94: 1049–1051.

DCLG (2012) *National Planning Policy Framework*. Department for Communities & Local Government, HMSO, London.

Defra (2011a) *The Natural Choice: Securing the Value of Nature. Natural Environment White Paper*. Department for Environment, Food and Rural Affairs, London.

Defra (2011b) *Biodiversity 2020:A Strategy for England's Wildlife and Ecosystem Services*. Department for Environment, Food and Rural Affairs, London.

Derby City Council (1990) *Nature Conservation Strategy*. Derby City Council, Derby.

Derbyshire County Council (1977) *Derbyshire Structure Plan: Report of Survey*. Derbyshire County Council, Matlock.

Derbyshire County Council (1980) *Derbyshire Structure Plan*. Derbyshire County Council, Matlock.

Derbyshire County Council & Naturalists' Trust (1985) *Derbyshire Wildlife Habitat Assessment: Report of Survey*. Derbyshire County Council & Naturalists' Trust, Matlock.

Derbyshire Wildlife Trust (2011) *Derbyshire Local Wildlife Sites Handbook volume 2*. Derbyshire Wildlife Trust, Belper.

Derbyshire Wildlife Trust (2014) Local Nature Conservation and Biodiversity Indicator Report April 2009 – March 2014. Unpublished Report, Derbyshire Wildlife Trust, Belper.

Desmond, R., Ed. (1994) *Dictionary of British and Irish Botanists and Horticulturalists 4th Ed.* Taylor & Francis, London.

Dickie, J.B., Gajjar, K.H., Birch, P. & Harris J.A. (1988) The survival of viable seeds in stored topsoil from opencast coal workings and its implication for site restoration. *Biological Conservation* 43: 257–265.

Dobson, L. (2001) *Common Trees in the Peak District*. Sorby Natural History Society, Sheffield.

Dony, J.G. (1967) *Flora of Hertfordshire*. Hitchin Museum, Hitchin.

Dower, J.W. (1945) *National Parks in England and Wales*. HMSO, London.

Dower, J.W. (1958) *National Parks in England and Wales*. HMSO, London.

Drabble, E. (1917) Additions to the flora of Derbyshire. *Journal of the Derbyshire Archaeological and Natural History Society* 39: 225.

Drabble, E. (1927) Derbyshire pansies. *Journal of the Derbyshire Archaeological and Natural History Society* NS 2: 135.

Drabble, E. (1929) Notes on the flora of Derbyshire. *Journal of the Derbyshire Archaeological and Natural History Society* NS 2: 210.

Drabble, E. & Drabble H. (1909) Notes on the flora of Derbyshire. *Journal of Botany* 47: 199–207.

Drabble, E. & Drabble H. (1911) Notes on the flora of Derbyshire. *Journal of Botany* 49: 313–317.

Drabble, E. & Drabble H. (1916) Notes on the flora of Derbyshire. *Journal of Botany* 54: 133–139.

Druce, G.C. (1932) *The Comital Flora of the British Isles*. Buncle, Arbroath.

Dudman, A.A. & Richards, A.J. (1997) *Dandelions of Great Britain and Ireland*. Botanical Society of the British Isles, London.

Edees, E.S. (1963) Notes on Derbyshire brambles. *Botanical Society of the British Isles Proceedings* 5: 13–19.

Edees, E.S. (1975) Notes on British *Rubi, 3. Watsonia* 10: 331–343.

Edwards, K.C. (1962) *The Peak District*. Collins, London.

Edwards, K.C., Ed. (1966) *Nottingham and its Region*. British Association for the Advancement of Science, Nottingham.

Egan, J. (1988) The flowering plants of the Sheffield and Tinsley Canal. *Sorby Record* 25: 89–94.

Ellis, G.E. (1994) Alien records. *BSBI News* 67: 50.

Elkington, T.T., Ed. (1986) *The Nature of Derbyshire*. Barracuda Books, Buckingham.

Elkington, T.T. & Willmot, A., Eds (1996) *Endangered Wildlife in Derbyshire*. Derbyshire Wildlife Trust, Derby.

Environment Agency (2009) *River Basin Management Plan, Humber River Basin District. Main Document*. Environment Agency.

Essex, S.J. (1988) The effectiveness of planning interventions on woodlands in the Peak District National Park. *East Midlands Geographer* 11: 48–56.

Ettlinger, D.M.T. (1991) Two new varieties of British *Dactylorhiza*. *Watsonia* 18: 307–309.

Eyre, S.R. (1957) The upward limit of enclosure on the East Moor of north Derbyshire. *Transactions & Papers (The Institute of British Geographers)* 23: 61–74.

Farey, J. (1813) *A General View of the Agriculture and Minerals of Derbyshire Volume 2*. The Board of Agriculture, London.

Ford, T.D. & King, R.J. (1969) The origin of the silica sand pockets in the Derbyshire limestone. *The Mercian Geologist* 3: 51–69.

Ford, T.D. & Rieuwerts, J.H., Eds (1983) *Lead Mining in the Peak District*. Peak Park Joint Planning Board, Bakewell.

Forestry Commission (1984) *County of Derbyshire Census of Woodlands and Trees*. Forestry Commission, Edinburgh.

Foster, J. (1968) *Alumni Oxonienses 1715–1886 volume 3*. Kraus, Nendeln.

Fox, B.W. (1980) The changing flora of a disused railway siding at New Mills, Derbyshire. *North West Naturalist* 1980: 2–3.

Fridley, J.D., Grime, J.P. & Bilton M. (2007) Genetic identity of interspecific neighbours mediates plant responses to competition and environmental variation in a species-rich grassland. *Journal of Ecology* 95: 908–915.

Frost, R.A. (1978) *Birds of Derbyshire*. Moorland, Ashbourne.

Fuller, R.M. (1987 The changing extent and conservation interest of lowland grasslands in England and Wales: a review of grassland surveys 1930–1984. *Biological Conservation* 40: 281–300.

Futter, K. & Raynes, P. (1989) *The Flora of Derby*. Futter, K. & Raynes, P., Derby.

Garland, S.P. (1983) Beetles as primary woodland indicators. *Sorby Record* 21: 3–38.

Garland, S.P. & Whiteley, D. (1984) Biological site recording at Sheffield Museum. *Newsletter of the Biological Curators Group* 3: 504–516.

Garnett, C.S. (1934) Reintroduction of *Cypripedium calceolus* L., Matlock district, Derbyshire. *Journal of Botany* 72: 57–58.

Garneys, W. (1881) *Contributions to the Flora and Fauna of Repton 2nd Ed*. Bemrose & Sons, London.

Gibson, E. (1695) *Camden's Britannia*. London.

Gilbert, O.L. (1976) An alkaline dust effect on epiphytic lichens. *The Lichenologist* 8: 173–178.

Gilbert, O.L. (1983) The lichen flora of Derbyshire – supplement 2. *The Naturalist* 108: 131–137.

Gilbert, O.L. (1992) The ecology of an urban river. *British Wildlife* 3: 129–136.

Gilbert, O.L. (1995) Botanical changes in the Sheffield canal 1984–1995. *Sorby Record* 32: 91–94.

Gilbert, O.L. & Pearman, M.C. (1988) Wild figs by the Don. *Sorby Record* 25: 31–33.

Glover, R. (1829) *History of the County of Derby*. Derby.

Godwin, H. (1923) Dispersal of pond floras. *Journal of Ecology* 11:160–164.

Godwin, H. & Willis, E.H. (1962) Cambridge University natural radiocarbon measurements V. *Radiocarbon* 4: 57–70.

Golson, D. (2012) *Wild about Ponds – End of Project Report*. Derby City Council, Derby.

Gorham, G.C. (1830) *Memoirs of John Martyn F.R.S. and of Thomas Martyn B.D., F.R.S., F.L.S. Professors of Botany in the University of Cambridge*. Hatchard & Son, London.

Grime, J.P. (1970) What are the priorities for conservation in Derbyshire? In *Plants and People*. Derbyshire Naturalists' Trust, Matlock.

Graham, G.G. & Primavesi, A.L. (1993) *The Roses of Great Britain and Ireland*. Botanical Society of the British Isles, London.

Grigson, G. (1975) *The Englishman's Flora*. Paladin, St Albans.

Grime, J.P. (1988) *Comparative Plant Ecology: a functional Approach to Common British Species*. Unwin Hyman, London.

Grime, J.P. & Blythe, G.M. (1969) An investigation of the relationship between snails and vegetation at the Winnats Pass. *Journal of Ecology* 57: 45–66.

Grime, J.P., Hodgson, J.G. & Hunt, R. (1990) *The Abridged Comparative Plant Ecology*. Unwin Hyman, London.

Groom, Q. (2006) The maps scheme. *BSBI News* 103: 18–19.

Hall, F.T. & Hall, R.H. (1942) Notes on the flora of Buxton and district. *Botanical Society and Exchange Club Report* 12: 338–355.

Harding, P. & Oxley, V. (2000) *Wildflowers of the Peak District*. The Hallamshire Press, Sheffield.

Hawksworth, D.L. (1969) The lichen flora of Derbyshire. *The Lichenologist* 4: 105–193.

Hawksworth, D.L. (1974a) The lichen flora of Derbyshire – supplement 1. *The Naturalist* 929: 57–64.

Hawksworth, D.L. (1974b) *Report on the Lichen Flora of the Peak District National Park*. Nature Conservancy Council, Shrewsbury.

Heath, J. (1982) *The Illustrated History of Derbyshire*. Barracuda Books, Buckingham.

Hicks, S.P. (1971) Pollen-analytical evidence for the effect of prehistoric agriculture on the vegetation of North Derbyshire. *New Phytologist* 70: 647–667.

Hicks, S.P. (1972) The impact of man on the East Moor of Derbyshire from Mesolithic times. *Archaeological Journal* 129: 1–21.

Hill, N.M. & Kloet, S.P.V. (2005) Longevity of experimentally buried seed in *Vaccinium*, relationship to climate, reproductive factors and natural seedbanks. *Journal of Ecology* 93: 1167–1176.

Hobhouse, A.L. (1947) *Report of the National Parks Committee*. HMSO, London.

Hodgson, J.G. (2002) *Umbilicus rupestris* – (slightly) Eastwards ho. *BSBI News* 91: 31–32.

Hollick, K.M. (1942) Botanical record for Derbyshire, 1941. *Journal of the Derbyshire Archaeological and Natural History Society* 62: 136–145.

Hollick, K.M. (1949) Botanical record for Derbyshire, 1948. *Journal of the Derbyshire Archaeological and Natural History Society* 68: 82.

Hollick, K.M. (1964) *The Parish Church of Saint Oswald Ashbourne*. Avian Press, Ashbourne.

Hollick, K.M. & Patrick, S. (1980) *Supplement to the Flora of Derbyshire*. Derby City Council, Derby.

How, W. (1650) *Phytologia Britannica Natales Exhibens Indigenarum Stirpium Sponte Emergentium*. London.

Huston, K. (2001) Changes in the Extent of Semi-natural Grasslands in Lowland Derbyshire between 1983 and 1999, and Recommendations for Future Conservation Action. Unpublished Report, Derbyshire Wildlife Trust, Belper.

Huston, K. (2009) The Status and Condition of Local Wildlife Sites in Derbyshire 1984–2008. Unpublished Report, Derbyshire Wildlife Trust, Belper.

Huston, K. (2014) Status of ponds in Derbyshire. Unpublished report, Derbyshire Wildlife Trust, Belper.

IPCC (2013) *Climate Change 2013: The Physical Science Basis*. Cambridge University Press, Cambridge.

Jackson, G. & Sheldon, J. (1949) The vegetation of Magnesian Limestone cliffs at Markland Grips near Sheffield. *Journal of Ecology* 37: 38–50.

Jacobi, R.M., Tallis, J.H. & Mellars, P.A. (1976) The southern Pennine Mesolithic and the ecological record. *Journal of Archaeological Science* 3: 307–320.

Jeayes, I.H. (1906) *Descriptive Catalogue of Derbyshire Charters*. Bemrose, Derby.

Jenkinson, R.D.S. & Gilbertson, D.D. (1984) *In the Shadow of Extinction*. Nottinghamshire and Derbyshire County Councils, Nottingham and Derby.

JNCC (2007) *Conservation Designations for UK Taxa*. Joint Nature Conservation Committee, Peterborough.

JNCC (2010) *Handbook for Phase 1 Habitat Survey*. Joint Nature Conservation Committee, Peterborough.

Johnson, C. & Sowerby, J.E. (1855) *The Ferns of Great Britain*. Sowerby, London.

Johnson, G.W. (1859) *The British Ferns 3rd edition*. Cottage Gardener Office, London.

Jones, M. & Rotherham, I.D. (2000) Seeing the woodman in the trees: some preliminary thoughts on Derbyshire ancient coppice woods. *Peak District Journal of Natural History and Archaeology* 2: 7–17.

Jump, A.S. & Woodward, F.I. (2003) Seed production and population density decline approaching the range-edge of *Cirsium* species. *New Phytologist* 160: 349–358.

Kent, D.H. (1992) *List of Vascular Plants of the British Isles*. Botanical Society of the British Isles, London.

Kirby, M. (1850) *A Flora of Leicestershire*. Hamilton, Adams & Co., London.

Kraehenbuehl, D.N. & Moyes, N. (1999) Joseph Whittaker: early English botanical visitor to South Australia. *South Australian Naturalist* 73: 44–60.

Laborde, J & Thompson, K. (2009) Post-dispersal fate of Hazel (*Corylus avellana*) nuts and consequences for the management and conservation of scrub-grassland mosaics. *Biological Conservation* 142: 974–981.

LDBP (1997) *Mid Derbyshire Local Biodiversity Action Plan*. Lowland Derbyshire Biodiversity Partnership, Matlock.

LDBP (2001) *Lowland Derbyshire Local Biodiversity Action Plan, Addendum*. Lowland Derbyshire Biodiversity Partnership, Matlock.

LDBP (2011) Lowland Derbyshire Biodiversity Action Plan. Published online, Lowland Derbyshire Biodiversity Partnership, Matlock.

Lawton, J. et al. (2010) *Making Space for Nature: a Review of England's Wildlife Sites and Ecological Network*. HMSO, London.

Leach, S. (1998) *Spergularia marina* on inland roadsides. *BSBI News* 79: 51–52.

Linton, D.L., Ed. (1956) *Sheffield and its Region*. British Association for the Advancement of Science, Sheffield.

Linton, E.F. (1908) The late Rev. W.R. Linton. *Journal of Botany* 46: 64–71.

Linton, E.F. & Linton, W.R. (1893) British hawkweeds. *Journal of Botany* 31: 145–149, 177–182 & 195–202.

Linton, W.R. (1890) *Hieracium holophyllum* sp.n. *Journal of Botany* 28: 376.

Linton, W.R. (1903) *Flora of Derbyshire*. Bemrose & Sons, London.

Linton, W.R. (1905) *An Account of the British Hieracia*. West Newman & Co., London.

Lloyd, P.S. (1968) The ecological significance of fire in limestone grassland communities of the Derbyshire Dales. *Journal of Ecology* 56: 811–826.

Lloyd, P.S. (1972a) Effects of fire on a Derbyshire grassland community. *Ecology* 53: 915–920.

Lloyd, P.S. (1972b) The grassland vegetation of the Sheffield region II Classification of grassland types. *Journal of Ecology* 60: 739–776.

Lloyd, P.S., Grime, J.P. & Rorison, I.H. (1971) The grassland vegetation of the Sheffield region I General features. *Journal of Ecology* 59: 863–886.

Lockton, A. & Whild, S. (1998) *Grass-wrack Pondweed in the Midlands region – a desk study*. The Environment Agency, Solihull.

Lousley, J.E. (1950) The habitats and distribution of *Gentiana uliginosa* Willd. *Watsonia* 1: 279–282.

Lousley, J.E. (1950) *Wild Flowers of Chalk & Limestone*. Collins, London.

Lowe, E.J. (1876) *Our Native Ferns*. George Bell & Sons, London.

Lysons, D. & Lysons, S. (1817) *Magna Britannica volume 5: Derbyshire*. London.

Mabey, R. (1996) *Flora Britannica*. Sinclair-Stevenson, London.

Maddock, A. (2011) UK Biodiversity Action Plan; Priority Habitat Descriptions. Published online, Defra, London.

Mallett, C. (2011) Was this tree rock-a-bye baby's cradle? Derby Telegraph May 9th: 15.

Martin, W.K. (1965) *The Concise British Flora in Colour*. Ebury Press and Michael Joseph, London.

Martin, W.K. (1968) *Over the Hills*. Michael Joseph, London.

Martyn, J. (1729) An account of some observations relating to natural history, made in a journey to the Peak in Derbyshire. *Philosophical Transactions of the Royal Society* 36: 22–32.

Martyn, T. (1763) *Plantae Cantabrigienses*. London.

Mathew, C. & Harrison, B.H., Eds (2004) *Oxford Dictionary of National Biography*. Oxford University Press, Oxford.

Matthews, J.R. (1955) *Origin and Distribution of the British Flora*. Hutchinson's, London.

Mayfield, B. & Pearson, M.C. (1972) Human interference with the north Derbyshire blanket peat. *East Midland Geographer* 5: 245–251.

McClintock, D. & Burns, A. (1995) Kathleen Margaret Hollick (1913–1993). *Watsonia* 20: 322.

McCosh, D. & Rich, T. (2011) *Atlas of British and Irish Hawkweeds*. Botanical Society of the British Isles, London.

McLellan, A.J., Law, R. & Fitter, A.H. (1997) Response of calcareous grassland plant species to diffuse competition: results from a removal experiment. *Journal of Ecology* 85: 479–490.

Mendelsohn, R. (2008) *Catalogue of the Pressed Flowers in the Herbarium given to Florence Nightingale by Margaret Stovin*. Short Publishing Company, Winchester.

Merton, L.F.H. (1970) The history and status of woods on the Derbyshire limestone. *Journal of Ecology* 58: 723–744.

Miller, A. (1985) Verge floras in the Peak District. *Sorby Record* 22: 59–61.

Mills, J.N. (1969) A new species of *Hieracium* in Derbyshire. *Watsonia* 7: 40–42

Mills, J.N. & Mills, J.R.J. (1970) *Hieracium* – Two Hieracia section Alpestria from the British mainland. *Watsonia* 8: 48–49.

Morgan, P. (1978) *Domesday Book, 27 Derbyshire*. Phillimore, Chichester.

Moseley, O. (1863) *The Natural History of Tutbury*. John van Voorst, London.

Moss, C.E. (1913) *Vegetation of the Peak District*. Cambridge University Press, Cambridge.

Moyes, N.J. & Willmot, A. (2002) *A Checklist of the Plants of Derbyshire*. Derby Museum, Derby.

Moyes, N.J. & Willmot, A. (2007) *An Update to the Checklist of the Plants of Derbyshire*. Derby Museum, Derby.

Moyes, N.J. & Willmot, A. (2009) *Red Data List of Derbyshire's Vascular Plants*. Derby Museum, Derby.

Murphy, R.J. (2009) *Fumitories of Britain and Ireland*. Botanical Society of the British Isles, London.

Natural England (2014) SSSI Condition Summary Report for Derbyshire. Unpublished Report, Natural England, Sheffield.

Newton, A. & Randall, R.D. (2004) *Atlas of British and Irish Brambles*. Botanical Society of the British Isles, London.

Nordal, I. (1988) *Cochlearia pyrenaica* DC., a species new to Scotland. *Watsonia* 17: 49–52.

North Wales Chronicle (1881) The Menai Society of Natural Science and Literature. *The North Wales Chronicle* August 20th: 5.

Page, W., Ed. (1905) *The Victoria History of the County of Derby*. Constable, London.

Painter, W.H. (1881) Notes upon the flora of Derbyshire. *Journal of Botany* 19: 210–216, 244–250, 293–301 & 374.

Painter, W.H. (1889) *A Contribution to the Flora of Derbyshire*. George Bell & Sons, London.

Painter, W.H. (1893) Botanical walks around Derby. *Journal of the Derbyshire Archaeological and Natural History Society* 15: 26–30.

Painter, W.H. (1902) *A Supplement to a Contribution to the Flora of Derbyshire*. Chorley & Pickersgill, Leeds.

Parkinson, J. (1640) *Theatrum Botanicum*. London.

Patrick, S.J. (1979) The botanical collections at Derby Museum. *Biological Curators' Group Newsletter* 2: 108–111.

Patrick, S.J. & Hollick, K.M. (1974) *Supplement to the Flora of Derbyshire*. Derby Borough Council, Derby.

PDNP (1974) *Structure Plan: Report of Survey*. Peak Park Joint Planning Board, Bakewell.

PDNP (1982) *Approved Structure Plan*. Peak Park Joint Planning Board, Bakewell.

PDNP (2001) *A Living Landscape – Biodiversity Action Plan for the Peak District*. Peak District National Park Authority, Bakewell.

PDNP (2011) *The Peak District Biodiversity Action Plan (BAP) 2011–2020.* On-line report, Peak District National Park Authority, Bakewell.

Pearsall, W.H. (1950) *Mountains and Moorlands.* Collins, London.

Peck T.W. & Wilkinson K.D. (1950) *William Withering of Birmingham.* John Wright & Sons, Bristol.

Perring, F.H. (1968) *Critical Supplement to the Atlas of the British Flora.* Botanical Society of the British Isles, London.

Perring, F.H. (1974) Foreword in, Gibbons, E.J., *The Flora of Lincolnshire*, 1975. Lincolnshire Naturalists' Union, Lincoln.

Perring, F.H. & Walters, S.M. (1962) *Atlas of the British Flora.* Botanical Society of the British Isles, London.

Philips, J., Yalden, D.W. & Tallis, J. (1981) *Peak District Moorland Erosion Study: Phase 1 report.* Peak Park Joint Planning Board, Bakewell.

Pigott, C.D. (1969) The status of *Tilia cordata* and *T. platyphyllos* on the Derbyshire limestone. *Journal of Ecology* 57: 491–504.

Pigott, C.D. (1970) Soil formation and development on the Carboniferous Limestone of Derbyshire. *Journal of Ecology* 58: 529–541.

Pigott, C.D. (1983) Regeneration of oak-birch woodland following exclusion of sheep. *Journal of Ecology* 71: 629–646.

Pigott, C.D. (1991) Professor A.R. Clapham. *New Phytologist* 119: 3–4.

Pilkington, J. (1789) *A View of the Present State of Derbyshire.* J. Drewry, Derby.

Pilkington, J. (1795) *The Doctrine of Equality of Rank and Condition.* J. Johnson, London.

Plantlife (2012) *Our Vanishing Flora – How Wildflowers are Disappearing across Britain.* Plantlife, Salisbury.

Porter, L. (1982) *A Visitors' Guide to the Peak District.* Moorland, Ashbourne.

Poulton-Smith, A. (2005) *Derbyshire Place-names.* Sutton Publishing, Stroud.

Precey, P. (2003) South Derbyshire Pondscape Survey. Unpublished Report. Derbyshire Wildlife Trust, Belper.

Press, M., Ferguson, P. & Lee, J. (1983) 200 years of acid rain. *The Naturalist* 108: 125–129.

Preston, C.D. (1988) The *Potamogeton* L. taxa described by Alfred Fryer. *Watsonia* 17: 23–35.

Preston, C.D. (2003) Perceptions of change in English county Floras, 1660–1960. *Watsonia* 24: 287–304.

Preston, C.D. & Hill, M.O. (1997) The geographic relationships of British and Irish vascular plants. *Botanical Journal of the Linnean Society* 124: 1–120.

Preston, C.D., Pearman, D.A. & Dines, T.D. (2002) *New Atlas of the British and Irish Flora.* Oxford University Press, Oxford.

Preston, C.D., Pearman, D.A. & Hall A.R. (2004) Archaeophytes in Britain. *Botanical Journal of the Linnean Society* 145: 257–294.

Pugsley, H.W. (1948) A prodromus of the British Hieracia. *Journal of the Linnean Society of London (Botany)* 54: 1–356.

Purchas, W. & Ley, A. (1889) *A Flora of Herefordshire.* Jakeman & Carver, Hereford.

Randle, J.A. (1953) Plant notes. *Watsonia* 2: 414.

Raven, C.E. (1947) *English Naturalists from Neckam to Ray.* Cambridge University Press, Cambridge.

Raven, C.E. (1950) *John Ray Naturalist: His Life and Works 2nd Ed.* Cambridge University Press, Cambridge.

Ray, J. (1660) *Catalogus Plantarum circa Cantabrigiam Nascentium.* Cambridge.

Ray, J. (1670) *Catalogus Plantarum Angliae.* London.

Ray, J. (1677) *Catalogus Plantarum Angliae 2nd Ed.* London.

Rich, T.C.G. & Scott, W. (2011) *British Northern Hawkweeds.* Botanical Society of the British Isles, London.

Riddelsdell, H.J. (1903) Further notes on Yorkshire plants in the Bicheno herbarium at Swansea. *The Naturalist* No. 556: 167–168.

Robertson, W.H. (1854) *A Handbook to the Peak of Derbyshire.* London.

Rotherham, I.D. (1986a) The introduction spread and current distribution of *Rhododendron ponticum* in the Peak District and Sheffield area. *The Naturalist* 111: 61–67.

Rotherham, I.D. (1986b) *Rhododendron ponticum* L. in the Sheffield area. *Sorby Record* 24: 19–24.

Rotherham, I.D. (1986c) The spread of *Rhododendron ponticum* at three sites in the Sheffield area. *Sorby Record* 24: 25–28.

Rotherham, I.D. & Ardron, P.A. (1993) *Thelypteris palustris* in the Peak District. *Pteridologist* 2: 188.

Rotherham, I.D. & Rose, J.C. (1993) Ancient woodlands in Sheffield and the eastern Peak District. In: Beswick, P. & Rotherham, I.D. eds, *Ancient woodlands.* Landscape Conservation Forum, Sheffield.

Rumsey, F.J., Jermy, A.C. & Sheffield, E. (1998) The independent gametophytic stage of *Trichomanes speciosum* Willd. (Hymenophyllaceae), the Killarney Fern and its distribution in the British Isles. *Watsonia* 22: 1–19.

Salt, J. (1889) *List of Plants Collected Chiefly in the Neighbourhood of Sheffield.* Sheffield Literary & Philosophical Society, Sheffield.

Sell, P.D. & Murrell, G. (2006) *Flora of Great Britain and Ireland volume 4 Campanulaceae – Asteraceae.* Cambridge University Press, Cambridge.

Sell, P.D. (1987) An introduction to the study of the British *Hieracia*, 1. History and classification. *Watsonia* 16: 365–371.

Shaw, J.M.H. (1995) *Sisymbrium volgense*: new to Derbyshire. *BSBI News* 68: 43.

Shaw, M.R., Ed. (1988) *A Flora of the Sheffield Area.* Sorby Natural History Society, Sheffield.

Shaw, M.R. (1974) Notes on Chickweed Wintergreen in the Sheffield area. *Sorby Record* 3: 55–56.

Shimwell, D.W. (1968) Notes on the distribution of *Thlaspi alpestre* L. in Derbyshire. *Proceedings of the Botanical Society of the British Isles* 7: 373–376.

Shimwell, D.W. (1973) Recent and fossil records for clubmosses on the Derbyshire limestone. *Watsonia* 9: 271–272.

Shimwell, D.W. (1974) Sheep grazing intensity in Edale, 1692–1747, and its effect on blanket peat erosion. *Derbyshire Archaeological Journal* 94: 35–50.

Shimwell, D.W. (1977) *Studies in the History of the Peak District Landscape: 1. Pollen Analysis of some Podzolic Soils on the Limestone Plateau.* University of Manchester, Manchester.

Simpson, I.M. (1982) *The Peak District.* Unwin, London.

Smith, C.U.M. & Arnott, R., Eds (2005) *The Genius of Erasmus Darwin.* Ashgate, Aldershot.

Smith, G. (1869) *The Ferns of Derbyshire 6th Ed.* W. Bemrose & Sons, London & Derby.

Smith, G. (1872) *Bemrose's Guide to Derbyshire.* Bemrose & Sons, Derby.

Smith, R. (1982) Some brambles from Derbyshire. *Watsonia* 14: 233.

Spray, M. (1970) Management of roadsides, hedgerows and grasslands for nature conservation and amenity. In: *People and Plants*, Derbyshire Naturalists' Trust, Matlock.

Spray, M. (1981) Holly as fodder in England. *The Agricultural Historical Review* 29: 97–110.

Spray, M. & Smith, D.J. (1977) The rise and fall of holly in the Sheffield region. *Transactions of the Hunter Archaeological Society* 10: 239–251.

Stace, C.A. (1975) *Hybridisation and the Flora of the British Isles.* Academic Press, London.

Stace, C.A. (1982) Segregation in the natural hybrid *Linaria purpurea* (L.) Mill. × *L. repens* (L.) Mill. *Watsonia* 14: 53–57.

Stace, C.A. (1991) *New Flora of the British Isles.* Cambridge University Press, Cambridge.

Stace, C.A. (1997) *New Flora of the British Isles 2nd Ed.* Cambridge University Press, Cambridge.

Stace, C.A. (2010) *New Flora of the British Isles 3rd Ed*. Cambridge University Press, Cambridge.

Stace, C.A., Ellis, R.G., Kent, D.H. & McCosh, D.J. (2003) *Vice-county Census Catalogue of the Vascular Plants of Great Britain* . Botanical Society of the British Isles, London.

Stewart, D.A., Pearman, D.A. & Preston, C.D. (1994) *Scarce Plants in Britain*. Joint Nature Conservation Committee, Peterborough.

Storer, L. (1984) Observations on the national Bee Orchid survey. *Sorby Record* 21: 87.

Stroh, P.A. *et al*. (2014) *A Vascular Plant Red List for England*. Botanical Society of Britain & Ireland, Bristol.

Stubbs, J. (1984) *A History of Cutthorpe Village, part II*. Stubbs, Chesterfield.

Syme, J.T. (1853) Remarks on plants sent to the Botanical Society of London in 1852. *The Phytologist* 4: 933–935.

Tallis, J.H. (1964a) The pre-peat vegetation of the southern Pennines. *New Phytologist* 63: 363–373.

Tallis, J.H. (1964b) Studies on southern Pennine peats I The general pollen record. *Journal of Ecology* 52*:* 323–331.

Tallis, J.H. (1964c) Studies on southern Pennine peats II The pattern of erosion. *Journal of Ecology* 52: 333–344.

Tallis, J.H. (1964d) Studies on southern Pennine peats III The behaviour of *Sphagnum*. *Journal of Ecology* 52: 345–353.

Tallis, J.H. (1965) Studies on southern Pennine peats IV Evidence of recent erosion. *Journal of Ecology* 53: 509–520.

Tallis, J.H. (1973) Studies on southern Pennine peats V Direct observations on peat erosion and peat hydrology at Featherbed Moss, Derbyshire. *Journal of Ecology* 61: 1–22.

Tallis, J.H. (1975) Tree remains in southern Pennine peats. *Nature* 256: 482–484.

Tallis, J.H. (1985) Mass movement and erosion of a southern Pennine blanket peat. *Journal of Ecology* 73: 283–315.

Tallis, J.H. (1987) Fire and flood at Holme Moss – erosion processes in an upland blanket mire. *Journal of Ecology* 75: 1099–1129.

Tallis, J.H. (1997) The pollen record of *Empetrum nigrum* in southern Pennine peats: implications for erosion and climate change. *Journal of Ecology* 85: 455–465.

Tallis, J.H. & Switzur, V.R. (1973) Studies on southern Pennine peats VI A radiocarbon-dated pollen diagram from Featherbed Moss. *Journal of Ecology* 61: 743–751.

Tallis, J.H. & Switzur, V.R. (1983) Forest and moorland in the south Pennine uplands in the mid-Flandrian period. I Macrofossil evidence of the former forest cover. *Journal of Ecology* 71: 585–600.

Tallis, J.H. & Johnson, R.H. (1980) The dating of landslides in Longdendale northern Derbyshire, using pollen analytical techniques. In: Cullingford, R.A., Davidson, D.A. & Lewin, J. Eds, *Timescales in geomorphology*. Wiley, Chichester.

Tansley, A.G. (1911) *Types of British Vegetation*. Cambridge University Press, Cambridge.

Tansley, A.G. (1931) Prof. C.E. Moss. *Nature* 127: 98–99.

Taylor, T. (2005) Derby City Ponds: Results from the Derby City Pond Survey. Unpublished Report. Derby City Council, Derby.

Telfer, M.G., Preston, C.D. & Rothery, P. (2002) A general method for measuring relative change in range size from biological atlas data. *Biological Conservation* 107: 99–109.

Thorpe, E. (1984) Cardamines on the Cromford Canal. *Sorby Record* 22: 51–58.

Trimen, H. (1874) *Carex ornithopoda* Willd. In England. *Journal of Botany* 12: 371.

Turner, D. & Dillwyn, L.W. (1805) *The Botanists' Guide through England and Wales*. Phillips & Fardon, London.

Waite, C.B. (1974) The hybrid bilberry (*Vaccinium × intermedium*). *Sorby Record* 13: 18.

Warren, P., Rotherham, I.D., Eades, P., Wright, S. & Howe, P. (1999) Invertebrate and macrophyte communities of dewponds in the Peak District with particular reference to the method of pond construction. *The Peak District Journal of Natural History and Archaeology* 1: 27–33.

Waterfall, C. (1891) Discovery of *Carex montana* etc. in Derbyshire. *The Naturalist* 1891: 50.

Watson, H.C. (1852) *Cybele Britannica 3rd Ed*. Longman & Company, London.

Watson, H.C. (1873) *Topographical Botany*. Thames Ditton.

Watson, W. (1811) *A Delineation of the Strata of Derbyshire*. W. Todd, Sheffield.

Webster, S.D. (1990) Three natural hybrids in *Ranunculus* L. subgenus *Batrachium* (DC.) A. Gray. *Watsonia* 18: 139–146.

Welch, D. (1998) Response of Bilberry (*Vaccinium myrtillus* L.) stands in the Derbyshire Peak District to sheep grazing and implications for moorland conservation. *Biological Conservation* 83: 155–164.

Whiteley, D., Ed. (1985) *The Natural History of the Sheffield Area and the Peak District*. Sorby Natural History Society, Sheffield.

Whittaker, J. (1847) A list of rare plants found in the neighbourhood of Breadsall Derbyshire. *The Phytologist* 2: 901–903.

Wikipedia (2012) Joseph Whittaker. en.wikipedia.org Accessed 15/01/2013.

Wildlife & Countryside Link (2011) Halting Biodiversity Loss by 2010, Final Progress Assessment. Unpublished report, Wildlife & Countryside Link, London.

Wiggington, M.J. (1999) *British Red Data Books I Vascular Plants 3rd Ed*. Joint Nature Conservation Committee, Peterborough.

Wilkinson, M.J. & Stace, C.A. (1989) The taxonomic relationship and typification of *Festuca brevipila* Tracey and *F. lemanii* Bastard (Poaceae). *Watsonia* 17: 289–299.

Wilkinson, M.J. & Stace, C.A. (1991) A new taxonomic treatment of the *Festuca ovina* L. aggregate (Poaceae) in the British Isles. *Botanical Journal of the Linnean Society* 106: 347–397.

Willmot, A. (1977a) A pteridophyte flora of the Derbyshire Dales Nature Reserve. *Fern Gazette* 11: 279–284.

Willmot, A. (1977b) *Sorbus torminalis* (L.) Crantz in Derbyshire. *Watsonia* 11: 339–344.

Willmot, A. (1980) The woody species of hedges with special reference to age in Church Broughton parish, Derbyshire. *Journal of Ecology* 68: 269–285.

Willmot, A. (1989) The phenology of leaf life spans in woodland populations of the ferns *Dryopteris filix-mas* (L.) Schott and *D. dilatata* (Hoffm.) A. Gray in Derbyshire. *Botanical Journal of the Linnean Society* 99: 387–395.

Wilmore, G.T.D., Lunn, J, & Rodwell, J.S. (2011) *The South Yorkshire Plant Atlas*. Yorkshire Naturalists' Union, York.

Wiltshire, M., Woore, S., Crisp, B. & Rich, B. (2005) *Duffield Frith*. Landmark, Ashbourne.

Withering, W. (1776) *A Botanical Arrangement of all the Vegetables Naturally Growing in Great Britain*. Swinney, Birmingham.

Withering, W. (1787) *A Botanical Arrangement of British plants 2nd Ed*. Swinney, Birmingham.

Withering, W. (1796) *Arrangement of British plants 3rd Ed*. Swinney, Birmingham.

Wyatt, W. & Thornton, C.G. (1866) *Flora Repandunensis*. Bemrose & Sons, London.

Yalden, D.W. (1996) Labrador Tea *Ledum groenlandicum* in the Peak District. *The Naturalist* 121: 81–86.

Yalden, P.E. & Yalden, D.W. (1988) The level of recreational pressure on blanket bog in the Peak District National Park England. *Biological Conservation* 44: 213–227.

Yeo, P.F. (1956) Hybridisation between diploid and tetraploid species of *Euphrasia*. *Watsonia* 3: 253–269.

Index

Taxa are arranged alphabetically by both the English name and the Latin binomial (***bold italic*** type). Page references to the main species accounts are given in **bold** type.